ROBERT W. PENNAK, Ph.D., University of Wisconsin, is Professor of Biology and Chairman of the Department at the University of Colorado, and has served also as a visiting investigator at the Oceanographic Institute at Woods Hole, Massachusetts. He is member of a number of professional societies and Past President of the American Society of Limnology and Oceanography, the Society of Systematic Zoology, the Invertebrate Section of the American Society of Zoologists, and the American Microscopical Society. Dr. Pennak has contributed a great many articles on lake and stream biology to professional journals and is the author of the *Collegiate Dictionary of Zoology*, published by The Ronald Press Company.

# FRESH-WATER

# INVERTEBRATES

## of the United States

By

### ROBERT W. PENNAK, Ph.D.

PROFESSOR OF BIOLOGY

UNIVERSITY OF COLORADO

THE RONALD PRESS COMPANY · NEW YORK

7

VR-VR

Library of Congress Catalog Card Number: 52–12522

PRINTED IN THE UNITED STATES OF AMERICA

To the memory of

C. Juday

# PREFACE

No comprehensive work on American fresh-water invertebrates has appeared since 1918, and in the meantime much new information has steadily accumulated in a wide variety of biological periodicals. To me, therefore, the need for the present volume is obvious. I hope it will prove useful to biologists and zoologists generally, and to aquatic zoologists, limnologists, fish biologists, and entomologists particularly. It will also serve as a text and reference pitched toward the level of the college senior and beginning graduate student.

Original material resulting from my own field and laboratory research forms only a small fraction of this book. Rather, my role as an author has been one of arrangement, organization, and selection from a very large mass of published information. Indeed, my most perplexing problem has been how *much* material on each taxonomic group to include within the covers of a single volume. General policies, however, have been clear from the outset; I have emphasized natural history, ecology, and taxonomy; I have minimized details in the sections on anatomy and physiology; I have tried to be complete, accurate, concise, and consistent from one chapter to another. During the preparation of this volume all of the chapters have been continually revised and kept up to date in accordance with new material appearing in the literature.

For the most part, only free-living, fresh-water invertebrates that occur in the United States are included. Cestodes, trematodes, parasitic nematodes, etc. are all omitted; their inclusion would have necessitated a much more extensive work and additional years of preparation. Furthermore, most aquatic biologists seldom need to refer to parasitic groups as contrasted with free-living groups.

It will be noted that some chapters contain keys to species, while others contain keys only as far as genera. In general, the chapters in the former category deal with small or comparatively stable taxonomic groups that are fairly well known and in which few new species are being described from time to time in the United States. The chapters in the latter category, however, are all concerned with larger taxonomic groups, as well as those that are less well known in the United States and in which new forms are being described so abundantly that any key to species is quickly out of date. It is assumed that users of this manual are familiar with the fundamentals of taxonomy and the construction of keys. Incidentally, each half of a key couplet consists of but a single sentence; changes in subject within a sentence are indicated by semicolons.

The list of references at the end of each chapter consists only of especially significant and comprehensive works; these include older classical papers as well as recent contributions. Except where sections are especially valuable, I have not listed the larger standard reference works such as Hyman's *The Invertebrates,* Schulze's *Biologie der Tiere Deutschlands,* Bronn's *Tierreich,* Kükenthal and Krumbach's *Handbuch der Zoologie,* Dahl's *Die Tierwelt Deutschlands,* Grassé's *Traité de Zoologie,* and *Faune de France.*

Almost all of the chapters (with or without figures) were sent to at least one specialist for criticisms, corrections, and suggestions. I am deeply grateful to all these specialists, who were most encouraging, generous, and cooperative. Without their help and assurance I would have had much less confidence in my efforts. Following is a list of these specialists, with the sections examined by each.

John L. Brooks (Cladocera); Royal B. Brunson (Gastrotricha); C. F. Byers (Odonata); Fenner A. Chace, Jr. (Crustacea Introduction, Mysidacea); B. G. Chitwood (Nematoda); W. R. Coe (Nemertea); R. E. Coker (Copepoda); Ralph W. Dexter (Eubranchiopoda); W. T. Edmondson (Rotatoria); T. H. Frison [deceased] (Plecoptera); R. E. Gregg (Insecta Introduction); H. H. Hobbs, Jr. (Decapoda); C. C. Hoff (Ostracoda); Leslie Hubricht (Amphipoda, Isopoda); H. B. Hungerford (Hemiptera); Libbie H. Hyman (Coelenterata, Turbellaria); F. P. Ide (Ephemeroptera); O. A. Johannsen (Diptera); M. W. de Laubenfels (Porifera); H. B. Leech (Coleoptera); James E. Lynch (Eubranchiopoda); J. G. Mackin (Isopoda); Ruth Marshall (Hydracarina); H. B. Mills (Collembola); J. Percy Moore (Hirudinea); L. E. Noland (Protozoa); Mary D. Rogick (Bryozoa); H. H. Ross (Plecoptera, Trichoptera); Henry van der Schalie (Gastropoda, Pelecypoda); Waldo L. Schmitt (Crustacea Introduction, Mysidacea); L. H. Townsend (Megaloptera, Neuroptera); H. C. Yeatman (Copepoda).

The introductory chapter was criticized by A. S. Pearse and by several of my graduate students. Other people have helped me in one way or another. A group of eight protozoologists, for example, selected the 300 most appropriate and common genera of Protozoa to be included in the Protozoa key. These men are: William Balamuth, Gordon H. Ball, A. M. Elliot, Harold Kirby (deceased); J. B. Lackey, L. E. Noland, K. L. Osterud, and D. H. Wenrich.

Obviously, a book of this sort is bound to have errors and ambiguities, and certainly such faults are clearly my own responsibility. I hope readers will bring them to my attention.

In a sense, this book constitutes a plea and encouragement for more work on our rich but poorly known fresh-water invertebrate fauna. I hope these chapters will kindle sparks and raise questions in the minds of our students and beginning investigators in zoology, for it is among these young people that we shall find our authorities and specialists of tomorrow.

ROBERT W. PENNAK

Boulder, Colorado

# CONTENTS

# FRESH-WATER INVERTEBRATES
## OF THE
## UNITED STATES

# Chapter 1

# INTRODUCTION

---

Excluding Protozoa and all parasitic classes but including aquatic insects, it is roughly estimated that the fresh-water invertebrate fauna of the United States consists of about 8,500 described species. Probably no competent aquatic biologist is of the opinion that this fauna is well known; certainly the total is bound to increase markedly in coming years, especially when the western half of the country is more thoroughly studied. Although a few groups are fairly well known and reasonably stabilized, such as the Cladocera, Decapoda, Odonata, Gastropoda, and Pelecypoda, the majority of American fresh-water invertebrate groups are in the process of taxonomic growth and development. In expanding categories that are composed mostly of noncosmopolitan species we are lagging behind European fresh-water taxonomy by about 10 to 30 years. All taxonomic questions aside, we are woefully lacking in our understanding of geographic distribution patterns, physiology, natural history, and ecology of fresh-water invertebrates in the United States.

The organization of an introductory chapter to a text such as this one is a problem because of the wide variety of major topics that might profitably be considered. However, to avoid becoming too involved, the subject matter of this chapter is restricted to very brief discussions of (1) origins of the fresh-water fauna, (2) fresh-water emigrants to the sea, (3) some major distinctions between fresh-water and marine invertebrates, (4) atypical fresh-water habitats, (5) dispersal and barriers, and (6) food webs. This particular selection was made only after considerable indecision. For the most part, these are important topics *not* generally discussed in other texts dealing with fresh-water biology. It also appears advisable to eliminate topics more strictly of a limnological nature.

## ORIGINS OF THE FRESH-WATER FAUNA

The generalization that most major fresh-water invertebrate groups originated from marine ancestors seems to be firmly established. Only a few groups, such as insects, Hydracarina, and pulmonate snails, are presumed to have clearly originated from terrestrial habitats. The fresh-water fauna is therefore appropriately termed an immigrant fauna.

The fundamental problem that must be solved before any marine animal can make its way into fresh water involves a major physiological readjustment. Body fluids of most marine invertebrates are roughly isotonic with sea water, that is, the internal dissolved salt concentrations are similar to or slightly higher than the 3.5 per cent average salt concentration of normal sea water. It is further true that the majority of marine invertebrates cannot endure

3

TABLE I. A COMPARISON OF THE TOTAL DISSOLVED SALT CONTENT OF FRESH WATERS, BRACKISH
WATERS, AND SEA WATER. Maximum and minimum values are merely approximations. The most
abundant salts in brackish waters are chlorides, carbonates, or bicarbonates, depending on the
degree of brackishness. In fresh waters the most abundant salts are usually carbonates and bicarbonates. In alkali and saline lakes they are usually carbonates, bicarbonates, chlorides, and sulphates in varying proportions.

|  | Per cent concentration | | Milligrams per liter | |
|---|---|---|---|---|
|  | Minimum | Maximum | Minimum | Maximum |
| Sea water | | 3.5 | | 35,000 |
| Brackish waters | 0.05 | 3.2 | 500 | 32,000 |
| Fresh waters | 0.001 | 0.05 | 10 | 500 |
| Alkali and saline lakes | 0.05 | 25.0 | 500 | 250,000 |

much dilution of sea water. Fresh waters commonly contain about 0.01 as much salt as the ocean, and the internal fluids of fresh-water invertebrates usually contain 0.03 to 0.40 as much salt as the ocean. From an osmotic standpoint, water therefore tends to pass into the hypertonic tissues of fresh-water animals. Consequently any successful fresh-water animal must have developed physiological mechanisms for maintaining a proper salt and water balance against this strong gradient.

It is difficult to imagine the appearance of such mechanisms *de novo*, and it is assumed that the transitions from marine to fresh-water environments were not sudden and rapid processes, but rather series of slow evolutionary processes occurring by way of littoral zones, marshes, swamps, and river estuaries where there are transition zones between salt and fresh water.

It should be borne in mind, however, that a river estuary is not a constant environment. Salinities, currents, tides, food, temperatures, and other ecological factors vary widely from time to time, and these conditions are by no means favorable to the evolution and gradual development of forms suited to fresh water. Pearse (1950) has stated the problem well:

An estuary has been called the doorway by which marine forms have populated fresh water. This statement is perhaps in part true,

but an estuarine doorway is not wide open and easily passed. There are many difficulties to be surmounted. Many animals struggle long ages to get through and fail. Only a few attain fresh water by this route.

Ideal conditions for the invasion of fresh water are afforded by such places as the Baltic Sea where there is a large area involved and where there is a permanent and very gradual transition from the sea to fresh water.

The generalization that marine invertebrates are isotonic with sea water is actually a slight exaggeration. Even pelagic, deep-sea, and the most primitive marine species maintain a dynamic steady state by which a difference in concentration of several ions commonly obtains across external membranes and which can be maintained only through physiological regulatory processes. The internal concentrations of magnesium and sulphate ions are often much lower than those in sea water. Potassium concentrations may be considerably higher or lower than in sea water, and calcium and chloride are also variable. Many marine invertebrates have the remarkable ability to concentrate astonishing amounts of elements that are present in the sea water only as traces. Examples are vanadium, iodine, strontium, and bromine.

A wide range in type and degree of

osmoregulatory control is found among littoral and estuarine invertebrates. Many species have limited ability to regulate the relative amounts of internal salt and water; their membranes are easily permeable so that the body fluids become more or less isotonic in diluted sea water, and death occurs rather promptly. A few stenohaline species can endure some dilution of sea water by regulating body volume and taking up more water into the tissues. A few other species can regulate their internal osmotic concentration only to a limited degree and venture into slightly brackish water; these species have a slight ability to remain hypertonic in diluted sea water. "Typical" brackish water species are euryhaline and can persist in habitats containing up to 30 to 85 per cent fresh water. Most of these invertebrates maintain a more or less hypertonic internal salt concentration, regardless of the degree of brackishness of their surroundings. They include representatives of many groups, especially arthropods, mollusks, and various kinds of worms. The active absorption of salts is an important mechanism, and perhaps in some species there is actually physiological control of the amounts of water absorbed. Marine and brackish species transferred directly to fresh water usually live a few hours at most, but when the transition is made very slowly, over days or weeks, they may live for weeks or months in fresh water.

Figure 1 is a diagram showing the relative composition of the aquatic fauna in relation to salinity. One of the most striking paradoxes of fresh-water, brackish, and marine faunas is the fact that animals thrive well on the one hand in one environment that is very low in salts and on the other hand in another environment that is high in salts, but environments of intermediate salinities (brackish) have a poor fauna. From the standpoint of total number of all types of species present, it should be noted that the minimum appears at a salinity of $7^0/_{00}$ (7 parts per thousand), which is well toward the fresh-water end

of the diagram in Fig. 1. This situation results from the fact that the number of fresh-water species drops very rapidly with a slight rise in salinity, while the number of marine species drops less rapidly with a decrease in salinity.

This diagram also poses a second paradox. It shows that specific brackish-water species, which occur chiefly or exclusively in such environments, are most abundant at salinities of 7 to $10^0/_{00}$, or about the place where the fresh-water forms decrease abruptly and where the total number of all species is smallest. This condition is not to be expected since most brackish-water species have obviously been derived from marine relatives and not from fresh-water relatives. It would be more logical to expect the maximum number of brackish species much farther toward the right in the diagram.

The invasion of fresh waters is a continuing process, and some American species are undoubtedly new arrivals or are in the process of becoming adapted to fresh waters. The colonial coelenterate *Cordylophora* and a few species in each of the following groups are all typical examples: polychaetes, grapsoid crabs, shrimps, isopods, clams, and snails. A comparable list may be cited for Europe where a few species are known to have invaded fresh waters within historical times. The mitten crab of the Old World has taken up permanent residence in rivers and returns to the sea only to breed. With few exceptions, the new fresh-water forms are thought to be physiological varieties of their close marine relatives.

Several species of European crustaceans are marine in northern Europe and both brackish and fresh, or fresh alone, in central and southern Europe. Certain tropical areas, especially around the Bay of Bengal, Indonesia, the Malay Archipelago, Madagascar, and tropical America are rich in species that have only recently made their way into fresh waters from the sea. It is presumed that constant temperatures and heavy rainfalls facilitate fresh-water inva-

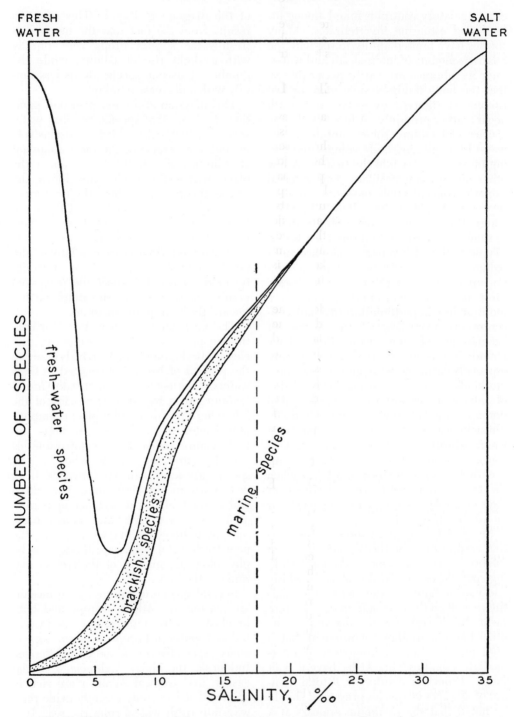

FIG. 1.—The composition of the aquatic fauna in relation to salinity of the environment. (Modified from Remane.)

sions via estuaries. An alternate, newer theory emphasizes temperate and sub-arctic regions as more likely areas for entry into fresh water, chiefly because lower temperatures minimize the physiological effects of the various ions.

## FRESH-WATER EMIGRANTS TO THE SEA

Once established in fresh water, few invertebrates have returned to brackish water and only rarely to undiluted sea water. Little is known about the major barriers to such migrations, but presumably they are physiological, and perhaps chiefly osmoregulatory. Potassium salts, which are abundant in the sea, are toxic to fresh-water invertebrates, but this effect may be partly neutralized by magnesium compounds. An impervious exoskeleton is advantageous for migrations into salt waters.

Only a few hemipterans, beetle larvae and adults, dipteran larvae and pupae (especially Culicidae, Ephydridae, and Tendipedidae), and several caddis larvae have successfully invaded estuaries, brackish waters, and the intertidal zone. Diptera larvae have occasionally been dredged from 10 to 15 fathoms off the coast of England. In Samoa there is a peculiar dipteran that is submarine for its entire life cycle. A few marine water striders occur regularly on the surface film of the seas well away from land.

Biologically, insects are considered a most successful group. They exhibit endless adaptations, occur in enormous numbers, and are found in almost every type of habitat. Yet they have not been successful in colonizing the seas. With the exception of some of the species noted above, a salt content in excess of 2.5 per cent appears to be toxic. However, brackish ponds with salt contents ranging up to 1.0 per cent are quickly colonized by certain "fresh-water" insects.

Occasionally typical fresh-water mollusks are reported from brackish estuaries. A few species of *Physa* and *Goniobasis* can endure up to 50 per cent sea water, *Amnicola* and *Planorbis* up to 30 per cent, and *Lymnaea* up to 25 per cent.

## MAJOR DISTINCTIONS BETWEEN MARINE AND FRESH-WATER INVERTEBRATES

**Osmoregulation.** Continuing the discussion of the foregoing sections, one of the basic physiological distinctions centers around the occurrence of more specialized osmoregulatory mechanisms in fresh-water organisms. Since their internal fluids are hypertonic to the greatly dilute surrounding water, there is a continuous and rapid inflow of water through all permeable surfaces of the body. Such surfaces may be epithelia, cuticle, chitin, gills, or other structures. The relative amounts of water absorbed through these various types of surfaces differ greatly from one taxonomic group to another. In general, chitin and thick cuticle are relatively impermeable.

Contractile vacuoles, flame bulb systems, nephridia, and different types of glandular structures have the function of forming a highly dilute urine which is excreted to the outside in considerable quantities. This urine is greatly hypotonic to the body fluids. By such means excessive water is prevented from accumulating in the body, and the relative concentrations of internal salts and water remain essentially constant. Figure 2 shows these relationships in a diagrammatic fashion.

Marine invertebrates usually have excretory organs that are basically more or less similar to those of their fresh-water relatives, but the urine they secrete is approximately isotonic with sea water and their body fluids. The fundamental problem

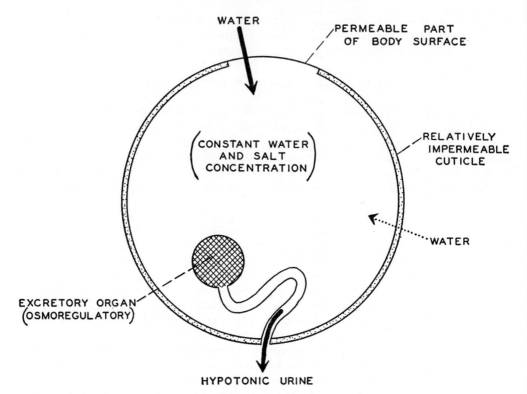

WATER

PERMEABLE PART
OF BODY SURFACE

CONSTANT WATER
AND SALT
CONCENTRATION

RELATIVELY
IMPERMEABLE
CUTICLE

WATER

EXCRETORY ORGAN
(OSMOREGULATORY)

HYPOTONIC URINE

Fig. 2.—Diagram showing the osmoregulatory water balance mechanism in a typical fresh-water invertebrate. (Greatly modified from Baldwin.)

that must be solved when a euryhaline animal invades fresh water is the physiological conversion of the osmoregulatory process to one that secretes dilute urine from hypertonic body fluids. Other things being equal, fresh-water invertebrates use more oxygen than their close marine relatives, probably because of the greater energy needed to maintain the proper internal osmotic pressure.

It is significant to note that contractile vacuoles are absent from most marine protozoans. Fresh-water isopods, amphipods, and decapods have larger excretory (osmoregulatory) glands than their marine relatives, and presumably this indicates greater activity and greater physiological and histological complexity.

Although the urine excreted by fresh-water invertebrates is highly dilute, it does contain traces of body salts. In most ani-

mals this loss is negligible and is apparently made up from food and by the slow absorption of ions through body surfaces. In a few groups of fresh-water invertebrates, however, it has been shown that there is active absorption of ions by special parts of the body, particularly in snails, mussels, leeches, dragonfly nymphs, crayfish, and some Diptera larvae. At the same time the ability to retain body salts is sometimes quite striking. Many insects and crustaceans may be placed in distilled water and kept there for weeks at a time without any apparent harm.

Although fresh-water invertebrates are generally considered stenohaline organisms, this generalization is true only in the gross sense. "Fresh water" is highly variable in total salt content and in the relative quantities of different ions present, but many common species in almost all orders of fresh-water invertebrates may be found in waters whose total salt content ranges from 0.002 to 0.04 per cent. This is actually a twenty-fold difference in dissolved salts! With the exception of a few species adapted to highly saline inland waters, however, the osmoregulatory mechanisms of most fresh-water invertebrates quickly break down when they are placed in solutions containing in excess of 25 per cent sea water (0.9 per cent salt).

**Eggs.** Fresh-water species regularly produce much smaller numbers of eggs than their marine counterparts. This difference is especially notable among mollusks and crustaceans. Fresh-water snails produce only about 20 to 500 eggs at a time, while most marine species produce thousands or tens of thousands. A large oyster produces up to 500,000,000 eggs per year, but fresh-water mussels produce only several thousand to a maximum of 3,000,000. A large marine crab may carry several million eggs, a crayfish only 10 to 800. Correlated with this difference in numbers is a further difference in size, fresh-water eggs generally being larger than marine eggs.

In fresh-water species eggs are often carried by the parent until they hatch and the young are released. This is true of certain rotifers, and essentially all cladocerans, mussels, copepods, amphipods, and isopods, in addition to some species in other groups. The egg-carrying habit is also true of some marine species, but it is by no means as frequent as in fresh-water forms. Internal fertilization is much more common among fresh-water organisms.

With the exception of some cladocerans and insects, floating and planktonic eggs are almost unknown among fresh-water species; eggs are usually heavy and sink or remain on the bottom. In marine forms, however, the production of planktonic eggs is a common occurrence. It is also generally true that fresh-water eggs are more yolky than marine eggs. A dense, tough covering or a gelatinous sheath is much more frequent among the former; many marine species have completely naked eggs.

**Larval stages.** The marine biologist is acquainted with a wealth of fascinating free-swimming larval forms produced by most worms, coelenterates, crustaceans, mollusks, echinoderms, etc. Familiar examples are ciliated trochophores, pilidia, auriculariae, planulae, and an abundance of crustacean larval types. The fresh-water biologist, on the other hand, sees few larval forms. Larval fresh-water sponges and those of a few bryozoans and coelenterates are free swimming for only a very short time. Mussel glochidia are active for only short periods. Copepods, Ostracoda, and Eubranchiopoda have series of free-swimming nauplius larvae. With the addition of certain insects, these few groups practically exhaust the list. In most fresh-water metazoans the young which hatches from the egg is a miniature unspecialized counterpart of the adult. Undoubtedly the greater abudance of yolky stored food in fresh-water eggs is correlated with the general lack of special larval stages. In marine groups where there is little yolk the newly hatched larvae must begin feeding promptly.

One theory advanced to explain the infrequency of fresh-water invasion by marine species is based on the poor adaptability of marine larvae. Although free-swimming, they are unable to make their way upstream against river currents. Even if the adults were to breed in an estuary or river, the unattached larvae would be swept downstream. It is also thought that the larval metabolism and hypertonic tissues are unable to withstand the severe and variable ecological conditions in fresh waters.

**Phylogenetic differences.** It is quite true that the seas are phylogenetically much richer than fresh waters, and there are many major taxonomic categories that are confined to salt water or are predominantly marine (lists A and B of

TABLE II. A CLASSIFICATION OF THE INVERTEBRATE KINGDOM ACCORDING TO ENVIRONMENTS. Various taxonomic categories are listed, including phyla, classes, and orders.

A. Exclusively marine
  Scyphozoa
  Anthozoa
  Ctenophora
  Echinodera
  Chaetognatha
  Brachiopoda
  Phoronidea
  Pogonophora
  Pterobranchia
  Enteropneusta
  Priapuloidea
  Archiannelida
  Poeobioidea
  Echiuroidea
  Sipunculoidea
  Echinodermata
  Mystacocarida
  Cirripedia
  Leptostraca
  Cumacea
  Tanaidacea
  Euphausiacea
  Stomatopoda
  Xiphosura
  Pycnogonida

B. Predominantly marine but with a few fresh-water species
  Porifera
  Hydrozoa
  Bryozoa
  Polychaeta
  Mysidacea
  Amphipoda

C. Chiefly marine but well represented in fresh waters
  Decapoda
  Pelecypoda

D. Abundant representatives in both marine and fresh waters
  Sarcodina
  Suctoria
  Copepoda
  Ostracoda

E. Abundant representatives in both marine and fresh waters; few terrestrial species
  Turbellaria

F. With more fresh-water species than marine
  Mastigophora
  Ciliata
  Gastrotricha
  Tardigrada

G. Predominantly fresh-water; few marine species
  Rotatoria
  Nematomorpha
  Cladocera
  Hydracarina

H. Exclusively fresh-water
  Eubranchiopoda
  Syncarida
  Thermosbaenacea

J. Chiefly marine but with a few fresh-water and terrestrial species
  Nemertea

K. Numerous marine, fresh-water, and terrestrial species
  Nematoda
  Oligochaeta
  Hirudinea
  Isopoda
  Gastropoda

L. Chiefly terrestrial, but with abundant fresh-water representatives; few marine species
  Insecta

M. Exclusively terrestrial
  Onychophora
  Progoneata (a few uncommon marine millipedes)
  Chilopoda
  Acarina (excluding Hydracarina)
  most other arachnid orders

N. Exclusively parasitic
  Sporozoa
  Trematoda
  Cestoidea
  Acanthocephala
  Linguatulida
  Myzostomata

Table II). Only three small groups, on the other hand, are exclusively fresh-water. These are the Eubranchiopoda, the Syncarida, and the single known species of Thermosbaenacea. Only the first of these three is represented in the United States. The Rotatoria, Nematomorpha, Cladocera, and Hydracarina have so few marine representatives, however, that these might just as well be considered fresh-water groups. In view of the fact that colonization of fresh waters probably

began earlier than Devonian times, it is significant that a longer list of fresh-water groups has not made its appearance.

With few exceptions, those taxonomic categories that are well represented in both environments are much richer in species in marine waters than in fresh waters. This is especially true of the Porifera, Hydrozoa, Bryozoa, Polychaeta, Mysidacea, Amphipoda, Decapoda, Pelecypoda, Copepoda, Isopoda, and Gastropoda.

For the sake of completeness, Table II

also includes strictly terrestrial and parasitic groups, and it is notable that these lists are quite short.

**Size.** As a whole, the marine fauna consists of a much greater percentage of large species. To anyone who has collected in both environments this is a striking difference, especially among coelenterates, worms, crustaceans, and mollusks. Possibly this size difference is the chief reason why marine invertebrate experimental physiology is so far advanced over the physiology of fresh-water invertebrates, since larger species are much more adaptable for many kinds of laboratory investigations.

**Coloration.** In general, fresh-water invertebrates are a rather monotonously colored lot. Most of the coloration is drab and subdued. Notable exceptions are a few brightly colored bryozoans, decapods, copepods, ostracods, amphipods, water mites, and leeches. This situation is in striking contrast to the bright coloration and distinctive patterns that are so common among marine coelenterates, worms of all kinds, crustaceans, and mollusks. No logical explanations seem to have been suggested to account for this distinction.

**Devices for withstanding unfavorable environmental conditions.** A further striking difference between marine and fresh-water animals is the frequent and regular occurrence in the latter of resting eggs, cysts, and desiccation adaptations and habits to withstand exceptionally unfavorable environmental conditions.

Such special adaptations as occur among marine animals are restricted chiefly to intertidal species and are for the most part merely special behavior patterns rather than distinctive morphological adaptations. To withstand unfavorable periods when the tide is out and when heavy rain may be falling or when the temperature is unfavorable, marine intertidal species close their shells, burrow into the sub-strate, hide in crevices or seaweeds, or remain in tide pools.

Many special resistant and dormant devices among fresh-water invertebrates are multipurpose. The same one may withstand desiccation, sometimes for long periods; it may overwinter; it may be blown about and thus increase the geographic range of the species; or it may withstand adverse chemical conditions, such as lack of oxygen, high concentrations of dissolved salts, or high temperatures. Protozoan cysts, sponge gemmules, desiccated tardigrades, bryozoan statoblasts, and desiccated bdelloid rotifers are all examples of special resistant devices. Under appropriate conditions, dormant and resistant eggs or cysts of comparable functions may also be produced by coelenterates, some turbellarians, nemerteans, gastrotrichs, rotifers, many crustaceans, and some oligochaetes.

Another common measure taken by fresh-water invertebrates is the habit of burying themselves in the substrate in a torpid state during dry or cold conditions. Some species secrete a protective layer of mucus. Examples are leeches, some snails, some copepods, a few ostracods, and some water mites.

**Neuston.** The surface film of salt water is virtually uninhabited by small metazoans, but the numerous fresh-water organisms associated with the surface film either constantly or intermittently constitute a special community, the neuston. Many hemipterans, collembolans, and even a few spiders run about on the upper face of the surface film, while some cladocerans and Protozoa are regularly attached to the under face of the film. Visitors to the film for varying lengths of time include dipteran larvae and pupae, hemipterans, beetles, planarians, hydras, a few ostracods, and some snails. The surface film is visited chiefly for food or to make brief contact with air in order to renew the supply of gaseous oxygen held on the surface of the body or in the tracheal system.

**Bioluminescence.** The phenomenon of bioluminescence is of common occurrence in a variety of animals including representatives of about 40 different and widely scattered orders. Most of these animals are marine, but there are a few terrestrial groups. In fresh waters, however, the physiological mechanisms responsible for bioluminescence have almost never evolved, and the process is very rare. Only four species of semiaquatic firefly larvae, one New Zealand fresh-water limpet, and a fresh-water shrimp in western China are bioluminescent.

**Euroky of fresh-water invertebrates.** If estuarine habitats are omitted, even the most casual comparison of marine and fresh-water environments emphasizes the much greater variations in ecological factors in the latter. This generalization holds true from one comparable fresh-water habitat to

another as well as from time to time within the same habitat. Seasonal and vertical temperature gradients in lakes and the greater variations in quiet shallows of ponds are much more pronounced than in salt water. Currents may vary seasonally from imperceptible to torrential in the same stream. Chemical conditions, including dissolved salts, dissolved organic matter, dissolved oxygen, and pH are highly variable and cannot be compared with the more monotonous conditions in typical marine habitats. Drying up of the habitat is a frequent and important hazard.

In general, therefore, our fresh-water invertebrates consist of a group of eurokous species that are physiologically, morphologically, and behavioristically adapted for maintaining themselves under trying circumstances that would be disastrous or impossible for the great majority of marine forms.

## ATYPICAL FRESH-WATER HABITATS

As a whole, fresh-water habitats are greater in variety (and often in complexity) than those of the marine environment, especially when the former include the complete series of running water habitats and many small, peculiar types of bodies of water.

If one is interested in collecting a wide variety of fresh-water invertebrates, the most favorable spots are small, weedy lakes and ponds. Such habitats afford large numbers of niches occupied by a correspondingly large variety of animals, especially mollusks, aquatic insects, crustaceans, and many representatives of the worms and wormlike groups. Food and population relationships are intricate, and presumably this complexity is the chief reason why so little comprehensive ecological work has been done on ponds and small lakes.

At the other extreme are highly specialized bodies of water in which one or more ecological conditions are so severe that

the fauna is restricted to a small number of species. Frequently, however, these few species attain great population densities, perhaps because of the lack of interspecific competition.

There is little advantage to be gained here by including a comprehensive outline classification of the many divisions and subdivisions of fresh-water communities. Several such outlines may be found in certain standard ecology texts. It may be worth while, nevertheless, to characterize some of the more peculiar habitats that represent extremes in ecological conditions. As compared with the usual sort of fresh-water habitat, these peculiar habitats are characterized by less variable ecological conditions.

**Alkali and salt lakes.** Alkali and salt lakes and ponds are common in many areas of the western states, especially where there are closed drainage basins, semiarid conditions, and soils containing large quantities of salts. Depending on surrounding soil chemistry, these waters may contain large quantities of chlorides, sulphates, or carbonates, especially those of sodium, potassium, and calcium. The expressions "salt" and "alkali" lakes are by no means sharply defined and are often interchangeable, but in general where the dissolved salts are of such composition and concentration as to produce persistent pH readings in excess of 9.4, a body of water is referred to, in common usage, as an "alkali lake."

At low concentrations, up to about 1 to 3 per cent dissolved salts, the fauna is still varied in species but much more restricted than in nonalkaline waters. Above this concentration species diminish rapidly in numbers, and the metazoan plankton becomes characterized by a few copepods and highly alkaline rotifers, particularly some species of *Brachionus* and *Pedalia* which may be extremely abundant. The insect fauna becomes highly restricted and consists mostly of Tendipedidae, occasionally one species of *Aedes*, and a few beetles.

Great Salt Lake, which contains about 25 per cent dissolved salt (chiefly sodium chloride), has been studied relatively carefully and has an extremely limited fauna. Protozoa include several ciliates, flagellates, and amoeboid forms; metazoans consist of only two species of *Ephydra* (the brine fly) and *Artemia salina* (the brine shrimp). *Artemia* populations sometimes attain an average density of five individuals per liter. In contrast to the situation in most normal lake beaches, no interstitial micrometazoan fauna has been found in the sandy beaches of Great Salt Lake.

**Polluted waters.** Waters grossly polluted with organic matter, especially sewage, likewise have a highly restricted fauna, one which is capable of thriving in very low concentrations of oxygen and high concentrations of dissolved and particulate organic matter. The chief "indi-

cator" metazoans are a few species of tubificid oligochaetes, red tendipedid dipteran larvae, psychodid larvae, and the rat-tailed maggot larva, *Tubifera*. Sometimes the bottom of polluted rivers is literally covered with a waving, writhing mass of tubificids. This habitat also supports large populations of ciliates and colorless flagellates.

At a certain distance below the entry of pollutants a river enters a "zone of recovery" in which the dissolved oxygen progressively increases and the polluting materials are oxidized or otherwise sufficiently removed from the water, especially as the result of bacterial action, so that the pollution fauna is slowly replaced by a "normal" river fauna. Depending on the intensity of pollution, size of the river, etc., the zone of recovery may begin anywhere between one-quarter mile and 100 miles downstream from the source of pollution. The fact that pollution with toxic industrial wastes of many kinds is sufficiently severe to produce biological deserts in many of our American rivers and streams is a familiar and discouraging story.

**Subterranean waters.** Subterranean streams, cave ponds, and an occasional artesian well sometimes contain endemic, primitive, or highly specialized amphipods, isopods, decapods, copepods, and turbellarians. The Ozarks and similar limestone areas are particularly rich in underground aquatic habitats. Most subterranean species are colorless, translucent, or whitish; eyes are nonfunctional or absent; tactile structures are often well developed and include long antennae and abundant long setae. The subterranean environment is completely monotonous, with constant ecological conditions. Basic food materials consist of fungi and small bits of organic debris washed underground. Populations are generally small, owing to the greatly limited food supply.

Endemic subterranean species are thought to have been derived from ancestral surface species which underwent evolutionary change and specialization concomitantly with the gradual submergence of their surface drainage habitats. It should be added that subterranean streams and ponds usually also contain common species that are regular members of aquatic communities on the surface of the ground.

**Cold springs, spring brooks.** Typical cold spring communities are restricted to a small area at and just below the point where the water issues from the ground. As soon as it flows any distance as a spring brook it becomes warmer, loses its characteristic growth of water cress, and contains a different animal community. Depending on local conditions, the typical spring and spring brook fauna zone usually extends from 10 meters to 500 meters below the source. Cold springs have an average temperature of about 8° in temperate areas, and the associated animals are mostly cold stenotherms. The list of characteristic animals is relatively small, including planarians, amphipods, and some of the following: beetles, caddis larvae, leeches, isopods, fingernail clams, small snails, and blackfly larvae. Frequently two or more of these species are numerically dominant. If the spring emerges from appropriate underground water courses in limestone areas it occasionally brings up typical subterranean species. The ecology of springs and spring brooks has been sadly neglected in the United States.

**Hot springs.** In addition to their high temperatures (above 35° C.), hot springs are often characterized by large quantities of dissolved salts. Sometimes the water is also high in dissolved carbon dioxide, hydrogen sulphide, or sulphur dioxide. Thus it is often difficult to distinguish between the limiting effects of temperature and the limiting effects of other ecological factors. In general, however, 25° to 30° seems to be the dividing line between a rich fauna at lower temperatures and a poor fauna at higher temperatures. Unlike cold springs, there do not seem to be any typical genera or species in hot springs, nor are hot spring animals ever abundant. Beetles are among the most characteristic metazoan inhabitants, many species having been reported from a wide variety of hot springs in the western states. Diptera larvae, especially Tendipedidae, are also common inhabitants, along with an occasional culicid or stratiomyid. Sometimes a few Hemiptera and Odonata may be collected. Most such records of insects are from springs whose temperatures range from 37° to 50° C. Other arthropods include amphipods, ostracods, and Hydracarina reported from springs with temperatures between 32° and 51° C. Micrometazoans are often present in exceptionally hot water, a few nematodes and rotifers having been taken as high as 60° C. Since the thermal death point of most fresh-water invertebrates is between 30° and 40°C., many hot spring animals must have developed considerable thermal acclimation.

## DISPERSAL AND BARRIERS

The successful establishment of the ancient marine ancestors of fresh-water animals in swamps and above estuaries was actually only the beginning of the story. From such footholds they must have developed a higher degree of euroky as they expanded to occupy new inland habitats.

Migration up and downstream through-out a single drainage system is comparatively easy for many fresh-water invertebrates over a long period of time. Superficially, it would appear that they are "landlocked" in separate drainage systems, with little access from one to another. In the long-time viewpoint, however, land barriers between different lakes and rivers are not effective for most groups within the confines of a single continental land mass. The ability of almost all microscopic species to form thick-shelled eggs, cysts, or resting stages that withstand partial drying or desiccation is a primary factor in ease of dispersal. Such small resting bodies are easily picked up and wind blown overland for long distances. If they drop into a favorable aquatic habitat with the appropriate combination of ecological conditions they again become active and may produce a new population nucleus.

The literature contains scattered but authentic records of live fish being transported overland by storms, tornadoes, and other strong winds, and there is no reason to doubt that plankton and bottom invertebrates are transported in the same manner. Much of the "dust" of dust storms is organic debris, and it is not improbable that a small fraction consists of cysts and eggs. Ducks, shore birds, and aquatic insects are undoubtedly important for increasing the ranges of many groups, though it should be emphasized that the literature contains little actual proof of such transport. Both resting and active stages are presumably transported in the detritus and mud that frequently sticks to the appendages. There is one authentic record of a 2½-ounce live mussel being transported overland by a duck!

Adult aquatic insects capable of flight easily migrate overland, often in what appears to be a completely random fashion, and come to occupy suitable new areas. Sometimes such flights are greatly aided by winds. Entomologists report collecting adult aquatic beetles and hemipterans five miles or more from the nearest open ponds. Occasionally such reports are for desert or semiarid regions. The surface of a concrete walk near the writer's home has a slight depression about 80 cm. in diameter which fills with water with every shower. On several occasions aquatic beetles have been found in this puddle, and the nearest spot from which they could have come is a pond more than one-half mile distant.

Anyone who follows the biological development of a new, man-made reservoir is bound to be impressed with the promptness with which the reservoir becomes colonized with aquatic animals.

Some highly eurokous and vagile species, mostly microscopic, have spread so effectively that they are essentially cosmopolitan and occur the world over in suitable habitats. The list includes a great many Protozoa and Rotatoria, several sponges, *Paracyclops fimbriatus*, perhaps *Plumatella repens*, a few oligochaetes, some Tardigrada, and several Cladocera, such as *Daphnia longispina* and *Chydorus sphaericus*. Many more species could be added to this list.

The fresh-water invertebrate faunas of North America and Europe, and to some extent northern Asia, have many of the species in the following groups in common: Protozoa, Rotatoria, Tardigrada, Bryozoa, Oligochaeta, and Cladocera. American gastrotrichs and nematodes are so poorly known that their European affinities are not established. In all of the other major taxonomic groups with low vagility, however, the great majority of species that occur in the United States are endemic and are not found in Europe.

The zoogeographic distribution of freshwater invertebrates has been rather well investigated in Europe, and zoogeographic regions have been suggested for several taxonomic groups, especially some of the orders of crustaceans and insects, and the mollusks. Numerous distribution patterns have been correlated with the effects of the advances and retreats of glaciers on the European continent. In the United States, however, comprehensive studies of fresh-water invertebrate zoogeography are largely lacking, with the notable exceptions of the mollusks, decapods, and perhaps one or two other groups.

Europe, Asia, and Africa have certain very ancient lakes where primitive species have been preserved and where geographic isolation has been effective for such a long time that independent speciation has resulted in many unique and endemic species, especially among Porifera, Turbellaria, Oligochaeta, Gastropoda, and crustaceans. Some of the better known lakes of this type are Baikal in Asia, Tan-ganyika and Nyasa in Africa, Ochrid in Jugoslavia, and the lakes of the Malili River system in the central Celebes. No such ancient lakes occur in the United States.

## FOOD WEBS

Some of the most fundamental problems of population dynamics and interrelationships are awaiting solution in the study of aquatic communities, especially in small streams, lakes, and ponds characterized by few species and few habitat niches. Using such bodies of water and some of the atypical bodies of water noted earlier in this chapter, it should be relatively easy to determine food habits of individual species and to make quantitative estimates of populations. Productivity indexes, food cycles, energy transfers from one trophic level to another, species interactions, and

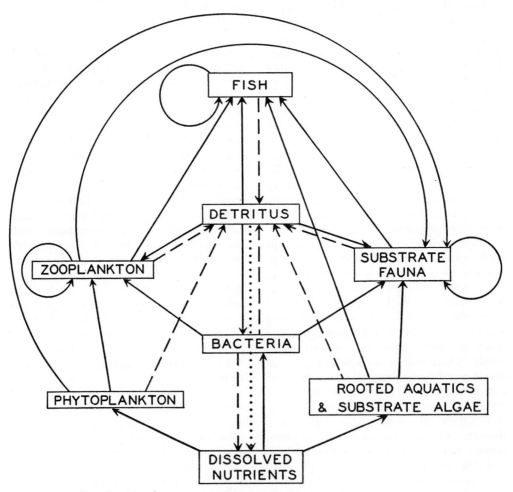

Fig. 3.—Basic features of aquatic food webs. See text for explanation.

seasonal population fluctuations are all important ecological concepts that may perhaps be derived from such studies. It is important to note that the measurement of associated physical and chemical factors in small streams, lakes, and ponds is simpler than is the case in more complex types of aquatic habitats and in terrestrial habitats.

Nevertheless, even in the simplest aquatic habitats the determination of pyramids of numbers and food chains (or better "food webs") is an involved problem, and only a very few thorough and inclusive studies have been attempted. In any such study the basic role played by detritus and bacterial action should not be minimized. In a schematic fashion Fig. 3 shows the fundamental food interrelationships for any aquatic habitat, regardless of size and complexity. The significance and role played by the various segments of this diagram vary enormously from one habitat to another. Some habitats, for example, have few or no fishes; other habitats have no rooted aquatics or a poor substrate fauna.

The solid lines in Fig. 3 indicate consumption or utilization as food. Broken lines indicate death and disintegration, or defecation by animals. The dotted line indicates disintegration of detritus as the result of certain bacterial activities. The circle arrows originating and ending at "zooplankton," "fish," and "substrate fauna" are meant to show that certain species in each of these categories are carnivorous and feed upon other individuals within the same category. Actually each such category may represent two, three, or more trophic levels. "Substrate fauna" includes all bottom invertebrates as well as the protozoans, micrometazoans, and macrometazoans associated with the surface of rooted aquatic plants and other objects. By inference "bacteria" also includes molds and their activities.

For the sake of simplicity, certain minor aspects of this food web have been omitted. For example, the contribution of excretory materials to the main reservoir of dissolved nutrients is not shown. By inference, "fish" should include other vertebrates such as frogs, salamanders, and turtles.

Not shown, but nevertheless intimately concerned with the continuing balance within the web, are the nitrogen, sulphur, and phosphorus cycles. These are fundamentally similar to the same cycles operating in terrestrial habitats.

Following is a selected list of general references. It includes (1) items referring specifically to the content of this introductory chapter, (2) texts covering essentially the same field as the present manual, (3) important accessory texts covering fields relating to the study of fresh-water invertebrates, (4) periodical references and texts covering major phases of fresh-water invertebrate biology, and (5) a few references giving laboratory and field methods. Some of these references are recent; others are older or important classics.

## GENERAL REFERENCES

ADOLPH, E. F. 1925. Some physiological distinctions between fresh-water and marine organisms. *Biol. Bull.* 48:327–335.

ALLEE, W. C., A. E. EMERSON, O. PARK, T. PARK, and K. P. SCHMIDT. 1949. *Principles of animal ecology.* 837 pp. Philadelphia, Penn.

AMERICAN PUBLIC HEALTH ASSOCIATION. 1946. *Standard methods for the examination of water and sewage.* 9th ed. 286 pp. New York, N. Y.

BADE, E. (n.d.). *Das Süsswasseraquarium. Die Flora und Fauna des Süsswasser und ihre* *Pflege im Zimmer-Aquarium.* 5th ed. 1212 pp. Berlin, Germany.

BALDWIN, E. 1937. *An introduction to comparative biochemistry.* 112 pp. New York, N. Y.

BARNES, T. C., and T. L. JAHN. 1934. Properties of water of biological interest. *Quart. Rev. Biol.* 9:292–341.

BEADLE, L. C. 1943. Osmotic regulation and the faunas of inland waters. *Biol. Rev.* 18:172–183.

BOND, R. M. 1933. A contribution to the study

of the natural food cycle in aquatic environments. *Bull. Bingham Oceanogr. Coll.* 4:1–89.

BRAUER, A. 1909–1912. *Die Süsswasserfauna Deutschlands.* 19 vols. by 32 authors. Jena, Germany.

BROOKS, J. L. 1950. Speciation in ancient lakes. *Quart. Rev. Biol.* 25:30–60, 131–176.

BRUES, C. T. 1932. Further studies on the fauna of North American hot springs. *Proc. Amer. Acad. Arts and Sci.* 67:185–303.

BUXTON, P. A. 1926. The colonization of the sea by insects: with an account of the habits of Pontomyia, the only known submarine insect. *Proc. Zool. Soc. London* 2:807–814.

CARPENTER, K. E. 1928. *Life in inland waters.* 267 pp. New York, N. Y.

CARTER, G. S. 1931. Aquatic and aerial respiration in animals. *Biol. Rev.* 6:1–35.

EDWARDS, F. W. 1926. On marine Chironomidae (Diptera); with descriptions of a new genus and four new species from Samoa. *Proc. Zool. Soc. London* 2:779–806.

ELLIS, M. M., B. A. WESTFALL, and M. D. ELLIS. 1946. Determination of water quality. *U. S. Fish and Wildlife Serv. Res. Rept.* 9:1–122.

EYFERTH, B. 1900. *Einfachste Lebensformen des Tier- und Pflanzenreiches.* 3d ed. 584 pp. Braunschweig, Germany.

FASSETT, N. C. 1940. *A manual of aquatic plants.* 382 pp. New York, N. Y.

FLORKIN, M. 1949. *Biochemical evolution.* 157 pp. New York, N. Y.

FOX, H. M., and B. G. SIMMONS. 1933. Metabolic rates of aquatic arthropods from different habitats. *Jour. Exp. Biol.* 10:67–74.

FURNEAUX, W. 1906. *Life in ponds and streams.* 406 pp. New York, N. Y.

GALTSOFF, P. S., *et al.* 1937. *Culture methods for invertebrate animals.* 590 pp. Ithaca, N. Y.

GURNEY, R. 1913. The origin and conditions of existence in the fauna of fresh water. *Trans. Norfolk and Norw. Nat. Soc.* 9:463–485.

HENTSCHEL, E. 1909. *Das Leben des Süsswassers.* 336 pp. Munich, Germany.

HESSE, R., W. C. ALLEE, and K. P. SCHMIDT. 1951. *Ecological animal geography.* Rev. ed. 715 pp. New York, N. Y.

HORA, G. L. 1930. Ecology, economics, and evolution of the torrential fauna. *Philos. Trans. Roy. Soc. London* 218B:171–282.

HUBALT, E. 1927. Contribution a l'étude des invertebres torrenticoles. *Bull. Biol. France et Belgique, Suppl.* 9:1–390.

JACOBS, W. 1935. Das Schweben der Wasserorganismen. *Erg. Biol.* 11:131–218.

KENK, R. 1949. The animal life of temporary and permanent ponds in southern Michigan. *Misc. Publ. Mus. Zool. Univ. Mich.* 71:1–66.

KROGH, A. 1939. *Osmotic regulation in aquatic animals.* 242 pp. Cambridge, England.

———. 1941. *The comparative physiology of respiratory mechanisms.* 172 pp. Philadelphia, Penn.

LAMPERT, K. 1925. *Das Leben der Binnengewässer.* 3d ed. 892 pp. Leipzig, Germany.

LOCHHEAD, J. H. 1942. Control of swimming position by mechanical factors and proprioception. *Quart. Rev. Biol.* 17:12–30.

LUCAS, C. E. 1947. The ecological effects of external metabolites. *Biol. Rev.* 22:270–295.

MACAN, T. T., and E. B. WORTHINGTON. 1951. *Life in lakes and rivers.* 272 pp. London, England.

MELLANBY, J. 1938. *Animal life in freshwater: a guide to British fresh-water invertebrates.* 296 pp. London, England.

MORGAN, A. H. 1930. *Field book of ponds and streams.* 448 pp. New York, N. Y.

MUENSCHER, W. C. 1944. *Aquatic plants of the United States.* 374 pp. Ithaca, N. Y.

NAUMANN, E. 1931. Limnologische Terminologie. *Handbuch der biol. Arbeitsmeth.*, Sect. 9, Part 8, Nos. 1–5:1–776.

NEEDHAM, J. 1930. On the penetration of marine organisms into freshwater. *Biol. Zentralblatt* 50:504–509.

NEEDHAM, J. G., and J. T. LLOYD. 1930. *The life of inland waters.* 2d ed. 438 pp. Springfield, Ill.

NEEDHAM, J. G., and P. R. NEEDHAM. 1938. *A guide to the study of fresh-water biology.* 4th ed. 89 pp. Ithaca, N. Y.

NEEDHAM, P. R. 1940. *Trout streams.* 233 pp. Ithaca, N. Y.

NICHOL, E. A. T. 1935. The ecology of a salt marsh. *Jour. Mar. Biol. Assoc. U. K.* 20:203–261.

NIELSEN, A. 1950. The torrential invertebrate fauna. *Oikos* 2:176–196.

PARK, T., *et al.* 1946. Dynamics of production in aquatic populations. *Ecol. Monogr.* 16:311–391.

PAX, F. 1951. Die Grenzen tierischen Lebens in mitteleuropäischen Thermen. *Zool. Anz.* 147:275–284.

PEARSE, A. S. 1928. On the ability of certain marine invertebrates to live in diluted sea water. *Biol. Bull.* 54:405–409.

———. 1932. Animals in brackish water ponds and pools at Dry Tortugas. *Publ. Carnegie Inst. Wash.* 435:125–142.

———. 1939. *Animal ecology.* 2d ed. 642 pp. New York, N. Y.

———. 1950. *The emigrations of animals from the sea.* 210 pp. Dryden, N. Y.

PLASKITT, F. J. W. 1926. *Microscopic fresh water life.* 278 pp. London, England.

PRATT, H. S. 1935. *Manual of the common invertebrate animals.* Rev. ed. 854 pp. Philadelphia, Penn.

REMANE, A. 1934. Die Brackwasserfauna. ( Mit besonderer Berücksichtigung der Ostsee.) *Verh. Deutsch. Zool. Ges.* **36**:34–74.

SCHLIEPER, C. 1930. Die Osmoregulation wasserlebender Tiere. *Biol. Rev.* **5**:309–356.

————. 1933. Die Brackwassertiere und ihre Lebensbedingungen vom physiologischen Standpunkt aus betrachtet. *Verh. Int. Verein. theor. angew. Limn.* **6**:113–146.

————. 1935. Neue Ergebnisse und Probleme aus dem Gebiet der Osmoregulation wasserlebender Tiere. *Biol. Rev.* **10**:334–360.

SEGERSTRÅLE, S. G. 1949. The brackish-water fauna of Finland. *Oikos* **1**:127–141.

SHELFORD, V. E. 1929. *Laboratory and field ecology.* 608 pp. Baltimore, Md.

SMITH, G. M. 1950. *The fresh-water algae of the United States.* Rev. ed. 719 pp. New York, N. Y.

STEUER, H. 1910. *Planktonkunde.* 723 pp. Leipzig and Berlin, Germany.

SUDIA, W. D. 1951. A device for rearing animals requiring a flowing water environment. *Ohio Jour. Sci.* **51**:197–202.

THIENEMANN, A. (ed.) 1926–1950 *et seq. Die Binnengewässer.* Vol. 1–18 *et seq.* Stuttgart, Germany.

THORPE, W. H. 1932. Colonization of the sea by insects. *Nature* **130**:629–630.

VON BRAND, T. 1946. *Anaerobiosis in invertebrates.* 328 pp. Normandy, Mo.

WARD, H. B., and G. C. WHIPPLE. 1918. *Freshwater biology.* 1111 pp. New York, N. Y.

WELCH, P. S. 1948. *Limnological methods.* 381 pp. Philadelphia, Penn.

————. 1952. *Limnology.* Rev. ed. 538 pp. New York, N. Y.

WELLS, M. M. 1932. *The collection and preservation of animal forms.* 72 pp. Chicago, Ill.

WESENBERG-LUND, C. 1939. *Biologie der Süsswassertiere.* 817 pp. Vienna, Austria.

WHIPPLE, G. C. 1927. *The microscopy of drinking water.* 586 pp. New York, N. Y.

WOODBURY, A. M. 1949. Animals and salinity in the Great Basin. *Amer. Nat.* **82**:171–187.

ZACHARIAS, O. 1891. *Die Tier- und Pflanzenwelt des Süsswassers.* 2 vols. 1–380, 1–369. Leipzig, Germany.

# Chapter 2

## PROTOZOA

BEGINNING with the observations on *Vorticella*, reported in 1675 in a letter to the Royal Society by the pioneer Dutch microscopist Leeuwenhoek, an enormous literature on the Protozoa has accumulated. Unquestionably this phylum has received more attention by zoologists than has any other fresh-water group. Because of the fact that a protozoan cell embodies all of the fundamental properties of living matter, it has long been a convenient object for the study of numerous phases of anatomy, cytology, physiology, behavior, and heredity; taxonomy has also been rather thoroughly investigated, but ecology is a relatively neglected phase of protozoan biology.

Protozoa occur in an extraordinary variety of habitats. Free-living species are found wherever there is water, from an accumulation of a few drops to the largest lakes and seas, and over a wide range of chemical and physical conditions. Parasitic species live in certain organs of most of the larger Metazoa that have been carefully examined. It is estimated that 15,000 to 20,000 species of Protozoa have been described, but this estimate is probably conservative. The discussion which follows is based almost exclusively on free-living fresh-water Protozoa, and emphasis is placed on features that are utilized as key characters, but most of the generalizations apply to the phylum and classes as a whole. Physiology, morphology, and anatomy are discussed only briefly; these phases of protozoan biology are thoroughly covered in many texts and review articles.

**General characteristics.** All Protozoa are single-celled organisms, though many species form colonies consisting of several to thousands of individuals. With the exception of certain reproductive individuals, however, all of the cells in a colony are fundamentally independent and similar in structure and function.

The physical nature of protoplasm is perhaps best studied in Protozoa. Essentially it consists of water in which are dissolved a wide variety of organic and inorganic materials and in which is suspended a variety of minute droplets and solid particles, the whole constituting a complex colloidal system. Fibrils, networks, alveoli, Golgi bodies, chondriosomes, and other granules and droplets larger than colloidal size serve to increase further the physical complexity. Viscosity is more or less variable and reversible from sol to gel states. Typical protozoan protoplasm is translucent and colorless or faintly tinted, but many species are colored by ingested foods, stored materials, or pigments such as chlorophyll. Thus green, yellowish, brown, gray, bluish, and reddish are common colorations.

Size ranges from about 5 microns to 5 mm., but the great majority of species are more than 30 microns and less than 300 microns long. Body shape is highly variable, but spherical, oval, elongated, and more or less flattened are the most common body forms. In flattened species the ventral surface is arbitrarily defined as that surface nearest the substrate and usually bearing the cytostome. Symmetry includes spherical, radial, and bilateral patterns, and asymmetry.

The Phylum Protozoa is clearly subdivided as follows:

SUBPHYLUM PLASMODROMA. Movement by means of pseudopodia or flagella, or without locomotion; with a single type of nucleus; holozoic, holophytic, saprozoic, or mixotrophic.

> Class Mastigophora. Locomotion by means of one or more flagella.
>
> Class Sarcodina. Locomotion by means of pseudopodia.
>
> Class Sporozoa. Without locomotor organelles; spore-producing; all parasitic. Not considered in this manual.

SUBPHYLUM CILIOPHORA. Move by means of cilia; usually with macronucleus and micronucleus; holozoic, saprozoic, or mixotrophic.

> Class Ciliata. Cilia present throughout life; usually free-swimming.
>
> Class Suctoria. Cilia only in immature stages; adult with suctorial tentacles; sessile.

The external surface of Sarcodina is usually a naked, thin, living plasmalemma, but in the ciliates, Suctoria, and many flagellates there is also a protective pellicle of varied composition. In addition, both flagellates and Sarcodina often have a thicker shell, case, or armor composed of cellulose, jelly, tectin (pseudochitin), calcium carbonate, or silicon dioxide. Frequently an outer protective sheath or lorica is distinctly separated from the periphery of the cell. Sometimes the outer case consists of foreign particles imbedded in a homogeneous matrix.

In ciliates and Sarcodina the layer of protoplasm just below the bounding membrane is usually a relatively clear ectoplasm in contrast to the more granular endoplasm internal to it.

The nucleus is nearly always difficult to distinguish in living, unstained material. In the ciliates and Suctoria the macronucleus is granular, large, and of variable shape, ranging from round or oval to elongated, beaded, branched, or horseshoe shaped; the one or more micronuclei are very small. Sarcodina have a single type of nucleus; a few genera, such as *Pelomyxa* and *Actinosphaerium*, are multinucleate. The nucleus of free-living flagellates is single, vesicular, and usually more or less centrally located.

**Locomotion.** Typical Sarcodina move about by means of streaming movements and temporary extensions of the cell called pseudopodia. The mechanics of pseudopodial movement have been most extensively studied by Mast and his students, and adequate descriptions are included in most standard zoology texts and reference books.

Four types of pseudopodia are generally recognized, though there are intergradations and none of them can be clearly separated from the others. Lobopodia are finger-like, tongue-like, rounded, or branched; they contain both ectoplasm and endoplasm (Figs. 4A–C). Filopodia are more or less filamentous, usually pointed, and consist of ectoplasm only (Figs. 26E–G). Reticulopodia are also filamentous and composed of ectoplasm but they are branching and anastamosing (Fig. 27D). Axopodia are semipermanent owing to a relatively stiff axial rod which in most cases ends internally in a small granule (Fig. 29).

In general, those Sarcodina having lobopodia move most rapidly, usually 0.5 to 3.0 microns per second, while those having other types of pseudopodia are more sluggish or do not move at all.

A flagellum is essentially a long, fine, whiplike protoplasmic thread which produces forward locomotion by spiral or un-

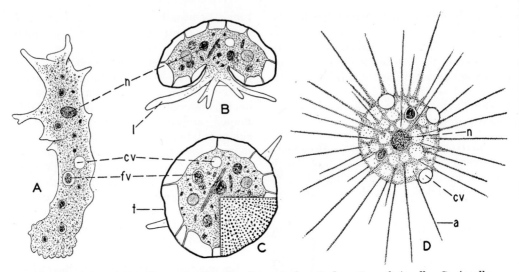

Fig. 4.—Typical Sarcodina. A, *Amoeba*; B, vertical optical section of *Arcella*; C, *Arcella*, showing partial horizontal section and partial external surface of test; D, *Actinophrys sol* Ehr. *a*, axopodium; *cv*, contractile vacuole; *fv*, food vacuole; *n*, nucleus; *l*, lobopodium; *t*, test.

dulating movements. Sometimes, however, the basal region is more or less rigid and only the distal half or tip moves about. Many Mastigophora have two flagella, both of which function in locomotion, but in some genera there are one to several accessory flagella which have little or no locomotor function. Accessory posteriorly directed flagella are thought to have a slight pushing or steering function in a few species.

Flagella are commonly inserted at or near the anterior end of the cell, often in a groove, pit, or cytopharynx. The attachment is variable, complex, and sometimes double, but it is not visible in unstained specimens. Usually the flagellum originates in a basal granule just within the periphery of the cell. The basal granule may or may not be combined with another granule, the blepharoplast, just below. A fine fibril, or rhizoplast, sometimes connects the basal granule and blepharoplast with the edge of the nucleus.

Flagellates usually move at the rate of 15 to 300 microns per second. Under adverse environmental conditions the flagella may be lost, but regeneration occurs promptly when conditions are again favorable.

Fundamentally, cilia are somewhat similar to flagella, but there are several important differences. Cilia are much shorter, very abundant, and have only a single basal granule. They are arranged in longitudinal, diagonal, or oblique rows, and their movements are often coordinated so that waves of beats pass along the entire animal. A single cilium is thought to have a pendular or side-to-side movement, usually in one plane or with an oval pattern at the tip. Ciliates move more rapidly than other Protozoa, the usual speed being 200 to 1,000 microns per second.

Cilia may also be fused to form more complex structures. A membranelle, for example, is a double lamella of cilia completely fused into a plate and found in the region of the cytostome, oral groove, or peristome (Figs. 7F, 36–39). Adoral membranelles occur in all ciliates except the Holotricha.

Undulating membranes of ciliates range in size from delicate aggregates no broader than the length of an ordinary

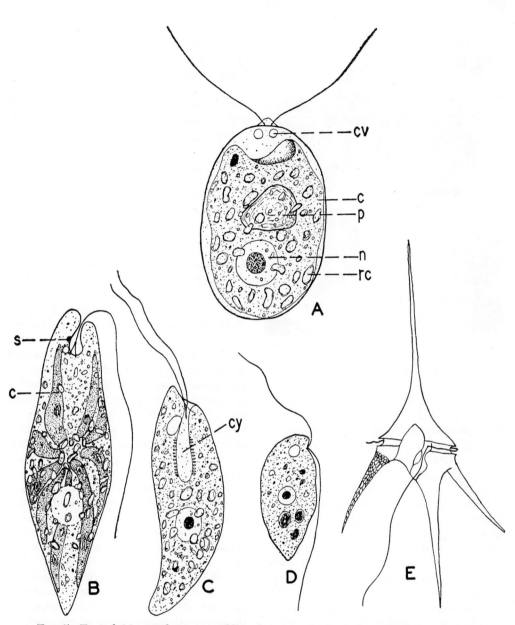

FIG. 5.—Typical Mastigophora. A, *Chlamydomonas*; B, *Euglena viridis* Ehr. (chromatophores very difficult to distinguish in living animal); C, *Chilomonas paramecium* Ehr.; D, *Bodo*; E, *Ceratium hirundinella* (O. F. M.) with only a portion of shell sculpturing shown. *c*, chloroplast; *cy*, cytopharynx; *cv*, contractile vacuole; *n*, nucleus; *p*, pyrenoid; *rc*, reserve carbohydrate granules; *s*, stigma.

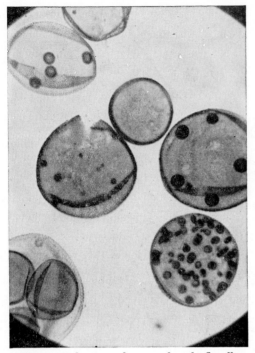

Fig. 6.—*Volvox*, a large colonial flagellate (×100); note mature colonies, young and old daughter colonies, and clusters of microgametes.

cilium to enormous balloon-like structures (Figs. 7F, 35E). An undulating membrane is composed of a single longitudinal row of fused cilia, but there is often a group of from two to as many as five or six such membranes in the peristomial area near the cytostome or in the cytopharynx.

Cirri are the most specialized ciliary organs and are particularly characteristic of the Hypotricha. They are highly variable in size and are located more or less definitely on the ventral surface (Fig. 7G). According to their location, they are known as frontal, marginal, ventral, anal, and caudal cirri. A cirrus has an elongated conelike shape and consists of a tuft of fused cilia. Unlike other locomotor organelles, cirri move about in any direction, and consequently they are used for walking, running, jerking, and jumping movements.

In addition to true locomotion, many Protozoa possess pronounced powers of contraction and extension. These movements are usually the result of contractility of unspecialized protoplasm, but in many ciliates there are fine contractile fibrils, or myonemes, in the ectoplasm just below the surface of the body.

Many genera of ciliates, flagellates, and amoeboid Protozoa are normally sessile and attached to the substrate, either with or without a stalk, but frequently these Protozoa metamorphose into temporary "swarmer" stages which are capable of moving to new locations where they again attach to the substrate and assume the usual body form. A temporary, motile telotroch of a stalked, sessile ciliate is shown in Fig. 41C.

**Feeding, nutrition.** Those Protozoa that ingest solid particles of food, including bacteria, algae, other Protozoa, small Metazoa, or debris, are said to be holozoic. Many flagellates possess chromatophores and chlorophyll and are plantlike, or photosynthetic, in their nutrition; carbon dioxide and water are absorbed from the surroundings and synthesized into carbohydrates in the presence of light and chlorophyll; this photosynthetic type of nutrition is called holophytic. From carbohydrates, and especially with the addition of absorbed nitrogen, phosphorus, and sulphur compounds, the other organic constituents of the cell are synthesized. Saprozoic nutrition involves absorbing dissolved salts and simple organic materials from the surrounding medium and synthesizing them into protoplasmic materials; this type of nutrition occurs in all classes of Protozoa. Parasitic nutrition is sometimes placed in a separate category, but since it usually involves the absorption of dissolved materials, it is essentially a specialized type of saprozoic nutrition. However, some parasites ingest particulate matter and might therefore be considered holozoic. Many Protozoa are mixotrophic, that is, they exhibit two of the above types of nutrition. Some ciliates, for example, are both holozoic and sapro-

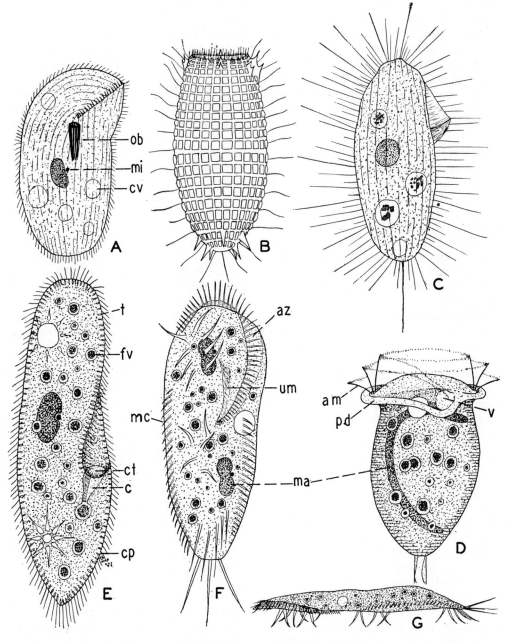

Fig. 7.—Typical Ciliata. A, *Chilodonella cucullula* (O. F. M.); B, *Coleps octospinus* Noland; C, *Cyclidium*; D, *Vorticella*; E, *Paramecium*; F, ventral view of *Stylonychia mytilus* (O. F. M.), showing eight frontal, five ventral, five anal, and three caudal cirri; G, lateral view of S. *mytilus*. *am*, adoral membrane; *az*, adoral zone; *c*, cytopharynx; *cp*, cytopyge; *ct*, cytostome; *cv*, contractile vacuole; *fv*, food vacuole; *ma*, macronucleus; *mc*, marginal cirrus; *mi*, micronucleus; *ob*, oral basket; *pd*, peristomial disc; *t*, trichocyst; *um*, undulating membrane; *v*, vestibule. (B modified from Geiman.)

zoic, and some flagellates are both holophytic and saprozoic. *Ochromonas* is a flagellate in which holozoic, holophytic, and saprozoic nutrition all occur.

Holozoic Protozoa may be conveniently classified according to their general food habits. *Spathidium, Dileptus, Didinium,* and *Actinobolina,* for example, are all carnivorous ciliates which feed on other Protozoa, usually only certain species. *Frontonia, Chilodon,* and most Sarcodina are herbivores which feed on algae, while many other genera are bacterial feeders. *Blepharisma, Spirostomum,* and *Stentor* are examples of omnivores which feed on all kinds of particulate matter, both living and dead. There are convincing data to show "selection" of certain types of food by some omnivorous ciliates, but in general such observations are variable and inconclusive.

Lobopodia commonly advance in such a way as to surround and enclose a food particle. The latter is then within the cell in a droplet of water, the whole constituting a food vacuole. Sometimes amoeboid Protozoa ingest particles by an invagination process when the particles come in contact with the general body surface. Occasionally large particles, such as algal filaments, are seen to "glide" into the cell by an "import" process. Pseudopodia of many amoeboid groups are sticky so that a food particle sticks to the general body surface on making contact and is then drawn within to form a food vacuole.

With few exceptions, the chlorophyll of holophytic flagellates is localized in chromoplasts (chloroplasts) which may be disc-, band-, bowl-, or cup-shaped, but sometimes the green color is masked by accessory yellow, orange, or brown pigments. A red pigment, hematochrome, often appears in some green flagellates, but it is distributed throughout the cytoplasm and is thought to be formed as a response to low concentrations of nitrogen and phosphorus. Pyrenoids are small proteinaceous bodies which are imbedded in chloroplasts and around which the carbo-

hydrate products of photosynthesis accumulate as laminae or granules. After they are formed, these particles (glycogen, paramylum, or starch) are evidently available to the general cytoplasm as reserve foods. Green flagellates vary widely with respect to their specific nitrogen requirements. Most species can use ammonium and nitrate compounds, others require amino acids, and some are even able to use peptones. These three groups of green flagellates are sometimes termed photoautotrophic, photomesotrophic, and photometatrophic, respectively.

Although many green flagellates are obligate phototrophs, there are numerous species that can also be grown in the dark, provided the correct dissolved nutrients are available in the culture medium. The Zoomastigina and many nonphotosynthetic Phytomastigina are holozoic, saprozoic, or mixotrophic. Like green flagellates, the colorless saprozoic species differ widely in their nitrogen requirements. In the holozoic species small food particles come in contact with the surface of the cell and sink or are drawn inward, sometimes by definite pseudopodial action. Many flagellates, both green and nongreen, possess an anterior cytostome, cytopharynx, and reservoir through which the flagellum projects, but particulate food is taken into the cell through this opening in only a very few holozoic forms.

Though many ciliates are saprozoic or mixotrophic, the great majority are holozoic. Movement through the water as well as beating of cilia, membranelles of the peristome, and undulating membranes all serve to collect the food and bring it into the cytostome and cytopharynx. In raptorial genera, however, such as *Coleps, Didinium, Prorodon,* and *Lacrymaria,* the prey is relatively large, and current production has little to do with food getting. At the lower end of the cytopharynx the particles enter the cell proper as food vacuoles. In some ciliates, especially Gymnostomata, the wall of the cytopharynx is stiffened by minute rodlike trichites which collectively form the cytopharyngeal basket (Figs. 31, 32).

Though the Suctoria are all holozoic and feed mostly on ciliates, much remains to be learned about the precise mechanisms of feeding. The struggling prey is held tightly at the tips of the tentacles, and contact with the tentacles often (but not always) kills the prey in a matter of seconds, the rigid tentacles being presumed to secrete a potent toxin. American fresh-water species have only one type of tentacles; they are suctorial and often knobbed. Only a few of the tentacles attached to the prey serve as cytostomes and these enlarge to a diameter twice or more that of the nonsucking tentacles. The protoplasm flows through these hollow tentacles and is formed into food vacuoles as it enters the cell proper. The entire contents of even large ciliates may be sucked up in as little as 20 minutes. Tentacles may be localized in bundles or more generally distributed over the body surface.

**Digestion.** In holozoic species the ingested food organisms may be killed in a few seconds after being taken into the food vacuole or they may stay alive for as long as an hour. Digestive enzymes are released into the food vacuoles from the surrounding cytoplasm. A variety of protein and carbohydrate digesting enzymes have been demonstrated, but the occurrence of fat-digesting enzymes is difficult to prove though they are undoubtedly present.

In most Protozoa that have been carefully studied the hydrogen ion concentration of the food vacuoles is variable but usually within the range of pH 4.0 to 7.6, most digestion being under acid conditions. Depending on the food supply and the activity of a protozoan, there may be few to many contained food vacuoles. As digested materials are absorbed into the cytoplasm through the membrane of the food vacuole the contents of the vacuole become progressively smaller, and the in-

digestible residue is voided through a temporary rupture in the cell membrane, though in ciliates and flagellates there is often a permanent pore, the cytopyge, for this purpose.

**Reserve foods.** Depending on ecological and physiological conditions, a protozoan cell may contain little to much reserve food. It may be in the form of glycogen, paraglycogen, starch, paramylum, or protein granules, or there may be droplets of reserve lipoids. Paramylum can be easily distinguished from starch by the fact that it does not stain blue with iodine.

**Respiration.** The great majority of Protozoa are aerobic, the oxygen being absorbed from the surroundings through the cell membranes. Nevertheless, it is probable that more than 90 per cent of our fresh-water species are capable of thriving in water that is less than 10 per cent saturated with oxygen. Indeeed, a great

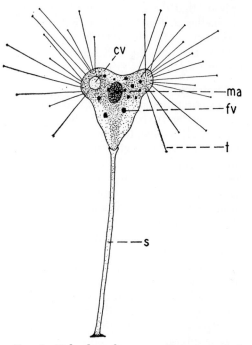

FIG. 8.—*Tokophrya lemnarum* Stein, a typical suctorian. *cv*, contractile vacuole; *fv*, food vacuole; *ma*, macronucleus; *s*, stalk; *t*, tentacle.

many species have been reported from anaerobic habitats such as sewage, the debris and mud of stagnant ponds, and the bottoms of lakes during periods of oxygen exhaustion, but these species are thought to be mostly facultative and temporary anaerobes capable of tolerating anaerobic conditions for variable periods but not able to maintain themselves indefinitely. The following genera, however, are known to have some obligatory anaerobic representatives: *Chlamydophrys, Vahlkampfia, Saprodinium, Mastigamoeba, Bodo, Holophrya, Trepomonas,* and *Metopus.* Under both permanent and temporary anaerobic conditions it is thought that energy is derived from reactions similar to fermentation processes.

**Excretion.** As in higher animals, the chief metabolic excretory products are water, carbon dioxide, and nitrogenous materials. Sometimes the latter are retained as granules or crystals for a variable time within the cell. It is now the general opinion that there are no special excretory organelles in Protozoa, but that dissolved excretory materials, notably urea, simply diffuse through the cell membranes into the surroundings.

**Contractile vacuoles.** These organelles are osmoregulatory devices which remove excess water from the cell. Since the internal salt concentration of fresh-water Protozoa is much higher than that of their surroundings, there is a continuous osmotic uptake of water through the cell membranes. The accumulation of water from the general cytoplasm and the release of water to the outside by the vacuoles therefore serve to maintain a constant internal salt-water balance.

Contractile vacuoles are found in all fresh-water Sarcodina and Mastigophora, and in all Ciliophora regardless of habitat. They do not occur in the Sporozoa or in most parasitic and marine Sarcodina and Mastigophora.

The Sarcodina have one or more contractile vacuoles of indefinite location.

Each one starts out as a coalescence of several minute adjacent droplets. The small vacuole then grows, reaches a certain size, and bursts and releases its contents to the outside through a temporary rupture in the plasmalemma. New vacuoles appear in any part of the cell. In the Mastigophora there is a single small contractile vacuole. It is constant in location and usually anterior in the Phytomastigina and posterior in the Zoomastigina. Ciliophora have one to many contractile vacuoles, all constant in position and opening through permanent pores in the pellicle; sometimes these vacuoles are supplied by a complex system of collecting canals in the cytoplasm.

The rate of pulsation of a contractile vacuole is dependent on such factors as temperature, age, physiological state, food, salt concentration, etc. In some Protozoa a volume of water equivalent to the volume of the entire cell may be voided in as short a time as two minutes; under other conditions and in other species an equivalent amount of water may be voided in 24 to 48 hours.

It is probable that insignificant quantities of dissolved nitrogenous wastes leave the cell in the expelled fluid of the vacuole, but this is merely incidental to the main osmoregulatory function.

**Irritability, behavior.** Basic perception and response to contact, food, gravity, light, chemicals, etc. are probably all due to the general irritability of protozoan protoplasm. Nevertheless many Protozoa have special receptors. The stigma, or eyespot, of some flagellates is a minute clump of granules with an adjacent light-sensitive area of cytoplasm; such stigmata commonly produce a directional locomotion toward a light source, as shown, for example, by the accumulation of *Euglena* along the lighted side of a culture jar set in a north window. Special cilia or bristles are thought to be touch receptors in some ciliates.

A great many observations have been

made on protozoan behavior, but only a few general examples can be cited here. Favorable environmental conditions elicit no visible responses, but under unfavorable circumstances, especially where there are gradients, Protozoa generally move away from the unfavorable and toward the favorable conditions. *Paramecium* and many other ciliates exhibit "trial and error" or "avoiding" reactions. Upon coming in contact with an unfavorable medium or object, they stop, retreat, turn slightly, and resume locomotion in a new direction; such movements may be repeated until the protozoan reaches favorable conditions. A few ciliates exhibit negative geotaxis.

As a group, only the stigma-bearing flagellates show reactions to light. They are generally photopositive to weak or medium light sources but photonegative to strong lights. Other Protozoa are mostly indifferent to usual light sources, though some are photonegative to exceptionally strong light.

Transmission of impulses is a regular function of the protoplasm, but in many ciliates a special neuromotor system of conducting fibrils has been demonstrated. Essentially, such a system consists of very fine longitudinal and transverse fibrils connecting the basal granules of the cilia. Many fibrils come together and are more or less centralized in the region of the cytopharynx. The neuromotor system functions as a coordinating apparatus for movements of the cilia, but elasticity, support, and contraction are also suggested functions.

Trichocysts are minute, cigar-shaped pockets of material which are symmetrically arranged and very abundant in the ectoplasm of numerous ciliates. When such ciliates are stimulated by pressure or various chemical substances, the trichocysts are discharged through minute surface pores, and on contact with water the substance of each trichocyst forms instantaneously into a long, rigid, needle-like projection from the cell. Little is known about the functions of trichocysts. In a

few species they are used for anchoring to a substrate; perhaps they are useful in carnivorous species for capturing prey; possibly they function in warding off enemies.

**Reproduction.** The usual method of reproduction involves mitosis and binary fission, resulting in two new individuals which quickly reconstitute themselves and form new organelles where necessary. Amitosis is probably limited to the macronucleus of Ciliophora. A few free-living fresh-water Protozoa exhibit multiple fission and plasmotomy.

Syngamy is best developed in some of the colonial green flagellates where certain of the vegetative cells become specialized as gametes. In some genera the uniting gametes are apparently identical, and the condition is called isogamy. At the other extreme, such as in *Volvox*, the condition is clearly heterogamous, one of the gametes being small, motile, and spermlike and the other being very large, nonmotile, and egglike. In all cases, however, the zygote eventually gives rise to a new individual or colony.

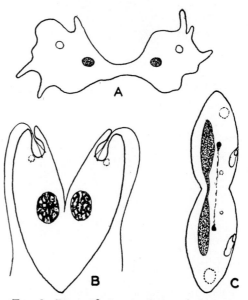

Fig. 9.—Binary fission in Protozoa, diagrammatic. A, *Amoeba*; B, *Euglena*; C, *Paramecium*.

Conditions most favorable for growth are also most favorable for rapid division, but under unfavorable, crowded conditions and in old cultures many ciliates commonly exhibit one of two complex phenomena—conjugation and autogamy.

Conjugating ciliates come together in pairs and unite temporarily along their lateral edges. Then follows a complex series of nuclear phenomena which differ from one species to another. In general, however, the process involves disintegration of the macronuclei, a series of mitotic and meiotic divisions of the micronuclei, and an exchange of micronuclear material. The migrating and stationary micronuclei then unite to form a single nucleus in each of the two conjugants. The animals separate, and there is a series of rapid nuclear and cell divisions accompanied by the reappearance of macronuclei derived from micronuclear material. Complex series of "mating types" have been found for several ciliates.

Autogamy involves nuclear changes within a single individual and includes segmentation and absorption of the macro-nucleus and a series of divisions of the micronuclei. Subsequent fusion of a pair of micronuclei is accompanied by reconstitution of the macronucleus. Like conjugation, the process of autogamy is completed within one to several days.

Basically, conjugation and autogamy seem to be rejuvenation phenomena by which there is a reshuffling of chromosomes and genes. General physiological vigor and fission rates appear to be increased in a population as a result of these processes. Figures of conjugation and autogamy are available in most elementary zoology textbooks.

Budding is almost restricted to the Suctoria where it is the common method of reproduction. In exogenous budding one to several ciliated buds, each with a nucleus, are constricted off from the external surface of the parent cell. Endogenous buds are liberated into internal spaces, or brood chambers, from which they soon escape to the outside. The ciliated embryos swim about for several hours, then become attached to the substrate, lose their cilia, and grow to mature size.

**Encystment.** The formation of resistant, protective cysts is rare among marine Protozoa but very common in fresh-water species. Cyst formation may be induced by any one of a variety of adverse environmental conditions, including drying, heat, cold, lack of food, and various chemical substances. The protozoan first rounds up and loses its flagella, cilia, and sometimes other organelles. The cyst wall which is then secreted around the periphery is usually double, consisting of a thin inner and a tough outer capsule. Sometimes a third innermost albuminous membrane is also formed.

Such cysts are extremely resistant to desiccation, freezing, and high temperatures. Dry cysts commonly remain viable for several months to several years, though there are records of some that were kept for as long as forty years.

Excystment of dry cysts and reconstitu-

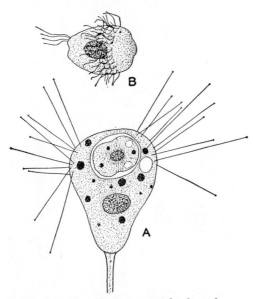

Fig. 10.—Reproduction in *Tokophrya lemnarum*. A, animal containing larva within brood pouch; B, released larva. (Modified from Noble.)

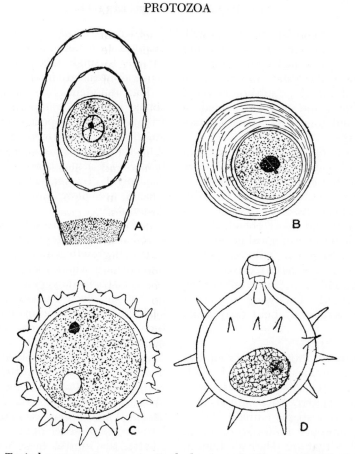

Fig. 11.—Typical protozoan cysts. A, *Euglypha* (amoeboid); B, *Colpoda* (ciliate); C, *Pleurotricha* (ciliate); D, *Ochromonas* (flagellate). (A modified from Kühn, 1926; B and D modified from Doflein, 1923; C modified from Ilowaisky.)

tion of the cells are induced in a few minutes when the cysts come in contact with suitable natural waters or culture solutions. Encysted Protozoa in old culture solutions will excyst when fresh water, salts, hay extracts, and various organic materials are added.

A few Protozoa are known to form reproductive cysts, in which fission occurs, or digestion cysts which are formed after a large food intake.

**Ecology.** In general, ponds and pools contain the greatest numbers of species though not necessarily the greatest numbers of individuals. Such waters consist of a large number of microhabitats and

afford a wide variety of niches. The open waters of lakes contain a characteristic assemblage but small number of species, including representatives of the following genera: *Dinobryon, Mallomonas, Peridinium, Ceratium, Gymnodinium, Trachelomonas,* and *Eudorina.* Sometimes summer populations of plankton species in lakes may reach more than five million individuals per liter.

Trickling filters, polluted waters, and Imhoff tanks have a rich and characteristic ciliate fauna. Certain species of *Euglypha, Pelomyxa, Trepomonas, Hexamita, Anthophysis, Carchesium,* and *Bodo* are commonly known as "sewage Protozoa." Colonial green flagellates, on the other hand, are usually most abundant in waters with a high oxygen content. Euglenoids are dominant in small ponds with a high organic content, while testate rhizopods are abundant and varied in sphagnum bogs. Even tree holes and the water held in large leaves and flowers have their characteristic faunas.

Owing to ease of transport, especially in the dry, cyst condition, most species are cosmopolitan, but local distribution seems to be governed by such factors as light, temperature, food, dissolved oxygen, acidity or alkalinity, and many chemical substances. Seldom can ecological generalizations be based on genera, only on species. Consequently an ecological classification of fresh-water Protozoa can be only of the most general sort. Following is such a classification suggested about forty years ago:

1. Katharobic Protozoa are found in springs, brooks, rivers, and ponds that are rich in oxygen and low in organic matter. Such habitats usually have a sparse fauna.

2. Oligosaprobic Protozoa occur in habitats that are relatively high in dissolved salts but low in organic matter; these habitats include the open waters of most lakes and reservoirs.

3. Mesosaprobic Protozoa occur in habitats where there is active oxidation and decomposition. The majority of Protozoa thrive under these conditions.

4. Polysaprobic Protozoa live in habitats where there is much organic matter and carbon dioxide and often quantities of hydrogen sulphide and methane. Pollution, sewage, and anaerobic Protozoa belong in this category.

Most free-living species show wide ranges of tolerance to single environmental factors, but at the same time it is thought that their activities may be af-fected by relatively slight environmental changes. In general, flagellates react more directly to single factors than do ciliates, while amoebae are intermediate.

The abundance of particulate or dissolved nutrients is important for the distribution of most species, but food is restrictive only when feeding is selective, as it is for carnivorous species. Otherwise food is only a quantitative limiting factor. As might be expected, euryphagous species are most common and widely distributed.

Noland (1925) stressed the distribution of ciliates with respect to food supply. Bacterial growth is most vigorous in acid habitats and where there are small quantities of dissolved oxygen and large quantities of dissolved carbon dioxide; under such circumstances forms feeding on bacteria become abundant. On the other hand, in alkaline habitats where dissolved oxygen is high and dissolved carbon dioxide low, the growth of algae is favored; in such habitats ciliates that feed on algae are abundant. Although certain physical and chemical factors may not in themselves determine the presence or absence of specific ciliates, the sum of these interdependent factors produces bacterial and algal growths in varying degrees, and the precise make-up of the ciliate populations is correspondingly determined.

Picken (1937) has emphasized the fact that an assemblage of Protozoa is not a collection of individuals depending on one source of food, but a complex of herbivores, carnivores, omnivores, and detritus feeders, forming a closed social structure. He analyzed the food chains in several protozoan communities characterized by widely different proportions of diatoms, blue-green algae, and bacteria. *Stentor* and *Dileptus* were at the ends of these chains.

The most pronounced seasonal population changes are quantitative, and temperatures below 10°C. and above 28° markedly affect the numbers of individuals present but not the numbers of species; summer and winter species lists from the same habitat are often strikingly similar. A few species have become adapted to hot springs where temperatures remain as high as 60°, but most species have a thermal death point somewhere between 30° and 43°. Optimum temperatures generally lie between 16° and 25°. Though trophic forms are killed by freezing, a great many species are active in water under ice throughout the winter.

The majority of species tolerate the wide range of ionic concentrations occurring in natural fresh waters, and although some species live in both fresh and marine waters, only a few can be transferred directly from one to the other. The transition is often successful, however, if it is carried out gradually in the laboratory. Seven species are known from the highly saline waters of Great Salt Lake.

Laboratory experiments have shown that many species can maintain themselves over a wide range in hydrogen ion concentration. *Euglena viridis* Ehr., for example, has been cultivated in hydrogen ion concentrations ranging from pH 2.3 to 11.0, *E. gracilis* Klebs in 3.0 to 9.9, *Glaucoma* sp. in 4.0 to 8.9, and *Chilomonas paramecium* Ehr. in 4.1 to 8.4. *Stylonychia pustulata* Ehr., however, will grow only between pH 6.0 and 8.0, and *Spirostomum ambiguum* Ehr. between 6.8 and 7.5. A few species are restricted to highly acid peat bogs in the range of pH 2.0 to 4.0; *Euglena mutabilis* is found in acid coalmine pits in the range of pH 1.8 to 3.9 and has been cultured in the range of pH 1.4 to 7.9. Nevertheless, the great majority of Protozoa have optimum conditions between pH 6.5 and 8.0.

**Succession.** Anyone who has kept hay infusions or other types of mixed cultures in the laboratory is aware of the fact that such cultures exhibit a rapid, complex, overlapping series of population growths and declines for the various species. Typically, the dominant hay infusion forms appear and become abundant in the following sequence: small flagellates, *Colpoda,* hypotrichs, *Paramecium, Vorticella,* and *Amoeba. Paramecium* does not usually become abundant until eight to fourteen days after the culture is begun, and *Amoeba* two to six weeks later when the culture is "dying out." No equilibrium is reached in such mixed cultures, and as yet sufficient information is not available to explain the sequence of species. Undoubtedly, such factors as food, temperature, light, dissolved oxygen, dissolved carbon dioxide, acidity, and the specific nature of the culture are important; and certainly the more intangible factors such as competition for food, available particulate and dissolved nutrients, and reproductive potential are also significant. Some investigators have presented evidence to indicate that a period of intensive growth of one species is brought to a halt by the accumulation of its own excretory products, and perhaps the growth cycle of one species may result in a favorable medium for another species. Seasonal and cyclic populations of Protozoa have also been studied in natural habitats, especially in the plankton, but these are likewise only poorly understood. The fundamental difficulty involved in protozoan succession studies is our inability to measure, control, and assess the relative significance of many interacting ecological factors.

**Ectocommensal Protozoa.** Many freshwater Metazoa have Protozoa living on their general external surfaces or gills, and some species are thought to be obligatory commensals, although it is sometimes difficult to decide just what special benefits the protozoan derives from such an association. Certain species of Suctoria, for example, are known only from the carapace of turtles; others are often abundant on the gills and appendages of Crustacea. Chonotricha, Peritricha, and sessile flagellates are also especially common on Crustacea. The curiously modified ciliates *Kerona* and *Trichodina* are common on the external surface of hydras where they run about rapidly in search of bits of food. However, some species of *Trichodina* are external parasites of fish, especially in hatcheries, but since they are frequently associated with other protozoan parasites such as *Chilodon, Costia,* and *Ichthyophthirius,* it is difficult to determine the relative importance of *Trichodina* as a true parasite.

**Organisms living in and on Protozoa.** Although there are a few Phycomycetes and many bacteria that are internal parasites of Protozoa, there are also some bacteria that are internal symbionts, or commensals, especially in amoeboid Protozoa, as well as a few bacteria that are apparently epiphytic on the external surface of Protozoa. Certain ciliates, including some species of *Paramecium, Stentor,* and others, commonly contain internal commensal green, blue-green, or yellow algae (therefore called zoochlorellae, zoocyanellae, and zooxanthellae, respectively). Such algae are ordinarily free-living and autotrophic species, but when they occur as symbionts they are presumed to obtain carbon dioxide and nitrogen and phosphorus compounds resulting from the protozoan metabolism and to contribute oxygen and carbohydrates to the protozoan. *Proales parasita* is a common parasitic or predatory rotifer in the interior of *Volvox* colonies.

**Economic importance.** Although parasitic Protozoa are of inestimable importance because of their adverse effects on the well-being and economic status of man, the free-living species are of little significance. During the summer months, however, some species become so abundant in municipal water supplies in rivers, lakes, and reservoirs as to impart an offensive odor to the water. Blooms of *Dinobryon, Chlamydomonas, Eudorina, Pandorina, Volvox, Glenodinium,* and *Peridinium* produce fishy odors. *Synura* smells like cucumber or muskmelon and has a bitter taste. *Mallomonas* has an aromatic, violet, or fishy odor. *Ceratium* produces a

"vile stench." Such disagreeable odors and tastes are more or less eliminated from water supplies by copper sulphate treatment, filtration, or aeration.

Of considerable theoretical importance is the role played by Protozoa in aquatic food chains. Holophytic and saprozoic species are producers which utilize dissolved nutrients and serve as food for small Metazoa. Holozoic species are consumers which form an essential link between particulate living and dead material on the one hand and rotifers, Crustacea, and other small Metazoa on the other hand.

**Collecting.** Plankton and littoral species may be collected with a fine townet, but other free-living species are best obtained by collecting submerged green and rotting vegetation, bottom debris and ooze, and surface scum. A useful device for collecting on and above soft substrates is a long sucking tube attached to a collecting bottle. Materials should be brought back to the laboratory in a quantity of water in which they occur. If desirable, they may be concentrated in a smaller volume by pouring off a part of the water through bolting silk. Stacked laboratory finger bowls are convenient containers. Collections should be allowed to stand in moderate diffuse light where the temperature is not too high. Stigma-bearing species then migrate toward the side facing the strongest light; amoeboid forms remain in the debris, but ciliates often swim about in the water above. If such containers are kept in the laboratory for one to several weeks, additional species often appear.

**Cultures.** Mixed cultures for general study are easily made with hay, lettuce powder, wheat, and rice infusions which are inoculated with pond water. The most successful cultures are obtained by excluding small Metazoa such as oligochaetes and entomostraca, and by adjusting light, food, temperature, and pH to favorable conditions. Moldy cultures should be discarded. Detailed directions for mixed and pure cultures are given in Kudo (1946) and Needham *et al* (1937).

**Examination, preparation.** There is no substitute for the study of *living* Protozoa; killing and fixing agents almost invariably distort specimens badly and make them unfit for accurate identification. Furthermore, instead of using an ordinary glass slide, it is better to use one that has a small, shallow concavity. If a drop of culture solution is placed in the concavity, covered with a Number 1 cover slip, and sealed with vaseline, evaporation is prevented and the living specimens may be studied with the high power of the microscope for hours at a time. Sometimes similar hanging-drop preparations are advantageous. For making careful observations on cilia and flagella dark-field illumination is occasionally useful. It is always important that clean slides, cover slips, and pipettes be used for working with live Protozoa.

Most ciliates move about so rapidly that they cannot be studied with the high powers of the microscope. Their movements may be impeded with cotton fibers or lens paper fibers. Narcotics, such as chloretone, isopropyl alcohol, or nickel chloride, are unsatisfactory because they usually alter body shape and physiology. Viscous agents such as agar, gelatin, tragacanth, or quince seed jelly are at best only moderately successful, but a viscous solution of methyl cellulose is excellent. This reagent is made up by dissolving 10 grams of methyl cellulose (viscosity rating of 15 centipoises) in 90 ml. of water. A drop of this syrupy solution is mixed with a drop of the protozoan culture on a slide before putting on the cover slip. A little experience will determine the relative amounts of culture solution and methyl cellulose that should be used. Movements of ciliates in this mixture are reduced to a minimum, and they may be carefully studied with the high powers. Furthermore, there is no distortion or detectable

impairment of the activities of the organelles or physiological processes.

The nucleus and certain organelles can best be distinguished in living Protozoa with the aid of vital stains. Methylene blue is perhaps the best general vital stain; a small amount is placed on the slide and allowed to dry before water containing the Protozoa is placed on it. One per cent aqueous solutions of Bismarck brown and neutral red are also good.

Noland's combined fixative and stain is excellent for demonstrating flagella and cilia in temporary mounts; it has the advantage of producing a minimum of distortion.

Phenol, saturated aqueous solution.. 80 ml.
Formalin ...................... 20 ml.
Glycerin ...................... 4 ml.
Gentian violet ................. 20 mg.

The dye should be moistened with 1 ml. of water before adding the other ingredients. A drop of this reagent should be mixed with a drop of the culture solution before putting on the cover slip.

Permanent, stained slides are mandatory for careful cytological work; a variety of fixatives, stains, and procedures are given in Kudo (1946) and in microtechnique handbooks. Schaudinn's fluid is perhaps the most generally used fixative. It is made up as follows:

Saturated aqueous mercuric chloride. 66 ml.
Absolute or 95 per cent alcohol..... 33 ml.
Glacial acetic acid .............. 1 ml.

The first two ingredients can be kept mixed without deterioration, but the acid should be added just before using. After fixation, specimens can conveniently be brought through changes of 50, 70, 95 per cent, and absolute alcohol in a centrifuge tube with gentle centrifuging between changes. A drop of the alcohol containing the concentrated Protozoa is then dropped with a pipette from a height of about one inch onto a slide coated with egg albumen. Following this, the slides are placed in absolute alcohol and thereafter treated as ordinary sections for staining.

**Taxonomy.** Unlike some metazoan phyla, the great majority of Protozoa die and disintegrate without leaving any fossil record, the only important exceptions being the skeleton-bearing Foraminifera and Radiolaria, both marine groups. Consequently, our ideas concerning the natural taxonomic relationships of the major groups are necessarily based on existing morphological traits, physiology, and development.

The older idea of amoeboid Protozoa being ancestral to the other groups has been discarded, and most protozoologists believe that the flagellates, especially green flagellates, are most primitive. This conviction is based on the fact that holophytic organisms utilizing dissolved nutrients must necessarily have preceded holozoic forms feeding on particulate organic materials. Furthermore, it is comparatively easy to derive the Sarcodina from holozoic flagellates. The origin of the Sporozoa (all parasitic), however, is obscure; they are probably polyphyletic, with flagellate and amoeboid ancestry. Both the Ciliata and Suctoria are highly evolved and complex in structure. The former probably originated from some of the more advanced flagellates, while the Suctoria undoubtedly arose from ciliated ancestors by loss of cilia and development of tentacles during the adult stage.

Morphologically, the ciliates and suctorians are sharply defined classes, but many flagellates are known that are more or less amoeboid, and some amoeboid forms have flagella. The flagellate order Rhizomastigina, for example, has holozoic representatives with well-developed pseudopodia, including *Mastigamoeba* and *Mastigella*. Many representatives of other flagellate orders also have pseudopodia in varying degrees; some of these are *Rhizochrysis*, *Oikomonas*, *Chrysamoeba*, and *Bodo*. On the other hand, some Sarcodina such as *Pseudospora* and *Dimastigamoeba* are flagellated swarmers during a short period of their life history.

The criteria to be used for subdividing the Class Mastigophora and distinctions between "true flagellate algae" and "true flagellate protozoa" are kindred and highly controversial problems which have been discussed for many years (see especially the reviews of Pringsheim, 1941, 1942, and Fritsch, 1944). Many members of the subclass Phytomastigina of the zoologist are classified by the botanist as members of the Chrysophyceae, Dinophyceae, Chlorophyceae, Euglenophyceae, and Cryptophyceae, and all of these classes of algae also include nonmotile genera. Most of the discussion has centered around the Phytomastigina, a group which contains pigmented and colorless forms, as well as holophytic, holozoic, saprozoic, and mixotrophic forms. At one extreme, a few investigators have advocated placing all chlorophyll-containing species with the Algae and all nonpigmented forms with the Protozoa. Most protistologists, however, have a broader viewpoint of these questions; they maintain that a sharp division of flagellates into "plant" and "animal" species is purely an artificial device and serves no useful purpose. Indeed, there is much to be said for considering flagellates as a mutual and primitive stage of organization of both the plant and animal kingdoms, and there is no real reason why many flagellates cannot be claimed by both zoologists and botanists. The widely accepted opinion emphasizes the fact that the flagellates do not constitute a natural taxonomic group but represent diverse branches in a stage of cellular organization, that some orders are quite artificial, and that the majority of orders contain both pigmented and nonpigmented forms. Some holozoic and saprozoic colorless forms are easily linked with their pigmented relatives, but in other cases few indications of affinities can be found. The following respective pairs of pigmented and nonpigmented genera appear to be closely related: *Cryptomonas* and *Chilomonas*, *Euglena* and *Astasia*, *Chlamydomonas* and *Polytoma*.

About 450 genera of free-living Protozoa

are known to occur in the fresh waters of the United States, but many of these are uncommon and have been reported only once or a few times. Such rare genera are mainly of interest only to the specialist. In order to determine just what genera should be included in this volume, however, the complete list of genera was sent to a group of American protozoologists along with a request that they strike from the list about 150 genera that they considered as being least likely to be encountered in field collections and laboratory cultures. Eight protozoologists [*] collaborated in this effort, and as the result of their "votes" the complete list was cut to 303 genera, all of which are included in the key which follows.

With few exceptions this key is drawn up for the identification of *living* Protozoa. Measurements are given chiefly for general information and should not usually be used as key characters. In each case the greatest dimension is noted; it is given for the cell proper and does not include stalk, flagella, cilia, cirri, tentacles, or case. In colonial species the measurements are given for single individuals of the colony. Except where size ranges are given, lengths are rough averages and are subject to a plus or minus one-third variation. In

[*] These men are listed and their kind assistance is acknowledged in the Preface to this volume.

general, a representative common species is figured for each genus Most of these figures are diagrammatic optical sections or surface views intended to emphasize key characters. Nuclei are often shaded, but it should be remembered that they are generally translucent in living Protozoa. Some of the figures have been drawn especially for this manual, but a large number are modified, simplified, or composites from a great many literature sources. Almost without exception, these latter figures are so considerably modified from their antecedents as to make acknowledgments unnecessary and superfluous. All figures have been drawn free hand.

The numbers of species known for the various genera are not usually included in the following key, chiefly because few genera have been thoroughly monographed. A few genera are monospecific; examples are *Uroglena*, *Distigma*, *Teuthophrys*, *Urocentrum*, and *Bursaria*. The great majority of genera occurring in the United States, however, are represented by more than three species, and some, such as the following, are represented by ten, twenty, or more species: *Euglena*, *Peridinium*, *Trachelomonas*, *Amoeba*, *Vorticella*, *Lionotus*, *Chilodonella*, *Cyclidium*, *Metopus*, *Euplotes*, *Epistylis*, and *Zoothamnium*.

## KEY TO COMMON GENERA OF PROTOZOA

1. With one or more flagella.
   Subphylum **PLASMODROMA**, Class **MASTIGOPHORA**, 4
   Without flagella. . . . . . . . . . . . . . . . . . . . . . . . . . . . . . . . . . .2
2. With pseudopodia. . . . . . . . . . . . . . . . . . . Subphylum **PLASMODROMA**, 120
   Without pseudopodia. . . . . . . . . . . . . . . . . . . . . . . Subphylum **CILIOPHORA**, 3
3. With cilia; free-swimming or sessile. . Class **CILIATA**, Subclass **EUCILIATA**, 161
   Adult with suctorial tentacles (Figs. 8, 42); cilia only in uncommon immature
      stages; usually sessile. . . . . . . . . . . . . . . . . . . . . . . . . . . Class **SUCTORIA**, 295
4. With one or more chromatophores. . . . . . . . . . . . . Subclass **PHYTOMASTIGINA**, 5
   Without chromatophores. . . . . . . . . . . . . . . . . . . . . . . . . . . . . . . . . . . . . . . .79
5. With two flagella, of which one extends transversely around the cell (Fig. 12).
   Order **DINOFLAGELLATA**, 6
   With one to four flagella, directed anteriorly or trailing. . . . . . . . . . . . . . . . . .14
6. Naked or covered with a thin exoskeleton (Figs. 12A–E). . . . . . . . . . . . . . . . .7
   Covered with a thick exoskeleton (Figs. 12F–H). . . . . . . . . . . . . . . . . . . . . . .11

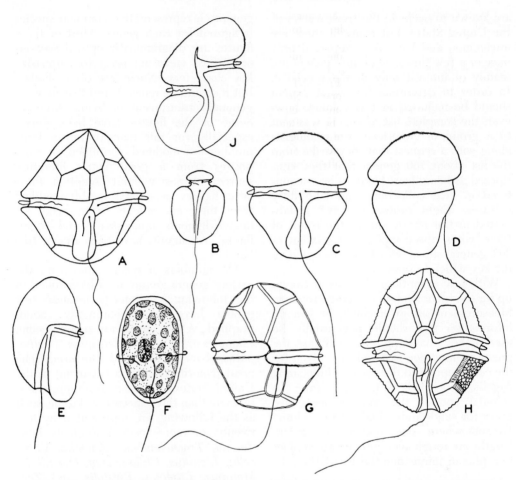

Fig. 12.—Representative Dinoflagellata. A, *Glenodinium cinctum* Ehr.; B, *Amphidinium* (chromatophores present or absent); C, ventral view of *Gymnodinium*; D, lateral view of *Gymnodinium*; E, *Hemidinium*; F, *Phytodinium*; G, *Gonyaulax*; H. *Peridinium tabulatum* (Ehr.) with only a small portion of shell sculpturing shown; J, *Gyrodinium*. (A and H modified from Eddy; C and D modified from Thompson.)

7.  Covered with a thin exoskeleton; several yellow to brown chromatophores; annulus complete (Fig. 12A); 40 microns; common.
    CYSTODINIIDAE, **Glenodinium**
    Naked; numerous chromatophores.........................GYMNODINIIDAE, 8
8.  Annulus anterior (Fig. 12B); 30 microns.......................**Amphidinium**
    Annulus not anterior............................................9
9.  Annulus spiral (Fig. 12J); 25 microns..........................**Gyrodinium**
    Annulus not spiral.............................................10
10. Annulus complete (Figs. 12C, D); 40 microns; common..........**Gymnodinium**
    Annulus incomplete (Fig. 12E); 28 microns....................**Hemidinium**
11. Exoskeleton with transverse and longitudinal grooves and divided into plates (Figs. 12G, H).......................................PERIDINIIDAE, **12**
    Exoskeleton without grooves; plates absent; spherical or ellipsoidal (Fig. 12F); 45 microns............................PHYTODINIIDAE, **Phytodinium**

12. Flattened and with one anterior and three posterior long, hornlike processes (Fig. 5E); highly variable; 100 to 500 microns; very common plankter in lakes and ponds.................................**Ceratium hirundinella** (Müller)
    Not flattened; without long hornlike processes; 40 microns.................**13**
13. Annulus displaced (Fig. 12G).....................................**Gonyaulax**
    Annulus not displaced (Fig. 12H); common in plankton............**Peridinium**
14. With yellow, brown, or orange chromatophores; usually quite small..........**15**
    With green chromatophores, or chromatophores absent......................**35**
15. With stored oil droplets; body often amoeboid...Order **CHRYSOMONADINA, 16**
    With stored carbohydrate granules; with a cuticle; body form constant; holophytic, holozoic, or saprozoic; 25 microns........Order **CRYPTOMONADINA, 32**
16. Motile stage dominant; often temporarily amoeboid; colonial or solitary.
                                    Suborder **EUCHRYSOMONADINA, 17**
    Inactive (palmella) stage dominant....................................**31**

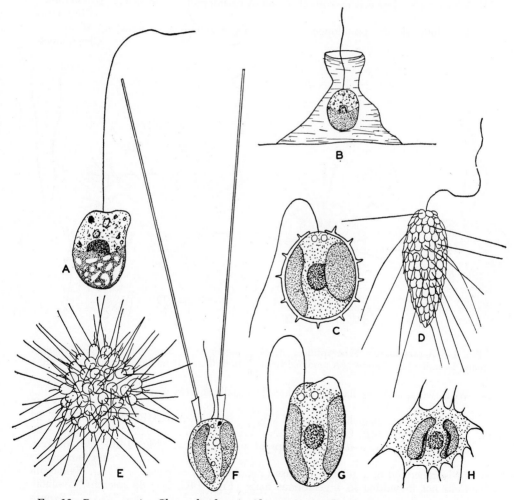

Fig. 13.—Representative Chromulinidae. A, *Chrysapsis*; B, *Chrysopyxis*; C, *Chrysococcus*; D, *Mallomonas*; E, colony of *Chrysosphaerella*; F, individual *Chrysosphaerella*; G, *Chromulina*; H, *Chrysamoeba*. (D modified from Smith, 1920.)

17. With a single flagellum...............................CHROMULINIDAE, **18**
    With two flagella.....................................................**24**
18. Cells in spherical colonies; each cell with two, long, siliceous rods (Figs. 13E, F);
    15 microns; plankton....................................**Chrysosphaerella**
    Not colonial ........................................................**19**
19. Cell with a lorica (Figs. 13B, C); 9 microns...........................**20**
    Cell without a lorica................................................**21**
20. Lorica more or less flattened; attached to algae (Fig. 13B)........**Chrysopyxis**
    Lorica not flattened (Fig. 13C)..........................**Chrysococcus**
21. Elongated; with siliceous scales and spines (Fig. 13D); 30 microns; plankton.
    **Mallomonas**
    Not elongated; without siliceous scales and spines......................**22**
22. Chromatophore diffuse or branching; amoeboid (Fig. 13A); 12 microns.
    **Chrysapsis**
    Chromatophore not diffuse or branching (Figs. 13G, H)....................**23**
23. Without pseudopodia, or with short, blunt pseudopodia (Fig. 13G); 16 microns.
    **Chromulina**
    With long, slender pseudopodia (Fig. 13H); flagellate stage transient; 20 microns.
    **Chrysamoeba**

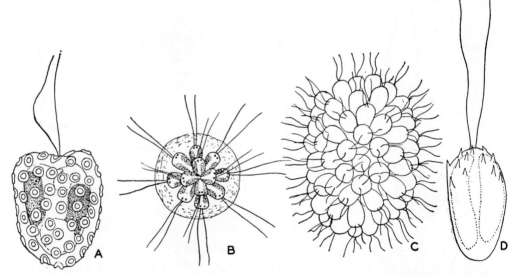

Fig. 14.—Representative Syncryptidae. A, *Hymenomonas*; B, *Syncrypta* colony; C, *Synura* colony; D, individual *Synura*. (A modified from Conrad; C and D modified from Smith, 1920.)

24. With two apical flagella of equal length; usually in acid waters.
    SYNCRYPTIDAE, **25**
    With two apical flagella of unequal length..........OCHROMONADIDAE, **27**
25. Colonial (Figs. 14B, C)................................................**26**
    Solitary; two chromatophores; ellipsoid to cylindrical (Fig. 14A); 35 microns.
    **Hymenomonas**
26. Cells imbedded in a gelatinous mass (Fig. 14B); 11 microns..........**Syncrypta**
    Cells not imbedded in a gelatinous mass (Figs. 14C, D); 35 microns; common.
    **Synura**
27. Each cell enclosed within a delicate lorica (Figs. 15A-C)..................**28**
    Each cell not enclosed within a lorica................................**29**

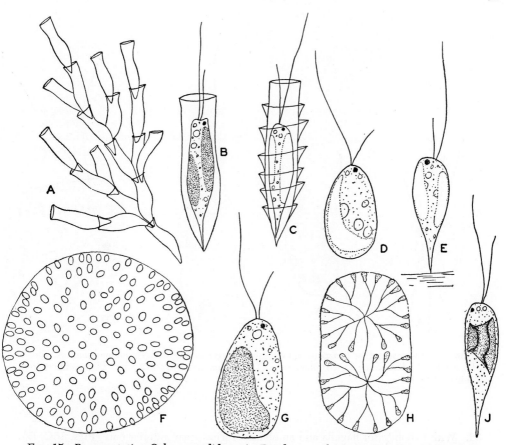

Fig. 15.—Representative Ochromonadidae. A, *Dinobryon* colony; B, *Dinobryon* individual; C, *Hyalobryon*; D, free-swimming *Ochromonas*; E, sessile *Ochromonas*; F, *Uroglenopsis* colony; G, *Uroglenopsis* individual; H, *Uroglena volvox* Ehr. colony; J, *U. volvox* single individual. (A modified from Smith, 1920.)

28. Lorica homogeneous, without growth rings (Figs. 15A, B); common in plankton.
                                                                        **Dinobryon**
    Lorica with growth rings (Fig. 15C); epiphytic; sometimes solitary...**Hyalobryon**
29. Solitary or colonial; individuals not arranged on periphery of a gelatinous mass
    (Figs. 15D, E); 22 microns...........................................**Ochromonas**
    Colonial and with individuals arranged on periphery of a gelatinous mass......**30**
30. Center of colony without dichotomously branched strands (Figs. 15F, G); 6
    microns; when present in abundance imparts an offensive odor to water.
                                                                   **Uroglenopsis** *
    Center of colony with dichotomously branched strands which are best seen in
    stained specimens (Figs. 15H, J); 16 microns........**Uroglena volvox** Ehr.*
31. Body amoeboid, with one or two chromatophores (Fig. 16A).
                                     Suborder **RHIZOCHRYSIDINA**, Rhizochrysis
    Cells imbedded in a branching gelatinous mass, 2 to 30 cm. long; attached to sub-
        strate in mosslike masses in cold mountain streams; with an acrid odor;
        recently divided cells often forming flagellated zoospores.
                              Suborder **CHRYSOCHRYSIDINA**, Hydrurus foetidus (Vill.)

* Some investigators contend that these two genera should be united into a single genus, *Uroglena.*

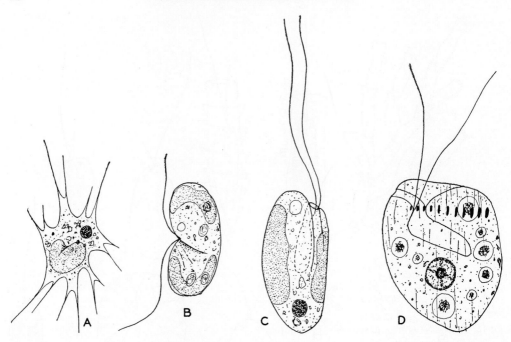

Fig. 16.—Representative Rhizochrysidina, Nephroselmidae, and Cryptomonadidae. A, *Rhizochrysis*; B, *Nephroselmis*; C, *Cryptomonas*; D, *Cyathomonas truncata* Ehr. (D modified from Ulehla, 1911.)

32. With two anterior flagella and an oblique furrow near anterior end (Figs. 16C, D).
     CRYPTOMONADIDAE, 33
     With two lateral flagella and an equatorial furrow (Fig. 16B).
     NEPHROSELMIDAE, **Nephroselmis**
33. With two chromatophores of variable coloration; dorsal periphery convex, ventral
     periphery almost flat (Fig. 16C)..........................**Cryptomonas**
     Without chromatophores; common in stagnant water and infusions...........34
34. Body oval, flattened, and obliquely truncate at anterior end (Fig. 16D); holozoic.
     **Cyathomonas truncata** Ehr.
     Body cylindrical and elongated (Fig. 5C); saprozoic..............**Chilomonas**
35. With stored starch granules and oil droplets; always two or more flagella; rarely
     elongated; without cytostome and cytopharynx.
     Order **PHYTOMONADINA, 37**
     With stored oil droplets and (or) paramylum granules; one or two flagella, usually
     one; commonly elongated; usually with cytostome and cytopharynx......36
36. With stored paramylum granules, sometimes oil droplets also; stigma present;
     common ..............................Order **EUGLENOIDINA, 60**
     With stored oil droplets, never paramylum granules; no stigma; rare.
     Order **CHLOROMONADINA, 77**
37. Solitary ........................................................38
     Colonial .........................................VOLVOCIDAE, 44
38. With an external bivalve membrane (Figs. 17A, B); 16 microns.
     PHACOTIDAE, 39
     Without a bivalve membrane.......................................40

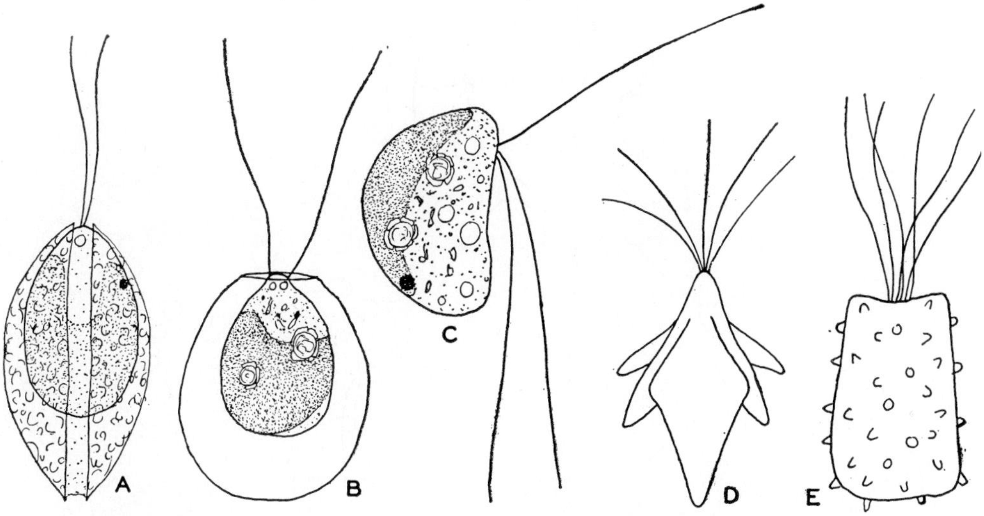

Fig. 17.—Representative Phytomonadina. A, *Phacotus*; B, *Pteromonas*; C, *Trichloris*; D, *Chloraster*; E, *Pocillomonas*.

**39.** Bivalve membrane sculptured, halves evident in vegetative cell (Fig. 17A); stagnant water.................................................................**Phacotus**
Bivalve membrane not sculptured, halves evident only in dividing cell (Fig. 17B).
**Pteromonas**
**40.** With two flagella.........................CHLAMYDOMONADIDAE, **51**
More than two flagella.................................................**41**
**41.** With three flagella; bean-shaped (Fig. 17C); 14 microns.
TRICHLORIDIDAE, **Trichloris**
More than three flagella...............................................**42**
**42.** With four flagella.................................CARTERIIDAE, **57**
With more than four flagella...........................................**43**
**43.** With five flagella; four anterior wings (Fig. 17D); 16 microns.
CHLORASTERIDAE, **Chloraster**
With six flagella (Fig. 17E); 13 microns..POLYBLEPHARIDIDAE, **Pocillomonas**
**44.** Colony a flat plate (Figs. 18A, B); cell 13 microns.......................**45**
Colony spherical or subspherical.......................................**46**
**45.** Gelatinous envelope with anterior-posterior differentiation; 16 or 32 cells (Fig. 18A).
**Platydorina**
Gelatinous envelope without anterior-posterior differentiation; 4 or 16 cells (Fig. 18B)................................................**Gonium**
**46.** Colony with at least 500 cells; colony up to 600 microns in diameter (Fig. 6).
**Volvox**
Colony with not more than 256 cells....................................**47**
**47.** With cells of two different sizes; 32, 64, or 128 cells per colony (Fig. 18C).
**Pleodorina**
Cells all of same size.................................................**48**
**48.** Cells more or less spherical...........................................**49**
Cells pear-shaped; 8 or 16 cells per colony.............................**50**
**49.** Cells close together; 4, 8, 16, or 32 cells per colony (Fig. 18D); cells 12 microns.
**Pandorina**
Cells farther apart; 16, 32, or 64 cells per colony (Fig. 18E); cells 17 microns.
**Eudorina**

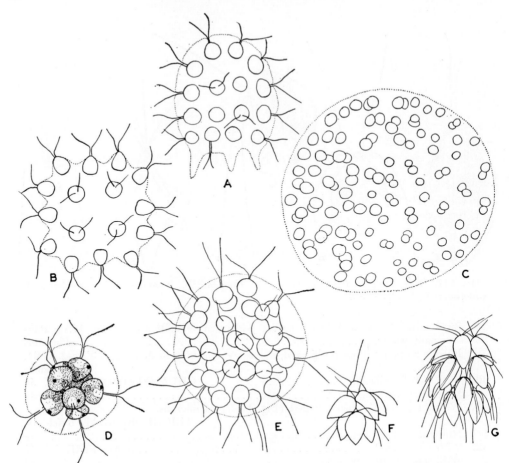

Fig. 18.—Representative Volvocidae. A, *Platydorina*; B, *Gonium*; C, *Pleodorina*; D, *Pandorina*; E, *Eudorina*; F, *Chlamydobotrys*; G, *Spondylomorum*. (C, D, and E modified from Smith, 1920.)

50. Cells with two flagella (Fig. 18F); cell 15 microns............**Chlamydobotrys**
    Cells with four flagella (Fig. 18G); cell 19 microns...........**Spondylomorum**
51. With chromatophores.................................................**52**
    Without chromatophores; saprozoic..................................**55**
52. Spindle-shaped (Fig. 19A); 50 microns.......................**Chlorogonium**
    Cell not spindle-shaped.............................................**53**
53. Cell apparently naked (Fig. 5A); 8 to 22 microns.............**Chlamydomonas**
    Cell not naked.....................................................**54**
54. Cell covered with gelatinous envelope (Fig. 19B); sometimes red pigmented; 10
    to 50 microns.....................................................**Haematococcus** *
    Cell surrounded by a capsular shell (Fig. 19C); 21 microns........**Coccomonas**
55. Spindle-shaped (Fig. 19D); 30 to 80 microns...................**Hyalogonium**
    Not spindle-shaped.................................................**56**
56. Ovoid (Fig. 19E); 23 microns.....................................**Polytoma**
    Anterior margin obliquely truncate (Fig. 19F); 15 microns.......**Parapolytoma**

    * This genus is sometimes called *Sphaerella*.

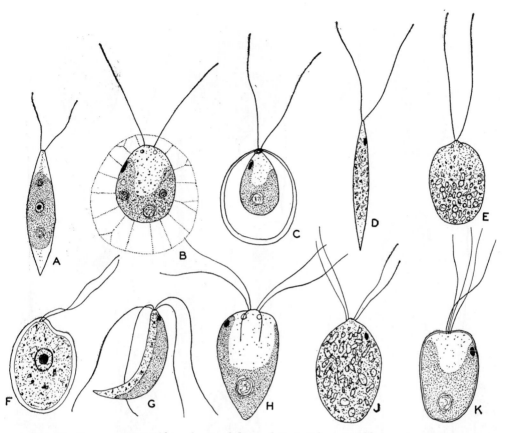

FIG. 19.—Representative Chlamydomonadidae and Carteriidae. A, *Chlorogonium*; B, *Haematococcus*; C, *Coccomonas*; D, *Hyalogonium*; E, *Polytoma*; F, *Parapolytoma*; G, *Spermatozopsis*; H, *Pyramimonas*; J, *Polytomella*; K, *Carteria*.

57. Sickle-shaped (Fig. 19G); rarely biflagellated; 8 microns........**Spermatozopsis**
    Not sickle-shaped...................................................**58**
58. Pyramidal or heart-shaped (Fig. 19H); 20 microns..............**Pyramimonas**
    Ovoid or ellipsoid..................................................**59**
59. Colorless (Fig. 19J); 14 microns...........................**Polytomella**
    Green (Fig. 19K); 6 to 24 microns..............................**Carteria**
60. With stigma; chromatophores almost invariably present (Figs. 20B–G).
                                                EUGLENIDAE, **62**
    Stigma and chromatophores absent..................................**61**
61. With one visible flagellum...............................ASTASIIDAE, **68**
    With two visible flagella............................ANISONEMIDAE, **73**
62. Highly flattened, asymmetrical, and often longitudinally striated and twisted (Fig. 20B); 30 to 170 microns.......................................**Phacus**
    Not highly flattened and asymmetrical...............................**63**
63. With a lorica, often spinous, and flagellum projecting from anterior aperture (Fig. 20G); 30 microns.................................**Trachelomonas**
    Without a lorica.....................................................**64**
64. With a short posterior spinous projection (Fig. 20C); 30 microns.....**Crumenula**
    Without a short posterior spinous projection.........................**65**

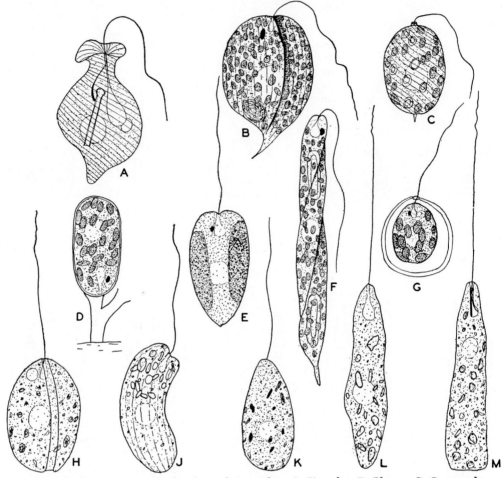

Fig. 20.—Representative Euglenidae and Astasiidae. A, *Urceolus*; B, *Phacus*; C, *Crumenula*; D, *Colacium*; E, *Cryptoglena*; F, *Euglena*; G, *Trachelomonas*; H, *Petalomonas*; J, *Menoidium*; K, *Scytomonas*; L, *Astasia*; M, *Peranema*. (A modified from Senn.)

65. Individuals stalked and colonial (Fig. 20D); flagellum present only in motile stage; often epizoic on copepods; 25 microns......................**Colacium**
    Not stalked and colonial...............................................**66**
66. Rigid, ovate, and somewhat compressed (Fig. 20E); 13 microns; uncommon.
                                                                   **Cryptoglena**
    Elongated and plastic................................................**67**
67. With chromatophores; often striated (Figs. 5B, 20F); stagnant water; about 50 species; 25 to 500 microns; very common......................**Euglena**
    Without chromatophores but otherwise similar to *Euglena*; saprozoic; 45 microns.
                                                                    **Khawkinea**
68. Flask-shaped, with a funnel-like neck (Fig. 20A); holozoic and saprozoic; 40 microns. ..........................................................**Urceolus**
    Not flask-shaped.....................................................**69**
69. With one or more longitudinal keels or grooves along one side (Fig. 20H); holozoic or saprozoic; 23 microns................................**Petalomonas**
    Without longitudinal keels or grooves................................**70**

**70.** Rigid, more or less curved; pellicle delicately striated (Fig. 20J); 15 to 80 microns.

**Menoidium**

Plastic; pellicle not striated.......................................................71

**71.** Elongated but more or less plastic (Figs. 20L, M); holozoic and saprozoic; stagnant water; 20 to 70 microns.........................................72

Not elongated, oval or pyriform (Fig. 20K); holozoic; 15 microns....**Scytomonas**

**72.** More or less spindle-shaped, posterior end drawn out (Fig. 20L)........**Astasia**

Posterior end broad, rounded, or truncate during locomotion (Fig. 20M); very common. ...............................................................**Peranema**

**73.** Both flagella directed forward; plastic (Fig. 21A); holozoic; 15 to 70 microns.

**Distigma proteus** Ehr.

One flagellum trailing.........................................................74

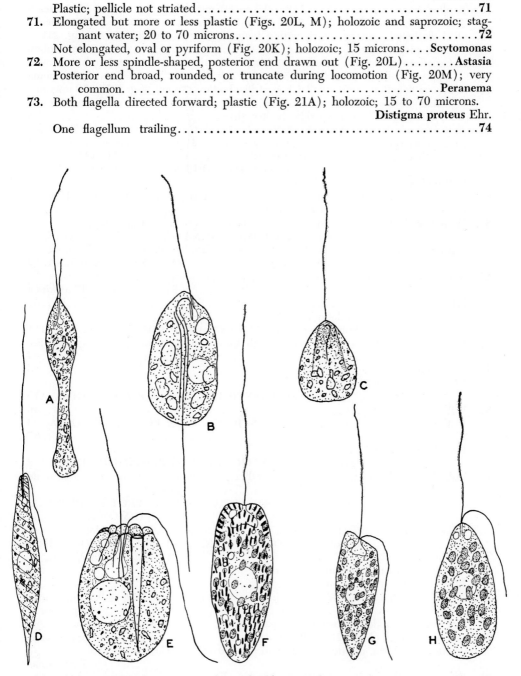

Fig. 21.—Representative Anisonemidae and Chloromonadina. A, *Distigma proteus* Ehr.; B, *Anisonema*; C, *Notosolenus*; D, *Heteronema*; E, *Entosiphon*; F, *Gonyostomum*; G, *Trentonia*; H, *Vacuolaria*.

74. With a long slitlike furrow (Fig. 21B, C)..............................75
    Without a furrow...................................................76
75. Trailing flagellum long (Fig. 21B); 15 to 60 microns.............Anisonema
    Trailing flagellum short (Fig. 21C); 8 to 25 microns.............Notosolenus
76. Oval, flattened, and furrowed; with a long pharyngeal rod apparatus (Fig. 21E);
      25 microns......................................................Entosiphon
    Rounded to elongated, sometimes ridged or striated; pharyngeal rod apparatus
      short or absent (Fig. 21D); 50 to 250 microns................Heteronema
77. With one flagellum; refractile trichocyst-like bodies present (Fig. 21F); 50 microns;
      acid waters....................................................Gonyostomum
    With two flagella; trichocyst-like bodies absent........................78
78. Anterior end obliquely truncate; flattened (Fig. 21G); 60 microns......Trentonia
    Anterior margin not truncate; highly plastic (Fig. 21H); 100 microns..Vacuolaria
79. Cell with an annulus and sulcus (Fig. 12).........Subclass **PHYTOMASTIGINA**,
                           Order **DINOFLAGELLATA**, GYMNODINIIDAE, 8
    Cell without an annulus and sulcus...................................80
80. Cell with cytostome and cytopharynx.........Subclass **PHYTOMASTIGINA**, 81
    Cell without cytostome and cytopharynx; holozoic or saprozoic...........83
81. With stored carbohydrate granules; two flagella, both projecting forward.
                  Order **CRYPTOMONADINA**, CRYPTOMONADIDAE, 34
    With stored paramylum granules, sometimes oil droplets also; one flagellum, or two
      flagella with one usually trailing..............Order **EUGLENOIDINA**, 82
82. Stigma present; saprozoic; similar to *Euglena* but colorless; 45 microns.
                                       EUGLENIDAE, **Khawkinea**
    Stigma absent.....................................................61
83. With well-defined pseudopodia in addition to flagella (Figs. 24G–L).
              Subclass **ZOOMASTIGINA**, Order **RHIZOMASTIGINA**, 111
    With flagella only, but occasionally with small blunt pseudopodia (Figs. 22, 23,
      25)...........................................................84
84. With one or two flagella.........................................85
    With three to eight flagella.
              Subclass **ZOOMASTIGINA**, Order **POLYMASTIGINA**, 115
85. With two flagella................................................86
    With one flagellum..Subclass **ZOOMASTIGINA**, Order **PROTOMONADINA**, 93
86. Flagella equally long.............................................87
    Flagella of unequal length.
              Subclass **ZOOMASTIGINA**, Order **PROTOMONADINA**, 102
87. Naked or with gelatinous envelope; solitary or colonial; one or two contractile
      vacuoles; motile or attached, often with small pseudopodia.
              Subclass **ZOOMASTIGINA**, Order **PROTOMONADINA**,
                                       AMPHIMONADIDAE, 88
    Naked; solitary; contractile vacuoles very small; motile; without pseudopodia.
              Subclass **PHYTOMASTIGINA**, Order **CRYPTOMONADINA**,
                                       CHLAMYDOMONADIDAE, 55
88. Without a lorica or gelatinous covering............................89
    With a lorica or gelatinous covering...............................91
89. Oval or rounded amoeboid; free swimming or attached by a long stalk (Fig. 22A);
      13 microns.....................................................Amphimonas
    Not oval or rounded amoeboid; stagnant water........................90
90. Spirally twisted (Fig. 22B); 10 microns...........................Spiromonas
    Ovate or pyriform, plastic; anterior end pointed (Fig. 22C); 15 microns.
                                                 Dinomonas
91. Each cell with a stalk and individual lorica (Fig. 22D); 15 microns....Diplomita
    Cells without individual stalks; in a common gelatinous mass or united tubes (Figs.
      22E, F); 6 to 12 microns.......................................92

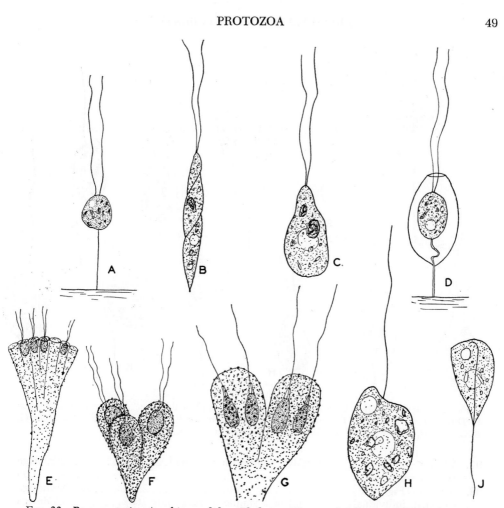

Fig. 22.—Representative Amphimonadidae, Phalansteriidae, and Oikomonadidae. A, *Amphimonas*; B, *Spiromonas*; C, *Dinomonas*; D, *Diplomita*; E, small part of colony of *Rhipidodendron*; F, small part of colony of *Spongomonas*; G, small part of colony of *Phalansterium*; H, *Oikomonas*; J, *Ancyromonas*.

92. Branched tubes united laterally (Fig. 22E).................**Rhipidodendron**
    Individuals imbedded in granular gelatinous masses which are not united laterally
       (Fig. 22F)....................................................**Spongomonas**
93. Cell with collar (Figs. 23A–C).........................................94
    Cell without collar.................................OIKOMONADIDAE, 96
94. Entire animal enclosed in gelatinous mass (Fig. 22G); 17 microns.
                                      PHALANSTERIIDAE, **Phalansterium**
    No gelatinous mass, or cell body only imbedded in gelatinous mass (Figs. 23A–F);
       free-swimming or sedentary; colonial or solitary.......................95
95. Without lorica (Figs. 23B, F); stalked; holozoic or saprozoic; 5 to 15 microns.
                                                   CODOSIGIDAE, 97
    With lorica (Figs. 23C, G–J); stalked or unstalked; holozoic.
                                                   BICOSOECIDAE, 99
96. Flagellum anterior; spherical or oval (Fig. 22H); 10 microns; stagnant water.
                                                         **Oikomonas**
    Flagellum trailing; ovate to triangular (Fig. 22J); 7 microns........**Ancyromonas**

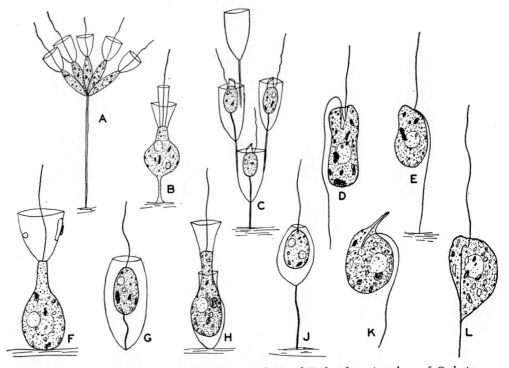

Fig. 23.—Representative Codosigidae, Bicosoecidae, and Bodonidae. A, colony of *Codosiga*; B, *Diplosiga*; C, colony of *Poteriodendron*; D, *Phyllomitus*; E, *Pleuromonas*; F, *Monosiga*; G, *Bicosoeca*; H, *Salpingoeca*; J, *Codonoeca*; K, *Rhynchomonas*; L, *Cercomonas*.

 97. With a double collar (Fig. 23B); solitary or clustered................**Diplosiga**
     With a single collar................................................................98
 98. Solitary (Fig. 23F)..........................................................**Monosiga**
     Colonial, individuals at the end of a simple or branching stalk.........**Codosiga**
 99. Lorica with a fine outer basal stalk (Figs. 23C, J).........................101
     Lorica without a fine outer basal stalk (Figs. 23G, H).....................100
100. Body small compared with lorica and attached to base of lorica with a fine stalk
        (Fig. 23G); sessile or free-swimming; often in clusters; 23 microns.
                                                                         **Bicosoeca**
     Body almost filling lorica, attached to base of lorica with a fine stalk or unattached
        (Fig. 23H); 16 microns.................................**Salpingoeca**
101. Colonial (Fig. 23C); 35 microns..........................**Poteriodendron**
     Solitary (Fig. 23J); 23 microns.............................**Codonoeca**
102. One flagellum trailing (Figs. 23D, E, K, L); somewhat amoeboid; stagnant water.
                                                                    BODONIDAE, 103
     Both flagella directed anteriorly (Figs. 24A–F); attached or free-swimming.
                                                                    MONADIDAE, 107
103. With an anterior projection (Fig. 23K); 6 microns...........**Rhynchomonas**
     Without an anterior projection..............................................104
104. Trailing flagellum about as long as body or slightly longer (Fig. 23L); 10 to 35
        microns.....................................................**Cercomonas**
     Trailing flagellum much longer than body (Figs. 23D, E)................105
105. Cytostome conspicuous (Fig. 23D); 25 microns.................**Phyllomitus**
     Cytostome inconspicuous.....................................................106

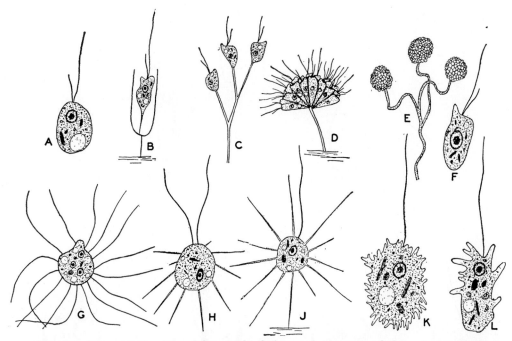

FIG. 24.—Representative Monadidae, Multiciliidae, and Mastigamoebidae. A, *Monas*; B, *Stokesiella*; C, portion of a *Dendromonas* colony; D, portion of a *Cephalothamnium* colony; E, small portion of an *Anthophysis* colony; F, single individual of *Anthophysis*; G, *Multicilia*; H, *Dimorpha*; J, *Actinomonas*; K, *Mastigella*; L, *Mastigamoeba*.

**106.** Usually attached by trailing flagellum (Fig. 23E); 8 microns......**Pleuromonas**
 Not attached; plastic (Fig. 5D); 15 microns.........................**Bodo**
**107.** Solitary ......................................................**108**
 Colonial ......................................................**109**
**108.** Without lorica; stalked or unstalked (Fig. 24A); 5 to 16 microns........**Monas**
 With lorica; stalked (Fig. 24B); 22 microns......................**Stokesiella**
**109.** Each individual attached at the end of a branch (Fig. 24C); 8 microns.
                                                          **Dendromonas**
 Individuals attached in clusters...................................**110**
**110.** Stalks colorless and rigid (Fig. 24D); often attached to plankton Crustacea; 8
  microns ........................................**Cephalothamnium**
 Stalks yellow or brown, usually bent (Fig. 24E); stagnant water; 6 microns.
                                                          **Anthophysis**
**111.** With many flagella; generally spherical but amoeboid (Fig. 24G); 35 microns.
                                         MULTICILIIDAE, **Multicilia**
 With one or two flagella; holozoic or saprozoic....MASTIGAMOEBIDAE, **112**
**112.** With two flagella and numerous fine radiating filopodia (Fig. 24H); pseudopods
  occasionally withdrawn; 18 microns........................**Dimorpha**
 With one flagellum and axopodia or filopodia..........................**113**
**113.** With filopodia; usually spheroidal and attached (Fig. 24J); 10 microns.
                                                          **Actinomonas**
 With lobopodia...............................................**114**
**114.** Pseudopodia very numerous; flagellum apparently not originating at nucleus
  (Fig. 24K); 130 microns...............................**Mastigella**
 Pseudopodia not so numerous; flagellum originating at nucleus (Fig. 24L); 20
  to 200 microns.................................**Mastigamoeba**

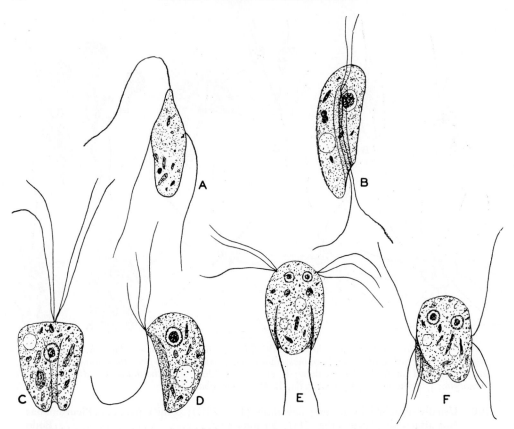

FIG. 25.—Representative Trimastigidae, Tetramitidae, and Hexamitidae. A, *Dallingeria*; B, *Costia*; C, *Collodictyon*; D, *Tetramitus*; E, *Hexamita*; F, *Trepomonas*.

115.  With three flagella, two of which are trailing (Fig. 25A); free-swimming or at-
          tached; 5 microns; stagnant water.........TRIMASTIGIDAE, **Dallingeria**
      With four or eight flagella....................................**116**
116.  With four flagella originating in one area............TETRAMITIDAE, **117**
      With eight flagella, not all originating at one area; anaerobic in stagnant water.
                                                       HEXAMITIDAE, **119**
117.  Flagella attached at or near anterior end; free-swimming in stagnant water...**118**
      Flagella attached at the base of a funnel-like depression (Fig. 25B); ectoparasites
          on fresh-water fishes; 10 microns................................**Costia**
118.  Spherical, ovoid, or heart-shaped (Fig. 25C); 45 microns.........**Collodictyon**
      Pyriform, with pointed posterior end (Fig. 25D); 12 microns.......**Tetramitus**
119.  Posterior end truncate; six flagella near anterior end, two posterior (Fig. 25E); 20
          microns. ...................................................**Hexamita**
      Broadly oval; two short and two long flagella laterally on each side; two cytostomes
          (Fig. 25F); 10 microns..................................**Trepomonas**
120.  With one or two chromatophores and filopodia; 10 to 40 microns.
                      Class **MASTIGOPHORA**, Order **CHRYSOMONADINA, 121**
      Without chromatophores; with lobopodia, filopodia, or axopodia; pseudopodia
          the chief means of locomotion throughout the life history.
                                                       Class **SARCODINA, 122**

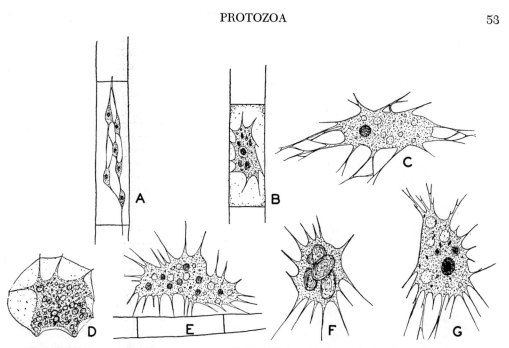

FIG. 26.—Representative Proteomyxa. A, *Labyrinthula* within an algal cell; B, *Pseudospora* within an algal cell; C, *Biomyxa*; D, *Hyalodiscus*; E, *Vampyrella* on a filamentous alga; F, *Protomonas*; G, *Nuclearia*.

121. Filopodia branching; one or two chromatophores; often aggregated (Fig. 16A).
     Suborder **RHIZOCHRYSIDINA**, Rhizochrysis
     Filopodia not branching; two chromatophores; usually solitary (Fig. 13H).
     Suborder **EUCHRYSOMONADINA**, CHROMULINIDAE, **Chrysamoeba**
122. With spherical symmetry and axopodia (Fig. 29)..Subclass **ACTINOPODA, 153**
     Without spherical symmetry; lobopodia or filopodia (Figs. 26–28).
     Subclass **RHIZOPODA, 123**
123. Naked, without a test or shell.....................................124
     With a sclerotized test or shell.....................Order **TESTACEA, 134**
124. With radiating reticulopodia (Fig. 26)............Order **PROTEOMYXA, 125**
     With lobopodia (Figs. 27A, B)....................Order **AMOEBINA, 131**
125. Small individuals grouped in a network of slightly branched and anastamosing
     reticulopodia (Fig. 26A); often colored by ingested algae; on *Vaucheria*.
     LABYRINTHULIDAE, **Labyrinthula**
     Cells solitary.................................................126
126. With many reticulopodia which branch freely and anastomose; body shape and
     size inconstant; many small contractile vacuoles (Fig. 26C).
     VAMPYRELLIDAE, **Biomyxa**
     Reticulopodia not anastomosing.....................................127
127. Parasitic and completely within cells of algae and Volvocidae (Fig. 26B); 20
     microns. .........................PSEUDOSPORIDAE, **Pseudospora**
     Not completely within cells of algae and Volvocidae....................128
128. Generally disc-shaped, with reddish endoplasm and clear ectoplasm (Fig. 26D);
     65 microns........................VAMPYRELLIDAE, **Hyalodiscus**
     Not generally disc-shaped; endoplasm reddish or not....................129
129. Heliozoa-like; when feeding on filamentous algae body shape may change
     markedly (Fig. 26E); 50 to 700 microns..VAMPYRELLIDAE, **Vampyrella**
     Not Heliozoa-like; not feeding on filamentous algae.....................133

**130.** Stored food consisting of starch granules (Fig. 26F).

                            PSEUDOSPORIDAE, **Protomonas**

     With other types of food inclusions; with or without mucous envelope (Fig. 26G); 45 microns............................VAMPYRELLIDAE, **Nuclearia**

**131.** With amoeboid and flagellated stages (Fig. 27A), the former with few, blunt pseudopodia; stagnant water; 10 to 50 microns.

                        DIMASTIGAMOEBIDAE, **Dimastigamoeba**

     Without a flagellated stage.............................AMOEBIDAE, **132**

**132.** Large, from 500 microns to 5 mm.; many small contractile vacuoles and refringent bodies; many nuclei; on bottom in stagnant waters......**Pelomyxa**

     Smaller, from 25 to 500 microns; a single nucleus........................**133**

**133.** With one broad pseudopodium (Fig. 27B); 35 microns............**Vahlkampfia**

     With numerous pseudopodia, never anastomosing (Fig. 4A); 25 to 500 microns.

                                              **Amoeba**

**134.** Shell simple and membranous though sometimes with bits of debris accidentally stuck on shell (Figs. 27C–M)......................................**135**

     Shell composed of scales, plates, sand grains, or bits of debris (Fig. 28)......**136**

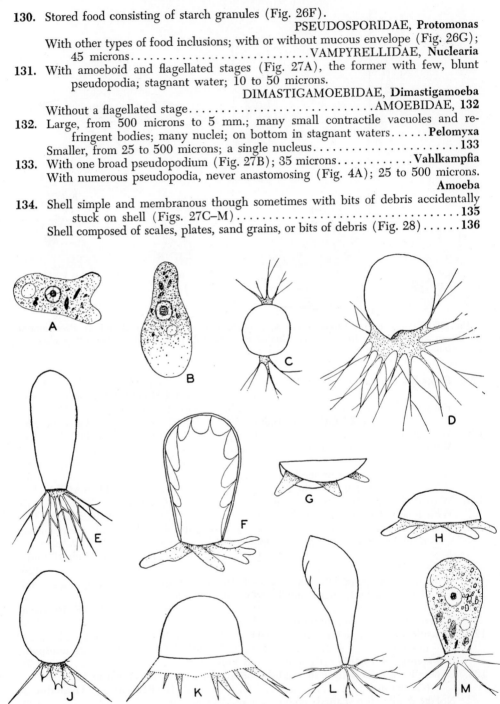

FIG. 27.—Representative Amoebina and Testacea. A, *Dimastigamoeba*; B, *Vahlkampfia*; C, *Diplophrys*; D, *Lieberkühnia*; E, *Gromia*; F, *Hyalosphenia*; G, *Pseudochlamys*; H, *Pyxidicula*; J, *Difflugiella*; K, *Cochliopodium*; L, *Pamphagus*; M, *Chlamydophrys*.

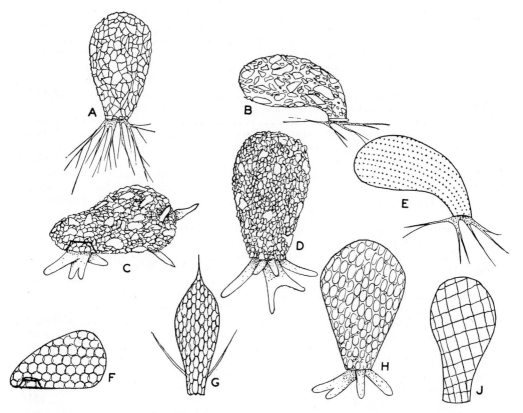

Fig. 28.—Representative Difflugiidae and Euglyphidae. A, *Pseudodifflugia*; B, *Campascus*; C, a spiny *Centropyxis*; D, *Difflugia*; E, *Cyphoderia*; F, *Trinema*; G, a spiny *Euglypha*; H, *Nebela*; J, *Quadrulella*.

**135.** With numerous branching reticulopodia, usually anastomosing (Figs. 27C–E).
GROMIIDAE, **137**
With lobopodia or a few, simple, branched filopodia (Figs. 27F–M).
ARCELLIDAE, **139**
**136.** Shell composed of foreign materials (Figs. 28A–D)......DIFFLUGIIDAE, **146**
Shell composed of symmetrical and similar plates or scales (Figs. 28E–J).
EUGLYPHIDAE, **149**
**137.** Test with one aperture.............................................**138**
Test with two apertures, thin, spherical (Fig. 27C); 14 microns......**Diplophrys**
**138.** Aperture lateral or subterminal (Fig. 27D); 110 microns.........**Lieberkühnia**
Aperture terminal (Fig. 27E); 100 to 400 microns..................**Gromia**
**139.** Aperture circular, central, and inverted like a funnel (Figs. 4B, C); 30 to 250 microns; common in ponds; many species.....................**Arcella**
Aperture otherwise.........................................**140**
**140.** Test patelliform and rigid; aperture very large (Fig. 27H); 20 microns.
**Pyxidicula**
Test not patelliform and rigid.....................................**141**
**141.** Test disclike, flexible when young, sometimes rolled up (Fig. 27G); 40 microns.
**Pseudochlamys**
Test otherwise.................................................**142**

142. With blunt pseudopodia only; test ovoid or pyriform; protoplasm partly filling test (Fig. 27F); 125 microns.................................**Hyalosphenia**

Not with blunt pseudopodia only; protoplasm filling test..................**143**

143. Median pseudopodia lobate or digitate and with pointed tips; lateral pseudopodia long, fine, and tapering to a point; test ovoid and flexible (Fig. 27J); 40 microns..............................**Difflugiella apiculata** Cash

All pseudopodia similar.....................................**144**

144. Aperture large; test thin and flexible; pseudopodia blunt or pointed (Fig. 27K); 25 to 60 microns.......................................**Cochliopodium**

Aperture small (Figs. 27L, M); pseudopodia long and branching.........**145**

145. Test hyaline and flexible; aperture very small (Fig. 27L); 40 to 100 microns. **Pamphagus**

Test rigid; aperture not so small (Fig. 27M); 20 microns.......**Chlamydophrys**

146. Test with a curved neck, covered with small sand particles; filopodia (Fig. 28B); 125 microns............................................**Campascus**

Test without a curved neck........................................**147**

147. With long, straight or branching filopodia; test ovoid; spines absent; aperture terminal (Fig. 28A); 25 to 70 microns..................**Pseudodifflugia**

Pseudopodia cylindrical, simple or branching; spines present or absent.......**148**

148. Aperture eccentric; test circular, discoid, or ovoid (Fig. 28C); 125 microns. **Centropyxis**

Aperture not eccentric; test variable in shape, composed of sand particles, diatoms, or other foreign bodies (Fig. 28D); 60 to 500 microns; very common. .......................................**Difflugia**

149. Test with a curved neck, thin and covered with discs or scales; pseudopodia long and thin (Fig. 28E); 60 to 200 microns.....................**Cyphoderia**

Test without a curved neck........................................**150**

150. Test compressed anteriorly; circular siliceous scales (Fig. 28F); 30 to 100 microns. .........................................**Trinema**

Test not compressed anteriorly.....................................**151**

151. With filopodia; test composed of siliceous scales arranged in longitudinal rows (Fig. 28G); often with spines; 20 to 150 microns.............**Euglypha**

With lobopodia; usually in acid waters................................**152**

152. Test composed of circular or oval plates (Fig. 28H); 130 microns......**Nebela**

Test composed of quadrangular plates (Fig. 28J); 80 to 140 microns. **Quadrulella**

153. Without scales, spicules, capsule, or an envelope of sand grains or diatoms....**154**

With scales, spicules, capsule, or an envelope of sand grains or diatoms......**156**

154. Pseudopodia branched and with thickened bases (Fig. 29A); 20 microns. ACTINOCOMIDAE, **Actinocoma**

Pseudopodia unbranched and without thickened bases..ACTINOPHRYIDAE, **155**

155. Granular endoplasm clearly set off from vacuolar ectoplasm (Fig. 29C); 70 to 300 microns.....................................**Actinosphaerium**

Endoplasm and ectoplasm not clearly divided (Fig. 4D); 40 microns. **Actinophrys**

156. With a chitinoid, perforated capsule and a stalk (Fig. 29B); 75 microns. CLATHRULINIDAE, **Clathrulina**

With chitinoid or siliceous spicules or scales, or with an envelope of sand grains or diatoms.....................................**157**

157. With numerous flagella among axopodia; siliceous scales (Fig. 29D); 40 microns. MYRIOPHRYIDAE, **Myriophrys**

Without flagella.............................................**158**

158. With an outer envelope of sand grains, diatoms, or debris (Fig. 29E); 45 microns. LITHOCOLLIDAE, **Lithocolla**

With chitinous or siliceous scales or spicules.........................**159**

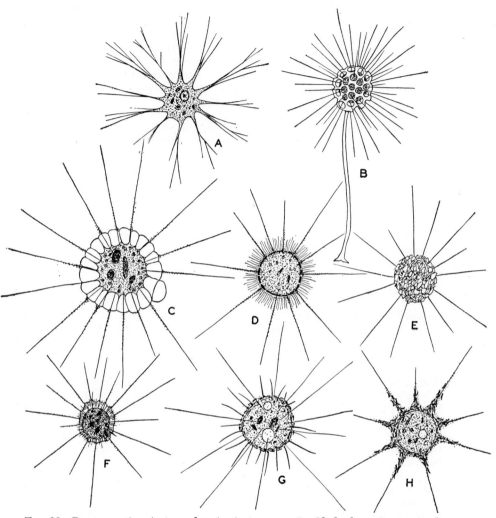

FIG. 29.—Representative Actinopoda. A, *Actinocoma*; B, *Clathrulina*; C, *Actinosphaerium*; D, *Myriophrys*; E, *Lithocolla*; F, *Heterophrys*; G, *Acanthocystis*; H, *Raphidiophrys*.

159.  Without siliceous scales; with indistinct radially arranged spicules projecting beyond the peripheral mucilaginous layer (Fig. 29F); 15 to 80 microns.

HETEROPHRYIDAE, **Heterophrys**

With siliceous scales..........................ACANTHOCYSTIDAE, **160**

160.  With tangentially arranged siliceous scales and radiating siliceous spines (Fig. 29G); 40 microns.....................................**Acanthocystis**

With scales clustered around basal portions of pseudopodia; radiating siliceous spines absent (Fig. 29H); 55 microns..................**Raphidiophrys**

161.  Without adoral zone of membranelles............Order **HOLOTRICHA, 163**

With adoral zone of membranelles.....................................**162**

162.  With adoral zone winding clockwise to cytostome (Figs. 36–39).

Order **SPIROTRICHA, 240**

With adoral zone winding counterclockwise to cytostome (Figs. 40, 41).

Order **PERITRICHA, 276**

163. Not commensal in mussels; without large ventral cilia.....................164
Commensal in mantle cavity and gill chambers of mussels; flattened; with large
ventral cilia for attachment (Fig. 30A); 60 to 250 microns.
Suborder **THIGMOTRICHA**, CONCHOPHTHIRIDAE, **Conchophthirus**
164. Cytostome on body surface or in peristome, without special cilia (Figs. 30–32).
Suborder **GYMNOSTOMATA, 166**
Cytostome in peristome, with special cilia or membranelles...............165
165. Peristome lined with rows of cilia (Fig. 33).
Suborder **TRICHOSTOMATA, 206**
Peristome with one or more membranelles, with or without cilia (Figs. 34, 35).
Suborder **HYMENOSTOMATA, 219**
166. Cytostome at or near anterior end.................................167
Cytostome not at or near anterior end.............................192
167. Region of cytostome more or less flattened; trichites present (Figs. 30B–E).
SPATHIDIIDAE, **168**
Region of cytostome not flattened.................................172
168. With three curved anterior arms; containing zoochlorellae (Fig. 30B); 225
microns............................**Teuthophrys trisulca** C. and B.
Without such arms................................................169
169. Body much elongated (Fig. 30C); 150 to 650 microns...........**Homalozoon**
Body not especially elongated.......................................170
170. Body with a long spiral ridge (Fig. 30D); 85 microns; usually in acid waters.
**Perispira**
Body without a spiral ridge.........................................171
171. Flask- or sack-shaped and compressed; cytostome very wide (Fig. 30E); 50 to
300 microns...........................................**Spathidium**
With an anterior swollen ring; not compressed (Fig. 30F); 110 microns.
**Enchelydium**
172. With a flask-shaped lorica; cytostome opening into a receptaculum; body ringed
(Fig. 30G); 100 microns..................METACYSTIDAE, **Vasicola**
Without a lorica; cytostome not opening into a receptaculum.............173
173. Cytostome at tip of an apical cone; one to several girdles of cilia (Figs. 30H, J).
DIDINIIDAE, **174**
Cytostome not at tip of an apical cone.............................175
174. With an equatorial furrow and tentacle-like processes around cytostome (Fig.
30H); 30 microns.........................................**Mesodinium**
Without an equatorial furrow; barrel-shaped (Fig. 30J); feeds on other ciliates;
60 to 200 microns.........................................**Didinium**
175. Body covered with regularly arranged, perforated plates; barrel-shaped; often
spinous (Fig. 7B); 40 to 110 microns..............COLEPIDAE, **Coleps**
Body not covered with plates......................................176
176. With tentacles scattered among cilia; ovate or spherical (Fig. 30K); 150 microns.
ACTINOBOLINIDAE, **Actinobolina**
Without tentacles.............................HOLOPHRYIDAE, **177**
177. Parasitic on the integument of many fresh-water fishes; oval (Fig. 30L); 100 to
1,000 microns; become mature on host within small pustules in integument.
**Ichthyophthirius**
Not parasitic....................................................178
178. With a finger-like process in front of cytostome; ovoid or ellipsoid (Fig. 30M);
40 microns.............................................**Chilophrya**
Without a finger-like process in front of cytostome......................179
179. With a large anterior groovelike pit (Fig. 30N); 250 to 550 microns....**Bursella**
Without a large anterior groovelike pit.............................180
180. With prominent longitudinal grooves; 30 to 80 microns.................181
Without prominent longitudinal grooves.............................182

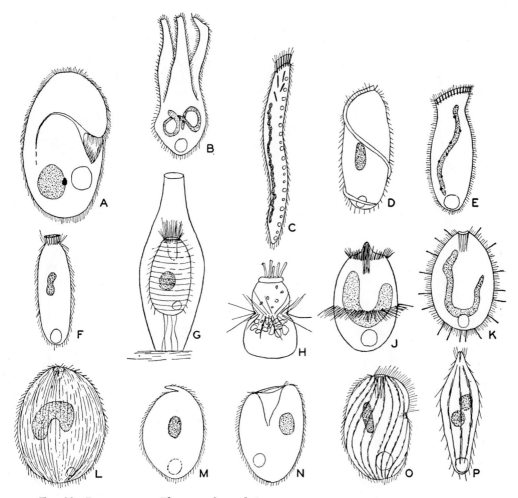

Fig. 30.—Representative Thigmotricha and Gymnostomata. A, *Conchophthirvus*; B, *Teuthophrys*; C, *Homalozoon*; D, *Perispira*; E, *Spathidium*; F, *Enchelydium*; G, *Vasicola*; H, *Mesodinium*; J, *Didinium*; K, *Actinobolina*; L, *Ichthyophthirius*; M, *Chilophyra*; N, *Bursella*; O, *Placus*; P, *Rhopalophrya*.

181. Grooves spiral; ellipsoid or ovoid; cytostome a narrow slit (Fig. 30O)....**Placus**
    Grooves not spiral; body not ovoid or ellipsoid; with few cilia (Fig. 30P).
                                                                 **Rhopalophrya**
182. Cytopharynx terminating anteriorly in a small more or less distinct conelike proc-
        ess; macronucleus spherical to oval; body ovoid to short cylindrical; one side
        convex, the other somewhat flattened (Fig. 31A); 80 microns..**Lagynophrya**
    Cytopharynx not terminating anteriorly in a small cone; with other characters..183
183. With three short, accessory rows of cilia extending dorsally from the cytostome;
        ovoid to cylindrical..........................................184
    Without three such rows of cilia................................185
184. Pharyngeal trichites usually long and extending out as far as the pellicle (Fig.
        31B); 170 microns...................................**Pseudoprorodon**
    Pharyngeal trichites shorter and not extending through the ectoplasm (Fig. 31C);
        100 to 200 microns.......................................**Prorodon**

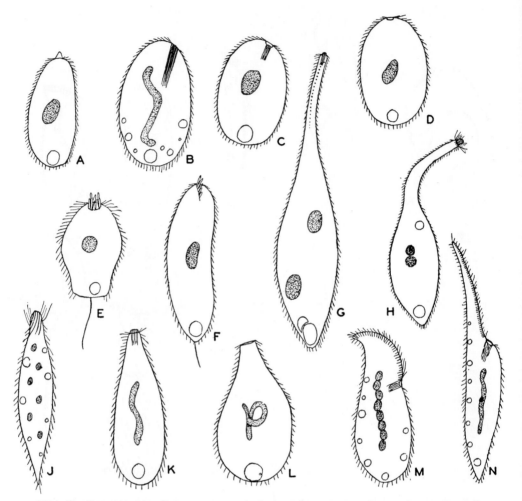

Fig. 31.—Representative Gymnostomata. A, *Lagynophrya*; B, *Pseudoprorodon*; C, *Prorodon*; D, *Holophrya*; E, *Urotricha*; F, *Plagiocampa*; G, *Trachelophyllum*; H, *Lacrymaria*; J, *Chaenea*; K, *Enchelyodon*; L, *Enchelys*; M, *Branchiocoetes*; N, *Dileptus*.

185. Body ovoid to short cylindrical (Figs. 31D–F)..........................186
     Body elongated (Figs. 31G–L).................................188
186. Cytostome entirely or partly fringed with small tentacle-like processes (Figs. 31E, F)...........................................187
     Cytostome without such processes; ovoid; without trichites (Fig. 31D); 35 microns. ..................................................**Holophrya**
187. Small tentacle-like processes surrounding cytostome; one or more long caudal cilia (Fig. 31E); 15 to 30 microns...............................**Urotricha**
     Small tentacle-like processes only partially surrounding cytostome; with or without long caudal cilium (Fig. 31F); 30 to 40 microns.........**Plagiocampa**
188. Greatly flattened, lancet-shaped or flask-shaped, sometimes ribbon-like (Fig. 31G).
     **Trachelophyllum**
     Not greatly flattened..............................................189

189. With a ringlike constriction around cytostome bearing long cilia; polymorphic and
       highly contractile (Fig. 31H); 70 to 1,000 microns. . . . . . . . . . .**Lacrymaria**
       Without such a ringlike constriction. . . . . . . . . . . . . . . . . . . . . . . . . . . . . . . .**190**
190. Elongated; anterior end drawn out into a narrow headlike structure which is
       spirally or longitudinally furrowed; usually with cilia at anterior end project-
       ing forward (Fig. 31J); 50 to 300 microns. . . . . . . . . . . . . . . . . . . . .**Chaenea**
       Not especially elongated, often flask-shaped; anterior cilia not projecting forward.
                                                           **191**
191. With a small, dome-shaped projection at anterior end (Fig. 31K); 80 to 400
       microns . . . . . . . . . . . . . . . . . . . . . . . . . . . . . . . . . . . . . . . . . . . . .**Enchelyodon**
       Without such a dome-shaped projection; anterior end obliquely truncated (Fig.
       31L); 40 to 200 microns. . . . . . . . . . . . . . . . . . . . . . . . . . . . . . . . . . .**Enchelys**
192. Cytostome lateral, slitlike or round (Figs. 31M, N; 32A–G) . . . . . . . . . . . . . . .**193**
       Cytostome on the flat ventral side, in anterior half (Figs. 32H–M) . . . . . . . . . .**201**

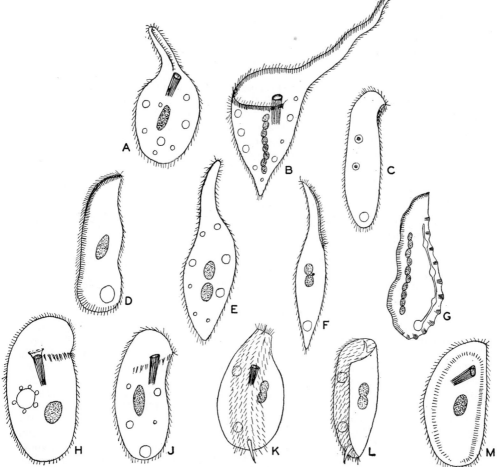

FIG. 32.—Representative Gymnostomata. A, *Trachelius*; B, *Paradileptus*; C, *Loxodes*; D,
*Bryophyllum*; E, *Amphileptus*; F, *Lionotus*; G, *Loxophyllum*; H, *Nassula*; J, *Chilodontopsis*;
K, *Trochilia*; L, *Dysteria*; M, *Chlamydodon*.

193. Cytostome a longitudinal cleft (Figs. 32C–G)........................197
     Cytostome round, at base of a long neck (Figs. 31M, N; 32A, B).
                                            TRACHELIIDAE, 194
194. Anterior end narrow and drawn out.................................195
     Anterior end not narrow and drawn out (Fig. 31M); 150 microns; ectocom-
     mensal on aquatic isopods and amphipods................Branchiocoetes
195. Body elongated and narrow (Fig. 31N); 200 to 600 microns.........Dileptus
     Body not especially narrow (Figs. 32A, B)...........................196
196. Anterior end drawn out into short finger-like process; small peristomial field;
     cytostome in neck region (Fig. 32A); 300 microns...........Trachelius
     Anterior end drawn out into a longer process; wide peristomial field; body broad
     at level of cytostome (Fig. 32B); 100 to 450 microns.........Paradileptus
197. Cytostome on convex side of anterior portion of body (Figs. 32D–G).
                                            AMPHILEPTIDAE, 198
     Cytostome on concave side of anterior end of body; lancet-shaped; anterior end
     curved ventrally (Fig. 32C); 100 to 700 microns....LOXODIDAE, Loxodes
198. Both left and right sides of body ciliated.............................199
     Without cilia on the left side.......................................200
199. With a prominent ventral ridge bearing trichocysts (Fig. 32D); 130 microns.
                                            Bryophyllum
     Flask-shaped, without such a ridge (Fig. 32E); often on other colonial Protozoa;
     sometimes parasitic on gills of fishes and tadpoles; 40 to 135 microns.
                                            Amphileptus
200. Without trichocyst borders; flask-shaped, elongated, and flattened; cilia only on
     right side (Fig. 32F); 80 to 500 microns......................Lionotus
     Ventral side with a trichocyst border; dorsal side with trichocyst border or clumps
     of trichocysts (Fig. 32G); shape variable; 100 to 700 microns..Loxophyllum
201. Ciliation complete; dorsal cilia less dense than those on ventral surface; ventral
     surface flat; 50 to 250 microns....................NASSULIDAE, 202
     Ciliation incomplete; dorsal surface without cilia or only with a few sensory
     bristles. ........................................................203
202. Usually brightly colored because of food vacuoles and symbiotic algae; opening
     of oral basket deep, in a vestibule (Fig. 32H)................Nassula
     Colorless; oral basket without vestibule (Fig. 32J)...........Chilodontopsis
203. Posterior ventral surface with a spinelike process (Fig. 32K, L).
                                            DYSTERIIDAE, 204
     Posterior end without such a process...........CHLAMYDODONTIDAE, 205
204. Ciliated portion of ventral surface free (Fig. 32K); 30 microns........Trochilia
     Ciliated portion of ventral surface more or less covered by a fold of the unciliated
     portion (Fig. 32L); 35 to 160 microns......................Dysteria
205. Variously shaped; dorsal surface without a transverse row of bristles; cytostome
     more or less elongated (Fig. 32M); 100 microns; rare.......Chlamydodon
     Ovoid; dorsal surface with a transverse row of bristles; cytostome round (Fig. 7A);
     very common; 50 to 300 microns..........................Chilodonella
206. With a gelatinous lorica (Fig. 33A); 40 microns....MARYNIDAE, Mycterothrix
     Without a gelatinous lorica........................................207
207. Ciliation sparse; with two to nine keel-like ridges; compressed (Figs. 33B–D).
                                            TRICHOPELMIDAE, 208
     Ciliation dense; without keel-like ridges.............................210
208. Cytostome one-third to one-half of way from anterior end...............209
     Cytostome near posterior end (Fig. 33B); 20 to 70 microns........Microthorax
209. Cytopharynx long and tubular (Fig. 33C); 40 microns...........Trichopelma
     Cytopharynx simple and short, near middle of body (Fig. 33D); 40 microns.
                                            Drepanomonas

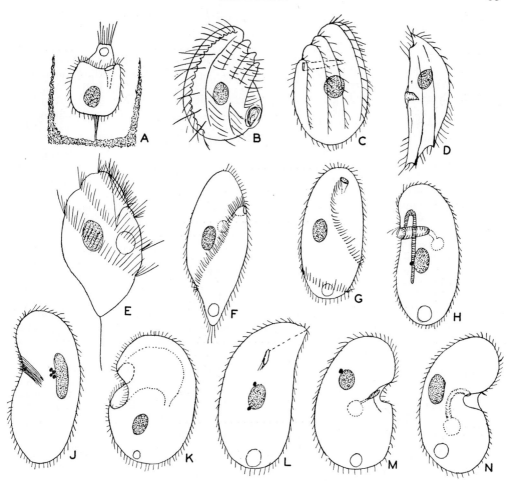

FIG. 33.—Representative Trichostomata. A, *Mycterothrix*; B, *Microthorax*; C, *Trichopelma*; D, lateral view of *Drepanomonas*; E, *Trimyema*; F, *Spirozona*; G, *Trichospira*; H, *Plagiopyla*; J, lateral view of *Clathrostoma*; K, *Bresslaua*; L, *Bryophrya*; M, *Colpoda*; N, *Tillina*.

210. With a long cilium at the posterior end; cilia in a few spiral rows (Fig. 33E);
     65 microns; usually in sewage..............TRIMYEMIDAE, **Trimyema**
     Without a single long posterior cilium; usually larger......................211
211. With a spiral zone of special cilia extending from cytostome to posterior end
     (Figs. 33F, G); 90 microns...................................212
     Without such special cilia.........................................213
212. Spiral zone of special cilia extending from right anterior to left posterior (Fig.
     33F); spindle-shaped; usually in sewage......SPIROZONIDAE, **Spirozona**
     Spiral zone of special cilia extending from left anterior to right posterior; cylin-
     drical (Fig. 33G)....................TRICHOSPIRIDAE, **Trichospira**
213. Peristome a ciliated cross furrow leading to cytostome; with a curved dorsal band
     originating in peristome (Fig. 33H); 100 microns.
                             PLAGIOPYLIDAE, **Plagiopyla**
     Peristome otherwise...............................................214

**214.** Cytostome slitlike and in a small, flat, oval groove which bears a ciliated ridge (Fig. 33J); 70 to 180 microns......CLATHROSTOMIDAE, **Clathrostoma**
Cytostome funnel-like and deep.................................**215**

**215.** Peristome extending from left anterior to right posterior; cigar- or slipper-shaped (Fig. 7E); 60 to 300 microns............PARAMECIIDAE, **Paramecium**
With a different type of peristome....................COLPODIDAE, **216**

**216.** Cytopharynx very large, occupying anterior half of animal (Fig. 33K); 80 to 250 microns; stagnant water..............................................**Bresslaua**
Cytopharynx not particularly large................................**217**

**217.** Ovoid to ellipsoid, anterior end slightly bent (Fig. 33L); 50 to 120 microns.
**Bryophrya**
Kidney-shaped. ................................................**218**

**218.** Cytopharynx short (Fig. 33M); 20 to 120 microns..................**Colpoda**
Cytopharynx long and curved (Fig. 33N); 80 to 400 microns..........**Tillina**

**219.** Cytostome not connected with peristome; peristome often obscure and apparently absent (Fig. 34)..............................FRONTONIIDAE, **220**
Cytostome at end or bottom of peristome..........................**235**

**220.** Without long caudal cilia (Figs. 34A–J)...........................**221**
With one or more long caudal cilia (Figs. 34K–Q)....................**229**

**221.** Cytostome opening pointed at anterior end (Figs. 34A, B)...............**222**
Cytostome opening more or less rounded at anterior end (Figs. 34C–J)......**223**

**222.** Cytostome less than one-sixth of body length; ovoid to ellipsoid (Fig. 34A); 60 to 600 microns.................................................**Frontonia**
Cytostome one-fourth to one-third of body length; pyriform (Fig. 34B); 120 microns. ................................................**Leucophrys**

**223.** Cytostome clearly oblique (Figs. 34C, D).........................**224**
Cytostome not clearly oblique; body ovoid to ellipsoid (Figs. 34E–J)......**225**

**224.** Ovoid or ellipsoid; with seven postoral ciliary meridians (Fig. 34D); 55 microns.
**Glaucoma**
Elongate reniform; usually with a single postoral ciliary meridian (Fig. 34C); 50 to 150 microns.................................................**Colpidium**

**225.** Cytostome and cytopharynx with a single membranelle (Fig. 34E); 75 microns.
**Monochilum**
Cytostome and cytopharynx with two to four membranelles (Figs. 34F–J)...**226**

**226.** Within a mucilaginous envelope; cytostome with a pocket-forming membrane (Fig. 34F); 30 microns..............................**Cyrtolophosis**
Without a mucilaginous envelope.................................**227**

**227.** Anterior end pointed (Fig. 34G); 70 microns; often in the pseudocoel of dead rotifers ................................................**Paraglaucoma**
Anterior end not pointed.......................................**228**

**228.** Cytostome about one-tenth or less the body length from anterior end; pyriform or variable body shape; cytostome in median line (Fig. 34H); 40 to 200 microns.
**Tetrahymena**
Cytostome about one-fifth the body length from anterior end; ellipsoid; cytostome slightly to left of median line (Fig. 34J); 40 microns............**Dichilum**

**229.** Cytostome three-fourths to four-fifths of body length; ventral side concave (Fig. 34K); 140 microns................................**Lembadion**
Cytostome much smaller.......................................**230**

**230.** With one or two wide ciliary bands; with a constriction at or near the middle (Figs. 34L, M) ................................................**231**
Cilia in longitudinal rows only..................................**232**

**231.** With a single ciliary band around the anterior half of the body (Fig. 34L); 30 microns. ................................................**Urozona**
With two ciliary bands; ventral surface flat; long canals associated with the contractile vacuole (Fig. 34M); 75 microns.....**Urocentrum turbo** (O. F. M.)

**232.** Cytostome on posterior half of body; highly flattened; cilia on flat ventral surface only (Fig. 34N); 30 microns..............................**Cinetochilum**

Cytostome on anterior half of body.......................................233

**233.** With cilia along anterior margin (Fig. 34O); 40 microns; often in decaying animal matter. .............................................................**Saprophilus**

Without cilia along anterior margin; ovoid to cylindrical...................234

**234.** With a small crescentic cytostome (Fig. 34P); 50 to 200 microns...**Loxocephalus**

With a large, elongated cytostome (Fig. 34Q); 40 microns............**Uronema**

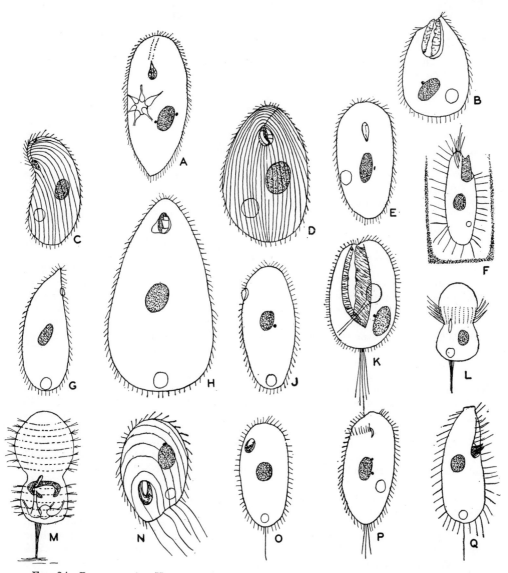

FIG. 34.—Representative Hymenostomata. A, *Frontonia*; B, *Leucophrys*; C, *Colpidium*; D, *Glaucoma*; E, *Monochilum*; F, *Cyrtolophosis*; G, *Paraglaucoma*; H, *Tetrahymena*; J, *Dichilum*; K, *Lembadion*; L, *Urozona*; M, *Urocentrum*; N, *Cinetochilum*; O, *Saprophilus*; P, *Loxocephalus*; Q, *Uronema*.

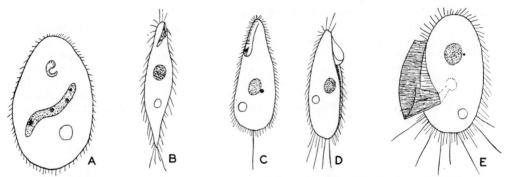

Fig. 35.—Representative Hymenostomata. A, *Ophryoglena*; B, *Cohnilembus*; C, *Philaster*; D, *Cristigera*; E, *Pleuronema*.

**235.** Peristome a small sickle-shaped slit; ellipsoid to cylindrical (Fig. 35A); some species parasitic in fresh-water invertebrates; 80 to 500 microns.
OPHRYOGLENIDAE, **Ophryoglena**

Peristome long, beginning at anterior end of body........................**236**

**236.** Peristome with a prominent membrane forming a pocket surrounding cytostome; with one to several stiff posterior cilia (Figs. 35D, E).
PLEURONEMATIDAE, **238**

Peristome without such a prominent membrane........................**237**

**237.** Body spindle-shaped; with several long cilia at posterior end (Fig. 35B); 60 microns.........................COHNILEMBIDAE, **Cohnilembus**

Body cylindrical; with a single long posterior cilium (Fig. 35C); 75 microns.
PHILASTERIDAE, **Philaster**

**238.** With a postoral depression or groove; compressed (Fig. 35D); 50 microns.
**Cristigera**

Without a postoral depression.......................................**239**

**239.** From 20 to 50 microns long; with refractile pellicle (Fig. 7C).......**Cyclidium**

From 70 to 180 microns long (Fig. 35E); some species commensal in fresh-water mussels. ...........................................**Pleuronema**

**240.** With cilia only, sometimes reduced or absent; rarely with additional small groups of cirrus-like structures.....................................**241**

With cirri only, confined to ventral surface; dorsal surface usually with rows of short bristles..........................Suborder **HYPOTRICHA, 259**

**241.** Body uniformly ciliated..................Suborder **HETEROTRICHA, 243**

Ciliation reduced or absent........................................**242**

**242.** Round in cross section; adoral zone consisting of cirri, bristles, or membranelles and enclosing a spiral peristomial field......Suborder **OLIGOTRICHA, 252**

Compressed and with a carapace; peristomial field consisting of eight membranelles; anaerobic......................Suborder **CTENOSTOMATA, 257**

**243.** Peristome sunken into the funnel-like anterior end (Figs. 36A, B).
BURSARIIDAE, **244**

Peristome exposed................................................**245**

**244.** Cytopharynx curved to the left (Fig. 36A); 500 to 1000 microns.
**Bursaria truncatella** O. F. M.

Cytopharynx curved to the right (Fig. 36B); 60 to 100 microns....**Bursaridium**

**245.** With a narrow nonciliated zone to the right of the adoral zone (Figs. 36C–G) .**246**

Without such a nonciliated zone...................................**250**

**246.** Adoral zone extending diagonally to right and posterior on ventral surface (Figs. 36C, E); anaerobic...............................METOPIDAE, **247**

Adoral zone longitudinal on flat ventral surface and turning to right before cytostome (Figs. 36D, F, G).....................SPIROSTOMIDAE, **248**

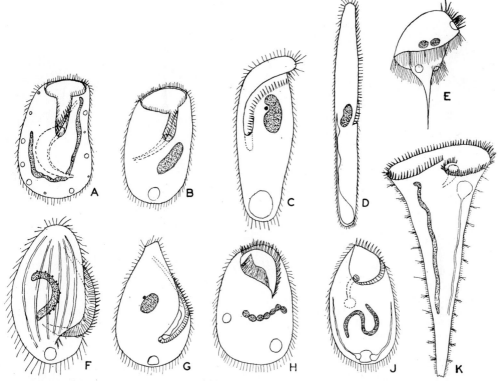

Fig. 36.—Representative Heterotricha. A, *Bursaria*; B, *Bursaridium*; C, *Metopus*; D, *Spirostomum*; E, *Caenomorpha*; F, *Phacodinium*; G, *Blepharisma*; H, *Condylostoma*; J, *Climacostomum*; K, *Stentor*.

**247.** Body shape variable but more or less oblong or fusiform (Fig. 36C); 80 to 300 microns. . . . . . . . . . . . . . . . . . . . . . . . . . . . . . . . . . . . . . . . . . . . . .**Metopus**

Bell-shaped and with long, pointed posterior end (Fig. 36E); 185 microns.
**Caenomorpha**

**248.** Cylindrical and very much elongated; large posterior contractile vacuole (Fig. 36D); 150 to 3,000 microns. . . . . . . . . . . . . . . . . . . . . . . . . . . . . . .**Spirostomum**

Not especially elongated; not cylindrical; contractile vacuole smaller. . . . . . . . .**249**

**249.** With marked grooves on body surface; cilia in cirrus-like fused groups; oval (Fig. 36F); 100 microns. . . . . . . . . . . . . . . . . . . . . . . . . . . . . . . . . . . .**Phacodinium**

Without grooves; without fused cilia; spindle-shaped or ellipsoid (Fig. 36G); 80 to 200 microns. . . . . . . . . . . . . . . . . . . . . . . . . . . . . . . . . . . . . . .**Blepharisma**

**250.** With a large undulating membrane; peristomial field not ciliated; ellipsoid (Fig. 36H); 100 to 400 microns. . . . . . . . . .CONDYLOSTOMIDAE, **Condylostoma**

Without a large undulating membrane; peristomial field ciliated.
STENTORIDAE, **251**

**251.** Highly contractile, trumpet-shaped or cylindrical when extended but oval to pyriform while swimming; adoral zone encircling peristome in a spiral (Fig. 36K); 200 to 3,000 microns. . . . . . . . . . . . . . . . . . . . . . . . . . . . . . . . .**Stentor**

Flattened and oval; adoral zone otherwise (Fig. 36J); 100 to 300 microns.
**Climacostomum**

**252.** Oral portion of peristome free on ventral surface; ovoid to spherical (Figs. 37A, B); 35 microns. . . . . . . . . . . . . . . . . . . . . . . . . . . . . . . . . ..HALTERIIDAE, **253**

Oral region enclosed by adoral zone (Figs. 37C–F) . . . . . . . . . . . . . . . . . . . .**254**

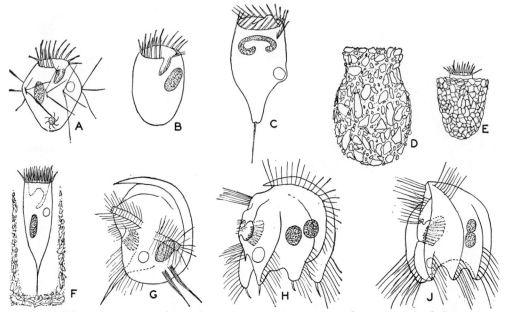

Fig. 37.—Representative Oligotricha and Ctenostomata. A, *Halteria*; B, *Strombidium*; C, *Strobilidium*; D, lorica of *Codonella*; E, *Tintinnopsis*; F, *Tintinnidium*; G, *Discomorpha*; H, *Saprodinium*; J, *Epalxis*.

253. With body bristles or cirri (Fig. 37A) ............................**Halteria**
    Without body bristles or cirri (Fig. 37B) ....................**Strombidium**
254. Without lorica; pyriform (Fig. 37C); 55 microns.
                                  STROBILIDIIDAE, **Strobilidium**
    With lorica or test, usually covered with debris...........TINTINNIDAE, **255**
255. Lorica divided into collar and basal portions (Fig. 37D); 65 microns..**Codonella**
    Lorica not so divided...........................................**256**
256. Lorica viscous, irregular in form, usually elongated, and translucent (Fig. 37F);
        40 to 200 microns.......................................**Tintinnidium**
    Lorica not viscous, thin, bowl-shaped (Fig. 37E); 50 microns......**Tintinnopsis**
257. With frontal cilia; with posterior marginal teeth or ridges (Figs. 37H, J).
                                     EPALCIDAE, **258**
    Without frontal cilia; oval; without marginal posterior teeth or ridges (Fig. 37G);
        80 microns.......................DISCOMORPHIDAE, **Discomorpha**
258. Some posterior teeth spiny (Fig. 37H); 50 microns..............**Saprodinium**
    Posterior teeth not spiny (Fig. 37J); 25 to 80 microns.................**Epalxis**
259. Adoral zone reduced or rudimentary; seven fronto-ventral cirri (Fig. 38A); 35
        microns.....................................ASPIDISCIDAE, **Aspidisca**
    Adoral zone well developed; usually larger...........................**260**
260. With two rows of marginal cirri......................OXYTRICHIDAE, **261**
    Without marginal cirri; ovoid; macronucleus band-shaped (Fig. 38B); 80 to 200
        microns..................................EUPLOTIDAE, **Euplotes**
261. Anal cirri absent (Figs. 38C–E) ..................................**262**
    Anal cirri present (Figs. 38F–K, 39) ...............................**264**
262. Ventral and marginal cirri spirally arranged (Figs. 38D, E); sometimes in gelati-
        nous tubes and colonial........................................**263**
    Ventral and marginal cirri not spirally arranged; elongated; tail-like region (Fig.
        38C); 175 microns.........................................**Uroleptus**

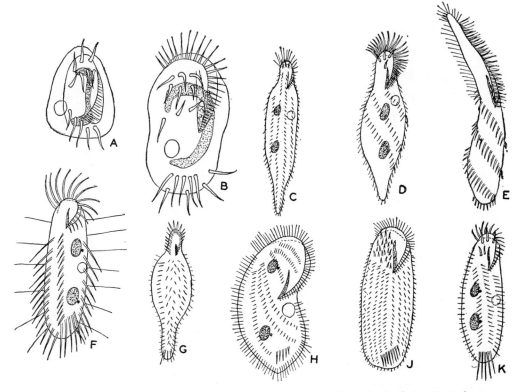

Fig. 38.—Representative Hypotricha; ventral views. A, *Aspidisca*; B, *Euplotes*; C, *Uroleptus*; D, *Strongylidium*; E, *Stichotricha*; F, *Balladyna*; G, *Epiclintes*; H, *Kerona*; J, *Urostyla*; K, *Holosticha*.

263. Peristome about one-fourth of body length (Fig. 38D); 80 to 250 microns.
**Strongylidium**
Peristome about one-half of body length (Fig. 38E); 50 to 200 microns.
**Stichotricha**
264. Frontal field without any special cirri (Figs. 38F, H) . . . . . . . . . . . . . . . . . . . . .265
Frontal field with a few, strong cirri (Figs. 38J, K, 39) . . . . . . . . . . . . . . . . . .267
265. Ellipsoid; one row of large anal cirri, one row of ventrals, and two rows of margi-
nals (Fig. 38F); 30 to 80 microns . . . . . . . . . . . . . . . . . . . . . . . . . . . .**Balladyna**
Not ellipsoid; with a much different pattern of cirri (Figs. 38G, H) . . . . . . . . .266
266. Elongated and spoon-shaped (Fig. 38G); free living; 375 microns. . . .**Epiclintes**
Reniform (Fig. 38H); commensal on *Hydra*; 160 microns.
**Kerona polyporum** Ehr.
267. Ventral cirri numerous and always arranged in long longitudinal rows (Figs.
38J, K) . . . . . . . . . . . . . . . . . . . . . . . . . . . . . . . . . . . . . . . . . . . . . . . . . . . . .268
Ventral cirri not particularly numerous and at least partly arranged in groups
(Fig. 39) . . . . . . . . . . . . . . . . . . . . . . . . . . . . . . . . . . . . . . . . . . . . . . . . . . . . .269
268. Ventral cirri in four or more rows (Fig. 38J); 200 to 800 microns . . . . . .**Urostyla**
Ventral cirri in one to three rows (Fig. 38K); 80 to 350 microns . . . . . .**Holosticha**
269. Ventral cirri arranged in one to three distinct longitudinal rows (Figs. 39A–D).
270
Ventral cirri not arranged in rows (Figs. 39E–G) . . . . . . . . . . . . . . . . . . . . . .273

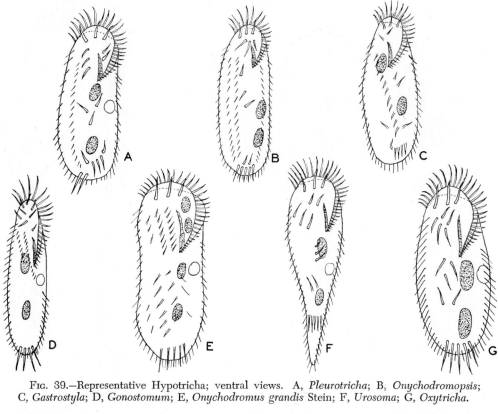

Fig. 39.—Representative Hypotricha; ventral views. A, *Pleurotricha*; B, *Onychodromopsis*; C, *Gastrostyla*; D, *Gonostomum*; E, *Onychodromus grandis* Stein; F, *Urosoma*; G, *Oxytricha*.

270. With one to three longitudinal and parallel ventral rows of cirri (Figs. 39A, B).
                                                            **271**
      With one or two oblique ventral rows of cirri (Figs. 39C, D)..............272
271. With two of the seven anal cirri more posterior (Fig. 39A); 170 to 400 microns.
                                                    **Pleurotricha**
      With a different arrangement of the anal cirri (Fig. 39B); 110 microns.
                                                **Onychodromopsis**
272. With a long row of ventral cirri (Fig. 39C); 150 to 320 microns.....**Gastrostyla**
      With one or two short rows of ventral cirri (Fig. 39D); 120 microns.
                                                **Gonostomum**
273. With 12 to 17 strong frontal cirri; four to eight macronuclei (Fig. 39E); 100 to
      300 microns............................**Onychodromus grandis** Stein
      With no more than ten frontal cirri; one to four macronuclei (Figs. 39F, G)..274
274. Posterior end tail-like (Fig. 39F); 110 to 250 microns..............**Urosoma**
      Posterior end not tail-like; 50 to 300 microns.........................275
275. Body soft and flexible; caudal cirri short (Fig. 39G)...............**Oxytricha**
      Body stiff; caudal cirri usually long (Fig. 7F)...................**Stylonychia**
276. Usually attached; rarely with body cilia (Figs. 40; 41A–H).
                                     Suborder **SESSILIA**, 277
      Free-swimming but with highly developed attachment disc on basal (aboral) sur-
          face....................Suborder **MOBILIA**, URCEOLARIIDAE, 293
277. Without a lorica but sometimes with a gelatinous envelope (Figs. 40; 41A, B).
                                                    278
      With a well-developed lorica......................................289

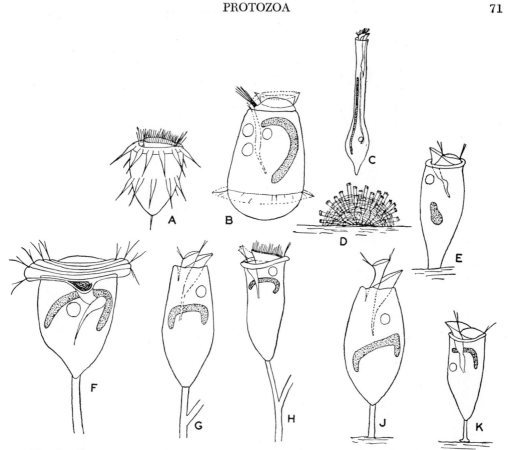

Fig. 40.—Representative Peritricha. A, *Hastatella*; B, *Opisthonecta*; C, *Ophrydium*; D, colony of *Ophrydium*; E, *Scyphidia*; F, *Campanella*; G, *Opercularia*; H, *Epistylis*; J, *Pyxidium*; K, *Rhabdostyla*.

278. Posterior end usually with one or two short spines; free swimming (Figs. 40A, B).
    ASTYLOZOONIDAE, **279**
    Posterior end without spines; sessile...................................**280**
279. Body with two to four rings of long conical processes (Fig. 40A); 40 microns; common in rivers......................................**Hastatella**
    Body without such processes; conical, ends broadly rounded; ring of cilia near aboral end (Fig. 40B); 160 microns.....................**Opisthonecta**
280. With a long, cylindrical, contractile neck; colonial; individuals imbedded in common gelatinous mass (Fig. 40C); 200 to 400 microns.
    OPHRYDIIDAE, **Ophrydium**
    Without a necklike region.............................................**281**
281. Without stalk; with posterior attachment disc (Fig. 40E); attached to debris, or epizoic; 40 to 100 microns.................SCYPHIDIIDAE, **Scyphidia**
    Stalk present........................................................**282**
282. Stalk not retractile.....................................EPISTYLIDAE, **283**
    Stalk retractile; bell-shaped; attached to plants and aquatic invertebrates.
    VORTICELLIDAE, **287**
283. Stalk branched; colonial (Figs. 40F–H)................................**284**
    Stalk not branched; attached to vegetation and a wide variety of aquatic invertebrates; 25 to 100 microns....................................**286**

Fig. 41.—Representative Peritricha. A, *Carchesium*; B, *Zoothamnium* colony; C, free-swimming telotroch stage of a vorticellid; D, *Lagenophrys*; E, *Cothurnia*; F, *Pyxicola*; G, *Vaginicola*; H, *Thuricola*; J, *Urceolaria*; K, *Trichodina*; L, *Cyclochaeta*.

**284.** Adoral zone with four to six turns (Fig. 40F); 130 to 350 microns...**Campanella**
Adoral zone simpler; attached to vegetation and many aquatic invertebrates; 40 to 150 microns............................................**285**

**285.** Peristome small, separated from peristome border and protrusible through it (Fig. 40G); often in polluted waters............................**Opercularia**
Peristome nearly as wide as body, attached to peristome border at margin (Fig. 40H); colonies often macroscopic; common in polluted waters......**Epistylis**

**286.** Frontal disc supported by style-like process (Fig. 40J)..............**Pyxidium**
Frontal disc not supported by style-like process (Fig. 40K)........**Rhabdostyla**

**287.** Solitary but often gregarious (Fig. 7D); 35 to 160 microns..........**Vorticella**
Colonial; colonies up to 6 mm. long.....................................**288**

**288.** Myonemes not continuous, individual stalks contract singly (Fig. 41A); 50 to 130 microns...........................................**Carchesium**
Myonemes continuous; entire colony contracting or expanding simultaneously (Fig. 41B); 40 to 90 microns.............................**Zoothamnium**

**289.** Distal margin not attached to lorica; with a posterior stalk (Figs. 41E–H).

VAGINICOLIDAE, **290**

Distal margin attached to aperture of lorica; unstalked; lorica with flattened attachment surface (Fig. 41D); often ectocommensal on invertebrates; 75 microns.

LAGENOPHRYIDAE, **Lagenophrys**

**290.** Lorica with a stalk (Figs. 41E, F)..................................**291**

Lorica without a stalk (Figs. 41G, H)................................**292**

**291.** With a discoidal corneous operculum which closes lorica when animal contracts (Fig. 41F); 70 to 160 microns...............................**Pyxicola**

Without an operculum (Fig. 41E); 50 to 110 microns..............**Cothurnia**

**292.** With a valvelike apparatus which closes the opening of the lorica when the animal is contracted (Fig. 41H); 160 to 220 microns.................**Thuricola**

Without such a valvelike apparatus (Fig. 41G); 50 to 200 microns....**Vaginicola**

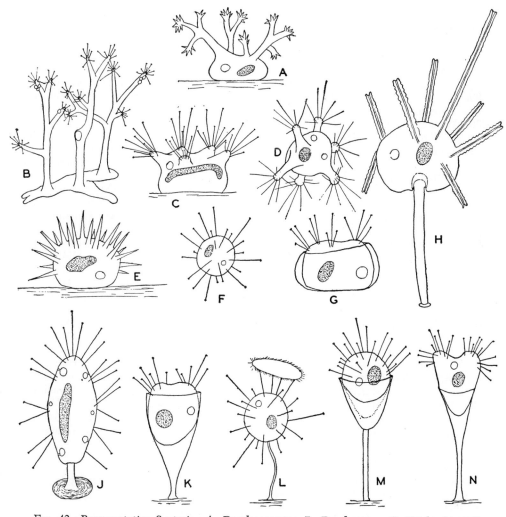

FIG. 42.—Representative Suctoria. A, *Dendrocometes*; B, *Dendrosoma*; C, *Trichophrya*; D, *Staurophrya*; E, *Stylocometes*; F, *Sphaerophrya*; G, *Solenophrya*; H, *Choanophrya*; J, *Discophrya*; K, *Metacineta*; L, *Podophrya* feeding on a ciliate; M, *Paracineta*; N, *Acineta*.

**293.** Peristome obliquely placed (Fig. 41J); 110 microns; commensal on Turbellaria.
**Urceolaria**

Peristome not obliquely placed; barrel-, bell-, or saucer-shaped...........294

**294.** Outer row of cilia of attachment disc not bent upward (Fig. 41K); 55 microns; commensal on *Hydra,* fishes, and amphibians; sometimes thought to be true parasites on fishes....................................**Trichodina**

Outer row of cilia of attachment disc stiff and bent upward (Fig. 41L); 45 microns; commensal on sponges and fishes................**Cyclochaeta**

**295.** Body asymmetrical or branched.....................................296

Body more or less symmetrical.......................................300

**296.** Without special arms..........................DENDROSOMIDAE, 297

With special arms (Figs. 42A, E); commensal on isopods, amphipods, etc.
DENDROCOMETIDAE, 299

**297.** Body dendritic, often large (Fig. 42B); up to 2.5 mm. high; on vegetation.
**Dendrosoma**

Body not dendritic.................................................298

**298.** Body rounded or elongated; tentacles knobbed; nucleus band-shaped (Fig. 42C); 30 to 240 microns; on vegetation and various invertebrates; also reported from gills of largemouth black bass.......................**Trichophrya**

Body rounded and with six processes; tentacles not knobbed; nucleus round (Fig. 42D); 50 microns; often in suspension as a plankter...........**Staurophrya**

**299.** With branched arms (Fig. 42A); 75 microns.................**Dendrocometes**

Arms not branched (Fig. 42E); 90 microns...................**Stylocometes**

**300.** Without a stalk....................................................301

With a stalk of variable length.....................................302

**301.** Without a lorica; spherical (Fig. 42F); 75 microns; stagnant water.
PODOPHRYIDAE, **Sphaerophrya**

With a lorica; tentacles in fascicles (Fig. 42G); 40 microns.
ACINETIDAE, **Solenophrya**

**302.** With 5 to 12 tubular expansible tentacles used for engulfing large food particles (Fig. 42H); 65 microns..............DISCOPHRYIDAE, **Choanophrya**

With normal type of tentacles.......................................303

**303.** With a large attachment plate at the base of the stalk; tentacles evenly distributed or in fascicles (Fig. 42J); 70 microns..DISCOPHRYIDAE, **Discophrya**

Without such a plate................................................304

**304.** Lorica drawn out, funnel-shaped, and attached at stalklike lower end (Fig. 42K); 550 microns...........................PODOPHRYIDAE, **Metacineta**

Lorica otherwise or absent..........................................305

**305.** Body spherical to ellipsoidal (Figs. 42L, M)...........PODOPHRYIDAE, 306

Body not spherical to ellipsoidal (Figs. 8, 42N)..........ACINETIDAE, 307

**306.** Without test or cup; tentacles distributed or in fascicles (Fig. 42L); 10 to 50 microns. ....................................................**Podophrya**

With a close-fitting cup or gelatinous envelope without a visible rim (Fig. 42M); tentacles distributed; 40 microns.........................**Paracineta**

**307.** Body completely or partly filling the delicate cup-shaped lorica; tentacles in one to three fascicles (Fig. 42N); 30 to 180 microns................**Acineta**

Lorica absent; tentacles in one to four fascicles (Fig. 8); 55 microns...**Tokophrya**

## PROTOZOA REFERENCES

AHLSTROM, E. H. 1937. Studies on variability in the genus Dinobryon. *Trans. Amer. Micros. Soc.* **56**:139–159.

ALLEGRE, C. F., and T. L. JAHN. 1943. A survey of the genus Phacus (Protozoa; Euglenoidina). *Ibid.* **62**:233–244.

BALAMUTH, W. 1940. Regeneration in protozoa: a problem of morphogenesis. *Quart. Rev. Biol.* **15**:290–337.

BARKER, A. N. 1946. The ecology and function of Protozoa in sewage purification. *Ann. Appl. Biol.* 33:314–325.

BHATIA, B. L. 1936. Protozoa: Ciliophora. *Fauna of British India*. 493 pp.

BOCK, F. 1938. Protozoa, Urtiere. *Biol. Tiere Deutschlands* 1:1–199.

BÜTSCHLI, O. 1887–1889. Protozoa. *Klassen und Ord. Thier-Reichs* 1:1–2035.

CALKINS, G. N. 1933. *The biology of the Protozoa*. 2d ed. 607 pp. Philadelphia, Pa.

CALKINS, G. N., and F. M. SUMMERS (eds.). 1941. *Protozoa in biological research*. 1148 pp. New York, N. Y.

CASH, J., J. HOPKINSON, and G. H. WAILES. 1905–1921. *The British freshwater Rhizopoda and Heliozoa*. 5 vols. London.

COLLIN, B. 1912. Études monographique sur les Acinétiéns. *Arch. Zool. Exp. Gen.* 51:1–457.

CONN, H. W. 1905. A preliminary report on the Protozoa of the fresh waters of Connecticut. *Bull. Conn. Geol. Nat. Hist. Surv.* 2:1–67.

DAVIS, H. S. 1947. Studies of the protozoan parasites of fresh-water fishes. *Fish. Bull. U. S. Wildlife Serv.* 51:1–29.

DEFLANDRE, G. 1928. Le genre Arcella Ehrenberg. *Arch. Protistenk.* 64:152–287.

———. 1929. Le genre Centropyxis Stein. *Ibid.* 67:322–375.

DOFLEIN, F., and E. REICHENOW. 1928–1929. *Lehrbuch der Protozoenkunde*. 5th ed. 1262 pp. Jena.

DOYLE, W. L. 1943. The nutrition of the Protozoa. *Biol. Rev.* 18:119–136.

EDDY, S. 1930. The fresh-water armored or thecate dinoflagellates. *Trans. Amer. Micros. Soc.* 49:277–321.

EDMONDSON, C. H. 1906. The Protozoa of Iowa. *Proc. Davenport Acad. Sci.* 11:1–124.

FINLEY, H. E. 1930. Toleration of freshwater Protozoa to increased salinity. *Ecology* 11:337–346.

FRITSCH, F. E. 1935. *The structure and reproduction of the algae. I.* 791 pp. New York, N. Y.

———. 1944. Present-day classification of algae. *Bot. Rev.* 10:233–277.

FURGASON, W. H. 1940. The significant cytostomal pattern of the "Glaucoma-Colpidium" group, and a proposed new genus and species, Tetrahymena geleii. *Arch. Protistenk.* 94:224–266.

GEIMAN, Q. M. 1931. Morphological variations in Coleps octospinus. *Trans. Amer. Micros. Soc.* 50:136–143.

GERLOFF, J. 1940. Beiträge zur Kenntnis der Variabilität und Systematik der Gattung Chlamydomonas. *Arch. Prostistenk.* 94:311–520.

HALL, R. P. 1939. The trophic nature of the plant-like flagellates. *Quart. Rev. Biol.* 14:1–12.

HOLLANDE, A. 1942. Étude cytologique et biologique de quelques flagellés libres. *Arch. Zool. Exp. Gen.* 83 (Suppl.) :1–268.

ILOWAISKY, S. 1926. Material zum Studium der Cysten der Hypotrichen. *Arch. Protistenk.* 54:92–136.

JAHN, T. L. 1934. Problems of population growth in the Protozoa. *Cold Spring Harbor Symp. Quant. Biol.* 2:167–180.

———. 1946. The euglenoid flagellates. *Quart. Rev. Biol.* 21:246–274.

JAKUS, M. A. 1945. The structure and properties of the trichocysts of Paramecium. *Jour. Exp. Zool.* 100:457–476.

JENNINGS, H. S. 1906. *Behavior of the lower organisms*. 366 pp. New York, N. Y.

JOHNSON, L. P. 1944. Euglenae of Iowa. *Trans. Amer. Micros. Soc.* 63:97–135.

JOHNSON, W. H. 1941. Nutrition in the Protozoa. *Quart. Rev. Biol.* 16:336–348.

———. 1941a. Populations of ciliates. *Amer. Nat.* 75:438–457.

KAHL, A. 1930–1935. Urtiere oder Protozoa. I: Wimpertiere oder Ciliata (Infusoria). *Tierwelt Deutschlands* 18, 21, 25, 30:1–886.

KIDDER, G. W., and V. C. DEWEY. 1945. Studies on the biochemistry of Tetrahymena. III. Strain differences. *Physiol. Zool.* 18:136–157.

KIMBALL, R. F. 1943. Mating types in the ciliate Protozoa. *Quart. Rev. Biol.* 18:30–45.

KING, R. L., and T. L. JAHN. 1948. Concerning the genera of amebas. *Science* 107:293–294.

KITCHING, J. A. 1938. Contractile vacuoles. *Biol. Rev.* 13:403–444.

KOFOID, C. A., and O. SWEZY. 1921. The free-living, unarmored dinoflagellates. *Mem. Univ. Calif.* 5:1–562.

KUDO, R. R. 1946. *Protozoology*. 3d ed. 778 pp. Springfield, Ill.

LACKEY, J. B. 1925. The fauna of Imhoff tanks. *Bull. N. J. Exp. Sta.* 417:1–39

———. 1932. Oxygen deficiency and sewage protozoa: with descriptions of some new species. *Biol. Bull.* 63:287–295.

———. 1936. Some freshwater protozoa with blue chromatophores. *Ibid.* 71:492–497.

———. 1938. Protozoan plankton as indicators of pollution in a flowing stream. *Publ. Health Rep. Wash.* 53:2037–2058.

———. 1938a. A study of some ecologic factors affecting the distribution of Protozoa. *Ecol. Monogr.* 8:501–527.

———. 1940. The microscopic flora and fauna of tree holes. *Ohio Jour. Sci.* 40:186–192.

LEIDY, J. 1879. Fresh-water rhizopods of North America. *Rept. U. S. Geol. Surv. Terr.* 12:1–324.

LOWNDES, A. G. 1944. The swimming of unicellular flagellate organisms. *Proc. Zool. Soc. London* 113A:99–107.

MAST, S. O. 1925. Structure, movement, locomotion, and stimulation in Amoeba. *Jour. Morph.* 41:347–426.

———. 1947. The food-vacuole in Paramecium. *Biol. Bull.* 92:31–72.

Mast, S. O., and W. J. Bowen. 1944. The food vacuole in the Peritricha, with special reference to the hydrogen-ion concentration of its contents and of the cytoplasm. *Ibid.* **87**:188–222.

Noble, A. E. 1932. On Tokophrya lemnarum Stein (Suctoria) with an account of its budding and conjugation. *Univ. Calif. Publ. Zool.* **37**:477–520.

Noland, L. E. 1925. A review of the genus Coleps with descriptions of two new species. *Trans. Amer. Micros. Soc.* **44**:3–13.

——. 1925a. Factors influencing the distribution of fresh water ciliates. *Ecology* **6**:437–452.

Noland, L. E., and H. E. Finley. 1931. Studies on the taxonomy of the genus Vorticella. *Trans. Amer. Micros. Soc.* **50**:81–123.

Owen, H. M. 1947. Flagellar structure: 1. A discussion of fixation and staining of the protozoan flagellum. *Ibid.* **66**:50–58.

Pascher, A. 1927. Volvocales. *Süsswasserfl. Deutschlands* **4**:1–506.

Penard, E. 1902. *Faune rhizopodique du bassin du Léman.* 714 pp. Geneva, Switzerland.

——. 1904. *Les heliozoaires d'eau douce.* 341 pp. Geneva, Switzerland.

——. 1922. *Études sur les infusoires d'eau douce.* 331 pp. Geneva, Switzerland.

Picken, L. E. R. 1937. The structure of some protozoan communities. *Jour. Ecol.* **25**:368–384.

Pochmann, A. 1942. Synopsis der Gattung Phacus. *Arch. Protistenk.* **95**:81–252.

Pringsheim, E. G. 1941. The interrelationships of pigmented and colourless Flagellata. *Biol. Rev* **16**:191–204.

——. 1942. Contributions to our knowledge of saprophytic algae and flagellata. III. Astasia, Distigma, Menoidium, and Rhabdomonas. *New Phytol.* **41**:171–205.

——. 1948. Taxonomic problems in the Euglenineae. *Biol. Rev.* **23**:46–61.

Rieder, J. 1936. Beitrag zur Kenntnis der Süsswasser-Suktorien und Revision der Schweizer Suktorien-Fauna. *Rev. Suisse Zool.* **43**:359–395.

——. 1936a. Biologische und ökologische Untersuchungen an Süsswasser-Suktorien. *Arch. Naturgesch.* **5**:137–214.

Roux, J. 1901. *Fauna infusorienne des eaux stagnantes des environs de Geneve.* 149 pp. Geneva, Switzerland.

Schaeffer, A. A. 1926. Taxonomy of the amoebas with descriptions of thirty-nine new marine and freshwater species. *Publ. Carnegie Inst. Wash.* **345**:1–116.

Shawhan, F. M., and T. L. Jahn. 1947. A survey of the genus Petalomonas Stein (Protozoa: Euglenidae). *Trans. Amer. Micros. Soc.* **66**:182–189.

Smith, G. M. 1920. Phytoplankton of the inland lakes of Wisconsin. Part I. *Bull. Wis. Geol. and Nat. Hist. Surv.* **57**:1–243.

——. 1950. *The fresh-water algae of the United States.* 2nd ed. 719 pp. New York, N. Y.

——. 1944. A comparative study cf the species of Volvox. *Trans. Amer. Micros. Soc.* **63**:265–310.

Stump, A. B. 1935. Observations on the feeding of Difflugia, Pontigulasia, and Lesquereusia. *Biol. Bull.* **69**:136–142.

Thompson, R. H. 1947. Fresh-water dinoflagellates of Maryland. *Publ. Chesapeake Biol. Lab.* **67**:1–28.

Unger, W. B. 1931. The protozoan sequence in five plant infusions. *Trans. Amer. Micros. Soc.* **50**:144–153.

Valkanov, A. 1940. Die Heliozoen und Proteomyxien. *Arch. Protistenk.* **93**:225–254.

Von Brand, T. 1935. Der Stoffwechsel der Protozoen. *Ergebnisse der Biol.* **12**:161–220.

Walton, L. B. 1915. A review of the described species of the Order Euglenoidina Bloch. Class Flagellata (Protozoa) with particular reference to those found in the city water supplies and in other localities in Ohio. *Bull. Ohio Biol. Surv.* **1**:341–449.

Wang, C. C. 1928. Ecological studies of the seasonal distribution of Protozoa in a freshwater pond. *Jour. Morph. and Physiol.* **46**:431–478.

Wenyon, C. M. 1926. *Protozoology.* 2 vols., 1563 pp. London.

West, G. S., and F. E. Fritsch. 1927. *A treatise on the British fresh-water algae.* 2d ed. 534 pp. Cambridge, England.

Woodruff, L. L. 1912. The origin and sequence of the protozoan fauna of hay infusions. *Jour. Exp. Zool.* **12**:205–264.

# Chapter 3

# PORIFERA (SPONGES)

THE GREAT MAJORITY of the 3,000 species of sponges are marine, only a single family, the Spongillidae, being represented in fresh waters. This family consists of about 150 species, of which about 30 have been reported from the United States.

Fresh-water sponges are common in clean ponds, lakes, streams, and rivers. Because they are sessile and because of their inconspicuous green, brown, gray, or yellowish coloration, however, they are frequently unnoticed. Indeed, until their morphology and physiology were first partially understood (beginning in 1825), sponges were often considered as plants. Syngamic reproduction has been known only since 1856. A suitable substrate for the matlike sponge growth may be provided by almost any stable submerged object, including rocks, pebbles, aquatic vegetation, logs, branches, and twigs. Sponges may be found on the upper surfaces, sides, or lower surfaces.

According to de Laubenfels (1936), the Phylum Porifera may be divided into three classes, which are distinguished on the basis of their skeletal structure. The Class Calcispongea consists of small marine sponges having a skeleton composed of calcium carbonate spicules which may be one-, three-, or four-rayed. Hyalospongea are the glass sponges, likewise all marine; their skeleton is an openwork structure and consists of siliceous triaxon spicules or some modification of triaxon. In the Demospongea the skeleton may consist of horny fibers (spongin), siliceous spicules (not triaxon), or both. Sponges of com-

mercial importance are in the Order Keratosa of the Demospongea; the skeleton consists entirely of spongin, spicules being absent. In four other orders there is no spongin, the skeleton being composed entirely of tetraxon spicules. In the three remaining orders, however, the skeleton consists of both monaxon spicules and variable amounts of spongin. One of these orders, the Haplosclerina, contains the Spongillidae. In addition to the skeletal materials already mentioned, it should be emphasized that the noncellular matrix, or mesoglea, of all sponges also functions in support and cohesion of the living tissues.

**General characteristics.** The size of a single fresh-water sponge is enormously variable, depending on the species, age, and various ecological conditions. Some species, for example, even when mature may consist of a thin, slimy, delicate mat having a surface area of only a few square centimeters. Other species may cover an area of as much as 40 square meters under highly favorable conditions. The thickness of a sponge growth is likewise variable; sometimes it may be only 1 or 2 mm. thick, while under other circumstances it may be as much as 4 cm. thick. The growth form may be typically encrusting and matlike, or there may be numerous papillae, finger-like outgrowths, branches, or an extremely irregular lobed growth form (Figs. 43, 44).

Furthermore, few of our American species are limited to one type of growth form, so that field identification by this

FIG. 43.—Colonies of *Spongilla lacustris* (L.) on twigs, ×0.3.

FIG. 44.—*Meyenia mülleri* (Lieberkühn). A, growth form on a branched twig, ×0.3; B, proliferating growth form on a single unbranched twig, ×0.8.

character is usually not feasible. *Spongilla fragilis* Leidy, for example, may be found as a fine-textured uniform crust; or it may be more robust, with an irregular surface and loose texture; or it may consist of luxuriant branching lobes. *S. lacustris* (L.) has every variation from a simple encrustation to tufts of long finger-like processes, and *Meyenia mülleri* (Lieberkühn) has a similar range. The more common growth forms for most of our species are indicated in the key which follows. In general, individuals of a particular species are usually more lobed and luxuriant in standing waters than in running waters.

Sponges are often collected in which the apparent thickness is as much as 30 to 60 mm., but if such growths are examined carefully it is usually found that the living portion of the mass forms only an outermost stratum 4 to 20 mm. thick, all of the underlying material being composed of the dead remains of the previous one or more years' growth.

Coloration of sponges may be produced by several factors. Most species found growing on the upper sides of objects are some shade of green owing to contained algal cells (see page 82). If these same species occur in deep waters or on the undersides of objects, however, there is little chlorophyll effect and the coloration may be some shade of dark brown, tan, gray, flesh color, or reddish (rarely). On the other hand, there are a few species that are seldom or never green, even when growing in an abundance of light. Coloration may be modified by the ingestion of food and inorganic particles of a certain shade or by the presence of pigmented metabolic materials in the tissues.

The sponge body is simply constructed. There are no organs, and the tissues are relatively unspecialized and loosely organized. The external surface bears openings of two general sizes. The very abundant microscopic ostia are merely more or less circular openings in the epidermal membrane. The few oscular openings are scattered over the sponge surface. Usually

Fig. 45.—Young spring sponges on bits of charred wood, ×1.7.

they are 0.5 to 2.0 mm. in diameter but may be as wide as 5 to 10 mm. An osculum is typically located at the distal end of a small chimney-like projection. By means of a carmine suspension it can be easily shown that minute currents of water pass into the sponge through the ostia and out through the oscula.

Internally, the sponge is a maze of interconnected and ramifying spaces, channels, and chambers (Figs. 46, 47). In typical fresh-water species the ostia open into an extensive subdermal cavity from which an abundance of minute narrow incurrent canals lead more deeply into the sponge. At their inner ends these incurrent canals open into small more or less spherical cavities, the flagellated chambers. At the opposite side each flagellated chamber empties into another minute canal, the excurrent canal, which, along with many other excurrent canals, empties into a much larger irregular central cavity. Each central cavity opens to the outside through an osculum. The opening of the incurrent canal into the flagellated chamber is called the prosopyle; the larger opening from the chamber into the excurrent canal is called the apopyle. The entire arrangement of canals and chambers in the Spongillidae is the rhagon type.

Judging from the available literature, there seems to be some variation in the structure of the thin, flat, outer epidermis. In some species it is apparently a syncitium with scattered nuclei, while in others

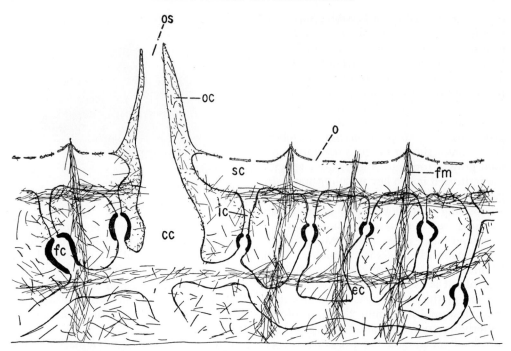

Fig. 46.—Diagrammatic section of peripheral portion of a typical fresh-water sponge. Heavy black lines represent layers of choanocytes lining flagellated chambers. Delicate matrix of spongin not shown. *cc*, central cavity; *ec*, excurrent canal; *fc*, flagellated chamber; *fm*, fascicle of megascleres; *ic*, incurrent canal; *o*, ostium; *oc*, oscular chimney; *os*, osculum; *sc*, subdermal cavity.

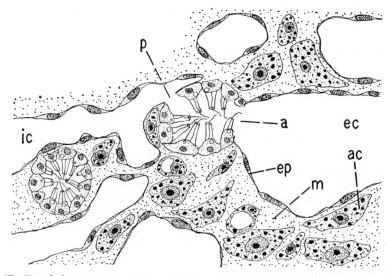

Fig. 47.—Detailed structure of Spongillidae, semidiagrammatic, showing two flagellated chambers. Spicules and delicate spongin matrix omitted. *a*, apopyle; *ac*, amoebocyte; *ec*, exhalent canal; *ep*, epithelial cell; *ic*, inhalent canal; *m*, mesoglea matrix; *p*, prosopyle. (Modified from Brien, 1936.)

there are definite cells with separating membranes. The ostia may be openings within special pore cells, but some workers maintain that the remnants of the pore cells eventually disappear, leaving the ostium as a simple opening in the epidermis.

In contrast to the situation in some marine sponges, the flagellated chambers of the Spongillidae are minute and lined with only a small number of collar cells, or choanocytes. Except for the flagellated chambers, all internal chambers and canals of a sponge are lined with a flat layer variously characterized as a syncitium, semisyncitium, or layer of colloidal material with contained cells.

The space between layers of epithelium is filled with a gelatinous noncellular matrix, or mesoglea, containing an abundance of several kinds of mesenchymal amoebocytes which have a wide variety of functions. Some secrete the skeleton; some function in nutrition, storage, transport, and excretion; others function in reproduction. Many amoebocytes are motile and move about slowly in the mesoglea.

**Skeleton.** Fresh-water sponges contain great numbers of needle-like microscopic spicules which aid in supporting the flimsy tissues. Such spicules are of two general types. The larger spicules, or megascleres (skeletal spicules), form a reticulate network through and in the tissues, and around and through the many cavities and channels. In addition to many megascleres arranged haphazardly, there are loose overlapping fascicles of megascleres radiating outward from the center or base of the sponge and frequently extending through the external epithelium to the outside. There are also transverse fascicles which run between the radiating fascicles. More or less minute amounts of fibrous and veil-like spongin bind the megascleres together.

The smaller type of spicules, or microscleres (flesh, or dermal spicules), are most abundant in the peripheral and epidermal portion of the sponge body, although there are also some lining the deeper channels. Microscleres are arranged in a scattered fashion, rarely in fascicles. Microscleres are lacking in some species.

Megascleres and microscleres may be sharp pointed or blunt and with few to many spines of variable size, depending on the species. A few species have spherical, stellate, or birotulate microscleres.

Additional types of spicules are found associated with the special reproductive bodies, or gemmules, and these are discussed on page 84.

The siliceous material of sponge spicules is often said to have the composition of "hydrated silica" or "opal." Analyses show about 92 per cent silicon dioxide, 7 per cent water, and small amounts of magnesium, potassium, and sodium oxides.

Small and simple spicules are formed within single specialized amoebocytes, called silicoblasts, but large and complex spicules are formed by two or more silicoblasts. The first sign of a spicule is an extremely thin organic axial thread within the silicoblast, the siliceous material being deposited around it in ever-increasing thickness.

**Nutrition.** Fundamentally, a sponge efficiently strains minute particles from the water in which it lives. The flagella of the choanocytes are directed more or less toward the apopyles of the flagellated chambers. Their spiral or undulating movements collectively produce weak water currents which enter the sponge through the ostia and leave through the oscula. As the water traverses the flagellated chambers, bacteria and bits of detritus are caught on the outer sticky surface of the collars of the collar cells as well as on the exposed surface of the cells proper. All digestion is intracellular, but little or no digestion occurs within the choanocytes. Food particles are passed on to the adjacent mesoglea and into the amoebocytes where digestion is completed and where there may be considerable storage.

Prosopyles are so small that they frequently become plugged, and in such cases the particles are carried off to one side by slow "flowing" movements of the epidermal protoplasm. They may later sink below the surface and be taken up by amoebocytes.

It is now thought that the inter- and intracellular "zoochlorellae" of Spongillidae are not essential to sponge metabolism, but there is some evidence to show that their presence results in better sponge growth. Such algae are certain ingested plankton species, including *Pleurococcus, Chlorella,* and other minute genera, that persist in the tissues, multiply, and are digested very slowly. In dim light or darkness they are digested much more rapidly than in bright light.

**Circulation.** There is no special circulatory mechanism in sponges. Materials are transferred by diffusion and amoebocytic transport.

**Respiration.** The exchange of oxygen and carbon dioxide occurs everywhere in exposed tissues of sponges, both externally and internally. Diffusion of these dissolved gases is probably rapid and efficient since all sponge cells are either directly in contact with water or only a few cells distant from it.

**Excretion.** Dissolved metabolic waste materials simply diffuse into the water surrounding and passing through the sponge body. Granular metabolic materials are usually given off from amoebocytes into the excurrent canals but may also be retained by the cells for varying periods of time.

Choanocytes and many amoebocytes sometimes contain one or two contractile vacuoles, and it is probable that they function mainly in keeping the proper osmotic pressure in the tissues.

**Contractile elements, impulse conduction.** Although sponges are completely sessile and there is no definite muscle system, a few specialized amoebocytes, or myocytes, have the ability to contract and relax.

The oscular chimneys are normally kept open by the excurrents, but if environmental conditions become unfavorable, the oscula will slowly close in several minutes. Such contraction is produced by the action of fusiform myocytes around the openings. In *Meyenia fluviatilis* Carter it has been shown that even under normal circumstances the oscular chimneys (1 to 3 mm. high) continuously and slowly change in form, from high to low and wide to narrow. The osculum will close and the chimney will collapse in several seconds if the latter is struck a sharp blow with a needle. Complete recovery takes 20 to 30 seconds. Sticking a needle into the tissues 2 mm. from the chimney base, however, has no effect on the chimney.

Some workers report that under unfavorable conditions ostia will slowly close as a result of contractility of the surrounding protoplasm, but there are no special sensory or nerve cells, and there is no coordination and no transmission of impulses (or perhaps transmission for 2 to 3 mm. at most).

**Reproduction, growth.** Many details of syngamic reproduction are still obscure and confused. Some investigators maintain that the Spongillidae are hermaphroditic and a single individual may produce eggs and sperm simultaneously, but others are convinced that the sexes are separate or that an individual may produce sperm at one time and eggs at another. Perhaps both conditions prevail, depending on the species.

Sperm and egg production are thought to occur mostly during July and August, and to a lesser extent in June and September. The oogonia are amoebocytes which grow by absorbing and ingesting many adjacent cells. By the time the egg is mature it is large and lies loosely in one of the internal cavities of the sponge.

Although earlier investigators thought

that sperm developed from amoebocytes, more recent work has shown that in at least two species they develop from choanocytes which lose their collars and flagella, become more or less amoeboid, migrate into the mesoglea, and function as spermatogonia. Mature flagellated sperm are formed in abundance in baglike "follicles." These sperm are released into the chambers of the sponge and out through the oscula into the surrounding water. Some of them are eventually drawn into the chambers of the same or other sponges where they fertilize the mature ova.

Several different and peculiar types of early embryology occur in the Spongillidae, but in all of them a flagellated embryo is formed which is released from the parent and swims about for a few hours or days before settling to the substrate and metamorphosing to form a minute young sponge.

Growth is mainly a process of proliferation and accretion with accompanying development of additional orifices, channels, and chambers. Usually most of the sponge body dies or becomes dormant in the autumn and partly disintegrates during the winter, and although it sometimes does not revive in the following spring, it is more common for the surviving remnant to revive and continue growth during the following season. In this way a specimen may remain more or less intact from year to year, growing in thickness, but with only the outermost layer being alive and active. This persistence of sponges occurs especially on firm, broad substrates and where there is little ice action.

Many times, however, a sponge may remain active and green throughout the winter, even under ice.

**Reduction bodies.** Under highly unfavorable conditions a large sponge forms numerous "reduction bodies," and a small sponge may form a single reduction body. The tissues shrink down into the skeleton and the canal system disappears, leaving the epidermis surrounding a mixture of mesenchyme cells, mesoglea, choanocytes, and spicules. Under favorable conditions such a reduction body may grow and regenerate a new sponge. Reduction bodies have been observed for only a few species, and it is not known whether they are produced regularly throughout the Spongillidae.

**Regeneration.** Like certain marine species, the Spongillidae have remarkable powers of regeneration. If bits of *Meyenia* or *Spongilla* are macerated and dissociated by squeezing through fine bolting silk, small clumps of cells will coalesce within a few hours, slowly reconstitute, and within several days grow into a new minute sponge.

**Gemmules.** The formation of gemmules is one of the most characteristic features of fresh-water sponges. These are highly resistant resting stages similar in function to the statoblasts of fresh-water bryozoans. Briefly, a gemmule is a spherical structure with a multiple, dead, secreted outer layer, a covering of spicules, and an internal mass of undifferentiated mesenchymal amoebocytes. Gemmule diameter ranges from about 150 to 1,000 microns. Coloration may be whitish or various shades of yellow or brown.

Formerly it was thought that gemmules appeared only at the close of the growing season, but it is now known that they may be formed at any time during the growing season. *Spongilla lacustris* is the only common species that regularly forms gemmules in September and October. Because of autumn disintegration of superficial tissues, however, it is much easier to observe gemmules in any species at that time.

Gemmules may be deposited in a compact basal layer in a sponge, or they may be scattered throughout the sponge body. The first sign of gemmule development is the grouping of many food-filled amoebocytes into discrete masses. A thin inner sclerotized membrane is formed around

Fig. 48.—Disintegrated winter appearance of sponges. A, crust of gemmules on bit of bark, ×1; B, gemmules of *Spongilla lacustris* on rock, ×3. (B from K. Berg, 1948, by permission.)

each mass of amoebocytes, followed by a heavier, middle (or outer) sclerotized membrane which has a single small foraminal area. The latter sometimes has a narrow, projecting foraminal tubule. Except for the location of the foraminal aperture or foraminal tubule, the gemmule is covered with a complete, crustlike, thick, honeycombed coating, or pneumatic layer. Sometimes a third thin, outer sclerotized membrane covers the pneumatic layer. In the Spongillinae an abundance of more or less cylindrical spicules are imbedded in the pneumatic layer and cover its outer surface. Such gemmule spicules are arranged tangentially or in a heterogeneous manner; they differ markedly from the megascleres and microscleres. In the Meyeninae, however, the pneumatic layer contains an abundance of radially arranged birotulate spicules, or amphidiscs. One of the wheel-like ends of a birotulate is called a rotule.

Gemmules may remain attached to the substrate or become freed and rise to the surface or sink to the bottom. They winter over easily, withstand repeated freezings and thawings, and have been found to be viable after being kept dried for one to three years or more.

Germination may occur any time at water temperatures of about 13° to 23°, but the process requires two weeks or more in the autumn and only a few days in the spring. Some investigators maintain that gemmules require a quiescent dormant period of one or two months or more before they will germinate. When a gemmule germinates the membrane covering the foramen disappears, and the inner creamy mass of amoebocytes slowly flows out of the foraminal aperture and more or less covers the empty gemmule shell. This process is usually completed in two to six days. The amoebocytes undergo histological differentiation and form the first cells of the several tissue types. Some spicules, channels, and subdermal spaces may be formed as early as the third day, and choanocytes may be functioning as early as the fifth day. Further development and growth result in typical sponge structure.

It is usually difficult to tell whether renewed growth of an old sponge in the spring is initiated by gemmule germination or by resumption of growth by dor-

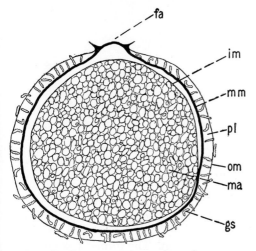

FIG. 49.—Diagrammatic section of a sponge gemmule, ×100. *fa*, foraminal area; *gs*, gemmule spicule; *im*, inner sclerotized membrane; *ma*, mesenchymal amoebocytes; *mm*, middle sclerotized membrane; *om*, outer sclerotized membrane (absent in some species); *pl*, pneumatic layer (containing gemmule spicules).

mant tissues, but probably both mechanisms are responsible.

**Ecology.** Sponges are most common in waters less than 2 meters deep. They are seldom found as deep as 4 meters, although there are records of collections as deep as 50 meters. In very favorable habitats sponge growths may almost obscure all suitable substrates. They are rarely found on a mud bottom, in silty water, or in small puddles. Contrary to Potts (1887), they are seldom found in extremely rapid waters. In general, individuals in running waters are smaller and more encrusting, and show little or no branching. *Spongilla lacustris* may often be found in both the branching and encrusting forms in the same body of water, but it is thought that the encrusting form is merely the earlier growth form which becomes branching as the sponge matures. Compared with most groups of freshwater invertebrates, sponges are quite sensitive to variations in environmental conditions. *Meyenia fluviatilis* will tolerate a minor amount of pollution, and a few other species a lesser degree.

Most species are more or less photopositive. *Spongilla ingloviformis* Potts, *Tubella pennsylvanica* Potts, and *Meyenia fluviatilis*, however, prefer dim light and are usually on the undersides of objects in clear water.

Much of our detailed information about the effects of dissolved inorganic materials has been provided by Jewell (1935, 1939). The most important limiting factors seem to be calcium, silicon, bound carbon dioxide, and pH (the last as a rough measure of the general suitability of water). The following species are acid (soft) water species seldom occurring where the pH reading is above 7.0 or 7.3: *Heteromeyenia repens* Potts, *H. argyrosperma* Potts, *Tubella pennsylvanica*, *Spongilla ingloviformis*, and *Meyenia everetti* (Mills). Alkaline species include *Heteromeyenia tubisperma* (Mills), *Meyenia mülleri*, and *M. fluviatilis*. A few species,

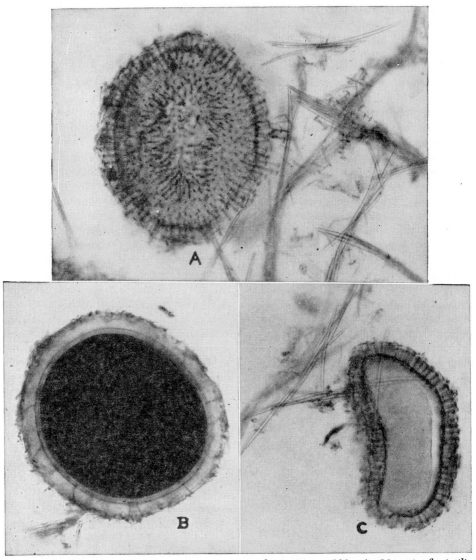

Fig. 50.—Gemmules of some common species of sponges, ×130. A, *Meyenia fluviatilis* Carter; B, *Spongilla lacustris*; C, *Heteromeyenia repens* Potts.

such as *Spongilla lacustris* and *S. fragilis*, tolerate a wide range in bound carbon dioxide and hydrogen ion concentration, although they fare better under alkaline conditions.

All common species regularly occur in waters having less than 12.0 ppm. of calcium. *Spongilla lacustris*, however, has been found where the calcium concentration was as high as 33.0 ppm., and *Hetero-*

*meyenia repens* where there was 53.4 ppm. The distribution of *Meyenia mülleri* and *Spongilla fragilis* appears to be restricted by low calcium. The former has not been reported from waters containing less than 5.6 ppm. and the latter 2.1 ppm. *Spongilla ingloviformis* and *Meyenia everetti*, on the other hand, appear to grow only where there are small quantities of calcium present; the former is restricted to waters having less than 3.2 ppm. of calcium, and the latter 2.5 ppm. *Spongilla lacustris* is independent of ordinary calcium concentrations and grows luxuriantly in waters containing from 0.16 to 32.4 ppm.

In view of the fact that sponges require large amounts of silicon for spicule formation, it is surprising to find that most species attain good growth in waters that may contain only a trace of silicon. The only important exception is *Meyenia mülleri* which requires a minimum of 1.6 ppm. of silicon dioxide. Nevertheless, some species show certain variations in spicule abundance and morphology, depending on the amount of silicon present. *Spongilla fragilis* has a poorly developed skeleton in water containing less than 1.0 ppm. of silicon dioxide. In *S. lacustris* both microscleres and megascleres become progressively attenuated in specimens collected in waters ranging from 13.0 ppm. of silicon dioxide down to only a trace. In fact, a concentration of 0.56 ppm. is the lowest value at which there is full microsclere development; there is no greater development above 0.56, but the microspines are absent below this concentration. In soft-water lakes this species has an abundance of spicules intermediate in size between megascleres and microscleres. *Tubella pennsylvanica* has progressively heavier spicules and closer approximation in the size of the two rotules in lakes of increasing mineralization.

It is common to find three different species in the same lake, less common to find four, and rare to find five or six. Often there are definite associations of certain species, suggesting similar but obscure habitat requirements. The following pairs of species are commonly associated in the same lake or stream: *Meyenia mülleri* and *Spongilla fragilis*, *Meyenia mülleri* and *Spongilla lacustris*, *S. fragilis* and *S. lacustris*, *S. lacustris* and *Tubella pennsylvanica*.

Larvae of Sisyridae (page 563) pierce the cells and suck out the contents and are entirely dependent on sponges as a food source, but no animals have been reported to devour healthy sponges bodily. Nevertheless the irregular growth form of many sponges affords a favorable substrate for a wide variety of metazoans, including insects, crustaceans, water mites, annelids, nematodes, and even mollusks.

Spongillidae have occasionally been reported to clog water pipes and conduits, but otherwise they are of no economic importance to man.

**Dispersal, geographic distribution.** Sponges easily spread throughout single drainage systems, and by virtue of their resistant gemmules they are probably transported overland by wind, insects, and birds.

*Spongilla lacustris*, *S. fragilis*, and *Meyenia fluviatilis* are essentially cosmopolitan and have been found the world over wherever intensive collecting has been done in suitable areas. *Tubella pennsylvanica*, *Heteromeyenia ryderi* Potts, *Meyenia crateriformis* (Potts), and probably several other species are widely distributed in the Northern Hemisphere. The four most common American species are *Spongilla lacustris*, *S. fragilis*, *Meyenia mülleri*, and *Heteromeyenia tubisperma*.

Certain other species, however, are rare and poorly known in the United States. *Spongilla heterosclerifera* Smith, *S. wagneri* Potts, *S. discoides* Penney, *Meyenia subdivisa* Potts, *M. millsi* Potts, *M. subtilis* (Weltner), *M. robusta* Potts, *Dosilia palmeri* (Potts), *Heteromeyenia conigera* Old, and *H. biceps* Lindenschmidt are each known only from a single locality.

**Collecting.** Hand-picking in the shallows and using a long-handled rake in deeper waters will produce an abundance of specimens. Sponges should be handled gingerly because of their fragility.

**Culturing.** Small *Meyenia fluviatilis* and *Spongilla* have been kept alive in aquaria up to five or six months, but these are exceptionally long periods. Usually sponges remain in good condition for only one to three weeks, then begin to lose color and disintegrate. Death occurs in such short periods even if there is a continuous flow of water through the aquarium.

If a small sponge or a bit of a larger one (about a cubic centimeter) is placed cut surface downward on a glass slide submerged under 5 to 10 cm. of water, the sponge will often adhere and grow for a time, especially if the water is changed frequently.

Germination of gemmules and early growth may be easily studied in the laboratory. Gemmules should be brought in and placed on slides or cover slips in shallow pans of water from the natural habitat. Germination will usually begin in 7 to 25 days, but sometimes the process may be hastened by first "vernalizing" the gemmules in water in a refrigerator at 5° to 10° for a day or two. After germination is completed and the young sponge securely attached, the slide should be removed to an aquarium in which the water is frequently renewed. Under favorable conditions the sponge may grow and cover as much as half of the slide and live for a month or two.

**Preserving, preparing.** If a whole large specimen is to be preserved, it should be removed from the water with or without its substrate and placed in a warm, shaded place to dry out completely. Incidentally, anyone who works with fresh or drying sponges never forgets their peculiar odor which is sometimes likened to that of garlic. Dried specimens must be stored and handled very carefully because of their fragility. Soft tissue paper, not cotton, should be used for shipping. Do not rub the eyes after handling dry sponges. Bits of sponge tissue and gemmules should be killed and preserved in 70 per cent alcohol.

For rapid identification place a small bit of sponge on a slide, add two drops of concentrated nitric acid, heat over a flame until dry, and add mounting medium and cover slip. This treatment destroys essentially everything except the spicules. A fragment of dry epidermis mounted in balsam will usually show the presence or absence of microscleres.

Permanent mounts require more care, and the following method is one of several suitable ones. Place 4 or 5 ml. of sponge in a small test tube, add 10 ml. of concentrated nitric acid, and heat to boiling. Let stand for one day, remove most of the supernatant acid with a pipette, and *carefully* add water to half fill the test tube. Let stand for one hour with occasional agitation and draw off most of the supernatant. Repeat this washing process twice more. Replace the water with 95 per cent alcohol and two changes of absolute alcohol (15 minutes each). Draw up some of the spicules and alcohol in a pipette and place on a slide, burn off the alcohol and add mounting medium and a cover slip.

Permanent mounts of gemmules are made by a slightly different technique. Place the gemmules in cold concentrated nitric acid in a test tube for 1 to 6 hours until they turn a translucent orange or yellow color, indicating that most of the pneumatic layer is dissolved away. Then wash with water several times, dehydrate, and mount as indicated in the preceding paragraph.

Glycerin jelly mounts are not desirable because the refractive index of this substance does not result in sufficient differentiation of the sponge spicules.

**Taxonomy.** American fresh-water sponges have been studied by only a few investigators, some of the more important contributors being Potts, Smith, Old, and Jewell. Much therefore remains to be done, especially from taxonomic, distributional, physiological, and ecological viewpoints.

Since general growth form is usually so variable within a species, it is a poor character for species identification. The detailed anatomy of gemmules, gemmule spicules, megascleres, and microscleres is essential for accurate identification.

There is still considerable disagreement

among specialists concerning dividing lines between genera. In this manual *Carterius* and *Ephydatia* (= *Meyenia*) *baileyi* Bowerbank have been incorporated into *Heteromeyenia*. *Tubella pennsylvanica*, however, has been kept separate from *Trochospongilla*. *Meyenia* is used rather than *Ephydatia* in accordance with de Laubenfels (1936).

Rough average or typical lengths of spicules are given in the key which follows, and it should be borne in mind that in most species these figures are subject to a variation of plus or minus 20 to 50 per cent. It should also be noted that the various spicule types for a particular species are not drawn to the same scale in Figs. 51 to 55. Furthermore, the spicule figures represent only typical specimens, and it must be noted that there is considerable variation even in the same sponge or same gemmule.

## KEY TO SPECIES OF PORIFERA

1.  Gemmule spicules elongated and more or less cylindrical, or gemmule spicules absent...................................SPONGILLINAE, **Spongilla, 2**
    Gemmule spicules always present and more or less birotulate (amphidisks).
    MEYENINAE, **8**
2.  Gemmule spicules absent; gemmules in the form of biconvex discs, with no foraminal aperture (Figs. 51A, B); with two types of megascleres (140 to 220 microns long) and three types of birotulate microscleres (24 to 50 microns long) (Fig. 51C); known only from Lexington Co., S. C..**Spongilla discoides** Penney
    Gemmule spicules present; gemmules more or less spherical (Figs. 50B, 51F)....**3**
3.  Megascleres smooth; microscleres present or absent; encrusting or branched and massive; in running or standing waters.....................................**5**
    Megascleres spiny (Figs. 51D, E); microscleres absent; encrusting species; in standing waters.........................................................**4**
4.  Gemmules arranged in domelike groups of 8 to 20, resting on the flat side, with the foraminal apertures all opening inward, and surrounded by a cellular pneumatic layer containing numerous coarsely spined gemmule spicules; megascleres 250 microns long, slightly curved, pointed, and with coarse spines (Fig. 51D); skeleton poorly developed; soft, alga-like encrusting growth form; usually in highly colored standing waters; reported from Mass., N. J., Mich., Wis., and La.
    **Spongilla ingloviformis** Potts
    Gemmules forming a definite pavement layer bound together into a firm crust by a cellular pneumatic layer which is closely crowded with various types of slender to stout and sparsely to densely spined gemmule spicules, 50 to 160 microns long; megascleres 250 microns long, slightly curved, pointed, and with many small spines except at the ends (Fig. 51E); reported only from Oneida Lake, N. Y...............................**Spongilla heterosclerifera** Smith
5.  Microscleres absent; usually with a firm, flat, spreading growth form, 0.2 to 5.0 cm. thick, and up to 30 cm. in diameter, but sometimes globular, cylindrical, or spindle-shaped; megascleres almost straight, 200 microns long; gemmules in a pavement layer or in groups of two to eight invested in a common pneumatic layer (Fig. 51F); gemmule spicules 85 microns long, cylindrical, with pointed or rounded ends, and covered with minute spines (Fig. 51H); common and widely distributed in running and standing waters....**Spongilla fragilis** Leidy
    Microscleres present........................................................**6**
6.  Microscleres spined, 70 microns long; gemmule spicules spined, 45 microns long, and more or less cylindrical and curved; megascleres 310 microns long (Fig. 51K); branched or unbranched growth form; in both standing and running waters; common and widely distributed...........**Spongilla lacustris** (L.)
    Microscleres smooth (Fig. 51L); gemmule spicules smooth or spined; uncommon..**7**

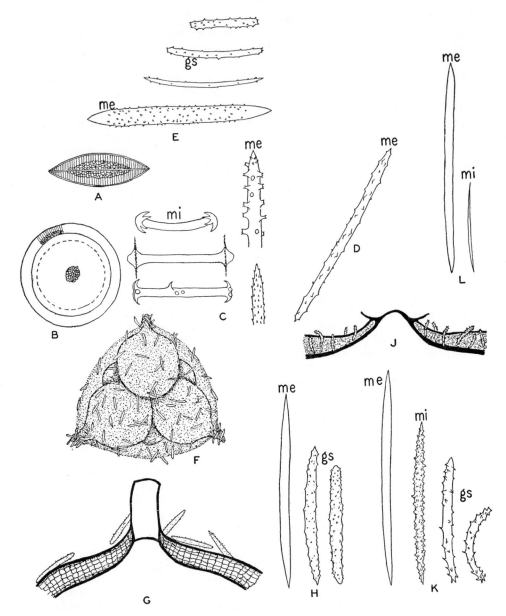

Fig. 51.—Structure of *Spongilla*. A, edge view of gemmule of *Spongilla discoides* Penney, ×80; B, surface view of gemmule of *S. discoides*, ×80; C, three microscleres and the ends of two megascleres of *S. discoides*; D, megasclere of *S. ingloviformis* Potts; E, one megasclere and three gemmule spicules of *S. heterosclerifera* Smith; F, group of gemmules of *S. fragilis* Leidy invested in a common pneumatic layer, ×50; G, section of foraminal region of gemmule of *S. fragilis*; H, typical spicules of *S. fragilis*; J, section of foraminal region of gemmule of *S. lacustris*; K, typical spicules of *S. lacustris*; L, typical spicules of *S. aspinosa* Potts. *gs,* gemmule spicules; *me,* megascleres; *mi,* microscleres. (A, B, and C modified from Penney, 1933a; F, G, and J modified from Sasaki.)

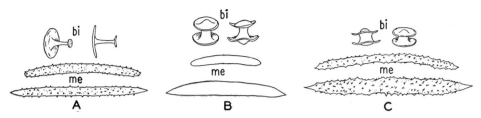

FIG. 52.—Spicules of typical Meyeninae. A, spicules of *Tubella pennsylvanica* Potts; B, spicules of *Trochospongilla leidyi* (Bowerbank); C, spicules of *T. horrida* (Weltner). *bi*, gemmule birotulate; *me*, megasclere.

7. Gemmule spicules smooth; megascleres 280 microns long; microscleres 35 microns long; an encrusting species reported only from N. J., Va., Fla., and Mich.
Spongilla aspinosa Potts
   Gemmule spicules long, spined, and curved; reported only from brackish waters of southwestern Fla..............................Spongilla wagneri Potts
8. Rotules of gemmule spicules unequal in size, the proximal being much the larger; margin of rotules entire, rarely finely incised; birotulates 15 microns long; megascleres 250 microns long, abundantly spined, and ends rounded or pointed (Fig. 52A); slimy and thin growth form, seldom more than 5 mm. thick, gray or flesh-colored; reported from S. C., Fla., La., and most states in the northeastern quarter of the country...............Tubella pennsylvanica Potts
   Rotules of gemmule spicules equal or subequal, margin entire to strongly spined. .9
9. Gemmules with one kind of birotulate.................................10
   Gemmules with two types of birotulates, one longer and the other shorter (Figs. 54, 55)......................................................20
10. Margins of rotules entire, not serrate; birotulates short (Figs. 52B, C); microscleres absent; encrusting growth form; running or standing waters.
Trochospongilla, 11
   Margins of rotules serrated or incised; birotulates short to long (Fig. 53).......12
11. Megascleres not spined (Fig. 52B); gemmules formed in a basal layer; color grayish or drab; reported from N. J., Penn., Ohio, Ken., Ill., La., and W. Va.
Trochospongilla leidyi (Bowerbank)
   Megascleres strongly spined (Fig. 52C); color gray, yellow, or brown; reported from Penn., Ill., Tex., S. C., and Dela.....Trochospongilla horrida (Weltner)
12. Microscleres absent.......................................Meyenia, 13
   Microscleres present, substellate to acerate; megascleres microspined; gemmule birotulates with spiny shafts, rotules serrate-laciniate; reported only once from Levy Co., Fla................................Dosilia palmeri (Potts)
13. With minute slender, birotulate microscleres about 10 microns long; gemmule birotulates 140 microns long, and with smooth, slender shafts; rotules composed of five or six stout, recurved hooks; megascleres 190 microns long, slender and smooth (Fig. 53A); skeleton poorly developed; finely branched filamentous growth form; most common in bogs; reported from Mass., Dela., and Wis......................................Meyenia everetti Mills
   Microscleres absent, if present then never birotulate......................14
14. Rays and spines of gemmule birotulates covered with microspines; megascleres smooth or microspined; massive, encrusting growth form; reported only from Fla. and La........................................Meyenia subdivisa Potts
   Rays and spines of gemmule birotulates without microspines................15
15. Margins of rotules finely serrate; megascleres entirely microspined; encrusting, loose-textured growth form; reported only from Sherwood Lake near De Land, Fla.......................................Meyenia millsi Potts
   Margins of rotules coarsely toothed....................................16

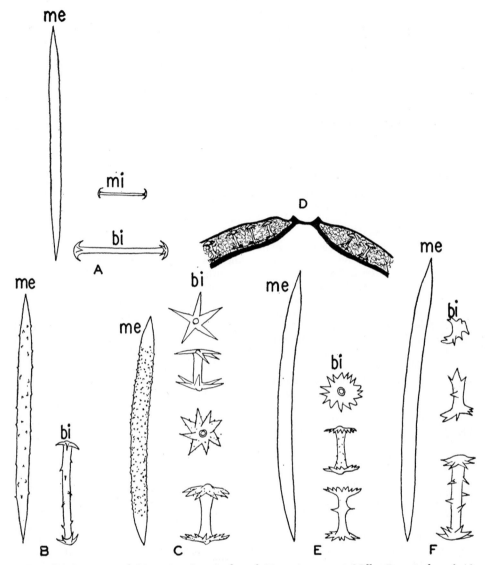

Fig. 53.—Structure of *Meyenia*. A, spicules of *Meyenia everetti* Mills; B, spicules of *M. crateriformis* Potts; C, spicules of *M. mülleri*; D, section of foraminal region of gemmule of *M. fluviatilis*; E, spicules of *M. fluviatilis*; F, spicules of *M. robusta* Potts. *bi,* gemmule birotulates; *me,* megascleres; *mi,* microscleres.

**16.** Birotulates 60 microns long, many times longer than diameter of rotules, shafts spined, rotules of three to six short recurved hooks; megascleres 250 microns long, slender, pointed, and sparsely microspined (Fig. 53B); gemmules small, white, and numerous; crust of gemmules very thick, the foraminal tubes being in crater-like depressions; thin, encrusting growth form; usually in running waters; generally distributed and common east of the Mississippi River but reported also from Texas....................**Meyenia crateriformis** Potts
Birotulates no more than three times as long as the diameter of rotules........**17**

17. Megascleres spined ..............................................**18**
    Megascleres smooth, rarely with a few microspines.......................**19**
18. Birotulates two or three times longer than diameter of rotules, which are split
    nearly to the center, and with 10 to 20 blunt rays; megascleres with scattered
    short spines; encrusting growth form; reported only from Kissimmee Lake, Fla.
    **Meyenia subtilis** (Weltner)
    Birotulate length 18 microns and equal to or less than diameter of rotules, which
    are irregularly serrate or dentate, and with few rays; megascleres 220 microns
    long and smooth or microspined except at tips (Fig. 53C); growth form highly
    variable but most luxuriant in standing waters where a single individual may
    cover as much as a square meter; usually in alkaline waters; common and
    generally distributed......................**Meyenia mülleri** (Lieberkühn)
19. Birotulate shafts usually smooth but sometimes with a few macrospines or micro-
    spines; shafts 20 microns long, slightly longer than diameter of rotules; mega-
    scleres 300 microns long, rarely with a few microspines (Fig. 53E); gemmules
    either basal or scattered; coloration and growth form highly variable but
    usually flat and encrusting; size ranging from a few square cm. to as much as
    40 square m.; more common in standing waters; generally distributed.
    **Meyenia fluviatilis** Carter
    Birotulate shafts about twice as long as rotule diameter and with numerous large
    spines; birotulates 24 microns long, often malformed; megascleres 260 microns
    long (Fig. 53F); reported only from northeastern Calif.
    **Meyenia robusta** Potts
20. Microscleres stellate (Figs. 54A, B)......................**Asteromeyenia, 21**
    Microscleres absent, or acerate if present...................**Heteromeyenia, 22**
21. Rotule rays of longer birotulates simply curved, shaft almost smooth; longer
    birotulates 190 microns long; shorter birotulates 60 microns long, shafts pro-
    fusely spined; megascleres 380 microns long (Fig. 54A); reported from one
    locality in each of Fla., La., Tex., Calif....**Asteromeyenia plumosa** (Weltner)
    Rotule rays of longer birotulates strongly recurved, shaft smooth, microspined, or
    with one or several macrospines; short birotulate shafts spined (Fig. 54B);
    reported only from Ohio and Ill.......**Asteromeyenia radiospiculata** (Mills)
22. Foraminal tubule prolonged and bearing long filamentous appendages (Figs. 54C,
    E, G; 55B); microscleres spined, slightly curved, and pointed............**23**
    Foraminal tubule short, filamentous appendages absent or inconspicuous; mega-
    scleres microspined.........................................**26**
23. Foraminal tubule with one or two very long tendrils, often enveloping the tubule
    (Fig. 54C); megascleres 270 microns long, smooth or sparsely microspined;
    shorter birotulates with rotules bearing deeply cut rays; longer birotulates with
    a smooth or sparsely macrospined shaft, rotules bearing deeply cut rays (Fig.
    54D); usually thin and encrusting in running waters; reported from several
    states in the northeastern quarter of the country.
    **Heteromeyenia latitenta** (Potts)
    Foraminal tubule with three or more tendrils of varying length; megascleres
    sparsely microspined........................................**24**
24. Foraminal tubule one-half to once the diameter of the gemmule body, with four to
    six long tendrils (Fig. 54E); shorter birotulates 40 microns long, with smooth
    shaft, and with rotules composed of three to five rays; longer birotulates 60
    microns long, usually with a thinner smooth shaft, and with rotules composed
    of 3 to 5 rays; megascleres 200 microns long; microscleres 90 microns long
    (Fig. 54F); an encrusting form with soft papillate projections; usually in
    running waters; probably cosmopolitan....**Heteromeyenia tubisperma** (Mills)
    Foraminal tubule one-fourth or less as long as diameter of gemmule body (Figs.
    54G, 55B); both types of birotulates with macrospined shafts (Figs. 54H,
    55A); encrusting growth form........................................**25**

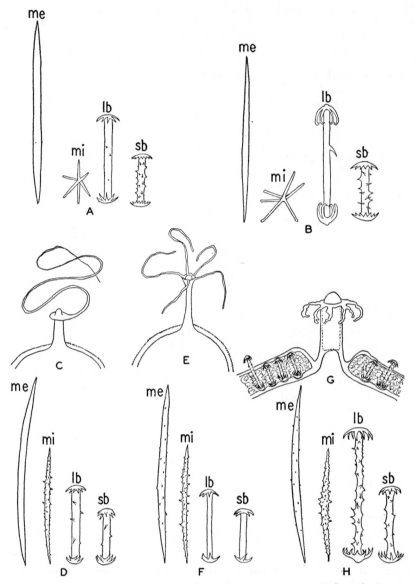

Fig. 54.—Structure of *Asteromeyenia* and *Heteromeyenia*. A, spicules of *Asteromeyenia plumosa* (Weltner); B, spicules of *A. radiospiculata* (Mills); C, foraminal region of gemmule of *Heteromeyenia latitenta* (Potts); D, spicules of *H. latitenta*; E, foraminal region of gemmule of *H. tubisperma* (Mills); F, spicules of *H. tubisperma*; G, foraminal region of gemmule of *H. baileyi* (Bowerbank); H, spicules of *H. baileyi. lb*, longer birotulates; *me*, megascleres; *mi*, microscleres; *sb*, shorter birotulates. (C and E modified from Potts, 1887; G modified from Sasaki.)

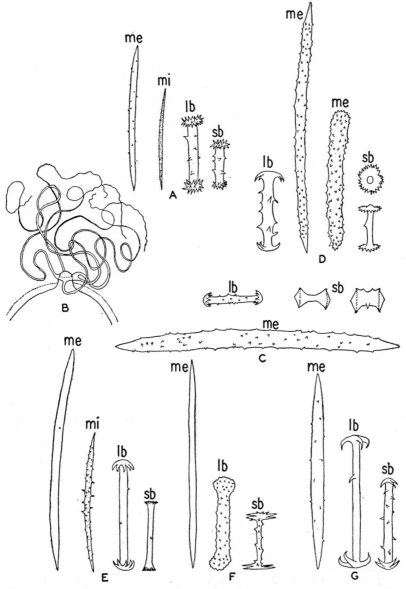

Fig. 55.—Structure of *Heteromeyenia*. A, spicules of *Heteromeyenia tenosperma* (Potts); B, foraminal region of gemmule of *H. tenosperma*; C, spicules of *H. conigera* Old; D, spicules of *H. ryderi* Potts; E, spicules of *H. repens*; F, spicules of *H. biceps* Lindenschmidt; G, spicules of *H. argyrosperma* Potts. *lb*, longer birotulates; *me*, megascleres; *mi*, microscleres; *sb*, shorter birotulates. (B modified from Potts, 1887; C modified from Old, 1931; D modified from Stephens.)

25. Rays of rotules of both types of birotulates deeply cleft and slightly incurved; longer birotulates 80 microns long; shorter birotulates 60 microns long; megascleres 250 microns long; microscleres 80 microns long (Fig. 54H); foraminal tubule variable, usually with six to ten irregular and sometimes branched tendrils (Fig. 54G), but tendrils sometimes fewer, reduced, or absent; reported once from each of N. Y., Penn., and Wis.

Heteromeyenia baileyi (Bowerbank)

Rays of rotules of both types of birotulates less deeply cleft and arranged so as to give the rotule a burlike appearance; megascleres 260 microns long; microscleres 70 microns long (Fig. 55A); foraminal tubule with about three to five long, irregular tendrils (Fig. 55B); reported from N. Y., N. J., Penn., and Ohio.

Heteromeyenia tenosperma (Potts)

26. Rotules of shorter birotulates finely serrate, shaft rarely microspined (Figs. 55C, D); microscleres lacking...........................................27

Rotules of shorter birotulates coarsely serrate (Figs. 55E–G); microscleres present or absent..................................................28

27. Both outer and inner surfaces of rotules of shorter birotulates broadly conical (Fig. 55C); reported only from the Chattahoochee River, Ga.

Heteromeyenia conigera Old

Rotules of shorter birotulates more nearly dislike; shorter birotulates 25 microns long; longer birotulates 45 microns long; megascleres 200 microns long (Fig. 55D); standing and running waters in eastern half of the U. S.

Heteromeyenia ryderi Potts

28. Microscleres present, 85 microns long, nearly straight, and heavily spined; megascleres 280 microns long, sparsely spined or smooth; shorter birotulates 55 microns long, with moderately serrated rotules, shaft smooth or with a few spines; longer birotulates 80 microns long, with rotules having many large recurved spines, and shaft usually with one or more macrospines (Fig. 55E); encrusting growth form, smooth or rugose; in standing or slow flowing waters; reported from many areas in eastern and midwestern states.

Heteromeyenia repens Potts

Microscleres absent; shorter birotulates with abundantly spined shafts, rotules with long rays (Figs. 55F, G).......................................29

29. Longer birotulates stout and 25 microns long; rotules knoblike and with numerous small spines, shaft with similar spines; shorter birotulates 20 microns long; megascleres 290 microns long, smooth to completely microspined (Fig. 55F); encrusting growth form, seldom more than 5 cm. in diameter; reported only from two streams near Douglas Lake, Mich.

Heteromeyenia biceps Lindenschmidt

Longer birotulates 130 microns long, slender; rays of rotules few and clawlike, shaft sparsely spined; megascleres 280 microns long, sparsely spined; shorter birotulates 80 microns long (Fig. 55G); encrusting growth form, sometimes with blunt projections, and seldom more than 15 cm. in diameter; more common in running waters; reported from Fla. and many localities in the northeastern quarter of the U. S.............Heteromeyenia argyrosperma Potts

# PORIFERA REFERENCES

ANNANDALE, N. 1909. Fresh-water sponges in the collection of the United States National Museum. Part II. Specimens from North and South America. *Proc. U. S. Nat. Mus.* 37:401–406.

ARNDT, W. 1928. Porifera, Schwämme, Spongien. *Tierwelt Deutschlands* 4:1–94.

BOWERBANK, J. S. 1863. A monograph of the Spongillidae. *Proc. Zool. Soc. London* (1863): 440–472.

BRIEN, P. 1932. Contribution à l'étude de la régénération naturelle chez les Spongillidae. *Arch. Zool. exp. gén.* **74**:461–506.

——. 1936. La réorganisation de l'éponge après dissociation par filtration et phénomènes d'involution chez Ephydatia fluviatilis. *Arch. Biol.* **48**:185–268.

DE LAUBENFELS, M. W. 1936. A discussion of the sponge fauna of the Dry Tortugas in particular and the West Indies in general, with material for a revision of the families and orders of the Porifera. *Publ. Carnegie Inst. Wash.* **467**:1–225.

ESHLEMAN, S. K. 1949. A key to Florida's fresh-water sponges, with descriptive notes. *Quart. Jour. Fla. Acad. Sci.* **12**:35–44.

GEE, N. G. 1932. Genus Trochospongilla of the fresh water sponges. *Peking Nat. Hist. Bull.* **6**:1–32.

——. 1932a. The known fresh-water sponges. *Ibid.*, 25–51.

JEWELL, M. E. 1935. An ecological study of the fresh-water sponges of northern Wisconsin. *Ecol. Monogr.* **5**:461–504.

——. 1939. An ecological study of the fresh-water sponges of Wisconsin, II. The influence of calcium. *Ecology* **20**:11–28.

JORGENSEN, C. B. 1944. On the spicule-formation of Spongilla lacustris (L.). I. The dependence of the spicule-formation on the content of dissolved and solid silicic acid of the milieu. *Biol. Meddel. Kjøbenhavn* **19**:1–45.

LEVEAUX, M. 1939. La formation des gemmules chez les Spongillidae. *Ann. Soc. Roy. Zool. Belg.* **70**:53–96

——. 1941, 1942. Contribution à l'étude histologique de l'ovogénèse et de la spermatogénèse des Spongillidae. *Ibid.* **72**:251–269; **73**:33–50.

LINDENSCHMIDT, M. J. 1950. A new species of fresh-water sponge. *Trans. Amer. Micros. Soc.* **69**:214–216

McNAIR, G. T. 1923. Motor reactions of the freshwater sponge, Ephydatia fluviatilis. *Biol. Bull.* **44**:153–166.

NEIDHOFER, J. R. 1940. The fresh-water sponges of Wisconsin. *Trans. Wis. Acad. Sci. Arts and Lett.* **32**:177–197

OLD, M. C. 1931. A new species of fresh-water sponge. *Trans. Amer. Micros. Soc.* **50**:298–299.

——. 1931a. Taxonomy and distribution of the fresh-water sponges (Spongillidae) of Michigan. *Papers Mich. Acad. Sci. Arts and Lett.* **15**:439–476.

——. 1932. Environmental selection of the fresh-water sponges (Spongillidae) of Michigan. *Trans. Amer. Micros. Soc.* **51**:129–137.

——. 1932a. Contribution to the biology of fresh-water sponges (Spongillidae). *Papers Mich. Acad. Sci. Arts and Lett.* **17**:663–679.

PENNEY, J. T. 1933. Reduction and regeneration in fresh water sponges (Spongilla discoides). *Jour. Exp. Zool.* **65**:475–495.

——. 1933a. A new fresh-water sponge from South Carolina. *Proc. U. S. Nat. Mus.* **82**:1–5.

POTTS, E. 1887. Fresh water sponges. A monograph. *Proc. Acad. Nat. Sci. Phila.* (1887): 157–279.

——. 1889. Report upon some fresh-water sponges collected in Florida by Jos. Willcox, Esq. *Trans. Wagner Inst. Phil.* **2**:5–7.

SASAKI, N. 1934. Report on the fresh-water sponges obtained from Hokkaido. *Sci. Repts. Tohoku Imp. Univ.* (*Ser. 4*) **9**:219–248.

SCHRÖDER, K. 1936. Beiträge zur Kenntnis der Spiculabildung der Larvenspiculation und der Variationsbreite der Gerüstnadeln von Süsswasserschwämmen. *Zeitschr. Morph. Ökol. Tiere* **31**:245–267.

SMITH, F. 1918. A new species of Spongilla from Oneida Lake, New York. *N. Y. State Coll. Forestry, Syracuse Univ., Tech. Publ.* **9**:239–243.

——. 1921. Data on the distribution of Michigan fresh-water sponges. *Pap. Mich. Acad. Sci. Arts and Lett.* **1**:418–421.

——. 1921a. Distribution of the fresh-water sponges of North America. *Bull. Ill. Nat. Hist. Surv.* **14**:9–22.

STEPHENS, J. 1920. The freshwater sponges of Ireland. *Proc. Roy. Irish Acad.* **35** (*Sect. B*): 205–254.

VAN TRIGT, H. 1919. A contribution to the physiology of the fresh-water sponges (Spongillidae). *Tijd. Nederl. Dierk. Vereen.* (*II.*) **17**:1–220.

WIERZEJSKI, A. 1935. Süsswasserspongien. Monographische Bearbeitung. *Mém. Acad. Polon. Sci. Lett., Sér. B,* **9**:1–242.

# Chapter 4

# COELENTERATA (HYDROIDS, JELLYFISH)

---

ALTHOUGH the Phylum Coelenterata contains in excess of 9,000 species, the vast majority are marine. Two classes, the Scyphozoa (true jellyfish) and the Anthozoa (corals, sea anemones, etc.), are exclusively marine, and in the third class, the Hydrozoa, only about 14 species are known from the fresh waters of the United States. These include 11 hydras, one uncommon "fresh-water jellyfish," one uncommon species of colonial polyp, and one rare protohydroid from brackish coastal waters.

Although not conspicuous, hydras are typical representatives of the fauna of ponds, spring brooks, unpolluted streams and rivers, and the littoral zone of lakes. They are all sessile and may be found attached to stones, twigs, vegetation, or debris, occasionally in enormous numbers.

**General characteristics.** Hydras should be familiar to all who have had an elementary college biology or zoology course. Like other coelenterates, they are radially symmetrical, the main body, or column, being an elongated cylinder from 2 to 25 mm. long. Attachment to the substrate is effected by a pedal disc which consists largely of special secretory cells. The distal end of the column has a circlet of tentacles whose length varies from one-half to five times the length of the column. Usually there are five or six tentacles, sometimes four, seven, or eight, and rarely up to 12. The end of the column in the center of the circlet of tentacles is raised and domelike to form a hypostome which bears a single opening, the combined mouth and anus. The single, continuous, internal body cavity is a gastrovascular cavity; it continues out into the hollow tentacles.

Although some hydras have a characteristic green or brown color, others have a variable coloration depending on age and the kind and amount of ingested food. Thus there may also be various shades of translucent whitish, grayish, tan, or red.

The body wall is simply constructed. Externally it consists of a layer of epidermis, and internally there is a layer of gastrodermis lining the gastrovascular cavity. Several different histological types of epidermal and gastrodermal cells can be distinguished. Between these two epithelia is a very thin, secreted, noncellular, cement-like mesoglea.

All coelenterates have minute stinging capsules, or nematocysts, imbedded in certain epidermal cells. Each nematocyst contains a coiled capillary thread, which, upon proper stimulation, can be "exploded" and extruded. Nematocysts function in food getting and protection by means of their entangling, adhesive, and paralyzing properties. Nematocysts are especially abundant on the tentacles and distal part of the column.

Although metagenesis and the alternation of medusoid and polyp stages are typical of marine hydrozoans, the hydras have only the polyp stage in their life history.

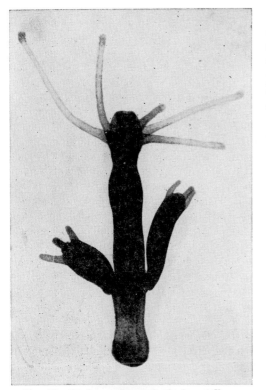

Fig. 56.–Hydra with two buds (partially contracted), ×12. (Courtesy General Biological Supply House, Inc., Chicago, Ill.)

**Locomotion.** Hydras are usually considered sessile creatures; when they are undisturbed the column is extended, the tentacles are spread out, and there is no movement visible to the naked eye. Occasionally, however, the tentacles wave about or the whole animal contracts and expands unaccountably. But hydras are also capable of moving slowly on the substrate. Most commonly they have a very slow gliding locomotion on the pedal disc. Occasionally they exhibit somersaulting or inchworm-like looping movements. More rarely they attach the distal end of the body to the substrate and pull themselves along by contractions and elongations. The central part of the basal disc may secrete a small gas bubble which enables the hydra to rise to the surface and remain suspended at the surface film in quiet waters.

**Feeding, digestion.** Hydrozoans are strictly carnivorous and eat many kinds of small metazoans, including cladocerans, copepods, insects, and annelids (but not ostracods). Occasionally hydras become a hatchery nuisance by killing fish fry, but *Hydra oligactis* (Pallas) is probably the only species large enough to be of any real importance. When a food organism is swimming or creeping about and by chance comes in contact with the tentacles or column, it is paralyzed and killed in a few seconds by the nematocysts which are discharged from those parts of the column or tentacles contacted. The organism is then manipulated so that it is taken into the mouth. The latter is variously described as star-shaped or round; both it and the column are capable of great distension, and a cladoceran four times the diameter of the column may be ingested. When the usual food supply is insufficient, hydras may feed on the organic material of the substrate, but this is certainly not a normal means of feeding.

Digestion is both extra- and intracellular. Preliminary extracellular digestion occurs in the gastrovascular cavity, resulting in the maceration of the food organisms into a mush within several hours. These small particles are then taken up by pseudopodial action of many of the gastrodermal cells. Further digestion is intracellular. Only the gastrodermal cells in the upper part of the column appear to function in digestion; those in the more basal part of the column (stalk) are highly vacuolated and have no digestive power.

Excess food is stored in the gastrodermal cells as fat and glycogen. Indigestible material is voided from the mouth.

*Chlorohydra viridissima* (Pallas) is the so-called "green hydra" because of the abundance of algal cells (probably mostly *Chlorella*) in the gastrodermis. Such living algae probably have a true symbiotic relationship with the hydra, but dead and disintegrating cells are digested and used as food. The algae are passed from one generation to the next in the egg cytoplasm.

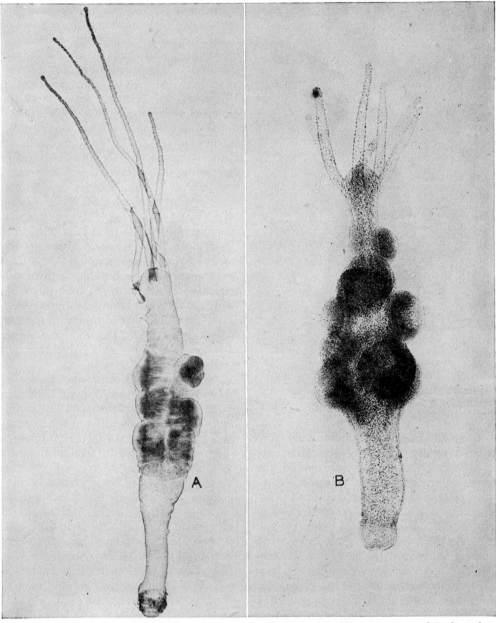

Fig. 57.—Sexually mature hydras, ×17. A, female; B, male. (Courtesy General Biological Supply House, Inc., Chicago, Ill.)

**Nematocysts.** A nematocyst is a spherical to elongated, capsular, sclerotized organoid ranging from 5 to 25 microns in length in fresh-water species. It is contained within a special epidermal cell, the cnidoblast. Inside of the nematocyst is a minute, coiled, hollow thread, or tubule, whose base is attached to the inner distal wall of the nematocyst. A lid, or operculum, covers the distal opening of the capsule, and a tiny, trigger-like bristle, or cnidocil, projects into the surrounding water from the surface of the cnidoblast near the edge of the operculum. In the Phylum Coelenterata as a whole there are many different types of nematocysts, but in the fresh-water hydras there are only four types, as follows:

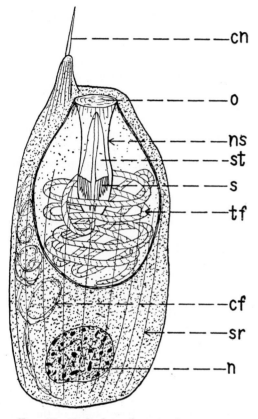

FIG. 58.—Undischarged stenotele nematocyst within its cnidoblast. *cf,* cnidoblast filament; *cn,* cnidocil; *n,* nucleus of cnidoblast; *ns,* nematocyst shaft (butt); *o,* operculum; *s,* spines; *sr,* supporting rods of cnidoblast; *st,* stylet; *tf,* tubular filament (actually much longer than shown).

Desmonemes (volvents) are small, pyriform, or spherical nematocysts. The tubule forms only one loop, is closed at the distal end, and is usually unarmed but may have extremely fine spinules (Figs. 59D, E). Desmonemes appear to function mainly in entangling and wrapping around bristles of the prey.

Stenoteles (penetrants) are large, spher-

ical nematocysts. The coiled tubule is open at the tip and has a definite butt, or enlarged basal portion, which bears three spines and three spiral rows of minute spinules (Figs. 58; 59F). Exploding stenoteles pierce the prey and inject a paralyzing material.

There are two types of isorhiza (glutinant) nematocysts, but both are characterized by a tubule which is open at the tip, by the absence of a butt, and by the secretion of a paralyzing material. Holotrichous isorhizas are larger and have the tubule covered with minute spinules (Fig. 59C); they function mainly in defense. Atrichous isorhizas are smaller and have a smooth tubule (Figs. 59A, B); they appear to function mainly in locomotion by discharging and sticking when the tentacles are placed in contact with a substrate.

Nematocysts have an unusual mode of origin and migration. They are formed within special interstitial cnidoblast cells of the epidermis. Most cnidoblasts first appear in the distal third of the column. Before their contained nematocysts are fully formed, many cnidoblasts pass through the mesoglea and gastrodermis into the gastrovascular cavity. Here they circulate about briefly before being taken up again by gastrodermal cells, especially in the tentacles. Then they are transported back through the mesoglea to their final location in the epidermis.

According to one theory, when the projecting cnidocil is touched, the operculum springs open and the nematocyst tubule instantaneously turns inside out as it whips out of the capsule. The base of the tubule emerges first and the rest follows from base to tip. According to a more recently elaborated theory, the external tubule is formed by the rapid extrusion of a fluid which hardens on contact with water. At the same time the internal coiled tubule disintegrates. Discharged nematocysts are lost and are of no further use to the hydra.

It is thought that stenotele and desmoneme discharge is usually dependent upon a combined chemical and mechanical stimulus. The juice and body fluids of the normal prey will not in themselves discharge nematocysts, nor will a fine glass rod touched to the cnidocils. In addition, these nematocysts of satiated animals do not react when food organisms touch the tentacles.

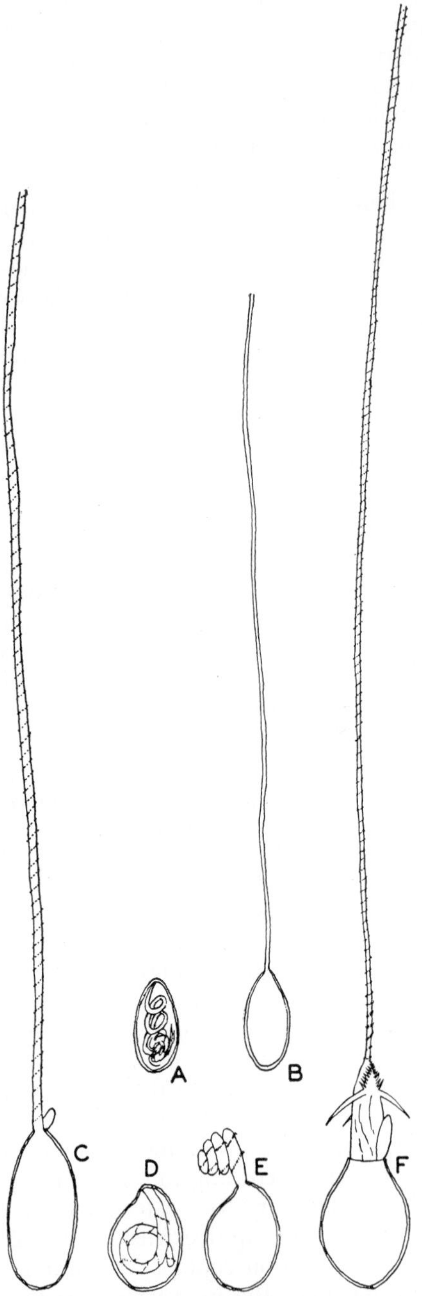

The physiological mechanisms of nematocyst action are poorly understood, but it is thought that the discharge is produced by an increased pressure within the capsule caused by increased permeability of the capsule wall. Perhaps a chemical stimulus acts first by reducing surface tension and lowering the resistance of the cnidoblast and cnidocil to mechanical stimuli.

One of the most unusual phenomena centering around nematocyst biology is the use of nematocysts by certain species of *Microstomum* for their own protection and food getting. When one of these turbellarians feeds on a hydra only the desmonemes and atrichous isorhizas are digested, and the other two types of nematocysts are passed through the mesenchyme of the *Microstomum* and into the epidermis. Here they are correctly oriented by associated phagocytes and discharged when touched by other animals.

**Physiology.** Circulation of materials within the gastrovascular cavity is effected by movements of the whole animal and by beating of the flagella of some of the gastrodermal cells. Such cells usually have one or two flagella.

Respiration occurs through the general body surface. None of the hydrozoans are active in the presence of reduced quantities of dissolved oxygen.

There seems to be no special excretory mechanism, and it is presumed that metabolic wastes simply diffuse out into the surrounding water. A few workers, however, have reported a small "aboral" or "excretory" pore in the center of the basal disc.

When strongly stimulated, and under adverse environmental conditions hydras

Fig. 59.—Typical hydra nematocysts. A, undischarged atrichous isorhiza; B, discharged atrichous isorhiza; C, discharged holotrichous isorhiza; D, undischarged desmoneme; E, discharged desmoneme; F, discharged stenotele. A to E, ×2,000; F, ×1,000. (Cnidoblasts not shown.)

contract markedly and assume a barrel-like shape with small, budlike contracted tentacles. Though there are no special bands or sheets of muscle tissue to produce such contractions and elongations, many of the epidermal cells and some gastrodermal cells have one or a few strand-like myonemes associated with their basal portions. Most of the longitudinal fibers are restricted to the epidermis and the circular fibers to the gastrodermis; the former are more abundant.

Elongated sensory cells are numerous in the epidermis of the tentacles and oral region. They are generalized receptors for touch, temperature, and substances in solution, and pass basally into one or more processes of the nervous system, which has the appearance of a nerve net ramifying everywhere at the base of the epidermis. The neurones are bi- and multipolar ganglion cells and their neurites, and although the entire system has the appearance of a continuous network, very delicate synapses are actually present. There are no coordinating or relay centers, and stimuli simply diffuse throughout the nerve net in all directions. The nervous system has no connections with the nematocysts.

**Reproduction, development.** Budding is the common asexual method of reproduction. Such buds usually originate at the junction of the gastric and stalk regions. A bud first appears as a hemispherical outpouching which later elongates, becomes cylindrical, and develops tentacles. The gastrovascular cavity of the budding individual and parent are continuous, but soon the base of the bud pinches off completely and the new individual becomes separated and independent. Under favorable conditions a new bud may be produced every two or three days.

Both transverse and longitudinal fission are occasionally observed in hydras, but these methods of reproduction are not normal and usually follow injuries or depression periods (page 107). Powers of regeneration and susceptibility to grafting are

well developed, and a large amount of experimental work has been done on these phases of hydra biology.

Syngamic reproduction is usually limited to the autumn months when water temperatures are dropping, but in a few species it may appear in spring or summer when the habitat is drying up. In hermaphroditic species the testes are distal and the ovaries proximal; sometimes ovaries and testes mature simultaneously, sometimes at different periods. In dioecious species the ovaries or testes may be distributed throughout most of the distal half or three-quarters of the column. In general, males far outnumber females.

A gonad consists of an accumulation of epidermal interstitial cells between mesoglea and epidermis, but in a developing ovary these cells fuse or engulf each other, leaving a single large food-filled ovum. A mature testis is usually hemispherical or helmet-shaped. It may or may not have a "nipple"; if present, many of the sperm escape to the outside through this small area. Ovaries are hemispherical or bulbous swellings.

When an egg is mature, the covering epidermis ruptures and withdraws, forming a small cup or cushion under the egg. If not fertilized promptly the egg dies. Sperm may come from the same or a different individual.

During late cleavage the embryo secretes a sclerotized yellowish shell, the embryonic theca. When the theca is being formed it is somewhat sticky, and at this stage the whole embryo drops off the parent or is fastened to the substrate by bending movements of the parent. It sticks to the substrate while the theca hardens. Such thecated embryos may be spherical or planoconvex, spinous or smooth. The diameter ranges from 0.40 to 1.00 mm. They are highly resistant to adverse environmental conditions and endure drying and freezing temperatures. After a dormant period of three to ten weeks or more, the theca softens and splits, permitting the exit of an embryo which

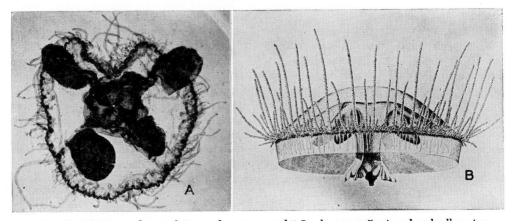

Fig. 60.—Mature medusae of *Craspedacusta sowerbii* Lankester, ×5. A, subumbrellar view of stained specimen; B, lateral view of living specimen. (B from Dejdar.)

already has a gastrovascular cavity and tentacles.

Little is known about the length of life under normal conditions. Under favorable conditions in the laboratory, however, hydras live for three to twelve months or more. A few specimens have been kept alive for more than two years during which time they produced scores of buds.

**Fresh-water jellyfish.** Although hydras are by far the most familiar fresh-water hydrozoans, there is one American species of "jellyfish," *Craspedacusta sowerbii* Lankester. Unlike large marine jellyfish, however, it has a velum and its life history includes a colonial (but simple) polyp.

*C. sowerbii* was first found in England in 1880; more recently it has been noted many times in Europe and on other continents. It has been found in about fifty localities in the United States since 1908, when it was discovered in this country. It has been reported mostly from small lakes, ponds, fishponds, and old water-filled quarries, especially between July and October.

A mature medusa stage of *C. sowerbii* has the typical umbrella or bell shape, manubrium, and four radial canals and one circular canal forming the gastrovascular cavity. The diameter of the bell is about 5 to 22 mm., and the circumference bears 50 to 500 solid tentacles of varying length and arranged in three to seven series, depending on the medusa size. The bell margin also bears many statocysts, often 60 to 100 or more. The velum is rather thick. Nematocysts are especially abundant around the mouth, at the edge of the bell, and on the tentacles. *Craspedacusta* actively swims up, down, or sideways in a dancing sort of movement produced by varying contractions of the bell.

Most populations appear to consist of all males or all females, the occurrence of mixed populations having been observed only a few times. The four gonads consist of convoluted or flaplike masses on the subumbrellar surface of the bell in the vicinity of the radial canals. Both eggs and sperm are released into the surrounding water where fertilization occurs.

The zygote develops into a simple, branching, colonial hydroid, 2 to 8 mm. long, usually consisting of two to four individuals (seldom up to ten). Single individuals are usually less than 2 mm. long, and tentacles are absent. The hydroid creeps about slowly on the substrate, feeding on small metazoans. The region around the mouth bears clumps of nematocysts. The body secretes a sticky, mucous material to which debris adheres and more or less covers the body. During the

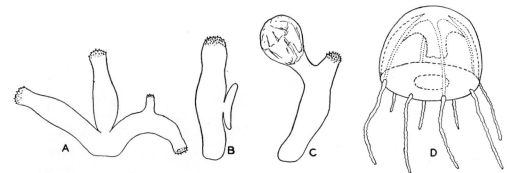

Fig. 61.—Stages in the life history of *Craspedacusta sowerbii.* A, typical colony of hydroids, ×12; B, hydroid with a maturing planula-like bud, ×15; C, hydroid with a maturing medusa bud, ×15; D, newly released medusa with eight tentacles, ×100. (A and D greatly modified from Payne.)

winter months the hydroids contract and secrete a sclerotized protective coat.

The hydroid stage has three methods of asexual reproduction. Ordinary budding is similar to that of the hydras, and new individuals may remain attached or constrict off from the parent. Nonciliated planula-like buds may also be produced. These constrict off, creep about slowly on the substrate for a time, and then develop into new polyps. The third method involves the production of medusa buds. When these break free from the parent the bell diameter is about 0.4 mm., and there are only eight tentacles, but rapid growth and development follow, resulting in the large, sexually mature medusae.

The appearance of the medusae is highly sporadic and unpredictable. In some years they may be found in abundance in certain ponds, but in subsequent years they may be absent, only to reappear several years later or in several successive years. In other ponds they have been found only once and have never reappeared, in spite of careful searching.

The hydroid generation has been found only a few times, probably chiefly because of its small size and inconspicuous nature. It is possible that the hydroids live undetected for long periods, only occasionally giving rise to the medusoid generation. For many years the hydroid was called *Microhydra ryderi,* and it was not until 1924 that it was definitely associated with *Craspedacusta sowerbii.*

The fresh-water jellyfish has been reported from nearly all of the states east of the Mississippi River, but is not known from Wisconsin or northern New England. West of the Mississippi it has been found in Iowa, Missouri, Kansas, Oklahoma, Arkansas, Louisiana, Texas, California, Washington, and Oregon.

Several related species of fresh-water medusae have been reported from other continents, including one species in China, two or three in Africa, one in India, and one in Trinidad.

**Colonial polyps.** Another unusual fresh-water coelenterate is *Cordylophora lacustris* (Allman). It is a profusely branching, mosslike colonial hydrozoan superficially similar to the marine *Obelia* and its many relatives. It occurs in brackish inlets and estuaries from New Jersey to the Gulf of the St. Lawrence, but has also been found in inland rivers in Illinois, Arkansas, and Louisiana. This species is probably cosmopolitan. It is widely distributed in northern Europe and has been found in numerous other parts of the world. Some taxonomists believe this species should be called *Cordylophora caspia* Pallas.

During the summer months brackish water colonies attain a height of 20 to 100 mm. from the substrate, but in fresh

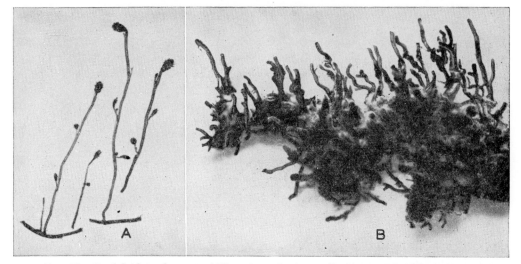

FIG. 62.—*Cordylophora lacustris* (Allman), ×5. A, small portions of summer growth of colony; B, colony in winter condition (lower portion of colony covered with detritus). (B from K. Berg, 1948, by permission.)

waters growths seldom exceed 30 mm. in height. There are two kinds of polyps making up such colonies; hydranths are spindle-shaped feeding individuals with a prominent manubrium and 10 to 20 thin scattered tentacles, and gonophores are ovoid reproductive polyps. It is notable that only a few gonophores are produced on colonies growing in strictly fresh waters. A single female gonophore usually produces six to 20 ova in brackish waters, but only three to six in fresh waters. Mature ova are retained on the gonophores, but the sperm from male gonophores are released into the water, and after swimming about for a short time they penetrate through the covering of the female gonophores and fertilize the eggs. The embryo develops on the gonophore and forms a free-swimming ciliated planula which is released from the colony. The planula attaches to the substrate and by growth and differentiation gives rise to a new colony. Thus there is no true medusoid generation in *Cordylophora*.

In the autumn the hydranths disintegrate and only a few horizontal and more basal upright portions of the colony winter over (Fig. 62B).

**Protohydroids.** A third unusual type of hydroid is *Protohydra leuckarti* Greeff. Although not a true fresh-water species, it occurs in brackish estuaries, swamps, and creeks, some of which are almost fresh. It has the general appearance of a hydra but has no tentacles. The body is usually less than 2 mm. long but may attain a maximum of 5 mm. The species exhibits dioecious syngamic reproduction and also reproduces by transverse and longitudinal fission. *Protohydra* has been reported several times along the New England coast and from numerous places in Great Britain and northwestern Europe.

**Ecology.** Although hydroids are typical members of the littoral and shallow stream associations, they have been reported from waters as deep as 40 to 350 meters. It is not unusual to find them in swift streams or in the wave-swept rocky littoral of large lakes. Unless there are large pieces of debris present, however, they do not occur on fine, muddy bottoms. Greatest populations are usually found in late spring and early summer, followed by a marked decrease in July or August. Sometimes there is also an autumn maximum in September or October. Populations may be vigorous in midwinter but are usually scanty by the time of the ice melt in late winter.

Gonad production is often induced in two or three weeks by lowered laboratory temperatures, usually 10° to 15°, but often a culture becomes sexual without any apparent stimulus. Medium hard waters with pH readings of 7.6 to 8.4 seem to be especially favorable for most species. Although little is known about minimal oxygen concentrations, about 0.3 ml. per liter seems to be a typical value. Hydras do not occur in oxygen-deficient depths of lakes. In general, any lasting contraction of the tentacles is an indication of unfavorable environmental conditions.

Periods of "depression" are often observed in laboratory cultures and are presumably induced by a variety of unfavorable conditions, including temperatures above 20°, lack of sufficient dissolved oxygen, toxic salts, transfer to clean water, and accumulation of metabolic materials. The bodies of hydras undergoing depression rapidly shorten and the tentacles contract

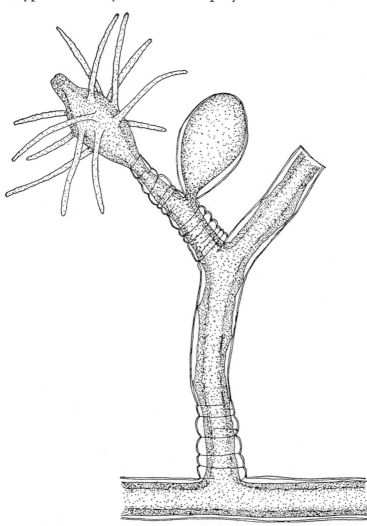

Fig. 63.—Small portion of colony of *Cordylophora lacustris*, ×15, showing one hydranth and one immature gonophore.

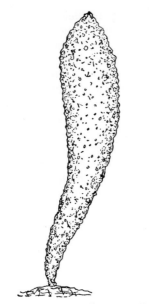

Fig. 64.—*Protohydra leuckarti* Greeff, ×35.

and then disappear. The column then further shortens into a small brownish mass which soon disintegrates. If not too far gone, hydras may recover upon being placed in more favorable conditions.

**Commensals, enemies.** Commensal ciliates, such as *Kerona* (page 69) and *Trichodina* (page 72), are common on the external surface of hydras where they feed on small bits of food. They do not discharge the nematocysts, although most free-living ciliates, both smaller and larger than *Kerona* and *Trichodina*, do easily discharge them.

Carnivorous enemies are not abundant or important but include a few turbellarians, nemertines, crustaceans, and aquatic insects. *Anchistropus minor* is a cladoceran that feeds exclusively on hydras. Epidemics of an external amoeboid parasite, *Hydramoeba hydroxena*, sometimes decimate vigorous hydra growths.

**Geographic distribution, dispersal.** *Chlorohydra viridissima* is known from North America, Europe, Greenland, South America, and New Zealand. *Hydra oligactis* is widely distributed in the Northern

Hemisphere and has been recorded in Australia. The other species of hydras occurring in the United States, however, have not been reported from continents other than North America. About 20 species are recorded in the literature as occurring outside of the continent of North America, but about half of these are so sketchily described as to be unrecognizable. Four American hydras are known from single localities, and several others have been reported from a few scattered areas. Undoubtedly when more intensive collecting is done, especially in the western half of the country, the geographical ranges of most species will be greatly extended.

Hydras attached to mollusk shells may be easily distributed through single drainage systems, and thecated embryos are probably easily blown or transported overland.

**Collecting.** Unless hydras are exceedingly abundant, they may be collected most easily by bringing small objects and aquatic plants into the laboratory where they may be picked off. If the containers are placed in semidarkness, the hydras will migrate to the surface film as the dissolved oxygen in the water decreases. The grayish or brownish thecated embryos should be sought for on aquatic vegetation or debris with the low power of binoculars.

**Culturing.** Specimens keep well in aquaria in moderate light if the temperature is below 20° and if they are well fed with cladocerans and copepods. Three or four daphnids per day per hydra will produce prolific budding. A fraction of the aquarium water should be changed frequently, and only pond water should be used, not tap water.

Periods of depression may be overcome by changing the culture water. If necessary, hand feed depressed individuals by holding (with fine forceps) a freshly killed daphnid in contact with the hydra.

**Preserving, preparing.** In order to kill hydras in an expanded condition they should first be squirted off their normal substrate into a dish. After they are fully expanded in about 2 ml. of water, dash a copious quantity of hot Bouin's fixative into the dish. After a few minutes place the specimens in cold Bouin's fluid for 12 hours. Then wash in several changes of alkaline 30 per cent alcohol, stain, dehydrate, and mount permanently.

Dissociation of the tissues to permit an examination of the nematocysts may be accomplished by placing hydras in a few drops of Hertwig-Schneider's fluid on a slide for 15 to 20 minutes. This solution consists of one part 0.02 per cent osmic acid and four parts 5.0 per cent glacial acetic acid. Dilute Bouin's fluid and one per cent nitric acid are also fairly useful for dissociation.

**Taxonomy.** Modern taxonomic concepts and generic designations date back to the important work of Schulze (1917). Essential characteristics for identification include shape of testes, form of the theca, relative body and tentacle length, hermaphroditism or the dioecious condition, and the shape, size, and structure of the nematocysts. The detailed anatomy of nematocysts can best be distinguished on macerated or dissociated specimens with an oil immersion objective. Preserved nematocysts are of little value.

Most of the information on our American hydras has been gained through the extensive and careful investigations of Dr. Libbie H. Hyman.

The following key includes all American species that have been adequately described in the literature. All lengths and proportions are based on measurements of the living, expanded animal. Ordinarily only living hydras can be accurately identified.

## KEY TO SPECIES OF HYDROZOA

1. Solitary polyps with tentacles; without a medusa stage in the life history.
   Order **HYDROIDA**, HYDRIDAE, 2
   Colonial polyps, free-swimming medusae, or solitary polyps without tentacles....12
2. Gastrodermis containing green algae; column up to 30 mm. long but usually less than 15 mm.; 4 to 12 tentacles, shorter than column; holotrichous isorhizas narrowed at basal end (Fig. 65L); hermaphroditic; the green hydra; generally distributed and common.................**Chlorohydra viridissima** (Pallas)
   Gastrodermis without green algae; hermaphroditic or dioecious..........**Hydra, 3**
3. Tentacles three to five times as long as column; dioecious...................4
   Tentacles less than three times as long as column.........................7
4. Theca spherical and spineless; testes without nipples, or pumpkin-shaped and with nipples (Figs. 65E, F); brownish coloration; common...................5
   Theca spherical and spined; testes pumpkin-shaped, with nipples; rare........6
5. Holotrichous isorhizas with lengthwise loops (Fig. 65D); testes without nipples (Fig. 65E); column up to 20 mm. long; the true brown hydra; common in northern states, from Mont., Wyo., and Colo. east to New England, north of the Ohio River..............................**Hydra oligactis** (Pallas)
   Holotrichous isorhizas with transverse loops (Fig. 65G); testes pumpkin-shaped, with nipples (Fig. 65F); column up to 25 mm. long; the false brown hydra; probably common in central states..........**Hydra pseudoligactis** (Hyman)
6. Theca thick and spined; column 8 to 20 mm. long; stenoteles pear-shaped, 15 microns long, with a downwardly directed stylet of three large spines, and four transverse coils of thread; reported only from ponds near Portland, Ore.
   **Hydra oregona** Griffin and Peters
   Theca extremely delicate and with scattered vestigial spines; column up to 17 mm. long; reported only from lakes near Edmonton, Alberta, Canada.
   **Hydra canadensis** Rowan

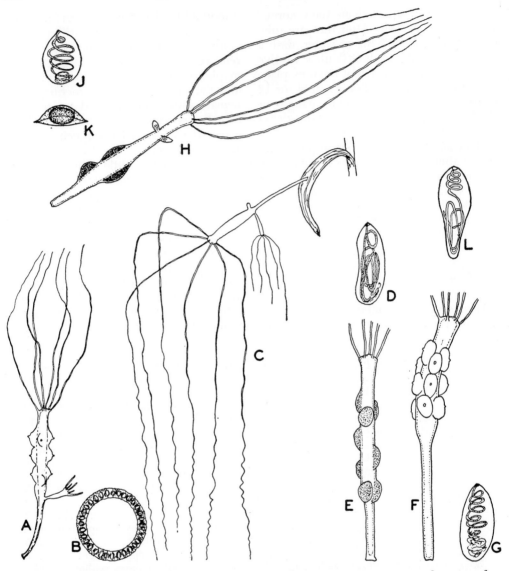

Fig. 65.—Structure of *Hydra*. A, male *Hydra cauliculata* Hyman, ×4; B, optical section of thecated embryo of *H. cauliculata*; C, *H. oligactis* (Pallas), ×2; D, holotrichous isorhiza of *H. oligactis*; E, male *H. oligactis* with testes, ×3; F, male *H. pseudoligactis* Hyman with testes, ×3; G, holotrichous isorhiza of *H. pseudoligactis*; H, sexually mature *H. utahensis* Hyman showing basal ovaries and distal testes, ×7; J, holotrichous isorhiza of *H. utahensis*; K, theca and contained zygote of *H. utahensis*; L, holotrichous isorhiza of *Chlorohydra viridissima* (Pallas). (A and B modified from Hyman, 1938; C to E modified from Hyman, 1930; F to K modified from Hyman, 1931b.)

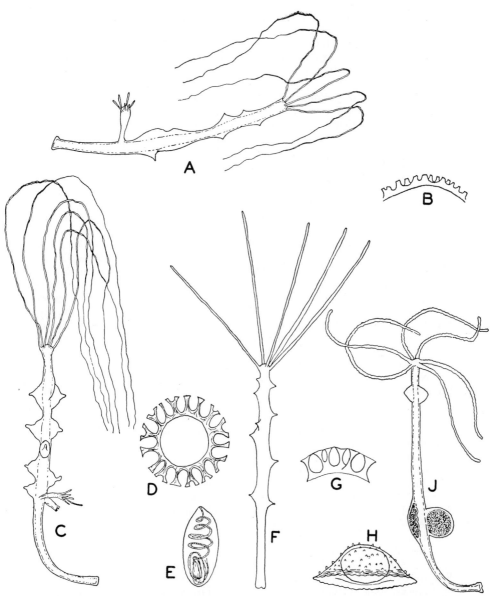

Fig. 66.—Structure of *Hydra*. A, mature *Hydra carnea* Agassiz, ×8, with four distal testes, three ovaries, one basal testis, and one bud; B, spines of embryonic theca of *H. carnea*; C, mature male *H. littoralis* Hyman with eight testes and two buds, ×5; D, optical section of thecated embryo of *H. littoralis*; E, holotrichous isorhiza of *H. littoralis*; F, mature male *H. americana* Hyman, ×6; G, portion of embryonic theca of *H. americana*; H, thecated embryo of *H. hymanae* Hadley and Forrest; J, sexually mature *H. hymanae* with two testes and two ovaries, ×6. (A and B modified from Hyman, 1931; C and D modified from Hyman, 1938; E modified from Hyman, 1931b; F and G modified from Hyman, 1929; H and J modified from Hadley and Forrest.)

7. Tentacles longer than column..........................................8
   Tentacles shorter than column; column up to 12 mm. long....................11
8. Holotrichous isorhizas broadly oval (Fig. 65J); theca spineless, helmet-shaped (Fig. 65K); hermaphroditic; with few small pyriform testes (Fig. 65H); column less than 10 mm. long; reported only from a pond near Salem, Utah.
   Hydra utahensis Hyman
   Holotrichous isorhizas elongated oval (Fig. 66E); theca spined and spherical (Figs. 65B, 66D)..........................................................9
9. Hermaphroditic, sometimes protandrous; testes small, conical, with pointed nipples; column up to 10 mm. long (Fig. 66A); in standing waters; generally distributed as far west as Nebr.......................Hydra carnea Agassiz
   Dioecious; testes large, with nipples; tentacles one and one-half to two times as long as column..............................................................10
10. Spines of embryonic theca moderately long (Fig. 65B); animal brownish; in standing waters; probably common in the Atlantic Coast states.
    Hydra cauliculata Hyman
    Spines of embryonic theca unusually long (Fig. 66D); in swift waters or on wave-swept shore; reported from scattered localities as far west as Okla.
    Hydra littoralis Hyman
11. Theca spined and spherical (Fig. 66G); dioecious, rarely hermaphroditic; testes numerous, conical, with well-developed nipples (Fig. 66F); in standing or slowly flowing waters; whitish to tan coloration; the white hydra; probably widely distributed throughout the eastern states....Hydra americana Hyman
    Theca spined and helmet-shaped (Fig. 66H); hermaphroditic; usually a single pair of distal testes, seldom three or four, rarely up to 12, hemispherical, and tapered to a blunt point (Fig. 66J); in ponds and rapid brooks; variable coloration, depending on contents of gastrovascular cavity; reported only from N. J. ...............................Hydra hymanae Hadley and Forrest
12. Macroscopic colonial polyps 10 to 100 mm. high and consisting of feeding hydranths and reproductive gonophores (Figs. 62, 63); uncommon in brackish waters of Atlantic and Pacific coasts; also reported from rivers in Ill., Ark., and La.
    Order HYDROIDA, CLAVIDAE, Cordylophora lacustris Allman
    Not macroscopic colonial polyps.........................................13
13. Free-swimming bell-shaped medusae with numerous peripheral tentacles; bell diameter ranging from 0.4 to 22 mm. (Fig. 60); sporadic and uncommon in ponds, small lakes, fishponds, and old flooded quarries.
    Order TRACHYLINA, PETASIDAE, Craspedacusta sowerbii Lankester
    Sessile solitary or simple colonial hydroids without tentacles................14
14. Simple colonial hydroids, 2 to 8 mm. long, usually consisting of two to four individuals and seldom up to 12 (Fig. 61); rare in ponds, small lakes, fishponds, and old flooded quarries.
    Order TRACHYLINA, PETASIDAE, Craspedacusta sowerbii Lankester
    Solitary hydroid up to 3 mm. long (Fig. 64); in brackish estuaries, swamps, and creeks, some of which are almost fresh; rare along New England coast.
    Order HYDROIDA, HYDRIDAE, Protohydra leuckarti Greeff

# COELENTERATA REFERENCES

BRYDEN, R. R. 1952. Ecology of Pelmatohydra oligactis in Kirkpatricks Lake, Tennessee. *Écol. Monogr.* 22:45–68.

BYERS, C. F. 1944. The fresh-water jellyfish in Florida. *Proc. Fla. Acad. Sci.* 7:173–180.

DEJDAR, E. 1934. Die Süsswassermeduse Cras- pedacusta sowerbii Lankester in monographischer Darstellung. *Zeitschr. Morph. Ökol. Tiere* 28:595–691.

EWER, R. F. 1947. On the function and mode of action of the nematocysts of Hydra. *Proc. Zool. Soc. London* 117:365–376.

――――. 1948. A review of the Hydridae and two new species of Hydra from Natal. *Ibid.* **118**: 226–244.

GRIFFIN, L. E., and D. C. PETERS. 1939. A new species of Hydra, Hydra oregona. *Trans. Amer. Micros. Soc.* **58**:256–257.

HADLEY, C. E., and H. FORREST. 1949. Taxonomic studies on the hydras of North America. 6. Description of Hydra hymanae, new species. *Amer. Mus. Novit.* **1423**:1–14.

HYMAN, L. H. 1929. Taxonomic studies on the hydras of North America, I. General remarks and description of Hydra americana, new species. *Trans. Amer. Micros. Soc.* **48**:242–255.

――――. 1930. Studies on hydras, II. The characters of Pelmatohydra oligactis (Pallas). *Ibid.* **49**:322–333.

――――. 1931. Studies on hydras, III. Rediscovery of Hydra carnea L. Agassiz (1850) with a description of its characters. *Ibid.* **50**:20–29.

――――. 1931a. Studies on hydras, IV. Description of three new species with a key to the known species. *Ibid.* 302–315.

――――. 1938. Taxonomic studies on the hydras of North America. V. Description of Hydra cauliculata, n. sp., with notes on other species, especially Hydra littoralis. *Amer. Mus. Novit.* **1003**:1–9.

JONES, C. S. 1941. The place of origin and the transportation of cnidoblasts in Pelmatohydra oligactis (Pallas). *Jour. Exp. Zool.* **87**:457–476.

――――. 1947. The control and discharge of nematocysts in Hydra. *Ibid.* **105**:25–60.

KEPNER, W. A., W. C. GREGORY, and R. J. PORTER. 1935. The manipulation of Hydra's nematocysts by Microstomum. *Science* **82**:621.

KEPNER, W. A., B. D. REYNOLDS, L. GOLDSTEIN, and J. H. TAYLOR. 1943. The structure, development and discharge of the penetrant of Pelmatohydra oligactis (Pall). *Jour. Morph.* **72**:561–587.

KEPNER, W. A., and others. 1951. The discharge of nematocysts of the hydra, with special reference to the penetrant. *Ibid.* **88**:23–48.

MILLER, D. E. 1936. A limnological study of Pelmatohydra with special reference to their quantitative seasonal distribution. *Trans. Amer. Micros. Soc.* **55**:123–193.

MUELLER, J. F. 1950. Some observations on the structure of Hydra, with particular reference to the muscular system. *Ibid.* **69**:133–147.

PAULY, R. 1902. Untersuchungen über den Bau und die Lebensweise der Cordylophora lacustris Allman. *Jenaische Zeitschr. Naturw.* **36**:737–780.

PAYNE, F. 1924. A study of the fresh-water medusa, Craspedacusta ryderi. *Jour. Morph.* **38**:387–430.

ROWAN, W. 1930. On a new Hydra from Alberta. *Trans. Roy. Soc. Canada, Sect. 5, Biol. Sci.* **24**:165–170.

SCHMITT, W. L. 1939. Freshwater jellyfish records since 1932. *Amer. Nat.* **73**:83–89.

SCHULZE, P. 1917. Neue Beiträge zu einer Monographie der Gattung Hydra. *Arch. Biontologie* **4**:33–119.

WELCH, P. S., and H. A. LOOMIS. 1924. A limnological study of Hydra oligactis in Douglas Lake, Michigan. *Trans. Amer. Micros. Soc.* **43**:203–235.

# Chapter 5

# TURBELLARIA (FLATWORMS)

CONSIDERING the Phylum Platyhelminthes as a whole, only a small fraction of the described species are free-living in fresh-water habitats. The classes Cestoidea (tapeworms) and Trematoda (flukes) are entirely parasitic, but the Class Turbellaria is almost exclusively a free-living group. Many of the species of turbellarians are marine and a few are terrestrial in warm, damp habitats or parasitic on marine invertebrates, but the remainder are fresh-water forms.

The Class Turbellaria is customarily divided into five orders. Two of these orders, the Acoela and Polycladida, are essentially marine. The Alloeocoela is a marine and fresh-water order, but the Tricladida and Rhabdocoela have fresh-water, marine, and terrestrial representatives.

Fresh-water turbellarians are to be found everywhere, usually on or closely associated with a substrate. The larger species are sometimes confused with small leeches which they resemble somewhat in shape and color; the microscopic species resemble large ciliates in size, shape, and general habits.

**General characteristics.** All fresh-water flatworms are more or less elongated. They may be highly flattened and leaflike, cylindrical, or spindle-shaped. Almost invariably, however, there is some evidence of flattening on the ventral surface. In many species the anterior end is differentiated and sufficiently specialized to resemble a "head."

Tricladida are usually 5 to 30 mm. long, but the Alloeocoela and Rhabdocoela are seldom more than 4 mm. in length, the majority being microscopic. Because of their habit of reproducing by fission, some rhabdocoels customarily occur in chains of several individuals, or zooids. The general surface of the body is usually more or less covered with cilia, and the term "Turbellaria" was coined by Ehrenberg in 1831 when he detected the minute vortical currents of water generated at the anterior end by ciliary action. In the familiar species of planarians, to which every zoology student is exposed in college, cilia are absent from the dorsal surface and edges of the body.

The body cavity of flatworms is a typical gastrovascular cavity having but a single external opening which functions as both mouth and anus. In the Tricladida the gastrovascular cavity has three main irregular branches, one median and anterior and the others posterior and lateral (Fig. 67). Both the Rhabdocoela and Alloeocoela have a single median gastrovascular chamber, but in some representatives of the latter order its outline is more irregular owing to small lateral caeca (Figs. 81, 83, 85).

In a few Turbellaria the mouth is terminal or subterminal. More characteristically it is ventral and somewhere between one-fifth and three-fifths of the way back from the anterior end. A protrusible or non-protrusible muscular pharynx surrounds that portion of the gastrovascular cavity just inside the mouth. If protrusible, the pharynx often lies in a separate pharyngeal chamber.

Almost all species are hermaphroditic and reproduce sexually. One or two genital pores are found on the ventral surface, usually posterior to the mouth.

A wide range of coloration occurs in fresh-water Turbellaria, although the brilliant patterns of marine species are rarely approached. The more familiar planarians (Tricladida) are various shades of gray, brown, or black; often there are dorsal stripes, spots, or mottlings. The ventral surface, however, is usually lighter in color or gray and without a color pattern. Some species have a highly variable coloration. *Dugesia tigrina* (Girard), for example, may be dark yellow, olive, brown, or brownish-black, and the pattern may range from lightly mottled to dense coloration (Fig. 68). The lighter shades usually develop in laboratory cultures. Cave species and a few noncave species are whitish.

Alloeocoels and rhabdocoels are characteristically grayish or colorless, but some are brilliant yellow, gold, orange, red, or rose. Other species are a bright green owing to internal symbiotic zoochlorellae. In all naturally light-colored Turbellaria the body may take on a variety of darker shades depending on the particular contents of the gastrovascular cavity.

Two darkly pigmented eyespots are usually present near the anterior end, but in some species eyespots are absent, and in a few others they are numerous.

Epidermal and subepidermal glands secrete an abundance of mucus which usually covers the body. Minute rodlike rhabdites are produced in the epidermis and subepidermal tissues of many genera, and these, upon being extruded to the surface of the body, disintegrate and produce an additional adhesive mucus.

Thin layers of circular and oblique, and a thicker layer of longitudinal muscle fibers lie below the basement membrane of the epidermis. The cells that line the gastrovascular cavity are large and

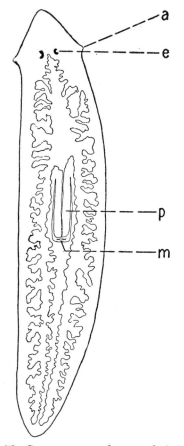

FIG. 67.—Gross anatomy of a typical planarian, showing the three divisions of the gastrovascular cavity, ×15. *a*, auricle; *e*, eyespot; *m*, mouth (on ventral surface of body); *p*, pharynx (lying in pharyngeal chamber).

phagocytic. Between the inner gastrodermis and the outer muscle fibers and epidermis the body consists largely of an undifferentiated mass of parenchyma cells. A few muscle fibers are found in the parenchyma, but otherwise it appears to function as a loose packing material between the excretory and reproductive organs. In the smaller turbellarians the parenchyma is often highly vacuolated, glandular, and watery.

**Locomotion.** Triclad flatworms cannot swim but are only capable of locomotion on a substrate or on the underside of the

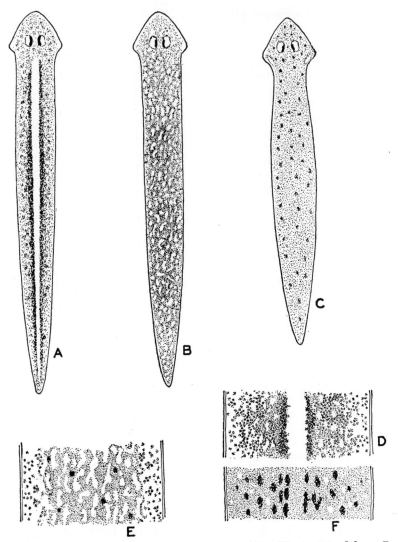

Fig. 68.—Variations in color pattern of *Dugesia tigrina* (Girard). A, striped form; B, spotted form; C, dark spots on uniform brown background; D, E, and F, enlarged views of similar patterns. (From Hyman, 1939).

surface film of the water. Smooth gliding movements are produced by the action of cilia upon the thin coat of mucus secreted onto the substrate by cyanophilous glands in the ventral parenchyma. Faint waves of muscular contractions pass longitudinally down the body and supplement ciliary action. Upon strong stimulation, planarians may crawl actively by means of pronounced waves of muscular contrac-

tion that pass from anterior to posterior. A few species have anterior adhesive organs which may be used as a leech uses its anterior sucker for locomotion.

Rhabdocoels and alloeocoels move on a substrate as do planarians, but many are also capable of swimming about freely in the water owing to their abundant cilia.

When conditions are unfavorable, when the water is too warm, or when fully fed, planarians are not active but remain more or less contracted for days at a time.

**Feeding, digestion.** The most familiar type of feeding occurs in the planarians. Here the pharynx is long, highly muscular, and protrusible through the mouth. When the presence of food (usually living, dead, or crushed animal matter) is detected in the water, the animals quickly move toward it and place the ventral surface of the body in contact with it. The pharynx is then extruded through the mouth, and its tip is placed against the food (Fig. 69). Sometimes the pharynx may be extended to as much as one-half of the body length. There appears to be no appreciable secretion of digestive juices from the tip of the pharynx, and apparently only soft or disintegrating tissues are capable of being sucked up into the main gastrovascular cavity by the muscular action of the pharynx. The gastrovascular cavity becomes filled with fluid and small bits of tissues after 30 to 80 minutes of feeding. There is no good evidence for extracellular digestion in planarians. Instead, individual particles are ingested by pseudopodial action of the large gastrodermal cells, and digestion is intracellular. Evidence based on the small amount of work that has been done on rhabdocoels, however, indicates that it is probable that they have considerable extracellular digestion.

Some species of *Phagocata* (Tricladida) are interesting in that they are polypharyngeal (Fig. 79F). In rhabdocoels and alloeocoels the pharynx is short and generally not greatly protrusible, but the normally small mouth may be expanded to a marked degree during feeding.

Although some rhabdocoels are sometimes said to be vegetarians, the great ma-

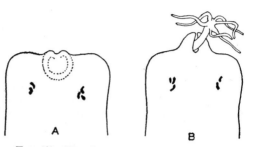

FIG. 70.—Dorsal views of head of *Procotyla fluviatilis* Leidy. A, with adhesive organ retracted; B, with adhesive organ grasping a hydra. (Modified from Redfield.)

jority of Turbellaria are zoophagous and feed on small living invertebrates. Nevertheless dead animal matter may often be ingested, and the microscopic species subsist on fresh corpses of larger metazoans as well as on whole living or dead Protozoa, rotifers, nematodes, and gastrotrichs. Small individuals, such as *Catenula* and *Macrostomum*, are especially abundant in decaying organic matter and perhaps are essentially omnivorous. Some species of *Macrostomum*, however, prefer animal tissues and eject plant material from the pharynx.

Some few species are so voracious that they will exterminate other species in a mixed culture. Cannibalism has occasionally been observed, especially in crowded cultures where there are injured specimens.

A few small rhabdocoels have been found to form an adhesive layer or mass on the substrate by the discharge of rhabdites at the anterior end. Such mucus with its entangled detritus, bacteria, algae, and protozoans is then gathered into a ball and ingested. Some investigators suggest that this method of feeding may be more common than is suspected. Planarians also exude rhabdites which form a mucus on coming in contact with water. Small crustaceans get caught in this material, as well as in the usual slime track, and are thus easy prey.

Dendrocoelidae have an anterior, adhesive, sucker-like organ which is used in

FIG. 69.—Planarian with extruded pharynx, just beginning to feed on a bit of food.

feeding. Such species pounce upon small crustaceans and hydras and grasp them firmly by bringing the lateral edges of the sucker together. The prey is then held against the substrate in the pharyngeal region while feeding proceeds. *Procotyla fluviatilis* Leidy feeds chiefly on living crustaceans; it cannot be cultured on raw meat.

When reared in the laboratory, planarians should be fed one to three times per week. They may be kept for months without any food, however, while the body gets progressively smaller and more simplified in structure. No reproduction occurs during such periods of starvation.

*Microstomum* and a few other genera have become curiously adapted for retaining the undischarged nematocysts of ingested hydras. Within ten to twenty hours after ingestion, the nematocysts are found distributed over the body surface between the epidermal cells. Such nematocysts are retained as defense devices for the remainder of the life of the turbellarian.

There is no special circulatory system in flatworms. Materials are distributed throughout the gastrovascular cavity by means of general muscular and body movements. The tissues are nowhere thick or bulky, and diffusion of materials from cell to cell is easily facilitated.

**Respiration.** The respiratory exchange of oxygen and carbon dioxide occurs through the general epidermis and perhaps to a slight extent through the gastrodermis also. Many rhabdocoels are characteristic of habitats where there is much decay and low concentrations of dissolved oxygen; some are able to withstand anaerobic conditions for variable lengths of time, although there is little definite information on this phase of rhabdocoel biology in the literature. Planarians, however, all require high concentrations of oxygen and occur only in well-oxygenated habitats.

Symbiotic zoochlorellae occur in the parenchyma and gastrodermis of many rhabdocoels, although they are not necessarily consistently present in a particular species. Photosynthesis releases oxygen to the turbellarian tissues, while the worm contributes carbon dioxide and nitrogenous compounds for algal metabolism. Algae may be passed on to the succeeding generation in the turbellarian egg.

**Excretion.** The flame bulb, or protonephridial, system of flatworms has a variable pattern. There may be few to many flame bulbs, but their ducts usually empty into two longitudinal collecting ducts (Fig. 71). *Stenostomum* and *Catenula* are exceptional in having a single median collecting duct. Collecting ducts open to the ventral surface by means of one or two pores which are variable in position.

As in certain other phyla, the excretory process is a function of the ducts rather than the flame bulbs themselves. Nevertheless the physiological significance of the whole flame bulb system appears to vary from one species to another. Sometimes the system has an important excretory function; sometimes it is apparently unimportant. Often it is of great importance in osmoregulation; in other species it appears to be relatively unimportant.

*Gyratrix hermaphroditus* Ehr. is a species occurring in fresh-water, brackish, and marine habitats. In the former it has a highly developed flame bulb system. In brackish habitats the system is less highly developed, with the bladder and ampullae lacking. In marine habitats, however, it is poorly developed or absent.

It is probable that a large fraction of the excretory materials are disposed of through the general epidermal surface and also perhaps to a slight extent through the gastrodermis into the gastrovascular cavity. Some excretory granules are commonly retained and stored in the tissues until the animal dies.

**Nervous system.** The brain consists of two more or less well-defined lobes, or ganglia, near the anterior end. Usually there are two prominent longitudinal

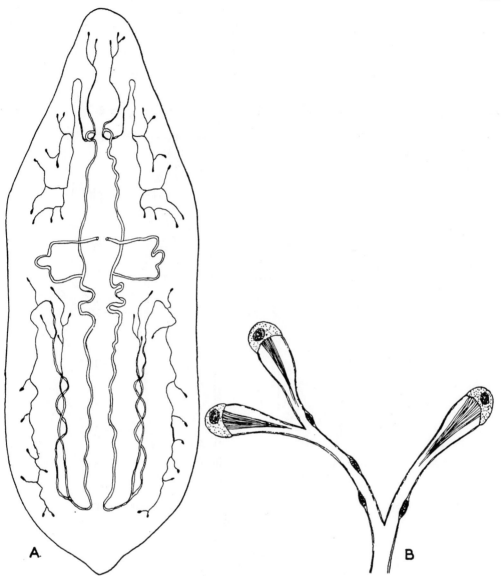

FIG. 71—Diagrams of protonephridial structures. A, protonephridial system of *Mesostoma* (the two proximal pores are located just inside the mouth); B, three flame bulbs at terminal endings of tubules.

nerve trunks, one originating in each ganglion, but often there are one to several additional, smaller trunks. Many cross commissures and small lateral nerves originate from the longitudinal trunks and innervate all of the organs and tissues. An abundance of sensory fibers are given off from the brain and innervate the anterior end (Fig. 72).

**Sensory receptors.** Eyespots are the most highly developed sense organs, especially in planarians. Each eyespot is shaped like a bean or a pigmented cup

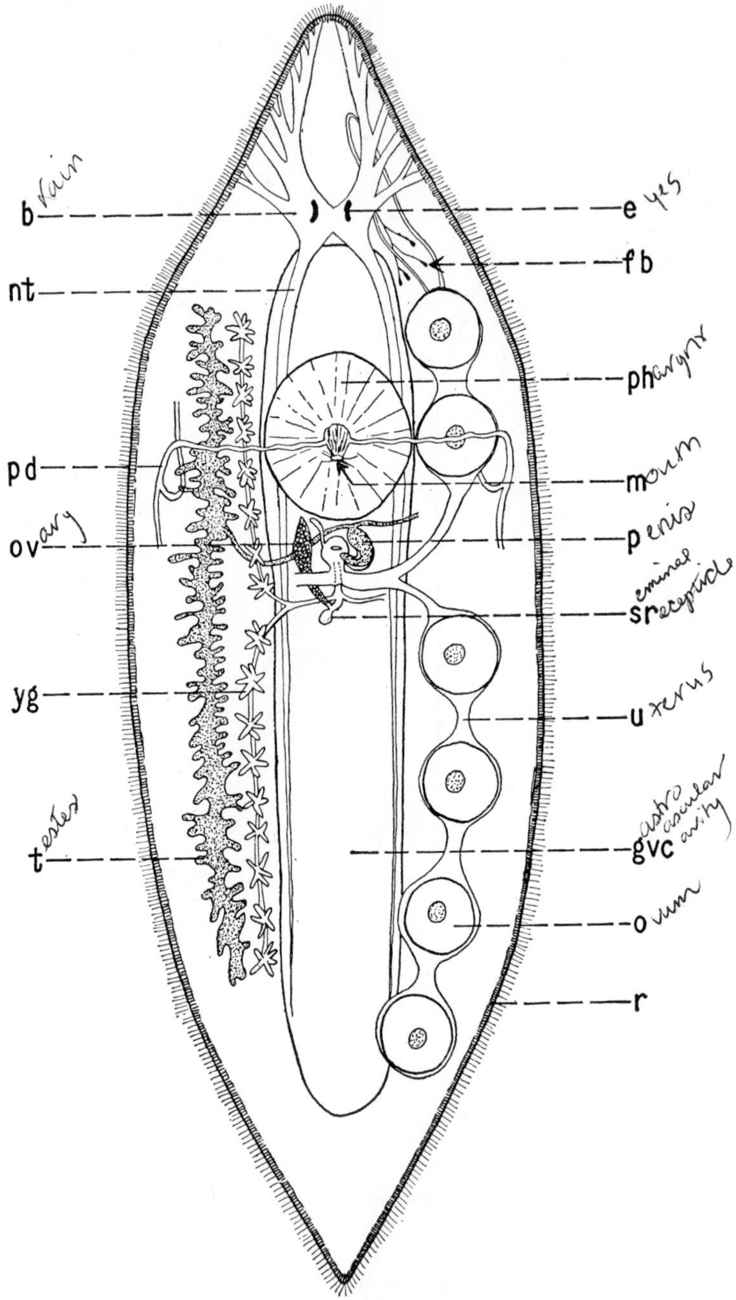


FIG. 72.–Structure of *Mesostoma ehrenbergi* Focke, ×20, ventral view. *b*, brain; *e*, eyespot *fb*, flame bulb (distributed over entire body); *gvc*, gastrovascular cavity; *m*, mouth; *nt*, longitudinal nerve trunk; *o*, ovum; *ov*, ovary; *p*, penis (projecting into genital atrium); *pd*, protonephridial duct; *ph*, pharynx; *r*, rhabdites in epidermis; *sr*, seminal receptacle; *t*, testes (shown only on right side of body); *u*, uterus (shown only on left side of body); *yg*, yolk gland. (Modified from Ruebush, 1940.)

containing translucent light-sensitive receptor cells which are attached to nerve fibers at the outer portion of the cup. Some spring and most cave species of Tricladida have no eyespots. The majority of rhabdocoels have one pair, but some are blind, and a few have multiple eyespots (Figs. 82–84).

Rhabdocoel eyespots are relatively simple in structure and are sometimes unpigmented and called light-refracting bodies rather than eyes. In *Stenostomum*, for example, the so-called eyespot is colorless and consists of a few to many basal refractive spherules and a distal low cone-shaped vesicle. Actually a visual function has not yet been definitely established for this structure.

Although eyespots may be well developed, most turbellarians are photonegative, especially in moderate to strong light, and as a consequence are usually found in shaded areas or under objects.

Some rhabdocoels have a pair of anterior sensory pits, often ciliated, which are presumably chemoreceptors. They may be rounded, oblong, slitlike, and shallow or deep (Fig. 81D).

Larval *Rhynchoscolex* and adult *Catenula* and *Otomesostoma* have a median anterior statocyst (Figs. 81A; 85B), but none of the other American fresh-water genera have such a structure.

In addition to the general coat of short cilia, many rhabdocoels have a few long sensory cilia, especially at the anterior and posterior ends (Figs. 74, 75). These move independently of each other and of the short cilia. In some species they are relatively stiff and are called "spines."

Other receptors, mostly in the epidermis, function in the detection of currents, in olfaction, and in response to contact. The pharynx and anterior end are especially sensitive.

**Reproduction, development.** With reference to their reproductive habits, there are three general groups of turbellarians: (1) species that reproduce only asexually,

by budding or fission; (2) species that reproduce solely by sexual methods; and (3) species that are capable of reproducing sexually or asexually, depending on the genetic strain, physiological strain, and prevailing ecological conditions.

Fission does not occur in the majority of triclads, though certain common species are in the third category. Among these latter species the relative frequency of sexual and asexual reproduction varies greatly from one species to another. In *Dugesia tigrina*, for example, there appear to be at least two physiological varieties. One variety reproduces only asexually. Under appropriate conditions of temperature and food supply individuals pinch in at about mid-length on each edge. The pinching in proceeds rapidly until the two halves are completely separated. Then the anterior end of the posterior individual reconstitutes a head, and the posterior end of the anterior individual forms a tail. External factors may change the rate of fission or inhibit it, but they do not change the reproduction to the sexual type. Fission occurs only above 10°, with frequency increasing to a maximum at 25° to 28°. Such fission strains have been kept as long as five years in the laboratory without development of sex organs.

In other physiological races of *D. tigrina* there may be an alternation of reproductive methods according to water temperature. Sex organs may develop during the winter and early spring, and egg capsules are deposited in May and June. As the water temperature increases, however, the reproductive organs degenerate, and in July, August, and September reproduction may be entirely by fission. By late autumn the sex organs are again beginning to develop. If the water temperature remains low throughout the year, however, sexual reproduction may be continuous.

It has also been suggested that there are still other strains of *D. tigrina* that reproduce sexually regardless of normal seasonal temperature variations.

*Dugesia dorotocephala* (Woodworth)

and a few other triclads also appear to exist in several physiological varieties comparable to the situation in *D. tigrina*. Nevertheless *D. dorotocephala* is rarely observed to reproduce sexually under natural conditions.

*Procotyla fluviatilis* is incapable of asexual reproduction; it is sexual and deposits egg cocoons during the winter months. Asexual reproduction is also unknown in *Curtisia foremani* (Girard), but it reproduces sexually at all seasons. In *Phagocata*

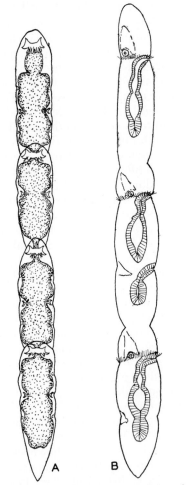

Fig. 73.—Chains of zooids in rhabdocoels. A, dorsal view of four zooids of *Stenostomum*, ×24 (gastrovascular cavity stippled); B, lateral view of three zooids of *Catenula*, ×85. (Modified from Marcus, 1945.)

*vernalis* Kenk and *P. velata* (Stringer), however, sexual reproduction is rare and apparently occurs only during the winter months in permanent bodies of water.

The seasonal reproductive habits of rhabdocoels and alloeocoels are poorly known, but most of the genera reproduce solely by the sexual method. *Catenula, Rhynchoscolex, Suomina, Microstomum,* and *Stenostomum* are the only genera capable of reproducing asexually. In these forms fission proceeds rapidly and often along several transverse planes so that there may be a series of two to eight zooids in a chain (Fig. 73). Occasionally a few species in this group of five genera have been observed to develop sex organs and reproduce sexually.

Fission in triclads is often a simple fragmentation, but in rhabdocoels a full complement of organs is usually developed before separation. Triclads have seldom actually been observed to divide, and there is some evidence to show that the process occurs at night and is completed within thirty minutes to several hours. Under favorable conditions divisions may occur as frequently as every five to ten days in triclads, but in rhabdocoels the time interval is much shorter.

All American fresh-water turbellarians are hermaphroditic, and the male and female organ systems are unusually complex in many genera. They are not present during periods of fission but develop later, presumably from undifferentiated parenchyma cells. The male organs sometimes mature before the female organs. Various types of reproductive systems are diagrammed in Figs. 72, 74, 75, and 76, and only a typical planarian arrangement will be described here (Fig. 76).

In the female reproductive system the two ovaries are on either side of the body near the anterior end. A longitudinal oviduct (or ovovitelline duct) proceeds posteriorly from each ovary and collects yolk cells from numerous lateral yolk glands. The two ovovitelline ducts unite near the mid-line, posterior to the mouth, and enter

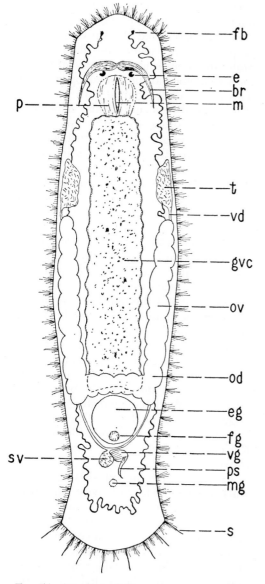

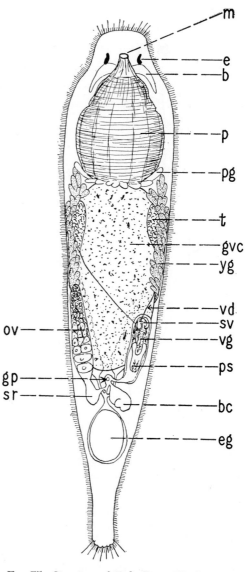

Fig. 74.—Structure of *Macrostomum appendic-ulatum* (Fabr.), ×140, a species common everywhere in fresh, brackish, and salt waters. *br*, brain; *e*, eyespot; *eg*, egg; *fb*, flame bulb; *fg*, female genital pore; *gvc*, gastrovascular cavity; *m*, mouth; *mg*, male genital pore; *od*, oviduct; *ov*, ovary; *p*, pharynx; *ps*, penis stylet; *s*, spine; *sv*, spermiducal vesicle; *t*, testes; *vd*, vas deferens; *vg*, prostatic vesicle. (Modified from Ferguson, 1939.)

Fig. 75.—Structure of *Dalyellia*, ×70, diagrammatic. *b*, brain; *bc*, bursa copulatrix; *e*, eyespot; *eg*, egg; *gp*, genital pore; *gvc*, gastrovascular cavity; *m*, mouth; *ov*, ovary; *p*, pharynx; *pg*, pharyngeal gland; *ps*, penis stylet; *sr*, seminal receptacle; *sv*, spermiducal vesicle; *t*, testes; *yg*, yolk glands; *vd*, vas deferens; *vg*, prostatic vesicle. (Modified from Ruebush and Hayes, 1939.)

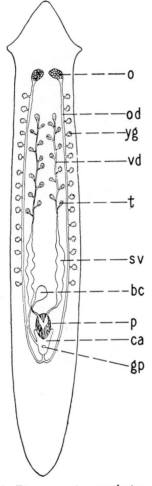

o

od

yg

vd

t

sv

bc

p

ca

gp

Fig. 76.—Diagrammatic ventral view of a typical triclad reproductive system, ×16. (The relationships of the male and female atria are distinct
only in a lateral view.) *bc*, bursa copulatrix;
*ca*, common atrium; *gp*, genital pore; *o*, ovary;
*od*, ovovitelline duct; *p*, penis; *sv*, spermiducal
vesicle; *t*, testis; *vd*, vas deferens; *yg*, yolk gland.

stored. The spermiducal vesicles, either
with or without uniting into a common
duct, enter the basal portion of the highly
muscular penis, and the tip of the latter
projects into a cavity, the male atrium.
Male and female atria unite ventrally to
form a common atrium which opens externally as a common genital pore.

Additional cement glands, copulatory
glands, and other accessory reproductive
structures occur in many turbellarians.
Rhabdocoels often have the distal end of
the penis modified to form a stylet, and
sometimes the basal part is a prostatic vesicle which secretes a granular material vital
to the sperm. Many rhabdocoels have two
genital pores.

As is the case in most hermaphroditic
animals, two turbellarians usually copulate
and exchange sperm. The penis of each
animal is elongated and protruded from its
genital pore and through the genital pore
of the other animal, the sperm being discharged into the bursal canal in planarians. Both animals exude quantities of
mucus from the genital pore region during
copulation. Upon completion of copulation, sperm are stored in the bursa copulatrix for a short time and then leave and
migrate up the oviducts to the region of
the ovaries. After a variable interval,
the eggs are fertilized as they leave the
ovaries.

As the zygote moves down the oviduct it accumulates yolk cells, and in the
male atrium aggregates of zygotes and
yolk cells become surrounded by a proteinaceous capsule. Such a cocoon usually
contains three to 15 zygotes and hundreds to thousands of yolk cells. It leaves
the body through the genital pore, and in
*Dugesia, Curtisia,* and a few other species
it is attached to the substrate by means of
a stalk (Fig. 77A). Each worm may deposit a series of cocoons during the breeding season.

Hypodermic impregnation appears to
be the rule in *Stenostomum.* A single egg
is ripened in each ovary during the reproductive season. It is fertilized inside the

a common cavity, the female atrium. A
saclike bursa copulatrix connects with the
female atrium by means of a bursal canal.

The testes are small round bodies arranged roughly in two longitudinal rows.
Each one connects with one of the two
vasa deferentia by means of a minute duct.
As the vasa deferentia proceed posteriorly
they are widened and convoluted to form
spermiducal vesicles where ripe sperm are

body and is liberated to the outside by a rupturing of the body wall.

More commonly, however, rhabdocoels copulate and exchange sperm in the usual fashion. Fertilized eggs are usually laid singly, each enclosed in a capsule or shell which is sometimes stalked (Fig. 77B). Many of the Typhloplanidae produce two kinds of eggs. Thin-shelled "summer" eggs hatch promptly after deposition, but the larger, thick-shelled "winter" eggs have delayed hatching and may be dormant during the winter; they are capable of withstanding unfavorable environmental conditions. Winter eggs may be extruded from the parent body in the customary way or they may be liberated upon the death and disintegration of the parent. Some species are regularly viviparous; the summer eggs hatch within the body and the young break out of the posterior region of the parent to the outside. In alloeocoel and rhabdocoel families other than the Typhloplanidae only eggs of the winter type are produced.

Self-fertilization is rare in the Tricladida and has been definitely demonstrated only for *Curtisia foremani*. Certain species sometimes produce sterile cocoons. Some investigators think that summer eggs of typhloplanid rhabdocoels are self-fertilized.

Cocoons of triclad turbellarians are 2 to 4 mm. in diameter and light-colored when recently deposited but soon become dark brown or blackish. Although they are resistant to low temperatures, they cannot withstand isolated drying. Depending on the season, a cocoon may winter over or hatch in about two weeks. The several worms that emerge are only 1 to 3 mm. long. Development is direct and there are no special larval stages in the American fresh-water species. With the exception of reproductive structures, the newly hatched worm often has the full complement of organ systems.

*Phagocata velata* and *P. vernalis* have an unusual habit of fragmenting, especially when their habitat becomes warm

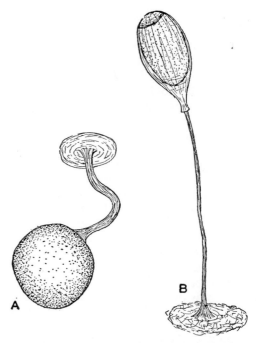

Fig. 77.—Turbellarian cocoon and rhabdocoel encapsulated egg. A, stalked planarian cocoon, ×7; B, stalked encapsulated egg of *Gyratrix*, ×100 (note operculum).

in late spring and summer. When a worm reaches a length of 12 to 15 mm. the internal organs degenerate and the whole worm fragments into numerous small bits. Each piece secretes mucus which hardens to form a small cyst, and a whole miniature individual is reconstituted within the cyst. Encystment of a whole mature animal has also been reported. Such cysts may hatch in a few weeks or may winter over.

Length of life is known chiefly from laboratory cultures. Sexually reproducing species live for only a few weeks or months, usually dying in summer or autumn after producing winter eggs. A few species, however, may survive a year or more by encysting during unfavorable conditions. Species capable of fission can presumably continue indefinitely under appropriate conditions. Such laboratory cultures have been kept going from two to eleven years.

The larger species of planarians, especially *Dugesia*, have long been classical objects for regeneration and grafting experiments. A great deal of such work was done in the United States, especially between 1910 and 1930. If extended specimens are carefully cut transversely into two or several pieces with a razor blade, a large percentage of the pieces will regenerate into whole new worms, the original longitudinal axis being maintained. Worms cut into two along the median line regenerate respective right and left halves to form two new worms. Partial longitudinal cuts at the anterior end often produce worms with two or more complete heads. Regeneration potentialities are most highly developed in the anterior half or three-quarters of the body.

In spite of this regeneration capacity, planarians are rather delicate, and when handled roughly in the laboratory they easily develop breaks and irregularities in the body.

**Ecology.** Springs, spring brooks, ditches, marshes, pools, ponds, lakes, and caves all have their characteristic turbellarian populations. Most species, and especially triclads, are photonegative and are found under objects or in debris during the daytime. Flatworms thrive on any kind of substrate where there is an appropriate food supply. Although they are most characteristic of the shallows, a few species have been collected from lake bottoms as deep as 100 meters.

Triclads are typical of brooks and streams; rhabdocoels and alloeocoels are never abundant in such habitats. Rheophile forms are also usually cold stenotherms; common species are *Curtisia foremani*, *Dugesia dorotocephala*, *Polycelis coronata* (Girard), *Phagocata velata*, and *P. morgani* (Stevens and Boring). The last-named species is restricted to water between 4° and 14°. *Procotyla fluviatilis* occurs in all kinds of habitats, including running waters, standing waters, and even brackish areas. In general, specimens from running waters attain greater size than those from standing waters. *Dugesia tigrina* and *Phagocata vernalis* are both standing-water triclads, but while the former species is a eurytherm, the latter is active only during the cold months in temperate zone ponds and ditches.

Small colonies of a well-known European species, *Crenobia alpina* (Dana), are restricted to cold brooks of the Alps, the Scandinavian countries, and Great Britain. The species is seldom found in water that becomes warmer than 12°, and 7° is the optimum temperature. Sexual reproduction is most rapid in the winter, but fission may occur in spring and early summer. Encystment is unknown. Because of its peculiar stenothermal distribution, this species is thought to be a glacial relict. No species of comparable habits are known from the United States.

The non-triclads are especially abundant during the warm months in pools and ponds containing quantities of algae, other vegetation, and organic debris. In a single lake, where many microhabitats or niches exist, as many as 30 species have been recorded. Almost any stagnant pool will contain one or more species of *Dalyellia*, and usually one or more additional species in each of *Stenostomum*, *Macrostomum*, *Microstomum*, and *Mesostoma*. Such species are eurythermal since they occur in habitats having a wide daily and seasonal temperature range. *Gyratrix*, *Phaenocora*, and *Otomesostoma* are also chiefly eurythermal. *Rhynchomesostoma rostratum* (O. F. M.) and certain species of *Macrostomum*, *Dalyellia*, and *Castrada*, however, are some of the few rhabdocoels known to be cold stenotherms.

The great majority of turbellarian genera occurring in fresh waters are restricted to that environment. *Macrostomum*, however, is the most distinct exception, with many species in brackish and marine environments. As implied in a previous section, *Gyratrix hermaphroditus* is one of the very few euryhaline species; it is found in fresh-water, brackish, and marine environments.

In those rhabdocoel genera occurring in both standing and running waters there is often a correlation of size and activity with habitat. Still waters are characterized by larger, more sedentary species, while the small, faster moving species are more abundant in waters where there is a current, however slow.

Some species of *Pseudophaenocora* thrive in the presence of only a trace of oxygen, and many other rhabdocoels occur in water where the concentrations are as low as 5 to 40 per cent saturation. Most triclads, however, are restricted to water whose oxygen concentration does not fall below 70 per cent saturation.

**Enemies, parasites.** Turbellaria are seldom an important element in the diet of other animals. Odonata nymphs consume a few planarians, and rhabdocoels and alloeocoels appear to be taken occasionally by nematodes, annelids, and a few crustaceans and aquatic insects.

Internal parasites of turbellarians include ciliates, gregarines, and (rarely) larval mermithid nematodes. Some turbellarians may be found in the brood pouch of isopods and amphipods, but they are probably commensals rather than true parasites.

**Geographical distribution.** So far as flatworms are concerned, that portion of the United States west of the Great Plains is almost a *terra incognita*. A few triclad records have been published for this region, but rhabdocoels have been even more greatly neglected. East of the Mississippi the triclads have been extensively studied, especially by Hyman, and although the non-triclads have been studied to a considerable degree by Kepner, Ferguson, and Ruebush, an enormous amount of work yet remains to be done. The number of species of rhabdocoels appears to be very large, and each new investigation turns up new species. As shown in the key

beginning on page 130, some triclads are common and widely distributed, while others are known from only one or two localities. Cave species are highly endemic, each form being restricted to a single cave or cave system, or to a group of caves in the same general area.

Although many rhabdocoels have thus far been reported from only one or several collecting areas, a few appear to be common and essentially cosmopolitan in the Holarctic region. Typical examples are *Macrostomum appendiculatum* (Fabr.), *Stenostomum leucops* (Dugès), *Castrella truncata* (Abildgaard), *Phaenocora unipunctata* (Ørsted), and *Bothromesostoma personatum* (Schmidt).

Little definite information is available concerning the dissemination of turbellarians. *Dugesia dorotocephala* is generally distributed in spring brooks and marshy springs, yet it probably is unable to migrate actively throughout a single drainage system because of its ecological preference for headwaters. The same is true of *Phagocata morgani*, which is widely distributed east of the Mississippi. *Dugesia tigrina*, however, is never found in springs or spring brooks, but it does occur in a wide variety of other lotic and lentic habitats and presumably can migrate actively through drainage systems over wide areas. *Procotyla fluviatilis* and *Curtisia foremani* also probably spread by active migration. Species such as *Phagocata vernalis,* however, which occur in temporary ponds and ditches, must rely entirely on passive means of distribution.

Even less is known about the dissemination of rhabdocoels, but the mechanisms of distribution must be fairly efficient, since the same species of rhabdocoel may be found everywhere in suitable habitats, even in temporary ponds and puddles that are dry during the late summer and early autumn.

Undoubtedly the cyst stages, winter eggs, and perhaps even cocoons are transported from place to place by natural agencies and larger animals that are capable of moving or flying overland from one pond, lake, or stream to another.

**Collecting.** Spring brooks may be "baited" for planarians with cubes of raw, lean beef, but this method is not usually successful in ponds. After 15 minutes the meat should be examined and the worms shaken off into a container of water. Otherwise they may be washed or picked off the undersides of objects with a pipette. If planarians are abundant in water cress, the plants should be placed in containers in the laboratory. As oxygen decreases the worms will migrate to the top where they may be picked off with a glass rod or pipette.

Because of their small size, rhabdocoels and alloeocoels are more difficult to obtain and concentrate in numbers. The uppermost one or two centimeters of bottom debris as well as algae and rooted vegetation from any body of water will yield these forms if such material is placed in wide-mouthed jars or aquaria in the laboratory. In six to twelve hours many of the specimens will migrate to the surface film and may be picked up with a pipette. Such containers should also be allowed to stand undisturbed for two to twenty days. As decomposition increases, more individuals and additional species will be found.

Sometimes a Birge cone net drawn through dense vegetation will take large numbers. Small species are common inhabitants of the under surface of lily pads.

**Culturing.** Planarians may be kept in standing water, provided it does not become too warm and is changed every other day. Tap water is often toxic. Enameled pans and glass or crockery containers are all suitable. Since they are photonegative animals, it is best to put objects into the container, such as pebbles or bits of broken flowerpots, in order to provide shaded places. Also, the whole container may be covered. Cubes of fresh meat (especially beef liver), earthworm fragments, or chopped meal worms are suitable foods

and should be supplied once or twice a week. *Procotyla fluviatilis,* however, requires small living crustaceans. After two or three hours any remaining food fragments should be removed, and if the cultures are in standing water, the water should be changed. Planarians will live for three to twelve weeks without any food but they get progressively smaller.

Most planarians are seldom found reproducing sexually, but if sexual specimens of *Dugesia tigrina* are collected in the field, they will usually continue producing egg capsules in the laboratory. *Procotyla fluviatilis* is especially useful for a study of sexual reproduction because of its translucency. Its sexual period extends from autumn through winter and sometimes into early spring. Nevertheless, *Curtisia foremani* is about the only species that can really be depended upon to produce egg capsules regularly under laboratory conditions.

Temporary cultures of rhabdocoels may develop and be kept for several weeks in the original containers of decaying aquatic vegetation and debris in the laboratory. More or less permanent cultures may be maintained in Petri dishes or finger bowls in a variety of ways. *Stenostomum* and certain other genera may be cultured in boiled wheat, rice, or rye grain infusions similar to those used for other micrometazoans and Protozoa. Subcultures should be started every five or six weeks. Pablum or cultures of similar foods are often successful. Some cold stenothermal species of *Macrostomum* can be cultured only in a refrigerator. Rhabdocoel food may be crushed entomostracans, chopped meal worms, or chopped aquatic oligochaetes.

**Preparing, preserving.** There are several suitable methods of killing and fixing planarians, but all methods should begin with the animals extended in a very small amount of water. Saturated mercuric chloride in 0.9 per cent sodium chloride is good. Two per cent nitric acid for one minute followed by 70 per cent alcohol is also fairly good. Two per cent nitric acid may be dropped on the planarians, and then they should be flooded with saturated mercuric chloride in 0.9 per cent sodium chloride. A biological supply company advocates narcotizing in strychnine water for a few minutes and then flooding with Gilson's fluid. The latter solution consists of the following: 5 g. mercuric chloride, 5 ml. 80 per cent nitric acid, 1 ml. glacial acetic acid, 25 ml. 70 per cent alcohol, and 220 ml. water; filter after three days.

Because of their greater translucency, alloeocoels and rhabdocoels are advantageously studied alive with the 4, 8, or 16 mm. objective in a hollow-ground slide or by placing them between two square cover slips sealed at the edges with vaseline. Such a mount may be turned over on a slide and both sides of the specimens examined. Slight pressure compresses the worms slightly so that they move about only slowly. If the preparation is carefully made, even an oil immersion lens may be used.

Non-triclads should usually be anesthetized with 0.1 per cent chloretone, 10 per cent alcohol, 1 per cent hydroxylamine hydrochloride, or near-freezing temperatures. Fixation with Helly's fluid produces little shrinkage. This reagent consists of the following: 2.5 g. potassium dichromate, 5 g. mercuric chloride, 1 g. sodium sulphate, 100 ml. water, and 5 ml. formalin. Hayes (1942) recommends Harper's modification of Allen's B-15 fixative. It consists of two solutions which should be mixed immediately before use. Solution A contains 380 ml. saturated picric acid, 40 ml. glacial acetic acid, and 8 g. chromic acid. Solution B contains 220 ml. saturated picric acid, 200 ml. formalin, and 8 g. urea.

Flatworm fixation usually takes 30 to 60 minutes. If the fixative contains mercuric chloride, the specimens should be washed several times in 50 per cent alcohol containing a little tincture of iodine. Pigmented specimens may be bleached in undiluted hydrogen peroxide. Seventy per cent alcohol and dioxan are suitable preservatives. Stained whole mounts of rhabdocoels are sometimes useful, orange G and Delafield's hematoxylin being suitable stains.

**Taxonomy.** If serial sections are not available, identification of triclads to genus or species should be made on living specimens whenever possible. Shape, and especially the shape of the anterior end, is highly variable in preserved specimens, even though carefully prepared.

Generic identification of non-triclads is usually possible with live specimens, but they must be mature.

On the other hand, species identification of almost all non-triclads and species identification of some triclads are entirely dependent upon serial sections, and especially on the detailed anatomy of the reproductive system of the mature individual. It is unfortunate that such work can be done only by the experienced specialist, and the considerable effort involved in making species identifications will probably always maintain a dearth of investigators.

As emphasized in a foregoing section, the turbellarian fauna of the United States is poorly known, especially in the western half of the country, and therefore a species name should never be given to a specimen simply because it is the only one previously reported from a particular region.

Many of our species have a long history of taxonomic confusion and synonymy, chiefly as the result of variable characters, poor fixation, and identification by inexperienced workers. It is thought that the key which follows incorporates the most accurate and recent taxonomic ideas. The section of the key which includes the rhabdocoel and alloeocoel genera has been modified from that of Ruebush (1941). The key does not take into account non-triclad family designations, but the following is a complete outline of the taxonomic relationships recognized in this manual. Essentially it follows that given by Bresslau in Kükenthal and Krumbach.

Order Tricladida
  Planariidae
    Curtisia
    Dugesia
    Hymanella
    Phagocata
    Planaria
    Polycelis
  Dendrocoelidae
    Dendrocoelopsis
    Procotyla
    Sorocelis
  Kenkiidae
    Kenkia
    Speophila
    Sphalloplana

Order Rhabdocoelida
  Catenulidae
    Catenula
    Rhynchoscolex
    Stenostomum
    Suomina
  Macrostomidae
    Macrostomum
  Microstomidae
    Microstomum
  Provorticidae
    Provortex
  Dalyelliidae
    Castrella
    Dalyellia
    Microdalyellia
  Typhloplanidae
    Amphibolella
    Bothromesostomum
    Castrada
    Krumbachia

Mesostoma
Microkalyptorhynchus
Olisthanella *
Opistomum
Phaenocora
Prorhynchella
Protoascus
Pseudophaenocora
Rhynchomesostoma
Strongylostoma
Typhloplana
  Gyratricidae
    Gyratrix
  Polycystidae
    Klattia
  Koinocystidae
    Koinocystis *

Order Alloeocoela
  Prorhynchidae
    Geocentrophora
    Prorhynchus
  Otomesostomidae
    Otomesostoma
  Bothrioplanidae
    Bothrioplana
  Plagiostomidae
    Hydrolimax

The figures associated with this key are all diagrammatic, and usually all anatomical details except significant key characters are omitted. Wherever possible, characters are used that do not require serial sections.

* These two genera are very rare in the United States. Only one poorly described species in each has been reported from Wisconsin.

# KEY TO GENERA AND SPECIES OF TURBELLARIA

1. Large species, usually longer than 5 mm.; gastrovascular cavity consisting of three main branches, one anterior and two posterior and lateral (Fig. 67).

    Order **TRICLADIDA, 2**

    Small species, rarely longer than 4 mm.; gastrovascular cavity almost invariably a single, median, longitudinal cavity (Figs. 81–85).

    Order **RHABDOCOELA** and Order **ALLOEOCOELA, 28**

2. Head long and triangular; two eyes (Figs. 68; 78A–C); up to 20 or 30 mm. long.

    PLANARIIDAE, **Dugesia, 3**

    Head truncate, low triangular, convex, or with a sucker or adhesive organ (Figs. 78D–G; 79, 80) . . . . . . . . . . . . . . . . . . . . . . . . . . . . . . . . . . . . . . . . . . . .5

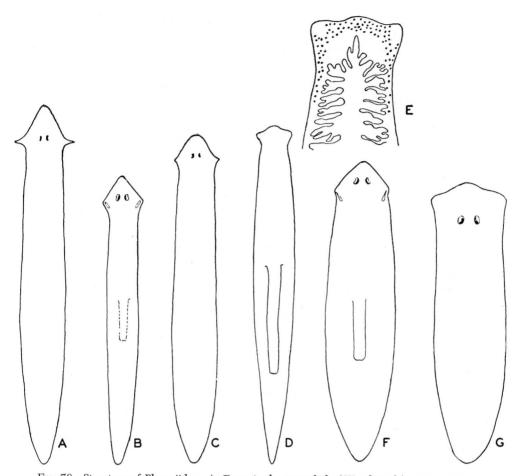

FIG. 78.—Structure of Planariidae. A, *Dugesia dorotocephala* (Woodworth), ×6; B, *Dugesia microbursalis* Hyman, ×8; C, *Dugesia tigrina* (Girard), ×6; D, *Polycelis coronata* (Girard), ×5; E, anterior end of *P. coronata*; F, *Curtisia foremani* Girard, ×6; G, *Hymanella retenuova* Castle, ×6. (B redrawn from Hyman, 1931b; D and E modified from Hyman, 1931; F modified from Kenk, 1935; G modified from Castle, 1941.)

3. Auricles elongated and pointed (Fig. 78A); coloration uniform, dark, brown to black; oviducts entering bursa stalk separately; penis bulb with paired or single large seminal vesicle; widely distributed in springs, spring brooks, and marshy springs and lakes.................**Dugesia dorotocephala** (Woodworth)
   Auricles short and blunt (Fig. 68); coloration uniform or spotty; oviducts uniting as they enter the bursa stalk; seminal vesicles small tubular enlargements of the termination of the vasa.......................................................4
4. Dorsal coloration blackish and uniform; auricle with a white dash (Fig. 78B); up to 12 mm. long; reported only from Conn. but probably common in New England ponds and streams.................**Dugesia microbursalis** Hyman
   Dorsal surface more or less brownish and with a highly variable striped or spotted pigment pattern (Figs. 68, 78C); up to 15 to 18 mm. long, often less; widely distributed in a variety of habitats but never in springs or spring brooks.
                                                                    **Dugesia tigrina** (Girard)

5. Prominent auricles present (Figs. 78D–G)..................PLANARIIDAE, **6**

   Auricles absent or small; head more or less truncate (Figs. 79, 80); coloration uniform or whitish........................................................**8**

6. With many eyes; pharynx long (Figs. 78D, E); brown to black coloration; up to 20 mm. long; reported from streams in the Black Hills, Colo., and Wyo. but probably occurs generally in the western states at suitable altitudes and temperatures............................**Polycelis coronata** (Girard)

   With two eyes; up to 15 mm. long.....................................**7**

7. Uniform gray, brown, or blackish coloration; an oblique dash on each auricle; head low triangular, with low blunt auricles (Fig. 78F); small creeks and rivers; reported from several states east of the Mississippi River.

   **Curtisia foremani** (Girard)

   Grayish coloration; without a dash on each auricle (Fig. 78G); known only from vernal ponds and swampy streams in R. I. and Mass.

   **Hymanella retenuova** Castle

8. With an adhesive organ at the anterior end (Figs. 70, 80); whitish or creamy coloration ....................................................**9**

   Without an adhesive organ; whitish or uniform coloration; two main eyes, or eyes absent......................................PLANARIIDAE, **13**

9. Eyes absent; whitish coloration.......................................**12**

   Eyes present; coloration whitish or variable..........DENDROCOELIDAE, **10**

10. With one to several eyes; up to 25 mm. long............................**11**

    With 6 to 20 eyes in an arc on each side of head (Fig. 79A); whitish coloration; less than 16 mm. long; a common Asiatic genus but only one species known from the U. S.; Ozark caves and springs........**Sorocelis americana** Hyman

11. Usually with two to seven eyes on each side (Fig. 70); coloration whitish; standing and running waters from New England to Mississippi R. and N. C.

    **Procotyla fluviatilis** Leidy

    With two eyes in the usual location; known only from shores and streams entering Flathead L., Mont.....................**Dendrocoelopsis vaginatus** Hyman

12. Reported only from Va. and Fla. ponds and springs; slender, up to 12 mm. long (Fig. 79C)..............DENDROCOELIDAE, **Procotyla typhlops** Kenk

    Restricted to caves...................................KENKIIDAE, **20**

13. Adult with numerous pharynges (Fig. 79F)....................**Phagocata, 18**

    Adult with a single pharynx; up to 17 mm. long..........................**14**

14. Two eyes situated far back (Fig. 79D) or with 10 to 60 eyes on each side......**15**

    Eyes in normal position (Fig. 79E)..........................**Phagocata, 16**

15. Whitish coloration; body elongated (Fig. 79D); rapid spring brooks in states east of Mississippi R.; usually two eyes but sometimes 10 to 60 eyes on each side.

    **Phagocata morgani** (Stevens and Boring)

    Body coloration gray to black; two eyes; reported from springs and spring-fed ponds in Va......................................**Planaria dactyligera** Kenk

16. Body elongated and tapered posteriorly; two normal eyes (Fig. 79E); dorsal coloration whitish to very dark gray; generally distributed from Atlantic Coast through Midwest.......................................................**17**

    Body stout and not tapered posteriorly; two eyes or two main eyes, one or both of which are accompanied by one or two small eyes; dorsal coloration dark gray; (a variety of a widely distributed species, reported only from Iowa).

    **Phagocata gracilis monopharyngea** Hyman

17. Testes numerous, separate, dorsal, and extending from ovaries to posterior end of body; permanent ponds, spring brooks, and spring-fed marshes; central states.

    **Phagocata velata** (Stringer)

    Testes few, prepharyngeal, and fused to form a compound testis on median side of each nerve cord; temporary ponds and ditches; active in winter and spring; central states..............................**Phagocata vernalis** Kenk

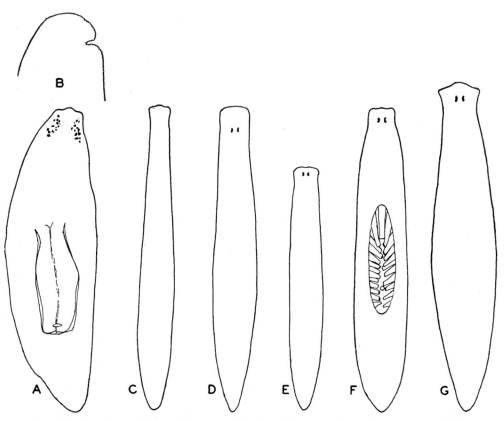

FIG. 79.—Structure of Planariidae and Dendrocoelidae. A, *Sorocelis americana* Hyman, ×18; B, longitudinal section of anterior end of *S. americana*, showing adhesive organ; C, *Procotyla typhlops* Kenk, ×7; D, *Phagocata morgani* (Stevens and Boring), ×7; E, *P. velata* (Stringer), ×5; F, *P. gracilis gracilis* (Haldeman), ×5; G, *P. gracilis woodworthi* Hyman, ×7. (A and B modified from Hyman, 1939b; G modified from Buchanan.)

18. Coloration dark gray, brown, or blackish; eyes present; margins of head expanded; up to 20 mm. long; springs and spring brooks..................**19**
    Whitish; eyes absent in adults; up to 5 mm. long; known only from several Indiana caves...........................**Phagocata subterranea** Hyman
19. Body not especially tapered posteriorly (Fig. 79F); penis elongated and pointed; occurring from Penn. and Va. westward through Ohio and Tenn. into Mo.
                                    **Phagocata gracilis gracilis** (Haldeman)
    Body tapered posteriorly (Fig. 79G); penis short and truncate; occurring in New England states....................**Phagocata gracilis woodworthi** Hyman
20. With about 50 pharynges; up to 35 mm. long; known only from Ezell's Cave, San Marcos, Texas...........................**Sphalloplana mohri** Hyman
    With a single pharynx; up to 15 mm. long................................**21**
21. Pharynx and copulatory apparatus at the posterior end of the body; adhesive organ in the form of a permanent, large, anterior snout; body concave ventrally (Fig. 80A); up to 5 mm. long; reported only from Malheur Cave, Ore.
                                    **Kenkia rhynchida** Hyman
    Pharynx and copulatory apparatus in the normal position; anterior snout present and small, or absent...............................................**22**

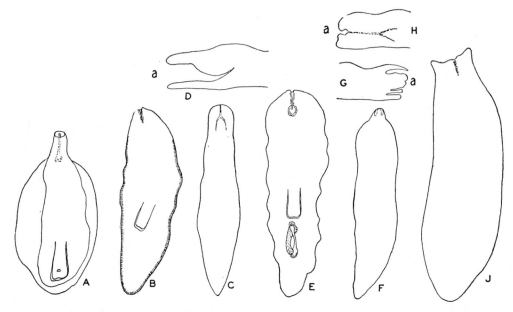

Fig. 80.—Structure of Kenkiidae. A, *Kenkia rhynchida* Hyman, ×11; B, *Sphalloplana virginiana* Hyman, ×4; C, *Speophila buchanani* Hyman, ×4; D, longitudinal section of anterior end of *S. buchanani*, showing the invaginated adhesive gland; E, *S. hubrichti* Hyman, ×3 (penis stippled); F, *S. pricei* Hyman, ×5; G, longitudinal section of anterior end of *S. pricei*, showing partly protruded adhesive gland; H, same, showing retracted adhesive gland; J, *Sphalloplana percoeca* (Packard), ×6. *a*, anterior end. (A, C, D, and F to H modified from Hyman, 1937a; B and E modified from Hyman, 1945; J modified from Buchanan.)

22. Anterior adhesive organ in the form of a pit (Figs. 80B, J); 5 to 20 mm. long.
    Sphalloplana, 23
    Anterior adhesive organ in the form of a long invaginated gland, eversible to the outside (Figs. 80C, D, G, H); up to 17 mm. or more in length.
    Speophila, 26
23. Total length about 5 to 7 mm.; known only from a cave near Limrock, Ala.
    Sphalloplana alabamensis Hyman
    Total length 8 to 20 mm..........................................24
24. Auricles present (Fig. 80J); Mammoth and adjacent caves, Ky.
    Sphalloplana percoeca (Packard)
    Auricles absent............................................25
25. Slender; margin supplied with unusually long rhabdites (Fig. 80B); reported only from Showhalter's Cave near Lexington, Va..Sphalloplana virginiana Hyman
    Broad; marginal rhabdites only a little larger than elsewhere; reported only from Purity Springs near Augusta, Kan...........Sphalloplana kansensis Hyman
26. Adhesive gland central at the anterior end (Figs. 80G, H).................27
    Adhesive gland ventral at the anterior end, and protrusible (Figs. 80C, D); Mammoth Cave, Ky.......................Speophila buchanani Hyman
27. Penis very large (Fig. 80E); Mo. and Ill. caves......Speophila hubrichti Hyman
    Penis of normal size; Penn. caves (Fig. 80F)..........Speophila pricei Hyman
28. Body usually composed of a series of two to eight zooids whose anterior and posterior extremities appear as paired lateral indentations; eyes usually absent (Figs. 73, 81C).............................................29
    Body composed of a single individual; eyes present or absent...............32

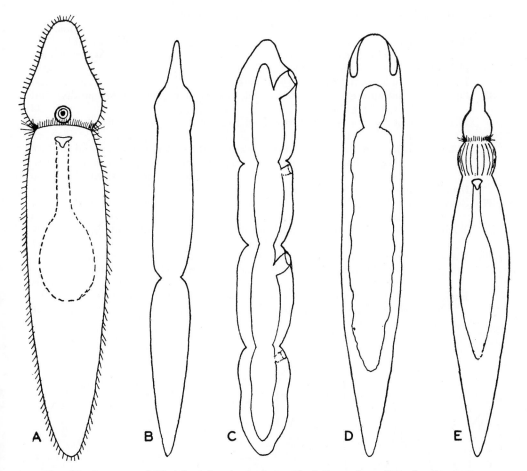

Fig. 81.—Structure of Rhabdocoela. A, single zooid of *Catenula*, ×230, showing statocyst, mouth, and gastrovascular cavity; B, two zooids of *Rhynchoscolex*, ×55; C, lateral view of four zooids of *Microstomum*, ×35; D, dorsal view of single zooid of *Stenostomum*, ×220; E, ventral view of *Suomina*, ×200, showing mouth, gastrovascular cavity, and ciliated anterior transverse groove. (A modified from Heinlein and Wachowski.)

**29.** With a statocyst at the anterior end of each zooid; each zooid composed of a
　　　cephalic lobe and body (Fig. 81A); two species . . . . . . . . . . . . . . .**Catenula**
　　Without a statocyst . . . . . . . . . . . . . . . . . . . . . . . . . . . . . . . . . . . . . . . . . . . . . . .30
**30.** With a narrow, proboscis-like structure at the anterior end (Fig. 81B).
　　　　　　　　　　　　　　　　　　　　　　　　　　　　　**Rhynchoscolex**
　　Without such a structure . . . . . . . . . . . . . . . . . . . . . . . . . . . . . . . . . . . . . . . . . .31
**31.** With a pre-oral blind pouch at the anterior end of the gastrovascular cavity (Fig.
　　　81C); common; many species . . . . . . . . . . . . . . . . . . . . . . . . . . . .**Microstomum**
　　Without such a pouch; with a ciliated pit on either side of the head (Fig. 81D);
　　　the most common of all rhabdocoels; generally distributed in a wide variety
　　　of habitats; many species . . . . . . . . . . . . . . . . . . . . . . . . . . . . . . . .**Stenostomum**
**32.** With a simple pharynx (Figs. 74, 81E) . . . . . . . . . . . . . . . . . . . . . . . . . . . . . . . .33
　　With a complex pharynx (Figs. 82–85) . . . . . . . . . . . . . . . . . . . . . . . . . . . . . . . .34

33. With a ciliated groove encircling the anterior region of the body (Fig. 81E).
............................................................................**Suomina**

Without such a groove; dorsoventrally flattened and somewhat spatulate (Fig. 74);
0.8 to 2.5 mm. long; many common species...............**Macrostomum**

34. Pharynx more or less bulbous (Figs. 82–84)...........................**35**
Pharynx not bulbous in shape (Figs. 85B–F).........................**55**

35. Pharynx at anterior end of gastrovascular cavity, directed anteroventrally, and
cask-shaped (Figs. 82B–E)......................................**36**
Pharynx not at anterior end of gastrovascular cavity, directed ventrally, and rosulate
in shape (Fig. 83).............................................**42**

36. A large species, up to 15 mm. long; dorsal surface dark gray, ventral surface
whitish; body plump and cylindroid; reported from N. J. and eastern Penn.
(Fig. 82A)............................**Hydrolimax grisea** Haldeman
Usually no more than 5 mm. long.......................................**37**

37. Body nearly cylindrical and more or less tapering to a pointed tail (Figs. 82B–D);
usually free swimming..........................................**38**
Triangular in section; posterior end truncate, with a small tail (Fig. 82E); usually
creeping ......................................................**41**

38. Each eye consisting of two pigmented spots connected by a pigmented band;
anterior end truncate (Fig. 82B); body usually darkly pigmented with blue
or black .............................................**Castrella**
Each eye a single concave mass; anterior end more rounded (Figs. 75, 82C, D);
brownish or green pigmentation...................................**39**

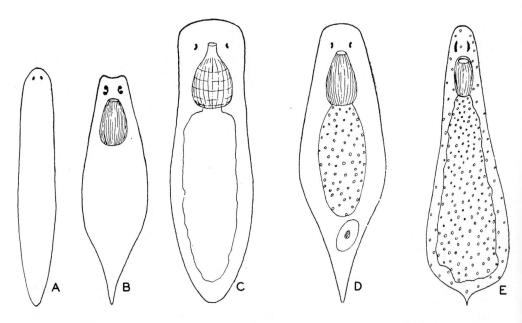

FIG. 82.—Structure of Rhabdocoela. A, *Hydrolimax grisea* Haldeman, ×4.5; B, *Castrella*, ×60, showing pharynx and eyespots; C, *Provortex*, ×125, showing eyespots, pharynx, and gastrovascular cavity; D, *Microdalyellia*, ×50, showing eyespots, pharynx, gastrovascular cavity, zoochlorellae, and single egg; E, *Phaenocora*, ×37, showing eyespots, pharynx, gastrovascular cavity, and zoochlorellae. (A modified from Hyman, 1938; B, D, and E modified from Ruebush, 1941; C modified from Ruebush, 1935a.)

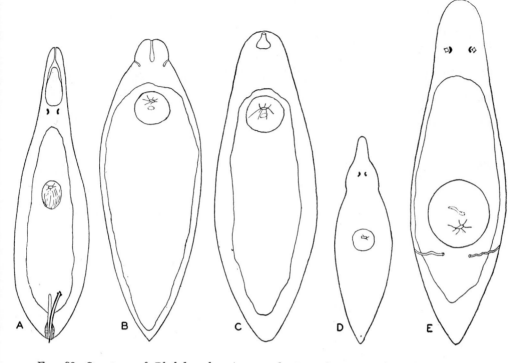

FIG. 83.—Structure of Rhabdocoela. A, ventral view of *Gyratrix hermaphroditus* Ehr., ×40, showing proboscis, eyespots, mouth, pharynx, gastrovascular cavity, and penis stylet; B, ventral view of *Prorhynchella*, ×100, showing anterior sensory pit, anterolateral ciliated pits, mouth, pharynx, and gastrovascular cavity; C, ventral view of *Microkalyptorhynchus*, ×80, showing anterior sensory pit, mouth, pharynx, and gastrovascular cavity; D, ventral view of *Rhynchomesostoma*, ×70, showing eyespots, mouth, and pharynx; E, ventral view of *Krumbachia minuta* Ruebush, ×180, showing eyespots, mouth, pharynx, gastrovascular cavity, protonephridial tubules, and protonephridial pores. (B modied from Ruebush, 1939; C modified from Ruebush, 1935; D modified from Ruebush, 1941; E modified from Ruebush, 1938.)

39. Mature animals about 0.5 mm. long; not pigmented; posterior end slightly rounded
    (Fig. 82C); each egg containing two embryos; only one or two species re-
    ported from the U. S...........................................**Provortex**
    Mature animals 1 to 3 mm. long; usually brown or green coloration; posterior end
    more or less pointed; each egg with a single embryo...................**40**
40. Mature animals 2 to 3 mm. long (Fig. 75); one to many eggs present and scattered
    throughout the body; with zoochlorellae and brownish pigment in parenchyma;
    several species in the U. S..................................**Dalyellia**
    Mature animals only 1 to 2 mm. long; only one egg carried at a time (Fig. 82D),
    rarely two to four; zoochlorellae, if present, restricted to the gastrovascular
    cavity; about 30 species..............................**Microdalyellia**
41. Mature animals up to 4.8 mm. long; without zoochlorellae; in sulphur springs.
    **Pseudophaenocora sulfophila** Gilbert
    Mature animals 1 to 3 mm. long; often with zoochlorellae in gastrovascular cavity
    and parenchyma (Fig. 82E); about five species.............**Phaenocora**
42. Anterior end with a heavy, muscular proboscis contained in a sheath; body usually
    cylindrical (Fig. 83A); free swimming..............................**43**
    Without such a proboscis; body usually flattened; usually creeping.........**44**

43. With a posterior penis stylet; eyes black (Fig. 83A); body coloration whitish; 2 mm. long; common..............................**Gyratrix hermaphroditus** Ehr.

     Without a posterior penis stylet.....................................**Klattia**

44. With a median anterior sensory pit (Figs. 83B, C) ........................**45**

     Without a sensory pit.............................................**46**

45. With a pair of anterolateral ciliated pits (Fig. 83B)...............**Prorhynchella**

     Without a pair of anterolateral ciliated pits (Fig. 83C)....**Microkalyptorhynchus**

46. With a retractile and sensory anterior end (Fig. 83D)......**Rhynchomesostoma**

     Without such a structure at the anterior end..........................**47**

47. Protonephridial tubules opening separately on the ventral surface of the body (Fig. 84A).............................................**48**

     Protonephridial tubules opening into the mouth cavity (Figs. 84D–F).......**51**

48. With a large refractive rectangle in each eye (Fig. 83E); with a bursa copulatrix; 0.5 mm. long...............................**Krumbachia minuta** Ruebush

     Eyes absent; with or without a bursa copulatrix...........................**49**

49. Body 2 to 3 mm. long, very opaque (Fig. 84A).

     **Krumbachia virginiana** (Kepner and Carter)

     Body up to 1.5 mm. long, more or less translucent; rare....................**50**

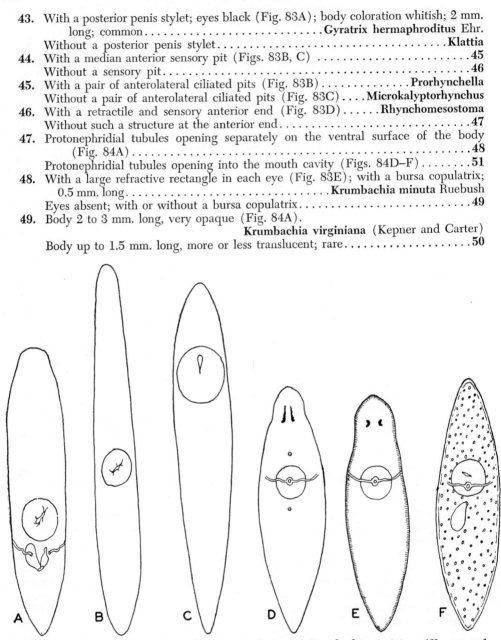

Fig. 84.—Structure of Rhabdocoela. A, ventral view of *Krumbachia virginiana* (Kepner and Carter), ×30, showing mouth, pharynx, penis, bursa copulatrix, protonephridial tubules, and protonephridial pores; B, ventral view of *Amphibolella*, ×125; C, *Protoascus wisconsinensis* Hayes, ×95; D, ventral view of *Bothromesostomum*, ×11, showing eyespots, pore of sensory pouch, protonephridial tubules, mouth, pharynx, and common genital pore; E, ventral view of *Strongylostoma*, ×50, showing eyespots, protonephridial tubules, mouth, pharynx, and epidermal rhabdites; F, ventral view of *Typhloplana*, ×65, showing zoochlorellae in parenchyma, mouth, pharynx, protonephridial tubules, protonephridial pore, and penis. (A, D, E, and F modified from Ruebush, 1941; B modified from Kepner and Ruebush, 1937.)

**50.** Pharynx near middle of body (Fig. 84B).......................**Amphibolella**
    Pharynx near anterior end (Fig. 84C); reported only from Wis.

**Protoascus wisconsinensis** Hayes

**51.** With a ventral pore leading into the sensory pouch anterior to mouth; common
    genital pore present (Fig. 84D); 5 to 7 mm. long.......**Bothromesostomum**
    Without a ventral sensory pouch; common genital pore present or combined with
    the mouth (Fig. 84E, F)........................................**52**

**52.** With rhabdites in the epidermis (Fig. 72)..............................**53**
    Without rhabdites in the epidermis.....................................**54**

**53.** Large species, usually 2 to 4 mm. long, but a few species as long as 10 mm.; with
    long parenchymal rhabdites; eyes, when present, black (Fig. 72); coloration
    brown, gray, or gold; very common; about ten species.........**Mesostoma**
    Small species, only 1 to 1.5 mm. long; without parenchymal rhabdites; eyes red
    (Fig. 84E); several species.............................**Strongylostoma**

**54.** About 1 mm. long; without bursa copulatrix; with abundant zoochlorellae in
    parenchyma (Fig. 84F).................................**Typhloplana**
    About 1 to 2 mm. long; with bursa copulatrix (Fig. 85A); with or without
    zoochlorellae; several species................................**Castrada**

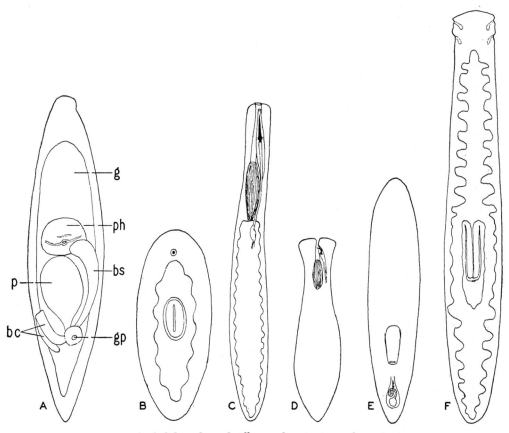

Fig. 85.—Structure of Rhabdocoela and Alloeocoela. A, *Castrada*, ×48; B, *Otomesostoma*,
×35; C, *Prorhynchus*, ×17; D, *Geocentrophora*, ×25; E, *Opistomum*, ×16; F, *Bothrioplana*,
×16. *bc*, bursa copulatrix; *bs*, blind sac of penis; *g*, gastrovascular cavity; *gp*, genital pore;
*p*, penis; *ph*, pharynx. (A modified from Kepner, Ruebush, and Ferguson; D modified from
Ruebush. 1941.)

## TURBELLARIA REFERENCES

BEAUCHAMP, R. S. A. 1932. Some ecological factors and their influence on competition between stream and lake-loving triclads. *Jour. Animal Ecol.* **1**:175–190.

BEAUCHAMP, R. S. A., and P. ULLYOT. 1932. Competitive relationships between certain species of freshwater triclads. *Jour. Ecol.* **20**:200–208.

BUCHANAN, J. W. 1936. Notes on an American cave flatworm, Sphalloplana percoeca (Packard). *Ecology* **17**:194–211.

CARTER, J. S. 1929. Observations on rhabdocoeles of Albemarle County, Virginia. *Trans. Amer. Micros. Soc.* **48**:431–437.

CASTLE, W. A. 1928. An experimental and histological study of the life-cycle of Planaria velata. *Jour. Exp. Zool.* **51**:417–483.

———. 1941. The morphology and life history of Hymanella retenuova, a new species of triclad from New England. *Amer. Midl. Nat.* **26**:85–97.

CASTLE, W. A., and L. H. HYMAN. 1934. Observations on Fonticola velata (Stringer), including a description of the anatomy of the reproductive system. *Jour. Amer. Micros. Soc.* **53**:154–171.

CURTIS, W. C. 1902. The life history, the normal fission, and the reproductive organs of Planaria maculata. *Proc. Boston Soc. Nat. Hist.* **31**:515–559.

FERGUSON, F. F. 1939–1940. A monograph of the genus Macrostomum O. Schmidt 1848. Parts I to VIII. *Zool. Anz.* **126**:7–20; **127**:131–144; **128**:49–68, 188–205, 274–291; **129**:21–48, 120–146, 244–266.

FERGUSON, F. F., and W. J. HAYES, JR. 1941. A synopsis of the genus Mesostoma Ehrenberg 1835. *Jour. Elisha Mitchell Sci. Soc.* **57**:1–52.

GILBERT, C. M. 1938. A new North American rhabdocoele—Pseudophaenocora sulfophila nov. genus, nov. spec. *Zool. Anz.* **124**:193–216.

GRAFF, L. VON. 1911. Acoela, Rhabdocoela, und Alloeocoela des Ostens der Vereinigten Staaten von Amerika. *Zeitschr. wiss. Zool.* **99**:1–108.

———. 1913. Turbellaria. II. Rhabdocoelida. *Das Tierreich* **35**:1–484.

HAYES, W. J., JR. 1941. Rhabdocoela of Wisconsin. I. Morphology and taxonomy of Protoascus wisconsinensis n. g., n. sp. *Amer. Midl. Nat.* **25**:388–401.

HEINLEIN, E., and H. E. WACHOWSKI. 1944. Studies on the flatworm Catenula virginiana. *Ibid.* **31**:150–158.

HYMAN, L. H. 1925. The reproductive system and other characters of Planaria dorotocephala. *Trans. Amer. Micros. Soc.* **44**:51–89.

———. 1928. Studies on the morphology, taxonomy, and distribution of North American triclad Turbellaria, I. Procotyla fluviatilis, commonly but erroneously known as Dendrocoelum lacteum. *Ibid.* **47**:222–255.

———. 1931. Studies on triclad Turbellaria, III. On Polycelis coronata (Girard). *Ibid.* **50**:124–135.

———. 1931a. Studies on triclad Turbellaria, IV. Recent European revisions of the triclads, and their application to the American forms, with a key to the latter and new notes on distribution. *Ibid.* **50**:316–335.

———. 1931b. Studies on triclad Turbellaria, V. Descriptions of two new species. *Ibid.* 336–343.

———. 1935. Studies on the morphology, taxonomy, and distribution of North American triclad Turbellaria. VI. A new dendrocoelid from Montana, Dendrocoelopsis vaginatus n. sp. *Ibid.* **54**:338–344.

———. 1937. Studies on the morphology, taxonomy, and distribution of North American triclad Turbellaria. VII. The two species confused under the name Phagocata gracilis, the validity of the generic name Phagocata Leidy 1847, and its priority over Fonticola Komarek 1926. *Ibid.* **56**:298–310.

———. 1937a. Studies on triclad Turbellaria, VIII. Some cave planarians of the United States. *Ibid.* 457–477.

————. 1938. North American Rhabdocoela and Alloeocoela. II. Rediscovery of Hydrolimax grisea Haldeman. *Amer. Mus. Novit.* **1004**:1–19.

————. 1939. North American triclad Turbellaria. IX. The priority of Dugesia Girard 1850 over Euplanaria Hesse 1897 with notes on American species of Dugesia. *Trans. Amer. Micros. Soc.* **58**:264–275.

————. 1939a. North American triclad Turbellaria. X. Additional species of cave planarians. *Ibid.* 276–284.

————. 1939b. New species of flatworms from North, Central, and South America. *Proc. U. S. Nat. Mus.* **86**:419–439.

————. 1945. North American triclad Turbellaria. XI. New, chiefly cavernicolous, planarians. *Amer. Midl. Nat.* **34**:475–484.

————. 1951. North American triclad Turbellaria. XII. Synopsis of the known species of fresh-water planarians of North America. *Trans. Amer. Micros. Soc.* **70**:154–167.

KENK, R. 1935. Studies on Virginian triclads. *Jour. Elisha Mitchell Sci. Soc.* **51**:79–126.

————. 1937. Sexual and asexual reproduction in Euplanaria tigrina (Girard). *Biol. Bull.* **73**:280–294.

————. 1941. Induction of sexuality in the asexual form of Dugesia tigrina (Girard). *Jour. Exp. Zool.* **87**:55–70.

————. 1944. The fresh-water triclads of Michigan. *Misc. Publ. Mus. Zool. Univ. Mich.* **60**:1–44

KEPNER, W. A., and J. L. BARKER. 1924. Nematocysts of Microstoma. *Biol. Bull.* **47**:239–251.

KEPNER, W. A., E. D. MILLER, and A. W. JONES. 1934. Observations upon Rhynchomesostomum rostratum. *Zool. Anz.* **107**:188–192.

KEPNER, W. A., and T. K. RUEBUSH. 1935. Microrhynchus virginianus n. gen. n. sp. *Ibid.* **111**:257–261.

KEPNER, W. A., T. K. RUEBUSH, and F. F. FERGUSON. 1937. Castrada virginiana n. sp. *Ibid.* **119**:307–314.

KROMHOUT, G. A. 1943. A comparison of the protonephridia of fresh-water, brackish-water, and marine specimens of Gyratrix hermaphroditus. *Jour. Morph.* **72**:167–169.

MARCUS, E. 1945. Sôbre Catenulida brasileiros. *Univ. S. Paulo, Bol. Fac. Filos. Cien. e Let., Zool.* No. **10**:3–100.

————. 1946. Sôbre Turbellaria limnicos brasileiros. *Ibid.* **11**:5–253.

NUTTYCOMBE, J. W., and A. J. WATERS. 1938. The American species of the genus Stenostomum. *Proc. Amer. Philos. Soc.* **79**:213–284.

PEARL, R. 1903. The movements and reactions of fresh-water planarians: a study in animal behaviour. *Quart. Jour. Micros. Sci.* **46**:509–714.

REDFIELD, E. S. P. 1915. The grasping organ of Dendrocoelum lacteum. *Jour. Animal Behavior* **5**:375–380.

REISINGER, E. 1923. Turbellaria. *Biol. Tiere Deutschlands* **4**:1–64.

RUEBUSH, T. K. 1935. The genus Olisthanella in the United States. *Zool. Anz.* **112**:129–136.

————. 1935a. The occurrence of Provortex affinis Jensen in the United States. *Ibid.* **111**:305–308.

————. 1937. The genus Dalyellia in America. *Ibid.* **119**:237–256.

————. 1938. Krumbachia minuta n. sp. (Turbellaria Rhabdocoela). *Ibid.* **122**:260–265.

————. 1939. A new North American rhabdocoel turbellarian, Prorhynchella minuta n. gen., n. sp. *Ibid.* **127**:204–209.

————. 1940. Mesostoma ehrenbergii wardii for the study of the turbellarian type. *Science* **91**:531–532.

————. 1941. A key to the American freshwater turbellarian genera, exclusive of the Tricladida. *Trans. Amer. Micros. Soc.* **60**:29–40.

RUEBUSH, T. K., and W. J. HAYES, JR. 1939. The genus Dalyellia in America. II. A new form from Tennessee and a discussion of the relationships within the genus. *Zool. Anz.* **128**:136–152.

STEINBÖCK, O. 1926. Zur Ökologie der alpinen Turbellarien. *Zeitschr. Morph. Ökol. Tiere* **5**:424–446.

# Chapter 6

## NEMERTEA (PROBOSCIS WORMS)

THE MAJORITY of fresh-water biologists never have the experience of observing living fresh-water nemerteans. One reason is the fact that they are seldom sought intentionally and are usually overlooked or disregarded in collections made with other taxonomic categories uppermost in mind. Another reason is their extremely "spotty" and local abundance. Weedy ponds, masses of filamentous algae, the undersides of lily pads, and the general substrate of littoral areas are preferred habitats, but often nemerteans may be taken from only one restricted area in a pond and are apparently absent elsewhere.

Presumably there is only one well-known American fresh-water species in the Phylum Nemertea. It is *Prostoma rubrum* (Leidy) which is widely distributed in the United States. This situation is in striking contrast to that prevailing in the marine littoral where many species are found.

**General characteristics.** *Prostoma rubrum* is translucent, elliptical in cross section, somewhat flattened ventrally, up to 20 mm. long, and 0.6 to 2.0 mm. in diameter. Coloration is highly variable. Young specimens are whitish or pale yellow, but mature specimens are yellowish-red, orange, or deep red. There is also a rare green variety. The anterior end is rounded and without a definite head; the posterior end is tapered to a point. Three pairs of ocelli are usually present, but occasionally there are two or four pairs. They are arranged in two longitudinal rows on the dorsal surface of the anterior end and are sometimes placed asymmetrically. The body is smooth, unsegmented, and covered with a columnar ciliated epithelium.

Owing to well-developed longitudinal and circular muscle tissues, these worms are highly contractile. A smooth, gliding type of locomotion is produced by cilia acting on a slime track secreted by the epidermis.

**Digestive system, feeding.** The subterminal mouth opens into a buccal cavity which is followed by an esophagus, stomach, intestine, and terminal anus. The entire length of the long intestine has pairs of small lateral diverticula, and from the anterior end of the intestine a pair of pyloric caeca extend forward. The digestive tract has no musculature of its own.

The proboscis apparatus is a unique feature of nemerteans. A fluid-filled longitudinal cavity, the rhynchocoel, runs throughout most of the body length dorsal to the digestive tract. The muscular wall of the rhynchocoel is called the proboscis sheath. Lying within the rhynchocoel is a tubular muscular proboscis which can be protruded anteriorly and withdrawn back into the rhynchocoel by a long retractor muscle. The proboscis is very long, sometimes two or three times the body length, and when not in use it is strongly contracted and coiled within the rhynchocoel. The rhynchodaeum is the cavity of the proboscis and it has an opening to the outside in common with the mouth. There are actually three parts to the proboscis. Anteriorly it is a thick-walled tube. Far-

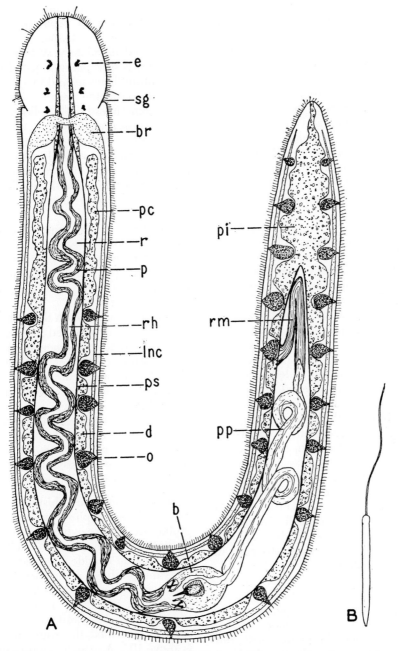

FIG. 86.—Structure of *Prostoma rubrum* (Leidy), semidiagrammatic. A, general anatomy, dorsal view, ×16; B, with protruded proboscis, ×1.5. *b*, bulbous portion of proboscis; *br*, brain; *d*, diverticulum of intestine; *e*, ocellus; *lnc*, lateral nerve cord; *o*, ovotestis; *p*, anterior portion of proboscis; *pc*, pyloric caecum; *pi*, posterior portion of intestine; *pp*, posterior portion of proboscis; *ps*, proboscis sheath; *r*, rhynchocoel; *rh*, rhynchodaeum; *rm*, retractor muscle of proboscis; *sg*, sensory groove.

ther back is a middle bulbous portion bearing a functional sclerotized stylet set in a heavy base along with two lateral pockets containing accessory stylets in various stages of development (Figs. 86, 88). The functional stylet is frequently lost and is then replaced by one from the lateral pockets. Posterior to the bulb is a blind tube. When the proboscis is protruded the bulb and posterior blind tube are everted through the anterior thick-walled tube and out of the mouth in such a fashion that the stylet is at the tip of the extended proboscis. Proboscis eversion is effected by muscle contraction exerting pressure on the fluid in the rhynchocoel.

The proboscis functions in both defense and food getting. While *Prostoma* creeps about on the substrate its extended proboscis probes and darts about constantly. If the proboscis comes in contact with a small metazoan, the stylet may be used to stab the animal repeatedly. A toxic material is thought to be secreted from the posterior chamber of the proboscis and discharged through the stylet apparatus. The proboscis is also coiled around the prey and quantities of sticky mucus are secreted, thus further immobilizing the prey. The mouth and buccal cavity are capable of great distension, and most food organisms are ingested intact. If the prey is too large, however, only the body juices are sucked out. *Prostoma* is chiefly carnivorous and feeds on all kinds of small metazoans, and especially on small oligochaetes. It may also feed on recently dead animals, and a few times it has been observed ingesting organic detritus.

Preliminary digestion occurs in the stomach and further digestion in the intestine and its diverticula. Specimens may be kept for six months or more without food, but the metabolic requirements during this period may produce a shrinkage to one-tenth or less of normal size.

**General anatomy, physiology.** Below the epidermis *Prostoma* has a thick connective tissue dermis and well-defined layers of longitudinal and circular muscle. Visceral organs are separated by mesenchymal connective tissue.

A closed circulatory system is present, the main vessels being a dorsal longitudinal contractile vessel and two lateral longitudinal contractile vessels. The blood is clear, sometimes faintly yellowish-reddish.

Excretion is effected by a protonephridial system which consists of many branched tubules with clusters of terminal flame bulbs and several nephridiopores along each side of the body. Presumably this apparatus also functions in osmoregulation.

The brain is dark-colored, four-lobed, and surrounds the esophagus. Two prominent lateroventral nerve cords pass from it and extend to the posterior end. Smaller paired nerves supply the head, proboscis, and proboscis sheath.

The ocelli lie beneath the epidermis and are irregular cup-shaped masses of black, brown, or reddish pigment granules. Anterior sensory grooves are presumably chemotactile, and sensory cells with long cilia are especially abundant at the extremities.

There are no special respiratory structures or adaptations. It is possible that some respiratory exchange occurs through the wall of the digestive tract in addition to the general body surface.

**Reproduction, life history.** *Prostoma rubrum* is hermaphroditic and generally protandric; saclike ovotestes alternate with the intestinal diverticula. Each ovotestis opens to the outside by a lateral genital pore and produces many sperm but only a single ripe egg. The additional oocytes degenerate. Breeding may occur at any time between May and November or December, provided the water temperature is above 10°. A sexually mature individual secretes a mucous sheath around itself, releases sperm and a double row of eggs into the sheath, and then crawls out of the sheath. Not infrequently two individuals,

one of which is at the time functionally
male and the other female occupy the
same mucous sheath and cross-fertilization
occurs. Contact with water causes dissolu-
tion of the germinal vesicles around the
eggs and they become fertilized. Development is direct and there is no special larval
stage. Young worms leave the mucous
mass and become independent.

*Prostoma* has considerable powers of
regeneration. The whole posterior portion
of the body may be regenerated provided
the remaining anterior portion contains at

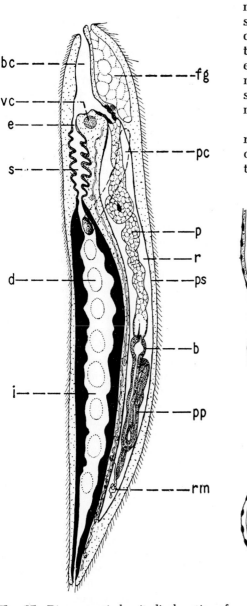

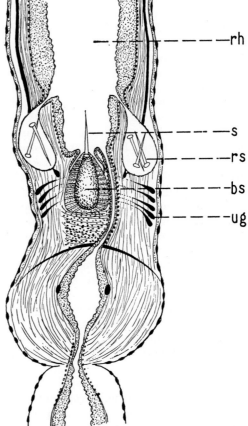

Fig. 87.—Diagrammatic longitudinal section of
*Prostoma*, ×7.5. *b*, bulbous portion of proboscis;
*bc*, buccal cavity; *d*, diverticulum of intestine; *e*,
esophagus; *fg*, frontal gland; *i*, intestine; *p*,
anterior portion of proboscis; *pc*, pyloric caecum;
*pp*, posterior portion of proboscis; *ps*, proboscis
sheath; *r*, rhynchocoel; *rm*, retractor muscle of
proboscis; *s*, stomach; *vc*, ventral commissure of
brain. (Modified from Reisinger.)

Fig. 88.—Bulbous portion of proboscis and
adjacent structures of *Prostoma*. *bs*, base of
stylet; *rh*, rhynchodaeum; *rs*, accessory stylet; *s*,
functional stylet; *ug*, unicellular glands. (Greatly
modified from Reisinger.)

least half of the esophageal region. A new proboscis may be regenerated if the old one is lost.

**Ecology.** *Prostoma rubrum* can be most easily found in the autumn when it is relatively abundant. It occurs only in well-oxygenated shallow and littoral standing waters and sluggish streams, especially in masses of filamentous algae, on rooted aquatics, or in the debris of the general substrate. No explanation is known for its localized distribution in such places. It is especially active at night when it does most of its feeding and egg deposition. It is highly thigmotactic and reacts positively to water currents. With the approach of autumn and freezing temperatures *Prostoma* migrates to deeper waters and returns to the shallows in spring.

Under adverse environmental conditions, such as insufficient oxygen, high temperature, abnormal substrate, and lack of food, *Prostoma* forms resting cysts by rounding up within a secreted outer layer of mucus which soon hardens and becomes covered with detritus. The worm may remain alive within such a cyst for a few days to a few weeks and emerges when ecological conditions are again appropriate. Cysts cannot withstand complete drying and are of limited value in dissemination.

Enemies of *Prostoma* include larger worms and carnivorous insects and crustaceans.

*Prostoma rubrum* is widely distributed throughout the United States, though usually in small numbers. Closely similar species are found in Central and South America.

**Culturing, preserving.** *Prostoma* may be successfully cultured in an aquarium which has a thin layer of soil on the bottom and plenty of rooted aquatics. Excessive bacterial decomposition will inhibit nemerteans and should be avoided. Feed the worms bits of liver, earthworms, or small metazoans.

Because it is so highly contractile, *Prostoma* should always be anesthetized before killing. Chloretone and other solutions may be used with varying success. Kill and preserve in 80 per cent alcohol.

**Taxonomy.** About 600 valid species of nemerteans are known. The great majority are marine, but a few occur on land and in fresh waters. About ten poorly known fresh-water species, representing five supposed genera, have been reported from such scattered places as Chile, Lake Nicaragua, Java, French Indochina, Brazil, and Asiatic Russia. The genus *Prostoma*, however, is essentially cosmopolitan, especially in the Northern Hemisphere, and about seven European and Asiatic species and our single American species are included in it.

Because most species have wide variations in color, number of reserve stylets, length of rhynchocoel, number of ocelli, and size, the taxonomy of *Prostoma* is confused and difficult. The situation has become especially involved because some of the descriptions and identifications have been based on contracted and faded alcoholic specimens. *Prostoma rubrum* has also gone under the generic designations of *Emea*, *Tetrastemma*, and *Stichostemma*, and under the species designations of *asensoriatum* and *aquarium*.

Stiasny-Wijnhoff takes another viewpoint of our American species and believes that *Prostoma rubrum* is of doubtful validity. This investigator further maintains that there are two species known thus far in North America, both of which also occur in Europe. These are *P. lumbricoideum* Dugès and *P. graecense* (Böhmig). Other workers have not generally followed these suggestions.

While it is probably true that European species have been introduced into this country on imported aquatic plants, it is not known how widespread they have become. Furthermore, it is quite possible that additional native species await discovery.

# NEMERTEA REFERENCES

Böhmig, L. 1898. Beiträge zur Anatomie und Histologie der Nemertinen. *Zeitschr. wiss. Zool.* **64**:479–564.

Child, C. M. 1901. The habits and natural history of Stichostemma. *Amer. Nat.* **35**:975–1006.

Coe, W. R. 1943. Biology of the nemerteans of the Atlantic coast of North America. *Trans. Conn. Acad. Arts and Sci.* **35**:129–328.

Cordero, E. H. 1943. Hallazgos en diversos paises de Sud América de nemertinos de agua dulce del género "Prostoma." *An. Acad. Brasil Cien.* **15**:125–134.

Montgomery, T. 1896. Stichostemma asensoriatum n. sp., a fresh-water nemertean from Pennsylvania. *Zool. Anz.* **19**:436–438.

Reisinger, E. 1926. Nemertini. *Biol. Tiere Deutschlands* **7**:1–24.

Rioja, E. 1941. Estudios hidrobiologicos. V. Hallazgo en Xochimilco de Stichostemma rubrum (Leidy), nemerte de agua dulce. *Mexico An. Inst. Biol.* **12**:663–668.

Stiasny-Wijnhoff, G. 1938. Das Genus Prostoma Dugès, eine Gattung von Süsswasser-Nemertinen. *Arch. Neérland. Zool., Suppl.* **3**:219–230.

# Chapter 7

# GASTROTRICHA

---

IN COMPANY with protozoans, rotifers, nematodes, and small oligochaetes, the Gastrotricha are a part of the characteristic assemblage of microorganisms on aquatic vegetation and on the debris commonly forming the substrates of standing waters.

Formerly it was thought that gastrotrichs were almost restricted to fresh waters, but they are now known to be abundant in marine habitats, and although the majority of described species in this phylum are fresh-water forms, the numerical preponderance of fresh-water over marine species is rapidly dwindling. The phylum consists of only two orders; the Order Macrodasyoidea is strictly marine, and the Order Chaetonotoidea is predominantly fresh-water.

**General characteristics.** Most fresh-water gastrotrichs range from 100 microns to 300 microns in length, although a few are as small as 70 microns or as large as 600 microns. The body is short to long and wormlike, with a flat ventral surface. Head and arched trunk regions are obvious, and often there is a more or less distinct neck. Two toelike projections, forming the furca, are commonly present at the posterior end.

The margin of the head is variable, even within the same genus. Sometimes the entire margin is smooth, sometimes it has a median anterior lobe and one or two pairs of variously developed lateral lobes. Tufts of sensory cilia are customarily situated in the depressions between lobes. The mouth is terminal, subterminal, or ventral, and is often surrounded by short delicate bristles. In fresh-water species the anus lies in a dorsal position at the base of the furca; rarely is it terminal or subterminal.

Locomotor cilia occur chiefly on the ventral surface of the head and trunk. Most commonly there are several patches on the head and two longitudinal bands running throughout most of the body length (Figs. 91H, J).

Coloration is variable, usually light gray to reddish-brown, and mostly determined by the contents of the digestive tract. A starved gastrotrich is grayish and completely translucent.

Internal organization is relatively uncomplicated. The digestive tract is tubular and without diverticula. The space between the digestive tract and thin body wall is a pseudocoel and it contains the simple muscle, protonephridial, nervous, and reproductive systems (Fig. 89). There are no special circulatory or respiratory structures.

Many workers have discussed the phylogenetic relationships with the Nematoda, Rotatoria, Kinorhyncha, Turbellaria, and other groups, but the Gastrotricha are here considered sufficiently distinctive to constitute a separate phylum.

**Cuticular structures.** The general body surface of gastrotrichs is covered with a cuticle secreted by the underlying syncytial hypodermis. In the great majority of species, however, the cuticle is not simple and thin but patterned and with a variety

148

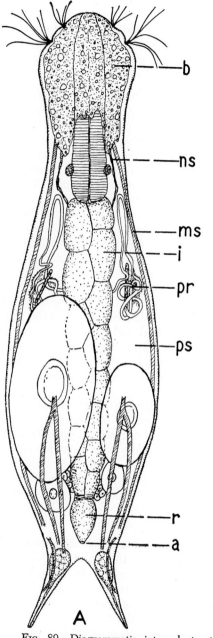
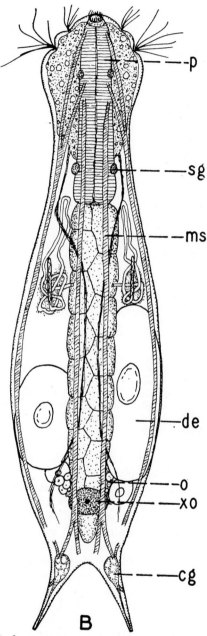

FIG. 89.—Diagrammatic internal structure of a typical gastrotrich. A, dorsal; B, ventral. *a*, anus; *b*, brain; *cg*, cement gland; *de*, developing egg; *i*, intestine; *ms*, muscle strand; *ns*, longitudinal nerve strand; *o*, ovary; *p*, pharynx; *pr*, protonephridium; *ps*, pseudocoel; *r*, rectum; *sg*, salivary gland; *xo*, "X organ." (Greatly modified from Zelinka.)

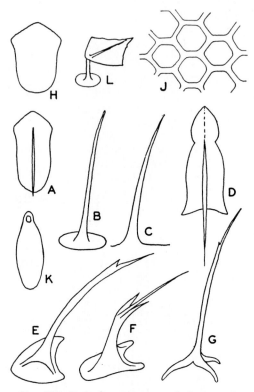

Fig. 90.—Cuticular structures of Gastrotricha. A to G, *Chaetonotus*; H and J, *Lepidodermella*; K, *Polymerurus*; L, *Aspidiophorus*. H, J, and K, simple cuticular plates; A, keeled plate; B, D, E, and F, spined plates; C and G, cuticular spines. (J from Brunson, 1950.)

of outgrowths, especially dorsally and laterally (Figs. 90, 94, 95).

In a few species the cuticle is locally thickened to form variously arranged plates, but more commonly there are series of cuticular scales which usually overlap more or less. Both plates and scales may have small keels or spines; the latter range from very short to exceedingly long and robust. In the absence of plates and scales, spines are often attached directly to the thin cuticle. Sometimes spines are barbed and have a triradiate or platelike base. A few species have midventral scales or plates. Size and shape of plates, scales, and spines commonly vary within the same individual, depending on the location on the body. A few simple setae are often

present, especially near the anterior and posterior ends of the body. The cephalic shield is a thickened cuticular plate covering the anterior end of the head above the mouth (Fig. 91G). Sometimes there are less distinct special plates posterior to the mouth and laterally on the head.

**Locomotion.** Beating movements of the ventral cilia against the substrate produce a characteristic smooth, graceful, gliding type of locomotion which is sometimes quite rapid; presumably the lateral tufts of head cilia are also of some importance. Such gliding locomotion is especially notable in the Chaetonotidae.

The long spines of the Dasydytidae are used in springing and leaping. Although the spines are not supplied with special muscles, they are moved vigorously toward the plane of the body when the arched body is straightened.

Most gastrotrichs may temporarily leave the substrate and swim about in the water with the ventral and head cilia, but they seldom go far above the substrate.

*Polymerurus* is said to have a sinuous type of locomotion characteristic of nematodes.

A cement gland is usually found in the base of each process of the furca, with its duct opening at or near the tip. The adhesive secreted material is used for temporary attachment to objects. A similar arrangement is found in rotifers. In the marine order Macrodasyoidea there is often an abundance of small lateral and posterior adhesive tubules.

**Feeding, digestive system.** Gastrotrichs browse about on the substrate, ingesting bacteria, algae, small protozoans, and organic detritus. Currents induced by head cilia aid in concentrating and bringing food particles to the mouth.

Often the mouth opening is surrounded by a projecting cuticular collar-like lip bearing the oral bristles. The mouth cavity opens directly into the pharynx, which is remarkably similar to the nematode pharynx. It is a long, cylindrical, muscu-

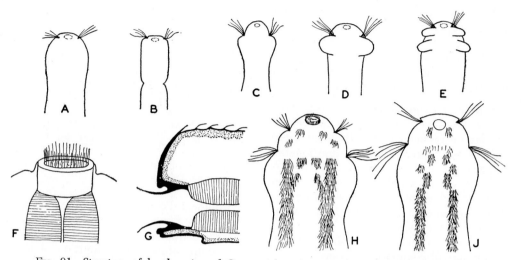

Fig. 91.—Structure of head region of Gastrotricha. A to E, dorsal view of typical heads, showing general shape and head lobes; F, semidiagrammatic ventral view of mouth region, showing circular collar, oral bristles, and anterior portion of pharynx; G, diagrammatic longitudinal section of anterior end, showing oral bristles, oral cavity, anterior portion of pharynx, and the cephalic shield; H, ventral view of anterior end of a typical *Chaetonotus*, showing arrangement of cilia; J, ventral view of anterior end of a typical *Ichthydium*, showing arrangement of cilia. (A to E modified from Brunson, 1950; F to J modified from Remane, 1935–1936.)

lar organ, usually slightly larger toward the inner end and sometimes with one or two indistinct bulbs. Its cavity is more or less triquetrous and lined with thin cuticle. Four small unicellular salivary glands are closely associated with the pharynx, one pair anteriorly and one posteriorly.

The intestinal wall consists of only four longitudinal rows of cells. There are no caeca, although a short rectum is distinguishable just before the anus.

One investigator has reported that reserve food materials are stored in special subepidermal cells which break loose and float about in the pseudocoel.

**Excretion.** The Chaetonotidae, including the great majority of fresh-water species, all have a single pair of flame bulbs at about mid-length. The two protonephridial tubules are considerably coiled in the pseudocoel and open ventrally near the mid-line. Undoubtedly the protonephridial system functions in both excretion and osmoregulation. Although there is some

disagreement, it is probable that the other families of the Chaetonotoidea also have a protonephridial system. Some investigators state that the marine species of Chaetonotidae have a protonephridial system; others maintain that it is absent. In the marine order Macrodasyoidea, however, the system is lacking. It is possible that the intestine of all gastrotrichs has an accessory excretory function.

**Muscle system.** The longitudinal muscle strands are quite prominent, especially ventrally. Usually there are about six pairs, with origins and insertions on the body wall. Their contraction produces shortening, curving, and partial rolling up of the body. A few delicate circular fibers in the body wall have recently been demonstrated for a few species, but they are thought to be of little importance in movement. In addition to the radial pharyngeal musculature, there are a few circular fibers on the outside of the pharynx and in the region of the rectum.

**Nervous system.** A large, dorsal, lobed, saddle-shaped brain covers the anterior portion of the pharynx, and two lateral nerve strands extend almost to the posterior end of the body. Fine branches innervate the body wall and viscera.

**Sensory receptors.** One or two pairs of pigmented "eyespots" have been seen on the lateral surfaces of the brain in a few species, but their function is questionable.

The tufts of cilia on the head are thought to function in touch, current detection, and the detection of dissolved materials. They are inserted in special thick glandular cells of the hypodermis.

Pairs of anterior and posterior tactile bristles are of common occurrence.

**Reproduction, life history.** Most marine gastrotrichs are hermaphroditic, and a few are protandrous. Fresh-water species, however, are all parthenogenetic females, males being unknown. The two parts of the ovary are more or less lateral to the intestine. Each portion consists of a few oocytes and eggs in varying stages of development. The oviduct is so skimpy that some investigators doubt its existence as a definite duct. The genital pore is ventral. A single ventral saclike "X organ" lies just inside the genital pore; possibly it represents a vestigial copulatory bursa.

A gastrotrich usually produces one to five eggs during its lifetime. A mature egg is quite large, and before leaving the parent it distends the body greatly. Nevertheless, it is plastic, and as it emerges from the genital pore it is momentarily constricted into a dumbbell shape. Upon coming in contact with the water an outer shell hardens. Sometimes the shell bears spines or other protuberances. Eggs are usually attached to some small object on the substrate.

Brunson (1949) distinguishes two definite types of eggs, differing slightly in size. Tachyblastic eggs begin cleavage as soon as deposited and hatch 12 to 70 hours later. Opsiblastic eggs are slightly larger and are produced in old cultures and when

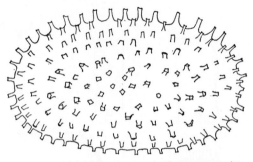

Fig. 92.—Opsiblastic egg of *Chaetonotus*. (Redrawn from Zelinka.)

environmental conditions become unfavorable. They have a heavier shell and survive desiccation, freezing, and unusually high temperatures. The duration of dormancy is variable, depending on ecological conditions, but it is known to last as long as two years. Opsiblastic eggs are usually the last ones laid by a particular gastrotrich, but there are some exceptions.

Development is direct. Upon emergence from the egg a gastrotrich is quite large, and during the ensuing several hours it grows by 20 to 30 per cent to attain mature size. As compared with the Macrodasyoidea, the Chaetonotoidea are composed of relatively few cells; perhaps the number is constant within each species. Little is known about the normal length of life; individuals in cultures live for three to 22 days, depending on the species and ecological conditions. Like the situation in rotifers, the cuticle is never shed during the life history.

**Ecology.** About 60 per cent of all known species of gastrotrichs are characteristic of fresh waters. Only seven genera, however, are restricted to this environment, including *Dasydytes*, *Dichaetura*, *Heterolepidoderma*, *Kijanebalola*, *Lepidodermella*, *Neogossea*, and *Proichthydium*. Four genera occur in both marine and fresh waters, or brackish and fresh waters. These are *Aspidiophorus*, *Chaetonotus*, *Ichthydium*, and *Polymerurus*. Only a very few species are known to occur in both types of environments, and some investigators believe that these are all actually pairs of varieties. About 24 genera are restricted to marine habitats.

Gastrotrichs are typical of puddles, marshes, wet bogs, and the shallow littoral, especially where there is detritus and decaying material. Old laboratory protozoan cultures or aquaria with disintegrating aquatic plants commonly have gastrotrich populations. They are uncommon in running waters generally and perhaps absent from swift streams.

Most species remain closely associated with the substrate, although the Neogosseidae and Dasydytidae may swim about above it. Their occurrence in the plankton of the shallows, however, is atypical and fortuitous. Little is known about the depth distribution and concentrations of fresh-water species, although *Chaetonotus* has been found in bottom deposits as deep as 36 meters. Recently it has been found that the capillary water of sandy beaches a meter or two from the water's edge supports a considerable population of gastrotrichs.

Although maximum numbers are usually found in summer and autumn, gastrotrichs may be collected at any time of the year. Other than opsiblastic eggs, no special desiccation or overwintering mechanisms are known.

Many species may be collected from habitats where there is much decay, and where the dissolved oxygen content consequently may be less than 1.0 part per million. Minimal oxygen concentrations are not definitely known, however, although it it probable that gastrotrichs may withstand at least temporary anaerobiosis.

**Geographical distribution, dispersal.** Except for some areas in Europe and three or four in the United States, there has been almost no intensive, systematic collection of gastrotrichs. Most records are the result of incidental or superficial studies, often associated with collections of other groups of fresh-water invertebrates. As a result, we know little about the geographical distribution of individual species. Most fresh-water genera, however, appear to be cosmopolitan and occur the world over in suitable habitats; these are *Aspidiophorus, Chaetonotus, Dasydytes, Ichthydium, Lepidodermella, Neogossea,* and *Polymerurus.* Overland dispersal is undoubtedly effected by the resistant opsiblastic eggs.

**Enemies.** In addition to the toll taken by browsing insects and crustaceans, gastrotrichs are also devoured by amoeboid protozoans, hydras, oligochaetes, turbellarians, and perhaps by tardigrades and nematodes.

**Collecting.** Sandy beach washings, and rinsings of aquatic vegetation often yield good collections. Specimens may be concentrated by straining the wash water through fine bolting silk. For bottom species the thin layer of surface mud and debris should be carefully scooped up and placed in a suitable container with water. After standing for a time in the laboratory, material at the debris and water interface should be sucked up with a long pipette and examined under the high power of the binoculars.

**Culturing.** Old protozoan cultures are sometimes suitable if gastrotrichs are seeded into them, and one investigator recommends using two drops of uncooked egg yolk in 100 ml. spring or pond water. In either case it is best to add a little bottom debris to the culture.

One-tenth per cent malted milk in well water is especially useful for pure cultures. After the water is brought to a boil, malted milk powder is added, and the solution is then further boiled for about a minute. Let stand a week before inoculating with gastrotrichs.

Regardless of the culture method used, about one-half the volume of fluid should be renewed every one to three weeks.

**Preserving, preparing.** Two per cent osmic acid is an excellent fixative. Place the living specimens in a drop of water on a slide and invert for five to ten seconds over the mouth of the bottle of osmic acid. Saturated mercuric chloride, 10 per cent formalin, and Bouin's fluid are alternative fixatives that often give good results. Specimens may be stored in 70 per cent alcohol or 5 per cent formalin. If glycerin is to be used for mounting, transfer the gastrotrichs to a concave watch glass containing 5 per cent glycerin in 50 per cent alcohol. Cover loosely to keep out dust and permit evaporation. After about a week the water and alcohol will all have evaporated and the specimens will be in concentrated glycerin. Any of the several mounting methods for rotifers may be used (page 185). Glycerin is excellent for permanent storage.

Some species require narcotization before fixing, and a wide variety of substances may be tried with varying success, including a concentrated aqueous menthol solution, chloretone, 2 per cent benzamine lactate, 2 per cent butyn, and 2 per cent hydroxylamine hydrochloride.

Scales, plates, and spines may be isolated by the judicious use of dilute acetic acid. Stain with fuchsin. Oil immersion is essential for critical work and species identification.

**Taxonomy.** Only two investigators have made important contributions to the biology of American gastrotrichs. Stokes published the results of his New Jersey observations in 1887 and 1888, and Brunson began his series of papers in 1947. Obviously, therefore, an enormous amount of work remains to be done in this country.

Some of the most important European investigations are those of Zelinka (1889), Grünspan (1910), and Remane (1935–1936).

The most reliable and significant characteristics for distinguishing genera are the nature of the furca, and the presence or absence and detailed structure and arrangement of cuticular plates, scales, and spines.

The vast majority of American species are unreported or undescribed. As a consequence, almost every study, however superficial, turns up new species. It is therefore fruitless to include a key to the approximately 20 American species known to date.

About 200 species have been described from the fresh waters of the world, but they may all be grouped into only 11 genera. The key which follows includes only nine genera; four of these have not yet been reported from the United States (*Aspidiophorus, Dichaetura, Heterolepidoderma,* and *Neogossea*), but at least the first three are widely distributed and will undoubtedly be found here eventually. Two other rare fresh-water genera are not included in the key; *Proichthyidium* has been collected only once in the Argentine, and *Kijanebalola* is known only from central Africa.

Remane (1935–1936) gives good evidence for grouping *Dasydytes, Setopus, Anacanthoderma, Stylochaeta,* etc., into a single genus, *Dasydytes,* and this practice is followed in the present manual. *Lepidoderma* is preoccupied and *Lepidodermella* is used instead.

## KEY TO GENERA OF GASTROTRICHA

**1.** Caudal furca present (Figs. 93, 94)..................................................2
     True caudal furca absent, but sometimes with rudimentary protuberances, long
          spines, or setose styloid processes (Figs. 95D–J).........................8
**2.** Caudal furca not forked; cuticle smooth, or with spines, plates, simple scales, or
          spined scales or plates; head usually with two to four tufts of cilia; cephalic
          shield present or absent; usually with one pair of posterior bristles (Figs. 93B–
          F; 94; 95A, B); two longitudinal bands of cilia; common and widely distributed;
          includes about 90 per cent of the known fresh-water species.
                                                          CHAETONOTIDAE, 3

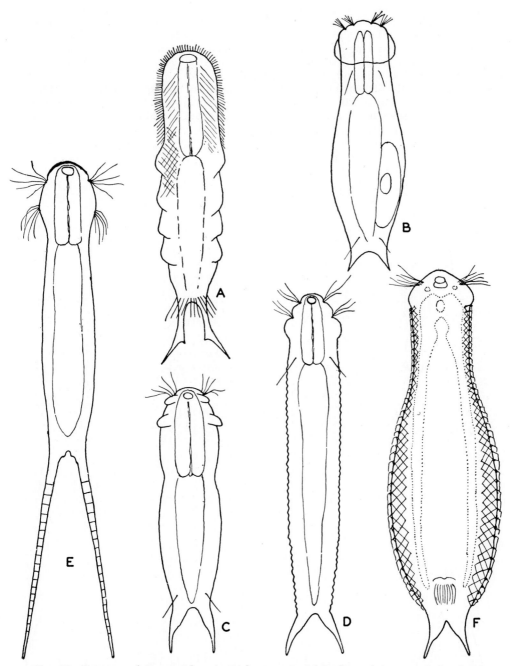

FIG. 93.—Structure of Gastrotricha. A, *Dichaetura*; B, *Ichthydium*, showing cephalic shield; C and D, *Ichthydium*; E, *Polymerurus*; F, ventral view of *Aspidiophorus*, showing arrangement of cilia. (A modified from Metschnikoff; B modified from Konsuloff; C modified from Brunson, 1949; D and E modified from Brunson, 1950; F modified from Saito.)

Caudal furca forked; cuticle covered with spined plates; head without tufts of cilia but with many single cilia; cephalic shield absent; four to many posterior bristles (Fig. 93A); several rare and poorly known species reported from Europe; not known in the U. S............DICHAETURIDAE, **Dichaetura**

3. Caudal furca very long and jointed; body usually with spines or spines and scales (Fig. 93E); several species.................................**Polymerurus**

Caudal furca not especially long, not jointed................................4

4. Cuticle smooth, without plates, scales, or spines, but sometimes with setae (Figs. 93C, D); about 20 species.................................**Ichthydium**

Cuticle not smooth..........................................................5

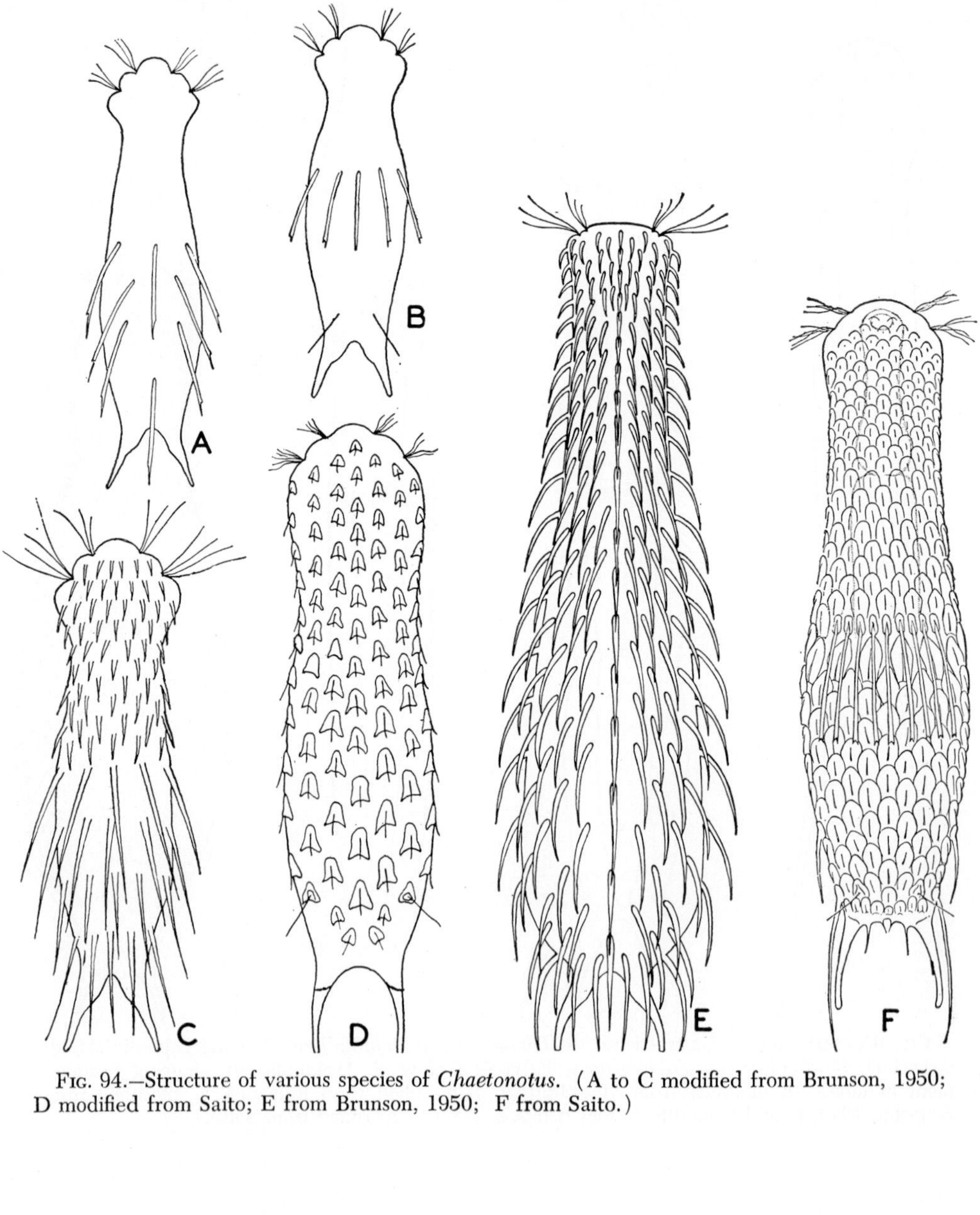

FIG. 94.—Structure of various species of *Chaetonotus*. (A to C modified from Brunson, 1950; D modified from Saito; E from Brunson, 1950; F from Saito.)

**5.** Body covered with complex stalked plates, each consisting of a rounded basal plate, a short stalk, and a rhombic endplate (Fig. 93F); several uncommon species; not yet reported from U. S..................................**Aspidiophorus**
Body with simple plates, scales, or spines...................................**6**

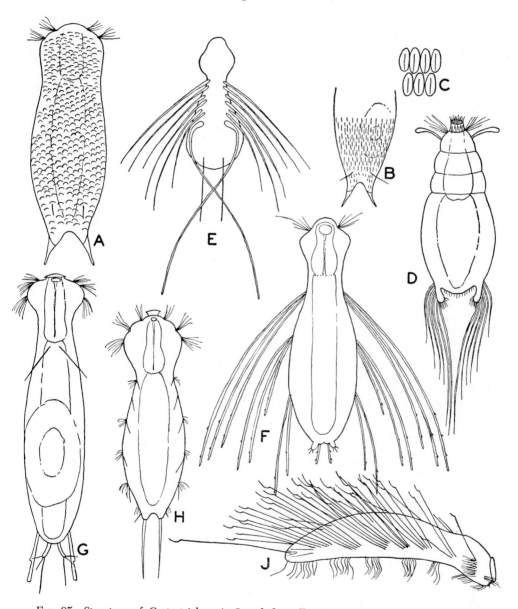

Fig. 95.—Structure of Gastrotricha. A, *Lepidodermella*; B, posterior end of *Heterolepidoderma*; C, keeled plates of *Heterolepidoderma*; D, *Neogossea*; E to H, dorsal views of *Dasydytes*; J, lateral view of *Dasydytes*. (A, B, C, and J modified from Remane, 1935–1936; E and F modified from Brunson, 1950; D modified from Daday; G modified from Voigt; H modified from Greuter.)

6. Body with spines or spined scales (Fig. 94); very common; about 100 species.

                                                          **Chaetonotus**

     Body without spines or scales but covered with plates.....................7

7. With flat broad plates or scales (Figs. 90H, J; 95A); about ten species.

                                                    **Lepidodermella**

     With small keeled plates (Fig. 95C); several uncommon species; not yet reported from U. S.....................................**Heterolepidoderma**

8. Head with two club-shaped tentacles; body with long spines, with or without basal plates; two long spines or two styloid processes at posterior end of body; several uncommon species (Fig. 95D); not yet reported from U. S.

                                        NEOGOSSEIDAE, **Neogossea**

     Head without tentacles; body with long spines, arranged singly or grouped; no plates or scales; ventral ciliation in two longitudinal bands or two longitudinal rows of tufts; head ciliation usually with three ventral transverse bands of cilia (Figs. 95E–J); a highly variable genus; about 20 species.

                                        DASYDYTIDAE, **Dasydytes**

# GASTROTRICHA REFERENCES

BRUNSON, R. B. 1947. Gastrotricha of North America. II. Four new species of Ichthyidium from Michigan. *Pap. Mich. Acad. Sci. Arts and Lett.* **33**:59–62

———. 1948. Chaetonotus tachyneusticus. A new species of gastrotrich from Michigan. *Trans. Amer. Micros. Soc.* **67**:350–351.

———. 1949. The life history and ecology of two North American gastrotrichs. *Ibid.* **68**:1–20.

———. 1950. An introduction to the taxonomy of the Gastrotricha with a study of eighteen species from Michigan. *Ibid.* **69**:325–352.

DAVISON, D. B. 1938. A new species of gastrotrichan—Chaetonotus robustus, new species. *Amer. Mus. Novit.* **972**:1–6.

DE BEAUCHAMP, P. M. 1934. Sur la morphologie et l'ethologie des Neogossea (gastrotriches). *Bull. Soc. Zool. France* **58**:331–342.

GRÜNSPAN, T. 1910. Die Süsswassergastrotrichen Europas. Eine zusammenfassende Darstellung ihrer Anatomie, Biologie und Systematik. *Ann. Biol. lacustre* **4**:211–365.

HATCH, M. H. 1939. Notes on two species of Gastrotricha from Washington. *Amer. Midl. Nat.* **21**:257–258.

MOLA, P. 1932. Gastrotricha delle acque dolci italiane. *Int. Rev.* **26**:397–423.

MURRAY, J. 1913. Gastrotricha. *Jour. Quekket Micros. Club* **12**:211–238.

PACKARD, C. E. 1936. Observations on the Gastrotricha indigenous to New Hampshire. *Trans. Amer. Micros. Soc.* **55**:422–427.

REMANE, A. 1927. Beiträge zur Systematik der Süsswassergastrotrichen. *Zool. Jahrb. Abt. Syst.* **53**:269–320.

———. 1935–1936. Gastrotricha. *Klassen u. Ordnungen des Tierreich* 4 (Abt. 2, Buch 1, Teil 2, Lfg. 1–2):1–242.

SAITO, I. 1937. Neue und bekannte Gastrotrichen der Umgebung von Hiroshima (Japan). *Jour. Sci. Hiroshima Univ., Ser. B, Div. 1,* **5**:245–265.

STOKES, A. C. 1887. Observations on Chaetonotus. *The Microscope* **7**:1–9, 33–43.

———. 1888. Observations on a new Dasydytes and a new Chaetonotus. *Ibid.* 261–265.

ZELINKA, C. 1890. Die Gastrotrichen. Eine monographische Darstellung ihrer Anatomie, Biologie und Systematik. *Zeitschr. wiss. Zool.* **49**:209–384.

# Chapter 8

# ROTATORIA (ROTIFERS)

IF WE were to designate a single major taxonomic category that is most characteristic of fresh waters, it could only be the Phylum Rotatoria. For the rotifers are one of the few groups that have unquestionably originated in fresh waters, and it is here that they have attained their greatest abundance and diversity. Probably 1,700 species have been described, but less than 5 per cent of these are restricted to marine and brackish waters. Only two species occur in mid-Atlantic.

Rotifers were first studied and described by Leeuwenhoek in 1703, and since his time they have become classical objects for study by the amateur microscopist and professional hydrobiologist alike. They are essentially all microscopic, the length range for the phylum being about 40 microns to 2.5 mm., but the great majority are between 100 microns and 500 microns long. These fascinating creatures have long been called Rotifera, or rotifers, because in some species the disclike ciliated anterior end, or corona, has a fancied and illusory resemblance to a pair of revolving wheels owing to the synchronized beating of the coronal cilia. Rotifers occur in an endless variety of aquatic and semiaquatic habitats, including the limnetic and deepest regions of the largest lakes and the smallest puddles. They are found in damp soil and vegetable debris, in mosses that may be wetted or dampened only occasionally, in the interstices between the sand grains of lake beaches, from the Arctic and Antarctic to the tropics, in small rock depressions, and even in cemetery flower urns and eaves troughs.

The vast majority of rotifers encountered under natural conditions are females. Males are definitely known for relatively few species; they are much smaller than the females, degenerate, and seldom live for more than two or three days. Most of the remarks in this chapter concern only female rotifers; the biology of males is discussed in a special section on page 176.

**General characteristics.** The Phylum Rotatoria is commonly divided into two classes, the Digononta and the Monogononta. The female members of the former class are characterized by paired ovaries, a ramate mastax, and by the absence of a secreted tube or lorica. The Class Digononta is subdivided into two orders, the Seisonidea and the Bdelloidea. The Seisonidea includes only a single genus, *Seison*, occurring as commensals on marine Crustacea; the ovaries have no vitellaria, males are well developed, and the corona is rudimentary. Almost all Bdelloidea, however, occur in fresh waters; the ovaries have vitellaria, males are unknown, reproduction is exclusively by parthenogenesis, and the corona is well developed. The Bdelloidea are appropriately named since the body is highly contractile and they creep about on the substrate in a leechlike manner.

The members of the Class Monogononta constitute about 90 per cent of the known species of rotifers and are characterized by

a single ovary, a mastax which is not ramate, and by the presence or absence of a
lorica or a secreted tube. Males are known
for some species and not for others; they
are small and degenerate. This class is
divided into three orders: Ploima, Flosculariacea, and Collothecacea.

The Order Ploima includes most of
the free-swimming, limnetic plankton, and
littoral species. These rotifers typically
have a posterior "foot" and two "toes."
The corona is not especially large.

The Order Flosculariacea includes some
species that are free-swimming and many
more that are sessile as adults. The foot,
when present, has no toes. Often there is
a secreted gelatinous envelope or case.
The corona is not especially large.

The Order Collothecacea includes those
rotifers with a very large, lobed corona
and a mouth which is centrally located at
the lower end of a funnel-like infundibulum; they are usually solitary and sessile.

As a group, the rotifers display an amazing range of morphological variations
and adaptations. Yet the great majority

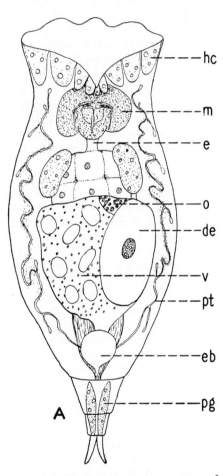 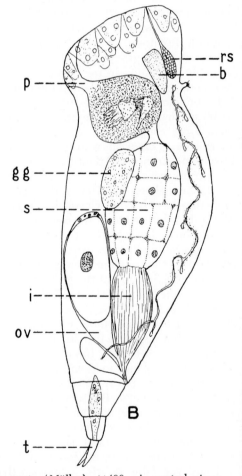

FIG. 96.—Diagrammatic structure of *Epiphanes senta* (Müller), ×400. A, ventral view;
B, lateral view. (Musculature and coronal ciliation not shown; see Fig. 100.) *b*, brain; *de*,
developing egg; *e*, esophagus; *eb*, excretory bladder; *gg*, gastric gland; *hc*, hypodermal cell
of head; *i*, intestine; *m*, mastax; *o*, ovary; *ov*, oviduct; *p*, pharynx; *pg*, pedal gland; *pt*, protonephridial tubule; *rs*, retrocerebral sac; *s*, stomach; *t*, toe; *v*, vitellarium.

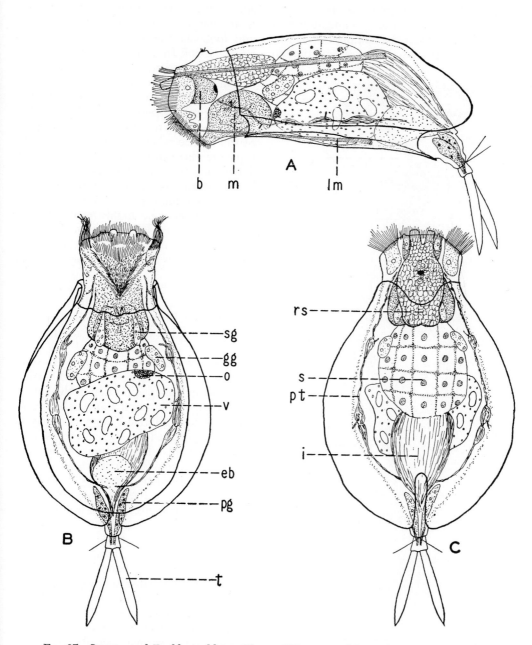

FIG. 97.—Structure of *Euchlanis dilatata* Ehr., ×320, a typical loricate rotifer, semidiagrammatic. A, lateral; B, ventral; C, dorsal. *b*, brain; *eb*, excretory bladder; *gg*, gastric gland; *i*, intestine; *lm*, longitudinal muscle; *m*, mastax; *o*, ovary; *pg*, pedal gland; *pt*, protonephridial tubule; *rs*, retrocerebral sac; *s*, stomach; *sg*, salivary gland; *t*, toe; *v*, vitellarium. (Modified from Myers, 1930.)

have several fundamental features in common. The body is usually elongated and cylindrical, though the complete range of shape extends from linear attenuation to spherical. Usually three main body regions may be distinguished: head, trunk, and foot. The head is more or less distinctly set off from the large trunk region, although there is rarely an elongated neck region. In the bdelloid rotifers the body appears to be composed of segments, but these are only superficial annuli which indicate the zones of folding and telescoping of the cuticle when the animal contracts; typically there are 15 to 18 such annuli. There is no true segmentation in rotifers. The posterior tapering foot usually consists of two or more superficial segment-like parts, or it may be highly retractile and annulated or creased; sometimes it is absent. When present, the foot usually has two (sometimes none, one, three, or four) terminal "toes."

The general body surface of a rotifer is covered with a cuticle which is secreted by a syncytial hypodermis. The hypodermis forms a thin layer under most of the cuticle, but at the anterior end it is thick, cushion-like, and inwardly lobed. In some rotifers the cuticle is very thin and flexible, but in many genera a portion of the cuticular surface is thickened, more or less rigid, and is termed a lorica. The lorica may be poorly developed and consist of several thin, elastic, platelike sections of the trunk cuticle, or it may be thick, rigid, boxlike, sculptured, inelastic, and may involve the entire surface of the trunk, much of the foot, and even a part of the head. Between these two extremes, every gradation in lorica development is to be found.

The periphery and more or less of the corona surface are ciliated, but the density and pattern of ciliation are highly variable. In general, these cilia serve the double function of locomotion and food getting.

The mouth may be anterior and in the center of the corona, peripheral, subterminal, or ventral. The anus, or cloacal aperture, is typically located dorsally at the base of the foot.

The mastax is a structure peculiar to the digestive system of rotifers, and no comparable device is known elsewhere in

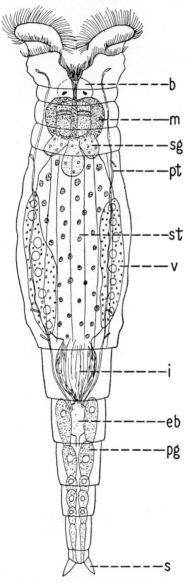

Fig. 98.—Ventral view of *Philodina*, a typical bdelloid rotifer, ×375, semidiagrammatic. *b*, brain; *eb*, excretory bladder; *i*, intestine; *m*, mastax; *pg*, pedal gland; *pt*, protonephridial tubule; *s*, spur (toes are completely retracted); *sg*, salivary gland; *st*, stomach; *v*, vitellarium. (Modified from Hickernell.)

the animal kingdom. Superficially, it has the appearance of a bulbous swelling lying between the pharynx proper and the esophagus. It consists of a complicated arrangement of muscles which activate a set of translucent sclerotized jaws (collectively called the trophi) which are used to seize, tear, grind, or macerate the food (Figs. 102–104).

True coloration of the tissues is usually grayish, yellowish, or sometimes a pink or bluish cast. The apparent coloration, however, is more often tan, green, or brownish owing to the varied contents of the digestive tract and stored excretory granules.

**Corona and its ciliation.** It is probable that the most primitive type of corona is that of the creeping and browsing notommatid Ploima. It consists merely of an anterior, ventral, or oblique surface more or less densely covered with cilia; the buccal area, which surrounds the mouth, is always densely ciliated, but this buccal field may be extended so that it covers

some or all of the corona (Fig. 99A). From this simple type, all of the more complicated and intergrading arrangements are presumed to be derived. In addition to the dense, short cilia of the coronal surface, for example, there may be a peripheral wreath of large, strong cilia (Figs. 99B–E). On the other hand, with the exception of the buccal and peripheral areas, some genera, such as *Eosphora* (Fig. 125K), have little or no ciliation on the coronal surface. *Epiphanes* and many other genera have a small buccal field, a strong peripheral wreath, and several transverse rows of long cilia and clumps of cilia located on protuberances on the corona. *Synchaeta* has several long sensory coronal bristles in addition to ordinary cilia (Fig. 99F). In many Notommatidae, *Synchaeta,* and a few other genera the corona bears a pair of lateral ciliated earlike processes, or auricles (Fig. 125D). In the Bdelloidea and Flosculariacea the surface of the corona is usually bare, but it has two peripheral concentric

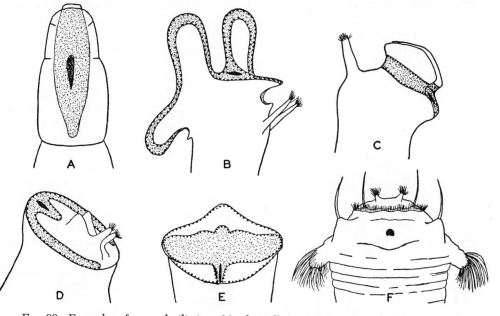

Fig. 99.—Examples of coronal ciliation. Membranelles and large cilia shown by large dots, smaller cilia by small dots. A, *Dicranophorus*, ventral; B, *Floscularia*, lateral, showing the ventral pellet-making concavity; C, *Philodina*, lateral; D, *Conochilus*, lateral; E, *Cyrtonia*, ventral; F, *Synchaeta*, dorsal. (Modified from de Beauchamp, 1909.)

wreaths of long, strong cilia with a densely ciliated furrow between (Figs. 128–132). In *Stephanoceros* and *Collotheca* the corona is a greatly concave infundibulum and its upper edge is folded and developed into prominent lobes or arms. These protuberances bear long, stiff setae. The mouth, at the bottom of the infundibulum, is surrounded by bands of cilia. In *Acyclus, Cupelopagis,* and *Atrochus* there are no coronal cilia.

In addition to these several types of corona, there are other arrangements and intergradations involving sparse to dense ciliation.

**Locomotion.** Movements through the water are mostly dependent upon the beating of the peripheral cilia, and many plankton and limnetic species remain in permanent suspension throughout life without ever coming in contact with a substrate. Such locomotion is often a combination of twisting on the longitudinal axis and spiral movements of the whole animal. A few plankton genera, such as *Filinia, Pedalia,* and *Polyarthra,* also move by sudden jerks and leaps, owing to sudden beating movements of their long appendages. Most of the free-swimming, non-plankton species having a foot and toes are able to creep about and browse on substrates as a result of the beating of the coronal cilia against

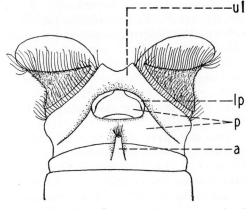

Fig. 101.—Dorsal view of anterior end of *Macrotrachela,* a typical bdelloid rotifer. *a,* antenna; *lp,* lamella of proboscis; *p,* proboscis; *ul,* upper lip.

the substrate combined with a pushing action of the toes. It is quite possible that the toes are useful in steering during both creeping and swimming.

In the Bdelloidea, however, the corona is retracted during creeping and in such a manner as to produce an anterior terminal sucker-like proboscis which functions in the leechlike movements. The toes of bdelloids are usually everted only during active creeping (Figs. 130C, F; 131K; 132C).

Most rotifers with a foot and toes have pedal glands. The Ploima usually have two pedal glands in the base of the foot or in the posterior part of the trunk, while the Bdelloidea have from four to 20 such glands. Pedal glands open via ducts at the tips of the toes, at the base of the toes, or, in some Bdelloidea, also into the spurs. The secretion is used for anchoring the animal to the substrate temporarily by the tips of the toes or spurs.

Most of the Collothecacea and Flosculariacea are sessile as adults, but their newly hatched young swim about actively for a short time before attaching to the substrate.

**Tube construction.** A wide variety of protective tubes are constructed or secreted by many genera of sessile rotifers,

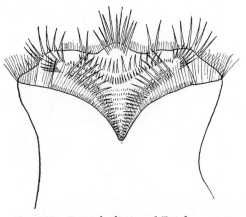

Fig. 100.—Coronal ciliation of *Epiphanes senta.* (Modified from de Beauchamp, 1909.)

and even by a few free-swimming species. In *Ptygura* the tube is usually gelatinous, sometimes flocculose, colorless to brown, and appears to be secreted by the general body surface; in many species it is more or less covered with bits of adherent debris, and in one species the tube is supplemented with fecal pellets. *Stephanoceros* secretes a thin, hyaline tube, and most species of *Limnias* form a thin, firm, and sometimes annulated tube.

Several species of *Floscularia* construct their tubes of small pellets of debris, and needless to say, it is a fascinating process to watch. The newly settled young *Floscularia* secretes a rough gelatinous tube which is to form the base of the main tube. On the ventral side of the body, just posterior to the mouth, there is a conical, ciliated depression into which a large gland secretes gelatinous material. As an accessory part of the coronal cilia action, small bits of detritus are collected and concentrated in the ciliated cup. This detritus is thoroughly mixed with the gelatinous secretion, and by means of ciliary action in the cup the mass is rotated on its axis and is formed into a hard symmetrical pellet having the shape of a pistol bullet. By appropriate movements of the head and trunk, the pellet is pushed into place at the top of the tube with the tip pointed outward. The upper edge of the tube is always level with the pellet-making cup, and as the animal elongates, it continuously manufactures pellets so that growth closely corresponds with the length of the tube (Edmondson, 1945).

According to the specific constituents of the pellets, the tubes are usually yellow, green, or brown in color, although in one species they are almost colorless and composed largely of the gelatinous secretion. Another species of *Floscularia* constructs its tube out of fecal pellets.

**Mastax and trophi.** The anatomy and action of the mastax and its contained trophi are so variously modified for special feeding habits that it is best to con-

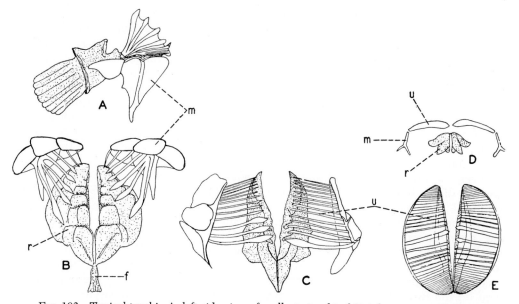

FIG. 102.—Typical trophi. A, left side view of malleate trophi of *Epiphanes senta*; B, anterior view of trophi of *E. senta*; C, anterior view of malleoramate trophi of *Floscularia*; D, optical section of ramate trophi of a bdelloid rotifer; E, anterior view of ramate trophi of a bdelloid rotifer. Inci are stippled. *f*, fulcrum; *m*, manubrium; *r*, ramus; *u*, uncus. (Modified from de Beauchamp, 1909.)

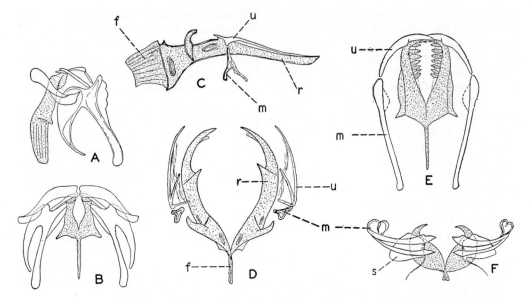

Fig. 103.—Typical trophi. A, lateral view of cardate trophi of *Lindia*; B, ventral view of trophi of *Lindia*; C, lateral view of incudate trophi of *Asplanchna*; D, anterior view of trophi of *Asplanchna*; E, anterior view of forcipate trophi of *Dicranophorus*; F, anterior view of uncinate trophi of *Stephanoceros*. Inci are stippled. *f*, fulcrum; *m*, manubrium; *r*, ramus; *s*, subuncus; *u*, uncus. (A and B modified from Harring and Myers, 1922; C, D, and F modified from de Beauchamp, 1909; E modified from Harring and Myers, 1928.)

sider these structures before discussing feeding and the digestive system.

Food is brought into the mouth by ciliary action, down the short pharynx, and into the mastax. Only the anterior, dorsal, or anterodorsal part of the mastax contains a cavity through which the food passes. The greater, basal part of this organ consists of minute muscles and the sclerotized trophi, whose movements the muscles bring about. In traversing the mastax, however, the food must pass through the moving, distal, toothlike portions of the trophi.

The trophi consist of one median piece and three paired lateral pieces, all of which are subject to morphological variation and specialization. The fulcrum is basal and median and serves as an attachment for the two rami; these three pieces collectively form the incus. The two unci are usually toothed to a varying degree, and each of these pieces is attached laterally to a manubrium. An uncus and its as-

sociated manubrium collectively form a malleus. Thus the trophi consist of one incus (composed of one fulcrum and two rami) plus two mallei (each composed of one manubrium and one uncus) (Figs. 102A, B). Eight basic, but variable, types of mastax are recognized according to the relative development and specialization of their parts. These are characterized briefly below, and their occurrence in the various families of rotifers is given in the taxonomic outline on pages 186–187.

Malleate (Fig. 102B). Specialized for horizontal grinding of plankton and particulate detritus. Feebly prehensile.

Virgate (Fig. 104). The fulcrum is long and expanded at the base for the attachment of the hypopharynx, a powerful domelike mastax muscle; the upper (dorsal) end of the hypopharynx is free and covered with cuticle, and when it contracts it acts as a piston and sucks food into the mouth and mastax cavity. Rotifers with a virgate mastax commonly extract the fluids of plant cells and the body fluids of microscopic animals by this suction mechanism. In addition to suction, the trophi of the virgate mastax may be used for biting or nibbling preliminary to ingestion and the grinding action. Plankton, periphyton, and particulate detritus are also used as the chief food by many rotifers with a virgate mastax.

Cardate (Figs. 103A, B). This type of mastax occurs only in the Subfamily Lindiinae. Like the virgate type, the cardate mastax functions by suction, but the whole mastax is able to oscillate on a transverse axis, and a complicated epipharynx supports the mouth. The Lindiinae are only incidentally predatory, the chief food being periphyton and particulate detritus.

Forcipate (Fig. 103E). The trophi of this type of mastax are elongated, strongly compressed dorsoventrally, and adapted for protrusion through the mouth and the capture and tearing of the prey (Protozoa and micrometazoa). The trophi can sometimes be protruded for half their length.

Incudate (Figs. 103C, D). The trophi

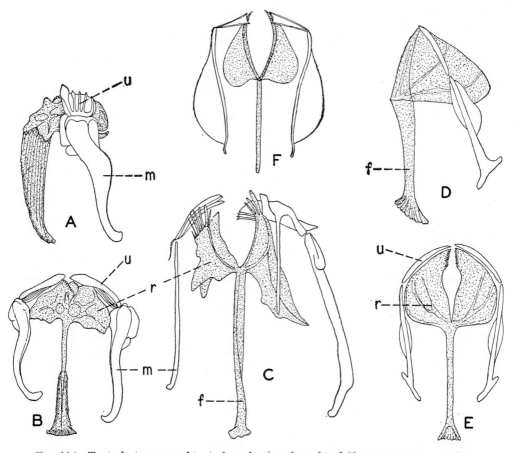

Fig. 104.—Typical virgate trophi. A, lateral view of trophi of *Notommata*; B, ventral view of trophi of *Notommata*; C, ventral view of trophi of *Trichocerca*; D, lateral view of trophi of *Cephalodella*; E, ventral view of trophi of *Cephalodella*; F, ventral view of trophi of *Synchaeta*. Inci are stippled. *f*, fulcrum; *m*, manubrium; *u*, uncus; *r*, ramus. (A and B modified from Harring and Myers, 1922; C modified from de Beauchamp, 1909; D and E modified from Harring and Myers, 1924.)

are prehensile and all parts are reduced except the pincer-like protrusile rami. The mastax musculature is likewise reduced. Food consists mostly of zooplankton.

Ramate (Figs. 102D, E). This mastax is specialized for the grinding of plankton, periphyton, and detritus. All parts of the trophi are reduced or vestigial except the semicircular unci which have opposing linear teeth. The fulcrum is usually absent.

Malleoramate (Fig. 102C.) This type is much like the ramate mastax, but the first few ventral teeth are larger, more highly developed, and detached, while the remaining teeth are progressively smaller striations. The fulcrum is present but small.

Uncinate (Fig. 103F). Specialized for laceration of ingested plankton, periphyton, and detritus. An intermediate piece, or subuncus, facilitates greater movement of the unci on the rami.

The trophi of all types of mastax are minutely sculptured, ridged, and barred. These complex markings can be discerned to advantage only with the oil immersion lens and they are mostly omitted in the trophi figures in this chapter.

**Food, feeding.** In both sessile and free-swimming nonpredatory rotifers the coronal cilia are of primary importance in creating localized currents which guide and concentrate the loose periphyton, small plankton organisms, and detritus at the region of the mouth. Indeed, the great majority of species are omnivorous and ingest all organic particles of the appropriate size. Common examples are *Cephalodella, Filinia, Keratella, Lecane, Proales, Euchlanis, Epiphanes, Brachionus,* the Bdelloidea, and most sessile species.

Predatory species probably detect their prey by touch or by biochemical stimuli. The following common genera feed on other rotifers and all kinds of small Metazoa, either in the plankton or on a substrate: *Asplanchna, Dicranophorus, Ploesoma, Synchaeta,* and *Trichocerca.* A care-

ful investigation has shown that *Asplanchna* will usually ingest all plankton organisms larger than 15 microns.

Many notommatids, as well as a few genera in other families, feed mostly on the fluid contents of filamentous algal cells.

*Cupelopagis, Acyclus,* and *Atrochus* are all sessile and without coronal cilia. They have a large funnel-like corona, or infundibulum, however, and when the prey wander into this cavity, they are quickly enclosed and ingested.

A few free-living rotifers have highly specialized food habits. *Acyclus inquietus* Leidy, for example, lives among *Sinantherina* colonies and eats the motile young. *Dicranophorus isothes* Harring and Myers is thought to subsist entirely on small Cladocera, and *D. thysanus* Harring and Myers feeds on dead copepods, Cladocera, and oligochaetes.

**Digestive system.** Most Flosculariacea, Bdelloidea, and Ploima have similar digestive systems (Figs. 105A, B, D–F). The mouth opens into a narrow ciliated pharynx which leads to the cavity of the mastax. A variable number of small salivary glands are closely associated with the mastax. After the food has been macerated in the mastax, it passes into the short to long esophagus which leaves the dorsal or posterodorsal surface of the mastax. The esophagus extends to the large, thick-walled, ciliated stomach where most of the digestion and absorption are thought to occur. Usually there is a pair of oval or bean-shaped gastric glands on the anterior margin of the stomach. The intestine may be distinctly or indistinctly set off from the stomach. It is much smaller, sometimes very narrow, thin-walled, and often ciliated. The cloaca is short and seldom ciliated; it opens to the outside dorsally at the base of the foot.

The anterior end of the Collothecacea digestive tract is much different (Fig. 105C). The buccal area is situated at the base of the large funnel-like infundibulum. Food taken into the mouth at the

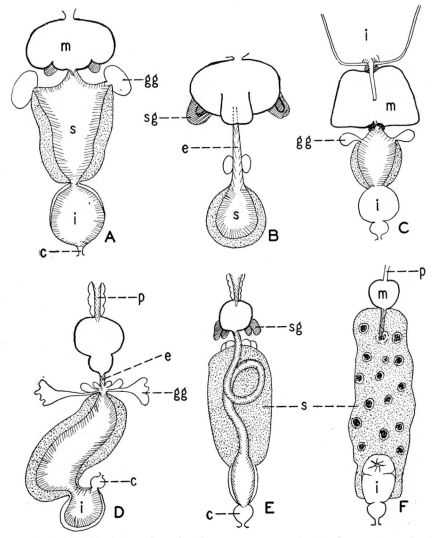

FIG. 105.—Diagrams of typical rotifer digestive systems. A, *Epiphanes*; B, *Asplanchna*; C, *Stephanoceros*; D, *Testudinella*; E, *Mniobia*; F, *Habrotrocha*. *c*, cloaca; *e*, esophagus; *gg*, gastric gland; *i*, intestine; *inf*, infundibulum; *m*, mastax; *p*, pharynx; *s*, stomach; *sg*, salivary gland. (A to E greatly modified from de Beauchamp, 1909; F modified from Burger.)

bottom of the infundibulum passes through a narrow esophageal tube which hangs freely in a very large cavity, the proventriculus. The small mastax is situated at the bottom of the proventriculus.

Digestion is regularly extracellular, but in a few genera, such as *Chromogaster*, *Ascomorpha*, and a few others, it is clearly intracellular. No gastric glands are pres-ent in these rotifers, but the stomach has large gastric caeca which fill much of the pseudocoel.

Although many rotifers have true symbiotic zoochlorellae in the stomach wall, it is now believed that some instances previously reported as symbiosis are in reality ingested algal cells that persist for several days during their very slow intracellular digestion in the cells of the stomach wall.

Only recently it has been discovered that in members of the bdelloid family Habrotrochidae there is no stomach cavity and that the stomach is a continuous syncytial mass. As food leaves the esophagus it enters the stomach protoplasm in the form of food pellets, or food vacuoles, which circulate about and become digested.

**Respiration.** Most littoral and plankton rotifers normally have rather high oxygen requirements, but it is well known that certain genera are capable of withstanding anaerobic conditions for short periods and very low concentrations of dissolved oxygen (0.1 to 1.0 part per million, for example) for extended periods.

Limnetic plankton genera, such as *Asplanchna, Filinia, Polyarthra,* and *Keratella,* commonly occur in the oxygen-poor hypolimnion of lakes during midsummer and midwinter. Rotifers living at a depth of a few centimeters in the interstices of sandy beaches likewise are in a region of low oxygen. Oxygen-deficient bottom muds and hay infusions characteristically contain species of *Lecane, Monostyla, Lepadella,* and bdelloids. Undoubtedly the creation of water currents by ciliary action ensures an adequate supply of oxygen to rotifers under most circumstances.

**Osmotic control, excretion.** Like most small fresh-water organisms, rotifers are readily permeable to water, but the internal osmotic pressure is kept constant by the action of the protonephridial system (Fig. 106). There are from four to 50 symmetrically arranged flame bulbs throughout much of the body. These are connected to a long convoluted collecting tubule on each side, a part of the tubule being thin-walled, another part thick-walled and glandular. The two collecting tubules empty into an excretory bladder which has a very short duct leading to the ventral side of the cloaca. Excess water and probably a certain amount of metabolic waste are absorbed from the fluid of the pseudocoel by the flame bulbs and wall of the collecting ducts and are excreted into the cavity of the ducts. The weak pressure produced by the beating of the tufts of cilia in the flame bulbs creates a slight current which aids in carrying the excretory fluid through the tubules to the bladder. Here it is stored only temporarily, since the bladder normally contracts and empties its contents to the outside through the cloacal aperture (anus) one to six times per minute. In a few Ploima and in typical Bdelloidea there is no separate bladder; the collecting tubules merely empty into the thin-walled

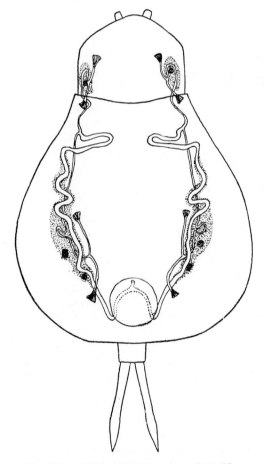

FIG. 106.—Protonephridial system of *Euchlanis.* (Modified from Stossberg.)

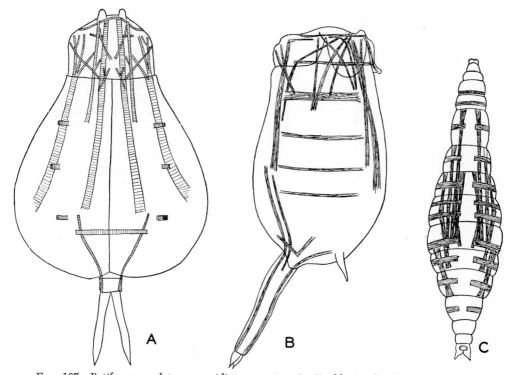

Fɪɢ. 107.—Rotifer musculature, semidiagrammatic. A, *Euchlanis*, dorsal; B, *Brachionus*, lateral; C, typical bdelloid, ventral. (A and B modified from Stossberg; C modified from Zelinka.)

posterior part of the cloaca, which is modified into a bladder.

Old rotifers are usually distinguished by their darker pigmentation, most of which consists of accumulated excretory granules retained in the tissues.

**Muscles.** Both smooth and striated muscle fibers occur in rotifers, the latter often associated with the rapid movement of long spines and special appendages, as in *Polyarthra* and *Pedalia*.

Muscles are always arranged in small bandlike groups of fibers, never in flat sheets. The circular muscle system consists of four to 15 bands attached just beneath the hypodermis. These bands are typically complete in the Monogononta, but in the Bdelloidea the bands usually have a ventral gap. One set of posterior longitudinal muscle bands are inserted in the foot or posterior part of the trunk. An anterior set of longitudinal bands have their insertions in the coronal region and their origins near the middle of the trunk. *Testudinella* has short dorsoventral muscles, no circular ones. *Cupelopagis* has a remarkably complex system of muscles.

A few delicate visceral and cutaneovisceral muscles help move and hold the internal organs in place.

**Nervous system.** The arrangement of the rotifer nervous system is nonlinear. The largest mass of nervous tissue is the sac-shaped cerebral ganglion, or "brain," lying on the dorsal surface of the mastax and esophagus and sometimes more or less obscured by the hypodermal syncytium of the corona. By means of fine paired nerve fibers it is connected with the mastax ganglion (sometimes absent) on the ventral surface of the mastax, and with the caudal ganglion in the foot region. A few

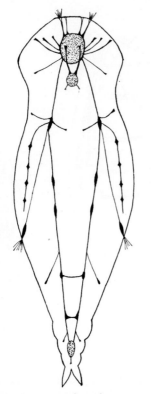

FIG. 108.—Diagram of rotifer nervous system. (Greatly modified from Remane, 1932.)

of lateral antennae in the posterior third of the body and often a minute caudal antenna on the dorsal surface of the foot. Special tufts of cilia, membranelles, setae, and sensory protuberances or papillae are of common occurrence on the corona of many Monogononta.

For many years the retrocerebral organ of rotifers went almost unnoticed. It consists of two parts: a retrocerebral sac situated dorsal or posterior to the brain and opening on two coronal papillae by a paired duct, and a small paired subcerebral gland on either side of the sac with ducts alongside those of the sac (Fig. 109). Either of these two components may be lacking, but usually it is the latter. "Bacteroids" often occur in the retrocerebral sac and occasionally in the subcerebral glands. A variety of functions have been postulated for the retrocerebral organ, none of them conclusive. The most plausible suggestion is that it is a special sense organ.

**Reproduction.** The Monogononta have a simple, ventral, elongated, saclike reproductive system (Figs. 96, 97). Just within the distal end of the sac is a small ovary consisting of a clump of developing oo-

additional fine connecting fibers and associated nerve cell bodies innervate the sensory areas, muscles, and viscera (Fig. 108).

**Sense organs.** Perhaps the most conspicuous sensory area is the cervical eyespot. Characteristically it lies at the lower end of the brain or is imbedded in the brain and consists of a cup- or bowl-shaped mass of red pigment granules containing a refractile globule. Occasionally it is double. Many rotifers have two additional frontal eyespots located on the corona and widely separated. Eyespots are lacking in the adults of most sessile species, but they are present in the active immature stages.

A small, median, dorsal, setose antenna is usually present; rarely it is paired. In addition, the Monogononta have a pair

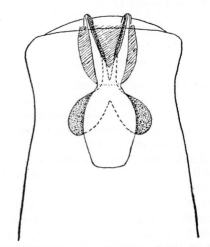

FIG. 109.—Diagram of a typical retrocerebral organ (dorsal view). Retrocerebral sac clear, subcerebral glands stippled, and brain with parallel diagonal lines.

cytes. The vitellarium is a syncytium with a few large nuclei; it occupies half or more of the capacity of the sac, and as eggs in the ovary mature one at a time and move downward slightly, the vitellarium contributes a large mass of yolk to the egg so that it becomes relatively large. Upon maturing, the egg passes down the short oviduct, into the cloaca, and out the cloacal aperture. The egg is quite elastic and is momentarily constricted and elongated as it passes through these small ducts.

The Bdelloidea reproductive system is similar to that of the Monogononta except that it is V- or Y-shaped and has two ovaries and two vitellaria (Fig. 110). The two oviducts are very delicate or rudimentary.

Males are unknown in the bdelloids, and reproduction is solely by parthenogenesis. In the Monogononta, however, males have been reported or described for most species whose biology has been carefully worked out, and it is thought that males occur regularly in this group, although there are a few genera in which males have never been seen, and perhaps in these groups reproduction is also exclusively parthenogenetic. It is commonly stated that males are rare, but this belief has arisen simply because the occurrence of males in most species is restricted to only one to three weeks during the year. If one collects during the brief time of male occurrence, they can be found in abundance.

Ploimate rotifers have two distinct types of females, which, with the exception of two or three species, are morphologically indistinguishable. During the greater part of the year the females reproduce exclusively by parthenogenesis. These females are said to be amictic, and both their body cells and their amictic eggs all have the diploid number of chromosomes. Their eggs undergo only one, nonreductional division during maturation in the ovary. The second type of female is called mictic. Such females appear only at critical

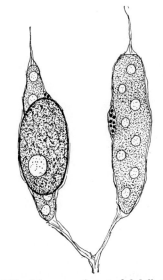

Fig. 110.—Diagram of typical bdelloid reproductive system, showing two vitellaria, two ovaries, two vestigial oviducts, and one developing egg.

times of the year, especially when there are marked changes in the factors of the environment (see page 177). The eggs of a mictic female undergo the usual double meiotic division and are therefore haploid. In contrast to amictic females, the mictic females are capable of being fecundated by the males. If fecundation does occur, the fertilized eggs (also called winter eggs, or resting eggs) which they deposit are thick-walled and highly resistant to adverse environmental conditions. If, however, a mictic female is not impregnated, she deposits eggs which promptly hatch into males. Fundamentally, a resting egg is a potential male-producing egg which has been fertilized and which, upon hatching, produces an amictic female.

One mictic female may produce both fertilized eggs and male eggs, but males and females, or fertilized eggs and females, are never produced by the same parent. In fact mictic females are commonly seen carrying both male eggs and fertilized eggs at the posterior end of the body. Fecundation of an amictic female by a male has no effect. The two kinds of

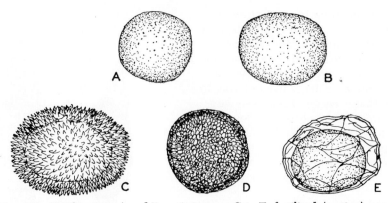

Fig. 111.—Rotifer eggs. A and B, amictic eggs; C to E, fertilized (resting) eggs.

female are always distinctly separate physiologically, not interchangeable. A typical sequence of generations is shown in Fig. 112. Under natural conditions, there are usually only one or two mictic generations per year, while there may be up to 20 or 40 amictic generations. The female which hatches from a resting egg is always amictic, but the following generation may be amictic or mictic.

The number of amictic eggs that a female may produce during her lifetime is highly variable and depends on both the species and environmental conditions. Specific laboratory cultures have shown that *Brachionus calyciflorus* Pallas averages only 3.6 eggs and *Testudinella elliptica* (Ehr.) only 5.0, while *Epiphanes senta* Müller averages 45.4 and *Proales sordida* Gosse 24.3. Little is known about the number of eggs that a mictic female produces, but presumably it does not differ greatly from the number produced by an amictic female.

Some rotifers are ovoviviparous, the eggs being retained in the oviduct or pseudocoel until hatched. These include two species of Notommatidae, many bdelloids, *Asplanchna, Conochilus, Rhinoglena,* and a few others. Their young are usually released through the cloaca, but many bdelloids are known to release the young through ruptures in the body wall. In *Asplanchna* the male may fecundate its

own mictic mother before it is released from the body of the mother.

Amictic, or summer, eggs are usually released from the body of the female and hatch within a day or two. The summer eggs of some plankton species contain large oil droplets which facilitate suspension and flotation. In the following genera, however, the summer eggs are usually carried loosely attached to the posterior end of the body until hatching: *Polyarthra, Pompholyx, Keratella, Pedalia, Brachionus,* and *Filinia.*

Resting (or winter, or fertilized) eggs are heavy, thick-shelled, and often sculptured. Upon release from the female they usually sink to the bottom, but in the autumn they may sometimes be found floating on the surface or blown ashore. They are remarkably resistant to desiccation, high temperatures, low temperatures, and adverse chemical conditions for long periods. Many species winter over in the resting egg stage. Unlike summer eggs, the resting eggs require a latent period of several weeks to several months before they can hatch. Hatching is stimulated by changes in temperature, osmotic pressure, water chemistry, and aeration.

A curious fourth type of rotifer egg has recently been reported from a culture of *Keratella quadrata* (Müller). It is an unfertilized "pseudosexual resting egg" produced by parthenogenesis. The mor-

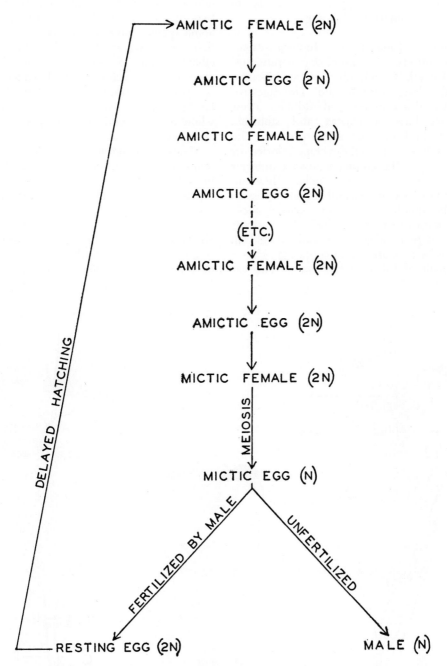

FIG. 112.—Diagrammatic sequence of generations in a typical ploimate rotifer.

phology and development are similar to those of ordinary resting eggs.

**Biology of males.** With few exceptions, male rotifers are minute, degenerate, and short-lived. Commonly they are about a third as long as the female. The digestive tract is absent or vestigial, although a few species have a mastax and stomach. Mouth and anus are never present. The males have no well-developed lorica or spines, and the corona is always anterior and well supplied with cilia. They are very rapid swimmers and are never sessile.

The simple reproductive system occupies most of the pseudocoel. The testis is pear-shaped or globular and is held in place by a small strand supposed to be a remnant of the digestive tract. The vas deferens is short to long and sometimes has two or four associated prostate glands. Some species have no true penis, the vas deferens being everted through a small ciliated orifice during copulation. Other species have a well-developed penis which is everted continually; sometimes it is larger than the foot. In a few males the whole posterior end of the body is tubelike and specialized for copulation.

Males of plankton species are the most strongly reduced. Some are not much more than a sperm sac surrounded by protoplasm and a cuticle, and having an anterior tuft of cilia.

Males are ready for copulation within an hour after hatching. They are extremely active, especially in the presence of females, and swim about erratically

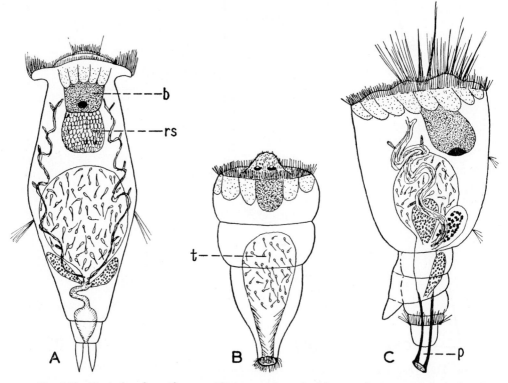

Fig. 113.—Typical male rotifers, semidiagrammatic and with musculature omitted. A, dorsal view of *Notommata*; B, dorsal view of *Filinia*; C, lateral view of *Brachionus*. b, brain (containing eyespot); p, penis; rs, retrocerebral sac; t, testis. (Greatly modified from Wesenberg-Lund, 1923.)

until they come in contact with one. Copulation and sperm transfer occur either through the cloacal aperture of the female or through the body wall (*Asplanchna*), and the male dies immediately thereafter. If a female is not located, the male lives for only two or three days; *Asplanchna* males, however, are known to live for as long as four to seven days.

Males have been reported for only about 10 per cent of the species of Monogononta. Few have been carefully studied and figured. Males have been reported for only three or four species in each of the large genera *Lecane* and *Monostyla*, and there are only three or four records for the family Trichocercidae.

In the so-called "perennial" species of rotifers, males usually appear in spring and autumn; in "summer" species they appear in autumn; and in "winter" species they ordinarily occur in spring.

**Development and longevity.** The rotifer zygote undergoes unequal and regular cleavage, and the gastrula consists of an outer layer of cells (ectoderm) enclosing an inner cell mass (mesoderm and endoderm). Cell division and differentiation proceed rapidly, with each organ developing from a definite cell complex. When all organs have received their full complement of cells, cell division ceases completely.

Most plankton and littoral species grow rapidly during the several hours after hatching, but thereafter very slowly if at all. Many sessile species, however, grow throughout life, chiefly as a result of the elongation of the posterior end. Although rotifers have no ecdyses, the mature adult may be three to ten times as large as the newly hatched young.

Although there may be considerable size variations among the individuals of a single species, it has been found, for the several species carefully studied, that there is an approximately constant number of cells in all adults of the same species. In *Epiphanes senta*, for example, there are about 959 nuclei. Each organ in the great majority of specimens has the same number of nuclei, though a few tissues, especially the vitellarium, show slight variations in the number of nuclei.

Length of life, from hatching until death, is highly variable. *Epiphanes senta* averages about 8 days, *Lecane inermis* (Bryce) 7.4 days, *Brachionus calyciflorus* 6 days, and *Proales decipiens* (Ehr.) only 5.5 days. At the other extreme, *Euchlanis incisa* Carlin averages 21 days, *Keratella quadrata* (Müller) 22 days, *Cupelopagis vorax* (Leidy) six weeks, and many bdelloids are active for three to six weeks.

As might be expected, the ability to regenerate lost or damaged organs is poorly developed. Amputation of the coronal lobes of *Stephanoceros* results in regeneration only in immature specimens; regeneration is lacking or very slow in full-grown individuals.

**Syngamic reproduction.** Since about 1904 there has been a vigorous and many-sided controversy over the relative significance of physiological, ecological, and genetic factors in the production of mictic females, males, and bisexual reproduction. Scores of papers dealing with a wide variety of field observations and controlled laboratory experiments have appeared. Reduced to simplest terms, the chief problem may be stated as follows: most ploimate rotifers reproduce by a series of parthenogenetic generations throughout most of the year; yet suddenly mictic females and males may appear in the population, and resting eggs are produced, usually in the autumn, but sometimes in the spring, or both. How may this phenomenon be explained? What factors are responsible for male production?

Most of the important observations and experimental work centering around this involved problem have stemmed from the laboratories of Shull, Whitney, Tauson, and Wesenberg-Lund, and their many papers should be consulted for a complete account. For our purposes, however, it is sufficient to summarize the present status of the matter and to mention some of the more significant items relating to sexual periodicity which have appeared as side issues in these studies.

To begin, it is obvious that species differ considerably from one another with respect to the nature and degree of ecological factors that instigate their bisexual periods. Furthermore, some species behave differently from one body of water to another and from one year to another. In one lake, for example, a species may regularly produce males in the autumn; in another lake it may have both spring and autumn bisexual periods; in a third lake the occurrence of bisexual periods may be sporadic. *Polyarthra*, for example, sometimes produces males at almost any time of the year, in both ponds and lakes.

In general, it has been shown that small populations of rotifers usually remain parthenogenetic, and that bisexuality appears during population increases. External factors, rather than genetic make-up, control sexual periodicity, but these factors are nonspecific. Careful experimental work indicates that the chief factors responsible for the appearance of males in a population are: (1) a change in the type of food (green to nongreen, and vice versa), (2) an increase in food supply, and (3) a decrease in food supply. Other factors that have been shown to be of importance in instigating male production are: crowding, addition of fresh culture medium, addition of distilled water, making the culture medium more alkaline, changing the temperature (rarely), and starving (rarely). Sometimes, however, even if measurable conditions remain unaltered, males unaccountably appear in a population.

The solution of the problem must, of course, be sought in a study of the amictic female, for whether she produces eggs that will hatch into more amictic females or eggs that will hatch into mictic females is a matter determined by her physiology. The decision as to which type of egg she will deposit is made in the three-hour period before she releases the egg from her oviduct. It has been noticed that those eggs which hatch into mictic females are slightly smaller than those eggs which hatch into amictic females, and several investigators contend that in this difference lies the crux of the whole problem. The production of a large or small egg might very well depend upon the available amount of yolk in the ovary, which in turn, might indirectly depend upon environmental conditions.

*Epiphanes senta* invariably has a sexual period under natural conditions, but experimentally this species has been carried through more than 500 successive parthenogenetic generations; such old cultures are characterized by a considerably lowered vigor and reproductive rate. *Proales decipiens*, however, has been carried through more than 250 successive parthenogenetic generations with no changes in vigor or fecundity, and it is interesting to note that the male is unknown in this species. Such facts appear to constitute some evidence that periodic bisexuality may have a rejuvenating effect upon rotifer populations through the associated meiotic and fertilization processes.

**Periodicity.** Like so many other plankton and littoral organisms, rotifers exhibit periodic and sometimes quite striking cycles of abundance during the year, a fact which is quite familiar to anyone who has done seasonal plankton work. Various investigators have designated certain species as monocyclic, dicyclic, polycyclic, or acyclic and perennial, according to whether their annual population curves have one, two, several, or no pronounced peaks. *Kellicottia longispina* (Kellicott) and *Conochilus unicornis* Rousselet are usually considered monocyclic, although they are both perennial in certain lakes. *Euchlanis dilatata* Ehr. commonly has an autumn maximum. *Brachionus angularis* Gosse and *Keratella cochlearis* (Gosse) are often considered dicyclic, with spring and autumn maxima, but are sometimes perennial. Other species are more variable. *Polyarthra* is dicyclic (summer and autumn), polycyclic, or perennial. *Keratella quadrata* may be most abundant in spring, summer, or autumn, or it may be perennial. *Asplanchna priodonta* Gosse is variously considered monocyclic, dicyclic, or perennial.

There has been an unfortunate tendency on the part of some investigators to generalize on the periodicity of a species on the basis of their observations of a few large lakes during only one or two years. As emphasized by Pennak (1949), however, the cycles of abundance for plankton species are highly variable within each species, variable from year to year within a single lake, and especially variable from one small lake to another.

**Variation, cyclomorphosis.** Like the cladocerans, many species of plankton rotifers exhibit a remarkable range of variation in size and lorica development from one habitat to another. The most striking examples of these local "races" occur in *Keratella* and *Brachionus*. In *Brachionus calyciflorus,* for instance, all degrees of development in the four posterior spines have been reported, ranging from long and well developed to very short or absent (Figs. 120B–D). Comparable variations in posterior spine development occur in *B. quadridentata* Hermann (Figs. 120H, J), *B. caudatus* Barrois and Daday (Fig. 120F), and *Platyias patulus* (Müller); to some extent the anterior spines are also variable. Until about 1915 these variations were often described as distinct species, and more recently taxonomists have had to contend with the resultant confusing synonymy. Now, however, they are recognized as forms or races comprising relatively few species.

Variations in the size of races from different localities are also striking. Ahlstrom (1940) gives the average width of the lorica of *Brachionus calyciflorus* for 21 localities all over the world, and the variation is 124 to 300 microns. This is a remarkable range of average size for a species having determinate cell division.

Superimposed on the confusion of varieties in some loricate plankton species is an annual cyclomorphic series, that is, a sequence of generations in the same strain marked by progressive modifications in morphology through a long parthenogenetic series. In *Keratella cochlearis* (Figs. 116A–D), for example, the lorica has a long posterior spine during the cold months followed by a gradual reduction in length until July and August when there is a very short spine or no spine. At this point syngamic reproduction often occurs, followed by a gradual reversal in spine length during the remainder of the year. Such well-defined cycles usually occur in small lakes which become quite warm in summer. In Lake Michigan there is no cycle, and in other bodies of water only a partial cycle. Sometimes the two extreme lorica forms have no transitional forms.

In *Keratella quadrata* (Figs. 116H–L) a form with long posterior spines initiates the cycle. The spines are progressively reduced in successive generations until a form with very short spines or no spines is dominant. Syngamic reproduction may then occur, and the cycle starts all over again with a long-spined form. But often this species is long-spined the year round, even in small ponds.

From these examples, and judging from the occurrence of two or three widely differing varieties in the same population, it is quite obvious that cyclomorphosis is a variable phenomenon within a single species. Certainly it cannot be ascribed to an inherent mechanism or simply to changes in environmental factors, but rather to a complicated interaction between organism and environment. In fact the problems of cyclomorphosis, population fluctuations, local races, and bisexual reproduction all seem to be inextricably bound up with each other and with a multitude of ecological factors. Although this complex is a most difficult one, it is probably capable of solution by means of careful field and laboratory observation and experimentation. To be sure, much has already been accomplished, but it is only a beginning.

**General ecology.** As emphasized above, rotifers occur in an extreme variety of habitats. They are poorly represented only in hot and cold springs, rushing streams, brackish waters, and extremely saline waters. Some common species are usually present in the same pond year after year, but sometimes unaccountably disappear for one or more years, then suddenly reappear.

Approximately 75 per cent of the known species occur in the littoral areas of lakes and ponds, but only about 100 species are limnetic or planktonic enough in their habits as to be completely emancipated from a substrate. The Bdelloidea are most characteristic of mosses and sphagnum. These habitats may be submerged, emergent, or terrestrial and only occasionally wet. Only a few species of the following genera of bdelloids regularly occur in the littoral zone: *Rotaria*, *Embata*, *Philodina*, and *Dissotrocha*; two or three other genera are uncommon in littoral waters. On the other hand, only a few ploimate species occur commonly in moss and only if it is kept wet.

A few free-living species are highly specific in their habitat preferences. *Acyclus inquietus* is invariably found among colonies of *Sinantherina*. *Collotheca algicola* (Hudson) appears to be restricted to clusters of *Gloeotrichia* filaments, and one or two other sessile species are also common on this alga. *Brachionus plicatilis* Müller and *B. pterodinoides* Rousselet are confined to extremely alkaline ponds and lakes, especially in the western states. *Proales rheinardti* (Ehr.) is unusual in that it occurs in mountain springs and among *Fucus* in marine bays and inlets! Only two genera, *Seison* and *Zelinkiella*, are known to be restricted to marine habitats.

Although the Rotatoria are primarily free-living organisms, a few species have become specialized for a parasitic existence. *Notommata trypeta* Harring and Myers is parasitic in colonies of the alga *Gomphosphaeria*. *Proales parasitica* (Ehr.) is a common parasite inside *Volvox* colonies. A few species of *Albertia* are ecto- and endoparasites of aquatic oligochaetes. *Drilophaga judayi* Harring and Myers has been found only in the free-living state, but a second species in this genus is parasitic on *Lumbriculus*, and a third on *Erpobdella*.

Aside from such true parasites, many free-living rotifers live as commensals or epizoics on a wide variety of fresh-water invertebrates, especially crustaceans and insects. Common examples include certain species of Bdelloidea, *Pleurotrocha*, *Lepadella*, and *Testudinella*.

The limnologist often collects plankton species that have much of the pseudocoel filled with peculiar sausage-shaped bodies. These are parasitic fungus growths which occasionally become epidemic.

Judging from the large plankton literature, it is obvious that most plankton communities average between 40 and 500 rotifers per liter, with populations in excess of 1,000 per liter being unusual. The waters of mountain lakes and large oligotrophic lakes, however, sometimes contain less than 20 rotifers per liter, especially during the cold months. The most dense plankton rotifer population ever recorded from unpolluted waters is 5,800 specimens per liter, cited by Pennak (1949).

The maximum density of rotifer populations appears to be closely correlated with the relative amount of available substrate and exposed surfaces. Using 5,800 per liter as a maximum for plankton, the corresponding maximum for sessile species inhabiting finely divided littoral plants is about 25,000 per liter (Edmondson, 1946). Furthermore, rotifers inhabiting the wet interstices of sandy beaches are reported to attain a maximum density of 1,155,000 individuals per liter of damp sand (Pennak, 1940). The greater the surface, therefore, the greater the population. Presumably this phenomenon is associated with more food, more attachment space, more nooks for protection, and reduced predation loss.

Sandy beaches as a habitat for rotifers have only recently been investigated. Below the water's edge the sand contains a negligible rotifer population, but the top three or four centimeters of sand extending from the water's edge as far as three or four meters landward is a favorable habitat. Although many of the sandy beach rotifers occur regularly in the littoral, about 40 psammobiotic species are known to be restricted to the sand habitat, especially species of *Trichocerca, Encentrum, Monostyla, Lecane,* and *Wierzejskiella.*

In contrast to littoral forms, the limnetic, or open-water, plankton genera occur over a wide depth range, even as deep as 100 or 200 meters. *Asplanchna, Filinia, Polyarthra,* and *Keratella* are all good examples.

Those pond and lake plankters having eyespots exhibit, in varying degrees, a 24-hour cycle of vertical movements in accordance with the variations in subsurface illumination. Beginning late in the afternoon a slow drift upward begins, and maximum abundance occurs near the surface in the early morning. Around dawn a reverse drift downward begins, until maximum concentrations in the deep waters are attained about noon. Such movements are also of general occurrence among copepods and cladocerans, but in rotifers they are of course much less pronounced, average amplitudes of only one to three meters being common and amplitudes as high as eight or ten meters being very unusual.

**Ecology of sessile rotifers.** The work of Edmondson (1944, 1945) has contributed much information to the ecology of sessile rotifers (Flosculariidae and Collothecidae). For the most part, sessile species are never present in quantities below a temperature of 15°, the largest populations always being present at temperatures above 20°. They are usually most plentiful in late spring, especially in small bays and littoral nooks in ponds and lakes. Although any substrate may be used, sessile species are by far the most abundant on submerged aquatic vegetation. *Utricularia vulgaris* var. *americana* has the most extensive, dense, and varied rotifer fauna of all species. Other favored plants are *Myriophyllum,* sphagnum, potamogetons, *Anacharis,* and *Vallisneria.*

Some species occur on a wide variety of plants, but others exhibit striking preferences. Thus, *Collotheca gracilipes* Edmondson is almost invariably on *Utricularia vulgaris americana, Ptygura melicerta* Ehr. inhabits *Gloeotrichia* and *Coleochaete,* while *Collotheca campanulata* (Dobie) and *Ptygura barbata* Edmondson are usually found on epiphytic algae. *Cupelopagis vorax,* however, is restricted to broad, flat leaf surfaces. Edmondson concludes that species distribution is determined mostly by water chemistry and available plant substrates.

**Hydrogen ion effect.** Harring and Myers (1928) first pointed out that there are some striking correlations between the pH of a body of water and the composition of its ploimate rotifer fauna. In general, alkaline waters (above pH 7.0) contain relatively few species but large numbers of individuals, while acid waters (below pH 7.0) contain large numbers of species and few individuals. In the hard-water lakes around Madison, Wisconsin, Myers identified 100 species in a week of collecting, but he found the same number of species in only one hour of collecting in a small acid lake in northern Wisconsin. In the alkaline Yahara basin of southern Wisconsin he collected 138 species, but in the acid waters of Mount Desert Island in Maine he collected 497 species (Myers, 1931–1934).

As the result of his extensive field collecting, Myers distinguished three ecological groups of species with reference to their occurrence in waters of various hydrogen ion concentrations. (1) Alkaline water species are those that are confined to waters having pH readings above 7.0. *Asplanchna, Asplanchnopus, Mytilina, Brachionus, Filinia, Lacinularia, Sinantherina, Eosphora,* and *Notholca* are all alkaline genera, but there are also species in other genera that are restricted to alkaline waters. (2) Transcursion species are those that occur in both alkaline and acid waters. By far the large majority of rotifers belong in this category. (3) Acid water species are those that are confined to lakes, ponds, and bogs having an acid reaction. There are no genera restricted to acid waters, only certain species in genera that also have transcursion and alkaline representatives. The following genera contain numerous acid water species: *Cephalodella, Lepadella, Lecane, Monostyla, Trichocerca,* and *Dicranophorus.*

Most genera contain representative species in each of these three groups, but a specialist can tell at a glance whether a particular collection came from an acid or alkaline body of water. Even though an acid lake and an alkaline lake may be separated by a ridge of land only 50 meters wide, the rotifer faunas are completely different.

In a study of many areas in Wisconsin and New England, Edmondson (1944) lists 8 alkaline, 36 transcursion, and 12 acid species of sessile rotifers. In an investigation of many ponds and lakes (mostly acid) of the Pocono Plateau in Pennsylvania, Myers (1940) found 4 alkaline species, 313 transcursion, and 75 acid water species. In a study of the acid waters of the Adirondacks, Myers (1937) found 42 acid water species and 171 transcursion species. On the other hand, he found (1936) a total of only 106 alkaline and transcursion species in the alkaline waters of southern California, even though he collected almost daily for three months.

To be sure, pH 7.0 is by no means a sharp dividing line between acid or alkaline water species; it is only an approximation. Some acid species, for example, are found in waters giving readings as high as pH 7.1 or 7.2, and alkaline species likewise occur as low as pH 6.9 or 6.8. It is not meant to imply that the hydrogen ion concentration itself is a governing factor in ecological distribution, since pH is a reflection of a whole complex of physical and chemical variables, and actually the limiting factor may be one or more of these ecological variables. Total dissolved salts, calcium and bicarbonate, for example, have been suggested as being fundamentally important. Acid water rotifers can easily be transferred to alkaline waters where they will live, and vice versa, but their parthenogenetic eggs will not hatch in the unfavorable environment.

The above remarks relating to pH refer only to ploimate rotifers; they do not apply to the Bdelloidea which are apparently all transcursional and capable of tolerating a relatively wide range of ecological conditions.

**Desiccation.** Even certain modern textbooks include the statement or inference that all rotifers can be dried to form a resistant cyst, which, when returned to water will excyst and become active again. In the first place, true desiccation is restricted to the majority of Bdelloidea and does not occur at all in the much larger ploimate group. Secondly, in the great majority of bdelloids desiccation involves drying and shrinking of the body contents and cuticle without the formation of a true cyst. Only a few bdelloids are known to form true secreted cysts; when subjected to drying, these species secrete a surrounding gelatinous material which quickly hardens and becomes resistant.

Bdelloids typically inhabit moss on old walls, bark, or ground; they are much more abundant on emergent sphagnum than on submerged sphagnum. Such habitats are wet only intermittently from rains, wave action, or high water, and the process of desiccation allows the rotifer to tide over the frequent unfavorable periods of dryness. Very few truly aquatic bdelloids are able to undergo desiccation.

Bdelloids that are isolated in a little water on a smooth, bare surface are unable to undergo desiccation and they die. They must be associated with irregular surfaces and interstices where drying occurs more gradually and where there is a protective effect, such as in debris, sand, or among moss or sphagnum. When drying begins, the bdelloid draws both ends of the body into the central portion of the trunk and then puckers the two ends as though they were drawn up by purse strings (Fig. 114). This globular body mass then becomes wrinkled and loses much water. The pseudocoel is almost nonexistent, and the volume of the animal is only one-third or one-fourth of its normal size.

A remarkable rearrangement of chromatin occurs during desiccation. Instead of remaining in its usual large karyosome mass in the center of the cell, it fragments, becomes highly dispersed, and adheres to the inner surface of the cell membrane. Presumably this adjustment facilitates suspended animation and the utilization of oxygen at a greatly retarded rate.

Desiccated rotifers may be kept dry as dust for months or even years. There is one record of specimens being revived from moss kept dry for 27 years. When the dried rotifers are placed in water they quickly absorb water and become extended and normally active. Sometimes complete recovery occurs in only ten minutes, but under other circumstances it may take a whole day.

Desiccation always produces some mortality, even under favorable conditions, and only a fraction of a group of desiccated rotifers are viable and can be revived. Rapid drying is injurious, and, in general, the longer the interval of desiccation, the lower will be the percentage of recovery. Nevertheless, even under natural conditions, bdelloids are able to survive several alternating periods of activity and desiccation.

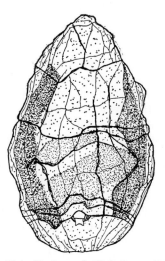

FIG. 114.—Desiccated *Philodina*. (Modified from Hickernell.)

**Dispersal, geographic distribution.** Overland transport of resting eggs or desiccated bdelloids is easily effected by winds and animals, and all rotifers are potentially cosmopolitan. By "cosmopolitan" we mean that similar habitats all over the world have similar rotifer faunas, and whether a given species is present in a particular body of water depends not on geographic location, but on the precise complex of ecological conditions prevailing there. As Jennings (1900) has said, "The problem of the distribution of the Rotifera is, then, a problem of the conditions of existence, not a problem of the means of distribution." The same species of rotifers are found in limnetic areas, in moss, in sandy beaches, in sphagnum bogs, in comparable farm ponds, etc. the world over. Even the "rare" species are being reported from localities everywhere that appropriate habitats prevail and where the collector is diligent.

A very few species appear to be generally distributed in restricted areas. *Paraploesoma formosum* (Myers) and *Trichocerca platessa* Myers, for example, are common in the acid waters of the northeastern states but have never been collected anywhere else in the world. Such instances are difficult to explain on the basis of our present knowledge of rotifer ecology.

**Collecting.** Plankton species are easily taken with a townet, thrownet, or a fine dipnet with a vial or centrifuge tube fastened to the lower open end.

Vegetated littoral areas are much richer collecting grounds, especially for browsing species, but nets are of little use there. Instead, masses of the plant material should be carefully placed in large screw-top jars along with water from the same habitat. The jars should be no more than half filled with plant material. When the jars are brought to the laboratory, they should be uncapped and placed in a north window. As the oxygen slowly decreases the rotifers will gather at the top of the water and usually toward the lighted side where they may be pipetted out. Sessile species may be found with the dissecting binoculars on bits of plants. Such temporary culture jars will keep well for a week or more if the lowermost third of the water is changed daily.

Bdelloids may be brought to the laboratory in handfuls of wet or dry moss which may be stored dry. When the material is to be studied it should be soaked for a few hours in water, then washed vigorously several times. The wash water and sediment should be kept in covered watch glasses or petri dishes for weeks or months and examined periodically under the microscope. Some bdelloids appear promptly, others not for two or three weeks.

**Culturing.** Many rotifer culture methods are suggested in the literature. Some methods are better for certain species than others, and if an investigator wishes to culture a previously uncultured species, he should try a variety of methods and modifications in order to get best results. Species of *Lecane* have been raised in 0.1 per cent malted milk in pond water, the solution being changed daily. The same genus has been cultured in rye extract prepared by grinding 20 grains of rye in a mortar

and boiling in 100 ml. of water for 20 minutes; the rotifers should be kept in drops of this solution and changed daily. Beef cube extract prepared by boiling one cube in 400 ml. of tap water is sometimes good. Dried breakfast oats may be used by boiling 8 to 30 flakes for three minutes in 100 ml. of water, filtering, and using after 24 hours. *Epiphanes* and certain other pond genera may be cultured in hay infusions which have been inoculated with a suitable protozoan or algal food organism. "Stable tea" is prepared by boiling 800 ml. of horse manure in 1,000 ml. of water for one hour; cool, strain, dilute with two parts boiled rain water, inoculate with a food organism, and age a week or ten days before inoculating with the rotifer. Sessile species are extremely difficult to culture.

The most important precaution to be observed in culturing rotifers is to change the culture solution frequently and prevent pronounced bacterial activity.

**Preparing, preserving.** Since the identification of loricate rotifers depends largely on the details of the lorica, they are conveniently killed and fixed by placing directly in 10 per cent formalin. This causes the soft parts of the animal to contract strongly, leaving the lorica well exposed for easy study.

The illoricate, free-swimming Ploima, however, require a much different technique. The identification of these forms depends very largely on anatomical details which can be studied only in an uncontracted, natural state. As a consequence, these rotifers must be narcotized before killing and fixing. The following method is adapted from Myers (1942) and should be performed under dissecting binoculars. With a fine pipette place the rotifers in about 3 ml. of water in a concave watch glass. If the specimens are from acid waters, add 3 or 4 drops of one per cent neosynephrin hydrochloride; repeat at five-minute intervals until the rotifers are all lying on the bottom and ciliary action has about stopped. Kill and fix by adding three drops of 0.5 or 1.0 per cent osmic acid from a dropping bottle and quickly stirring into the water. Pour the contents of the watch glass into a small vial, and after five minutes decant or pipette off most of the fluid, then add water. Repeat the decantation and addition of wash water three times at 15-minute intervals.

If the rotifers are from alkaline waters, a 5 per cent solution of novocain or cocaine hydrochlorate in 50 per cent methyl alcohol gives better results than the neosynephrin. Usually, however, these narcotics are very difficult to obtain, even for such scientific purposes, and other more readily available substitutes must be used. Chloretone and 2 per cent benzamine lactate are useful, and the writer has had considerable success with 2 per cent butyn and 2 per cent hydroxylamine hydrochloride.

The osmic acid solution will last much longer without deteriorating if it is dissolved in one per cent chloroplatinic acid (platinic chloride) and kept in a dropping bottle which is painted black. If rotifers are exposed to osmic acid too long they will blacken but they can be bleached in weak potassium hydroxide.

Many illoricate species, especially Notommatidae and bdelloids, are so delicate and sensitive that narcotization is not successful, and in such cases it is advisable to flood the specimens with an equivalent amount of *boiling* water in a watch glass; this treatment kills a large fraction of the animals in a well-expanded and lifelike condition. Formalin or other fixative should then be added.

Hanley (1949) strongly recommends the following procedure. Narcotize by adding several drops of 2 per cent benzamine hydrochloride to a small amount of water containing the rotifers, the time being variable from one species to another. Kill in 10 per cent formalin. Wash at least six times in 5 per cent formalin in order to remove all of the benzamine hydrochloride which might later crystallize out.

After killing and fixing, all rotifers can be stored in 2 to 5 per cent formalin containing 2 per cent glycerin. Many workers add a little eosin as this colors the rotifers and makes them easier to study and handle.

Preserved specimens can be studied and kept for several days in a shallow, hollow-ground slide provided the cover slip is sealed with vaseline.

Permanent mounts are best made with glycerin or glycerin jelly. In either case the rotifers should be slowly run up to pure glycerin. This is done by placing the perserved specimens in 5 per cent glycerin in a depression embryology slide or concave watch glass and leaving it loosely covered for about a week so that all of the water evaporates. In this way the specimens are penetrated slowly and partially cleared, and they retain their turgidity and natural shape.

Individual specimens in glycerin should never be picked up with a pipette since they usually stick to the inner surface of the glass and are easily lost. Instead, they may be readily picked out of glycerin under the dissecting binoculars with a flat toothbrush bristle glued to the tip of a matchstick. The bristle is simply slid under the specimen and quickly lifted straight upward and out of the glycerin; usually the specimen adheres to the tip of the bristle in a droplet of glycerin. Specimens handled in this way may be conveniently set aside while other preparations are being made. Glycerin jelly slides are made by placing a drop of melted jelly on a slide, touching the drop with the tip of the bristle holding the rotifer, and quickly orienting the specimen under the binoculars before putting on the round cover slip. The glycerin jelly should be allowed to set for several hours. Then the excess may be trimmed from the edge of the cover slip and several coats of Murrayite applied to its edge with a camel's hair brush and turntable at 24-hour intervals.

Fluid glycerin mounts are much more

difficult to prepare but are superior for some purposes. Detailed directions for one method are given in Harring and Myers (1928). An alternative method is as follows. Three or four bits of *passe partout* or gummed paper are fixed symmetrically to a 1 x 3 slide and spaced about 10 or 12 mm. apart to act as supports for the cover slip and thus prevent crushing of the specimen. The rotifer is then placed in a droplet of glycerin in the center of the slide and midway between the supports. The cover slip is next lowered into place very carefully, and by touching a camel's hair brush of Murrayite to the edge of the cover slip, capillarity will draw the Murrayite between the cover slip and slide and it will surround the glycerin droplet and completely fill the capillary space. Such slides should be set aside to dry for several hours and then given several rings of Murrayite at 24-hour intervals for greater permanence.

**Trophi mounting.** Since genus and species identifications are often dependent upon the anatomical details of the trophi, it is sometimes essential that permanent or semipermanent mounts of these jaws be made. The following method, requiring some skill and practice and much patience, is modified from Myers (1937). Place a drop of 1:10 Chlorox, or similar caustic alkali, just inside the concavity of a shallow concavity slide, and place a similar drop just outside the concavity. Then place a 22 mm. square cover slip on the outside drop and push it over the concavity until it is almost in contact with the inside drop. Next place the rotifer in the inner drop by means of a bristle. If cover slip is pushed slowly over the inner drop, the rotifer will be drawn under. And by working the cover slip over the concavity by short pushes, and adding small quantities of solution after each advance, the rotifer will be forced into the acute angle formed by the edge of the concavity and the under surface of the cover slip. The edges of the cover slip

should then be carefully dried and painted with vaseline or Murrayite. The position of the rotifer should be noted, and in about a half hour it will all have dissolved except the trophi. Such trophi slides will last for several to many months, and if a vaseline seal is used, the trophi may be oriented by tapping or moving the cover slip slightly.

**Taxonomy.** Rotifer taxonomy owes much to Harring's painstaking *Synopsis of the Rotatoria* which appeared in 1913 and which brought order out of chaotic nomenclature. Nevertheless, with the exception of specialists, many aquatic biologists still clung to old, ambiguous, and confused nomenclature. Ward and Whipple (1918) included 79 genera of rotifers, 34 of which were shown to be invalid in 1913. Even to this day, much outdated terminology still perists.

The arrangement of genera and families used here is a modification of the plan given by Remane in *Das Tierreich* (1929–1933). It is based primarily on the fundamental structure and modifications of the mastax. The outline presented below includes the genera given in the key which follows.

Class Digononta
  Order Seisonidea
  Order Bdelloidea (ramate mastax)
    Philodinidae
      *Dissotrocha, Embata, Macrotrachela, Mniobia, Philodina, Pleuretra, Rotaria*
    Habrotrochidae
      *Ceratotrocha, Habrotrocha, Scepanotrocha*
    Philodinavidae
      *Philodinavus*
    Adinetidae
      *Adineta, Bradyscela*
Class Monogononta
  Order Flosculariacea (malleoramate mastax)
    Flosculariidae
      *Beauchampia, Floscularia, Lacinu-*

laria, Limnias, Octotrocha, Pseudo-
ecistes, Ptygura, Sinantherina
Conochilidae
Conochilus, Conochiloides
Filiniidae
Filinia, Pedalia, Tetramastix
Testudinellidae
Pompholyx, Testudinella
Trochosphaeridae
Trochosphaera
Order Collothecacea (uncinate mastax)
Collothecidae
Acyclus, Atrochus, Collotheca, Cu-
pelopagis, Stephanoceros
Order Ploima
Notommatidae
Notommatinae (virgate or virgate-
forcipate mastax)
Cephalodella, Dorria, Driloph-
aga, Enteroplea, Eosphora, Eo-
thinia, Itura, Monommata, No-
tommata, Pleurotrocha, Restic-
ula, Rousseletia, Scaridium, Sphy-
rias, Taphrocampa, Tylotrocha
Proalinae (modified malleate mas-
tax)
Bryceella, Proales, Proalinopsis
Tetrasiphoninae (modified virgate
mastax)
Tetrasiphon
Lindiinae (cardate mastax)
Lindia
Birgeinae (aberrant mastax, with a
pair of pseudunci)
Birgea
Dicranophorinae (forcipate mas-
tax)
Albertia, Aspelta, Dicranophorus,
Encentrum, Erignatha, Myersi-
nella, Pedipartia, Streptognatha,
Wierzejskiella

Pseudoploesomatinae * (virgate
mastax)
Pseudoploesoma
Synchaetidae (virgate or virgate-for-
cipate mastax)
Polyarthra, Synchaeta
Microcodonidae (forcipate mastax)
Microcodon
Ploesomatidae (virgate mastax)
Ploesoma
Gastropodidae (virgate mastax)
Ascomorpha, Chromogaster, Gas-
tropus
Trichocercidae (virgate mastax)
Elosa, Hertwigia, Trichocerca
Asplanchnidae (incudate mastax)
Asplanchna, Asplanchnopus, Har-
ringia
Brachionidae (malleate mastax)
Brachioninae
Anuraeopsis, Brachionus, Cyr-
tonia, Epiphanes, Euchlanis, Eu-
dactylota, Kellicottia, Keratella,
Lophocharis, Macrochaetus, Mi-
krocodides, Mytilina, Notholca,
Platyias, Rhinoglena, Trichotria
Colurinae
Colurella, Lepadella, Paracolu-
rella, Squatinella
Lecaninae
Lecane, Monostyla

The following key includes all genera
likely to be encountered in the United
States. It does not include about eight
rare fresh-water genera which have been
found only on other continents. Much of
this key is not based on natural and family
relationships but rather on the most obvious and reliable morphological and anatomical characters.

## KEY TO GENERA OF ROTATORIA

1. With a single ovary (Figs. 96, 97); mastax not ramate; lorica or secreted tube
present or absent..........................Class **MONOGONONTA, 3**
With paired ovaries (Figs. 98, 110); mastax ramate (Fig. 102E); without a lorica
or secreted tube..............................Class **DIGONONTA, 2**

---

* New subfamily.

2. Ovaries without a vitellarium; male well developed; corona disc rudimentary; one genus and several species commensal on marine Crustacea.
$$\text{Order SEISONIDEA}$$

Each ovary with a vitellarium (Fig. 110); males absent; reproduction entirely by parthenogenesis; corona usually well developed; body cylindrical, highly contractile, and telescopic; free-swimming or with leechlike creeping movements; with a dorsal proboscis; toes, when present, usually retracted within foot except when creeping; two nonretractile spurs usually present.
$$\text{Order BDELLOIDEA, 92}$$

3. Adult female almost invariably free-swimming or creeping; lorica present or absent; without a secreted tube; corona not especially large; foot, when present, typically with two toes; solitary......................................5
Adult female usually sessile; without a lorica but often in a secreted tube; corona large; foot, when present, long and annulated and without toes but with a terminal attachment disc; solitary or colonial......................4

4. Corona surrounded by two concentric wreaths of cilia with a ciliated furrow between (Figs. 99B, D); cilia of outer wreath always shorter than inner; mouth not central; usually with one or two well-developed antennae; mastax malleoramate (Fig. 102C); solitary or colonial............Order **FLOSCULARIACEA, 79**
Corona very large, without such a double wreath of cilia; without well-developed antennae; mouth central; mastax uncinate or poorly developed; buccal field horseshoe-shaped and located at the bottom of a large concave infundibulum; (Fig. 129); solitary; often sessile.
$$\text{Order COLLOTHECACEA, COLLOTHECIDAE, 88}$$

5. Foot and toes always absent.................................................6
Foot always present; toes usually present.................................20

6. With 12, movable, sword- or blade-shaped lateral appendages (Fig. 115B); body short and more or less cylindrical; several common plankton species.
$$\text{Order PLOIMA, SYNCHAETIDAE, Polyarthra}$$
Without 12 such appendages................................................7

7. With six, stout, muscular, setose appendages; body conical; with a double ciliary wreath and a ciliated groove between (Fig. 115A); the "jumping rotifer"; usually in small lakes and ponds during the summer months; several species.
$$\text{Order FLOSCULARIACEA, FILINIIDAE, Pedalia}$$
Without six such appendages.............................................8

8. Without a lorica but with three or four long movable spines (Figs. 115E, F).
$$\text{Order FLOSCULARIACEA, FILINIIDAE, 9}$$
Lorica present or absent; spines, if present, rigid and confined to anterior and posterior margins of lorica.................................................10

9. With two lateral and one posterior spine; several common limnetic species (Fig. 115E) ...................................................**Filinia**
With two unequal lateral and two unequal posterior spines (Fig. 115F); one uncommon plankton species...................**Tetramastix opoliensis** Zach.

10. With a spinous lorica composed of two plates immovably fused laterally.
$$\text{Order PLOIMA, BRACHIONIDAE, Brachioninae, 11}$$
Lorica absent, or present and not spinous..................................13

11. With one very long posterior spine and four or six anterior spines, of which three are very long (Figs. 115H, J); two limnetic species, one of which is very common. ...................................................**Kellicottia**
With one, two, or no posterior spines, and with six short to medium anterior spines; highly variable plankton and limnetic species.........................12

12. Dorsal surface of lorica with a pattern of polygonal facets (Figs. 116A–L); about ten species, of which several are very common..................**Keratella**
Dorsal surface of lorica plain, pustulose, or longitudinally striated (Figs. 116M, N); several species..................................................**Notholca**

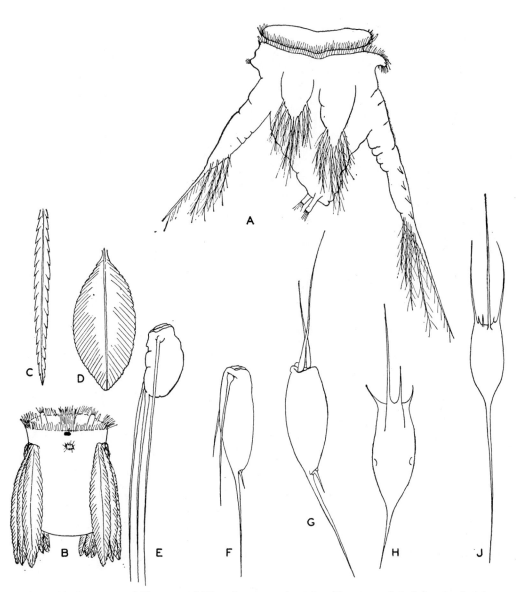

FIG. 115.—Structure of Ploima and Flosculariacea. A, right side view of *Pedalia*; B, dorsal view of *Polyarthra*; C and D, single appendages of *Polyarthra*; E, lateral view of *Filinia*; F, *Tetramastix opoliensis* Zach. with anterior spines in normal position; G, *T. opoliensis* with anterior spines retracted forward; H, dorsal view of lorica of *Kellicottia bostoniensis* (Rousselet); J, dorsal view of *K. longispina* (Kellicott).

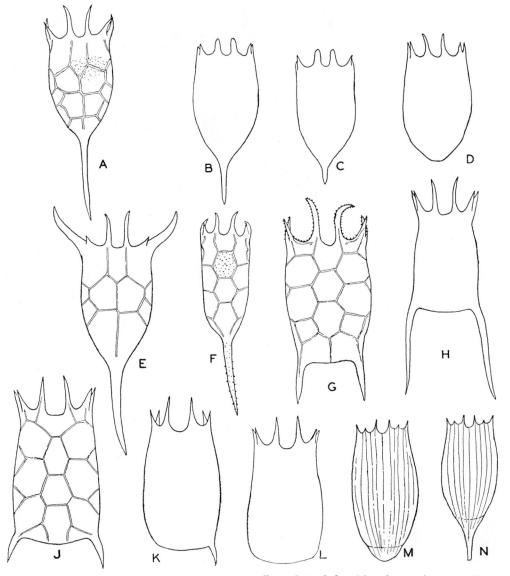

Fig. 116.—Lorica of typical species of *Keratella* and *Notholca* (dorsal views). A to D, *Keratella cochlearis* (Gosse); E, *K. taurocephala* Ahlstrom (an acid water species); F, *K. gracilenta* Ahlstrom; G, *K. serrulata* (Ehr.) (common in acid waters); H to L, *K. quadrata* (Müller); M and N, *Notholca*. Dorsal plates shown only for A, E, F, G, and J; small amount of pustulation shown only in A and F. (A to L modified from Ahlstrom, 1943.)

13. Large, transparent species, usually 400 to 2,000 microns long................**14**
    Small, more opaque species, less than 200 microns long....................**15**
14. Sac-shaped, with a well developed corona; intestine and anus lacking; mastax in-
       cudate; vitellarium horseshoe-shaped or globose (Figs. 117A, B); often vivip-
       arous; body of one species with humps or winglike processes; several very
       common plankton species. .Order **PLOIMA, ASPLANCHNIDAE, Asplanchna**
    Spherical and without a true corona, the body being divided into unequal hemis-
       pheres by a ciliary band; intestine and anus present; mastax malleoramate
       (Fig. 117C); up to 750 microns in diameter; very rare; more likely to be
       found in southern states....................Order **FLOSCULARIACEA,**
                      TROCHOSPHAERIDAE, **Trochosphaera solstitialis** Thorpe
15. With a thin lorica, or lorica absent; sac-shaped; with a very large lobed stomach
       filling much of the body cavity; anus absent; usually densely colored or
       opaque (Fig. 117D); mastax virgate; several species.
                      Order **PLOIMA, GASTROPODIDAE, Ascomorpha**
    With a thick lorica; not sac-shaped.....................................**16**

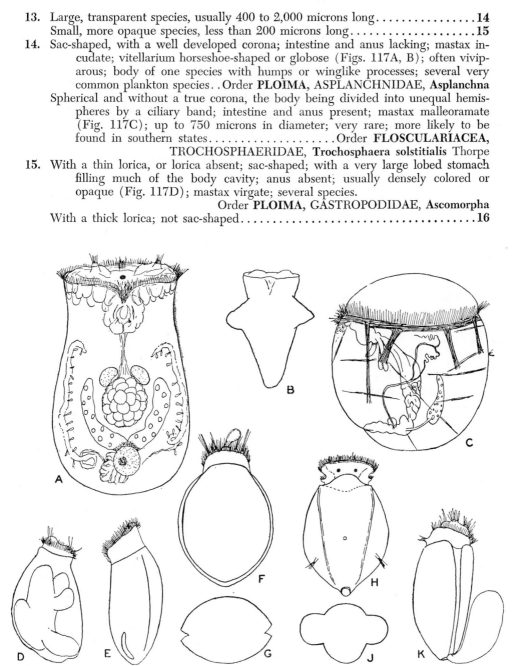

Fig. 117.—Structure of Ploima and Flosculariacea. A, ventral view of *Asplanchna* (muscle
fibers not shown); B, *Asplanchna* with winglike processes; C, lateral view of *Trochosphaera
solstitialis* Thorpe; D, lateral view of *Ascomorpha* showing lobed stomach; E, lateral view of
*Elosa worralli* Lord; F, dorsal view of *Chromogaster*; G, cross section of *Chromogaster*; H,
dorsal view of *Pompholyx*; J, cross section of *Pompholyx*; K, lateral view of *Anuraeopsis fissa*
(Gosse) carrying egg. (H and J modified from Wulfert.)

16. Lorica composed of a single cylindrical piece (Fig. 117E); trophi asymmetrical (Fig. 104C)...................Order **PLOIMA**, TRICHOCERCIDAE, **17**
    Lorica composed of a dorsal and a ventral plate (Figs. 117F–K); trophi symmetrical ........................................................**18**

17. Lorica trilobate in section, and with a crescentic opening posteriorly on the left side (Fig. 117E); one uncommon free-living species........**Elosa worralli** Lord
    Lorica round in section, and without a crescentic opening; parasitic in *Volvox* colonies; one species........................**Hertwigia volvocicola** Plate

18. Corona with one to three finger-like processes in addition to ciliated papillae; lorica composed of two convex plates fused laterally (Figs. 117F, G); mastax virgate; probably two species.
    Order **PLOIMA**, GASTROPODIDAE, **Chromogaster**
    Corona without finger-like processes...................................**19**

19. Lateral edges of dorsal and ventral plates of lorica closely confluent; flat or four-lobed in cross section; two frontal eyespots (Figs. 117H, J); mastax malleoramate; several species.
    Order **FLOSCULARIACEA**, TESTUDINELLIDAE, **Pompholyx**
    Lateral edges of dorsal and ventral plates of lorica connected by infolded cuticle; ventral plate flat, dorsal plate arched (Fig. 117K); mastax malleate; one rare species..............Order **PLOIMA**, BRACHIONIDAE, BRACHIONINAE,
    **Anuraeopsis fissa** (Gosse)

20. With a well-developed rigid lorica.....................................**21**
    Lorica absent, or present and poorly developed and flexible....Order **PLOIMA, 42**

21. Foot and toes attached to the ventral surface; lorica composed of one rigid piece, never dorsoventrally flattened; foot usually annulated (Figs. 118A, B); mastax virgate...........................................Order **PLOIMA, 22**
    Foot and toes terminal or subterminal.................................**24**

22. Surface of lorica plain; body laterally compressed; lorica with a small ventral opening for the foot; foot with one or two toes (Fig. 118A); three species.
    GASTROPODIDAE, **Gastropus**
    Surface of lorica marked with ridges or vesicles; body not laterally compressed; lorica usually open along the midventral line; foot with two toes (Figs. 118B, C) ........................................................**23**

23. Corona with frontal palps; foot annulated; lorica open along the midventral line (Fig. 118B); mastax virgate and adapted for prehension; about four species.
    PLOESOMATIDAE, **Ploesoma**
    Corona without frontal palps but with two unique juxta-buccal protuberances; foot composed of two telescoping segments and emerging from an oval opening in the lorica (Fig. 118C); mastax virgate but not adapted for prehension; one rare species in acid waters......NOTOMMATIDAE, PSEUDOPLOESOMATINAE,
    **Pseudoploesoma formosum** (Myers)

24. Body cylindrical, more or less curved, and asymmetrical; lorica a single cylindrical piece, often with teeth and longitudinal grooves or ridges; toes spinelike, of unequal length, and with several small spinules at their base (Figs. 118D–J); creeping or free-swimming; mastax virgate; trophi asymmetrical (Fig. 104C); many species........Order **PLOIMA**, TRICHOCERCIDAE, **Trichocerca** *
    With another combination of characters; rarely asymmetrical; toes not spinelike. .**25**

25. Foot long, retractile, annulated, and terminating in a tuft of cilia; dorsal and ventral plates of lorica completely fused laterally; greatly flattened dorsoventrally and sometimes nearly circular (Fig. 119B); mastax malleoramate; 120 to 300 microns long; about ten species.
    Order **FLOSCULARIACEA**, TESTUDINELLIDAE, **Testudinella**
    Foot ending in one or two toes........................Order **PLOIMA, 26**

* In accordance with the suggestion of Edmondson (1935), *Diurella* and *Trichocerca* have been combined into a single genus.

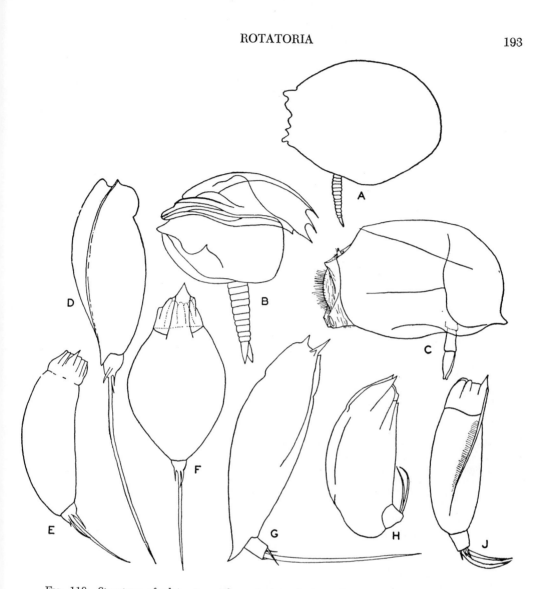

Fig. 118.—Structure of ploimate rotifers. A, lateral view of *Gastropus*; B, lateral view of *Ploesoma*; C, lateral view of *Pseudoploesoma formosum* (Myers); D to J, common species of *Trichocerca* (contracted). (B modified from Wesenberg-Lund, 1930; C modified from Myers, 1934; G and H modified from Ahlstrom, 1938.)

26. Entire margin spiny; lorica heavy, with four to ten long dorsal spines and six
       posterior spines; foot short (Fig. 119A); mastax malleate; about five species.
                                 BRACHIONIDAE, Brachioninae, **Macrochaetus**
    Entire margin of body not spiny................................................27
27. Head bearing a wide circular shield; lorica cylindrical or pyriform, often with one
       or two median dorsal spines, or several spines on posterior margin of lorica;
       sometimes with a spine at the base of the toes (Figs. 119C, D); mastax
       malleate; about six species.... BRACHIONIDAE, Brachioninae, **Squatinella**
    Head without a wide circular shield................................28

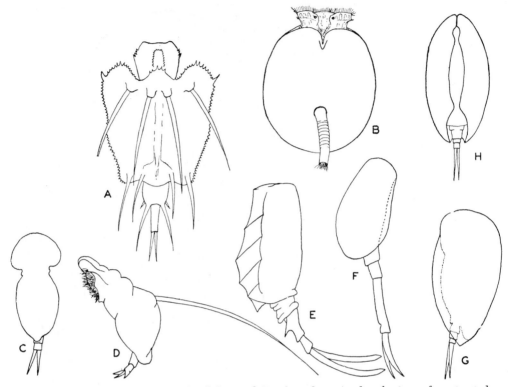

Fig. 119.—Structure of Testudinellidae and Brachionidae. A, dorsal view of contracted *Macrochaetus*; B, ventral view of *Testudinella*; C, dorsal view of *Squatinella*; D, lateral view of a spined species of *Squatinella*; E, lateral view of contracted *Trichotria*; F, lateral view of contracted *Paracolurella*; G, lateral view of contracted *Colurella*; H, ventral view of contracted *Colurella*. (D modified from Hauer, 1935; F modified from Myers, 1934.)

**28.** Usually with two spines at base of foot, or rarely with two posterior dorsolateral spines on the lorica; lorica composed of one boxlike piece, usually thick and with large facets (Fig. 119E); mastax malleate; about six species.

BRACHIONIDAE, Brachioninae, **Trichotria**

Without two such spines.........................................................29

**29.** Body moderately flattened dorsoventrally; dorsal and ventral plates of lorica completely fused laterally; anterior dorsal margin of lorica usually with four or six spines; posterior margin with or without spines; two toes; mastax malleate.

BRACHIONIDAE, Brachioninae, **30**

With another combination of characters; mastax usually malleate or submalleate; never dorsoventrally flattened and never with four or six spines on anterior dorsal margin of lorica.......................................................31

**30.** Foot segmented and retractile (Figs. 120N, O); three species.........**Platyias**

Foot long, annulated, retractile, not segmented (Fig. 120K); about 15 plankton species, some of which are common and highly variable..........**Brachionus**

**31.** Strongly compressed laterally; lorica composed of two lateral plates; frontal head hood present; toes long and tapering; lorica open along anterior, ventral, and posterior margins (Figs. 119F, G); small species.

BRACHIONIDAE, Colurinae, **32**

Not strongly compressed laterally; lorica of different construction; frontal hood absent. ..........................................................33

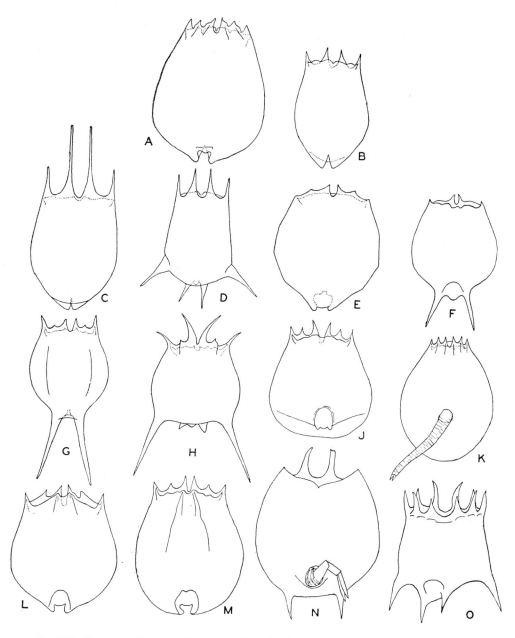

FIG. 120.—Structure of lorica of some common species of *Brachionus* and *Platyias*. A, dorsal view of *Brachionus plicatilis* Müller, a species characteristic of highly alkaline waters; B, ventral view of *B. calyciflorus* Pallas; C and D, dorsal view of *B. calyciflorus*; E, dorsal view of *B. angularis* Gosse; F, ventral view of *B. caudatus* Barrois and Daday; G, dorsal view of *B. havanaensis* Rousselet; H, dorsal view of *B. quadridentata* Hermann; J, ventral view of *B. quadridentata*; K, ventral view of *B. pterodinoides* Rousselet, a species characteristic of highly alkaline waters; L, dorsal view of *B. rubens* Ehr.; M, ventral view of *B. urceolaris* Müller; N, ventral view of *Platyias quadricornis* (Ehr.); O, ventral view of *P. patulus* (Müller). (Redrawn and modified from Ahlstrom, 1940.)

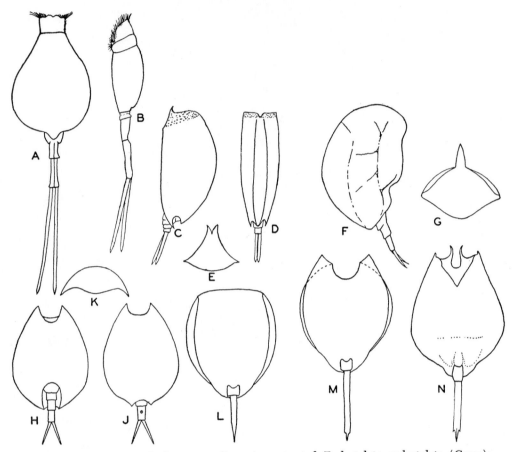

Fig. 121.—Structure of ploimate rotifers. A, contracted *Eudactylota eudactylota* (Gosse); B, lateral view of *Scaridium longicaudum* (Müller); C, lateral view of contracted *Mytilina*; D, dorsal view of contracted *Mytilina*; E, cross section of *Mytilina*; F, lateral view of contracted *Lophocharis*; G, cross section of *Lophocharis*; H, ventral view of contracted *Lepadella*; J, dorsal view of contracted *Lepadella*; K, cross section of *Lepadella*; L to N, ventral views of three contracted species of *Monostyla*.

32. Terminal foot segment long (Fig. 119F); two rare species.........**Paracolurella**
    Terminal foot segment short; about ten species, some common (Fig. 119G).
                                                       **Colurella**
33. Foot long; toes long; lorica without spines or plates.......................34
    Foot short; toes short to long........................................35
34. Lorica vase-shaped; toes shorter than rest of body (Fig. 121B); mastax virgate; one species.
            NOTOMMATIDAE, Notommatinae, **Scaridium longicaudum** (Müller)
    Lorica pear-shaped; toes about as long as rest of body (Fig. 121A); mastax mal-leate; one species.
            BRACHIONIDAE, Brachioninae, **Eudactylota eudactylota** (Gosse)
35. Lorica composed of a ventral plate and two lateral plates, the edges of the latter forming two dorsal ridges; often with anterior and posterior spines (Figs. 121C–E); about six species....BRACHIONIDAE, Brachioninae, **Mytilina**
    Lorica constructed differently............................................36

36. Lorica composed of one piece, capacious, rigid, boxlike, and with a prominent dorsal keel or low ridge extending the entire length of the lorica (Figs. 121F, G); several species. . . . BRACHIONIDAE, BRACHIONINAE, **Lophocharis**
Lorica usually composed of a dorsal and a ventral plate. . . . . . . . . . . . . . . . . . .37

37. Dorsal and ventral plates rigidly united at the edges; with an anterior opening for the protrusion of the head and a posterior opening through which the foot projects; foot well developed (Figs. 121H–K); about 20 small species.

BRACHIONIDAE, COLURINAE, **Lepadella**

Dorsal and ventral plates not united at the edges; foot not well developed; associated with the substrate but occasionally found in the plankton. . . . . . . . . . .38

38. With a single long toe; strongly compressed dorsoventrally and oval to ovate in outline (Figs. 121L–N). . . . . . . . . BRACHIONIDAE, LECANINAE, **Monostyla**
With two toes. . . . . . . . . . . . . . . . . . . . . . . . . . . . . . . . . . . . . . . . . . . . . . . . . . . . . .39

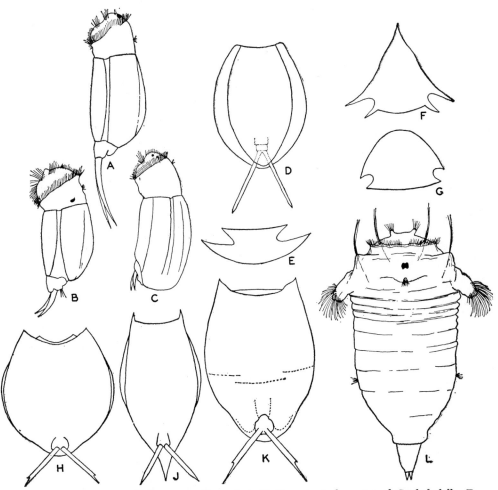

FIG. 122.—Structure of ploimate rotifers. A to C, three typical species of *Cephalodella*; D, dorsal view of retracted *Euchlanis*; E to G, cross sections of three species of *Euchlanis*; H to K, ventral views of typical species of *Lecane* (contracted); L, dorsal view of *Synchaeta*. (D to G modified from Myers, 1930; H to K modified from Harring and Myers, 1926.)

39. Prismatic or spindle-shaped; toes tapering, usually curved; lorica thin and poorly developed (Figs. 122A–C); mastax virgate; many species.

NOTOMMATIDAE, Notommatinae, **Cephalodella**

More or less flattened dorsoventrally; toes long and slightly fusiform or parallel-sided and straight; lorica rigid and well developed (Figs. 122D–K); mastax malleate or submalleate..........................BRACHIONIDAE, **40**

40. Dorsal plate much smaller than ventral plate (Fig. 122E); cuticle connecting the dorsal and ventral plates in the form of a deep groove dividing the body cavity into two unequal portions (Fig. 122D); one species.

Brachioninae, **Euchlanis**

Dorsal plate the same size or larger than the ventral plate..................**41**

41. Foot with two rudimentary segments, of which only the posterior is movable; toes parallel-sided; strongly compressed dorsoventrally (Figs. 122H–K).

Lecaninae, **Lecane**

Foot with two or three obscure segments; toes usually slightly fusiform; ventral plate flat; dorsal plate arched and convex, sometimes keeled (Fig. 97); about 12 species, some very common..................Brachioninae, **Euchlanis**

42. With four long, prominent sensory bristles on the corona; body conical; toes small (Fig. 122L); mastax virgate; about ten plankton species, several of which are common..........................SYNCHAETIDAE, **Synchaeta**

Without four such bristles...........................................**43**

43. Foot very long, about half of total length; a single toe; corona flat and circular (Fig. 123B); mastax forcipate; a single uncommon species.

MICROCODONIDAE, **Microcodon clavus** Ehr.

Foot much shorter; almost invariably with two toes.......................**44**

44. Corona complex, with an outer band of cilia and an inner band of cilia, sometimes also with accessory rows of cilia and ciliated protuberances (Figs. 123A, C, D); mastax malleate; large species........BRACHIONIDAE, Brachioninae, **45**

Corona simple, with a single peripheral band of cilia; general surface of corona without cilia, with few scattered cilia, or with cilia more or less covering the corona; corona occasionally with two slight sensory protuberances.......**48**

45. With a single toe; sometimes a small spur at the base of the toe; foot thick (Fig. 123A); one species......................**Mikrocodides chlaena** (Gosse)

With two toes...................................................**46**

46. With a large dorsal proboscis at the anterior end bearing two eyespots (Fig. 123C); one species....................................**Rhinoglena frontalis** Ehr.

Without such a proboscis.........................................**47**

47. Eyespot absent; body not strongly tapered posteriorly (Fig. 96); common during spring in stock ponds and puddles containing much organic matter; probably three species.............................................**Epiphanes**

Eyespot present; body strongly tapered posteriorly (Fig. 123D); one species.

**Cyrtonia tuba** Ehr.

48. Large, globular species; mastax incudate (Figs. 103C, D).

ASPLANCHNIDAE, **49**

Smaller species, more or less opaque; mastax not incudate; mostly illoricate or weakly loricate..............................NOTOMMATIDAE, **50**

49. Intestine and anus absent (Fig. 123F); three species..........**Asplanchnopus**

Intestine and anus present (Fig. 123E); two species...............**Harringia**

50. Mastax forcipate; trophi strongly compressed dorsoventrally and adapted for protrusion and tearing prey (Fig. 103E); corona oval and ventral, or subcircular and strongly oblique; marginal cilia short, with the exception of two lateral, auricle-like tufts of long cilia; rostrum large; buccal field evenly ciliated; retrocerebral sac present.............................Dicranophorinae, **71**

Mastax not forcipate; corona frontal or oblique..........................**51**

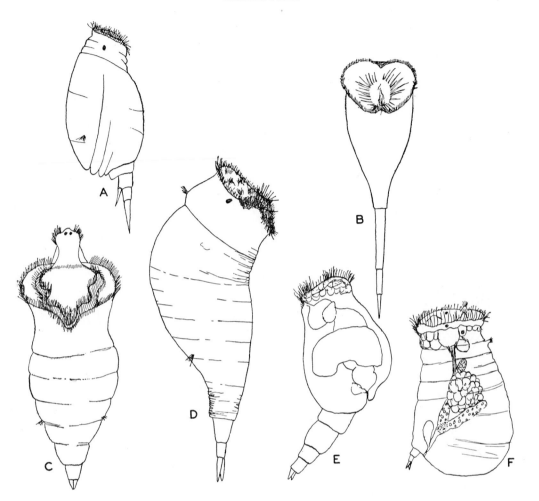

Fig. 123.—Structure of ploimate rotifers. A, *Mikrocodides chlaena* (Gosse); B, *Microcodon clavus* Ehr.; C, ventral view of *Rhinoglena frontalis* Ehr.; D, *Cyrtonia tuba* Ehr.; E, *Harringia*; F, *Asplanchnopus*.

51. Mastax virgate or virgate-forcipate, adapted for sucking out the contents of plant cells and animals (Fig. 104); a pair of lateral auricles often present; retrocerebral sac present...........................................................52
   Mastax not virgate or virgate-forcipate; retrocerebral sac rudimentary or absent..53
52. Lateral antennae located near base of foot, long, knobbed, and with excessively long setae; ovary long, slender, and ribbon-like; auricles absent; dorsal antenna double and very long (Fig. 124C); corona oblique; total length 750 to 1,000 microns; one rare species....Tetrasiphoninae, **Tetrasiphon hydrocora** Ehr.
   Lateral antennae not located near base of foot; ovary not long, slender, and ribbon-like; auricles present or absent; dorsal antenna not especially long; corona frontal or oblique....................................Notommatinae, **55**

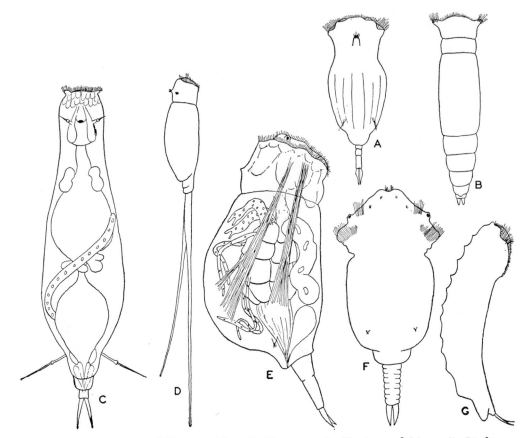

FIG. 124.—Structure of Notommatidae. A, *Birgea enantia* Harring and Myers; B, *Lindia*; C, *Tetrasiphon hydrocora* Ehr.; D, *Monommata*; E, *Enteroplea lacustris* Ehr.; F, *Sphyrias lofuana* (Rousselet); G, *Taphrocampa*. (A to C modified from Harring and Myers, 1922; D to G modified from Harring and Myers, 1924.)

53. Mastax modified malleate; unci adapted for crushing and grinding; corona oblique, with two lateral tufts of cilia but no auricles (Figs. 126D–F); total length 90 to 400 microns.....................................PROALINAE, **69**

   Mastax not modified malleate or malleate-virgate; corona oblique or frontal; auricles present or absent...............................................**54**

54. Body cylindrical and tapering posteriorly, sometimes indistinctly annulated; foot not set off sharply from body (Fig. 124B); mastax cardate (Figs. 103A, B); total length 250 to 1,200 microns; about ten species......LINDIINAE, **Lindia**

   Foot slender and sharply set off from the wide body (Fig. 124A); trophi aberrant, with a pair of pseudunci; 240 to 275 microns long; one rare species.
   BIRGEINAE, **Birgea enantia** Harring and Myers

55. Toes longer than rest of body, usually unequal in length (Fig. 124D); about 20 species. ...............................................**Monommata**

   Toes short ...............................................................**56**

56. Gastric glands long, ribbon-like, and bifurcated; with four slender accessory gastric appendages; body short and saclike (Fig. 124E); one uncommon species.
   **Enteroplea lacustris Ehr.**

   Without such glands...........................................................**57**

**57.** Head very broad and truncate anteriorly; two eyespots widely separated on protuberances; foot annulated (Fig. 124F); one species.

**Sphyrias lofuana** (Rousselet)

With other characters..............................................................**58**

**58.** Body marked with transverse folds or annuli; elongated and spindle-shaped; foot
rudimentary (Fig. 124G); several species.................**Taphrocampa**

Body not so marked....................................................**59**

**59.** Toes relatively long, pointed, and usually curved; foot rudimentary and unjointed;
body prismatic or spindle-shaped (Figs. 122A–C); retrocerebral sac absent;
lorica present, more or less sclerotized and composed of a dorsal and a ventral
plate; both rami and unci of very simple construction (Figs. 104D, E); more
than 50 species, some of which are very common.............**Cephalodella**

Toes comparatively short; foot present and distinct; retrocerebral sac present; lorica
absent; rami and unci more complicated...............................**60**

**60.** Foot unsegmented, though sometimes annulated (Figs. 125A–C)............**61**

Foot segmented (Figs. 125D–K).........................................**63**

**61.** With a single toe; retrocerebral sac absent (Fig. 125A); trophi highly specialized
virgate; one species...................**Tylotrocha monopus** (Jennings)

With two toes; retrocerebral sac present or absent; trophi not highly specialized
virgate..............................................................**62**

**62.** Retrocerebral sac absent; eyespot absent; foot short (Fig. 125B); one species ectoparasitic on oligochaetes, a second ectoparasitic on *Erpobdella,* and one other
possibly free-living; often covered by a gelatinous secretion......**Drilophaga**

Retrocerebral sac present; eyespot present; foot long (Fig. 125C); one species.

**Rousseletia corniculata** Harring

**63.** With a projecting auricle on each side of the head, each auricle bearing long cilia;
trophi usually asymmetrical (Figs. 104A, B).........................**64**

Without definite auricles but often with a tuft of long cilia in the usual location of
an auricle; trophi symmetrical......................................**65**

**64.** Rami roughly hemispherical (Figs. 104A, B); with a cervical eyespot only (Fig.
125D); total length 100 to 1,000 microns, usually more than 300 microns; a
few species covered by a gelatinous secretion; many species, some very
common. ......................................................**Notommata**

Rami lyrate, broad, and strongly divergent at the base, continuing as parallel rods
toward the tips (Fig. 125E); with a cervical eyespot and two frontal eyespots
(Fig. 125F); about four uncommon species........................**Itura**

**65.** Eyespot absent (Fig. 125G); in mountain brooks among submerged moss; one
species..............................**Dorria dalecarlica** Myers

One or three eyespots present; not in mountain brooks in moss...............**66**

**66.** Retrocerebral sac absent (Fig. 125H); rami without teeth (Fig. 125J); toes
separate or fused; total length 110 to 250 microns; five species

**Pleurotrocha**

Retrocerebral sac present (Fig. 125K); rami with one or more teeth; toes separate.

**67**

**67.** Each uncus with a single simple tooth; rami bent at right angles and with one or
two teeth at mid-length and many small ones more distally (Fig. 125L); total
length 300 to 500 microns; about five species...................**Eosphora**

One or both unci with a single main tooth plus accessory teeth (Fig. 126B); rami
more or less bent at right angles but with a different arrangement of teeth;
total length 170 to 400 microns.....................................**68**

**68.** With one eyespot, or eyespot absent (Fig. 126A); each uncus with one main tooth
and with accessory teeth on either the left or right uncus; probably four species.

**Resticula**

With three eyespots (Fig. 126C); both unci with one main tooth and accessory
teeth (Fig. 126B); probably three species....................**Eothinia**

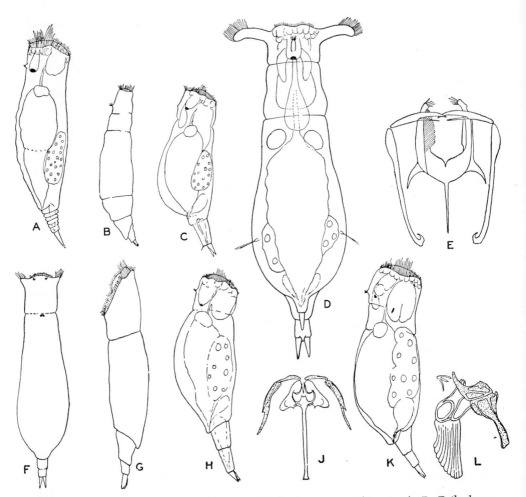

FIG. 125.—Structure of Notommatidae. A, *Tylotrocha monopus* (Jennings); B, *Drilophaga*; C, *Rousseletia corniculata* Harring; D, dorsal view of *Notommata*; E, ventral view of *Itura* trophi; F, *Itura*; G, *Dorria dalecarlica* Myers; H, *Pleurotrocha*; J, ventral view of *Pleurotrocha* trophi (mallei stippled); K, *Eosphora*; L, lateral view of *Eosphora* trophi (malleus stippled). (A, C, H, and J modified from Harring and Myers, 1924; B, D, K, and L modified from Harring and Myers, 1922; E and F modified from Harring and Myers, 1928; G modified from Myers, 1933.)

69. With a very long stylet on each side of the head (Fig. 126D); two species.
                                                                          **Bryceella**
    Without such stylets...................................................70
70. Tail region or basal foot segment with a knoblike papilla bearing a tuft of setae or
    a spine (Fig. 126E); five species.........................**Proalinopsis**
    Without such a tuft of setae or spine (Fig. 126F); one species with a single toe;
    about 20 species, some quite common.........................**Proales**
71. Trophi asymmetrical (Fig. 126H)...............................72
    Trophi symmetrical (Figs. 127C, E, G, L)........................73

72. Corona ventral; retrocerebral sac present; toes long (Fig. 126G); about ten species, usually in acid waters and sphagnum bogs.......................**Aspelta**
    Corona oblique; retrocerebral sac absent; toes short (Fig. 126J); one rare species known from sandy beaches....................**Pedipartia gracilis** (Myers)
73. Foot one-fourth to one-third the total length, composed of one to four segments (Fig. 127A); three uncommon species....................**Wierzejskiella**
    Foot shorter........................................................74
74. Incus Y-shaped and composed of rods; with a long naviculoid sclerite attached to the tip of each uncus (Fig. 127C); a single acid water species.
    **Streptognatha lepta** Harring and Myers
    With incus and unci of different construction............................75
75. Rami slender and bent at nearly a right angle at mid-length and terminating in long, slender, single teeth (Fig. 127E); retrocerebral sac absent; corona oblique (Fig. 127D); about four species.............................**Erignatha**
    Rami not slender and bent at nearly a right angle at mid-length; retrocerebral sac present or absent; corona oblique or ventral..........................76

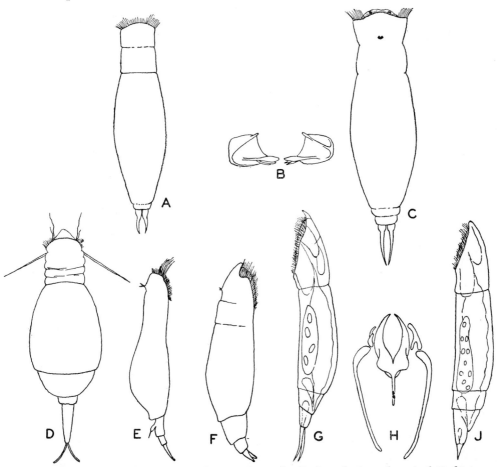

FIG. 126.—Structure of Notommatidae. A, *Resticula*; B, frontal view of unci of *Eothinia*; C, *Eothinia*; D, *Bryceella*; E, *Proalinopsis*; F, *Proales*; G, *Aspelta*; H, trophi of *Aspelta*; J, *Pedipartia gracilis* (Myers). (A, E, and F modified from Harring and Myers, 1922; B and C modified from Harring and Myers, 1924; G and H modified from Harring and Myers, 1928; J modified from Myers, 1936.)

**76.** With a posterior projection at the external angles of the rami (Fig. 127G); retrocerebral sac absent; corona oblique or ventral (Fig. 127F); two species.

**Myersinella**

Without such projections on the rami.................................77

**77.** Toes minute and fused, or lacking; corona oblique; eyespots lacking; rostrum minute; retrocerebral sac absent (Fig. 127H); several species, most or all of which are ecto- or endoparasites of oligochaetes..................**Albertia**

Toes prominent, not fused; corona oblique or ventral; eyespots present or absent; rostrum conspicuous; retrocerebral sac present or absent; not parasitic.....**78**

**78.** Corona essentially ventral; two frontal eyespots; retrocerebral sac present and large (Fig. 127J); rami often with shearing teeth; unci robust (Fig. 103E); about 40 species.........................................**Dicranophorus**

Corona oblique; one eyespot, or eyespots absent; retrocerebral sac present or absent (Fig. 127K); rami never with shearing teeth; unci weak and needle-like (Fig. 127L); about ten species..................................**Encentrum**

**79.** With a ventral gap in the ciliary wreath; mouth on the corona, nearer the dorsal edge; gelatinous case (Figs. 128A–C); limnetic species.

CONOCHILIDAE, 80

Ciliary wreath with a dorsal gap or without a gap; mouth ventral to the corona; eyespots usually absent (Figs. 128D–L); adults usually sessile.

FLOSCULARIIDAE, 81

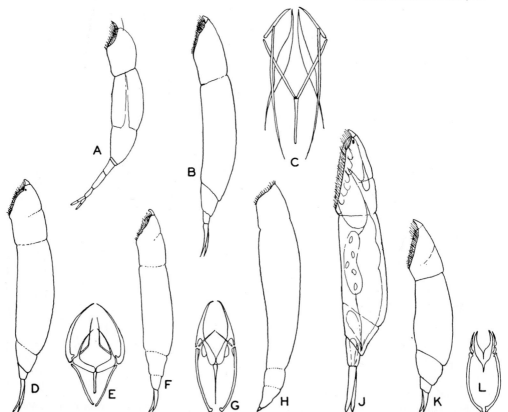

Fig. 127.—Structure of Dicranophorinae. A, *Wierzejskiella*; B, *Streptognatha lepta* Harring and Myers; C, trophi of *S. lepta*; D, *Erignatha*; E, trophi of *Erignatha*; F, *Myersinella*; G, trophi of *Myersinella*; H, *Albertia*; J, *Dicranophorus*; K, *Encentrum*; L, trophi of *Encentrum*. (B to L modified from Harring and Myers, 1928.)

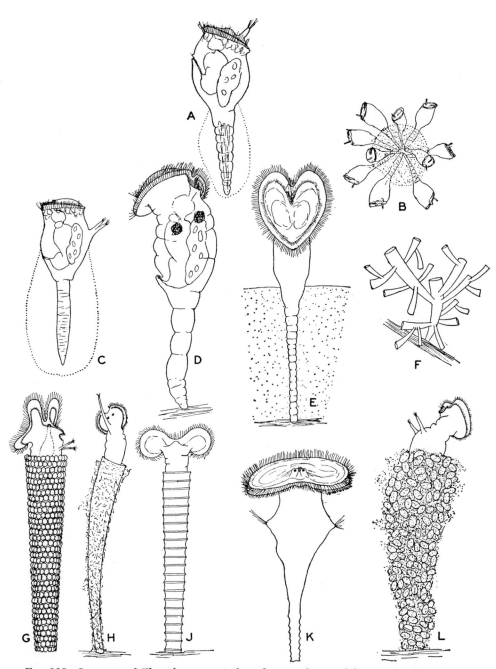

FIG. 128.—Structure of Flosculariacea. A, lateral view of *Conochilus*; B, sketch of a small colony of *Conochilus* showing common gelatinous case; C, lateral view of a solitary *Conochiloides* in gelatinous case; D, lateral view of *Sinantherina*; E, *Lacinularia* in gelatinous matrix of colony; F, cluster of empty *Floscularia* tubes; G, lateral view of *Floscularia* (note pellet-making concavity on ventral surface of head); H and J, dorsal views of *Limnias*; K, *Pseudoecistes rotifer* Stenroos; L, *Ptygura*. (All greatly modified from various sources.)

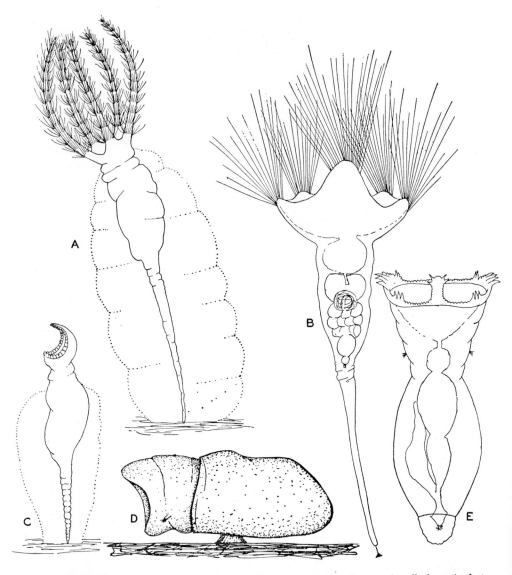

Fig. 129.—Structure of Collothecacea. A, *Stephanoceros*; B, dorsal view of *Collotheca* (gelatinous tube omitted); C, lateral view of *Acyclus inquietus* Leidy; D, lateral view of *Cupelopagis vorax* (Leidy); E, dorsal view of *Atrochus tentaculatus* Wierzejski. (C modified from Leidy, 1882; E modified from Wierzejski, 1893.)

80. With one or two antennae on the corona; colonies composed of radiating individuals inhabiting coherent gelatinous tubes; two common species (Figs. 128A, B)...............................................................**Conochilus**

With one or two ventral antennae below the corona; solitary or colonial; probably four species, of which two are common (Fig. 128C)..........**Conochiloides**

81. Adults in spherical, sessile colonies attached to aquatic plants...............82

Adults solitary or colonial, but colonies never spherical......................83

**82.** Colonies without tubes; trunk usually with two to four opaque protuberances; corona roughly kidney-shaped (Fig. 128D); about eight species.

**Sinantherina**

Colonies with adhering gelatinous tubes; trunk without protuberances; corona heart-shaped and with the sinus ventral (Fig. 128E); about ten species.

**Lacinularia**

**83.** Corona with eight prominent lobes and one small median dorsal lobe; in a gelatinous tube; one species.....................**Octotrocha speciosa** Thorpe

Corona with less than eight lobes, or not lobed...........................84

**84.** Corona four-lobed; two large ventral antennae; with a tube composed of gelatinous material, pellets of debris, or fecal pellets (Figs. 128F, G); about six species.

**Floscularia**

Corona two-lobed and elliptical, circular, or kidney-shaped.................85

**85.** Tube chitinoid, often opaque and more or less covered with debris; corona of two distinct lobes, or nearly circular; dorsal antenna short to long (Figs. 128H, J); about eight species.....................................**Limnias**

Tube not chitinoid, or tube absent.....................................86

**86.** Tube absent (Fig. 128K); able to leave substrate and swim about; one rare species.

**Pseudoecistes rotifer** Stenroos

Tube present ............................................................87

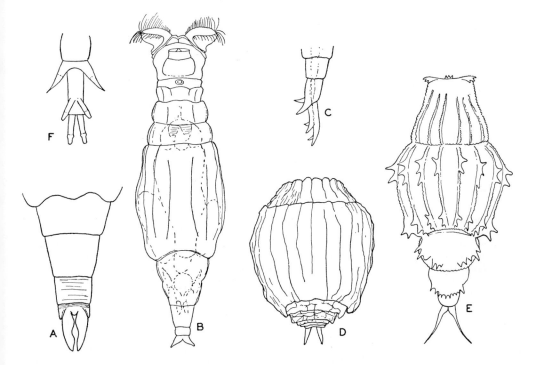

Fig. 130.—Structure of Bdelloidea. A, posterior end of *Embata* while swimming (toes retracted); B, dorsal view of *Philodina* (toes retracted); C, foot of *Philodina* (toes protruded); D, contracted *Philodina*; E, dorsal view of partly contracted *Dissotrocha*; F, dorsal view of foot of *Philodina* (toes protruded). (A modified from Murray, 1906; B and E modified from Murray, 1911; C and D modified from Hickernell.)

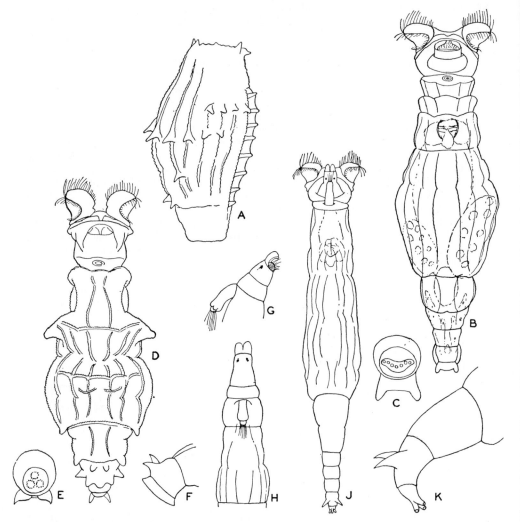

FIG. 131.—Structure of Bdelloidea. A, lateral view of contracted *Pleuretra*; B, dorsal view of *Mniobia* (toes retracted); C, ventral view of spurs and disc of *Mniobia*; D, dorsal view of *Macrotrachela* (toes retracted); E, end view of foot of *Macrotrachela* (toes retracted); F, lateral view of foot of *Macrotrachela* (toes retracted); G, lateral view of head of creeping *Rotaria*; H, dorsal view of anterior end of creeping *Rotaria*; J, dorsal view of swimming *Rotaria* (toes shown extruded); K, lateral view of foot of *Habrotrocha* (toes extruded). (A to J modified from Murray, 1911.)

87. Dorsal antenna small or apparently absent; ventral (lateral) antennae short to long; corona a wide oval or nearly circular, indistinctly bilobed; tube made of debris, fecal pellets, or gelatinous and more or less covered with debris (Fig. 128L); one species free-swimming; 24 species....................**Ptygura**
   Dorsal antenna very long; corona of two distinct lobes; tube irregular, translucent, and gelatinous; one rare species......**Beauchampia crucigera** (Dutrochet)
88. With setae but no cilia on the corona; sessile; in a gelatinous tube; foot terminated by a long nonretractile peduncle, ending in an adhesive disc............89
   Without setae or cilia on the corona; gelatinous case present or absent.........90

89. Corona drawn out into long pointed arms, which bear whorls of setae (Fig. 129A); two species...............................................................**Stephanoceros**

    Corona circular, lobed, or pointed in shape (Fig. 129B); setae not arranged in whorls; some species free-swimming.........................................**Collotheca**

90. Body long, with a long, annulated, tapering stalk and with or without a gelatinous case; corona produced into a large dorsal lobe, and bordered by a thin festooned membrane (Fig. 129C); lives in *Sinantherina* colonies; one rare species.
    **Acyclus inquietus** Leidy

    Body shorter, without a gelatinous case; foot absent........................91

91. Body saclike, with a flat attachment disc on the ventral surface; corona a large concave chamber (Fig. 129D); usually on broad flat leaves of aquatic plants; one rare species.............................**Cupelopagis vorax** (Leidy)

    Body spindle-shaped; corona with numerous small peripheral tentacles (Fig. 129E); one species.........................**Atrochus tentaculatus** Wierzejski

92. With a well developed rostrum and corona, the latter always capable of being retracted into the mouth........................................................93

    With rostrum imperfect or corona absent................................102

93. Stomach with a true lumen (Fig. 105E); intestine ciliated; oviparous or viviparous.
    PHILODINIDAE, 94

    Stomach without a lumen (Fig. 105F); food formed into vacuoles in the stomach protoplasm; intestine unciliated; oviparous......HABROTROCHIDAE, 100

94. With four plain toes, of which two are dorsal and two terminal (Figs. 130C, F)..95

    Toes otherwise.....................................................98

95. Cuticle smooth.........................................................96

    Cuticle coarse or leathery, and folded (Figs. 130E, 131A).................97

96. Spurs long (Fig. 130A); ectocommensals on many aquatic invertebrates; about three species...........................................................**Embata**

    Spurs short (Figs. 130B–D, F); not usually commensals; about 15 species.
    **Philodina**

97. Cuticle coarse, with few or no transverse folds but often with few to many spines, or spines absent (Fig. 130E); viviparous; about four species....**Dissotrocha**

    Cuticle leathery, with many transverse folds (Fig. 131A); oviparous; probably two rare species..........................................................**Pleuretra**

98. With three plain toes, one dorsal and two terminal (Figs. 131E, J)...........99

    With toes bearing cuplike suckers or united to form a broad disc or twin discs (Figs. 131B, C); about ten species.............................**Mniobia**

99. Eyes absent; oviparous; about 20 species (Figs. 131D–F)........**Macrotrachela**

    Two eyes usually present on proboscis; viviparous; some species greatly elongated; about ten species (Figs. 131G–J).................................**Rotaria**

100. Corona of the normal type; with three toes (Fig. 131K); many species.
     **Habrotrocha**

     Corona modified (Fig. 132)...........................................101

101. Corona with two hornlike processes (Fig. 132B); several rare species.
     **Ceratotrocha**

     Corona screened by a wide dorsal membranous plate (Fig. 132A); several uncommon species.............................................**Scepanotrocha**

102. Rostrum present and perfect but no corona; with four toes (Figs. 132C, D); one uncommon species..PHILODINAVIDAE, **Philodinavus paradoxus** (Murray)

     Rostrum imperfect; corona cannot be retracted within mouth; no ciliary wreaths but only with cilia distributed on corona (Fig. 132G); unable to swim.
     ADINETIDAE, 103

103. Foot slender, with two spurs and three toes (Fig. 132E); about ten species.
     **Adineta**

     Foot stout; spurs absent and replaced by a row of papilliform lobes (Figs. 132F, G); one uncommon species............**Bradyscela clauda** (Bryce)

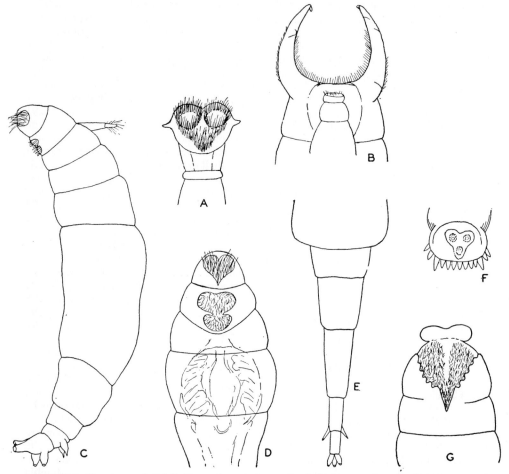

Fig. 132.—Structure of Bdelloidea. A, anterior end of *Scepanotrocha*; B, dorsal view of anterior end of *Ceratotrocha cornigera* (Bryce); C, *Philodinavus paradoxus* (Murray) with protruded toes; D, ventral view of anterior end of *P. paradoxus*; E, posterior end of *Adineta* with protruded toes; F, ventral view of posterior end of *Bradyscela clauda* (Bryce) showing papilliform lobes and region of three retracted toes; G, ventral view of anterior end of *B. clauda*. (A modified from Bryce, 1910; C and D modified from Murray, 1906.)

# ROTATORIA REFERENCES

AHLSTROM, E. H. 1934. Rotatoria of Florida. *Trans. Amer. Micros. Soc.* **53**:251–256.

———. 1934a. A quantitative study of Rotatoria in Terwilliger's Pond, Put-in-Bay, Ohio. *Bull. Ohio State Univ. Nat. Hist. Surv.* **6**:1–36.

———. 1938. Plankton Rotatoria from North Carolina. *Jour. Elisha Mitchell Sci. Soc.* **54**:88–110

———. 1940. A revision of the rotatorian genera Brachionus and Platyias with descriptions of one new species and two new varieties. *Bull. Amer. Mus. Nat. Hist.* **77**:143–184.

———. 1943. A revision of the rotatorian genus Keratella with descriptions of three new species and five new varieties. *Ibid.* **80**:411–457.

BARTÔS, E. 1948. On the Bohemian species of the genus Pedalia Barrois. *Hydrobiologia* **1**:63–77.

——. 1951. The Czechoslovak Rotatoria of the Order Bdelloidea. *Věstník Čs. zool. spol.* **15**:241–500.

Bérziņš, B. 1951. On the collothecacean Rotatoria. With special reference to the species found in the Aneboda district, Sweden. *Ark. Zool.* **1**:565–592.

Brakenhoff, H. 1937. Zur Morphologie der Bdelloidea. *Zool. Jahrb. Abt. Anat. Ont. Tiere* **63**:125–182

Bryce, D. 1893. On two new species of macrotrachelous Callidinae. *Jour. Quekket Micros. Club* **5**:196–201.

——. 1910. On a new classification of the bdelloid Rotifera. *Ibid.* **11**:61–92.

Buchner, H. 1941. Experimentelle Untersuchungen über den Generationswechsel der Rädertiere. II. *Zool. Jahrb. Abt. Allg. Zool. Physiol. Tiere* **60**:279–344

Budde, E. 1925. Die parasitischen Rädertiere mit besonderer Berücksichtigung der in der Umgegend von Minden I. W. beobachteten Arten. *Zeitschr. Morph. Ökol. Tiere* **3**:706–784.

Burger, A. 1948. Studies on the moss dwelling bdelloids (Rotifera) of Eastern Massachusetts. *Trans. Amer. Micros. Soc.* **67**:111–142.

Campbell, R. S. 1941. Vertical distribution of the plankton Rotifera in Douglas Lake, Michigan, with special reference to depression individuality. *Ecol. Monogr.* **11**:1–19.

Carlin, B. 1939. Über die Rotatorien einiger Seen bei Aneboda. *Medd. Lunds Univ. Limn. Inst.* **2**:1–68.

——. 1943. Die Planktonrotatorien des Motalaström. *Ibid.* **5**:1–255.

Cori, C. 1925. Zur Morphologie und Biologie von Apsilus vorax Leidy. *Zeitschr. wiss. Zool.* **125**:557–584.

De Beauchamp, P. M. 1909. Recherches sur les rotifères: les formations tégumentaires et l'appareil digestif. *Arch. Zool. Exp. Gen.* (4) **10**:1–410.

——. 1912. Instructions for collecting and fixing rotifers in bulk. *Proc. U. S. Nat. Mus.* **42**:181–185.

——. 1928. Coup d'oeil sur les recherches récentes relatives aux rotifères et sur les méthodes qui leur sont applicables. *Bull. Biol. France et de la Belgique* **62**:51–125.

——. 1932. Contribution à l'étude du genre Ascomorpha et des processus digestifs chez les rotifères. *Bull. Soc. Zool. France* **57**:428–449.

Dobers, E. 1915. Über die Biologie der Bdelloidea. *Int. Rev.* **7** (Suppl. 1):1–128.

Donner, J. 1951. Erste Übersicht über die Rotatorienfauna einiger Humusboden. *Österreich. Zool. Zeitschr.* **3**:175–240.

Edmondson, W. T. 1935. Some Rotatoria from Arizona. *Trans. Amer. Micros. Soc.* **54**:301–306.

——. 1936. Fixation of sessile Rotatoria. *Science* **84**:444.

——. 1939. New species of Rotatoria, with notes on heterogonic growth. *Trans. Amer. Micros. Soc.* **58**:459–472.

——. 1940. The sessile Rotatoria of Wisconsin. *Ibid.* **59**:433–459.

——. 1944. Ecological studies of sessile Rotatoria. Part I. Factors affecting distribution. *Ecol. Monogr.* **14**:31–66.

——. 1945. Ecological studies of sessile Rotatoria. Part II. Dynamics of populations and social structures. *Ibid.* **15**:141–172.

——. 1946. Factors in the dynamics of rotifer populations. *Ibid.* **16**:357–372.

——. 1948. Ecological applications of Lansing's physiological work on longevity in Rotatoria. *Science* **108**:123–126.

——. 1949. A formula key to the rotatorian genus Ptygura. *Trans. Amer. Micros. Soc.* **68**:127–135.

Finesinger, J. E. 1926. Effects of certain chemical and physical agents on fecundity and length of life, and on their inheritance in a rotifer Lecane (Distyla) inermis (Bryce). *Jour. Exp. Zool.* **44**:63–94.

Hanley, J. 1949. The narcotization and mounting of Rotifera. *Microscope* **7**:154–159.

Harring, H. K. 1913. Synopsis of the Rotatoria. *Bull. U. S. Nat. Mus.* **81**:1–226.

——. 1914. A list of the Rotatoria of Washington and vicinity with descriptions of a new genus and ten new species. *Proc. U. S. Nat. Mus.* **46**:387–405.

——. 1916. A revision of the rotatorian genera Lepadella and Lophocharis with descriptions of five new species. *Ibid.* **51**:527–568.

Harring, H. K., and F. J. Myers. 1922. The rotifer fauna of Wisconsin. *Trans. Wis. Acad. Sci. Arts and Lett.* **20**:553–662.

——. 1924. The rotifer fauna of Wisconsin, II. A revision of the notommatid rotifers, exclusive of the Dicranophorinae. *Ibid.* **21**:415–549.

——. 1926. The rotifer fauna of Wisconsin, III. A revision of the genera Lecane and Monostyla. *Ibid.* **22**:315–423.

——. 1928. The rotifer fauna of Wisconsin, IV. The Dicranophorinae. *Ibid.* **23**:667–808.

Hauer, J. 1924. Zur Kenntnis des Rotatorien genus Colurella Bory de St. Vincent. *Zool. Anz.* **59**:177–189.

——. 1937. Die Rotatorien von Sumatra, Java, und Bali nach den Ergebnissen der Deutschen Limnologischen Sunda-Expedition. *Arch. Hydrobiol., Suppl.* **7**:296–384.

——. 1938. Die Rotatorien von Sumatra, Java, und Bali nach den Ergebnissen der Deutschen Limnologischen Sunda-Expedition. ii. *Ibid.* 507–602.

Hickernell, L. M. 1917. A study of desiccation in the rotifer Philodina roseola, with special reference to cytological changes accompanying desiccation. *Biol. Bull.* **32**:343–407.

HLAVA, S. 1904. (Monograph of the Melicertidae.) *Arch. Přír. Prozk. Čech.* **13**:1–79.

HUDSON, C. T., and P. H. GOSSE. 1889. *The Rotifera; or wheel-animalcules, both British and foreign.* 2 vols. 272 pp. London, England.

JACOBS, M. H. 1909. The effects of desiccation on the rotifer Philodina roseola. *Jour. Exp. Zool.* **6**:207–265.

JENNINGS, H. S. 1903. Rotatoria of the United States. II. A monograph of the Rattulidae. *Bull. U. S. Fish Comm.* (1902):273–352.

JENNINGS, H. S., and R. S. LYNCH. 1928. Age, mortality, fertility, and individual diversities in the rotifer Proales sordida Gosse. I. *Jour. Exp. Zool.* **50**:345–407.

———. 1928a. Age, mortality, fertility, and individual diversities in the rotifer Proales sordida Gosse. II. *Ibid.* **51**:339–381.

LANSING, A. I. 1942. Some effects of hydrogen ion concentration, total salt concentration, calcium and citrate on longevity and fecundity of the rotifer. *Jour. Exp. Zool.* **91**:195–212.

LUCKS, R. 1929. Rotatoria. Rädertiere. *Biol. Tiere Deutschlands* **10**:1–176.

LUNTZ, A. 1926. Untersuchungen über den Generationswechsel der Rotatorien. I. Die Bedingungen des Generationswechsels. *Biol. Zentralbl.* **46**:233–278.

MILLER, H. M. 1931. Alternation of generations in the rotifer Lecane inermis Bryce. Life histories of the sexual and non-sexual generations. *Biol. Bull.* **60**:345–381.

MONTGOMERY, T. H. 1903. On the morphology of the rotatorian family Floscularidae. *Proc. Acad. Nat. Sci. Phila.* **55**:363–395.

MURRAY, J. 1905. On a new family and twelve new species of Rotifera of the order Bdelloidea, collected by the Lake Survey. *Trans. Roy. Soc. Edinburgh* **41**:367–386.

MYERS, F. J. 1930. The rotifer fauna of Wisconsin, V. The genera Euchlanis and Monommata. *Trans. Wis. Acad. Sci. Arts and Lett.* **25**:353–411.

———. 1931. The distribution of Rotifera on Mount Desert Island. *Amer. Mus. Novit.* **494**:1–12.

———. 1933. A new genus of rotifers (Dorria). *Jour. Roy. Micros. Soc.* **53**:118–121.

———. 1933a. The distribution of Rotifera on Mount Desert Island. III. New Notommatidae of the genera Pleurotrocha, Lindia, Eothinia, Proalinopsis, and Encentrum. *Amer. Mus. Novit.* **660**:1–18.

———. 1934. The distribution of Rotifera on Mount Desert Island. Part V. A new species of the Synchaetidae and new species of Asplanchnidae, Trichocercidae, and Brachionidae. *Ibid.* **700**:1–16.

———. 1934a. The distribution of Rotifera on Mount Desert Island. Part VII. New Testudinellidae of the genus Testudinella and a new species of Brachionidae of the genus Trichotria. *Ibid.* **761**:1–8.

———. 1936. Psammolittoral rotifers of Lenape and Union lakes, New Jersey. *Ibid.* **830**:1–22.

———. 1937. A method of mounting rotifer jaws for study. *Trans. Amer. Micros. Soc.* **56**:256–257.

———. 1937a Rotifera from the Adirondack region of New York. *Amer. Mus. Novit.* **903**:1–17.

———. 1941. Lecane curvicornis var. miamiensis, new variety of Rotatoria, with observations on the feeding habits of rotifers. *Notulae Naturae* **75**:1–8.

———. 1942. The rotatorian fauna of the Pocono plateau and environs. *Proc. Acad. Nat. Sci. Phila.* **94**:251–285.

NACHTWEY, R. 1925. Untersuchungen über die Keimbahn, Organogenese und Anatomie von Asplanchna priodonta Gosse. *Zeitschr. wiss. Zool.* **126**:239–492.

PAWŁOWSKI, L. K. 1938. Materialen zur Kenntnis der mossbewohnenden Rotatorien Polens. I. *Ann. Mus. Zool. Polon.* **13**:115–159.

PAX, F., and K. WULFERT. 1941. Die Rotatorien deutscher Schwefelquellen und Thermen. *Arch. Hydrobiol.* **38**:165–213.

PENNAK, R. W. 1940. Ecology of the microscopic Metazoa inhabiting the sandy beaches of some Wisconsin lakes. *Ecol. Monogr.* **10**:537–615.

———. 1949. Annual limnological cycles in some Colorado reservoir lakes. *Ibid.* **19**:233–267.

REMANE, A. 1929. Intrazellulare Verdauung bei Rädertieren. *Zeitschr. Vergl. Physiol.* **11**:146–154.

———. 1929a. Rotatoria. *Tierwelt der Nord- und Ostsee.* **7**:1–156.

———. 1929–1933. Rotatorien. *Klassen und Ordnungen des Tier-Reichs* 4 (Abt. 2, Buch 1) Lief. 1–4:1–576.

ROUSSELET, C. F. 1902. The genus Synchaeta: a monographic study, with descriptions of five new species. *Jour. Roy. Micros. Soc.* (1902): 269–290, 393–411.

RUTTNER-KOLISKO, A. 1946. Über das Auftreten unbefruchteter "Dauereier" bei Anuraea aculeata (Keratella quadrata). *Österreich. Zool. Zeitschr.* **1**:179–181.

———. 1949. Zum Formwechsel- und Artenproblem von Anuraea aculeata. *Hydrobiologia* **1**:425–468.

SEEHAUS, W. 1930. Zur Morphologie der Rädertiergattung Testudinella Bory de St. Vincent. *Zeitschr. wiss. Zool.* **137**:175–273.

STOSSBERG, K. 1932. Zur Morphologie der Rädertiergattungen Euchlanis, Brachionus und Rhinoglena. *Ibid.* **142**:313–424.

VALKANOV, A. 1936. Beitrag zur Anatomie und Morphologie der Rotatoriengattung Trochosphaera Semper. *Trav. Soc. Bulgare Sci. Nat.* **17**:177–195.

VIAUD, G. 1940. Recherches experimentales sur le phototropisme des rotifères. *Bull. Biol. France et Belgique* **74**:249–308; **77**:68–93, 224–242.

WATZKA, M. 1928. Die Rotatorienfauna der Cakowitzer Zuckerfabriksteiche und Versuche über das Auftreten von Rotatorien-Männchen und über die Entwicklungszeit der Dauereier. *Int. Rev.* **19**:430–451.

WEBER, E. F. 1898. Faune rotatorienne du bassin de Léman. *Rev. Suisse Zool.* **5**:263–785.

WESENBERG-LUND, C. 1923. Contributions to the biology of the Rotifera. I. The males of the Rotifera. *D. Kgl. Vidensk. Selsk. Skr. Naturv. Math.* (8) **4**:189–345.

——. 1930. Contributions to the biology of the Rotifera. II. The periodicity and sexual periods. *Ibid.* (9) **2**:1–230.

WISZNIEWSKI, J. 1934. Les rotifères psammiques. *Ann. Mus. Zool. Polon.* **10**:339–399.

WULFERT, K. 1938. Die Rädertiergattung Cephalodella Bory de St. Vincent. *Arch. Naturgeschichte* **7**:137–152.

ZACHARIAS, O. 1902. Zum Kapital der "wurstförmigen Parasiten" bei Räderthieren. *Zool. Anz.* **25**:647–649.

# Chapter 9

# NEMATODA (ROUNDWORMS)

ALMOST any collection of sand, mud, debris, or vegetation from the bottom or margin of a pond, lake, brook, or river will be found to contain small roundworms, or nematodes, sometimes in great abundance. Yet as a group, the fresh-water species are poorly known, and few American investigators have been concerned with them since the extensive taxonomic and ecological studies of N. A. Cobb, of the United States Department of Agriculture, whose many papers appeared during the first third of the present century.

Most of the available information about the Phylum Nematoda is concerned with the thousands of parasitic species, some of which are of extreme importance to the health and economic well-being of man. Probably no more than 1,000 free-living species have been reported from the fresh waters of the world, but this figure must represent only a small fraction of the actual number of species living in this environment. They occur in such widely differing habitats as pools of polar ice, hot springs, puddles, and the bottoms of the deepest and largest lakes.

The account of the Nematoda as given in this chapter is written specifically from the standpoint of the free-living fresh-water species of the United States, but most of the generalizations apply also to the phylum as a whole.

**General characteristics.** With the exception of the family Mermithidae, nematodes occurring in the substrates of fresh waters are almost invariably less than a centimeter long. Their nearly constant and rapid whiplike movements in a dorsoventral plane are quite characteristic, there being no changes in body diameter and proportions. These thrashing, serpentine movements usually produce little or no locomotion in water alone, but debris and vegetation afford sufficient friction to result in forward locomotion. A few species move along the substrate in an inchworm manner, and the rare free-swimming forms are able to move through the water just above the substrate.

Most aquatic species have three unicellular glands in the tail. Their secretion is carried to the posterior end by one to three minute ducts, and the flow to the outside is regulated by a special pore, or spinneret, at the tip of the body (Figs. 135A, B, D). This secretion is sticky and is used for temporary attachment to objects.

Members of the Class Phasmidia have a pair of lateral caudal pores, or phasmids, of uncertain function (Fig. 135C).

In cross section the nematode body is more or less round. The mouth is terminal, but the transverse slitlike anus is subterminal. Though coloration ranges from

---

DETAILS OF FIG. 133:

A genital bursa is shown in the male, but this structure is rare in free-living species. *a*, amphid; *cb*, cardiac bulb of esophagus; *cs*, copulatory spicule; *ec*, excretory canal; *eg*, ejaculatory gland; *ep*, excretory pore; *g*, gubernaculum; *i*, intestine; *mb*, middle bulb of esophagus; *nr*, nerve ring; *o*, ovary; *od*, oviduct; *ov*, mature fertilized ovum; *p*, pharynx; *r*, renette; *rg*, rectal gland; *sg*, salivary gland (glands and ducts solid black; present in both sexes but shown only in figure of male); *sr*, seminal receptacle; *sv*, seminal vesicle; *t*, testis; *u*, uterus; *v*, vulva and genital pore; *vd*, vas deferens.

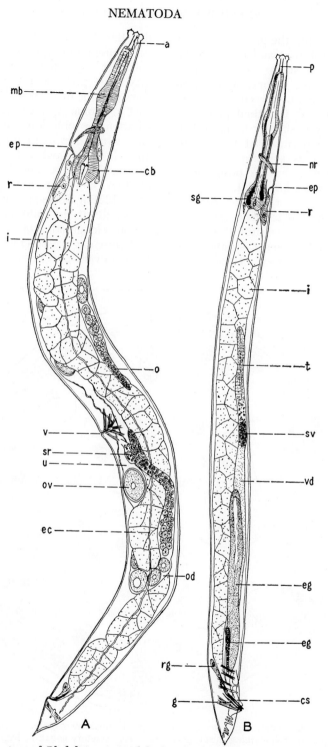

FIG. 133.—Structure of *Rhabditis,* a typical fresh-water nematode, ×95. A, female; B, male. (Modified from Chitwood, 1937, by permission.) See bottom of page 214 for details.

colorless to blackish, the great majority of species are translucent and therefore fascinating objects for study under the microscope. Most of the coloration of nematodes is determined by the contents of the digestive tract and intestinal cell inclusions. The body is slightly tapered, truncate, or bluntly rounded at the anterior end where there is sometimes a poorly defined head region, but the posterior end generally tapers to a fine point.

The outermost layer of the body is a dead, secreted proteinaceous cuticle which is variously marked, sculptured, or scaly. Sometimes the transverse striations are composed of lines or rows of dots so fine that they may be detected only with critical illumination and the oil immersion lens. At the other extreme, the cuticle may have prominent transverse grooves, rows of dots, or even scalelike folds (Fig. 136C). Some species have longitudinal striations or long, low, keel-like wings, or alae, which appear to aid in stiffening the animal. In the males of a few fresh-water species there is a caudal bursa composed of two more or less prominent alae (Fig. 133B). Setae are sometimes present, especially at the anterior end; these are simply elongated projections of the general cuticular exoskeleton. The cuticle extends inward and lines the mouth cavity,

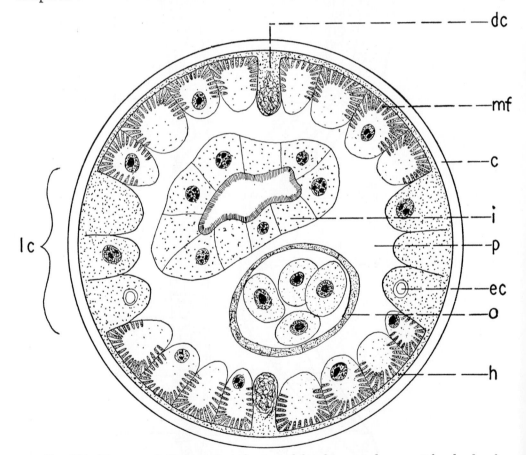

Fig. 134.—Diagrammatic cross section of a typical female nematode. *c*, cuticle; *dc*, dorsal chord of hypodermis containing dorsal nerve cord; *ec*, excretory canal; *h*, hypodermis; *i*, intestine, showing rodlike layer on inner surface; *lc*, lateral chord of hypodermis; *mf*, muscle fibers of muscle cell; *o*, oviduct with four developing eggs; *p*, pseudocoel.

esophagus, vulva, and posterior portion of the digestive tract.

The hypodermis, or subcuticle, is usually a syncytial tissue; it secretes the cuticle and lies just below it. This layer is thin except dorsally, ventrally, and laterally, where it is greatly thickened and protruded inward to form the four chords (Fig. 134).

The remainder of the body wall consists of an innermost layer of muscle cells comprising four groups, or fields, of cells separated by the four chords. In meromyarian nematodes there are usually only two to four cells per field, but in polymyarian nematodes each field has numerous cells. A muscle cell is long, spindle-shaped, and contains numerous ribbon-shaped muscle fibrils. The fibrils may all lie at the base of the cell and adjacent to the hypodermis (platymyarian arrangement), or the fibrils may extend varying distances up the sides of the cells and partially enclose the sarcoplasm (coelomyarian arrangement) (Fig. 134).

The body cavity of a nematode is properly called a pseudocoel and contains only a few connective tissue cells. There is no true mesodermal epithelium covering the digestive tract.

**Digestive system.** The mouth is characteristically surrounded by lips, each with a small papilla on its summit. Six appears to be the basic number of lips, but often there is fusion to form three, and sometimes distinct lips are absent. The lips show innumerable modifications. In some species they are muscular, mobile, and modified for sucking or gripping (*Enoplus*); in others they are modified for ripping (*Ironus*); sometimes they form tooth-like odontia (*Mononchus*).

The mouth opening is minute to large, round or triangular, and often capable of great distension. The mouth cavity, or pharynx, is lined with cuticle and varies enormously in size and structure. Sometimes it is inconspicuous or absent; in other species it is capacious. It may be cylindrical, subglobular, cup-shaped, conoid, or some other shape. Its wall is often supplied with stiffening rods or plates; rasps and special teeth, or onchia, are common. In some herbivorous and carnivorous species the pharynx is supplied with a solid or hollow stiletto-like protrusile spear (Figs. 136, 139).

The structure of the esophagus is an important taxonomic character. It is round in cross section, lined with cuticle, composed mostly of radial muscle fibers, and has a small triquetrous cavity. Three unicellular salivary glands are usually imbedded in the esophageal wall; their ducts open into the lumen of the pharynx or esophagus. In some species the esophagus is elongated, plain, and more or less cylindrical, but more commonly there are one or two ellipsoid or spherical bulbar swellings. If a single bulb is present, it is usually located at the posterior end of the esophagus and is termed the cardiac bulb, while the second (middle) bulb is located somewhere near mid-length. The esophagus is a suctorial and peristaltic organ, with the bulbs serving to increase the pumping action. Sometimes esophageal valves are present which aid in sucking and prevent regurgitation.

The long intestine extends from esophagus to rectum and is devoid of caeca or loops in fresh-water species. It consists of a single layer of epithelial cells, though rarely there is a flimsy covering of connective tissue or muscle fibers. The inner surface of the intestine is lined with a layer of curious minute rodlike outgrowths (Fig. 134). These are sometimes mistaken for cilia, but true cilia are unknown in this phylum. Most intestinal digestion is thought to occur in the anterior half of this organ.

The junction of esophagus and intestine is supplied with an obscure valvular apparatus, and there is often a comparable structure separating the intestine proper from its short, narrow, muscular posterior end, the rectum. Several unicellular rectal and anal glands are characteristic of this region of the body.

**Feeding.** All varieties of food habits are represented in free-living fresh-water nematodes. Some feed only on dead plant material, others only on dead animal material. A third group are detritus feeders which consume both dead plant and dead animal material. Herbivorous species are variously specialized for biting and chewing living plant tissues, while others are equipped with a rigid hollow stylet which pierces plant cells and through which the protoplasm is sucked by the action of the esophagus. Similarly, the predaceous and carnivorous forms, such as *Mononchus, Dorylaimus, Nygolaimus,* and *Actinolaimus,* show a variety of anatomical modifications for feeding. The lips may be specialized for seizing or tearing the prey, and the pharynx is often partially eversible and supplied with onchia or rasps for crushing, rasping, or macerating. Many carnivorous species have the hollow stylet type of feeding. The prey consists of Protozoa and all types of small Metazoa, including oligochaetes, rotifers, gastrotrichs, tardigrades, and other nematodes.

Material digested in the alimentary canal is absorbed into the fluid of the surrounding hemocoel and thence to all of the internal organs and body wall by circulation resulting from the incessant body movements. There is no special circulatory system.

**Excretion.** The excretory system presents a varied picture in the phylum as a whole. It is simplest in the Class Aphasmidia where there is a single ventral excretory cell, or renette, which opens through an excretory pore on the midventral line in the region of the esophagus by way of a short to long duct. In the Class Phasmidia there are two lateral excretory canals imbedded in the lateral chords of the hypodermis throughout most of the body length. They are connected anteriorly and ventrally by a transverse canal, thus forming an H or U shape. A very short duct connects the transverse duct with the excretory pore. There may or may not be two special cells (the renette) associated with the transverse duct (Fig. 133).

In a few genera, including *Dorylaimus,* no excretory system has been found. Considerable excretion through the digestive tract may occur in all nematodes.

**Nervous system.** A ring of nerve fibers and associated ganglia encircle the esophagus. From this mass six small nerves are given off which innervate the anterior end. Four or more longitudinal nerves extend posteriorly in the hypodermis, of which the dorsal and ventral nerves are usually the most prominent. Especially at the extremities of the body, there are scattered small ganglia and numerous branch nerves which connect the longitudinal nerves with each other. In general, the nervous system is considerably more complicated than most elementary textbooks indicate.

**Sense organs.** Paired eyespots occur in some species of *Chromadora* and *Monhystera,* as well as in a few other genera. Such eyespots are small clumps of reddish, violet, or blackish granules imbedded in the esophagus or between the esophagus and body wall. A minute lenslike device may be present in front of each clump of pigment, or it may be absent. There appears to be some difference of opinion as to whether there are nervous connections between eyespots and nervous system.

Tactile receptors are mainly associated with the cephalic papillae and setae and with the caudal setae. The somatic setae, often present between anterior and posterior ends, are probably also tactile.

Amphids are peculiar nematode structures, and though there is still considerable controversy about their function, it appears most likely that they are chemoreceptors rather than organs of equilibration. A typical fresh-water nematode has two amphids, one on each side of the body near the anterior end. Externally, an amphid may have the shape of a narrow slit, of an oval, a circle, or of spiral grooves and ridges on the cuticle. Internally, it consists of a small pouch and often a minute longitudinal posterior canal. The pouch has recently been shown to be innervated. Chitwood (1937) maintains that amphids are always present, but often they are so minute, reduced, or vestigial as to be indistinguishable to the average observer.

**Reproduction, development.** Both males and females are known for most species of nematodes, and reproduction is syngamic, but in many species males are rare or unknown, and reproduction is usually parthenogenetic, as in *Rhabdolaimus, Monhystera,* and *Alaimus.* Hermaphroditic species occur in *Hoplolaimus, Mononchulus, Aphanolaimus, Ironus, Trilobus, Mononchus,* and a few other genera. The female is usually the larger, but the sexes can be distinguished by the sex characters.

In general, the reproductive systems are simpler and less extensive than those of parasitic species and produce relatively few gametes. In the mature female the genital pore, or vulva, can be seen as a transverse slit on the ventral mid-line near the middle of the body. There is a short muscular vagina which may connect with a single thin-walled tapering reproductive tubule or, more typically, may branch to form two tubules, one anterior and one posterior. Beginning at the vagina, each tubule consists of a wide uterus, an oviduct, and a fine terminal ovary composed of very small oocytes. Sometimes the uterus has a small associated seminal receptacle (Fig. 133). A reproductive tubule may be outstretched or reflexed. Thus, the reproductive system of a female nematode may have one of four configurations: double and outstretched, double and reflexed (Fig. 135G), single and outstretched (Fig. 138D), or single and reflexed.

The male reproductive system is ordinarily a single tapering tubule which opens ventrally into the posterior part of the digestive tract. Beginning basally, the tubule consists of a long vas deferens, short seminal vesicle, and thin testis (Fig. 133B). Rarely the testis is bifurcated or reflexed. Ejaculatory glands sometimes open into the basal part of the vas deferens. Since the rectum of the male is common to both the reproductive and digestive ducts, it is more appropriately called a cloaca. A pair of sclerotized copulatory spicules are contained within a delicate pouch on the dorsal side of the cloaca. During copulation these spicules are extruded through the cloacal aperture, or anus, of the male and into the vulva. They are moved back and forth by muscles so that the vulva and vagina are kept open and so that sperm are more easily propelled into the vagina. The gubernaculum is a sclerotized thickening in the dorsal wall of the male cloaca which acts as a spicular guide and prevents the spicules from rupturing the spicular pouch and cloaca when exserted.

A clasping device, or copulatory bursa (Fig. 133B), is common in parasitic species but is rare in the males of fresh-water species. It consists of two thin, transparent, longitudinal flaps of cuticle near the posterior end. It is widest opposite the anus and may or may not be long enough to encompass the posterior tip of the animal.

Fertilization occurs in the upper end of the uterus and the egg shell is laid down in the lower uterus. The fertilized eggs usually leave the body before the onset of segmentation, but some species are viviparous or ovoviviparous. The embryo is formed and hatches in a few hours to a few weeks, depending on the particular species and ecological conditions. The newly hatched young are fully developed except for size, reproductive system, and certain specializations of the lips, pharynx, and esophagus. It is thought that there is almost always a series of four molts (five instars) in the complete life history. In addition to the general body covering, a molt also includes shedding of the cuticular lining of pharynx, esophagus, vulva,

and rectum. The secondary sex characters are not apparent until after either the
penultimate molt or the last molt. Little is
known about the longevity of free-living
nematodes, but males are thought to be
much shorter lived than females.

**Ecology.** The eggs of soil and parasitic
nematodes are highly resistant to desiccation (even for periods up to ten or twenty
years) and to high and low temperatures;
they are easily transported by animals and
blown about as dust. The larvae and
adults of many soil species likewise are
viable after being dried and shriveled up
in a state of anabiosis. Nevertheless, there
seems to be very little information about
encystment and desiccation among aquatic
nematodes, and it is not known how important these mechanisms are for dissemination. Judging from the available
scanty distribution records, however, most
aquatic genera and many species are cosmopolitan and world-wide.

Furthermore, some species show an
amazing ability to thrive in a wide variety
of habitats and a wide range of ecological
conditions. Among all the metazoan
phyla, nematodes are perhaps the most
highly adaptable from ecological and
physiological standpoints. The same species, for example, may be found from the
tropics to the subarctic, from warm springs
to cold alpine lakes, and on many types of
substrates. Only a few genera appear to
be restricted to fresh waters; examples are
*Cryptonchus, Chronogaster, Anonchus,*
and *Udonchus. Oncholaimus* and *Chromadora* are both marine and fresh-water
genera. The following genera, among
others, occur in both fresh waters and terrestrial soils: *Prismatolaimus, Mononchus,
Trilobus, Tripyla,* and *Ironus. Monhystera,* however, is a genus with terrestrial,
marine, and fresh-water representatives.
In addition to being found in fresh waters
and soils, *Diplogaster, Rhabditis,* and
*Cephalobus* also have parasitic representatives. A few genera show specific habitat
preferences in fresh waters, and some of

these are mentioned in the key which follows. Many soil nematodes often occur in
fresh waters as the result of wash.

Present ideas emphasize the probable
origin of nematodes in fresh waters and
their subsequent migration and colonization of salt water and terrestrial environments.

As pointed out long ago by Cobb,
nematode populations often reach tremendous numbers both in terrestrial soils
and in the substrates of bodies of water
where they are of great mechanical importance in continuously working over and
mixing soils in much the same way as
oligochaetes. Even in the wet sand of lake
beaches near the water's edge, which is
not an especially favorable habitat for
nematodes, the writer has found up to
eight adult nematodes per cubic centimeter of sand. Some of the most dense
populations, especially species of *Mononchus, Ironus,* and *Tripyla,* occur in the
sand and gravel filter beds of sewage dis-
posal plants. A wide variety of species
occur around the roots of aquatic plants.
In natural fresh-water habitats most specimens are confined to the uppermost five
centimeters of the substrate.

Although populations of aquatic nematodes can be maintained indefinitely in
low concentrations of dissolved oxygen,
2 to 10 per cent saturation, for example, it
is thought that active nematodes are capable of withstanding anaerobic conditions
only for one to several weeks at a time.
The eggs, however, are highly resistant
and may remain viable after many months
in the absence of oxygen and after repeated freezing and thawing.

**Collecting, preparing, preserving.** Perhaps the chief reason for the general neglect of the nematodes by investigators in
aquatic zoology is the fact that they almost
invariably occur in quantities of bottom
mud and fine organic debris from which
it is difficult to separate them. If a small
quantity of the material containing nematodes is placed in a petri dish or water,

they can be detected by their movements and picked out with a fine pipette under the dissecting binoculars and transferred to clean water. This is a tedious method, however, and if a relatively large quantity of nematode-containing material is available, many worms may be concentrated by the following method: (1) wash the material through a sieve of 2 or 3 mm. mesh and then (2) through a 1 mm. mesh sieve in order to remove the larger pieces of debris; (3) wash the material through number 20 bolting silk which will retain the nematodes and allow the fine debris to pass; (4) transfer the retained nematodes and debris to a small container of water, agitate, and decant quickly as soon as the heavy sand particles settle out; repeat this step if desirable; (5) agitate and allow to stand two to four minutes, which is sufficient time to allow the nematodes to sink to the bottom, and then decant off the muddy water. The residue will then contain most of the nematodes with a minimum of fine debris; specimens should be picked up individually with a fine pipette or bristle for further treatment. Cobb (1918) gives methods for estimating nematode populations of terrestrial soils, and perhaps certain modifications can be used for estimating population densities in aquatic substrates.

Live nematodes are so active that it is useless to study them with a compound microscope. They should first be narcotized with chloroform, chloral hydrate, magnesium sulphate, or other narcotic.

Hot saturated mercuric chloride or hot 70 to 80 per cent alcohol are probably the best fixatives, but for routine fixation in the field cold 85 per cent alcohol and 5 per cent formalin are quite reliable.

Simple temporary formalin mounts ringed with vaseline are excellent for routine purposes.

For permanent mounts and identification there is probably no better or more convenient mounting medium than glycerin jelly. But glycerin, like most substances, penetrates the nematode cuticle very slowly. If, however, the worms are placed in an open concave watch glass of 5 per cent glycerin in 50 per cent alcohol, the alcohol and water will evaporate in three to ten days and the worms will be infiltrated in concentrated glycerin. They may be stored thus or mounted directly in glycerin jelly. Like all other glycerin jelly slides, the round cover slips should be ringed with Murrayite or similar cement.

Stained balsam mounts are tedious to prepare and often exasperating, because unless meticulous care is taken in the reagent transfers, the final mounted nematodes collapse or become distorted and opaque. Cobb (1918) devised a glass "differentiator" for gradually transferring nematodes from one fluid to another so as to avoid distortion. Chatterji (1935) reports success with the following brief procedure: 70 per cent alcohol, dioxan overnight, fresh dioxan one hour, clove oil two hours, and balsam. Chitwood and Chitwood (1930) give detailed directions for imbedding in paraffin.

Many aquatic nematodes may be cultured in the laboratory in 3 per cent agar in tap water with a little added soil and debris.

**Taxonomy.** The taxonomic relationships of free-living nematodes, especially with respect to family designations, are uncertain and in a state of flux. Of the several modern plans which have been proposed, that of Chitwood (1937) is used in this manual. Following is a skeleton outline of a part of the Chitwood taxonomic arrangement; it includes only those families and the great majority of genera having representatives in fresh waters. A few genera are included that have not yet been reported from the United States, but it is highly probable that they will be found when more extensive collecting has been accomplished. Fifty-eight genera are listed in this outline as compared with 32 listed by Cobb in 1918. Asterisks show genera most frequently collected.

Class Phasmidia—with a pair of small lateral cuticular pores (phasmids) on the tail; no caudal glands; caudal alae usually present; amphids porelike.

Order Rhabditida—esophagus divisible into three regions, especially in the larva; free living and parasitic.

Suborder Rhabditina

Rhabdiasidae
* *Rhabdias*

Rhabditidae
*Bunonema*
*Diploscapter*
* *Rhabditis*

Cephalobidae
* *Acrobeles*
* *Cephalobus*
* *Macrolaimus*
* *Panagrolaimus*

Diplogasteridae
*Diplogaster*

Suborder Tylenchina

Criconematidae
* *Criconema*
*Criconemoides*
*Hemicycliophora*

Aphelenchidae
*Aphelenchoides*
*Aphelenchus*
*Metaphelenchus*
*Paraphelenchus*
*Seinura*

Heteroderidae
*Dolichodorus*
*Hoplolaimus*
*Pratylenchus*

Tylenchidae
* *Psilenchus*
* *Tylenchus*

Class Aphasmidia—phasmids absent; caudal glands present or absent; amphids variable; caudal alae rarely present; free living or parasitic.

Order Chromadorida—free living; amphids spiral, circular, vesiculate, or other forms derivable from spiral; caudal glands present; esophagus of three definite regions.

Plectidae

* *Anaplectus*
* *Anonchus*
* *Plectus*
* *Rhabdolaimus*
* *Teratocephalus*
* *Wilsonema*

Bastianiidae
*Bastiania*

Camacolaimidae
* *Aphanolaimus*
*Paraphanolaimus*

Axonolaimidae
* *Cylindrolaimus*

Monhysteridae
* *Monhystera*

Chromadoridae
* *Chromadora*

Microlaimidae
*Microlaimus*

Cyatholaimidae
* *Achromadora*
* *Ethmolaimus*
*Prodesmodora*

Order Enoplida—amphids pocket-like and elongated, porelike, or tuboid; caudal glands present or absent; esophagus divisible into two parts; free living and parasitic.

Suborder Dorylaimina

Superfamily Mermithoidea

Superfamily Dorylaimoidea

Diphtherophoridae
Leptonchidae
Belondiridae
Dorylaimidae
* *Actinolaimus*
*Dorylaimus*
*Nygolaimus*
*Tylencholaimus*
*Xiphinema*

Suborder Enoplina

Alaimidae
* *Alaimus*
*Amphidelus*

Ironidae
* *Cryptonchus*
*Ironus*

Tripylidae
* *Prismatolaimus*
* *Trilobus*

\* *Tripyla*
*Trischistoma*
Mononchidae
*Anatonchus*
*Iotonchus*
*Mononchulus*
\* *Mononchus*
*Mylolonchus*
*Prionchulus*
*Sporonchulus*

After considerable experience, identification to genus can sometimes be made with the 4 mm. objective of the microscope, but critical illumination and the oil immersion objective are usually essential in order to study the smaller details.

For species descriptions Cobb devised a numerical formula method of indicating certain morphological features by conventional characters and significant body measurements expressed as percentages of the total body length, but this method is now seldom used.

The following key is modified from one constructed for the writer by Dr. B. G. Chitwood. It includes the great majority of genera reported from fresh waters and will be found to be reliable for more than 98 per cent of all specimens collected.

## KEY TO GENERA OF NEMATODA

1. Amphids porelike (Fig. 136A); phasmids (lateral caudal pores) present (Fig. 135C); caudal glands and spinneret absent; lateral excretory canals present, at least on one side.............Class **PHASMIDIA**, Order **RHABDITIDA**, 2
   Amphids circular, spiral, reniform, crescentic, or pocket-like (Figs. 137–140); phasmids absent; caudal glands and spinneret often present (Figs. 135A, B, D, E); lateral excretory canals absent............Class **APHASMIDIA**, 23
2. Stylet absent.................................Suborder **RHABDITINA**, 3
   Stylet present (Figs. 136C, D)..................Suborder **TYLENCHINA**, 11
3. Lower end of esophagus terminated by a valved bulb (Fig. 133)..............4
   Lower end of esophagus not terminated by a valved bulb.
                    DIPLOGASTERIDAE, **Diplogaster**
4. Pharyngeal wall rigidly cylindrical, terminated by minute triad of cups (Fig. 133)..........................................5
   Pharyngeal wall not rigidly cylindrical, not terminated by minute triad of cups (Fig. 136A); common.......................CEPHALOBIDAE, 8
5. Cuticle highly ornamented with flanges; usually in moss.
                    RHABDITIDAE, **Bunonema**
   Cuticle not highly ornamented with flanges.............................6
6. Head with outwardly acting teeth at terminus; uncommon.
                    RHABDITIDAE, **Diploscapter**
   Head with simple lips, no teeth.......................................7
7. Male with a single narrow bursa.................RHABDIASIDAE, **Rhabdias**
   Male with a single wide bursa or a double narrow bursa (Fig. 133B); common in decaying material........................RHABDITIDAE, **Rhabditis**
8. Pharyngeal cavity distinct...........................................9
   Pharyngeal cavity indistinct.........................................10
9. Pharynx short and wide; cephalic papillae setose................**Macrolaimus**
   Pharynx not particularly wide; cephalic papillae not setose (Fig. 136A); in decaying material..............................................**Panagrolaimus**
10. With prominent and elaborate appendages encircling the mouth, papillae at their base................................................**Acrobeles**
    Without such appendages; papillae on lips......................**Cephalobus**
11. Very short, thick-bodied; cuticle heavily annulated (Fig. 136C); feeding on plant roots.....................................CRICONEMATIDAE, 12
    Not very short or thick-bodied; cuticle variously striated but not annulated.....14

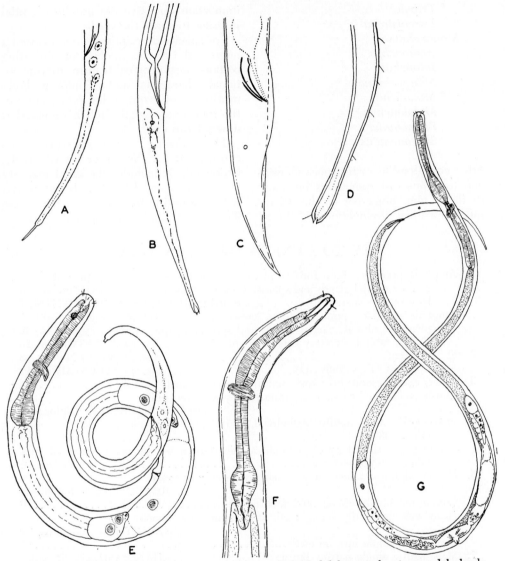

FIG. 135.—Structure of nematodes. A, posterior end of *Rhabdolaimus*, showing caudal glands and spinneret; B, posterior end of *Aphanolaimus*, showing caudal glands, spinneret, and phasmid; C, posterior end of male *Tylenchus*, showing phasmid; D, posterior end of *Trilobus*, showing spinneret; E, female *Achromadora*, ×350; F, anterior end of *Plectus*; G, female *Diplogaster*, ×170. (A, B, E, F, and G modified from Cobb, 1914; C and D modified from Micoletzky.)

12. Cuticle with spines or scales (Fig. 136C); usually common in swamps and
        acid waters...........................................................**Criconema**
    Cuticle without spines or scales.................................................13
13. With 160 annules or less.....................................**Criconemoides**
    With 200 or more annules; uncommon........................**Hemicycliophora**
14. Dorsal esophageal gland orifice situated in median esophageal bulb; feeding on
        higher plants and fungi........................APHELENCHIDAE, 15
    Dorsal esophageal gland orifice situated near base of stylet...................19

15.  Female with bluntly rounded tail....................................16
     Female with conoid to filiform tail................................17
16.  Esophageal glands free, extending beyond beginning of intestine; uncommon.
                                                         **Aphelenchus**
     Esophageal glands enclosed in wall of esophagus, not extending beyond beginning
        of intestine; uncommon..............................**Metaphelenchus**
17.  Tail attenuated to filiform.............................................**Seinura**
     Tail conoid........................................................18
18.  Esophageal glands free, extending beyond beginning of intestine...**Aphelenchoides**
     Esophageal glands enclosed in wall of esophagus, not extending beyond beginning
        of intestine; uncommon...............................**Paraphelenchus**
19.  Body distinctly striated; feeding on plant roots........HETERODERIDAE, **20**
     Body faintly striated; feeding on stem, leaf, or roots of higher plants or even
        mycelia........................................TYLENCHIDAE, **22**
20.  Females with one ovary; parasites of plant roots..................**Pratylenchus**
     Females with two ovaries..........................................**21**
21.  Stylet three or more times as long as head diameter (Fig. 136D)....**Dolichodorus**
     Stylet about one to two times as long as head diameter............**Hoplolaimus**
22.  Stylet without basal knobs.......................................**Psilenchus**
     Stylet with basal knobs (Fig. 136E)...............................**Tylenchus**

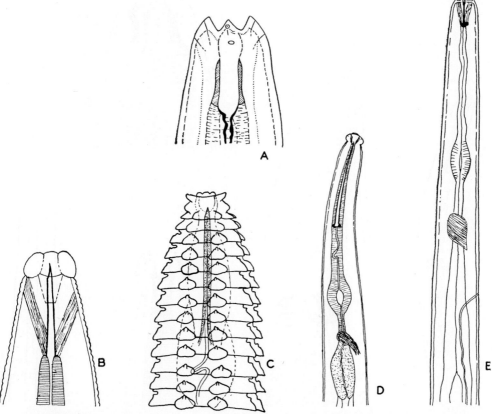

Fig. 136.—Structure of anterior end of nematodes of the Class Phasmidia. A, *Panagrolaimus*; B, *Aphelenchus*; C, *Criconema*; D, *Dolichodorus*; E, *Tylenchus*. (A modified from Thorne, 1937; B modified from Chitwood, 1937, by permission; C modified from Cobb, 1915; D modified from Cobb, 1914; E modified from Micoletzky.)

23. Amphids circular, spiral, or transversely reniform (Figs. 137, 138).
                                                    Order **CHROMADORIDA, 24**
    Amphids pocket-like, externally slit or transversely crescentic (Figs. 139, 140).
                                                    Order **ENOPLIDA, 39**
24. Terminal excretory duct tubular; common...................**PLECTIDAE, 25**
    Terminal excretory duct not tubular......................................29
25. Pharyngeal cavity wide, walls jointed (Fig. 137B); esophagus without valved bulb.
                                                    **Anonchus**
    Pharyngeal cavity more or less tubular or conoid; esophagus with valved bulb...**26**
26. Head with elaborate ornamentation (Figs. 137D, E).......................27
    Head with plain lips.....................................................28
27. With membranes between setae of head.......................**Wilsonema**
    With six inwardly directed teeth (Figs. 137D, E)..............**Teratocephalus**
28. Male with conoid supplementary organs.......................**Anaplectus**
    Male with papilloid supplementary organs.......................**Plectus**
29. Anterior part of body distinctly attenuated...............................30
    Anterior part of body not distinctly attenuated............................32
30. With ten cephalic setae (Fig. 137F)...............**BASTIANIIDAE, Bastiania**
    With four cephalic setae (Fig. 137A)...............**CAMACOLAIMIDAE, 31**

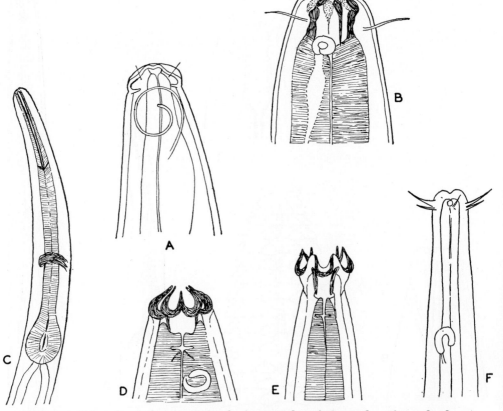

Fig. 137.—Structure of the anterior end of nematodes of the Order Chromadorida. A, *Aphanolaimus*; B, *Anonchus*; C, *Rhabdolaimus*; D and E, *Teratocephalus*; F, *Bastiania*. (A, C, D, and E modified from Cobb, 1914; B modified from Cobb, 1913; F modified from Chitwood, 1937, by permission.)

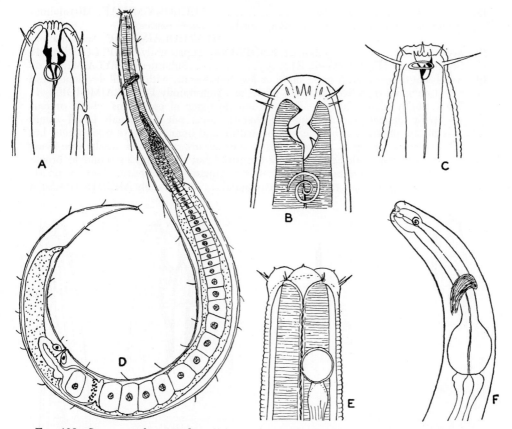

FIG. 138.—Structure of nematodes of the Order Chromadorida. A, anterior end of *Microlaimus*; B, anterior end of *Achromadora*; C, anterior end of *Chromadora*; D, female *Monhystera*, ×110; E, anterior end of *Monhystera*; F, anterior end of *Ethmolaimus*. (A and C modified from Chitwood, 1937, by permission; B, D, and F modified from Cobb, 1914; E modified from Micoletzky.)

31. Pharyngeal cavity distinct; uncommon........................**Paraphanolaimus**
    Pharyngeal cavity rudimentary (Fig. 137A); common...........**Aphanolaimus**
32. Pharynx elongated, tubular (Fig. 137C)................................33
    Pharynx not elongated and tubular....................................34
33. Ovaries reflexed.............................PLECTIDAE, **Rhabdolaimus**
    Ovaries outstretched; common............AXONOLAIMIDAE, **Cylindrolaimus**
34. Pharynx rudimentary (Figs. 138D, E); common.
                                        MONHYSTERIDAE, **Monhystera**
    Pharynx well developed, teeth usually present (Figs. 138A, B)..............35
35. Amphids reniform (Fig. 138C); esophago-intestinal valve inconspicuous; common.
                                        CHROMADORIDAE, **Chromadora**
    Amphids circular to spiral (Figs. 138A, B); esophago-intestinal valve elon-
        gated. ........................................................36
36. Pharyngeal cavity small.................CYATHOLAIMIDAE, **Prodesmodora**
    Pharyngeal cavity large (Figs. 138A, B)................................37
37. Pharynx cylindrical (Fig. 138F); feeding mostly on algae; common.
                                        CYATHOLAIMIDAE, **Ethmolaimus**
    Pharynx not cylindrical (Figs. 138A, B)................................38

38. Amphids circular (Fig. 138A)..............MICROLAIMIDAE, **Microlaimus**
    Amphids spiral (Fig. 138B); feeding mostly on algae; common.
                                    CYATHOLAIMIDAE, **Achromadora**
39. Stylet absent.........Suborder **ENOPLINA**, Superfamily TRIPYLOIDEA, **48**
    Stylet present (Figs. 139A–C, E)...............Suborder **DORYLAIMINA**, **40**
40. Total length less than 5 mm.; more or less translucent; with a well-developed and
    functional digestive tract; not parasitic..Superfamily DORYLAIMOIDEA, **41**
    Total length 15 to 300 mm.; opaque; muscle tissue of esophagus wholly or par-
    tially degenerate; intestine degenerate; anus not functional; larval stages
    mostly parasitic in body cavity of mature and immature terrestrial insects, but
    a few occurring in aquatic insects, crustaceans, and snails; adults free-living
    but do not feed; adults usually terrestrial but some species found in brooks
    and ponds after emergence from the aquatic or terrestrial host; a poorly
    known group, not treated in this manual....Superfamily MERMITHOIDEA

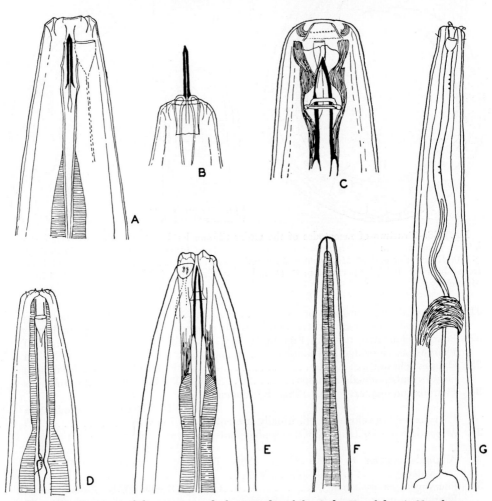

Fig. 139.—Structure of the anterior end of nematodes of the Order Enoplida. A, *Nygolaimus*;
B, *Nygolaimus* with protruded spear; C, *Actinolaimus*; D, *Cryptonchus*; E, *Dorylaimus*; F,
*Alaimus*; G, *Ironus*. (A and B modified from Thorne, 1930; C and D modified from Cobb,
1913; E modified from Micoletzky; F and G modified from Cobb, 1914.)

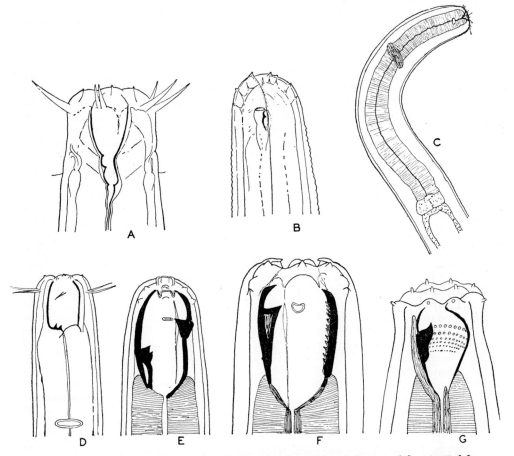

FIG. 140.—Structure of the anterior end of nematodes of the Order Enoplida. A, *Trilobus*; B and C, *Tripyla*; D, *Prismatolaimus*; E, *Mononchus*; F, *Prionchulus*; G, *Mylonchulus*. (A and B modified from Micoletzky; C and D modified from Cobb, 1914; E, F, and G modified from Cobb, 1917.)

**41.** Esophagus with pyriform posterior bulb.............................**42**
    Esophagus with cylindrical posterior third or more enlarged (Fig. 139A)......**43**
**42.** Amphids externally crescentic; one testis............DIPHTHEROPHORIDAE
    Amphids externally slitlike; two testes....................LEPTONCHIDAE
**43.** Enlarged posterior part of esophagus surrounded by spiral muscles.
                                                             BELONDIRIDAE
    Enlarged posterior part of esophagus not surrounded by spiral muscles.
                                                        DORYLAIMIDAE, **44**
**44.** Pharynx with heavily sclerotized walls (Fig. 139C); very common.
                                                              **Actinolaimus**
    Pharynx without heavily sclerotized walls (Figs. 139A, B, E)..............**45**
**45.** Stylet not hollow, attached to side of pharynx wall (Figs. 139A, B)...**Nygolaimus**
    Stylet hollow, attached posteriorly to pharynx wall on all sides (Fig. 139E)....**46**
**46.** Stylet without posterior flanges or knobs (Fig. 139E); a very large genus; common.
                                                                **Dorylaimus**
    Stylet with posterior flanges or knobs...................................**47**

**47.** Stylet about one-eighth to one-tenth as long as esophagus, knobs weak.
Tylencholaimus

Stylet about one-third or more as long as esophagus, with well-developed flanges.
Xiphinema

**48.** Esophagus greatly elongated; anterior end attenuated (Fig. 139F).
ALAIMIDAE, 51

Esophagus not greatly elongated; anterior end not attenuated..............49

**49.** Pharyngeal cavity cylindrical (Figs. 139D, G)...............IRONIDAE, 52

Pharyngeal cavity not cylindrical (Fig. 140)...........................50

**50.** Esophagus terminated by bulbar esophago-intestinal structure; dorsal esophageal gland orifice at base of pharyngeal region; pharynx surrounded by esophageal tissue (Figs. 140A–D).............................TRIPYLIDAE, 53

Esophagus not terminated by bulbar esophago-intestinal structure; dorsal gland orifice posterior to nerve ring; pharynx not surrounded by esophageal tissue (Figs. 140E–G)..............................MONONCHIDAE, 56

**51.** Amphids externally slitlike; common..............................Alaimus

Amphids externally crescentic..................................Amphidelus

**52.** Cephalic setae absent; single dorsal tooth at base of pharynx (Fig. 139D); common.
Cryptonchus

With four cephalic setae; pharynx with three or four teeth at anterior end (Fig. 139G)................................................Ironus

**53.** Pharynx cylindrical (Fig. 140D); common..................Prismatolaimus

Pharynx somewhat conoid or obscure (Figs. 140A–C).....................54

**54.** Lips massive, deeply cut, dividing head into three jaws...........Trischistoma

Lips not massive, three or six, but head not appearing to be divided into jaws (Figs. 140A–C); common...........................................55

**55.** Pharynx collapsed (Figs. 140B, C)...........................Tripyla

Pharynx conoid, divided (Fig. 140A)............................Trilobus

**56.** Pharynx rather conoid, with small dorsal tooth and one large and one small subventral tooth......................................Mononchulus

Pharynx not conoid; dorsal tooth largest (Figs. 140E–G)..................57

**57.** Ventral pharyngeal ridge bearing longitudinal row of denticles (Fig. 140F).
Prionchulus

Ventral longitudinal pharyngeal ridge absent............................58

**58.** Numerous subventral denticles present in pharynx (Fig. 140G)............59

No such denticles in pharynx (Fig. 140E)..............................60

**59.** Pharyngeal denticles in transverse rows (Fig. 140G)..............Mylonchulus

Pharyngeal denticles irregular..............................Sporonchulus

**60.** Teeth small, middle or posterior to middle of pharynx, if middle, then retrorse...61

Dorsal tooth usually large, not retrorse, in anterior or middle part of pharynx (Fig. 140E); common..................................Mononchus

**61.** Teeth retrorse.......................................Anatonchus

Teeth not retrorse.......................................Iotonchus

# NEMATODA REFERENCES

BASTIAN, H. C. 1865. Monograph on the Anguillulidae, or free nematodes, marine, land, and fresh water; with descriptions of 100 new species. *Trans. Linn. Soc. London* 25:74–184.

BAYLIS, H. A., and R. DAUBNEY. 1926. *A synopsis of the families and genera of Nematoda.* 277 pp. British Museum of Natural History, London.

CHATTERJI, R. C. 1935. Permanent mounts of nematodes. *Zool. Anz.* 109:270.

CHITWOOD, B. G. 1931. A comparative histological study of certain nematodes. *Zeitschr. Morph. Ökol. Tiere* 23:237–284.

CHITWOOD, B. G., and M. B. CHITWOOD. 1930. A technique for the embedding of nematodes. *Trans. Amer. Micros. Soc.* 49:186–187.

CHITWOOD, B. G., *et al.* 1937–1940. *An introduction to nematology.* Section I, Parts I, II, and III; Section II, Part I; pp. 1–240. Baltimore, Md.

———. 1950. *Ibid.* Revised edition of Section I; pp. 1–213.

COBB, M. V. 1915. Some fresh-water nematodes of the Douglas Lake region of Michigan, U. S. A. *Trans. Amer. Micros. Soc.* 34:21–47.

COBB, N. A. 1913. New nematode genera found inhabiting fresh water and non-brackish soils. *Jour. Wash. Acad. Sci.* 3:432–444.

———. 1914. The North American free-living fresh-water nematodes. *Trans. Amer. Micros. Soc.* 33:69–134.

———. 1914–1935. *Contributions to the science of nematology.* 490 pp. Baltimore, Md. (Issued in 26 parts, bound in one volume; some parts are reprints of previously published articles, others are original.)

———. 1915. Nematodes and their relationships. *Yearbook U. S. D. A. for 1914*:453–490.

———. 1917. The mononchs. A genus of free-living predatory nematodes. *Soil Science* 3:431–486.

———. 1918. Estimating the nema population of soil. *U. S. D. A. Bur. Plant Ind. Agric. Tech. Circ.* 1:1–48.

———. 1918a. Filter-bed nemas: nematodes of the slow sand filter beds of American cities (including new genera and species) with notes on hermaphroditism and parthenogenesis. *Contrib. Sci. Nematology* 7:189–212.

———. 1919. The orders and classes of nemas. *Ibid.* 8:213–216.

———. 1935. A key to the genera of free-living nemas. *Proc. Helminth. Soc. Wash.* 2:1–40.

FILIPJEV, I. N. 1934. The classification of the free-living nematodes and their relation to the parasitic nematodes. *Smithson. Misc. Coll.* 89:1–63.

———. 1936. On the classification of the Tylenchinae. *Proc. Helminth. Soc. Wash.* 3:80–82.

GOODEY, T. 1951. *Soil and freshwater nematodes. A monograph.* 390 pp. New York and London.

HOEPPLI, R. J. C. 1926. Studies of free-living nematodes from the thermal waters of Yellowstone Park. *Trans. Amer. Micros. Soc.* 45:234–255.

LINFORD, N. B. 1937. The feeding of some hollow-stylet nematodes. *Proc. Helminth. Soc. Wash.* 4:41–46.

MAN, J. G. DE. 1884. *Die frei in der reinen Erde und im süssen Wasser lebenden Nematoden der Niederländischen Fauna.* 206 pp. Leiden.

MICOLETZKY, H. 1925. Die freilebenden Süsswasser- und Moornematoden Dänemarks. *D. Kgl. Danske Vidensk. Selsk. Skr. Naturv. Math. Afd.* 10:57–310.

SCHNEIDER, W. 1937. Freilebende Nematoden der Deutschen Limnologischen Sundaexpedition nach Sumatra, Java und Bali. *Arch. Hydrobiol.* 15 (Suppl. Bd.): 30–108.

STEINER, G. 1914. Freilebende Nematoden aus der Schweiz. *Ibid.* 9:259–276, 420–438.

———. 1915. Beiträge zur geographischen Verbreitung freilebender Nematoden. *Zool. Anz.* 46:311–335, 337–349.

THORNE, G. 1930. Predaceous nemas of the genus Nygolaimus and a new genus Sectonema. *Jour. Agric. Res.* 41:445–466.

———. 1935. Notes on free-living and plant-parasitic nematodes. II. *Proc. Helminth. Soc. Wash.* 2:96–98.

———. 1937. A revision of the nematode family Cephalobidae Chitwood and Chitwood. *Ibid.* 4:1–16.

———. 1939. A monograph of the nematodes of the superfamily Dorylaimoidea. *Capita Zool.* 8:1–261.

# Chapter 10

# NEMATOMORPHA (HORSEHAIR WORMS, GORDIAN WORMS)

BECAUSE of their fancied resemblance to animated horsehairs, members of the Phylum Nematomorpha have long been known as "horsehair worms," and because of their habit of becoming inextricably entangled in masses of two to many individuals, they are also commonly called "gordian worms," after the Gordian knot episode of antiquity.

The adults swim clumsily by slow undulations or writhe about in puddles and in the shallows of marshes, ponds, lakes, and streams. Sometimes they occur on the shore near the water's edge, especially if the substrate is wet. The immature stages are internal parasites of insects, usually crickets, terrestrial beetles, and grasshoppers.

**General characteristics.** Adult gordian worms range from about 10 cm. to 70 cm. in length with a diameter of 0.3 to 2.5 mm. The diameter is the same throughout the body length except for slight tapering at the extremities, especially anteriorly. Coloration includes opaque yellowish, gray, tan, dark brown, or blackish. There is considerable variation in size and coloration within single species. Males are consistently smaller than females and often exhibit slight coiling of the posterior end. The two sexes occur in about equal numbers.

The small mouth is terminal or subterminal, and sometimes absent. The cloacal aperture is terminal, subterminal, or ventral. Sexes of several genera can be distinguished by the structure of the posterior end. Females of *Paragordius* have three lobes. Males of *Gordius, Parachordodes, Paragordius,* and *Gordionus* have two lobes. In females of *Gordius, Gordionus,* and *Parachordodes* the posterior end is simple and rounded, and this is also the situation in both sexes for *Neochordodes, Chordodes,* and *Pseudochordodes.* In some species the posterior end of the female is slightly bulbous.

These worms were not separated from the nematodes until 1886, and they are often confused with mermithid nematodes. Externally, however, Mermithidae are easily differentiated by their pointed ends, tapered body, smooth cuticle, and location of the anus.

**Cuticle.** The gordian cuticle is unusually complex, lamellated, and fibrous (Figs. 143, 146). Areoles are irregular, rounded, or polygonal thickened surface areas of the cuticle which are present in most species. Sometimes they are poorly differentiated or flat and project only slightly from the general surface of the cuticle; in other species they may be papillate to a varying degree. Often the areoles bear small pore canals, granules, setae, or filamentous processes. The furrows or flat areas between areoles likewise may contain setae, granules, papillae, or filamentous processes. In the cloacal region of the male there are often special tracts of setae, thorns, or adhesive wartlike structures which presumably aid in copulation.

232

**Internal anatomy, physiology.** In addition to cuticle, the body wall consists of a flat to columnar hypodermis and an innermost layer of longitudinal muscle fibers. There are no circular fibers, and consequently the diameter of the body cannot be varied. Locomotion consists of localized bending and writhing movements produced by contractions of the longitudinal muscle fibers in one or two quadrants at a time. Males are able to swim in an undulatory manner, but such locomotion is not to be compared with the rapid wriggling of small nematodes.

Food is never ingested at any time during the life history, the digestive tract being degenerate and completely functionless. A pharynx is usually differentiated but has no cavity, and the midgut is a simple narrow tubule. The posterior end of the digestive tract is a cloaca into which the two genital ducts open.

The gonads consist of a pair of long cylindrical bodies which fill most of the pseudocoel in mature animals. Ripe eggs and sperm pass posteriorly through short

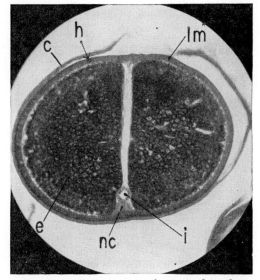

FIG. 142.—Cross section of a typical gordian, ×60. *c*, cuticle (partly torn away from underlying hypodermis); *e*, developing eggs; *h*, hypodermis; *i*, intestine; *lm*, longitudinal muscle; *nc*, nerve cord.

paired oviducts and sperm ducts, respectively, into the cloaca, and thence to the outside. In the female there is a median ventral seminal receptacle extending forward from the anterior end of the cloaca.

A cerebral mass, or brain, encircles the digestive tract at the anterior end, and a longitudinal ventral nerve cord extends throughout the body.

One or two ocelli have been described at the anterior end of some species, but otherwise sensory receptors are limited to tactile areas near the brain and perhaps also to some of the cuticular outgrowths on the general body surface.

There are no special circulatory, respiratory, or excretory structures. The residual pseudocoel space between body wall and visceral organs is filled with loose mesenchyme.

**Reproduction, life history.** Probably depending on the species and ecological conditions, copulation usually occurs in spring, early summer, or autumn. Although it is not uncommon to find up to

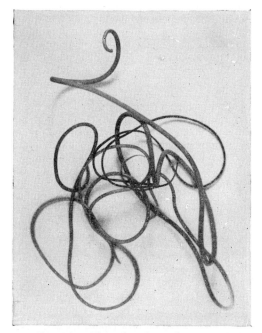

FIG. 141.—Three female gordians, ×1.

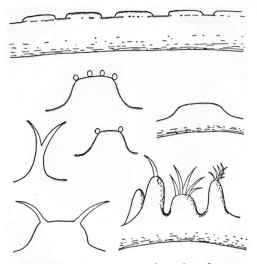

FIG. 143.—Various types of areoles, diagrammatic. (Partly modified from Müller.)

10 or 20 worms aggregated in a single writhing mass in the springtime, only one female and one male are involved in a copulation. A male coils the posterior tip of his body around the posterior end of the female and deposits sperm at her cloacal opening. The sperm then migrate into the female cloaca and may be stored for a short time in the seminal receptacle. Fertilization is internal, and presumably the eggs are fertilized just before being extruded from the cloacal opening of the female. Eggs are deposited in long gelatinous strings which swell and may exceed the size of the parent. Such masses contain up to several million eggs. Males die after copulation and females after egg deposition.

Depending on water temperature, the incubation period is usually 15 to 80 days. The resulting larva (Fig. 144) is unlike the adult and has a very brief free-swimming existence. It is cylindrical, often annulated, only about 250 microns long, and divided into a trunk and large muscular presoma. The anterior end of the presoma has an eversible proboscis bearing three long stylets and three circlets of hooks. The anterior portion of the trunk contains a large glandular mass which opens at the tip of the presoma via a long duct. Posteriorly the trunk contains a blind nonfunctional intestine which opens to the outside by means of a pore.

The immediate and ultimate fates of this larval stage have been the subject of a long and confusing controversy, and even the most recent investigations do not seem to have completely cleared up the problem. Within 24 hours after hatching the larva is usually thought to encyst on vegetation or any other convenient substrate at or near the water's edge. The

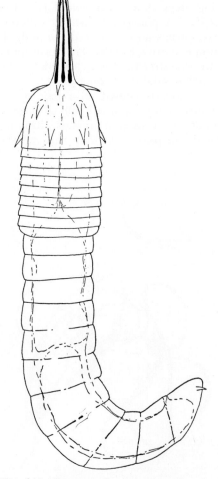

FIG. 144.—Diagram of a typical gordian larva, ×500, with protruded proboscis.

colder the water the more readily encyst-ment occurs. Such cysts may remain via-ble for two months in water and up to one month in a moist habitat such as grass and other vegetation along the waterside. The latter condition may result when the water level of a stream or pond is falling.

Assuming favorable circumstances, a wide variety of crickets, grasshoppers, and terrestrial and aquatic beetles ingest these cysts along with the vegetation to which they are attached. Within the digestive tract the cyst wall disintegrates, and the released larva bores its way through the wall of the intestine and into the hemocoel of the host.

Large numbers of cysts are undoubtedly ingested by abnormal hosts (snails, oligo-chaetes, aquatic insects, fish, etc.), but in these hosts the larva dies or re-encysts in the tissues instead of developing further. If such an abnormal host is eaten by an omnivorous insect that is a normal host, the contained larva then burrows through the well of the digestive tract to the hemo-coel of the latter and undergoes further development.

There is also the possibility (but one that is losing favor) that motile larvae actively penetrate through the body wall of almost any small aquatic or waterside animal but develop further only within such insects as crickets, grasshoppers, and beetles.

Within the host the larva digests and absorbs the surrounding tissues as a source of nourishment. Metamorphosis and de-velopment to the adult stage are com-pleted in several weeks to several months by which time the worm is a tightly coiled mass in the hemocoel. Usually there are one to several worms per host. Sometimes gordians overwinter in the host body.

If the host falls into water or becomes wetted at a time when the contained worm is mature or nearly mature, the latter breaks through the body wall and is thenceforth free living. There is some evi-dence to show that hosts tend to seek water when their worms are ready to emerge. Newly released worms that do not have access to water soon die. If emer-gence from the host occurs in spring or summer, copulation usually soon follows, but sometimes emergence occurs in the autumn and then the worms remain soli-tary and customarily hibernate in water-side grass and roots and become active and copulate in the water in the following spring. Length of the complete life cycle is quite variable, ranging from about two to 15 months.

Unlike most parasites, gordians gener-ally have little host specificity, and the same species may develop in a variety of grasshoppers or beetles. A few gordians have even been reported emerging from caddis flies and dragonflies.

Adults have occasionally been recorded as human parasites, but such cases are undoubtedly fortuitous and produced by accidental ingestion of worms in food or water.

**Ecology.** Little is known about gordian ecology. The worms occur in suitable habitats wherever appropriate hosts are found, from the tropics to cold-temperate latitudes, and to altitudes above tim-ber line in mountainous areas. Some spe-cies are widely distributed throughout North and South America, and a few occur in both Europe and the United States or are Holarctic. The genus *Gordius* is essen-tially cosmopolitan. The most common and widely distributed species in the United States are *Gordius robustus* Leidy and *Paragordius varius* (Leidy).

There seem to be few habitat prefer-ences, and the same species may be found in both running and standing waters. Oc-casionally they are on the shore just above the water's edge but more usually in water 2 cm. to 20 cm. deep. Even small puddles and stock tanks are fruitful collecting areas. A few observations indicate that the worms are more active at night, but there is no evidence for a true negative phototaxis. Males are much more active than females and move about in a serpentine manner for hours in the water and on the bottom. Females are sluggish and move about but little.

**Preparing.** Seventy to 90 per cent alcohol is a suitable fixative and preservative, but for more critical work hot saturated mercuric chloride containing 5 to 10 per cent acetic acid is much better, especially if histological sections are contemplated.

For a study of the extremities, cut anterior to the cloacal aperture and posterior to the dark ring near the anterior end; mount in lactophenol, clarite, or balsam after dehydrating. Small bits of cuticle should be sliced from the middle third of the body with a sharp razor blade by stretching the worm firmly over the left forefinger. Such pieces should be placed in a drop of glycerin for about an hour. Then gently scrape off the soft tissues from the underside with needles. Rinse the cleaned cuticle in a change of glycerin and mount, outer surface up, in glycerin jelly on a slide. Lactophenol and clarite mounts are often preferable for certain cuticular structures. Thin razor-blade sections of the whole body are sometimes also desirable.

**Taxonomy.** The Phylum Nematomorpha is divided into the Nectonematoidea and Gordioidea. The former category contains a single marine species whose larvae are parasitic in crustaceans. All of the other species are fresh-water, totaling about 80 for the whole world, and belong in the Gordioidea. This category consists of two families, the Gordiidae and the Chordodidae. The former contains a single genus, *Gordius*; the latter contains about 12 genera, of which six are presumed to occur in the United States.

Some generic characters and most species characters are based largely on the surface pattern and sculpturing of the cuticle. For studying some of these details it is often necessary to use oil immersion.

Only a negligible amount of work on American gordians has been published since the papers of Montgomery and May, and the taxonomy and distribution of our species are very poorly known. Many of the descriptions published prior to 1910 were quite brief and did not include sufficient fine details, and for this reason some such descriptions are not now very trustworthy. Until the gordian fauna of the United States is more thoroughly investigated, therefore, it seems fruitless to draw up a key to species which would be unreliable and soon out of date. For this reason the following key includes only generic categories. Most of the delimitations and suggestions of Carvalho and Heinze have been followed.

## KEY TO GENERA OF NEMATOMORPHA

1. Posterior end with three lobes (Fig. 145B); cuticle with scattered areoles of one kind (Fig. 146A); widely distributed and common; several species; females.
   **Paragordius**

   Posterior end blunt or bilobed (Figs. 145C, D, F, G)......................2
2. Posterior end bilobed and often with a tendency toward coiling (Figs. 145C, D, G); males................................................3

   Posterior end blunt and without lobes; males and females..................6
3. Postcloacal region with a crescentic fold; areoles present (Fig. 145D) or absent; widely distributed; several species............................**Gordius**

   Postcloacal region without a crescentic fold.............................4
4. With two kinds of areoles (Fig. 146E); poorly known in the United States.
   **Parachordodes**

   With one kind of areole (Figs. 146A, C)................................5

5. Posterior lobes about two and one-half to three times as long as wide; without rows of hairs or papillae lateral to cloacal aperture (Fig. 145C); widely distributed and common; several species.............................**Paragordius**

   Posterior lobes about twice as long as wide; with rows of long papillae on either side of cloacal aperture (Fig. 145G); several species...........**Gordionus**

6. Interareolar furrows clear and without setae, pore canals, or large granulations; areoles often absent or indistinct; only one kind of areole (Fig. 146B); common and widely distributed; several species; females...............**Gordius**

   Interareolar furrows usually with setae, pore canals, granulations, or other structures; one, two, or more kinds of areoles always present.................7

7. With one kind of areole..........................................8

   With two or more kinds of areoles; pore canals in areoles or between adjacent areoles (Figs. 146E–H), sometimes absent...........................9

8. With a few pore canals in furrows between areoles (Fig. 146C); several species; females...........................................**Gordionus**

   Without pore canals in furrows between areoles (Fig. 146D); poorly known in the United States; males and females........................**Neochordodes**

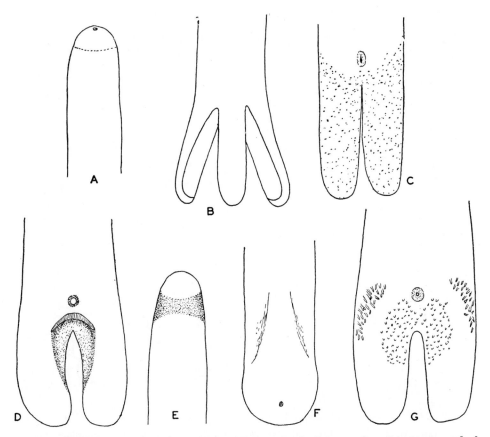

Fig. 145.—Extremities of Nematomorpha. A, anterior end of *Paragordius;* B, posterior end of female *Paragordius;* C, posterior end of male *Paragordius;* D, posterior end of male *Gordius;* E, anterior end of *Gordius;* F, posterior end of female *Gordius;* G, posterior end of male *Gordionus.*

9. Pore canals in center of large areoles (Fig. 146E); body of mature individuals usually less than 1 mm. thick; poorly known in the United States; females.
**Parachordodes**
Pore canals absent, or between large areoles (Figs. 146F, H); body of mature individuals usually more than 1 mm. thick; males and females...............**10**
10. Cuticle with two or more types of prominent papillate areoles, the highest ones often bearing a tuft of slender filaments; interareolar furrows with scattered tubercles, bristles, and granules (Figs. 146F, G); several species..**Chordodes**
Cuticle with two types of nonpapillate areoles; interareolar furrows free of tubercles, bristles, and granules (Fig. 146H); uncommon in the United States.
**Pseudochordodes**

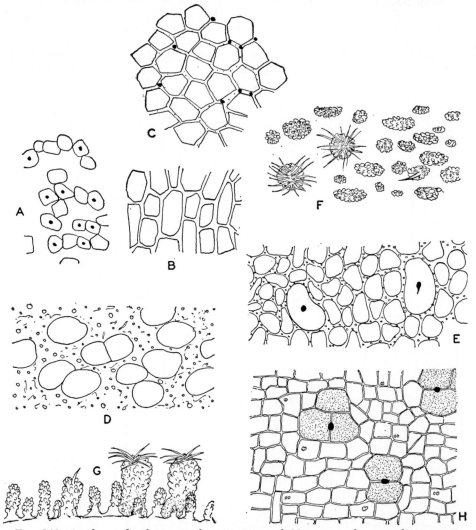

Fig. 146.—Areoles and other cuticular structures of Nematomorpha, semidiagrammatic. (Pore canals shown in solid black.) A, *Paragordius*; B, *Gordius*; C, *Gordionus*; D, *Neochordodes*; E, *Parachordodes*; F, surface view of *Chordodes* areoles; G, side view of *Chordodes* areoles; H, *Pseudochordodes*. (E modified from Heinze, 1935; F and G modified from Camerano, 1897; H modified from Carvalho.)

# NEMATOMORPHA REFERENCES

CAMERANO, L. 1897. Monografia dei Gordii. *Mem. R. Accad. Sci. Torino* (2) **47**:339–419.

——. 1915. Revisione dei Gordii. *Ibid.* **66**:1–66.

CARVALHO, J. C. M. 1942. Studies on some Gordiacea of North and South America. *Jour. Parasit.* **28**:213–222.

DORIER, A. 1930. Recherches biologiques et systématiques sur les Gordiacés. *Trav. Lab. Hydrobiol. Piscicult. Grenoble* **22**:1–180.

HEINZE, K. 1935. Über das genus Parachordodes Camerano 1897 nebst allgemeinen Angaben über die Familie Chordodidae. *Zeitschr. Parasitenk.* **7**:657–678.

——. 1935a. Über Gordiiden. *Zool. Anz.* **111**:23–32.

——. 1937. Die Saitenwürmer (Gordioidea) Deutschlands. Eine systematisch-faunistische Studie über Insektenparasiten aus der Gruppe der Nematomorpha. *Zeitschr. Parasitenk.* **9**:263–344.

——. 1941. Saitenwürmer oder Gordioidea. *Tierwelt Deutschlands* **39**:1–78.

MAY, H. G. 1919. Contributions to the life histories of Gordius robustus Leidy and Paragordius varius (Leidy). *Ill. Biol. Monogr.* **5**:1–118.

MÜLLER, G. W. 1927. Über Gordiaceen. *Zeitschr. Morph. Ökol. Tiere* **7**:134–219.

MONTGOMERY, T. H., JR. 1898. The Gordiacea of certain American collections with particular reference to the North American fauna. *Bull. Mus. Comp. Zool. Harvard Univ.* **32**:23–59.

——. 1898a. The Gordiacea of certain American collections, with particular reference to the North American fauna. II. *Proc. Calif. Acad. Sci.* (3) **1**:333–344.

——. 1899. Synopses of North American invertebrates. II. Gordiacea (hair worms). *Amer. Nat.* **33**:647–652.

SCHUURMANS STEKHOVEN, J. H., JR. 1943. Contribution a l'étude des gordiides de la fauna Belge. *Bull. Mus. royal d'Hist. nat. Belg.* **19**:1–28.

# Chapter 11

# TARDIGRADA (WATER BEARS)

ALTHOUGH tardigrades are strictly aquatic animals, they are seldom abundant in the usual types of habitats harboring fresh-water invertebrates. They are not plankton organisms; they are only occasionally collected in aquatic mosses and algae, on rooted aquatics, or in the mud and debris of puddles, ponds, and lakes. More typically, active tardigrades are found in the droplets and film of water on terrestrial wet mosses, liverworts, and certain angiosperms with a rosette growth form. They also occur in the capillary water between the sand grains of sandy beaches up to two or three meters from the water's edge.

Mature individuals range from 50 microns to 1,200 microns in length but are usually less than 500 microns long. Many species have a considerable size variation. The short, stout, cylindrical body, the four pairs of stumpy lateroventral legs, and a deliberate "pawing" sort of locomotion produce a fancied resemblance to a miniature bearlike creature, and the Tardigrada have been generally called "water bears" since they were given that name by Huxley in 1869.

The great majority of species have been reported from lichens, liverworts, and terrestrial and fresh-water mosses. Less than 10 per cent of the known species have been reported from marine habitats.

Nearly all of what we know about tardigrade biology has been contributed through the efforts of British, German, and French investigators. Water bears have been almost completely ignored in the United States, even though we undoubtedly have a rich fauna. Only about 20 species have been reported from this country and about 40 species from the whole of North America, and these figures include marine, moss, and fresh-water forms. About 340 species have been described the world over.

**General characteristics.** The body consists of a distinct head and four indefinite "body segments." Each leg is armed with four claws or two pairs of double claws. Crawling and creeping are more or less sluggish, the claws being used for clinging to vegetation and debris. The mouth is anterior, subterminal, or ventral, and the cloacal aperture, or anus, lies between the bases of the last legs. The entire surface of the body is covered with a cuticle secreted by the thin hypodermis, which consists of polygonal cells. Depending on the species, the cuticle may be variously thickened and marked. Cilia do not occur in this phylum. Only liquid materials are ingested, and the anterior part of the digestive tract has a sucking pharynx and a pair of long, piercing stylets.

Sexes are separate, but the great majority of individuals are females. Usually there are four to six ecdyses in the life history.

A remarkable feature of most aquatic and semiaquatic fresh-water tardigrades is their ability to tide over dry periods in a shriveled, rounded, anabiotic state. When normal moisture conditions return, the ani-

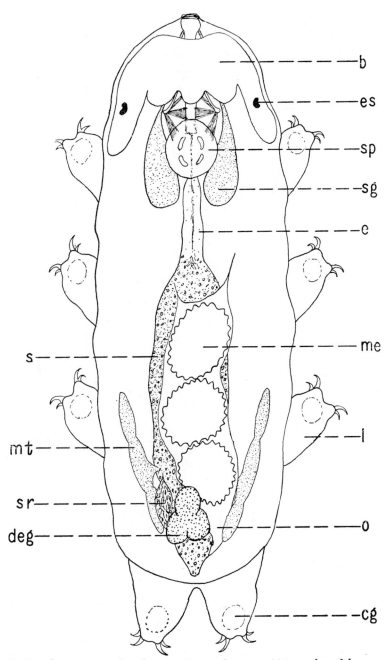

FIG. 147.—Semidiagrammatic dorsal view of *Macrobiotus*, ×220; trunk and leg muscles not shown. *b*, brain; *cg*, claw gland; *deg*, dorsal excretory gland; *e*, esophagus; *es*, eyespot; *l*, leg; *me*, mature egg in saclike ovary; *mt*, Malpighian tubule; *o*, oviduct; *s*, stomach; *sr*, seminal receptacle; *sg*, salivary gland; *sp*, sucking pharynx. (Greatly modified from Marcus, 1928b.)

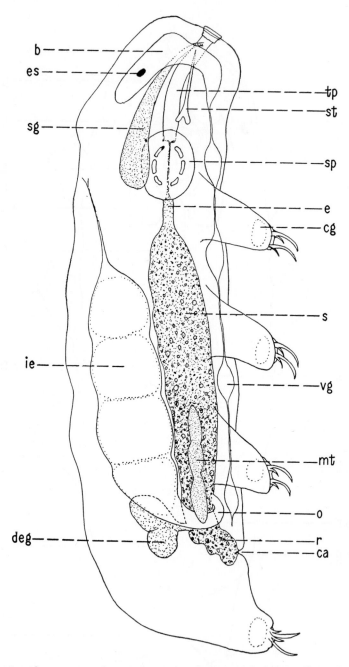

Fig. 148.—Semidiagrammatic lateral view of a typical tardigrade, ×220; all musculature omitted. *b*, brain; *ca*, cloacal aperture; *cg*, claw gland; *deg*, dorsal excretory gland; *e*, esophagus; *es*, eyespot; *ie*, immature egg in saclike ovary; *mt*, Malpighian tubule; *o*, oviduct; *r*, rectum; *s*, stomach; *sg*, salivary gland; *sp*, sucking pharynx; *st*, stylet; *tp*, tubular pharynx; *vg*, ventral ganglion.

mal resumes its normal appearance and activity.

Coloration is variously produced by the pigmentation of the cuticle and hypodermis, dissolved materials in the body fluid, reserve food bodies, and the contents of the digestive tract. Gray, bluish, yellow-brown, reddish, or brown are common colors. Some species are relatively dark and opaque, especially among older individuals; others are translucent and pale.

There are no special circulatory or respiratory systems. Materials diffuse and circulate about easily in the body fluid, and respiration occurs through the general body surface.

**Feeding, digestive system.** Tardigrades are mostly plant feeders. The cellulose wall of moss leaflet cells and algal filaments are pierced with the stylets and the fluid contents are sucked out by pharyngeal pumping action. Occasionally, however, the body fluids of small metazoans, such as nematodes and rotifers, are used as food. *Milnesium tardigradum* Doyère is said to be chiefly carnivorous.

The periphery of the mouth is stiffened and surrounded by two or three folded and superimposed rings of cuticle. That portion of the digestive system extending from the small mouth cavity to the anterior end of the esophagus is called the buccal apparatus (Fig. 149). It consists of the tubular pharynx, the muscular or sucking pharynx, and the stylet mechanism. The tubular pharynx is narrow and sclerotized and extends into the mass of the sucking pharynx. The latter is football-shaped, with thick walls composed of radial muscle fibers, and its small triquetrous cavity is lined with a thin epithelium. Six longitudinal ridges or fragmented sclerotized bars give stiffness to the sucking pharynx and provide for insertions of muscle fibers. The individual sclerotized pieces in the pharynx are called macroplacoids (Figs. 149, 150). Sometimes there is a single small posterior piece, called a microplacoid or comma.

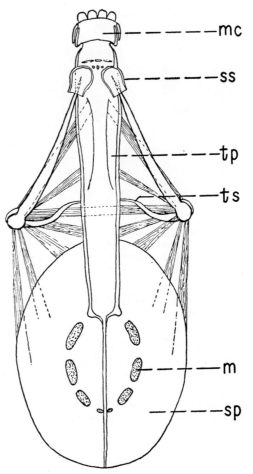

Fig. 149.—Semidiagrammatic dorsal view of buccal apparatus and associated musculature; stylets are shown retracted. *m*, macroplacoids; *mc*, mouth cavity; *sp*, sucking pharynx; *ss*, stylet sheath; *tp*, tubular pharynx; *ts*, transverse support.

The two stylets lie at an angle on either side of the tubular pharynx and the sharp tips project into the anterior end of the pharyngeal cavity through special lateral slots, or stylet sheaths. A transverse support extends from the tubular pharynx to the basal portion of each stylet. Several pairs of small muscles extending from the base of the stylets to the tubular pharynx and the sucking pharynx are capable of withdrawing and protruding the stylets a considerable distance out of the mouth.

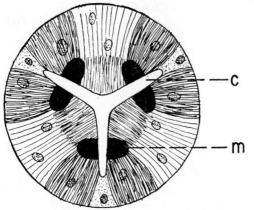

Fig. 150.—Diagrammatic cross section of a typical tardigrade sucking pharynx showing radial muscle fibers. *c*, triquetrous cavity; *m*, macroplacoid.

A pair of large salivary glands open into the mouth cavity. They also function in the secretion of new stylets and stylet supports at molting and for this reason are sometimes called stylet glands. Some investigators believe that they have an excretory function, especially in the Heterotardigrada. A few small unicellular glands of unknown function occur near the mouth. They are ingrowths of the hypodermis.

The esophagus ranges from long to very short. It empties into the capacious stomach, or midgut, which is usually without diverticula but may have slight lateral caeca. The hindgut, or rectum, is short and has a small cavity. In the Class Eutardigrada it is a true cloaca. The anus or cloacal aperture is a longitudinal or transverse slit.

Digestion in the anterior portion of the stomach is acid; posteriorly it is alkaline. Reserve food may be stored in hypodermal cells or in special reserve food bodies which float about in the body cavity. Feces are often released into the old cuticle during molting, especially in *Echiniscus*.

**Excretion.** In the Eutardigrada there are three small glands situated at the junc-tion of midgut and hindgut, each of which consists of only three cells. One gland is dorsal and two are lateral. All supposedly have an excretory function, and perhaps they are also osmoregulatory. The paired glands are commonly called Malpighian tubules. Some excretory material is stored in the hypodermal cells, some excretory granules are left within the old exoskeleton at ecdysis, and some are given off at the anterior end when the stylet mechanism is shed just preceding an ecdysis.

**Muscle system.** In addition to the pharynx and the stylet muscles, a tardigrade usually has from about 40 to 140 long, thin body muscles, the number depending on the species. Each such muscle is merely a single fibrillar cell with one nucleus, or several such cells. Most origins and insertions are on the body wall (Fig. 151). Contractions of the dorsal and ventral longitudinal muscles bring about a slight shortening or curvature of the body. Each leg is moved by a set of muscles originating on the dorsal and ventral body wall and inserting near the tip of the leg. The body wall is devoid of circular muscle fibers, but the turgor of the body fluid presumably acts as an antagonist to the longitudinal and leg muscles. Muscles extending from the body wall to the cloaca facilitate egg deposition and defecation. A few species have longitudinal fibers associated with the stomach.

**Nervous system.** The large dorsal brain commonly has two long lateral lobes and two or three median lobes; it covers much of the tubular pharynx (Fig. 152). Two broad circumpharyngeal connectives pass around the pharynx and unite with a subpharyngeal ganglion. In the trunk there is a chain of four conspicuous ventral ganglia united by two longitudinal nerve strands. Frequently these ganglia are slightly bilobed. Paired nerve strands originating in the brain and ganglia innervate all parts of the body. Some of the longer strands, especially those extending into the legs, have small terminal ganglionic masses.

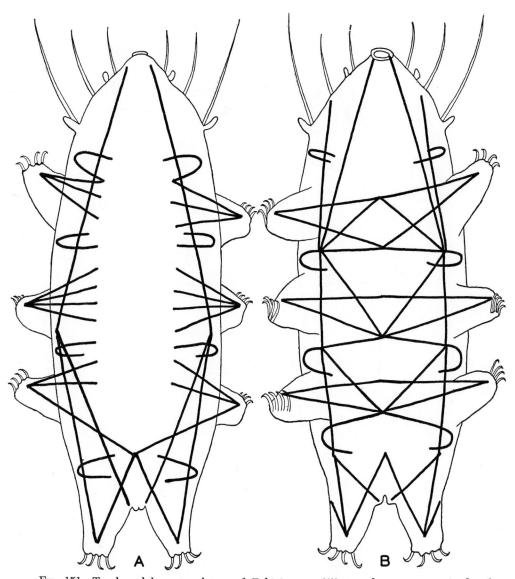

FIG. 151.—Trunk and leg musculature of *Echiniscus*, ×350, semidiagrammatic. A, dorsal view; B, ventral view. (Greatly modified from Marcus, 1928b.)

**Sense organs.** The great majority of tardigrades have a pair of eyespots in the lateral lobes of the brain. Each consists of a cup-shaped mass of black or red pigment granules.

Head cirri are usually tactile, but there is some question about the presumed sensory function of body cirri and filaments.

**Cuticular structures.** Fresh-water species usually have a thicker cuticle than marine species, and semiaquatic species have a thicker cuticle than aquatic species. The surface may be smooth or variously sculptured, granular, or papillate. Often there are long cirri. Some species of Eutardigrada have transverse grooves or

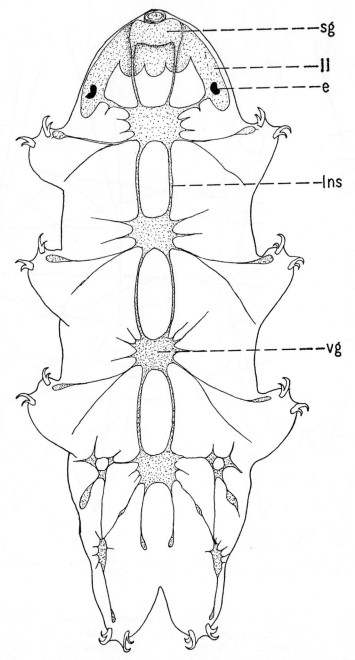

Fig. 152.—Ventral view of nervous system of *Macrobiotus*, ×220. *e*, eyespot; *ll*, lateral lobe of brain; *lns*, longitudinal nerve strand; *sg*, subpharyngeal ganglion; *vg*, ventral ganglion. (Modified from various sources.)

folds, but *Echiniscus* and *Pseudechiniscus* have dorsal armor-like thickened plates. Beginning at the anterior end, these are as follows (Fig. 156F): head plate, shoulder plate (first trunk plate), a small median first intercalary, second trunk plate (divided longitudinally), second intercalary, third trunk plate (usually divided longitudinally), third intercalary (often indistinct), and the anal plate (usually grooved).

**Reproduction, growth.** The bulk of a population is always composed of females, and males reach their peak of abundance during the winter or early spring. Males are unknown in *Oreella*, *Parechiniscus*, and *Echiniscus*, and these genera probably reproduce exclusively by parthenogenesis.

Some species show sexual dimorphism in the shape and cuticular structure of the last legs, in the size and curvature of the claws, and in the smaller size of the males. The gonad is an unpaired sac dorsal to the digestive tract and with one or two attachment fibers at the anterior end. In the male there are two vasa deferentia which curve around each side of the intestine and have a small swollen portion which acts as a seminal vesicle. The female has a single oviduct on the right side of the intestine. On the other side a blind seminal receptacle may sometimes be found in *Hypsibius* and *Macrobiotus*, especially in the late fall, winter, and early spring. In the Eutardigrada the genital ducts open into the rectum which is therefore more appropriately a cloaca. In the Heterotardigrada there is a separate preanal genital pore.

Two distinct types of eggs have been observed in some species, thin-shelled and thick-shelled, and perhaps they are similar to the tachyblastic and opsiblastic eggs produced by gastrotrichs, or the summer and winter eggs produced by rotifers. At least there is some evidence to show that thick-shelled eggs are produced when environmental conditions are unfavorable; there is the further possibility that thin-shelled eggs are parthenogenetic and thick-shelled eggs are fertilized. The peak of the reproductive period is from November to May, but females with eggs may be found at any time of the year.

In most of the true aquatic species "external" fertilization is the rule. One or more males clamber about on the body of a female before she is ready to release her eggs but after the old cuticle has become loosened in preparation for a molt. The males release sperm through the cloacal aperture or genital pore of the old cuticle, and the eggs are fertilized when they are released into the cavity between the new and old cuticle.

In typical semiaquatic species fertilization is "internal" and does not necessarily occur just before an ecdysis. Sperm enter the genital pore or cloacal aperture and fertilize the eggs before their release from the body of the female. Sometimes the sperm may be stored in the seminal receptacle.

Most female Echiniscoidea produce only two to six eggs, but in other groups a female produces anywhere from one to 30 eggs. Sometimes the whole complement may be released in 15 to 30 minutes.

In *Macrobiotus* and some species of *Hypsibius* the eggs are deposited freely and singly, or in groups. In other freshwater forms they are contained in the newly shed cuticle. Free eggs are often sticky for attachment to the substrate and frequently faceted, spinous, tuberculate, or variously sculptured. Eggs released into the old cuticle usually have a smooth surface. Inside the true shell a thin membrane surrounds the developing embryo.

Depending on the species and ecological conditions, a thin-shelled egg usually completes development in three to 12 days and a thick-shelled egg in ten to 14 days.

The young emerge from the egg by rupturing the shell with their stylets. Newly hatched individuals are one-third to one-fifth the size of mature specimens, and all growth occurs by enlargement of cells al-

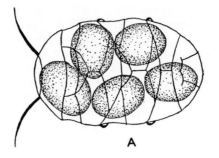

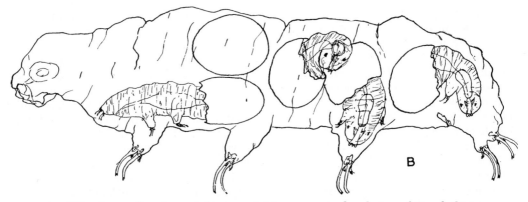

FIG. 153.—Cast tardigrade exoskeletons containing eggs. A, dorsal view of *Pseudechiniscus*; B, lateral view of *Milnesium tardigradum* Doyère (four of five eggs in process of hatching). (A modified from Ramazotti; B greatly modified from Marcus, 1929.)

ready present. Aside from their smaller size, immature tardigrades may be recognized by their undeveloped reproductive system, slight differences in the details of the buccal apparatus, and sometimes by the fact that there only two claws per leg.

Most investigators indicate four to six molts during the life history, and sexual maturity is usually attained sometime after the second or third molt. The old cuticle is usually shed after a period of growth, but it may also be shed as a response to hunger and unfavorable environmental conditions. Several days before a molt the sclerotized portions of the buccal apparatus are ejected and new ones (attached to the old muscles) promptly begin to be formed by the salivary glands. A day or two before a molt, the animal shrinks temporarily and slightly. Then the old cuticle ruptures at the anterior end and the animal crawls out. The lining of the rectum and the claws are lost at molting, and new claws are secreted by special claw glands in the tip of each leg.

There appears to be considerable variation in longevity, assuming that the animal is continuously active. Three months and 30 months are perhaps the extremes.

**General ecology.** A few species of *Macrobiotus* and *Hypsibius* are truly aquatic and some are both aquatic and semiaquatic, but the majority of species in these genera are semiaquatic only and occur chiefly on terrestrial mosses and lichens. *Milnesium tardigradum* occurs in both semiaquatic and aquatic habitats. All of the species in the other fresh-water genera are semiaquatic and occur in true aquatic habitats only rarely and fortuitously.

Active tardigrades can usually be found if one searches diligently in masses of filamentous algae, washings of higher aquatic plants, or in the debris on the bottom of ponds and pools. The semiaquatic species, however, are active only when the plant has been wetted by rain or when it is splashed at streamside. Many mosses, liverworts, lichens, and rosette angiosperms contain large tardigrade populations. Mosses on rocks or on the bark of trees contain tardigrades, even though they may be wet enough to allow them to be active for less than 5 per cent of the time. Concentrations up to 22,000 dry and inactive anabiotic tardigrades per gram of dry moss have been reported. Mosses with especially thick cellulose cell walls, such as *Polytrichum*, usually do not harbor tardigrades. Presumably their stylets cannot penetrate such walls. Favorable portions of sandy beaches sometimes contain 300 to 400 tardigrades per ten cubic centimeters of wet sand. Sometimes they occur as deep as ten centimeters in the sand.

Most species appear to be eurythermal and are normally active anywhere between near-freezing temperatures and 25° to 30°C. Some forms have been found in warm springs where they are continuously exposed to temperatures of 40°.

Although aquatic species are generally characteristic of the littoral, there are records of collections as deep as 100 meters on lake bottoms. Semiaquatic species occur from the tropics to the Arctic and Antarctic and from sea level to mountain tops up to 6,000 meters high. The annual period of activity varies correspondingly, from the year round to only a week or two.

Little is known about minimal oxygen requirements, but it is usually inferred that tardigrades cannot endure low dissolved oxygen concentrations as do many other small aquatic metazoans.

Aquatic species are usually most abundant between January and May, and sometimes there is a second maximum in the autumn months. Moss dwellers do not have pronounced seasonal maxima. Individuals are active as long as the moss is damp.

Tardigrades are chiefly preyed upon by amoeboid protozoans, nematodes, and perhaps by each other to a certain extent.

**Anabiosis.** When a bit of moss dries, many of the associated Tardigrada have the unusual ability to assume an inactive anabiotic state which may persist for as long as four to seven years. When normal ecological conditions again prevail, the tardigrades come out of their quiescent state and resume normal activity. Most marine species and true aquatic freshwater species do not apparently have the ability to assume an anabiotic condition.

Under drying conditions the head, posterior end, and legs are retracted, and the whole body becomes more or less rounded. Considerable water is lost from the body cavity and the anabiotic animal is therefore shriveled and wrinkled (Fig. 154). Internal visceral structures are not greatly modified. Although drying is almost always responsible for bringing on anabiosis, a lack of sufficient dissolved oxygen and perhaps other unfavorable conditions may also be responsible.

Metabolic processes proceed very slowly, but the length of time a specimen can remain in continuous anabiosis depends on the amount of stored food in the body. Death occurs as soon as the supply is exhausted.

Anabiotic tardigrades are highly resistant to abnormal environmental conditions. Some remain viable even after being kept experimentally in strong brine solutions, at 100°C. for six hours, and at −190°C. for as long as 20 months.

Revival from anabiosis takes but a short time when individuals are properly wetted. Usually the interval is four minutes to several hours, and occasionally a day or two. The animal absorbs water,

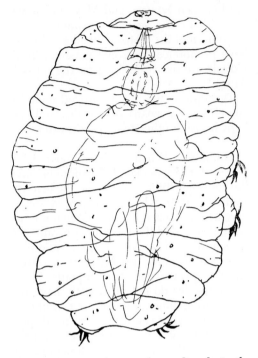

FIG. 154.—Dorsal view of a tardigrade in the anabiotic state, ×300.

swells, and promptly becomes active. Moss species usually go through numerous alternating periods of activity and anabiosis during their life cycle, depending on the nature of their habitat. One author states that the life cycle may be as long as 60 years, including anabiotic periods. Laboratory animals can easily be dried and revived ten times or more.

**Cysts.** Damage, hunger, and other abnormal ecological conditions sometimes bring about the formation of resistant cysts, especially in true aquatic species of *Macrobiotus* and *Hypsibius*. The animal contracts inside the old wrinkled cuticle and forms a dark-colored, thick-walled inner cyst (Fig. 155). The internal organs undergo a variable degree of degeneration. When ecological conditions are favorable the animal becomes reconstituted, the cyst wall ruptures, and the tardigrade emerges.

A "simplex" stage has been observed in many tardigrades, especially in species of *Macrobiotus*. Such animals are inactive and have a more or less reduced buccal apparatus. The macroplacoids are abortive, the esophagus is very slender, and the stylets are nonfunctional and reduced; sometimes all of the digestive system anterior to the stomach disappears and there is no mouth. Little is known about the factors responsible for the appearance of the simplex stage, but it is thought that it may occur in animals about to encyst or in those just emerged from a cyst.

**Asphyxy.** A third type of inactive condition in tardigrades is called asphyxy. It usually comes about when there is insufficient oxygen. The body swells and becomes rigid and turgid. There are no movements, and it is difficult to decide whether the animal is alive. After a maximum of about five days in this condition the animal dies, but if food and oxygen are supplied promptly the animal again resumes normal activity. Sometimes individuals emerging from anabiosis go into the state of asphyxy.

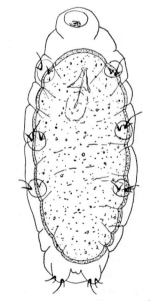

FIG. 155.—Cyst of *Hypsibius*, semidiagrammatic, ×75. (Greatly modified from Marcus, 1928.)

**Geographical distribution, dispersal.** The great majority of tardigrades are undoubtedly widely distributed, and an abundance of species first found in Europe have since been found scattered over a broad range. Some are Holarctic, generally distributed in the Northern Hemisphere, or even cosmopolitan (*Macrobiotus hüfelandi* Schultze, *Hypsibius oberhäuseri* (Doyère), and *Milnesium tardigradum*). Other species, of course, have been reported only from single mainland or island localities. The tropics contain notably few species and few individuals.

Passive distribution is effected by currents, animals (usually insects), waves, and wind, especially in the anabiotic and cyst stages. There is considerable positive evidence for wind as an important distributive agency.

**Collecting.** Almost any bit of suitable moss will yield tardigrades. If the moss is wet, simply rinse it out in water and examine the washings. Masses of filamentous algae and rooted aquatics may be treated similarly. Dry mosses and lichens should be soaked for 30 minutes to several days. At intervals rinse such plant material, and the tardigrades will be found as they emerge from cysts and the anabiotic state.

**Culturing.** Tardigrades are easy to culture, although little actual culture work seems to have been done. They may be kept in masses of filamentous algae or wet moss. Change a large fraction of the water every three or four days.

**Preserving, preparing.** Unlike many other small fresh-water metazoans, tardigrades are easy to fix in extended form. A large percentage will be suitable when killed and fixed in 5 per cent formalin or 85 per cent alcohol. Especially fine specimens may be secured by inducing asphyxy under a vaseline-sealed cover slip before killing and fixing. This procedure usually requires ten minutes to three hours. Some investigators recommend the use of one of a variety of narcotics before fixation. Fixatives that are particularly useful for staining and histological work are osmic acid, saturated mercuric chloride, and 2 per cent acetic acid. Piercing the body wall with a fine needle permits better staining and dehydration. Simple unstained permanent mounts may be made in glycerin jelly.

The sclerotized parts of the buccal apparatus may be isolated on a slide by the judicious use of 10 per cent potassium hydroxide.

**Taxonomy.** The phylogenetic affinities of tardigrades are highly debatable. During early embryology five coelomic pouches are formed from the mesoderm, but only one posterior pair persists as the gonads and their ducts; the others degenerate. The main body cavity is therefore probably something of a hemocoel.

Often they are placed near the mites in the Phylum Arthropoda, especially because of their indistinct segmentation, four pairs of legs, and piercing stylets. Some workers consider them crustaceans, and a further suggestion places them near the Onychophora. Others workers, however, consider the Phylum Tardigrada one of the wormlike groups of various affinities and place it after the Nematoda and either before or after the Chaetognatha and Bryozoa in the phylogenetic series. For the time being and until more definite evidence is forthcoming, this last suggestion is the one followed in the present manual.

Only about 15 genera are recognized in the whole phylum, of which eight contain a total of about 315 semiaquatic and aquatic fresh-water species. Five of these genera have been reported from the United States; they are *Echiniscus*, *Pseudechiniscus*, *Milnesium*, *Macrobiotus*, and *Hypsibius*. Three other genera, each known from a single species, have not yet been reported from the United States, but are included in the following key for the sake of completeness; these are *Oreella mollis*

Murray, *Parechiniscus chitonides* Cuénot, and *Mopsechiniscus imberbis* (Richters).

The chief taxonomic structures used in generic and specific determinations include details of the buccal apparatus (especially macroplacoids), armor, claws, cirri, filaments, and eggs. *Echiniscus, Macrobiotus,* and *Hypsibius* are large genera that are often subdivided into species groups for taxonomic convenience. Most of the earlier descriptions are insufficient owing to the false supposition that the structures of the claws alone were sufficient and trustworthy characters.

The following key includes data for all fresh-water genera of the world.

## KEY TO GENERA OF TARDIGRADA

1. Head with anterior cirri (rarely absent) and lateral filaments; with four separate but similar claws on each leg (Fig. 156); semiaquatic.
   Class **HETEROTARDIGRADA, 2**
   Head without anterior cirri and lateral filaments (Figs. 157O–Q); each leg with two double claws or two unlike pairs of claws (Figs. 157C–E, L–N); semi-aquatic and aquatic. . Class **EUTARDIGRADA,** Order **MACROBIOTOIDEA, 6**
2. Posterior legs stout and not set off from body by cuticular folds.
   Order **ECHINISCOIDEA,** SCUTECHINISCIDAE, **3**
   Posterior legs slender and set off from body by distinct cuticular folds (Fig. 156A); up to 230 microns long; one species reported from Alps and New South Wales.
   Order **ARTHROTARDIGRADA,** NUDECHINISCIDAE, **Oreella mollis** Murray
3. Body with thick dorsal plates, variously sculptured; with a variable number of cirri and filaments (Figs. 156D–G); eggs deposited in shed exoskeleton (Fig. 153A). . . . . . . . . . . . . . . . . . . . . . . . . . . . . . . . . . . . . . . . . . . . . . . . . . . . **4**
   Body with thin dorsal plates (Fig. 156B); up to 200 microns long; one species reported from Europe. . . . . . . . . . . . . . . . . . .**Parechiniscus chitonides** Cuénot
4. Armor consisting of head plate, three trunk plates, and anal plate (plus intercalaries) (Figs. 156D–F); up to 350 microns long; about 120 species. . . . . . .**Echiniscus**
   Armor consisting of head plate, four trunk plates, and anal plate (plus intercalaries) (Fig. 156G). . . . . . . . . . . . . . . . . . . . . . . . . . . . . . . . . . . . . . . . . . . . . . . . . . **5**
5. Head with anterior cirri (Fig. 156G); up to 500 microns long; about 30 species; widely distributed. . . . . . . . . . . . . . . . . . . . . . . . . . . . . . . . . . . . .**Pseudechiniscus**
   Head without anterior cirri; one species reported from South Georgia Island and the state of São Paulo, Brazil. . . . . . . . . . . .**Mopsechiniscus imberbis** (Richters)
6. Sucking pharynx with macroplacoids (Figs. 147, 148); eyes present or absent; each leg with two double claws (Figs. 157C–E, L–N). . . . . . .MACROBIOTIDAE, **7**
   Sucking pharynx elongated and without macroplacoids (Fig. 157B); mouth surrounded by six prominent papillae; eyes present; each leg with two long, slender claws and two short, heavy claws (Figs. 157A, C); up to 1,200 microns long; one cosmopolitan species. . . . ARCTISCIDAE, **Milnesium tardigradum** Doyère
7. The two double claws of each leg similar in shape; the two larger claws of each leg more or less turned toward each other, the two smaller claws more or less turned away from each other (Figs. 157D, E); cuticle smooth; eggs mostly free and sculptured (Figs. 157F, G); up to 1,100 microns long; about 80 species.
   **Macrobiotus**
   The two double claws of each leg usually dissimilar; the two larger claws of each leg more or less parallel; the two smaller claws more or less parallel (Figs. 157L–N); cuticle smooth or sculptured; eggs smooth or sculptured and deposited in the shed exoskeleton (Figs. 157H–J); up to 700 microns long; about 80 species. . . . . . . . . . . . . . . . . . . . . . . . . . . . . . . . . . . . . . . . . . . . . . . . . .**Hypsibius**

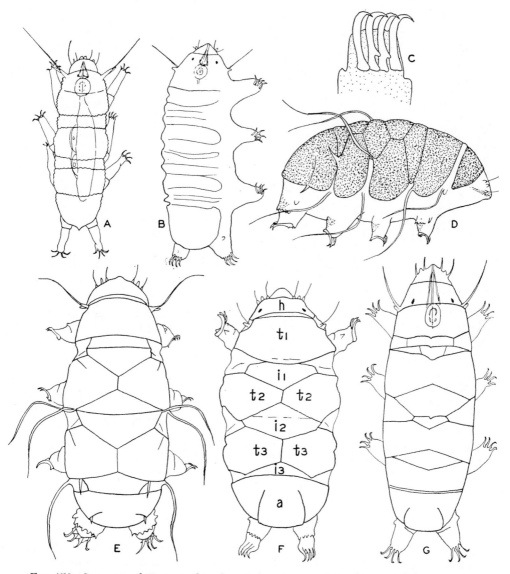

Fig. 156.—Structure of Heterotardigrada. A, dorsal view of *Oreella mollis* Murray, ×280; B, *Parechiniscus chitonides* Cuénot, ×430; C, claws of *Echiniscus*; D to F, typical species of *Echiniscus*, ×240; G, dorsal view of *Pseudechiniscus*, ×340. Armor sculpturing omitted on E, F, and G. *a*, anal plate; *h*, head plate; *i1*, *i2*, and *i3*, intercalaries; *t1*, first trunk plate; *t2*, second trunk plate (divided); *t3*, third trunk plate (divided). (Modified from various sources.)

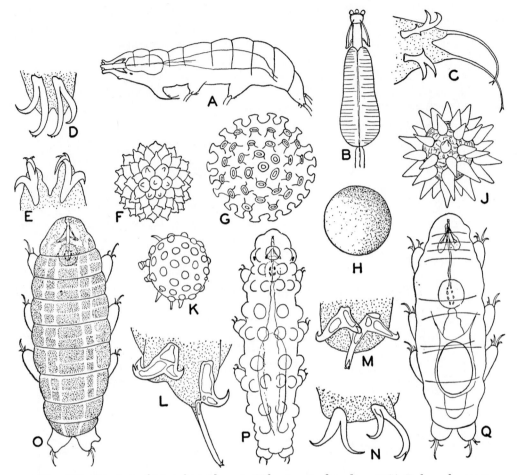

Fig. 157.—Structure of Macrobiotoidea. A, *Milnesium tardigradum*, ×75; B, buccal apparatus of *M. tardigradum*; C, claws of *M. tardigradum*; D and E, claws of *Macrobiotus*; F and G, eggs of *Macrobiotus*; H to K, eggs of *Hypsibius*; L to N, claws of *Hypsibius*; O to Q, dorsal view of typical species of *Hypsibius*, ×220. (Modified from various sources.)

## TARDIGRADA REFERENCES

Bartos, E. 1941. Studien über die Tardigraden des Karpathengebietes. *Zool. Jahrb. Abt. Syst. Ökol. Geogr. Tiere* 74:435–472.

Baumann, H. 1921. Beiträge zur Kenntnis der Anatomie der Tardigraden (Macrobiotus hüfelandi). *Zeitschr. wiss. Zool.* 68:637–652.

———. 1922. Die Anabiose der Tardigraden. *Zool. Jahrb. Abt. Syst. Geogr. Biol. Tiere* 45:501–556.

Cuénot, L. 1932. Tardigrades. *Faune de France* 24:1–96.

Doyère, L. 1840, 1842. Mémoire sur les Tardigrades. *Ann. Sci. Nat. Zool.* (2) 14:269–361; 17:193–205; 18:5–35.

Hennecke, J. 1911. Beiträge zur Kenntnis der Biologie und Anatomie der Tardigraden (Macrobiotus macronyx Duj.). *Zeitschr. wiss. Zool.* 97:721–752.

Marcus, E. 1928. Spinnentiere oder Arachnoidea. IV. Bärtierchen (Tardigrada). *Tierwelt Deutschlands* 12:1–230.

———. 1928a. Zur Ökologie und Physiologie der Tardigraden. *Zool. Jahrb. Abt. Allg. Zool.* 44:323–370.

———. 1928b. Zur vergleichenden Anatomie und Histologie der Tardigraden. *Ibid.* 45:99–158.

———. 1929. Tardigrada. *Tierreich* 5, Abt. 4, Buch 3;1–608.

——. 1929a. Zur Embryologie der Tardigraden. *Zool. Jahrb. Abt. Anat.* **50**:333–384.

——. 1935. Über die Verdauung bei den Tardigraden. *Zool. Jahrb. Abt. Allg. Zool.* **54**:385–404.

——. 1936. Tardigrada. *Das Tierreich* **66**:1–340.

MARCUS, E. B.-R. 1944. Sobre Tardigrados Brasileiros. *Com. Zool. Mus. Hist. Nat. Montevideo* **1**:1–19.

MATHEWS, G. B. 1938. Tardigrada from North America. *Amer. Midl. Nat.* **19**:619–626.

MAY, R.-M. 1948. La vie des Tardigrades. *Hist. Naturelles* **8**:1–133.

MÜLLER, J. 1935. Zur vergleichenden Myologie der Tardigraden. *Zeitschr. wiss. Zool.* **147**:171–204.

MURRAY, J. 1907. Scottish Tardigrada, collected by the Lake Survey. *Trans. Roy. Soc. Edinburgh* **45**:641–668.

——. 1907a. Encystment of Tardigrada. *Ibid.* 837–854.

——. 1907b. Water-bears, or Tardigrada. *Jour. Quekket Micros. Club* **10**:55–70.

——. 1910. Tardigrada. *Sci. Reports, Brit. Antarctic Exped. 1907–1909* **1**:81–185.

——. 1911. Water-bears, or Tardigrada. (Supplementary notes.) *Jour. Quekket Micros. Club* **11**:181–198.

RAHM, G. 1927. Tardigrada. Bärtierchen. *Biol. Tiere Deutschlands* **22**:1–56.

RAMAZOTTI, G. 1945. I Tardigradi d'Italia. *Mem. Istit. Ital. Idrobiol.* **2**:29–166.

RODEWALD, L. 1939. Systematische und ökologische Beiträge zur Tardigradenfauna Rumäniens. *Zool. Jahrb. Abt. Syst. Ökol. Geogr. Tiere* **72**:225–254.

THULIN, G. 1911. Beiträge zur Kenntnis der Tardigradenfauna Schwedens. *Ark. Zool.* **7**:1–60.

——. 1928. Über die Phylogenie und das System der Tardigraden. *Hereditas* **11**:207–266.

# Chapter 12

# BRYOZOA (MOSS ANIMALCULES)

UNPOLLUTED and unsilted waters, especially ponds and the shallows of lakes and slow streams, characteristically contain colonies of Bryozoa, or Polyzoa. To the casual observer such colonies are often mistaken for a mat of moss, and certainly some of the common species do have a superficial plantlike appearance. A large, encrusting, sessile colony may consist of thousands of individuals covering an area of several square feet, and a massive gelatinous species may attain the size of a grapefruit or a small watermelon. Usually bryozoans occur on the undersides of logs and stones, or on twigs and other objects where the light is dim.

Bryozoa are much more generally distributed and obvious in salt-water habitats than in fresh waters, and about 3,500 marine species have been described the world over, as contrasted with about 40 freshwater species. Only about 14 species have been reported from American fresh waters.

**General characteristics.** The unit of organization is a microscopic, more or less cylindrical zooid, or polypide (Figs. 160, 161). Superficially it resembles certain coelenterate polyps, and it wasn't until 1830 that the Bryozoa were distinguished from the Coelenterata as a separate phylum. The living body wall is very thin, and the Y-shaped digestive tract is suspended in the extensive coelomic cavity. The mouth is situated on a very large, distal, circular, oval, or horseshoe-shaped lophophore which bears numerous ciliated tentacles, but the anus is located posterior to or below the lophophore rather than on it. Sometimes the lophophore and its tentacles are collectively called the tentacular crown. Typically the individuals of a colony are all connected in a highly branched, twiglike manner. In some species the coelom is continuous from one polypide to another, but in others there are complete or incomplete septa.

Only the tentacular crown and distal portion of the body are exposed to the water, the rest of the body and the whole colony being invested by an ectocyst, or zooecium, which is secreted by the body wall. This protective layer may be thin to massive, corneous, cuticular, gelatinous, delicate, or tough, depending on the particular species and variety. According to the mode of growth and type of zooecium, there are three general but intergrading growth forms: (1) branching and threadlike, (2) matlike or crustlike, and (3) gelatinous and massive. In the older portions of colonies the zooecium is commonly opaque, brownish, and more or less covered with detritus, algae, and microscopic animals. But the polypide proper, which comprises the living portions of the zooid, is delicate, translucent, and only slightly pigmented. Internal structures can therefore usually be observed only in the younger individuals.

When undisturbed, the bryozoan tentacular crown is extended through the distal aperture of the zooecium. It is large and beautifully expanded, and a colony has the appearance of a patch of tiny and delicate flowers, but at the slightest disturbance the tentacular crowns are retracted within the zooecia in a flash. After a few minutes they are again slowly extruded and expanded.

Growth and proliferation of a colony is a matter of simple asexual budding. Sexual reproduction is restricted to a few weeks during the year. Each individual is hermaphroditic, and early development takes place within the coelom. Upon being released to the outside, the ciliated embryo soon becomes fixed to the substrate and gives rise to a new colony.

Statoblasts are asexual internal buds whose functional cells are enclosed by two tightly fitting convex sclerotized and sculptured valves (Figs. 165–167). Upon being released from the colony, statoblasts are distributed at random by currents and winds; they may float or remain on the bottom. A statoblast is highly resistant to drying, cold, and other adverse environmental conditions, but under appropriate conditions it germinates to produce a new colony.

The Phylum Bryozoa is divided into two classes, the Phylactolaemata and the Gymnolaemata. All species in the former are restricted to fresh waters, but the much larger Class Gymnolaemata is almost exclusively marine. Four of the five orders in this class are marine, and in the fifth order, the Ctenostomata, only two American species occur in fresh waters. Unlike marine species, fresh-water bryozoans exhibit no polymorphism.

The Endoprocta is a phylum which is mainly marine and closely related to the Bryozoa. In addition to the true Bryozoa, the key on page 270 includes the one American fresh-water species of Endoprocta. The differentiating features of this peculiar and uncommon species are given in the key.

**Locomotion.** Although bryozoan colonies are generally sessile, a few fresh-water species are capable of sluggish creeping

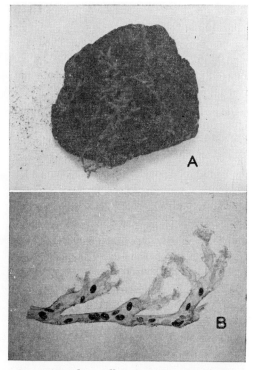

Fig. 158.—*Plumatella repens* L. A, bit of colony on piece of wood, ×1.5; B, bit of colony, ×6.

movements. *Cristatella mucedo* Cuvier (Fig. 171B) is the most active form, and a colony may progress as much as one to ten centimeters per day. The small colonies of *Lophopus crystallinus* Pallas and *Lophopodella carteri* (Hyatt), as well as young colonies of *Pectinatella magnifica* Leidy, also move but usually less than two centimeters per day.

The mechanism of colony locomotion is obscure, but it is probable that ciliary action on the tentacles, the musculature of the body wall, and perhaps polypide retractor muscle action are of some importance.

**Feeding, digestive system.** When the lophophore is expanded under normal conditions, the tentacles are almost motionless, but their abundant cilia beat constantly and create miniature currents along the lophophore which bring algae, protozoans, micrometazoa, and detritus to

Fig. 159.—Massive colonies of *Pectinatella magnifica* Leidy photographed in natural habitat; relative size can be judged from the two tree trunks at the water's edge in the immediate background. (Photo courtesy of Percy Viosca, Jr.)

the region of the mouth. If large and inedible particles reach the mouth, the individual tentacles may bend over in such a way as to brush the particles away and alter the ciliary currents. In all fresh-water Phylactolaemata the base of the lophophore is surrounded by a membranous cup, or calyx, which is festooned or scalloped; presumably this structure increases the efficiency of feeding. The distal end of the animal may extend upward from the substrate or downward from the underside of an object, but feeding goes on effectively regardless of position. Phylactolaemata have a flaplike epistome over the mouth. It may cover the mouth or aid in rejecting or warding off undesirable particles.

The anterior portion of the esophagus is slightly modified to form a somewhat muscular pharynx. Food passes through the mouth, pharynx, and into the esophagus, and when a sufficient quantity has accumulated in the esophagus, the esophageal valve relaxes and the food passes into the stomach where most of the digestion occurs. Below the stomach and corresponding to the basal leg of the Y is a long baglike absorptive organ, the caecum. Connecting the lower end of the caecum and the body wall is a long strand of tissue, the funiculus. The tubular intestine passes from the upper end of the caecum to the anus; its terminal portion is slightly modified to form a rectum. The anus is located just below the lophophore.

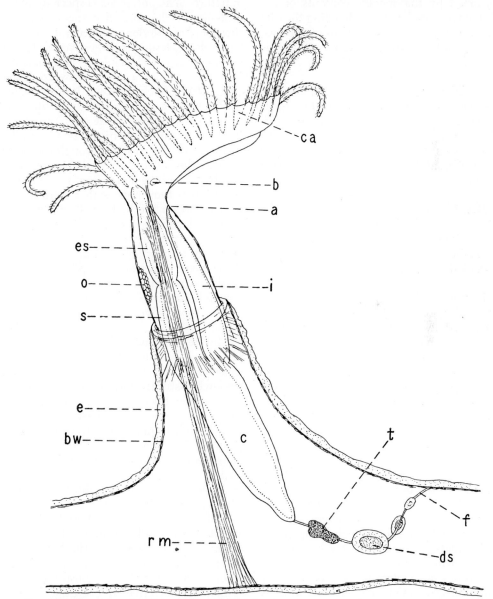

Fig. 160.—Structure of a *Plumatella* polypide, diagrammatic. Tentacles and retractor muscle shown for only one side. *a*, anus; *b*, brain; *bw*, body wall; *c*, caecum; *ca*, calyx; *ds*, developing statoblasts (3); *e*, ectocyst; *es*, esophagus; *f*, funiculus; *i*, intestine; *o*, ovary; *rm*, retractor muscle *s*, stomach; *t*, testis.

The Phylactolaemata alimentary canal is ciliated only around the mouth and in the pharynx, but in the Gymnolaemata cilia extend as far as the upper portion of the stomach.

Much of the polypide coloration is determined by the specific contents of the alimentary canal, and by changing the diet experimentally it is possible to get yellow, green, and brown coloration all in the same day.

**Circulation.** There is no circulatory mechanism in bryozoans, but materials are undoubtedly distributed quickly and efficiently via the coelomic fluid owing to the movements of the alimentary canal and retractions and extrusions of the tentacular crown.

**Respiration.** No special respiratory devices are present. The greater portion of the carbon dioxide and oxygen exchange undoubtedly occurs through the basal portion of the lophophore.

**Excretion.** No excretory system occurs in the Gymnolaemata. In some Phylactolaemata, however, a few investigators have seen a simple excretory system situated between the rectum and pharynx, often at the base of the epistome. It is said to consist of two short ciliated collecting ducts opening into a minute bladder which, in turn, opens by means of a short duct through an external pore. Coelomic amoebocytes containing engulfed excretory granules supposedy enter the collecting ducts and pass through the bladder and its duct to the outside.

In *Cristatella, Lophopus, Plumatella,* and possibly some other genera the epidermal cells of the tentacles apparently accumulate excretory substances and liberate them to the outside. In addition, quantities of metabolic wastes are undoubtedly retained in many of the body tissues until the animal dies and disintegrates. A true intertentacular organ is unknown in fresh-water bryozoans.

A few Phylactolaemata, including *Hyalinella, Lophopus, Cristatella,* and *Lophopodella,* sometimes undergo "brown body" formation, especially under unfavorable conditions, and it is thought that this phenomenon is at least partially excretory in nature. The polypides (especially older individuals) first retract permanently and then begin to undergo degeneration. The lophophore, tentacles, digestive tract, and nervous system degenerate and become rounded up into a small brownish mass (Fig. 161). Such a brown body remains unchanged, or it may further disintegrate into small fragments that circulate about in the coelom. Sometimes, however, the brown body is extruded through the body wall to the outside, or perhaps occasionally by way of the anus. Frequently a new polypide is then regenerated from an internal bud on the body wall; it comes to occupy the space vacated by the old polypide. Sometimes the same zooid may undergo brown body formation two or three times a season. In spite of certain textbook statements to the contrary, a brown body has never been seen to regenerate a new polypide.

**Muscle system.** All bryozoan muscle fibers are smooth. The most prominent muscles are the two retractors, which are somewhat stringy and not at all compact. They originate at the base of the zooecium and are inserted on the base of the lophophore and uppermost portion of the digestive tract, one on each side (Fig. 160). Their contraction pulls the whole distal end of the polypide back into the coelom and zooecium. Some short indistinct fibers connect the upper part of the polyp with the nearby body wall, and a few associated fibers aid in rotating the tentacular crown and depressing the lobes.

The thin body wall contains a few loosely arranged fibers, mostly circular, which are effective in everting the polypide. Other indistinct muscles elevate the epistome, move the alimentary canal slightly, and act as dilators and sphincters.

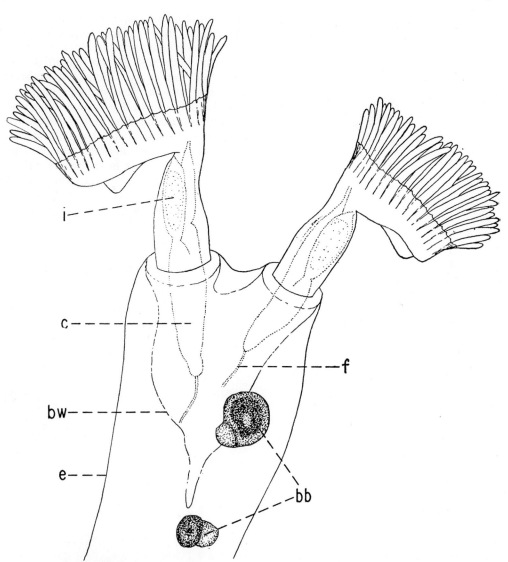

FIG. 161.—Semidiagrammatic view of a small portion of a *Lophopodella carteri* (Hyatt) colony, ×50, showing two brown bodies. *bb,* brown bodies; *bw,* body wall; *c,* caecum; *e,* ectocyst; *f,* funiculus; *i,* intestine. (Greatly modified from Rogick, 1938.)

**Nervous system.** A single large ganglion, or "brain," is situated at the distal end between the mouth and anus. From it a series of flimsy fibers with a few associated nerve cell bodies radiate out to all tissues and organs. There are no nervous connections between adjacent polypides.

Special sense organs are absent, but bryozoans are remarkably sensitive to light and other stimuli, certain epidermal cells being specialized as receptors.

**Reproduction, development.** Growth of a colony is an asexual form of proliferation, often dichotomous, whereby a part of the body wall grows outward and eventually forms a new polypide surrounded by the contiguous zooecium, or ectocyst.

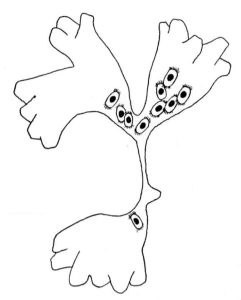

FIG. 162.—Diagram of dividing colony of *Lophopodella carteri*, ×5. Polypides are shown contracted; ten statoblasts present. (Redrawn from Rogick, 1935.)

coelomic fluid just as it leaves the ovary. The zygote then becomes implanted in a special pouchlike ooecium which develops from the body wall in the immediate vicinity of the ovary. Here the embryo develops into a pear-shaped, oval, or round ciliated larva 1 to 2 mm. long and usually containing one to five immature polypides. A *Cristatella* larva, however, may have up to twenty-five polypides or polypide buds. This larva breaks out of the parent through a special large pore at the base of the lophophore, or it escapes when the parent degenerates (Fig. 163). It is free-swimming for only a few minutes or for as long as twenty to twenty-four hours and then settles on the substrate, evaginates, and eventually gives rise to a mature colony.

Little specific information is available concerning the natural longevity of individual zooids, but presumably the great majority live for three weeks to four months in temperate climates. Large, old

In this way, beginning with a single polypide in the spring, the resulting colony may consist of thousands of living and dead individuals by autumn. Developing *Hyalinella*, *Pectinatella*, *Cristatella*, and *Lophopodella* colonies often undergo fission, thus giving rise to two or more new colonies (Fig. 162).

The period of sexual reproduction usually lasts only about three or four weeks, some time between May and July. Individual zooids are hermaphroditic. The single ovary develops from the peritoneum of the body wall near the distal end of the zooid, and the testis develops from the peritoneum of the funiculus. Unlike the situation in the great majority of hermaphroditic animals, there seems to be little or no evidence for cross-fertilization in fresh-water Bryozoa, although it could presumably occur in species having no septa between adjacent individuals. Mature eggs and sperm are produced either simultaneously or in rapid succession. Ordinarily only a single ovum matures at a time and is fertilized by sperm in the

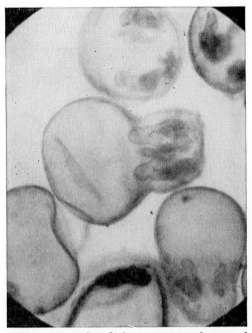

FIG. 163.—Ciliated free-swimming larvae of *Plumatella*, ×27. Center embryo contains three developing polypides.

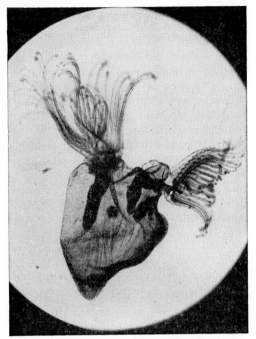

FIG. 164.—Young colony of *Pectinatella magnifica*, ×33.

colonies contain many dead zooids in the parts of the colony that were first formed.

Although colonies customarily die out in the late summer or autumn, there are records of *Paludicella* and *Lophopus* colonies being active throughout the winter, especially if it is mild and the water temperature does not drop below 4°.

**Statoblasts.** The production of highly resistant statoblasts is a unique feature of fresh-water Phylactolaemata. They function mainly in tiding the species over unfavorable environmental conditions and in geographic dissemination.

Statoblasts develop by asexual budding from the funiculus, and in some zooids several stages of development may be found. A mature statoblast is roughly biconvex, but the central portion is considerably thickened into a capsule owing to its contained mass of undifferentiated germinative cells. The peripheral portion (annulus, or float) consists of air cells and is relatively thin; sometimes it bears spiny,

barbed, or hooked processes (Fig. 165A). Except for the germinative cells, a statoblast therefore consists of two sclerotized, dead valves which are tightly attached to each other in the region of the annulus. Early stages in statoblast development are almost smooth; older ones are strongly ridged and tan, brown, or black in color. Usually each zooid produces two to eight statoblasts.

Three general types of statoblasts are distinguished. Floatoblasts are free or floating; they have no peripheral processes; they are annulated when mature and

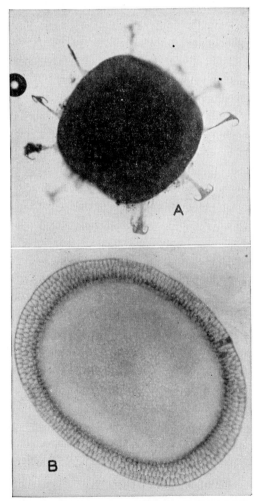

FIG. 165.—Bryozoan statoblasts. A, *Pectinatella magnifica*, ×40; B, *Plumatella repens*, ×175.

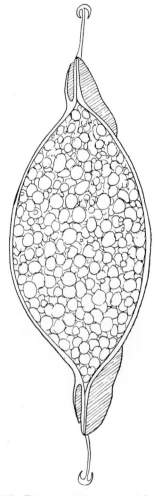

length is 0.3 to 0.6 mm. *Fredericella, Hyalinella, Plumatella,* and *Stolella* produce sessoblasts (Figs. 167; 172A, C).

Formerly it was thought that statoblast production is limited to late summer and autumn just before the colonies die off, but it is now well established that statoblasts may also be regularly produced during the earlier portion of the growing season. In the tropics statoblasts appear with the onset of hot weather. Sexual reproduction and statoblast production may occur simultaneously in the same zooid; there is little evidence for alternation of the two methods.

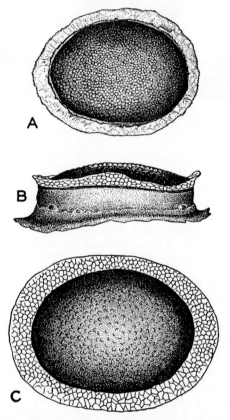

Fig. 166.—Diagrammatic section of statoblast of *Pectinatella magnifica*, showing the two valves, hooked spines, central capsule filled with germinative cells, and float.

are 0.2 to 0.7 mm. long. *Hyalinella, Plumatella,* and *Stolella* produce floatoblasts (Figs. 173A–C; 174B, C, E).

Spinoblasts are also free or floating, but they are provided with spined, barbed, or hooked processes. Length ranges from 0.7 to 1.8 mm. *Cristatella, Lophopodella, Lophopus,* and *Pectinatella* produce spinoblasts (Figs. 165A; 171C, D).

Sessoblasts are sessile, fixed, or attached to the zooecium wall with cement; an annulus may be present or absent. The

Fig. 167.—Sessoblasts of *Plumatella*, ×120. A, unattached surface view of sessoblast of *P. repens* var. *emarginata*; B, side view of sessoblast of *P. repens* var. *typica* phase *beta* (note sclerotized lamella which resembles the float of floatoblasts); C, unattached surface view of same. (From Rogick, 1940.)

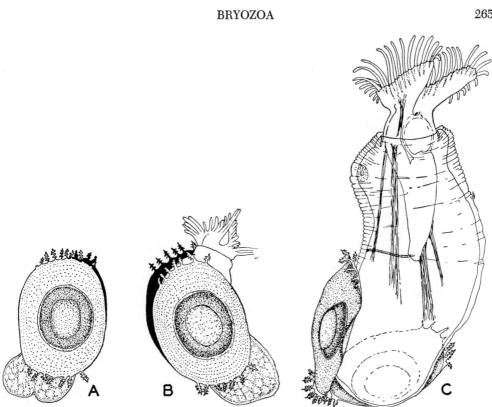

Fig. 168.—Germinating statoblast of *Lophopodella carteri*, ×33. A, valves separating and mass of undifferentiated yolky cells extruded; B, primary polypide emerging; C, primary polypide almost mature (note small bud on left side near distal end). (Modified from Rogick, 1935.)

Upon distintegration of the polypides, the spinoblasts and floatoblasts are released to the vagaries of currents, waves, and wind. Some of them sink or remain on the bottom. Others float to the surface, and under appropriate conditions may be found in such abundance as to form windrows on the shore, especially in spring and autumn. Sessoblasts, however, remain attached to the substrate until the last bit of old zooecium has disintegrated.

The length of the statoblast dormant period is highly variable, depending on the species, the individual, temperature, and other environmental conditions. In north temperate and higher latitudes there is usually only one generation per year, and the majority of statoblasts winter over and germinate the following spring, but

south of the 40th parallel it appears that the growing season is often sufficiently long for two main crops of statoblasts. Colonies mature in the spring, and their statoblasts hatch out and produce a second group of mature colonies by late summer or early autumn. These individuals, in turn, give rise to statoblasts which winter over. In spite of their ability to survive drying and freezing temperatures, it should be borne in mind that statoblasts have a very high natural mortality rate.

The natural period of dormancy and germination is usually 30 to 150 days, the chief governing factors being low temperatures and desiccation. Germination begins in the spring when the water reaches 10° to 19°. The first evidence of germination is the gradual separation of

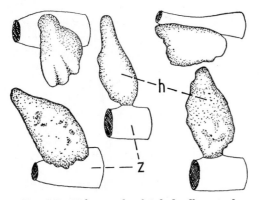

Fig. 169.—Hibernacula of *Paludicella articulata* (Ehr.), ×50. *h*, hibernaculum; *z*, bits of old zooecium. (Modified from Rogick, 1935.)

the two statoblast valves along the equator, a process that may take one to eight days. A mass of undifferentiated yolky cells slowly grows and protrudes from between the valves. These cells are whitish or grayish, very contractile, and they adhere to the substrate. The primary polypide meanwhile develops between the valves, hidden from view. It utilizes the abundant stored food of the undifferentiated yolk cells, and as it enlarges it protrudes, pushes the valves farther apart, and absorbs and incorporates more and more of the yolk mass so that the latter soon becomes an indistinguishable part of the polypide. As growth proceeds, additional polypides appear by budding, and eventually a colony results.

A very large amount of experimental laboratory work has been conducted on the viability of statoblasts, but the results vary so much from one species to another and from one investigator to another that it is difficult to generalize. Most workers, however, seem to agree that natural freezing and normal winter temperatures have little effect on the percentage of later germination, but little is known about the lethal effects of unusually low temperatures.

Viability of statoblasts dried and kept at room temperature differs widely from one species to another. Rogick (1940)

found that all *Hyalinella*, *Pectinatella*, and *Plumatella* statoblasts died within 23 to 34 months under such conditions. *Fredericella*, on the other hand, showed 50 to 100 per cent germination after 24 months. Seventy per cent of *Lophopodella* statoblasts were capable of germinating after being dry for 50 months, but none germinated after 74 months. In general, wet storage in the refrigerator produces a lower statoblast mortality than drying at room temperature for the same length of time.

Under natural conditions the period of statoblast dormancy or desiccation extends from the end of one growing season to the beginning of the next, which is usually four to nine months, and most workers are agreed that a majority of statoblasts of all species are viable for the duration of such periods.

When statoblasts are placed in water and germinated in the laboratory the period of incubation is highly variable. Some individuals and species germinate in four to ten days; others require one to four months for germination.

**Hibernacula.** The Paludicellidae, including *Paludicella* and *Pottsiella*, do not form statoblasts, but rather hibernacula, which are similar to statoblasts in function. A hibernaculum is a specially modified external winter bud. Like statoblasts, they consist of masses of cells protected by a thick sclerotized coat (Fig. 169).

**Ecology.** Quiet ponds, backwaters, bays, and slow streams, especially where there are sunken logs, twigs, rocks, and aquatic vegetation, are ideal places for Bryozoa. Sandy and pebbly bottoms are poor habitats, but *Plumatella* and *Fredericella* are sometimes found on rocky shoals where there is considerable wave action. Although they are common in stagnant waters, bryozoans are never found under polluted conditions and only sparingly where the quantity of dissolved oxygen falls below 30 per cent saturation. Silting also discourages establishment and growth, and strongly acid waters and bogs almost never contain bryozoans. *Lophopodella carteri* is probably the species that is most tolerant of decay and stagnation.

Light is not necessary for development and growth, as shown by the occurrence of bryozoans in water pipes and closed conduits. On the other hand, they are seldom present in bright light, although *Cristatella mucedo* occurs regularly on the upper sides of objects in the shallows. All other species found in shallow water are attached to the undersides or shaded sides of rocks, logs, vegetation, and boards. In the dim light of deep waters, however, all species apparently are able to grow on the upper surfaces of objects.

Most Bryozoa are collected in waters less than a meter deep, but they commonly occur at considerably greater depths, and if appropriate collecting equipment is used, almost all of our common species may be taken in lakes at depths up to 5 or 10 meters. *Paludicella* has been taken as deep as 36 meters and *Fredericella* up to 214 meters.

*Lophopodella* and *Lophopus* are generally restricted to standing waters. *Paludicella*, *Cristatella*, *Pectinatella*, *Fredericella*, and *Hyalinella* are more common in standing waters but are found also in slowly running waters. *Urnatella* and *Plumatella* may, in addition, be found in fairly rapid waters. *Pottsiella* is presumably restricted to rapid waters. Sometimes *Fredericella*, *Plumatella*, *Pectinatella*, and *Cristatella* are all found in the same pond or lake at the same time.

Most American species attain their greatest abundance in the summer when the water temperature reaches 19° to 23° and begin to die off in the autumn when the water cools to 10°. *Pectinatella*, however, tolerates a much smaller range of temperature and usually dies when the water temperature goes below 16°. *Fredericella* and *Lophopus*, on the other hand, are unusually tolerant and do well anywhere between 5° and 23°.

**Economic importance.** Occasional summer plagues of large floating gelatinous colonies of *Pectinatella magnifica* clog the screens of water intakes and the grates of hydroelectric plants so effectively that it requires the full time of a man to keep them clear.

In communities using unfiltered and unchlorinated water, bryozoans sometimes become established in the pipes, and dead and living masses clog the valves and meters. The usual offenders are *Paludicella*, *Fredericella*, and *Plumatella*.

Bryozoa are an incidental and relatively unimportant element in the diet of many fresh-water invertebrates, including planarians, snails, insects, oligochaetes, Hydracarina, and crustaceans. Statoblasts are often eaten by small fish. The ectocyst forms an excellent substrate for a variety of commensals and browsers, especially ciliates and rotifers.

**Geographical distribution, dispersal.** *Plumatella repens* L. and *Fredericella sultana* (Blumenbach) are the only known truly cosmopolitan species; they occur in suitable habitats all over the world. *Hyalinella punctata* Hancock and *Paludicella articulata* (Ehr.) occur in North America, Europe, and Asia, and the latter species is also reported from New Zealand; *Lophopus crystallinus* occurs in North America, South America, Europe, and Asia; *Cristatella mucedo* is common in North America and Europe. It is probable that all four of these species occur on other continents but as yet have not been recorded. *Pectinatella magnifica* is probably native only to North America but has been recently introduced into Japan and Germany.

The other seven species reported from the United States have much more spotty distributions. *Lophopodella carteri* has been recorded only from Lake Erie, New Jersey, and Ohio in this country, but it is widely distributed in both Africa and Asia. *Stolella indica* Annandale has been collected in Pennsylvania, South America, and Asia. *Fredericella australiensis* Goddard is known from New South Wales, the Transcaucasian area, and northern Africa, but in the United States it has been collected only in Wyoming. *Plumatella casmiana* Oka also has a puzzling distribution; it has been reported from Japan, Java, the Volga drainage, and Lake Erie. Only two records are known for *Hyalinella vaihiriae* Hastings; one is Tahiti and the other Bear River, Utah. *Urnatella gracilis* Leidy (an endoproct) has been collected from scattered localities in the northeastern quarter of this country; otherwise it is known only from the Meuse River, Belgium. *Pottsiella erecta* Potts was first collected in southeastern Pennsylvania in 1884 and has never been found since, except for one questionable recent Texas record.

Unquestionably the paucity of records for some of the American species is a reflection of the fact that little systematic and intensive collecting has been done. Future collecting, especially in the South, and west of the Mississippi River, will probably show that some of our "rare" species are actually widely distributed.

Chiefly by virtue of their resistant statoblasts and hibernacula, bryozoans are one of the few fresh-water groups that are clearly capable of being transported overland from one body of water to another by animals. There are definite records of statoblast occurrence in mud on the feet of waterfowl, and Brown (1933) has shown that some statoblasts are capable of germinating after passing through the alimentary canal of waterfowl, turtles, frogs, and salamanders.

**Collecting.** Bits of colonies, sessoblasts, and hibernacula should be carefully removed from their substrate with forceps, spatula, and scalpel, but if the colonies are on small pieces of wood, twigs, or stones, they may be brought to the laboratory intact. A dredge or double rake is necessary for collecting below a depth of a meter.

Floating statoblasts may often be obtained in abundance at the right season by skimming the surface of the water with a net or by scooping them up from windrows.

**Culturing.** Bryozoa are among the most difficult of all fresh-water invertebrates to culture in the laboratory. If intact colonies are used, they may sometimes be kept alive in finger bowls for five to fifteen days provided the water is replaced frequently with fresh pond water, preferably from their natural habitat. Sometimes a small quantity of fresh yeast is beneficial to the culture.

Rogick reports some success using water from aquatic plant aquaria along with a bit of the organic debris from the bottom of such aquaria. Such debris usually contains an abundance of suitable microorganisms for food. Both water and debris should be changed every two or three days.

Brandwein (1938) uses the following technique for maintaining cultures of *Pectinatella magnifica*. Pour about 5 mm. of 2 per cent agar into a finger bowl and embed half a petri dish in the agar before it hardens. Also place 15 equally spaced wheat grains in the agar. Make up a stock culture solution as follows: 1.2 g. sodium chloride, 0.03 g. potassium chloride, 0.04 g. calcium chloride, 0.02 g. sodium bicarbonate, 50 ml. Sorenson's phosphate buffer pH 6.9–7.0, and distilled water to 1,000 ml. This stock solution should be diluted 1:10 for use. Pour enough into the finger bowl to come about 1 cm. above the edge of the petri dish. Inoculate with *Chilomonas* or *Colpidium* and let stand for two or three days. Then introduce three to five zooids and 20 ml. of water from their habitat. Subculture every three or four weeks and do not allow the water to become cloudy with protozoans.

Other investigators have had success by adding a variety of protozoans and their culture water to the finger bowl containing bryozoans.

**Preparing, preserving.** Bryozoans are highly sensitive to foreign substances, and if ordinary methods of fixation are used the tentacular crown contracts into the zooecium so strongly as to make the whole animal useless for study. Consequently some method of narcotization must first be used so that the animals can be killed and fixed with the lophophore expanded.

The colonies and a part of their substrate should be placed in a finger bowl one-third to one-half full of water from their habitat, and the subsequent narcotization must be done very gradually and patiently. If chloretone or chloral hydrate is used, a saturated solution should be added slowly over a period of one to three hours. When the animals no longer respond appreciably to jarring or touching, most of the fluid should be withdrawn with a large pipette. Then Bouin's fixative or 50 per cent formalin should be poured over the animals, and if the narcotization has been successful, they will be killed in a beautifully expanded condition.

The following effective method is modified from Hurrell (1936). Place the colonies and a bit of their substrate in a finger bowl of water. Sprinkle a teaspoonful of menthol crystals on top of the water, cover the finger bowl with a glass plate, and let stand overnight. By morning the bryozoans should be fully narcotized. Then withdraw most of the fluid from the finger bowl, add concentrated formalin equivalent to the amount of water remaining in the finger bowl, and let stand for one hour.

Five per cent formalin and 50 per cent alcohol are suitable preservatives.

Bryozoa may be mounted either unstained or stained with hematoxylin or borax carmine. Before mounting or staining, however, the ectocyst should be gently brushed as free of debris as possible. If glycerin jelly mounts are to be made, the animals must first be run up into glycerin. Place them in a watch glass containing a solution of 5 per cent glycerin in 30 per cent alcohol and cover with a loose cover to keep out dust and permit evaporation of the alcohol and water. When nearly pure glycerin remains, they are ready for mounting.

**Taxonomy.** Fresh-water Bryozoa are one of a long list of groups of American fresh-water invertebrates greatly in need of much more systematic collecting and critical work. Indeed, between 1904 and 1935, this group was almost completely forgotten, but in more recent years much fundamental work has been accomplished by the outstanding American investigator Mary D. Rogick.

Most of our species are quite distinctive, especially if both the colonies and their statoblasts are available for identification. But the most common and widely distributed species, *Plumatella repens,* is extremely variable and puzzling. At least six different varieties and two "phases" of this species have been reported from the United States, and although all of them are perhaps best placed in the single species, there are some investigators, especially Europeans, who prefer to consider these several varieties as distinct species. Some of the more striking intergrading and variable characters are (Rogick, 1935): colony composed of two discrete masses or not, branching compact to open, zooecia furrowed or not furrowed, tubes attached to the substrate along their entire length or tubes more or less erect, keel present or absent, and statoblasts relatively long or short. Sometimes the variations differ according to the age of the animals, but often they are apparently controlled and induced by certain obscure factors of the many different types of habitats in which *P. repens* occurs. The problem awaits solution by means of controlled laboratory cultures.

## KEY TO SPECIES OF BRYOZOA

1. Anus outside the lophophore; zooids not stalked; tentacular crown capable of being
   retracted within zooecium; without a protonephridial system; statoblasts
   present or absent.............................Phylum **BRYOZOA, 2**
   Anus on the lophophore; each zooid on a flexible stalk composed of sclerotized urn-
   shaped segments; one to six such stalks arising from one basal plate; stalks
   may be branched or unbranched and up to 5 mm. long; lophophore circular,
   with 8 to 16 tentacles, and incapable of being retracted within zooecium
   **(Fig. 170A)**; with a simple protonephridial system; without statoblasts; on
   objects in running waters or in large lakes; one uncommon species reported
   from scattered localities in eastern half of U. S., but there is also one Texas
   record..................Phylum **ENDOPROCTA, Urnatella gracilis** Leidy
2. Lophophore circular and without an epistome (Fig. 170B); colony covered with a
   corneous or membranous cuticle; statoblasts absent; hibernacula produced
   (Fig. 169)..............................Class **GYMNOLAEMATA,**
                              Order **CTENOSTOMATA, PALUDICELLIDAE, 3**
   Lophophore horseshoe-shaped, oval, or circular, and with an epistome (Figs. 160,
   161, 168); statoblasts produced.
                              Class **PHYLACTOLAEMATA,** Order **PLUMATELLINA, 4**

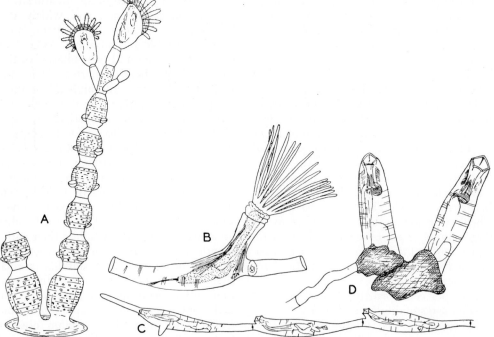

FIG. 170.—Structure of Endoprocta and Paludicellidae. A, small portion of a colony of
*Urnatella gracilis* Leidy, ×32; B, zooid of *Paludicella articulata*, ×33; C, portion of a young
colony of *P. articulata* showing three retracted individuals and two buds; D, young colony of
*Pottsiella erecta* Potts, ×33, showing two hibernacula. (A modified from Leidy, 1884; B and C
modified from Rogick, 1940; D modified from Kraepelin, 1887.)

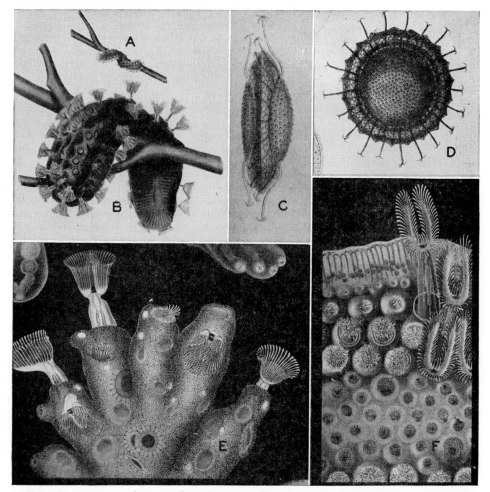

FIG. 171.—Structure of *Cristatella* and *Pectinatella*. A, colony of *Cristatella mucedo* Cuvier, ×50; B, colony of *C. mucedo*, ×40; C, edge view of *C. mucedo statoblast*, ×50; D, surface view of *C. mucedo* statoblast; E, rosette of *Pectinatella magnifica*; F, edge of colony of *Cristatella mucedo* showing three rows of marginal polypides. (A to D from Allman; E and F from Kraepelin, 1887.)

3. Colony consisting of a series of club-shaped zooecia arranged end to end and separated from each other by partitions; 16 to 18 tentacles; zooecium openings on upper surface; zooids about 2.0 mm. long; colony recumbent or partially erect (Figs. 170B, C); standing and slowly flowing waters; reported from scattered localities, probably cosmopolitan in U. S........**Paludicella articulata** (Ehr.)
   Colony consisting of a stolon from which single erect individuals arise; zooecium openings terminal; 19 to 21 tentacles; zooids about 1.5 mm. long (Fig. 170D); on upper surface of stones in rapid water; reported only from streams in southeastern Penn. in 1884......................**Pottsiella erecta** (Potts)

4. Statoblasts all free, annulated, and with processes (Figs. 168; 171D); colony soft, gelatinous, transparent, and not dendritic (Figs. 171E; 172H, J)......**5**
   Usually with two types of statoblasts; one unattached, funicular, and annulated (floatoblasts); the other attached and without float cells (sessoblasts); statoblasts without processes; colony dendritic..........**PLUMATELLIDAE, 7**

5. Ectocyst a transient secretion elaborated by flat base of colony; colony elongated and slowly motile (Fig. 171A); statoblasts with two circlets of hooked spines; dorsal circlet with 10 to 34 hooks and ventral circlet with 20 to 50 hooks (Figs. 171C, D); zooids on upper surface and arranged marginally in three rows; all polypides contracting into a common cavity; usually 80 to 90 tentacles; long dimension of colony sometimes as much as 10 to 30 cm. but more typically 2 to 6 cm.; in standing water or slow currents, on upper side of submerged objects and vegetation; widely distributed but not common.

CRISTATELLIDAE, **Cristatella mucedo** Cuvier

Ectocyst present throughout life of colony and sometimes very well developed (Fig. 171E); colony not usually motile; statoblasts never with two circlets of hooked spines (Figs. 165A, 168)..................LOPHOPODIDAE, **6**

6. Statoblasts more or less circular, with 11 to 22 peripheral hooked spines, and about 1 mm. in diameter (Fig. 165A); ectocyst translucent to brownish; colonies massive, sometimes up to 40 cm. long and 15 cm. thick by autumn; polypides arranged in rosette-shaped groups of 12 to 18 individuals on surface of ectocyst; colonies commonly investing twigs and other submerged objects, especially in shaded places in quiet water (Figs. 159, 171E); 60 to 84 tentacles; very young colonies motile; widely distributed but uncommon west of the Mississippi Valley.........................**Pectinatella magnifica** Leidy

Statoblasts broadly oval or subtruncate and with a graduated series of 6 to 17 barbed spines at each pole (Fig. 168); ectocyst transparent; colonies small, circular to oval, and mound-shaped when only a few polypides are present, but lobate when many polypides are present; average colony 4 mm. wide, 5 mm. long, and with 20 to 45 polypides; 52 to 82 tentacles, usually about 64; rare, reported only from Lake Erie, N. J., and Ohio.

**Lophopodella carteri** (Hyatt)

7. Lophophore circular or elliptical; colony tubular, branched, and antler-like (Figs. 172B, G); zooecium usually opaque and brown; all statoblasts (sessoblasts) attached to walls of zooecia (Fig. 172A); no free, annulated statoblasts (floatoblasts)..............................FREDERICELLINAE, **Fredericella, 8**

Lophophore horseshoe-shaped; floatoblasts present; sessoblasts also present in most species...................................PLUMATELLINAE, **9**

8. With 24 to 30 tentacles; polypides short; zooecia not especially slender; ectocyst thin, chitinoid, and opaque (Fig. 172B); most sessoblasts rounded or broadly elliptical (Fig. 172A); reported only from Uinta Co., Wyo.

**Fredericella australiensis** Goddard

With 17 to 24 tentacles; polypides longer; zooecia slender, with antler-like branching (Fig. 172G); most sessoblasts reniform or elongated (Fig. 172C); on submerged objects and vegetation in standing and slowly flowing waters; common and widely distributed........**Fredericella sultana** (Blumenbach)

9. Colony sac-shaped, erect, often lobed, and usually less than 1 cm. across; zooecium gelatinous (Figs. 172H, J); statoblasts drawn out into a sharp tip at each end (Figs. 172D, E); with about 60 tentacles; usually attached to vegetation in standing water...........................**Lophopus crystallinus** Pallas

Colony larger, branching, and tubular (Figs. 173, 174); statoblasts not drawn out into a sharp tip (Figs. 173A–C; 174B, C)...........................**10**

10. Basal portions of zooecia slender and tapered (Fig. 173H); ectocyst thin; reported only from a pond in Westtown, Penn.............**Stolella indica** Annandale

Basal portions of zooecia not especially slender and tapered.................**11**

11. With soft, hyaline, gelatinous ectocyst; horizontal branches only; thickly branched, often completely covering the substrate (Fig. 173D)..........**Hyalinella, 12**

With a thin, firm, and sometimes horny ectocyst; zooecia long and tubular, pale and transparent to dark brown in color; in masses up to 5 cm. high or closely adherent to substrate (Fig. 174); in a variety of habitats......**Plumatella, 13**

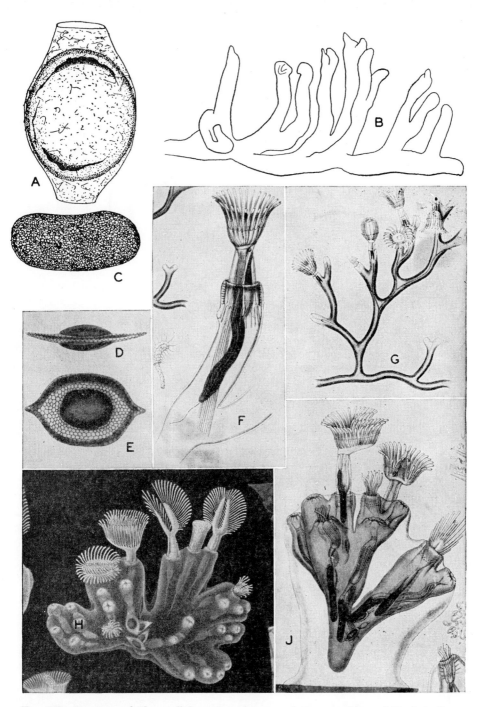

Fig. 172.—Structure of Plumatellidae. A, endocyst enclosing sessoblast of *Fredericella australiensis* Goddard, ×100 (markings of sessoblast not shown); B, branching in colony of *F. australiensis*, ×12 (polypides shown retracted); C, sessoblast of *F. sultana* (Blumenbach), ×85; D, edge view of statoblast of *Lophopus crystallinus* Pallas, ×40; E, surface view of same statoblast; F, polypide of *Fredericella sultana*, ×15; G, small colony of *F. sultana*, ×3; H and J, small colonies of *Lophopus crystallinus*, ×7. (A and B modified from Rogick, 1945; C modified from Rogick, 1937; D to G, and J from Allman; H from Kraepelin, 1887.)

273

12. Floatoblasts averaging 0.37 mm. wide and 0.54 mm. long (Figs. 173B, C); coenecium adherent throughout; ectocyst soft, swollen, colorless, or yellowish (Fig. 173D); widely distributed and common....**Hyalinella punctata** (Hancock)
　Floatoblasts averaging 0.25 mm. wide and 0.36 mm. long (Fig. 173A); reported only from Bear River, Utah................**Hyalinella vaihiriae** Hastings

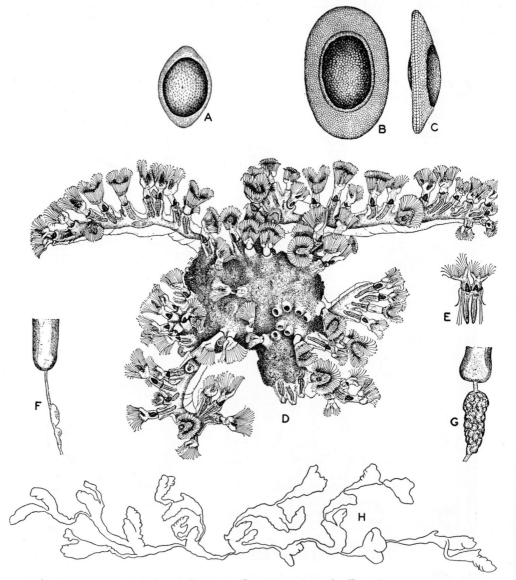

Fig. 173.—Structure of Plumatellinae. A, floatoblast of *Hyalinella vaihiriae* Hastings, ×60; B, surface view of floatoblast of *H. punctata* (Hancock), ×65; C, edge view of floatoblast of *H. punctata*, × 65; D, entire colony of *H. punctata*, ×6; E, twin polypides of *H. punctata*; F, three developing statoblasts on funiculus of *H. punctata*; G, immature sperm mass on funiculus of *H. punctata*; H, outline of colony of *Stolella indica* Annandale, ×6 (all polypides shown retracted). (A from Rogick, 1942; B and C from Rogick, 1940; D to G from Rogick, 1935; H modified from Rogick, 1943a.)

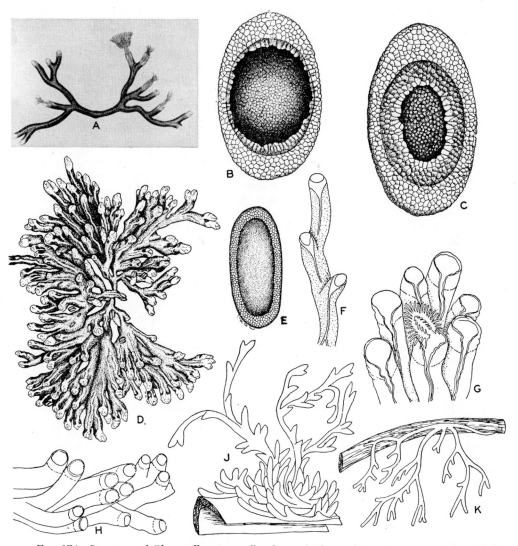

FIG. 174.—Structure of *Plumatella*. A, small colony of *Plumatella repens* var. *jugalis*, ×4;
B and C, opposite surfaces of floatoblasts of *P. repens* var. *jugalis*, ×100; D, colony of
*P. casmiana* Oka, ×5; E, floatoblast of *P. casmiana*, ×65; F, diagram of small portion of
colony of *P. repens* var. *furcifer* (polypides all retracted); G, small portion of colony of *P.
repens* var. *emarginata* (only one polypide partially expanded); H, small portion of colony of
*P. repens* var. *appressa* (all polypides retracted); J, diagram of small portion of colony of
*P. repens* var. *typica* phase *beta* (all polypides retracted); K, diagram of small portion of
colony of *P. repens* var. *fruticosa* (all polypides retracted). (A from Allman; B to D from
Rogick, 1941; E from Rogick, 1943; F modified from Newcomer; G and H modified from
Rogick, 1935; J modified from Rogick, 1940.)

**13.** With two types of floatoblasts; the more common type is somewhat narrow, very thin-walled, and has the annulus the same width all around the capsule (Fig. 174E); the less common type is the usual thick-walled capsuled form similar to those of the other forms in this genus; colony without free, upright branches; zooecia keeled (Fig. 174D); reported only from Lake Erie and the Tippecanoe River, Ind . . . . . . . . . . . . . . . . . . . . . . . . . . . . . . . . . . . . . . .**Plumatella casmiana** Oka

With only thick-walled capsuled floatoblasts; annulus not of the same width all around capsule (Figs. 174B, C); zooecia often keeled; 40 to 60 tentacles; at least six varieties and two phases; on underside of vegetation and objects; typically in lakes and ponds but also occurring in running waters; the most common American species . . . . . . . . . . . . . . . . . . . .**Plumatella repens** L., **14**

**14.** Floatoblasts twice or more as long as wide . . . . . . . . . . . . . . . . .variety **fruticosa**

Length of floatoblasts less than twice the width . . . . . . . . . . . . . . . . . . . . . . . .**15**

**15.** Colony divided into two main masses (Fig. 174A); rare . . . . . . . . . . . . . . . . .**16**

Colony not divided into two main masses . . . . . . . . . . . . . . . . . . . . . . . . . . . .**17**

**16.** Branching very compact; tips of zooecia slightly inclined upward . .variety **flabellum**

Branching very open; zooecia adherent to the substrate throughout their entire length (Fig. 174A) . . . . . . . . . . . . . . . . . . . . . . . . . . . . . . . . .variety **jugalis**

**17.** Zooecia with a bifurcated furrow (Fig. 174F); uncommon . . . . . . . .variety **furcifer**

Zooecia without a bifurcated furrow . . . . . . . . . . . . . . . . . . . . . . . . . . . . . . .**18**

**18.** Zooecia strongly keeled, furrowed, and with an emarginate orifice (Fig. 174G); ectocyst dark; common . . . . . . . . . . . . . . . . . . . . . . . . . . . . .variety **emarginata**

Zooecia not strongly keeled . . . . . . . . . . . . . . . . . . . . . . . . . . . . . . . . . . . . .**19**

**19.** Zooecia adherent to the substrate throughout most of their length (Fig. 174H) . .**20**

Zooecia not adherent to the substrate throughout their entire length (Fig. 174J); zooecia reddish amber . . . . . . . . . . . . . . . . . . . . . . .variety **typica** phase **beta**

**20.** Branching very open; zooecia reddish amber . . . . . . . .variety **typica** phase **alpha**

Branching very close or thickly intertwined (Fig. 174H); common.

variety **appressa**

# BRYOZOA REFERENCES

ALLMAN, J. 1856. *A monograph of the fresh-water Polyzoa.* 119 pp. Ray Society, London, England.

ANNANDALE, N. 1911. Freshwater sponges, hydroids, and Polyzoa. *Fauna of British India,* 251 pp.

BRANDWEIN, P. F. 1938. The culture of Pectinatella magnifica Leidy. *Amer. Nat.* 72:94–96.

BROOKS, C. M. 1929. Notes on the statoblasts and polypids of Pectinatella magnifica. *Proc. Acad. Nat. Sci. Phila.* 81:427–441.

BROWN, C. J. D. 1933. A limnological study of certain fresh-water Polyzoa with special reference to their statoblasts. *Trans. Amer. Micros. Soc.* 52:271–316.

DAVENPORT, C. B. 1893. On Urnatella gracilis. *Bull. Mus. Comp. Zool. Harvard Coll.* 24:1–44.

———. 1904. Report on the fresh-water Bryozoa of the United States. *Proc. U. S. Nat. Mus.* 27:211–221.

GEISER, S. W. 1937. Pectinatella magnifica Leidy an occasional river-pest in Iowa. *Field & Laboratory* 5:65–76.

HARMER, S. F. 1913. The Polyzoa of waterworks. *Proc. Zool. Soc. London* 426–457.

HURRELL, H. E. 1936. Freshwater Polyzoa in English lakes and rivers. *Turtox News* 14:1–2, 20–21.

JULLIEN, J. 1885. Monographie des Bryozoaires d'eau douce. *Bull. Soc. zool. France* 10:91–207.

KRAEPELIN, K. 1887. Die deutschen Süsswasser-Bryozoen. Eine Monographie. I. Anatomisch-systematischer Teil. *Abhandl. natw. Vereins Hamburg* 10:1–168.

———. 1892. Die deutschen Süsswasserbryozoen. Eine Monographie. II. Entwickelungsgeschichtlicher Teil. *Ibid.* 12:1–68.

LEIDY, J. 1884. Urnatella gracilis, a fresh-water polyzoan. *Jour. Acad. Nat. Sci. Phila.* 9:5–16.

LOPPENS, K. 1908. Les Bryozoaires d'eau douce. *Ann. biol. lacustre* 3:141–183.

MARCUS, E. 1925. Bryozoa. *Biol. Tiere Deutschlands* 47:1–46.

———. 1926. Beobachtungen und Versuche an lebenden Süsswasserbryozoen. *Zool. Jahrb. Abt. Syst. Ökol. Geogr. Tiere* 52:279–350.

———. 1934. Über Lophopus crystallinus (Pall.). *Zool. Jahrb. Abt. Anat.* 58:501–606.

ROGICK, M. D. 1934. Studies on freshwater Bryozoa. I. The occurrence of Lophopodella carteri (Hyatt) 1866 in North America. *Trans. Amer. Micros. Soc.* **53**:416–424.

———. 1935. Studies on freshwater Bryozoa. II. The Bryozoa of Lake Erie. *Ibid.* **54**:245–263.

———. 1937. Studies on fresh-water Bryozoa. VI. The finer anatomy of Lophopodella carteri var. typica. *Ibid.* **56**:367–396.

———. 1938. Studies on fresh-water Bryozoa. VII. On the viability of dried statoblasts of Lophopodella carteri var. typica. *Ibid.* **57**:178–199.

———. 1940. Studies on fresh-water Bryozoa. IX. Additions to New York Bryozoa. *Ibid.* **59**:187–204.

———. 1940a. Studies on fresh-water Bryozoa. XI. The viability of dried statoblasts of several species. *Growth* **4**:315–322.

———. 1941. Studies on fresh-water Bryozoa. X. The occurrence of Plumatella casmiana in North America. *Trans. Amer. Micros. Soc.* **60**:211–220.

———. 1943. Studies on fresh-water Bryozoa. XIII. Additional Plumatella casmiana data. *Ibid.* **62**:265–270.

———. 1943a. Studies on fresh-water Bryozoa. XIV. The occurrence of Stolella indica in North America. *Ann. N. Y. Acad. Sci.* **45**:163–178.

———. 1945. Studies on fresh-water Bryozoa. XV. Hyalinella punctata growth data. *Ohio Jour. Sci.* **45**:55–79.

———. 1945a. Studies on fresh-water Bryozoa. XVI. Fredericella australiensis var. browni, n. var. *Biol. Bull.* **89**:215–228.

ROGICK, M. D., and C. J. D. BROWN. 1942. Studies on fresh-water Bryozoa. XII. A collection from various sources. *Ann. N. Y. Acad. Sci.* **43**:123–144.

ROGICK, M. D., and H. VAN DER SCHALIE. 1950. Studies on fresh-water Bryozoa. XVII. Michigan Bryozoa. *Ohio Jour. Sci.* **50**:136–146.

TWITCHELL, G. B. 1934. Urnatella gracilis Leidy, a living Trepostomatous bryozoan. *Amer. Midl. Nat.* **15**:629–655.

WILLIAMS, S. R. 1921. Concerning "larval" colonies of Pectinatella. *Ohio Jour. Sci.* **21**:123–127.

# Chapter 13

# ANNELIDA (AQUATIC EARTHWORMS, LEECHES, POLYCHAETES)

---

TYPICAL segmented worms, constituting the Phylum Annelida, are constructed on a tube-within-tube plan. The body wall is soft, muscular, and covered with a very thin cuticle. The specialized digestive tract has a terminal mouth and anus and is supported in the coelom by thin transverse septa which mark the internal segmental divisions. Unlike the condition in arthropods, segmentation is homonomous. There is an extensive closed circulatory system, and most segments have a pair of long tubular nephridia, or excretory organs. The two ventral nerve cords and their segmental ganglia are fused along the median line; the brain typically consists of a pair of cerebral ganglia, and these connect with the nerve cord by two circumpharyngeal connectives. Anterior eyespots are present in some genera. Except for certain aquatic species that reproduce by budding, reproduction is syngamic, and individuals are hermaphroditic. Cross-fertilization is the rule.

Three classes of annelids are represented in fresh waters. Oligochaeta, or earthworms, have many fresh-water representatives; the Hirudinea, or leeches, are dominantly a fresh-water group; the Polychaeta, however, which are so varied and richly represented in salt water, occur in fresh water only as a few rare and sporadic species. These three classes are easily distinguished from each other, and because they are so different they are considered in separate sections of this chapter.

Polychaeta have muscular, paired, lateral projections from the body wall, called parapodia; these are absent in the other two classes occurring in fresh water. Groups of setae accompany the parapodia of polychaetes, and setae are also present in the Oligochaeta though not in the Hirudinea. Polychaetes usually have accessory tentacles or other appendages at the anterior end but these are absent in the other two groups. Leeches are dorsoventrally flattened, have an oral and a caudal sucker, and the body segments are subdivided into superficial annuli. None of these features occur in the oligochaetes and polychaetes.

## OLIGOCHAETA (AQUATIC EARTHWORMS)

Aquatic oligochaetes have the same fundamental structure as the common terrestrial earthworms, and the anatomy, physiology, and behavior of the latter are so familiar to everyone who has been exposed to an elementary course in college zoology that it would be superfluous to repeat these details here. Instead, the various specializations and peculiarities of aquatic oligochaetes will be emphasized.

**General characteristics.** Representatives of ten families of oligochaetes occur in the fresh waters of the United States. The

278

Aeolosomatidae, Naididae, Tubificidae, Branchiobdellidae, and Lumbriculidae are strictly aquatic. Some species of Haplotaxidae, and Enchytraeidae are semiaquatic or amphibious and occur especially in debris at the edges of streams, ponds, or in marshes and soggy ground; other species, however, are essentially terrestrial and never occur in water. The Glossoscolecidae, Megascolecidae, and Lumbricidae are almost entirely terrestrial, and only occasional and accidental individuals of a few species may be found in water.

The great majority of true aquatic species are common in the mud and debris substrate of stagnant pools and ponds and in streams and lakes everywhere. They are sometimes especially abundant in masses of filamentous algae. Tubificidae occur even in the deepest parts of large lakes, but the shallows down to a depth of a meter are the usual habitat for the great majority of species.

Compared with amphibious and terrestrial forms, the true aquatic oligochaetes are much more delicately constructed and small, the usual length range being 1 to 30 mm. The body wall is thin, and the internal organs can be easily seen in living specimens.

The prostomium is a half-segment at the extreme anterior end of the body; it projects in a rooflike fashion above the mouth and is sometimes elongated into a proboscis. In locating various external and internal structures of oligochaetes it is customary to designate the body segments serially by Roman numerals, beginning at the anterior end. Thus the first complete body segment immediately behind the prostomium is designated as I.

Only in the Branchiobdellidae is there a constant and definite number of segments. All species in this family have a distinct head region and 11 trunk segments, but in the other families the number of segments is quite variable, even in mature individuals, and commonly there is a plus or minus 25 per cent variation from the aver-

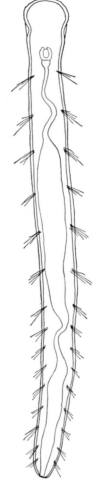

FIG. 175.—Dorsal view of *Aeolosoma leidyi* Cragin, a typical aquatic oligochaete, ×50. Note formation of posterior zooid behind zone of fission. (Modified from Kenk.)

age for various specimens of a particular species. The threadlike Haplotaxidae have the largest number of segments, sometimes up to 500. At the opposite extreme the Aeolosomatidae and Naididae usually have between 7 and 40 segments. The other six families have an intermediate number of segments, tubificids, for example, usually consisting of 40 to 200 segments.

The chitinoid setae are arranged in four bundles, two dorsolateral and two ventro-

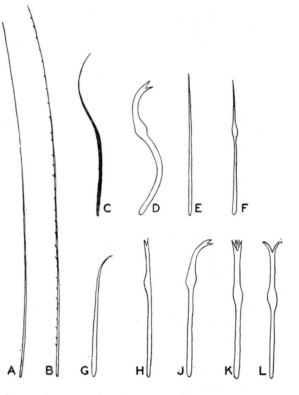

FIG. 176.—Typical setae of aquatic Oligochaeta. A and B, capilliform; C through L, aciculate; B, serrated; C and D, sigmoid; D, H, and J, bifurcate; G, uncinate; J, hooked; K, pectinate; L, biuncinate.

lateral. Setae are never found on segment I, but usually begin on II, although in some genera they are absent from several successive segments, either dorsally, ventrally, or both. Detailed structure of the setae and their arrangement are important as taxonomic characters. A bundle may consist of from one to as many as 20 setae, and the number in a particular bundle may be constant from one specimen to another within a species, or it may vary. Setae may be long, short, straight, curved, sigmoid, capilliform, aciculate, pectinate, bifurcate, hooked bifurcate, or uncinate (Fig. 176). Two-thirds or more of the total length of a capilliform seta usually projects from the body wall, but only about a quarter or less of an aciculate seta is exposed.

**Locomotion.** Usually locomotion is a crawling movement on or in the superficial layers of the substrate; it is similar to that of the earthworm and involves contractions of the muscular body wall and obtaining a purchase with the setae. A few naids, such as *Pristina* and *Stylaria*, are effective swimmers which move along just above the substrate in a serpentine manner. Some species of *Aeolosoma* swim about with the aid of the beating of the cilia of the anterior end.

**Feeding.** The great majority of aquatic oligochaetes obtain nutriment by ingesting quantities of the substrate after the manner of the earthworm, the organic component being digested as it passes through the alimentary canal. Sometimes the food is ingested at a depth of two or three centimeters below the water-substrate interface. Under some circumstances the food may consist largely of filamentous algae, diatoms, or simply miscellaneous plant and animal detritus. *Chaetogaster* is one of the few carnivorous forms. It feeds on entomostraca, insect larvae, and other oligochaetes. *Aeolosoma* feeds on particulate debris and microorganisms which are swept toward the mouth by ciliary currents set up at the anterior end.

**Respiration.** Because of the fact that the body wall is thin and often well supplied with capillaries, most of the carbon dioxide and oxygen exchange occurs through the general body surface. In most naids and in some tubificids water is taken into the anus and passed forward for a variable distance by antiperistalsis and ciliary action, and these processes are thought to constitute an accessory respiratory mechanism.

*Dero* and *Aulophorus* have handsome ciliated gills surrounding the anal region. The posterior extremity has the form of a shallow cup, and the gills originate within the cup or from its margin. *Branchiura* has a finger-like dorsal and ventral gill on each of the posterior segments. All oligochaete gills are well supplied with blood vessels. Gilled species remain quietly in position with the anterior portion of the body hidden in the substrate and in a tube which is constructed of fine debris and projects up from the substrate for a variable distance. The posterior end projects vertically out of the tube and into the water. When disturbed, the worm withdraws into its tube and the substrate in a fraction of a second.

Most tubificids also build tubes, the projecting posterior end of the animal being waved about vigorously in the water, presumably to circulate the water and make more oxygen available to the body surface. Tubificids are commonly

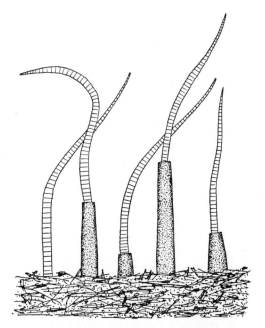

Fig. 177.—*Tubifex*, a typical tube-builder, ×3.

red, owing to dissolved erythrocruorin in the blood.

**Epidermal sensory structures.** Many species of Naididae have a pair of eyespots. They are entirely epidermal, the overlying cuticle being unmodified. Each eye consists of a transverse row of five or six small visual cells and a large number of pigment granules which cover the sensory cells medially and posteriorly. Other epidermal sense organs, consisting of either single cells or aggregates and often arranged symmetrically, occur over the general body surface of all oligochaetes but are especially concentrated at the anterior end. Sensory hairs are common in the Naididae, and in *Slavina appendiculata* (Udek.) they are borne on prominent sensory papillae. Epidermal sensory cells are generally assumed to be sensitive to tactile, thermal, and chemical stimuli.

**Reproduction.** In the Aeolosomatidae and Naididae asexual reproduction by budding is the rule, only a few instances of syngamic reproduction having been reported. The budding zone is localized in one of the segments toward the posterior end, and the number of segments anterior to the budding segment is often designated by $n$. The location of the budding segment is usually constant within a single individual, but under experimental conditions it is possible to alter its position slightly; favorable temperature, food, and oxygen conditions will move the zone anteriorly a segment or two; unfavorable conditions may move it posteriorly a segment or two. On the other hand, the specific location of the fission zone varies greatly from one individual to another within a species. Thus, in *Nais elinguis* O. F. M., $n$ varies from 12 to 20, and in *Stylaria fossularis* Leidy, $n$ varies from 8 to 23 but is usually 18.

The budding segment grows and undergoes repeated transverse divisions which result in four or more anterior segments of a new posterior worm and several new posterior segments of the anterior parent worm. These regions rapidly become differentiated (Fig. 178). The two animals remain attached for a variable length of time, and the more posterior individual may in turn produce a third individual posterior to its budding zone. This process may be repeated so that in some species there may be chains of as many as four to eight zooids in various stages of development. After an interval, however, two adjacent and mature zooids separate and become completely independent individuals. Under favorable conditions most naids reproduce a new individual every two or three days. In *Dero* it is unusual to find a chain of more than two zooids.

Syngamic reproduction in the other eight families is essentially similar to the familiar story in the earthworm. In the true aquatic species, however, the clitellum is often thin and inconspicuous. Cocoons containing embryos are deposited on rocks, vegetation, and debris, especially in the late summer and early autumn, but syngamic reproduction has

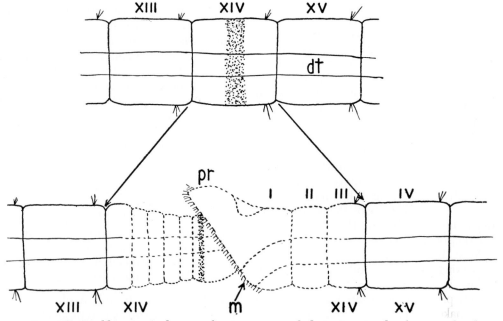

Fig. 178.—Budding in *Aeolosoma*, showing segmental derivatives in daughter zooids. *dt*, digestive tract; *m*, mouth; *pr*, prostomium. (Modified from Marcus, 1944.)

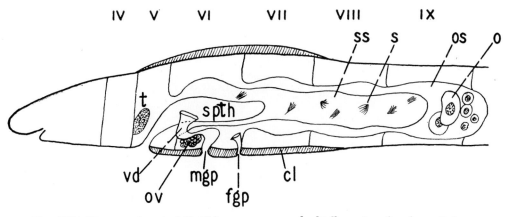

IV    V    VI        VII        VIII        IX

FIG. 179.—Diagram of typical Naididae sex organs. *cl*, clitellum; *fgp*, female genital pore; *mgp*, male genital pore; *o*, ovum; *os*, ovisac; *ov*, ovary; *s*, sperm; *spth*, spermatheca; *ss*, sperm sac; *t*, testis; *vd*, vas deferens. (Modified from Stephenson.)

often been reported as early as July. Under rare circumstances reproduction in isolated tubificids indicates self-fertilization.

The capacity to regenerate lost or damaged anterior or posterior segments varies within the aquatic oligochaetes, but it is

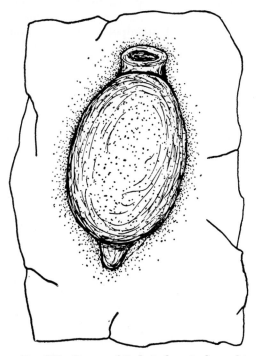

FIG. 180.—Cocoon of *Stylaria* deposited on a bit of debris, ×60.

best developed in the Naididae and Tubificidae.

**Ecology.** Aquatic oligochaetes occupy a niche which is equivalent to that occupied by terrestrial species, and they feed on bottom mud and mix it much as earthworms effectively mix the surface layers of garden and meadow soils.

Temperature is not usually a limiting factor, but it often determines the relative abundance of oligochaetes. Some amphibious species, especially enchytraeids and lumbriculids are notable because they are commonly found in cold mountain streams and in brooks originating from snowbanks and glaciers.

Some species of *Aeolosoma* are known to encyst when the water temperature is 6° or lower. A translucent, hardened coat of mucus is formed around the tightly coiled worm. Emergence from the cyst occurs at about 20°.

Tubificidae are the dominant forms at depths exceeding one meter, and in the deep waters of lakes there are sometimes more than 8,000 individuals per square meter. By far the most concentrated populations are found in streams and rivers that are polluted with sewage. Here tubificids, especially the common and cosmopolitan *Tubifex tubifex* (O. F. M.), occur

Fig. 181.—Mixed colony of *Tubifex* (longer, more flexible individuals) and *Lumbriculus* (shorter, less flexible individuals), ×1. (From Von Wagner.)

in dense waving masses. In fact this species is usually considered an "indicator" of organic pollution, especially where the water is between 10 and 60 per cent saturated with oxygen. *Tubifex,* some enchytraeids, and a few other macroscopic forms are common inhabitants of sewage settling tanks and trickling filters.

Most of the true aquatic species are able to thrive in low concentrations of dissolved oxygen, and many are also able to withstand the complete absence of oxygen for extended periods. Tubificids, for example, can endure the summer and winter periods of stagnation in lakes. Nevertheless, populations cannot be maintained indefinitely in the absence of oxygen. Dausend (1931) found that only one-third of the specimens of *Tubifex* that he used were able to survive anaerobic conditions for 48 days at 0° to 2°C., and at higher temperatures the fraction was progressively smaller. Other workers report the survival of very small percentages of *Tubifex* populations after 120 days under anaerobic conditions. In general, the lower the oxygen concentration the more the animal projects from its tube and the more vigorous are the waving aeration movements of the posterior part of the body, but when the oxygen concentration nears complete exhaustion most tubificids become relatively quiescent.

Naididae are often found in the internal cavities of fresh-water sponges where they probably have the role of commensals.

**Branchiobdellidae.** This family is so unusual in structure and habits that it merits separate consideration. In fact, branchiobdellids are so similar to leeches that they were considered a family of leeches until their true oligochaete affinities were definitely established in 1912. From a morphological standpoint, however, the Branchiobdellidae form a connecting link between typical oligochaetes and true leeches.

The body ranges from 1 to 12 mm. in in length and consists of head, trunk, and muscular caudal sucker. The cylindrical head consists of four fused segments, which are sometimes superficially annulated. The prostomium is absent. The mouth is surrounded by a dorsal and a ventral lip, and just inside the mouth is a pair of chitinoid jaws.

The trunk always consists of 11 segments, although the last three are often indistinct and somewhat fused into the base of the sucker. Trunk segments are usually subdivided by a transverse sulcus. Setae are absent, and there are only two pairs of nephridia. The anus is on the dorsal side of segment X.

A spermatheca opens on the ventral mid-line of V, and there is a male genital pore on the ventral mid-line of VI. A few species have a single pair of testes in V, but most have a pair of testes in each of V and VI. Ordinarily the testes are more easily seen in immature worms. A pair of ovaries is present in VII, and there are two ventral female genital pores. Large eggs may be seen in sexually mature specimens. The glandular clitellum forms around V, VI, and VII. Cocoons are formed, but almost nothing is known about the embryological development.

Branchiobdellids are always associated with crayfish. They occur on the gills, on the inner surface of the gill chambers, and on the general anterior external surface of the body. It is thought that the worms are essentially commensals since their digestive tracts usually contain only diatoms, other algae, and organic debris. Nevertheless, the possibility that they occasionally take some blood from the host does not seem to be completely ruled out.

Species of branchiobdellids reported from western crayfish (*Astacus*) have never been found on eastern crayfish (Cambarinae), and vice versa; otherwise there seems to be no host specificity.

*Cambarincola macrodonta* Ellis, for example, has been reported from 11 species of Cambarinae.

One of the most convenient places to find branchiobdellids is in the debris at the bottom of jars of preserved crayfish. If living specimens are collected, they are best killed and fixed in FAA, which consists of 85 ml. of 85 per cent alcohol, 10 ml. formalin, and 5 ml. glacial acetic acid. Either stained or unstained specimens may be dehydrated and mounted permanently on slides in Canada balsam or in a similar medium. Branchiobdellids seldom contract as strongly as other oligochaetes upon fixation.

**Dispersal, geographic distribution.** Oligochaetes undoubtedly migrate easily throughout whole drainage systems, but passive and accidental overland transport presumably is most effective during the cocoon stage in those species that have syngamic reproduction. *Aeolosoma*, however, forms a resistant cyst stage which may be easily transported from place to place.

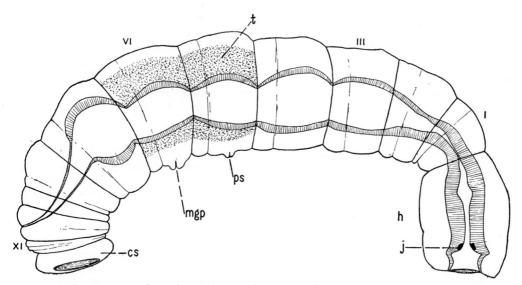

Fig. 182.—Diagram of *Cambarincola*, lateral view, showing digestive tract, ×70. *cs*, caudal sucker; *h*, head; *j*, jaw; *mgp*, male genital pore; *ps*, pore of spermatheca; *t*, testes (shaded areas).

The aquatic oligochaete fauna of the United States is poorly known. Collecting has been scanty and sporadic, and there have been less than 15 important American papers published since 1900. Nevertheless, as additional records slowly accumulate, it is becoming increasingly apparent that many of our species are cosmopolitan and occur the world over or are widely distributed in the Northern Hemisphere. *Aeolosoma variegatum* Vejd., several species of *Chaetogaster, Nais obtusa* (Gerv.), *Slavina appendiculata, Dero limosa* Leidy, and *Tubifex tubifex* are all examples of common and cosmopolitan species. Of the species of Aeolosomatidae and Naididae occurring in the United States, less than 20 per cent have not yet been reported from other continents.

The Lumbricidae are restricted to temperate and cold-temperate zones, while most of the Megascolecidae and Glossoscolecidae are tropical to subtropical. Some few species have an interesting sporadic distribution. The rare *Branchiurus sowerbyi* Bedd., for example, has been collected in Ohio, Michigan, Great Britain, Germany, Belgium, France, Japan, China, Java, and Australia.

**Collecting.** If the bottom material is finely divided, a sieve or strainer may be used for field collecting. Otherwise, the bottom debris should be brought into the laboratory where it may be examined immediately or allowed to stand until the worms can be seen at the surface of the debris or crawling up the sides of the container. Masses of filamentous algae can be rinsed or washed out with a stream of water. The small species can best be found with the aid of dissecting binoculars. Amphibious and large species can usually be picked up with tweezers by sorting stream and lakeside trash.

**Culturing.** The success of a laboratory culture often depends on the amount and kind of water supply and the available oxygen, but many species can be grown in their natural substrate when it is kept in shallow pans into which water drips or slowly flows. Water should never be changed rapidly. Needham *et al.* (1937) give directions for raising Naididae in rice-agar cultures. Naids often become abundant in protozoan cultures.

**Preparation.** For gross structure and even for many fine details of small oligochaetes there is no substitute for the examination of living specimens. Nevertheless, preserved specimens are unavoidable for lengthy examinations and comparisons. Perhaps the greatest difficulty encountered in working with Aeolosomatidae, Naididae, Tubicifidae, and Lumbriculidae is the usual strongly contracted and distorted condition which makes careful anatomical work impossible. Chloretone, chloroform vapors, and magnesium sulphate have all been suggested as narcotic agents, but almost invariably the posterior end of the worm being narcotized disintegrates long before the anterior end has become quiet. Nevertheless, the writer has had some success with 2 per cent hydroxylamine hydrochloride. Regardless of the method used, it is almost impossible to kill *Dero* and *Aulophorus* with expanded gills.

Most investigators advocate killing and fixing small oligochaetes without the use of a narcotic. Some tubificids will die in an extended condition if diluted fixatives are used. Stephenson recommends placing a glass slide on edge along the center of the flat surface of another slide, thus making a right angle. When one to several worms are placed in the angle in a small quantity of water, they usually extend and begin to crawl, and at that point they are flooded with Schaudinn's fixative. If many specimens are being fixed, they may be placed in a shallow dish, and then the water is poured off. The worms thereupon elongate and crawl about, and if they are flooded with hot Schaudinn's fixative, a good percentage of the worms will remain elongated and in good condition. Seventy per cent alcohol is a suitable preservative, and permanent glycerin jelly mounts are generally satisfactory, either with or without staining.

Large amphibious or terrestrial species are best killed and preserved in an extended condition in accordance with standard methods. If the specimens are to be sectioned, they should be first kept in water or on wet filter paper until the digestive tract is free of grit.

The number, arrangement, and structural details of the setae are essential for the identification of Aeolosomatidae, Naididae, Tubificidae, and some Lumbriculidae, but whole mounts do not often allow an examination of the finer details. If living specimens are available, it is best to place one in water on a slide with a circular cover slip. Then remove most of the water at the edge of the cover slip with blotting paper and allow the mount to dry. The worm will be compressed, and then it will burst and flatten, leaving the body wall and setae nicely in place. If a drop of glycerin is placed at the edge of the cover slip, capillarity will draw it under, and such a slide can be made semipermanent by ringing with Murrayite.

Similar preparations of larger dead or preserved specimens of Enchytraeidae, Tubificidae, and some Lumbriculidae may be made if they are left in water for a day or two until they begin to decompose and are soft enough for setae preparations.

**Taxonomy.** In addition to setae, other characters of taxonomic significance in small species are the location of the bud-ding zone, gill structure, shape and size of the prostomium, and the arrangement of certain blood vessels. Body length is of little value since preserved specimens exhibit varying degrees of contraction. In addition, the published literature is often confusing because it is not made clear whether lengths refer to a single anterior zooid or a whole chain of zooids.

It is unfortunate that the identification of Enchytraeidae, Lumbricidae, Megascolecidae, Glossoscolecidae, and some Lumbriculidae depends on internal details of the reproductive system, and though careful dissections are often adequate, it is frequently necessary to make stained serial sections of the segments containing the reproductive structures. Usually cross sections are sufficient, but some workers advocate longitudinal sections in addition. It is chiefly this tedious procedure that has discouraged taxonomic investigations of these annelids.

Because of the fact that the aquatic oligochaetes of the United States are relatively poorly known, the key below has certain limitations. Nevertheless, with the exception of a few very rare and poorly described and unrecognizable species, this key includes all known species of Branchiobdellidae, Aeolosomatidae, and Naididae. The Lumbriculidae and Tubificidae are keyed to some genera and some species. Haplotaxidae and Enchytraeidae are carried to genera. The Lumbricidae, Megascolecidae, and Glossoscolecidae are almost exclusively terrestrial and are not considered beyond the family characters.

## KEY TO GENERA AND SPECIES OF OLIGOCHAETA

1. With a caudal sucker; setae absent; body composed of 11 trunk segments the last three of which are often indistinct; commensal on crayfish; 1 to 12 mm. long (Figs. 190, 191)......Order **PROSOPORA**, BRANCHIOBDELLIDAE, **70**
   Without a caudal sucker; setae present; not commensal on crayfish............2
2. Reproduction normally by fission, producing chains of individuals; living animals more or less translucent and delicate; with one to six setae per bundle; less than 25 mm. long; cosmopolitan and common on the substrate of pools, ponds, and lakes...................................Order **PLESIOPORA, 3**
   Reproduction always sexual; no chains of individuals; living animal more or less opaque; more than 25 mm. long...................................4

3. Single zooids usually less than 5 mm. long, but a few species sometimes reaching 10 mm.; usually with minute red, yellow, or greenish pigment globules in the epithelium of living animals; with cilia on ventral and sometimes lateral surfaces of prostomium; dorsal bundles of setae present on anterior segments; usually without septa (Figs. 175, 183); cerebral ganglia permanently connected with epidermis...........AEOLOSOMATIDAE, **Aeolosoma, 10**
Usually 5 to 25 mm. long; without colored oil globules in epithelium; without cilia anteriorly; dorsal bundles of setae usually lacking in first several segments (Figs. 184, 186); with septa; cerebral ganglia free in coelom..NAIDIDAE, 17

4. Body threadlike, 0.5 to 1.0 mm. in diameter and 100 to 300 mm. long; with two large ventral and two small dorsal sigmoid setae per segment; up to 500 segments; semiaquatic; in wet earth, marshes, ditches, mud, and under rocks at streamside; one or two species.
Order **OPISTHOPORA,** HAPLOTAXIDAE, **Haplotaxis**
Not threadlike; with a different pattern of setae...........................5

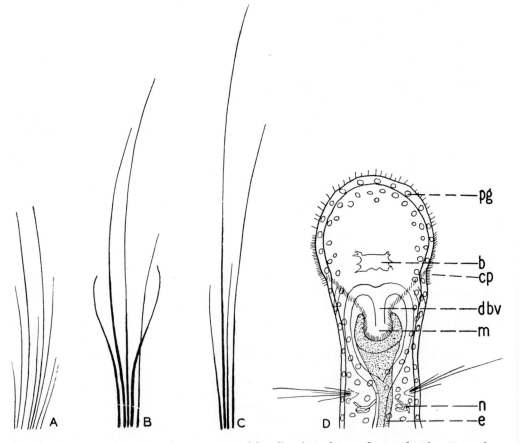

Fig. 183.—Structure of *Aeolosoma*. A, setal bundle of *Aeolosoma hemprichi* Ehr.; B, setal bundle of *A. leidyi;* C, setal bundle of *A. headleyi* Bedd.; D, ventral view of anterior end of *A. leidyi.* b, brain; cp, ciliated pit; dbv, dorsal blood vessel; e, esophagus; m, mouth; n, nephridium; pg, pigment globules. (B to D redrawn from Kenk.)

5. Large, thick-bodied worms which are essentially terrestrial, but occasionally occur in mud or debris of stream and lake margins or in trickling filters of sewage plants; setae sigmoid; true earthworms; usually 5 to 30 cm. long.

Order **OPISTHOPORA, 8**

Smaller, thin worms, mostly aquatic; setae sigmoid or some other shape; usually less than 8 cm. long but a few up to 15 cm.............................**6**

6. Whitish to pinkish; spermathecae opening on IV or V; without a tube; usually two to six setae per bundle; setae all similar; usually 10 to 30 mm. long; aquatic or terrestrial; many species; common in debris along margins of streams and lakes.....................Order **PLESIOPORA, ENCHYTRAEIDAE, 65**

Red to brown; spermathecae opening behind VI; anterior end of worm sometimes hidden in a tube which projects vertically from the substrate and is composed of mud and debris; two setae per bundle, or an indeterminate number per bundle; dorsal and ventral setae similar or dissimilar; typically aquatic..**7**

7. Setae all of one form, single-pointed or sometimes more or less distinctly bifurcate; four bundles of two setae each per segment; usually reddish or brownish in color; up to 8 cm. long; in mud or debris of pools, ponds, and lakes.

Order **PROSOPORA, LUMBRICULIDAE, 61**

Dorsal and ventral setae different; ventral setae bifurcate, dorsal setae bifurcate or a mixture of two or three types; four bundles of an indeterminate number each per segment; usually reddish in color.

Order **PLESIOPORA, TUBIFICIDAE, 53**

8. With a well-formed gizzard at the beginning of the intestine; four pairs of setae per segment; clitellum beginning at or behind XVIII......LUMBRICIDAE

Without a gizzard at the beginning of the intestine; clitellum beginning before XVIII; mostly tropical and subtropical...............................**9**

9. Male genital pores on XVII, XVIII, or XIX; eight, twelve, or more setae per segment, in the latter case forming rings which may be either closed or broken dorsally and ventrally; clitellum beginning with or in front of XV.

MEGASCOLECIDAE

Male genital pores in anterior portion of clitellum or in front of it; eight setae per segment; clitellum beginning with or in front of XXV.

GLOSSOSCOLECIDAE

10. Epidermis colorless...............................................**11**

Epidermis with pigment globules (Fig. 183D).........................**12**

11. Aciculate setae present, at least ventrally, in the posterior region.

**Aeolosoma beddardi** Mich.

Aciculate setae absent..........................**Aeolosoma niveum** Leydig

12. With orange, red, or carmine pigment globules.........................**13**

With green, bluish, yellowish, or brown pigment globules.................**14**

13. Prostomium about as wide as subsequent segments.

**Aeolosoma quaternarium** Ehr.

Prostomium wider than subsequent segments.........**Aeolosoma hemprichi** Ehr.

14. Sigmoid setae present (Fig. 183B).................................**15**

Sigmoid setae absent (Fig. 183C)..................................**16**

15. With biuncinate sigmoid setae beginning on the fourth setigerous segment; the most common species......................**Aeolosoma tenebrarum** Vejd.

With one to three simple sigmoid setae per bundle on second and third setigerous segments (Fig. 183B); first zooid in a chain consisting of six to twelve segments......................................**Aeolosoma leidyi** Cragin

16. Zone of division in VII to X; nephridia absent from esophageal region.

**Aeolosoma variegatum** Vejd.

Zone of division in XI to XV; nephridia present in esophageal region.

**Aeolosoma headleyi** Beddard

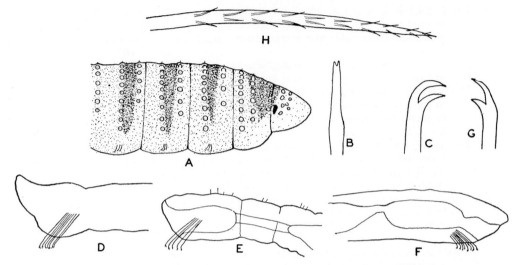

Fig. 184.—Structure of Naididae. A, anterior end of *Ophidonais serpentina* (O. F. M.); B, dorsal seta of *O. serpentina;* C, tip of seta from II of *Chaetogaster bengalensis* Annand.; D, anterior end of *C. diastrophus* (Gruith.); E, anterior end of *C. langi* Bretscher; F, anterior end of *C. bengalensis;* G, terminal bifurcation of seta of *C. diaphanus* (Gruith.); H, tip of dorsal capilliform seta of *Vejdovskyella*.

17. Dorsal setae completely lacking........................................18
    Dorsal setae present in nearly all segments............................19
18. Ventral setae absent from III to V; ventral setae uncinate; prostomium absent or
        very short; mostly carnivorous; mouth and pharynx large (Figs. 184D–F).
                                                                **Chaetogaster, 30**
    Ventral setae all present beginning with II; rare.................**Schmardaella**
19. All dorsal setae aciculate; capilliform setae lacking.........................20
    Some capilliform setae in dorsal bundles (Figs. 186, 187)....................22
20. Segment III two or three times as long as other anterior segments; rare.
                                                    **Amphichaeta americana** Chen
    Segment III not especially elongated..................................21
21. Dorsal and ventral setae both bifurcate at the tips; several uncommon species.
                                                                    **Paranais**
    Dorsal and ventral setae with different tips; the ventral setae hooked bifurcate,
        the dorsal weakly bifurcate or uncinate (Fig. 184B); four dark anterior pig-
        ment bands; pair of eyespots (Fig. 184A); body more or less covered with
        foreign particles; usually in mud substrates; up to 30 mm. long.
                                                **Ophidonais serpentina** (O. F. M.)
22. With ciliated posterior gills surrounding the anus (Fig. 185).................23
    Without ciliated posterior gills.......................................24
23. Without long, nonciliated accessory terminal processes in addition to gills; on
        mud bottom or vegetation; usually in tubes built of debris or mucus (Figs.
        185A–D); three recognizable species.........................**Dero, 36**
    With two long, nonciliated, ventral, finger-like terminal processes in addition to
        gills (Figs. 185E–G); often with a portable tube built of debris, mucus, or
        vegetable material...................................**Aulophorus, 38**
24. Dorsal setae beginning on any segment from XIV to XXII; rare......**Haemonais**
    Dorsal setae beginning much nearer to anterior end.......................25
25. Dorsal setae beginning on II (rarely III)...............................26
    Dorsal setae beginning on VI..........................................27

26. Prostomium developed into a long tentacular process (Fig. 186H); often in tubes; eight recognizable species and several poorly described and unrecognizable forms....................................................Pristina, 40

Prostomium not developed into a long tentacular process..........Naidium, 47

27. Capilliform setae of dorsal bundles with a series of prominent teeth (Fig. 184H); rare. ...................................................Vejdovskyella

Capilliform setae of dorsal bundles not toothed (Figs. 187B, D, G)..........28

28. Prostomium developed into a very long tentacular process; eyes present (Figs. 187E, F)................................................Stylaria, 49

Prostomium not developed into a long tentacular process...................29

29. Body covered with foreign particles; zones of sensory papillae present.
                                    Slavina appendiculata (Udek.)

Body not covered with foreign particles; without sensory papillae; often with a flimsy tube; several common species and several poorly known species.
                                                        Nais, 50

30. Prostomium distinct, usually with a pore on anterior margin (Fig. 184D).
                                    Chaetogaster diastrophus (Gruith.)

Prostomium indistinct.................................................31

31. First postesophageal dilation of digestive tract surrounded by 12 or more pairs of nonanastomosing transverse blood vessels; six to seven setae per bundle.
                                    Chaetogaster pellucidus Walton

First postesophageal dilation of digestive tract covered with anastomosing network of blood vessels.....................................................32

32. Esophagus as long as pharynx (Fig. 184E).............................33

Esophagus shorter than pharynx, often indistinct (Fig. 184F)..............34

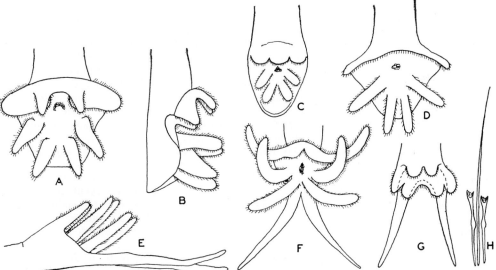

FIG. 185.—Structure of Naididae. A, dorsal view of posterior end of *Dero limosa* Leidy; B, lateral view of posterior end of *D. limosa*; C, dorsal view of posterior end of *D. obtusa* Udek.; D, dorsal view of posterior end of *D. pierrieri* Bousf.; E, lateral view of posterior end of *Aulophorus furcatus* (Müller); F, dorsal view of posterior end of *A. furcatus*; G, dorsal view of posterior end of *A. vagus* Leidy; H, dorsal bundle of setae of *A. vagus*. (B and E modified from Bousfield; D modified from Chen, 1940; F modified from Marcus, 1943; H modified from Walton.)

33. Chain of zooids 2.5 to 7.0 mm. long; setae of II about 165 microns long.
                                        **Chaetogaster crystallinus** Vejd.
     Chain of zooids 0.8 to 2.0 mm. long; setae of II about 75 microns long; four to
        seven setae per bundle......................**Chaetogaster langi** Bretscher

34. The two branches of the terminal bifurcation of the setae equal or nearly equal
        (Fig. 184C); five to 20 setae per bundle.............................**35**
     The two branches of the terminal bifurcation of the setae unequal (Fig. 184G);
        five to nine setae per bundle; feeding mostly on entomostraca.
                                   **Chaetogaster diaphanus** (Gruith.)

35. Chain of zooids usually 6 to 10 mm. long; often epizoic on aquatic snails and
        sponges; nine or ten segments in first animal of a chain.
                                 **Chaetogaster bengalensis** Annand.
     Chain of zooids usually 2 to 6 mm. long; epizoic on the surface of aquatic snails
        or in the mantle cavity; eight segments in first animal of a chain.
                                 **Chaetogaster limnaei** v. Baer

36. With four pairs of gills or gill-like structures, the dorsal pair being small and the
        others being large and sometimes lobed (Figs. 185A, B); very common.
                                        **Dero limosa** Leidy
     With two pairs of gills (Figs. 185C, D)..............................**37**

37. Branchial fossa narrow (Fig. 185C).....................**Dero obtusa** Udek.
     Branchial fossa wide (Fig. 185D)......................**Dero pierrieri** Bousf.

38. Dorsal bundles beginning on V; usually three long pairs of gills (Figs. 185E, F).
                                   **Aulophorus furcatus** (Müller)
     Dorsal bundles beginning on VI...................................**39**

39. Three pairs of flat, semilunar gills (Fig. 185G)..........**Aulophorus vagus** Leidy
     Two pairs of long gills.....................**Aulophorus oxycephalus** Schmarda

40. Capilliform setae of dorsal bundles smooth..............................**41**
     Capilliform setae of dorsal bundles provided with teeth (Figs. 186C, D).......**43**

41. Last segment provided with three terminal finger-like processes (Fig. 186J).
                                      **Pristina flagellum** Leidy
     Last segment without such processes.................................**42**

42. Usually 16 to 18 segments in first zooid; $n = 16$ to 18; dorsal bundles consisting
        of two or three equally long capilliform setae and usually two aciculate setae;
        reported only from N. J......................**Pristina schmiederi** Chen
     Usually 18 to 23 segments in first zooid; $n = 12$ to 15; dorsal bundles consisting of
        one (rarely two) capilliform and one (rarely two unequally long) aciculate
        setae; common....................................**Pristina aequiseta** Bourne

43. Dorsal capilliform setae of III long, twice or more as long as those of subse-
        quent bundles (Fig. 186G)..........................................**45**
     Dorsal capilliform setae of III less than twice as long as those of subsequent
        bundles. ..........................................................**44**

44. Dorsal capilliform setae of III slightly longer than those of subsequent bundles
        (Fig. 186H).............................**Pristina serpentina** Walton
     Dorsal capilliform setae of III shorter than those of subsequent bundles (Fig.
        186K); reported only from Ga..................**Pristina plumaseta** Turner

45. Zone of division usually situated between XIII and XVIII; common and widely
        distributed. ......................................................**46**
     Zone of division situated at or beyond XXV; reported only from Va.
                                   **Pristina tangiseta** Hayden

46. With three to five setae in each ventral bundle of III, about one-half the number
        in II or IV; serrations in the middle part of capilliform setae about 2 microns
        apart (Fig. 186C).............................**Pristina longiseta** Ehr.
     With four to six setae in each ventral bundle of III, nearly as numerous as in
        adjacent segments; serrations in the middle part of capilliform setae about
        8 to 16 microns apart (Fig. 186D).................**Pristina leidyi** Smith

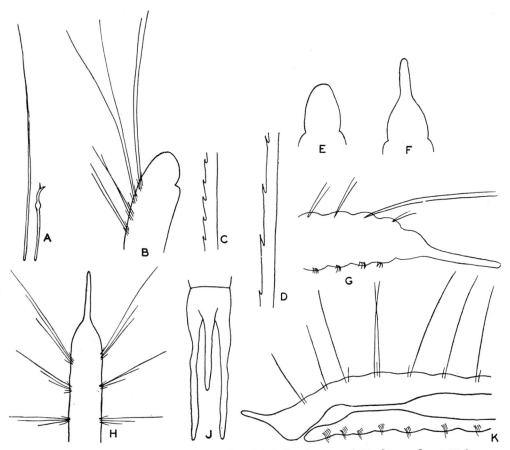

Fig. 186.—Structure of Naididae. A, dorsal bundle of setae of *Naidium osborni* Walton;
B, anterior end of *N. bilongata* Chen; C, part of dorsal capilliform seta of *Pristina longiseta*
Ehr.; D, part of dorsal capilliform seta of *P. leidyi* Smith; E and F, extreme variations in
anterior end of *Naidium breviseta* (Bourne); G, anterior end of *Pristina longiseta*; H, anterior
end of *P. serpentina* Walton; J, posterior end of *P. flagellum* Leidy; K, anterior end of *P.
plumaseta* Turner. (A and H modied from Walton; B modified from Chen, 1944; C and D
redrawn from Chen, 1940; G modified from Marcus, 1943; J modified from Leidy, 1880;
K modified from Turner.)

47. Dorsal bundles beginning on III; capilliform setae of bundles of III and IV very
    long (Fig. 186B); reported from N. J. . . . . . . . . . . .**Naidium bilongata** Chen
    Dorsal bundles beginning on II; capilliform setae of bundles of III and IV not
    especially long. . . . . . . . . . . . . . . . . . . . . . . . . . . . . . . . . . . . . . . . . . . . . . . . .48
48. Each dorsal bundle consisting of one long capilliform seta and one short biuncinate
    seta (Fig. 186A) . . . . . . . . . . . . . . . . . . . . . . . . . . . . . . .**Naidium osborni** Walton
    Each dorsal bundle consisting of two capilliform and two short biuncinate setae;
    prostomium variable from blunt to slightly produced (Figs. 186E, F).
                                           **Naidium breviseta** (Bourne)
49. Proboscis projecting from apex of prostomium (Fig. 187E).
                                         **Stylaria fossularis** Leidy
    Proboscis inserted into a prostomial notch (Fig. 187F).
                                       **Stylaria proboscidea** (O. F. M.)

50. Some or all of dorsal aciculate setae with plain tips . . . . . . . . . .**Nais obtusa** (Gerv.)
    All dorsal aciculate setae bifurcate or pectinate (Figs. 187B, D) . . . . . . . . . . .**51**
51. Eyespots present (Fig. 187A) . . . . . . . . . . . . . . . . . . . . . . . . . . . . . . . . . . . . . . .**52**
    Eyespots absent . . . . . . . . . . . . . . . . . . . . . . . . . . . . . . . . . . . .**Nais josinae** Vejd.
52. Bifurcations of dorsal aciculate setae long, about equal in length, and set at an acute
    angle to each other (Fig. 187D) . . . . . . . . . . . . . . . . . .**Nais elinguis** O. F. M.
    Bifurcations of dorsal aciculate setae short and weak (Fig. 187B); very common.

    **Nais communis** Piguet

Fig. 187.—Structure of Tubificidae. A, dorsal view of anterior end of *Nais communis* Piguet; B, dorsal bundle of setae of *N. communis*; C, ventral bundle of setae of *N. communis*; D, dorsal bundle of setae of *N. elinguis* O. F. M.; E, anterior end of *Stylaria fossularis* Leidy; F, anterior end of *S. proboscidea* (O. F. M.); G, dorsal bundle of setae of *S. proboscidea*.

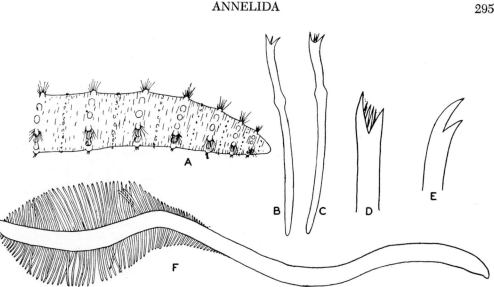

Fig. 188.—Structure of Tubificidae. A, anterior end of *Peloscolex*; B and C, dorsal pectinate setae of *Tubifex tubifex* (O. F. M.); D, distal end of dorsal pectinate seta of *Ilyodrilus*; E, distal end of seta of *Limnodrilus claparedianus* Ratzel; F, lateral view (diagrammatic) of *Branchiura sowerbyi* Bedd., ×1.1, showing dorsal and ventral gills.

53. With a dorsal and a ventral gill on each segment in the posterior 25 to 40 per cent of the body; 40 to 140 pairs of such gills (Fig. 188F); 20 to 185 mm. long; pinkish gray; probably introduced; ponds, lakes, and streams; reported from Ill., Ohio, Mich., Tenn., Iowa, and Wis.

**Branchiura sowerbyi Bedd.**

Without gills...........................................................**54**

54. With capilliform setae in dorsal bundles.............................**55**

With no capilliform setae in dorsal bundles............................**57**

55. With prominent sensory papillae around segments; with three to 14 setae per dorsal bundle near anterior end (Fig. 188A); often with a sheath of mucus and foreign particles; among roots of aquatic plants or in vegetable debris; several uncommon species........................................**Peloscolex**

Without such sensory papillae; common..................................**56**

56. With the two lateral teeth of the dorsal pectinate setae widely divergent (Figs. 188B, C); length of atrium and penis combined much shorter than the remainder of the sperm duct; 30 to 100 mm. long; several species reported from the U. S. but only one is common; it has the anterior end imbedded in mud bottoms, sometimes in a special tube, and waves the posterior end about in the water for aeration; especially common in polluted waters; sometimes present in enormous numbers.................**Tubifex tubifex (O. F. M.)**

With the two lateral teeth of the dorsal pectinate setae not widely divergent (Fig. 188D); length of atrium and penis combined at least two-thirds as long as the remainder of the sperm duct; several rare species described from ditches, springs, streams, and ponds in Calif.................................**Ilyodrilus**

57. Setae not bifurcate; one rare species reported from Calif. marshes and ponds.

**Telmatodrilus**

Setae bifurcate (Fig. 188E)...........................................**58**

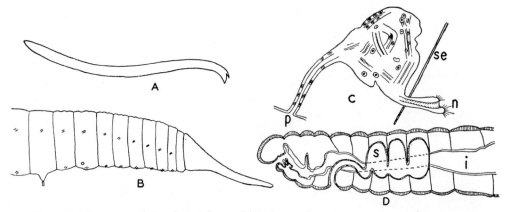

FIG. 189.—Structure of Lumbriculidae and Enchytraeidae. A, ventral seta from posterior part of body of *Lumbriculus*; B, anterior end of *Rhynchelmis*; C, section of nephridium of *Mesenchytraeus*; D, longitudinal section of anterior end of *Mesenchytraeus*. *s*, spermatheca; *se*, septum; *i*, intestine; *n*, nephrostome; *p*, nephridiopore. (B to D modified from Altman.)

**58.** With a single spermatheca pore on ventral side of X; among roots of aquatic plants; rare.........................................**Monopylephorus**
With two spermatheca pores on ventral side of X; in stagnant water, often in tubes; about ten species known from the U. S. but only three are common.
**Limnodrilus, 59**

**59.** With 160 to 205 segments; five to eight setae per bundle at anterior end.
**Limnodrilus hoffmeisteri** Clap.
With less than 140 segments; four to six setae per bundle at anterior end......**60**

**60.** Body with 60 to 85 segments; no spermatophores present in spermathecae.
**Limnodrilus claparedianus** Ratzel
Body with 65 to 124 segments; spermatophores usually present in spermathecae.
**Limnodrilus udekemianus** Clap.

**61.** Setae posterior to clitellum bifurcate (Fig. 189A); prostomium never drawn out into a proboscis; several species but only one common.
**Lumbriculus inconstans** Smith
Setae posterior to clitellum simple; prostomium often elongated to form a proboscis (Fig. 189B).........................................**62**

**62.** With a single spermatheca in VIII; male genital pores in IX; several rare western species. ...............................................**Sutroa**
With two or more spermathecae.....................................**63**

**63.** With spermathecal pores on VIII, or VIII and IX; two male genital pores on X (Fig. 189B); several species...........................**Rhynchelmis**
With three pairs of spermathecal pores; uncommon........................**64**

**64.** With two spermathecal pores on each of IX, X, and XI; two male genital pores on IX; one species reported from Wash.......................**Kincaidiana**
With two spermathecal pores on each of VIII, IX, and X or XI; one or two male genital pores on X; widely distributed; several species..........**Eclipidrilus**

**65.** Setae straight and paired, inner pairs in bundle successively smaller than outer; dorsal pores present in body wall.............................**Fridericia**
Setae straight or sigmoid and in pairs in bundle with smaller ones within; dorsal pores absent........................................**66**

**66.** Esophagus expanding abruptly into intestine........................**Henlea**
Esophagus merging gradually into intestine (Fig. 189D)..................**67**

**67.** Setae straight..................................................**Enchytraeus**
Setae sigmoid....................................................**68**

68. Testes divided..........................................**Lumbricillus**
    Testes not divided...................................................**69**
69. Nephridial duct loosely coiled, cell mass of postseptal part well developed;
    spermathecae confined to a single segment....................**Marionina**
    Nephridial duct closely wound, cell mass reduced to a minimum; spermathecae con-
    fined to V or extending posteriorly through one or more additional segments
    (Fig. 189D) ........................................**Mesenchytraeus**
70. With one pair of testes, located in trunk segment V; about 5.0 mm. long.
          BRANCHIOBDELLINAE,* **Branchiobdella, 71**
    With two pairs of testes, located in trunk segments V and VI (Fig. 182).
          CAMBARINCOLINAE,* **72**
71. Peristomium entire; on eastern crayfish......**Branchiobdella americana** Pierantoni
    Peristomium bilobed; on western crayfish (*Astacus*).
          **Branchiobdella tetradonta** Pierantoni
72. Body with appendages (Figs. 190A, B)................................**73**
    Body without appendages.........................................**76**
73. With blunt, cylindrical projections along the median dorsal line (Fig. 190A); 0.5
    to 2.0 mm. long; on eastern crayfish...................**Pterodrilus, 74**
    With irregular bands encircling the dorsal surface of body (Fig. 190B); 2.0 to 3.0
    mm. long; on western crayfish............**Cirrodrilus thysanosomus** (Hall)
74. With a large funnel-shaped collar encircling VII and VIII; reported from Ind. and
    Mich....................................**Pterodrilus durbini** Ellis
    Without such enlargements........................................**75**
75. Dorsal appendages on trunk segments II to VIII (Fig. 190A); widely distributed.
          **Pterodrilus distichus** Moore
    Dorsal appendages on III, IV, V, and VIII; reported only from Fla., N. C., and Va.
          **Pterodrilus alcicornus** Moore
76. Accessory sperm duct present (Fig. 190H)...........................**77**
    Accessory sperm duct absent.....................................**87**
77. Body cylindrical; posterior end not conspicuously enlarged (Figs. 190G, H); 2.0
    to 9.0 mm. long.................................**Cambarincola, 78**
    Body flattened, posterior end greatly enlarged (Fig. 191B); 2.0 to 6.0 mm. long.
          **Xironogiton, 86**
78. Upper lip divided............................................**79**
    Upper lip entire except for a small median emargination...................**81**
79. Upper lip composed of four subequal lobes (Fig. 190E); widely distributed and
    common. ................................................**80**
    Upper lip with four finger-like processes (Fig. 190C); reported from *Astacus* in
    Wyo....................**Cambarincola macrocephala** Goodnight
80. Major annulations of body segments distinctly elevated over minor annulations;
    lower jaw with several median and lateral denticles (Fig. 190D).
          **Cambarincola chirocephala** Ellis
    Major annulations of body segments not distinctly elevated over minor annula-
    tions; lower jaw with several minute denticles on each side (Fig. 190F).
          **Cambarincola philadelphica** (Leidy)
81. Major annulations of trunk segments II to VIII usually all distinctly elevated over
    minor annulations (Fig. 190G)....................................**82**
    Only major annulation of VIII distinctly elevated, or no major annulations dis-
    tinctly elevated (Fig. 190H)......................................**83**
82. Upper jaw with five distinct teeth; reported only from Fla.
          **Cambarincola floridana** Goodnight
    Upper jaw with one distinct median tooth and two small denticles on each side;
    reported only from Ky.................**Cambarincola meyeri** Goodnight

---

* Key modified from Goodnight (1940).

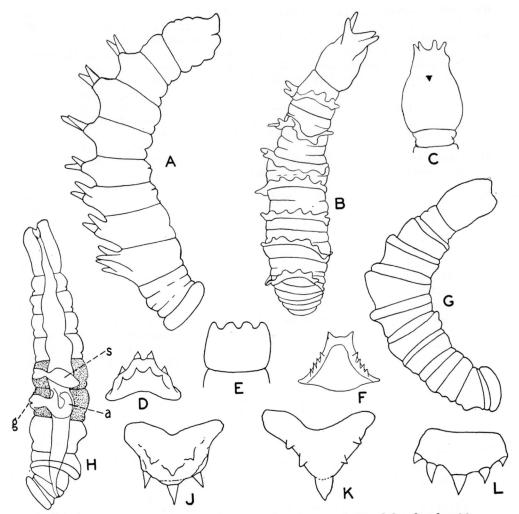

FIG. 190.—Structure of Branchiobdellidae. A, lateral view of *Pterodrilus distichus* Moore, ×85; B, dorsal view of *Cirrodrilus thysanosomus* (Hall), ×35; C, dorsal view of head of *Cambarincola macrocephala* Goodnight; D, lower jaw of *C. chirocephala* Ellis; E, upper lip of *C. philadelphica* Leidy; F, lower jaw of *C. philadelphica*; G, lateral view of *C. floridana* Goodnight, ×24; H, lateral view of *C. elevata* Goodnight, ×30; J, upper jaw of *C. inversa* Ellis; K, upper jaw of *C. macrodonta* Ellis; L, upper jaw of *C. vitrea* Ellis. *a*, accessory sperm duct; *g*, male genital pore; *s*, spermatheca; testes shown as shaded areas in H. (B modified from Hall, 1915; D, J, and L modified from Ellis, 1920; F redrawn from Moore, 1893; G modified from Goodnight, 1941; H modified from Goodnight, 1940; K modified from Ellis, 1912.)

83. Major annulation of VIII distinctly elevated over minor annulation (Fig. 190H); reported from Midwest.................**Cambarincola elevata** Goodnight
    Major annulation of VIII not distinctly elevated over minor annulation........84
84. Upper jaw with three large teeth (Fig. 190J); if five teeth are present then the two lateral ones are very small; on western crayfish.
                                                                **Cambarincola inversa** Ellis

    Upper jaw with five teeth (Figs. 190K, L); widely distributed and common on eastern crayfish.................................................85

**85.** Middle tooth of upper jaw prominent and long (Fig. 190K).
> **Cambarincola macrodonta** Ellis

Middle tooth of upper jaw only slightly larger than the other four (Fig. 190L).
> **Cambarincola vitrea** Ellis

**86.** With glandular concave discs located laterally on the ventral surface of trunk segments VIII and IX; body usually spatula-shaped; on western crayfish.
> **Xironogiton occidentalis** Ellis

Without such glandular concave discs; body usually flask-shaped (Fig. 191B); one subspecies on western crayfish and another subspecies on eastern crayfish.
> **Xironogiton instabilius** (Moore)

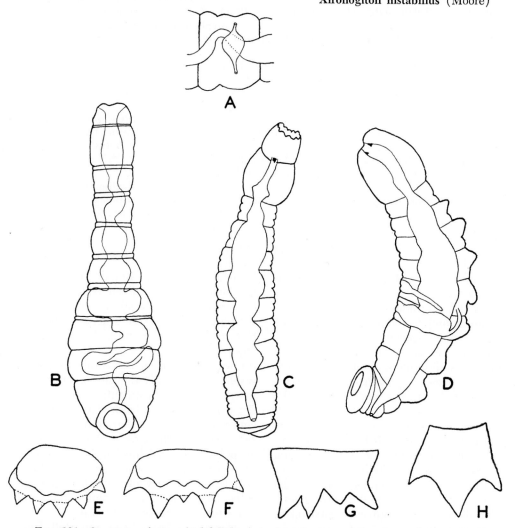

Fig. 191.—Structure of Branchiobdellidae. A, lateral view of fourth trunk segment of *Bdellodrilus illuminatus* (Moore) showing lateral gland; B, ventral view of *Xironogiton instabilius* (Moore), ×18; C, dorsal view of *Triannulata montana* Goodnight, ×21; D, lateral view of *Stephanodrilus obscurus* Goodnight, ×30; E, upper jaw of *Xironodrilus formosus* Ellis; F and G, upper jaw of *X. dentatus* Goodnight; H, upper jaw of *X. appalachius* Goodnight. (B redrawn from Moore, 1893; C and D modified from Goodnight, 1940; E and F modified from Ellis, 1919; G and H modified from Goodnight, 1943.)

87. With a pair of large clear glands on each of the trunk segments (Fig. 191A); scattered distribution..................Bdellodrilus illuminatus (Moore)
    Without such glands.............................................88
88. Major annulations of trunk segments secondarily divided, especially in middle of body (Fig. 191C); 2.0 to 8.0 mm. long; on western crayfish.
    Triannulata, 89
    Major annulations of trunk segments not secondarily divided.................90
89. Lips divided into lobes (Fig. 191C)...........Triannulata montana Goodnight
    Lips entire except for a slight median emargination.
    Triannulata magna Goodnight
90. Body not flattened; sucker terminal (Fig. 191D); 2.0 to 3.0 mm. long; on western crayfish........................Stephanodrilus obscurus Goodnight
    Body flattened; sucker ventral; up to 6.0 mm. long; on eastern crayfish.
    Xironodrilus, 91
91. With four to six teeth in upper jaw (Figs. 191E–G); widely distributed.......92
    With three teeth in upper jaw (Fig. 191H).............................93
92. Middle tooth of upper jaw the longest if teeth are odd in number, middle pair longest if teeth are even in number (Fig. 191E).
    Xironodrilus formosus Ellis
    Middle tooth of upper jaw shorter than either of the two adjacent teeth (Figs. 191F, G)..............................Xironodrilus dentatus Goodnight
93. Middle tooth of upper jaw longer than the two lateral teeth (Fig. 191H); reported from Great Smoky Mountains National Park.
    Xironodrilus appalachius Goodnight
    Middle tooth of upper jaw shorter than the two lateral teeth; reported from N. C.
    Xironodrilus pulcherrimus (Moore)

# POLYCHAETA

Polychaetes are almost exclusively marine annelids, and an amazing variety of species and enormous numbers of individuals are found in many types of marine habitats. Some species (especially Nereidae) are euryhaline and occur also in estuaries and brackish waters, but only about 17 species of polychaetes are known to be restricted to the fresh waters of the world (Feuerborn, 1931; Johnson, 1903).

The colonization of inland waters by these few polychaetes is by no means restricted to one family or a few genera. The Serpulidae, Capitellidae, Nereidae, and Eunicidae are all represented, and the 17 species belong to nine different genera. All of these species, however, have close marine relatives.

In addition to being found in the United States, fresh-water polychaetes have been reported sporadically from Jugoslavia, Lake Baikal in Asia, French Indo-China, French Guinea, Hawaii, Java, Sumatra, China, Trinidad, and Brazil. With few exceptions, they have been collected from fresh-water rivers, lakes, and springs within 20 miles of the seacoast, and this fact seems to be an indication that polychaetes, in spite of their phylogenetic antiquity, are relative newcomers to fresh waters. Presumably the physiological and morphological adjustments necessary for the marine-brackish-fresh-water transition constitute almost insurmountable barriers. Perhaps the most striking incidence of polychaete distribution is the occurrence of two fresh-water species in Lake Baikal, a body of water which is geologically ancient and more than a thousand miles from the nearest salt water.

Six species have been reported from North America. *Nereis limnicola* Johnson, one of the Nereidae, was first collected in 1895 from Lake Merced near San Francisco, a body of fresh water less than a quarter of a mile from the ocean and formed in very recent geological times. Another nereid, *Lycastoides alticola* Johnson, was described from a single small specimen collected in 1892 in a mountain stream at an altitude of 7,000 feet in "Sierra Laguna, Lower California." Neither of these two species has been recovered since they were first described.

A third member of the Nereidae, *Neanthes lighti* Hartman, occurs in brackish tidal streams as well as in strictly fresh-water streams and ponds north of San Francisco. *Neanthes saltoni* (Hartman) is known only from the Salton Sea, California. In the limnological sense this large body of water is a lake, but chemically it is much like the ocean. Both of these species inhabit loosely constructed tubes in vertical burrows in the shallows.

In 1858 and in several papers published later the great microscopist Leidy described an interesting serpulid polychaete, *Manayunkia speciosa* Leidy, from the Schuylkill River near Philadelphia; it was later found in other areas in southeastern Pennsylvania and New Jersey. Nothing is known about the present distribution and occurrence of this species.

In 1939, however, another species in the same genus, *Manayunkia eriensis* Krecker, was described from mud samples taken at a depth of 17 meters in Lake Erie, near Put-in-Bay, Ohio. It was subsequently collected in the same general area, and more recently was found on the bottom of the Duluth harbor area in Lake Superior. It is quite possible that a careful search would reveal that it is generally distributed throughout the Great Lakes.

*Manayunkia speciosa* and *M. eriensis* are very similar, and most of the following description of *M. speciosa* applies equally well to the other American species. The mature worm is 3 to 5 mm. long and inhabits a tube built of mud and mucus. The head bears two large lateral lophophore-like structures each of which has about 18 long ciliated tentacles used in feeding. There is a pair of eyes near the median line of the head, and also a linear

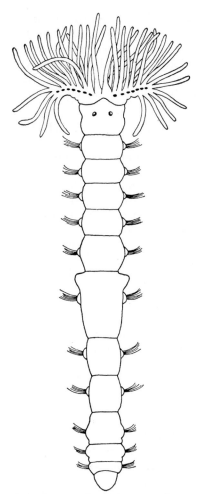

FIG. 192.—*Manayunkia speciosa* Leidy, ×37, a fresh-water polychaete. (Modified from Leidy, 1883.)

group of pigmented spots on each half of the lophophore which are presumed to be light sensitive. Each of the first 11 of the 12 trunk segments has a pair of reduced, knoblike parapodia bearing a bundle of four to ten setae. The circulatory system is well developed, and the bright green chlorocruorin of the blood colors the whole body. Leidy showed that development is direct and that there is no free-swimming trochophore larva. The large size and lateral swellings of the sixth trunk segment may be an indication that these polychaetes also reproduce by budding.

The two American species of *Manayunkia* may be differentiated on the basis of three morphological characters. *M. speciosa* has a pair of haemal loops in each segment; *M. eriensis* has none. In *M. speciosa* the tentacles on each side are arranged in two regular rows; in *M. eriensis* the tentacles are not arranged in rows. In the latter species there is an open collar surrounding the base of the tentacles; in the former species there is no such structure.

# HIRUDINEA (LEECHES)

The leeches are predominantly a fresh-water group, although there are many marine as well as numerous terrestrial species, the latter mostly in the tropics. About 44 fresh-water species are known from the United States, and they are common inhabitants of ponds, marshes, lakes, and slow streams, especially in the northern half of the country. To the layman, leeches are collectively known as "blood-suckers," but many forms are predators and scavengers, and only a minority of our species will take blood from warm-blooded animals. Unlike the great majority of fresh-water invertebrates, leeches are often brightly colored and patterned, and in some species the coloration is highly variable. The length of mature leeches ranges from minute species only 5 mm. long to some of the giant *Haemopis* that have been reported to reach a length of 18 inches when swimming.

**General characteristics.** Unlike oligochaetes, the Hirudinea are dorsoventrally flattened. The mouth is surrounded by an oral sucker which may be large, or small, fused with the anterior end, and liplike. The caudal sucker usually faces ventrally and is much larger, discoid, powerful, and expanded over a central attachment pedestal. The anus is dorsal and in front of the sucker. The surface of the body may be smooth, wrinkled, tuberculate, or papillated. Although most genera have rather characteristic shapes, it should be borne in mind that leeches are highly muscular and contractile, and the body outline may vary greatly with locomotion, reaction to stimuli, and method of killing and fixation.

From the standpoint of basic body segmentation, external appearances are deceiving. All leeches are composed of only 34 true segments, but each segment is subdivided into a definite and constant number of superficial annuli. In the middle portion of the body of most leeches a segment typically has three, five, or six annuli, but in some of the Piscicolidae (fish leeches) there are seven, 12, or 14 annuli. Toward the extremities of the body annulation is incomplete so that there are fewer annuli per segment than in the mid-body segments. In *Haemopis marmorata* (Say), for example, mid-body segments all have five annuli, but segments I through VII are represented by 1, 1, 1, 2, 2, 3, and 4 or 5 annuli, respectively; and XXIII through XXVII are represented by 5, 4, 3, 2, and 1 annuli. Furthermore, in all leeches there is considerable fusion of the true segments of the body at the extremities, and especially at the posterior end. In *H. marmorata* segments XXVIII through XXXIV are all fused to form the caudal sucker.

The true body segmentation has been precisely established by a study of the nervous system. Each of the 34 segments is represented by a ganglion and paired nerves, but these structures are crowded together and partially fused at the anterior and posterior ends.

Some investigators distinguish the following major body regions in leeches: head (I to VI), preclitellar (VII to IX), clitellar (X to XIII), postclitellar (XIV to XXIV), anal (XXV to XXVII), and caudal sucker (XXVIII to XXXIV). The degree of differentiation of these regions is highly variable from one species to another.

The Class Hirudinea is divided into two

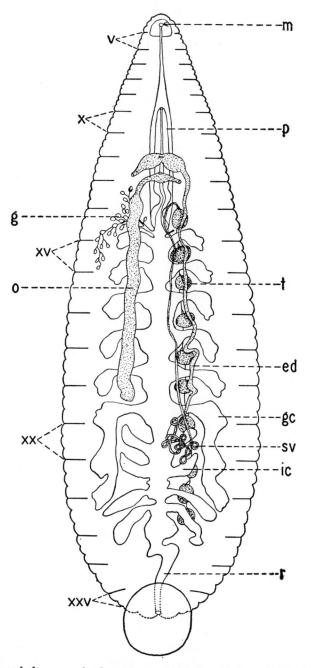

F<small>IG</small>. 193.—Ventral diagram of *Glossiphonia complanata* (L.), ×10, showing annulations, reproductive system, and digestive system. Reproductive system stippled; female organs shown only on the left; male organs shown only on the right. *ed,* ejaculatory duct; *ic,* intestinal caecum (second); *g,* salivary glands; *gc,* gastric caecum (sixth); *m,* mouth; *o,* ovary; *p,* proboscis; *r,* rectum; *t,* testis; *sv,* seminal vesicle. (Modified from Harding and Moore.)

orders. Each member of the Order Rhynchobdellida has a small porelike mouth in the oral sucker through which a muscular proboscis can be protruded; jaws are absent; the blood is colorless; and there are three or six or more annuli per segment in the middle of the body. Members of the Order Arhynchobdellida have a medium to large mouth, no proboscis, jaws present or absent, red blood, and usually 5 annuli per segment in the middle of the body.

The Order Rhynchobdellida is subdivided into two American families. The Glossiphoniidae generally have a flattened body, the anterior sucker more or less fused with the body, one to four pairs of eyes, and typically three annuli in each of the mid-body segments. The American Piscicolidae, on the other hand, are somewhat cylindrical, with a distinct anterior sucker, one or two pairs of eyes, and usually six or more annuli per mid-body segment; these leeches are almost invariably found as parasites on the body of fish or crustaceans.

The Order Arhynchobdellida is also subdivided into two families represented in North America. The Erpobdellidae have three or four pairs of eyes (never arranged in an arch), no jaws, and no gastric caeca. The Hirudidae, however, have five pairs of eyes (forming a regular arch), toothed jaws, and one to several pairs of gastric caeca.

**Color.** When collecting specimens in the field, notes on coloration should always be taken, since they quickly fade in preservatives, with only red, brown, and black pigments persisting. Uniform coloration is a rather rare condition, most leeches being brightly mottled, spotted, or segmentally striped; sometimes the color pattern is arranged transversely, sometimes longitudinally. The ventral surface is almost always paler than the dorsal. The Glossiphoniidae range from translucent and pinkish to an opaque and brightly colored condition. *Glossiphonia complanata* (L.), for example, is dull green to brownish, with six longitudinal rows of yellowish spots and two dark longitudinal paramedian lines. *Macrobdella decora* (Say), the American medicinal leech, is very showy; the general coloration is green with obscure longitudinal stripes or short median lines; in the mid-line are bright orange or reddish spots, while the marginal spots are black. The ventral surface is rich orange, either plain or spotted with black. *Placobdella parasitica* (Say) is richly and variably colored, and it is difficult to find two specimens with exactly the same coloration and intensity. The general ground color is some shade of greenish-brown, but the body is variously spotted, striped, or blotched with yellow and orange. A histological study of this species has revealed three types of pigment granules: (1) a pale yellowish granular reflecting substance, (2) chromatophores which range from black (contracted) to green (expanded), and (3) reddish-brown chromatophores which form a fine network in the expanded state. Leeches show no background color adaptation, but usually become paler in darkness and darker under illumination. Color changes are thought to be governed through the central nervous system.

**Locomotion.** All leeches can move about on the substrate with characteristic creeping, looping, or inchworm movements, by getting a firm grip alternately with the oral and caudal suckers. The body shape changes greatly during such locomotion. The Hirudidae and Erpobdellidae are excellent swimmers which move along rapidly with graceful up-and-down or side-to-side undulations. The Glossiphoniidae are poor swimmers, however, and when disturbed they usually roll up like a pillbug and fall to the substrate.

**Feeding, digestive system.** The structure of the digestive system is partially correlated with food habits. In the Rynchobdellida there are no jaws, and the mouth is normally a small pore in the oral sucker.

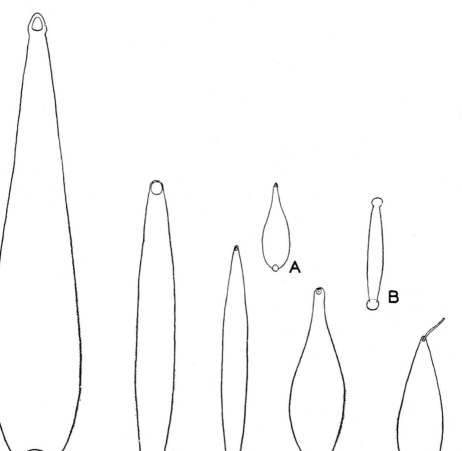

Fig. 194.—Relative shape and size of typical American leeches, ×1. A, *Helobdella*; B, *Piscicola*; C, *Haemopis*; D, *Macrobdella*; E, *Erpobdella*; F, *Placobdella*; G, *Glossiphonia*, with extruded proboscis.

The anterior portion of the digestive tract contains an elongated, muscular, protrusible proboscis which lies in a proboscis sheath and is thrust forward and out of the mouth during feeding. There is a very short esophagus at the base of the proboscis, but the unicellular salivary glands in this region have long ducts which carry their secretion through the proboscis to its tip. The large stomach extends approximately through the middle third of the body and has from one to ten pairs of lateral gastric caeca (often branched), in which quantities of ingested food may be stored for long periods prior to digestion. The gastric caeca are capable of great distension, and after a large meal a rhynchobdellid leech may weigh two to four times as much as it did before the meal. Digestion occurs in the intestine, and this part of the digestive tract is also supplied with caeca; usually, however, there are only four small pairs. The rectum is an unspecialized part of the digestive tract just before the anus. The Glossiphoniidae have a wide variety of food habits; many species are scavengers which feed on dead animal matter, but more

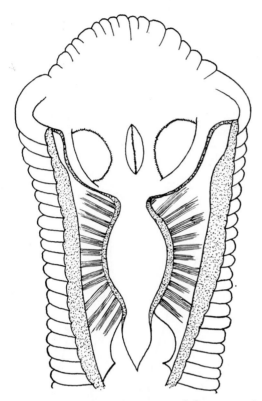

Fig. 195.—Diagrammatic ventral dissection of the anterior end of *Hirudo*. Stippling denotes cut edges of oral chamber, pharynx, and body wall. (Greatly modified from Pfurtscheller.)

commonly they are carnivorous and feed on snails, oligochaetes, and other small invertebrates. *Glossiphonia complanata* (L.) and *Helobdella stagnalis* (L.) are almost always associated with snails upon which they feed and are consequently commonly called "snail leeches." *Placobdella* and *Helobdella* are often temporary parasites on fish, frogs, and turtles, and they have occasionally been reported as taking a blood meal from man, especially from an open abrasion on the skin. Except during the breeding season, the Piscicolidae are almost invariably found as parasites on fish or crustaceans; they feed on the surface mucus as well as on blood and tissue fluids. The fact that certain Rynchobdellida are capable of taking blood from vertebrates does not seem to

have been satisfactorily explained, especially since these leeches have no teeth with which to make an incision in the host epidermis. It is probable, however, that digestive enzymes are given off through the pore at the tip of the proboscis where it is in contact with the skin of the host and that these enzymes digest away the superficial layers and permit blood to flow.

The general plan of the Arhynchobdellida digestive system is similar to that of the Rynchobdellida, but there are several striking differences. For one thing, there is no proboscis, and in its place is a strong, muscular, sucking pharynx. Some of the Hirudidae, or true "bloodsuckers," have three sharp-toothed jaws behind the large mouth. These are used in making incisions in the skin of the host. Other Hirudidae, especially *Haemopis*, have no teeth or only vestigial teeth and normally feed on small invertebrates or dead animal matter, though *H. marmorata* (Say) will occasionally attack man. The latter species is called the "horse leech" because it commonly lives in ponds and troughs where it attacks drinking cattle and horses. The Erpobdellidae never have true jaws. They are scavengers or feed mostly on small invertebrates which they sometimes swallow whole; occasionally they suck blood from fish, frogs, and man, especially at bleeding epidermal abrasions. None of the American Arynchobdellida have intestinal caeca. The Hirudidae have one to several pairs of gastric caeca, but the Erpobdellidae have none.

*Macrobdella* and *Philobdella* are the only common American leeches that regularly take human blood. Like all other bloodsuckers, they attach to the host with the caudal sucker and explore with the anterior end until a suitable spot is located, especially where the skin is thin. The oral sucker is then attached tightly and three fine painless incisions are made by back-and-forth rotary motions of the jaws. Sufficient blood is taken to distend the stomach and its caeca greatly so that the leech may be five times as heavy as it was when it began feeding. Much of the fluid of the ingested blood is excreted by the nephridia during feeding, the stored organic components, both cellular and noncellular, being considerably concentrated. When the leech has filled its digestive tract it leaves the host voluntarily, but the incisions keep on bleeding for a variable time because of the persistence of small quantities of the salivary anticoagulant, hirudin, in the adjacent tissues.

True bloodsucking leeches require only an occasional full meal, the stored blood being digested and utilized very slowly. Specimens have been kept for more than two years without feeding.

**Circulatory system.** Unlike the condition in oligochaetes, where there is a spacious coelom regularly divided by transverse septa, the coelom of leeches is largely obliterated and reduced by the greatly developed muscular, botryoidal, and parenchymatous tissues. The remaining sinus-like cavities consist of several longitudinal canals interconnected by smaller branch canals. The nerve cord, larger blood vessels, and reproductive organs are located in these sinuses.

The main portion of the circulatory system of typical Rynchobdellida consists of a large dorsal longitudinal blood vessel and a large ventral longitudinal blood vessel which are connected near the two extremities by a series of convoluted branch vessels. The muscular wall of the anterior portion of the dorsal vessel acts as a heart. Near the posterior end the dorsal vessel is greatly expanded into an intestinal blood sinus which envelops the intestine and its caeca, and muscular contractions of the intestine are thought to aid in forcing the blood anteriorly out of this sinus and through the dorsal vessel proper. All of the body tissues are well supplied with capillaries. In addition to the blood circulatory system, the coelomic sinuses contain a lymphlike fluid which circulates slowly. The two systems are unconnected, blood flowing in one and

lymph in the other, both fluids being colorless. In some of the Piscicolidae the lymphatic system has a series of paired lateral pulsating vesicles which force the lymph around the body.

In the Arhynchobdellida the true blood vascular system has disappeared, and the system of coelomic sinuses alone remains in a modified form. It contains blood which is red because of dissolved erythrocruorin.

**Respiration.** Some marine leeches have special lateral gill-like structures, but none of the American fresh-water species have any special respiratory structures. The oxygen and carbon dioxide exchange readily occurs through the general body surface since there is a rich network of capillaries just below the epidermis. Many species attach to the substrate with one or both suckers and undulate the body, probably to facilitate respiration. Little is known about the ability of active leeches to tolerate low concentrations of dissolved oxygen. They do not appear to be able to tolerate highly acid conditions or decomposition gases at low oxygen concentrations.

**Excretion.** There are never more than 17 pairs of nephridia and these are all segmentally arranged in the middle body segments. The internal openings, located in the sinus system, are simple ciliated funnels in some species and simple to complex, variable "ciliated organs" in others. The paired external openings, or nephridiopores, are in the ventral furrows between annuli.

**Nervous system.** The brain is in the region of segments V and VI and consists of the fused ganglia and basal portions of the nerves of the first six body segments. There is a small suprapharyngeal mass, a small connective passing around each side of the pharynx, and a very large subpharyngeal mass. The posterior ganglionic mass, in segments XXV and XXVI, represents the more or less fused ganglia of XXV

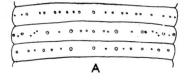

A

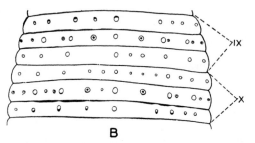

B

FIG. 196.—Arrangement of sensillae and papillae in typical segments in two species of *Placobdella*. Sensillae are shown with central dots; all other areas are cutaneous papillae. Note that sensillae occur only on the middle annulus of each segment and that they are symmetrically arranged.

through XXXIV. The ventral nerve cord connects brain and posterior ganglionic mass, and each of VII through XXIV has a ganglion with three pairs of nerves.

**Sense organs.** Typical leeches have a variable number of small papillae arranged in transverse rows or extending completely around the body. These are of two general types. Ordinary cutaneous papillae are tactile and possibly chemical receptors. Sensillae, however, are more specialized, light-colored or whitish, and sensitive to light. While there may be numerous transverse rows or rings of cutaneous papillae in a single segment, there is never more than one row or ring of sensillae per segment. Usually a ring of sensillae consists of a dorsal transverse row of six or eight sensillae and a ventral row of six sensillae. Such a ring of sensillae is often called the neural ring, or sensory ring, and is always situated on the neural or sensory annulus of every somite. The term is usually applied to the annulus and not to the sense organs themselves.

True paired eyes are found at the ante-rior end of the body. Each eye consists of a clump of dark-colored pigment granules, often cup-shaped, and an adjacent sensory area. Glossiphoniidae have one to four pairs of eyes, Piscicolidae one or two or more, Erpobdellidae three or four, and Hirudidae five. A few leeches have eyespots on the caudal sucker or body somites.

**Reproduction.** In a very few leeches there is a common genital pore for both sets of reproductive organs, but usually there are two genital pores located on the median ventral line in XI and XII and separated by one to five or more annuli, the male genital pore always being more anterior than the female.

The female reproductive system is much simpler than that of the male. It consists of two saclike ovaries of variable size and two very short narrow oviducts which unite to form a vagina. The vagina, in turn, opens to the outside through the female genital pore. In the Hirudidae the female reproductive system also has an albumen gland, vaginal caecum, and muscular vagina.

Usually there are five to 12 pairs of segmentally arranged rounded testes, but in some of the Erpobdellidae they may be minutely subdivided like linear bunches of grapes. On each side of the body the testes are connected to a long vas deferens by means of short vasa efferentia. Each vas deferens has a modified seminal vesicle region which, in turn, becomes an ejaculatory duct. The two ejaculatory ducts unite to form a median atrium which is often complex and glandular.

The relative development and size of the seminal vesicles and ejaculatory ducts vary greatly from one species to another. They may be short to long, straight or much convoluted, and small to massive. In the seminal vesicles sperm become cemented together and stored for future use.

An eversible muscular bursa is associated with the male atrium. In the Glossiphoniidae it is rudimentary, but in the other families it is generally larger and functional. In the Hirudidae, however, the bursa region contains a coiled filamentous tubular penis which often has a complicated structure.

As the sperm leave the seminal vesicle and pass down the ejaculatory ducts into the region of the atrium they are formed into spermatophores (except in the Hirudidae) for conveyance to another individual during copulation. These double club-shaped structures, which have a chitinoid covering, consist of two more or less adherent tubes containing sperm bundles (Fig. 197). Spermatophores are formed by glandular areas of the atrium and adjacent portions of the ejaculatory ducts.

Like most hermaphroditic animals, an individual leech does not fertilize itself, but copulates with another individual and exchanges sperm. In the Rhynchobdellida and Erpobdellidae copulating pairs implant spermatophores on the ventral or dorsal surface of each other, usually in the clitellar region, but sometimes only one member of a copulating pair releases spermatophores. The sperm issue out of the spermatophores and penetrate the superficial tissues to the sinuses of the recipient leech with the aid of local histolysis. Soon the sperm reach the ovaries in the ventral sinuses and fertilize the eggs.

In the Hirudidae the penis of each member of a copulating pair is extruded so that sperm are deposited at the genital pore or in the vagina of the recipient.

The clitellum of a leech is relatively inconspicuous, but in the breeding season it secretes ringlike structures which slip off the anterior end of the body to form cocoons, just as in the earthworm. As the cocoon passes the female genital pore it receives and encloses from one to several fertilized eggs. The Piscicolidae and most Arhynchobdellida fasten their cocoons to the substrate, but some of the Hirudidae superficially bury their cocoons in soft substrates, often in or on exposed mud along the shores of bodies of water. Cocoons

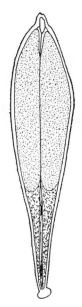

Fig. 197.—Spermatophore of *Glossiphonia*, showing two oval bundles of sperm. (Modified from Brumpt.)

are usually 2 to 15 mm. long, more or less oval, and flattened on the attachment surface. The outer surface may be gelatinous, spongy, tough and membranous, horny, or chitinoid. After a variable period of growth, the young leeches emerge from the cocoons and become independent.

The Glossiphoniidae do not form true cocoons but carry their fertilized eggs in membranous capsules on the ventral surface of the body. After hatching, the young remain on the body of the parent in the same area. They are attached by means of mucous threads and probably feed on mucus until they attain quite a large size at which time they leave the parent.

Copulation usually begins in the spring after a good meal has been obtained, and most cocoons are deposited between May and August. Some species produce batches of eggs for periods of five to six months, and empty cocoons may be found as late as October or November.

Little is known about the length of life of leeches. *Macrobdella decora* takes two

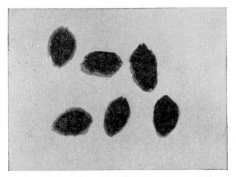

Fig. 198.—Cocoons of *Haemopis*, ×1.5.

to three years to mature, certain other Hirudidae may require four to five years, and it is claimed that some specimens may live for ten to 15 years.

**Ecology.** Leeches abound in warm protected shallows where there is little wave action and where plants, stones, and debris afford concealment. In such habitats population densities of 700 leeches per square meter of bottom have been reported. Superficial daylight examination of a likely body of water may be disappointing, but it must be borne in mind that leeches are chiefly nocturnal in their activities, and that they are hidden under stones, vegetation, and debris during the hours of daylight. The great majority of specimens are collected between the water's edge and depths of two meters, but a few species have been collected as deep as 50 meters. Leeches require substrates to which they can adhere and consequently are rare on pure mud or clay bottoms.

Few species and few individuals occur in strongly acid lakes, and they are generally absent from sphagnum bogs. There is some evidence which indicates that low calcium content of waters may be a limiting factor in leech distribution.

Unlike most groups of fresh-water invertebrates, there is very little habitat preference among leeches. The same species (*Helobdella stagnalis*, for example) may occur in lakes, ponds, springs, slow streams, marshes, and on all kinds of suitable substrates. A few species of Erpobdellidae and Glossiphoniidae may be collected in swift streams, and some of them even tolerate some degree of pollution.

The leech fauna of intermittent ponds persists because of the fact that some species are able to tide over dry periods by burrowing into the mud bottom, losing considerable weight, and constructing a small mucus-lined cell. Leeches have been known to aestivate in this manner for more than four weeks at a time. Winters are spent in a lethargic dormant state buried in the upper parts of the substrate but below the frost line.

Although our American leeches are all considered to be aquatic organisms, there are some that are actually amphibious. *Haemopis*, for example, commonly crawls out of the water and wanders about on the moist shore and ground, sometimes as much as a quarter of a mile from the water, where it feeds on living and dead invertebrates, especially earthworms.

Semipermanent and permanent parasites, such as the Piscicolidae and *Placobdella parasitica*, remain on the body of the host except during the breeding season when they become free-living long enough to deposit their eggs on the substrate. But some of the fish leeches are completely dependent and deposit their cocoons on the host fish.

**Economic importance.** The common medical practice of bloodletting as treatment for a wide variety of human ills supported a considerable leech industry in eighteenth- and nineteenth-century Europe. *Hirudo medicinalis* L. was raised

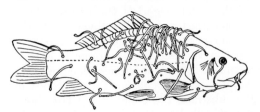

Fig. 199.—A small carp heavily infected with *Piscicola geometra* (L.), ×0.5. (From Plehn, 1924.)

commercially in so-called leech ponds, especially in France, Hungary, and Russia, and it is estimated that 25,000,000 leeches were used in France in 1846 and 7,000,000 in London hospitals in 1863.

Leeching never attained such great importance in the United States, and between 1840 and 1890 it is doubtful if more than 1,500,000 leeches were used in any one year, including both the imported and native species (usually *Macrobdella decora*). The maximum wholesale price was about one hundred dollars per thousand. By 1890 the use of leeches had dwindled greatly and by the turn of the century it was difficult to find a drugstore that still carried leeches in stock. Bloodletting by the use of leeches is now extremely rare in this country and is confined to a few older European elements of our population. The practice is mostly resorted to as a home remedy for boils, contusions, and abscessed teeth. A report persists, however, that leeches have been used occasionally in hospitals within the past 20 years for relieving inflammation of the iris after glaucoma operations.

Leeches sometimes become so abundant in northern lake resort areas as to constitute a nuisance for bathers. Disturbances in the water, such as splashing and currents, are known to attract bloodsuckers quickly. Unfortunately there are usually no effective remedial measures that can be taken to reduce leech populations, but if the water level of a lake can be lowered at least a meter in the late fall, dormant leeches in the exposed muddy shallows will be killed by temperatures of 20°F. or less. Leeches may be temporarily controlled in localized bathing beach areas by applying 100 pounds of powdered lime per acre per day in the shallows.

With reference to fish populations, the Glossiphoniidae, Hirudidae, and Erpobdellidae can be dismissed as being of no real importance as parasites. Heavy infections of Piscicolidae, however, have sometimes caused considerable mortality in both hatcheries and the natural environment.

**Dispersal, geographic distribution.** Since many leeches temporarily attach to or definitely parasitize ducks and shore birds, they are easily transported overland from one body of water or drainage system to another. In fact, the leeches are one of the few fresh-water groups in which such transport is definitely known to occur. Within a single drainage system, however, passive dispersal by attachment to fish is undoubtedly of great importance.

In addition, leeches actively and readily spread from place to place and colonize suitable habitats within individual drainage systems. Peculiar seasonal upstream mass migrations of great numbers of leeches have been reported several times.

Some American leeches, including *Actinobdella, Oligobdella, Theromyzon,* some species of *Placobdella, Dina anoculata* Moore, *Macrobdella sestertia* Whitman, *Philobdella floridana* Verrill, and most Piscicolidae have very restricted distributions or have been reported only once or a few times. Others, however, occur in suitable habitats throughout the United States as well as in other continental areas. Two species of *Glossiphonia,* for example, occur throughout Europe and much of Asia; *Helobdella stagnalis* and *Theromyzon tessulatum* (O. F. M.) are widely distributed in the north and south temperate zones. The most common European member of the Piscicolidae, *Piscicola geometra* (L.), on the other hand, has been recorded only a few times from this country. Similarly, the common European bloodsucker, *Hirudo medicinalis* L., has presumably become established only recently in the United States and has been recorded a few times from the northeastern states.

**Collecting, preparing.** Usually specimens are collected individually with forceps by turning over rocks, logs, and debris in the shallows. A small dipnet should be carried to capture the rapid swimmers and to retrieve sluggish glossiphonids as they roll up and fall to the bottom. Some collectors have had success by placing the body of a dead and bleeding small animal as bait in the water where there is a slight current.

If leeches are kept in aquaria, they must be provided with food, especially the Hirudidae, which otherwise have a habit of crawling out and wandering about on the floor.

For close examination in the living state leeches should be narcotized. Carbonated water, chloretone, chloroform vapors, chloral hydrate, nicotine sulphate, and magnesium sulphate are all variously successful for different species. Specimens to be killed and preserved should receive similar treatment until they no longer respond to pinching. If carefully done, exceptionally good specimens may require one to five hours or more for narcotization. They are then placed in a flat dish and flooded with the killing agent which may be any one of a variety of standard fixatives. Schaudinn's fluid, 0.5 per cent chromic acid, and 2 per cent formalin in 50 per cent alcohol are all suitable. If an acid-containing fixative is used, care must be exercised to remove all acid after fixation, otherwise the connective tissues swell greatly. Permanent preservation should be in 80 per cent alcohol or 5 per cent formalin. Preserved leeches should be straight, moderately extended, undistorted, and not too hard or too soft.

Bennike (1943) advises narcotizing leeches in 15 per cent alcohol for 15 minutes. Then they should be removed, stretched to normal size, and placed in 10 per cent formalin or 70 per cent alcohol. If they bend or contract, they have not been kept in the weak alcohol long enough.

**Laboratory cultures.** With the exception of the Piscicolidae, laboratory cultures can be easily maintained, especially since leeches need to be fed only infrequently. It is most important that the culture water be kept cool and clean. Although leeches are tolerant of a wide range of temperatures, they do not usually survive in the laboratory in direct sunlight or water that is too warm. A wide variety of common substances are toxic, even in minute quantities; copper and chlorine are especially harmful. Dead leeches, feces, and unused food material should always be removed promptly. Water should be changed as soon as it shows signs of becoming foul.

Small Glossiphoniidae may be kept in finger bowls or similar dishes of pond water containing a few shoots of *Anacharis* or other aquatic plants. Pieces of shell or pebbles afford additional concealment and protection. Small balanced aquaria also make excellent containers for leeches in the laboratory. Living snails should be added occasionally for food. Large blood-sucking glossiphonids should be kept in larger containers and require a feeding of turtle, frog, or toad blood every month or two. Glossiphonids thrive and readily reproduce under suitable conditions, but care should be taken to prevent overcrowding.

Erpobdellidae are very active, especially at night, and require large containers with tightly fitting covers or screens so that they will not crawl out. Stones and pieces of shell are a suitable substrate for the deposition of cocoons. Earthworms, immature insects, and ground fresh meat are appropriate foods for maintaining satisfactory cultures.

Hirudidae may be kept in large, low aquaria or eathernware jars, but similar precautions must be taken against wandering. They do not require vegetation, but since they are somewhat amphibious there should be room for them to crawl up on the side of the container above the water level, and it is well to have a sloping bank of sandy soil at one end with a partial cover of moss, stones, or sticks. A vertebrate blood meal should be supplied at intervals of about six months, but the diet may be varied with frog eggs, immature insects, and earthworms. Cocoons are mostly deposited in wet soil just above the water's edge.

**Taxonomy.** Most of the United States has had only sporadic collecting, and much remains to be done. Extensive work has been accomplished only in the northeastern quarter of the country, especially in Minnesota, Michigan, Missouri, Illinois, and Ohio. Consequently, aside from those leeches that are undoubtedly generally distributed throughout much of the coun-try, it is fruitless to indicate geographic distribution for the species given in key.

External key characters are used wherever possible, but in a few couplets it has been necessary to use internal anatomical features which require dissection. Lengths are for average specimens when at rest. The 44 species listed in this key are believed to be essentially a complete list for the United States. Only a few poorly described, unrecognizable, and rare species are not included.

## KEY TO SPECIES OF HIRUDINEA

1. Mouth consisting of a small pore in the oral sucker through which a muscular proboscis can be protruded; jaws absent (Figs. 193, 194G); with three or six or more annuli per segment in middle of body; blood colorless.
   Order **RHYNCHOBDELLIDA, 2**
   Mouth medium to large; without a proboscis; jaws present or absent; usually five annuli per segment in middle of body; blood red.
   Order **ARHYNCHOBDELLIDA, 3**

2. Body flattened, never cylindrical; oral sucker ventral and more or less fused with body; no distinct clitellum; usually three annuli per segment in middle of body (Fig. 200A); one to four pairs of eyes; eggs in membranous sacs on ventral side of adult; young clinging to ventral side of adult; poor swimmers.
   **GLOSSIPHONIIDAE, 4**
   Body cylindrical, often divided into a narrow anterior and a wide posterior region; oral sucker distinctly separated from body; six or more annuli per segment in middle of body, but one rare species with three annuli per segment (Fig. 202E); one to three pairs of eyes, or none; 6 to 30 mm. long; eggs deposited in cocoons on host or substrate; almost invariably found as parasites on the body of fishes; most records from eastern and northeastern parts of U. S. but undoubtedly widely distributed; the fish leeches.
   **PISCICOLIDAE, 34**

3. Three or four pairs of eyes (rarely absent), never arranged in a regular arch (Fig. 201C); jaws absent; gastric caeca absent; body linear.
   **ERPOBDELLIDAE, 21**
   Five pairs of eyes forming a regular arch (Fig. 201B); jaws typically present and toothed, but may be toothless or absent; with one to several pairs of large gastric caeca; medium to very large size................HIRUDIDAE, **26**

4. With one pair of eyes (Fig. 200A).........................................5
   With three or four pairs of eyes (Figs. 200G–J)...........................8

5. With two annuli per segment in middle of body; about 7 mm. long; poorly known and reported only once from salamanders in N.C.
   **Oligobdella biannulata** (Moore)
   With three or six annuli per segment in middle of body (Fig. 200A)...........8

6. Body essentially without papillae; with six or fewer pairs of gastric caeca; caudal sucker without prominent marginal papillae; 5 to 20 mm. long; scavengers, or feeding on small invertebrates, occasionally parasitic on fish and frogs, will rarely take blood from man; very common...................**Helobdella, 9**
   Body with variable papillae; with seven pairs of gastric caeca; caudal sucker with or without prominent marginal papillae......................................7

7. Caudal sucker without prominent marginal papillae and glands, but small serrations present in one species; proboscis pore at the anterior margin of the cephalic sucker; three annuli per segment; up to 90 mm. long; free-living forms or temporary parasites on fish, frogs, and turtles; one or two species will occasionally take blood from man.........................................Placobdella, 11

Caudal sucker with prominent marginal papillae and glands (Fig. 200F); proboscis pore not at the anterior margin of the cephalic sucker; three or six annuli per segment; up to 15 mm. long; uncommon; reported only from a few areas in the northeastern states; habits largely unknown....Actinobdella, 17

8. With three pairs of eyes (Figs. 200G, H); six pairs of gastric caeca; feeding mostly on snails, oligochaetes, and other small aquatic invertebrates; up to 30 mm. long; very common and widely distributed throughout the U. S.; the snail leeches.............................................................Glossiphonia, 19

With four pairs of eyes (Fig. 200J); nine pairs of gastric caeca; body translucent; up to 35 mm. long; a poorly known genus in the U. S.; widely distributed but not common...................................................Theromyzon, 20

9. With a brown chitinoid plate on the dorsal surface of VIII (Fig. 200A); five pairs of gastric caeca; the most cosmopolitan of all American leeches.
Helobdella stagnalis (L.)

Without such a plate.....................................................10

10. Greatly elongated and slender; translucent and colorless; one pair of gastric caeca.
Helobdella nepheloidea (Graf)

Short, flat, and broad; deeply pigmented; six pairs of gastric caeca.
Helobdella fusca (Castle)

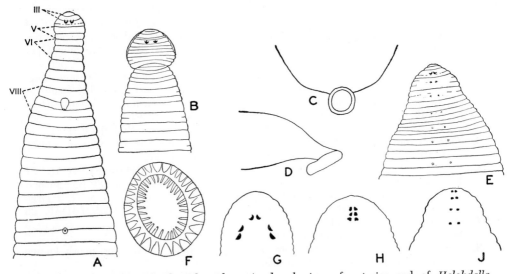

Fig. 200.—Structure of Glossiphoniidae. A, dorsal view of anterior end of *Helobdella stagnalis* (L.), position of genital pores on ventral surface also indicated; B, dorsal view of anterior end of *Placobdella montifera* Moore; C, ventral view of posterior end of *P. pediculata* Hemingway (annulations not shown); D, lateral view of same; E, dorsal view of anterior end of *P. hollensis* (Whitman) (note transitions between well-developed pair of eyes and sensillae); F, caudal sucker of *Actinobdella inequiannulata* Moore; G, eyes of *Glossiphonia heteroclita* (L.); H, eyes of *G. complanata* (L.); J, eyes of *Theromyzon*. (A, C, D, and E modified from Moore, 1912; B and F modified from Moore, 1901.)

**11.** Anterior segments widened to form a headlike structure which is constricted from the body (Fig. 200B); with three low dorsal keels; uncommon.

**Placobdella montifera** Moore

Anterior segments not widened; no dorsal keels............................12

**12.** Caudal sucker on a narrow stalk (Figs. 200C, D); no dorsal papillae; anus between XXIII and XXIV; a rare species, usually found on fish.

**Placobdella pediculata** Hemingway

Caudal sucker not on a narrow stalk; anus behind XXVII...................13

**13.** Papillae small, few, smooth, and rounded...................................14

Papillae prominent, abundant, rough, and pointed (Fig. 196)..............15

**14.** Coloration highly variable, but usually a deeply pigmented pattern of dark greenish-brown, variously spotted, blotched, and striped with yellow and orange which may more or less replace the ground coloration; triangular reddish-brown marginal spots; third annulus of each segment in the middle of the body with no trace of a secondary furrow; free living during the breeding season but otherwise a very common parasite found clinging to the legs of the common snapping turtle; the largest species in this genus.

**Placobdella parasitica** (Say)

Dark brownish-green, finely marked with orange; with a row of semicircular orange spots along the lateral margins; third annulus of each segment in the middle of the body with a distinct cross furrow; rare....**Placobdella picta** (Verrill)

**15.** Margin of caudal sucker serrated; with a pale band across VI; rare.

**Placobdella phalera** (Graf)

Margin of caudal sucker not serrated; without a pale band across VI; up to 60 mm. long; free-living or parasitic on turtles and fish.......................16

**16.** Dorsal papillae numerous (Fig. 196); accessory eyes absent; very common.

**Placobdella rugosa** (Verrill)

Dorsal papillae not numerous; accessory eyes present (Fig. 200E); uncommon.

**Placobdella hollensis** (Whitman)

**17.** With six annuli per segment in middle of body............................18

With three annuli per segment in middle of body.

**Actinobdella triannulata** Moore

**18.** Caudal sucker with about 30 marginal papillae (Fig. 200F).

**Actinobdella inequiannulata** Moore

Caudal sucker with about 60 marginal papillae......**Actinobdella annectens** Moore

**19.** Eyes arranged in a roughly triangular pattern of three groups of two each (Fig. 200G); body translucent, with little pigmentation.

**Glossiphonia heteroclita** (L.)

Eyes in two nearly parallel rows near the median line (Fig. 200H); body opaque, deeply pigmented; very common............**Glossiphonia complanata** (L.)

**20.** With two annuli between genital pores; with nine or ten pairs of gastric caeca.

**Theromyzon occidentale** (Verrill)

With four annuli between genital pores; with nine to 11 pairs of gastric caeca.

**Theromyzon tessulatum** (O. F. M.)

**21.** Segments of middle of body all with five annuli; three pairs of eyes; oral sucker small; mature specimens brownish in color, with four irregular longitudinal rows of black dots; body parallel-sided; up to 100 mm. long; common and widely distributed; feeds on aquatic invertebrates, fish, and frogs; sometimes a scavenger; occasionally attacks man........**Erpobdella punctata** (Leidy)

With one or more annuli of middle of body subdivided (Fig. 201C); three or four pairs of eyes, or eyes apparently absent............................22

**22.** All or nearly all annuli of middle of body subdivided (Fig. 201A); with four pairs of eyes; gray to brownish coloration, more or less thickly spotted with black; feeds on aquatic invertebrates, also a scavenger; up to 100 mm. long; widely distributed................................**Nephelopsis obscura** Verrill

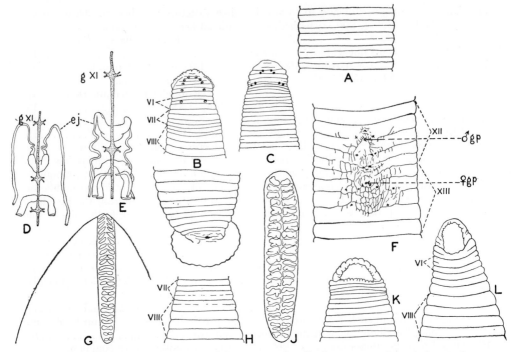

FIG. 201.—Structure of Arhynchobdellida. A, typical midbody segment of *Nephelopsis obscura* Verrill, showing subdivided annuli; B, anterior and posterior ends of *Macrobdella decora* (Say); C, anterior end of *Dina parva* Moore; D, dorsal view of part of reproductive system of *D. parva*; E, dorsal view of part of reproductive system of *D. fervida* (Verrill); F, ventral view of XII and XIII of *Philobdella gracile* Moore, showing copulatory gland region and genital pores; G, edge view of median jaw of *P. gracile*; H, segments VII and VIII of *Haemopis marmorata* (Say); J, edge view of teeth of median jaw of *H. lateralis* (Say); K, ventral view of anterior end of *H. plumbeus* Moore; L, ventral view of anterior end of *H. grandis* (Verrill). *gXI*, eleventh ganglion; *ej*, ejaculatory duct; nervous tissue stippled. (B, C, D, K, and L modified from Moore, 1912; E, F, G, and J modified from Moore, 1901.)

Only with the fifth annulus of each segment in middle of body subdivided; with three or four pairs of eyes, or eyes absent (Fig. 201C); feed mostly on aquatic invertebrates. . . . . . . . . . . . . . . . . . . . . . . . . . . . . . . . . . . . . . . . . . . . . . .**Dina, 23**

23. Without pigmented eyes; up to 25 mm. long; genital pores separated by two annuli; with longitudinal stripes; reported from Calif. .**Dina anoculata** Moore

With eyes; genital pores separated by two or more annuli; without longitudinal stripes; not heavily pigmented. . . . . . . . . . . . . . . . . . . . . . . . . . . . . . . . . . . . .**24**

24. Anterior loops of ejaculatory ducts reaching as far as ganglion XI (Fig. 201D); four pairs of eyes (Fig. 201C); up to 25 mm. long; genital pores separated by three to three and one-half annuli. . . . . . . . . . . . . . . . . . . .**Dina parva** Moore

Ejaculatory ducts without such long anterior loops (Fig. 201E); three or four pairs of eyes; genital pores separated by two or three annuli; up to 70 mm long. .**25**

25. With a small caudal sucker; genital pores separated by three annuli; three pairs of eyes. . . . . . . . . . . . . . . . . . . . . . . . . . . . . . . . . . . . . . . . .**Dina microstoma** Moore

With a large caudal sucker; genital pores separated by two annuli; three or four pairs of eyes. . . . . . . . . . . . . . . . . . . . . . . . . . . . . . . . . . . . . . . . .**Dina fervida** (Verrill)

26. With large jaws and numerous teeth (Fig. 195); numerous pairs of gastric caeca; in small lakes, ponds, and swamps. . . . . . . . . . . . . . . . . . . . . . . . . . . . . . . . . . .**27**

Jaws small and with few teeth, or jaws absent; a single pair of gastric caeca. . . .**29**

27. Coloration variable but usually green with four or six brown stripes; without copulatory glands; each jaw with about 50 small teeth (Fig. 195); up to 100 mm. long; the introduced European medicinal leech; uncommon in northeastern states...................................**Hirudo medicinalis** L.
Dorsal surface with segmental median red and lateral black spots; with large copulatory glands, having ventral openings in the region of XIII and XIV; each jaw with about 38 to 48 teeth, or with about 65 teeth.
**Macrobdella, 28**

28. With five annuli between genital pores; the American medicinal leech (Fig. 201B); up to 230 mm. long; each jaw with about 65 teeth; feeds almost exclusively on vertebrate blood; common in the northern half of the U. S.
**Macrobdella decora** (Say)
With two and one-half annuli between genital pores; up to 150 mm. long; each jaw with about 38 to 48 teeth; rare and poorly known.
**Macrobdella sestertia** Whitman

29. Jaws short and high; teeth small, partly in a single series and partly in a double series (Fig. 201G); genital pores separated by three or four annuli and surrounded by copulatory glands (Fig. 201F); common in Gulf Coast states; the southern bloodsuckers...............................**Philobdella, 30**
Jaws small or absent; when present, teeth coarse and all in a double series (Fig. 201J); genital pores separated by five annuli; often very large; scavengers and feeding on invertebrates, not normally bloodsuckers; widely distributed and common, especially in the northern half of the U. S...........**Haemopis, 31**

30. With about 35 small teeth on each jaw (Fig. 201G); with long yellow stripes and a few brown spots; up to 100 mm. long; common...**Philobdella gracile** Moore
With about 20 small teeth on each jaw; with two faint reddish-brown stripes separated by a narrow black line on each side of the dorsal mid-line; up to 50 mm. long; reported from Fla.; rare..........**Philobdella floridana** Verrill

31. Jaws small, with few teeth (Fig. 201J)...................................**32**
Jaws and teeth absent; incapable of taking vertebrate blood.................**33**

32. With 10 to 16 pairs of teeth on each jaw; last annulus of VII and first annulus of VIII enlarged but not completely subdivided (Fig. 201H); coloration variable but usually blotched with brown or black; up to 160 mm. long; often found in or on mud at edge of water; the common "horse leech"; occasionally attacks man............................. **Haemopis marmorata** (Say)
With 20 to 25 pairs of teeth on each jaw (Fig. 201J); last annulus of VII and first annulus of VIII completely subdivided; few or no dark blotches; up to 200 mm. long; one variety has been found on soil as much as one-half mile from water; feeds on aquatic invertebrates and earthworms.....**Haemopis lateralis** (Say)

33. Lip broad and flat (Fig. 201K); uniform grayish coloration with few or no dorsal blotches; with a reddish or orange band along lateral margins; often found in or on soil away from water; up to 160 mm. long.
**Haemopis plumbeus** Moore
Lip narrow and arched (Fig. 201L); greenish, grayish, or slaty color with dark blotches; up to 300 mm. long; often in or on soil along borders of lakes, ponds, and swamps...............................**Haemopis grandis** (Verrill)

34. Caudal sucker flattened, as wide or wider than the widest part of body........**35**
Caudal sucker concave, narrower than the widest part of body (Figs. 202J, K)..**40**

35. Body divided into two distinct regions (Figs. 202A, B)....................**36**
Body not divided into two distinct regions......................**Piscicola, 37**

36. Segments in middle of body with seven annuli; reported from Ill. (Fig. 202A).
**Cystobranchus verrilli** Meyer
Segments in middle of body with six annuli; reported from *Fundulus* in fresh and salt water in southern New England; (Fig. 202B); rare.
**Trachelobdella vivida** (Verrill)

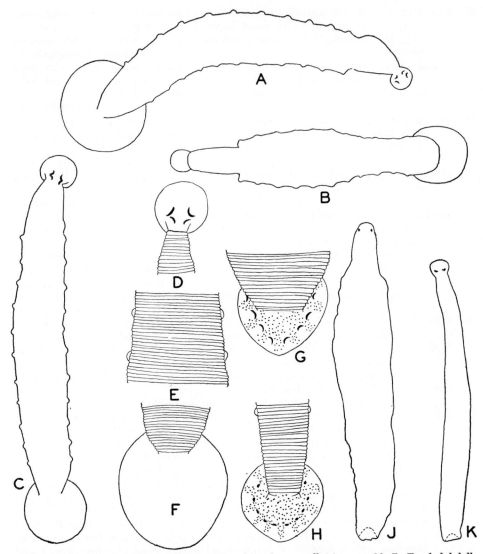

Fɪɢ. 202.—Structure of Piscicolidae. A, *Cystobranchus verrilli* Meyer, ×10; B, *Trachelobdella vivida* (Verrill), ×4; C, *Piscicola punctata* (Verrill), ×6.5; D, E, and F, anterior, middle, and posterior portions of *P. punctata*; G, posterior end of *P. salmositica* Meyer; H posterior end of *P. geometra* (L.); J, *Illinobdella moorei* Meyer, ×6.5; K, *I. alba* Meyer, ×8. (A, C, J, and K modified from Meyer, 1940; D, E, F, and H modified from Meyer, 1946; B modified from Moore, 1899; G modified from Meyer, 1946a.)

37. Caudal sucker without oculiform spots or dark rays; widely distributed in north-eastern states (Fig. 202C)...................**Piscicola punctata** (Verrill)
    Caudal sucker with oculiform spots and (or) dark rays (Figs. 202G, H).......**38**
38. Caudal sucker centrally attached to body; eight to ten crescent-shaped spots on caudal sucker (Fig. 202G); reported from steelhead trout in Wash.
    **Piscicola salmositica** Meyer
    Caudal sucker eccentrically attached to body (Fig. 202H); more common and widely distributed.............................................**39**

**39.** Ten or 12 oculiform markings on caudal sucker, which are not separated by dark rays......................................**Piscicola milneri** (Verrill)
Caudal sucker with 14 dark rays and a corresponding number of oculiform spots (Fig. 202H)................................**Piscicola geometra** (L.)
**40.** Segments in middle of body composed of three or 12 annuli................**41**
Segments in middle of body composed of 14 annuli; widely distributed and common in eastern half of U. S......................**Illinobdella, 42**
**41.** Segments in middle of body composed of three annuli; length:width ratio about 4:1; reported from N. J. and Ill...............**Piscicolaria reducta** Meyer
Segments in middle of body composed of 12 annuli; length:width ratio about 18:1; Ill...............................**Illinobdella elongata** Meyer
**42.** Body divided into two regions of different width; length:width ratio about 5:1 (Fig. 202J)...............................**Illinobdella moorei** Meyer
Body not divided into two regions.......................................**43**
**43.** Length:width ratio about 15:1; annuli distinct....**Illinobdella richardsoni** Meyer
Length:width ratio about 9:1 (Fig. 202K); annuli distinct.

**Illinobdella alba** Meyer

# ANNELIDA REFERENCES

ALSTERBERG, G. 1922. Die respiratorischen Mechanismen der Tubificiden. *Lunds Univ. Årsskrift, N. F. Avd 2* 18:1–176.

ALTMAN, L. C. 1936. Oligochaeta of Washington. *Univ. Wash. Publ. Biol.* 4:41–137.

BEDDARD, E. F. 1892. A new branchiate oligochaeta (Branchiura sowerbyi). *Quart. Jour. Micros. Sci.* 33:325–340.

———. 1895. *A monograph of the Order Oligochaeta.* 769 pp. Oxford, England.

BOLDT, W. 1940. Oligochaeta. *Biol. Tiere Deutschlands* 12a:1–39.

BOUSFIELD, E. C. 1887. The natural history of the genus Dero. *Jour. Linn. Soc.* (Zool.) 20:91–107.

CASTLE, W. E. 1900. Some North American fresh-water Rhynchobdellidae, and their parasites. *Bull. Harvard Mus. Comp. Zool.* 36:15–64.

CHEN, Y. 1940. Taxonomy and faunal relations of the limnetic Oligochaeta of China. *Contr. Biol. Lab. Sci. Soc. China, Zool. Ser.* 14:1–132.

———. 1944. Notes on naidomorph Oligochaeta of Philadelphia and vicinity. *Notulae Naturae* 136:1–8.

DAUSEND, K. 1931. Über die Atmung der Tubifiziden. *Zeitschr. vergl. Physiol.* 14:557–608.

EISEN, G. 1885. Oligochaetological researches. *Rept. U. S. Fish. Comm. for 1883* 11:879–964.

ELLIS, M. M. 1912. A new discodrilid worm from Colorado. *Proc. U. S. Nat. Mus.* 42:481–486.

———. 1919. The branchiobdellid worms in the collections of the United States National Museum, with descriptions of new genera and new species. *Ibid.* 55:241–265.

FEUERBORN, H. J. 1931. Ein Rhizocephale und zwei Polychaeten aus dem Süsswasser von Java und Sumatra. *Verh. Int. Verein. theor. angew. Limn.* 5:618–660.

GALLOWAY, T. W. 1911. The common freshwater Oligochaeta of the U. S. *Trans. Amer. Micros. Soc.* 30:285–317.

GOODNIGHT, C. J. 1940. The Branchiobdellidae (Oligochaeta) of North American crayfishes. *Ill. Biol. Monogr.* 17:1–75.

———. 1941. The Branchiobdellidae (Oligochaeta) of Florida. *Trans. Amer. Micros. Soc.* 60:69–74.

———. 1943. Report on a collection of Branchiobdellidae. *Jour. Parasit.* 29:100–102.

HALL, M. C. 1914. Description of a new genus and species of the discodrilid worms. *Proc. U. S. Nat. Mus.* 48:187–193.

HARDING, W. A., and J. P. MOORE. 1927. Hirudinea. *Fauna of British India.* 302 pp.

HARTMAN, O. 1936. New species of polychaetous annelids of the family Nereidae from California. *Proc. U. S. Nat. Mus.* 83:467–480.

———. 1938. Brackish and freshwater Nereidae from the northeast Pacific with the description of a new species from central California. *Univ. Calif. Publ. Zool.* 43:79–82.

HAYDEN, H. E. 1914. Further notes on Pristina with descriptions of three new species. *Trans. Amer. Micros. Soc.* 33:135–138.

———. 1922. Studies on American naid oligochaetes. I. Preliminary note on naids of Douglas Lake Michigan. *Ibid.* 41:167–171.

HERLANT-MEEWIS, H. 1950. Cyst-formation in Aeolosoma hemprichi (Ehr.). *Biol. Bull.* 99:172–180.

HERTER, K. 1932. Hirudinea. *Biologie der Tiere Deutschlands* 12b:1–158.

HOTZ, H. 1938. Protoclepsis tesselata (O. F. Müller); Ein Beitrag zur Kenntnis von Bau und Lebensweise der Hirudineen. *Rev. Suisse de Zool.* (Suppl.) 45:1–380.

JOHNSON, H. P. 1903. Fresh-water nereids from the Pacific Coast and Hawaii, with remarks on fresh-water Polychaeta in general. *Mark Anniv. Vol.* 205–222.

KENK, R. 1941. Notes on three species of Aeolosoma (Oligochaeta) from Michigan. *Occ. Pap. Mus. Zool. Univ. Mich.* 435:1–7.

KEYL, F. 1913. Beiträge zur Kenntnis von Branchiura sowerbyi Bedd. *Zeitschr. wiss. Zool.* 107:199–304.

KRECKER, F. H. 1939. Polychaete annelid worms in the Great Lakes. *Science* 89:153.

LEIDY, J. 1883. Manayunkia speciosa. *Proc. Phila. Acad. Nat. Sci.* (1883):204–212.

MARCUS, E. 1942. Sôbre algumas Tubificidae do Brasil. *Univ. São Paulo, Bol. Fac. Filos. Cien. e Letras, Zool.* 6:153–228.

——. 1943. Sôbre Naididae do Brasil. *Ibid.* 7:1–247.

——. 1944. Sôbre Oligochaeta limnicos do Brasil. *Ibid.* 8:5–135.

MEEHEAN, O. L. 1929. Manayunkia speciosa (Leidy) in the Duluth harbor. *Science* 70:479–480.

MEYER, M. C. 1940. A revision of the leeches (Piscicolidae) living on fresh-water fishes of North America. *Trans. Amer. Micros. Soc.* 59:354–376.

——. 1946. Further notes on the leeches (Piscicolidae) living on fresh-water fishes of North America. *Ibid.* 65:237–249.

——. 1946a. A new leech, Piscicola salmositica n. sp. (Piscicolidae), from steelhead trout (Salmo gairdneri gairdneri Richardson, 1838). *Jour. Parasitol.* 32:467–473.

MILLER, J. A. 1929. The leeches of Ohio. *Contrib. Franz Theodore Stone Lab.* 2:1–38.

——. 1937. A study of the leeches of Michigan with key to orders, suborders and species. *Ohio Jour. Sci.* 37:85–90.

MOORE, J. P. 1894. On some leech-like parasites of American crayfish. *Proc. Acad. Nat. Sci. Phila.* (1893):419–428.

——. 1895. The anatomy of Bdellodrilus illuminatus, an American discodrilid. *Jour. Morph.* 10:497–540.

——. 1898. The leeches of the U. S. National Museum. *Proc. U. S. Nat. Mus.* 21:543–563.

——. 1898a. The Hirudinea of Illinois. *Bull. Ill. State Lab. Nat. Hist.* 5:479–547.

——. 1906. Hirudinea and Oligochaeta collected in the Great Lakes region. *Bull. U. S. Bur. Fish.* 25:153–172.

——. 1923. The control of blood-sucking leeches, with an account of the leeches of Palisades Interstate Park. *Roosevelt Wild Life Bull.* 2:1–53.

——. 1924. The leeches (Hirudinea) of Lake Nipigon. *Univ. Toronto Studies, Biol. Ser.* 25:15–31.

NACHTREIB, H. F., E. E. HEMINGWAY, and J. P. Moore. 1912. The leeches of Minnesota. *Geol. Nat. Hist. Surv. Minn. Zool. Ser.* 5:1–150.

REYNOLDSON, T. B. 1947. An ecological study of the enchytraeid worm population of sewage bacteria beds. *Jour. Animal Ecol.* 16:26–37.

SMITH, F. 1900. Notes on species of North American Oligochaeta III. *Bull. Ill. State Lab. Nat. Hist.* 5:441–458.

——. 1918. A new North American oligochaete of the genus Haplotaxis. *Bull. Ill. State Nat. Hist. Surv.* 13:43–49.

SMITH, R. I. 1942. Nervous control of chromatophores in the leech Placobdella parasitica. *Physiol. Zool.* 15:410–417.

SPENCER, W. P. 1932. A gilled oligochaete Branchiura sowerbyi new to America. *Trans. Amer. Micros. Soc.* 51:267–272.

SPERBER, C. 1948. A taxonomical study of the Naididae. *Zool. Bidrag f. Uppsala* 28:1–296.

STEPHENSON, J. 1923. Oligochaeta. *Fauna of British India*, 518 pp.

——. 1930. *The Oligochaeta*. 978 pp. Oxford, England.

TURNER, C. D. 1935. A new species of fresh-water oligochaete from the southeastern United States with a description of its sexual organs. *Zool. Anz.* 109:253–258.

VON WAGNER, P. 1916. Zur Oecologie des Tubifex und Lumbriculus. *Zool. Jahrb. Abt. Syst.* 23:295–318.

WALTON, L. B. 1906. The Naididae of Cedar Point, Ohio. *Amer. Nat.* 40:683–706.

WELCH, P. S. 1920. The genera of the Enchytraeidae (Oligochaeta). *Trans. Amer. Micros. Soc.* 39:25–50.

——. 1923. New records of North American Enchytraeidae. *Ibid.* 42:91–94.

# Chapter 14

# INTRODUCTION TO THE CRUSTACEA

FOUR obvious features clearly distinguish the members of the Class Crustacea: with few exceptions, they are all aquatic arthropods; respiration occurs through gills or through the general body surface; they all have two pairs of antennae; most of the body segments, or at least the more anterior ones, bear paired, jointed appendages which are fundamentally biramous.

The great majority of the 30,000 known species of the world are marine, and of the 23 orders occurring in the United States and surrounding waters, 11 are represented in fresh waters, but only three are restricted to our fresh waters. The number of species represented for each of the 11 orders in the United States ranges from two (Mysidacea) to about 160 (Eucopepoda, Podocopa, and Decapoda), the total number being about 760. These 11 orders are treated in detail in Chapters 15 to 22, so the present chapter is merely a summary and tabulation of their chief distinguishing characteristics and affinities.

A few carcinologists distinguish fine gradations in meaning in the usage of "somite," "metamere," and "body segment" to denote the primary body divisions of adult Crustacea. Nevertheless, these expressions are more generally used interchangeably and without confusion; in this manual "body segment," "trunk segment," or simply "segment" are used consistently.

In the primitive condition the trunk segments are distinct, but the segments forming the head are completely fused. The trunk is usually subdivided into thorax and abdomen so that there are three body regions, though fusion of some thoracic and abdominal segments is the common condition. One or more thoracic segments, for example, are often fused with the head to form a cephalothorax, which in many crustaceans is completely or partly covered by a shieldlike carapace. In groups such as the Cladocera and Ostracoda body segmentation has disappeared. The general body plan of the various orders is outlined in Table IV.

In the strict sense, the most posterior division of the body which bears the anus is not considered a true body segment and is usually referred to as the telson. This term is universally used in the orders of Malacostraca where this structure is comparatively small and flattened and does not bear any processes. In the other orders, however, the telson typically resembles the preceding body segment; furthermore, it bears a pair of terminal caudal rami, cercopods, or heavy claws. In common usage it is often referred to as a "segment" in the non-malacostracan orders. The writer can see no real objection to this practice.

The paired appendages are serially homologous; each is fundamentally biramous and consists of a basal protopod, a segmented endopod, and a segmented exopod. They are usually more or less specialized for a wide variety of functions, many such modifications being figured and considered rather completely in Chapters 15 to 22.

TABLE III. Fundamental Environmental Affinities of the Orders of Crustacea Found in the United States and Surrounding Waters.

| Restricted to marine waters | Chiefly marine; few fresh-water representatives | Well represented in both marine and fresh waters | Chiefly in fresh waters; few marine representatives | Exclusively fresh water | Approximate number of species occurring in U. S. fresh waters |
|---|---|---|---|---|---|
| Myodocopa<br>Cladocopa | Mysidacea | | | | 2 |
| Platycopa | | Podocopa | | | 160 |
| Thoracica | | Eucopepoda | | | 160 |
| Ascothoracica | | Branchiura | | | 15 |
| Acrothoracica | | Isopoda | | | 50 |
| Rhizocephala | | Amphipoda | | | 50 |
| Nebaliacea | | Decapoda | | | 160 |
| Cumacea | | | | | |
| Tanaidacea | | | Cladocera | | 120 |
| Euphausiacea | | | | | |
| Stomatopoda | | | | Anostraca | 20 |
| Mystacocarida | | | | Notostraca | 5 |
| | | | | Conchostraca | 20 |

Because of variations in early embryology from one order to another and because of the variety of interpretations which may be drawn from such embryological material, the "head problem" of arthropods is still unsettled. Some investigators maintain that the adult crustacean head represents the fusion of five segments or four segments plus a large anterior cephalic lobe (Snodgrass, 1951); others hold to an older theory that the head represents six fused segments. Henry (1948) maintains that the older theory is the more acceptable, and that none of the six segments forming the head are "preoral." Aside from this controversy, the typical adult crustacean head bears five pairs of serially homologous appendages. Beginning at the anterior end, these are: first antennae, second antennae, mandibles, first maxillae, and second maxillae. Compound eyes are not considered true segmental appendages. In the Cladocera the second maxillae are lacking, and in the Ostracoda the second maxillae are completely lacking. More posteriorly the situation is variable, with some groups having an additional complement of thoracic or body appendages modified as mouth parts, and others not. Further, the number of thoracic and abdominal appendages and their modifications vary widely from one group to another, even within single genera.

Some textbooks still use the old method of dividing the Crustacea into two subclasses, Entomostraca and Malacostraca. The latter group is a clearly defined and natural section of the Crustacea, all of its members having abdominal appendages, a gastric mill, an eight-segmented thorax, and an abdomen of six (rarely seven or eight) segments. The Entomostraca, however, is a heterogeneous assemblage of orders which differ from one another as widely as each of them does from the Malacostraca, and for this reason the use of "Entomostraca" as a specific taxonomic category should be discouraged. Nevertheless, "entomostraca" is a convenient general descriptive term which might be legitimately used to designate collectively all small fresh-water Crustacea.

The taxonomic categories used for the Class Crustacea in this manual (Table VI) are generally accepted by the majority of carcinologists. The only important point of disagreement lies in the grouping of the

TABLE IV. GROSS MORPHOLOGICAL FEATURES OF THE ORDERS OF FRESH-WATER CRUSTACEA OF THE UNITED STATES.

| Order | Main body features | Length range, in mm. | Number of thoracic segments fused with head to form cephalothorax | Number of free thoracic segments | Number of abdominal segments | Number of pairs of thoracic appendages — modified for use as mouth parts | Number of pairs of thoracic appendages — not used as mouth parts | Number of pairs of abdominal appendages | Posterior end |
|---|---|---|---|---|---|---|---|---|---|
| Anostraca | Head and trunk; body cylindrical. | 7–100 | 0 | 19 trunk segments | | 0 | 11 pairs of trunk appendages | | telson and caudal rami |
| Notostraca | Head and trunk; shieldlike carapace covering most of body; depressed dorsoventrally. | 10–58 | 0 | 25 to 44 trunk segments | | 0 | 35 to 71 pairs of trunk appendages | | telson and caudal rami |
| Conchostraca | Head and trunk; body enclosed in a bivalve carapace; laterally compressed. | 2–16 | 0 | 10 to 32 trunk segments | | 0 | 10 to 32 pairs of trunk appendages | | telson and caudal rami |
| Cladocera | Head, trunk, and postabdomen; segmentation obscure; body laterally compressed and covered with a folded carapace. | 0.2–18.0 | — | — | — | 0 | 5 or 6 | 0 | postabdomen and claws |
| Podocopa | Head indistinctly set off from trunk; segmentation obscure; body laterally compressed and covered with a bivalve shell. | 0.3–4.2 | — | — | — | — | 3 | 0 | caudal rami |
| Eucopepoda | Cephalothorax, thorax, and abdomen; body cylindrical. | 0.3–3.2 | 1 or 2 | usually 5 | 3 to 5 | 1 | 5 | 0 | caudal rami |
| Branchiura | Cephalothorax, thorax, and abdomen; large, expanded cephalothoracic carapace; body strongly depressed; parasitic. | 5–25 | 1 or 2 | 3 (4th and 5th fused with abdomen) | fused | 1 | 4 | 0 | caudal rami |
| Mysidacea | Cephalothorax, thorax, and abdomen; carapace covering cephalothorax and most of thorax; body slightly compressed laterally. | 10–30 | 1 | 7 | 6 | 2 | 6 | 6 | telson |
| Isopoda | Cephalothorax, thorax, and abdomen; body depressed. | 5–20 | 1 | 7 | 6 (usually fused) | 1 | 7 | 6 | telson (obscure) |
| Amphipoda | Cephalothorax, thorax, and abdomen; body slightly compressed laterally. | 5–25 | 1 | 7 | 6 | 1 | 7 | 6 | telson |
| Decapoda | Cephalothorax and abdomen; carapace covering all of cephalothorax; body subcylindrical. | 15–130 | 8 | 0 | 6 | 3 | 5 | 6 | telson |

## TABLE V. ARRANGEMENT AND TERMINOLOGY OF SEGMENTAL APPENDAGES OF TYPICAL FRESH-WATER CRUSTACEA.

| Body region | | Eubranchiopoda | Cladocera | Copepoda | Ostracoda | Mysidacea | Isopoda | Amphipoda | Decapoda |
|---|---|---|---|---|---|---|---|---|---|
| Head | | 1st antennae | 1st antennae | 1st antennae | 1st antennae | 1st antennae | 1st antennae | 1st antennae | 1st antennae |
| | | 2d " | 2d " | 2d " | 2d " | 2d " | 2d " | 2d " | 2d " |
| | | mandibles | mandibles | mandibles | mandibles | mandibles | mandibles | mandibles | mandibles |
| | | 1st maxillae | maxillae | 1st maxillae | maxillae | 1st maxillae | 1st maxillae | 1st maxillae | 1st maxillae |
| | | 2d " | – * | 2d " | – | 2d " | 2d " | 2d " | 2d " |
| Trunk segments | 1 | | 1st legs | maxillipeds *** | 1st legs | 1st maxillipeds | maxillipeds | maxillipeds | 1st maxillipeds |
| | 2 | | 2d " | 1st legs | 2d " | 2d " | 1st legs (gnathopods) | 1st legs (gnathopods) | 2d " |
| | 3 | | 3d " | 2d " | 3d " | 1st legs | 2d " (pereiopods) | 2d " | 3d " |
| | 4 | | 4th " | 3d " | | 2d " | 3d " " | 3d " (pereiopods) | 1st legs (pereiopods) |
| | 5 | | 5th " ** | 4th " | | 3d " | 4th " " | 4th " " | 2d " |
| | 6 | | 6th " | 5th " | | 4th " | 5th " " | 5th " " | 3d " |
| | 7 | 10 to 71 pairs of appendages on 10 to 44 trunk segments | – | – | | 5th " | 6th " " | 6th " " | 4th " |
| | 8 | | – | – | | 6th " | 7th " " | 7th " " | 5th " |
| | 9 | | – | – | | 1st pleopods | 1st pleopods | 1st pleopods | 1st pleopods |
| | 10 | | | – | | 2d " | 2d " | 2d " | 2d " |
| | 11 | | | – | | 3d " | 3d " | 3d " | 3d " |
| | 12 | | | | | 4th " | 4th " | 1st uropods | 4th " |
| | 13 | | | | | 5th " | 5th " | 2d " | 5th " |
| | 14 | | | | | uropods | uropods | 3d " | uropods |

* The fifth pair of head appendages is lacking in the Cladocera.
** These appendages are present only in three small families of Cladocera.
*** Some copepod specialists consider the maxillipeds as head appendages.

orders Anostraca, Notostraca, and Conchostraca in the Division Eubranchiopoda as opposed to the Division Oligobranchiopoda which contains the single Order Cladocera. Justification for this taxonomic arrangement is outlined on page 339.

TABLE VI. CLASSIFICATION OF CRUSTACEA OCCURRING IN THE FRESH WATERS OF THE UNITED STATES.

Class Crustacea
    Subclass Branchiopoda
        Division Eubranchiopoda
            Order Anostraca (fairy shrimps)
            Order Notostraca (tadpole shrimps)
            Order Conchostraca (clam shrimps)
        Division Oligobranchiopoda
            Order Cladocera (water fleas)
    Subclass Ostracoda
        Order Podocopa (seed shrimps)
    Subclass Copepoda
        Order Eucopepoda (copepods)
        Order Branchiura (fish lice)
    Subclass Malacostraca
        Division Peracarida
            Order Mysidacea (opossum shrimps)
            Order Isopoda (aquatic sow bugs)
            Order Amphipoda (scuds, sideswimmers)
        Division Eucarida
            Order Decapoda (fresh-water shrimps, crayfish)

# GENERAL CRUSTACEA REFERENCES

CALMAN, W. T. 1911. *The Life of Crustacea.* 289 pp. London.

CRAMPTON, G. C. 1928. The evolution of the head region in lower arthropods and its bearing upon the origin and relationships of the arthropodan groups. *Canad. Ent.* **40**:284–302.

HENRY, L. M. 1948. The nervous system and the segmentation of the head in the Annulata. *Microentomology* **13**:1–26.

KÜKENTHAL, W., and T. KRUMBACH. 1926–1927. Crustacea. *Handbuch der Zoologie* 3(1):277–1078.

SCHMITT, W. L. 1938. Crustaceans. *Smithsonian Scientific Series* **10**:85–248.

SMITH, G., and W. F. R. WELDON. 1909. Crustacea. *Cambridge Nat. Hist.* **4**:1–217.

SNODGRASS, R. E. 1938. Evolution of the Annelida, Onychophora, and Arthropoda. *Smithson. Misc. Coll.* **97**:1–159.

———. 1951. *Comparative studies on the head of mandibulate arthropods.* 118 pp. Ithaca, N. Y.

# Chapter 15

## EUBRANCHIOPODA (FAIRY, TADPOLE, AND CLAM SHRIMPS)

THE EUBRANCHIOPODA are among the most characteristic inhabitants of temporary ponds and pools, especially during spring and early summer. They move along the bottom or swim and glide about gracefully, often with the ventral side uppermost. They are absent from running waters, and there are no true marine representatives, although one species, *Artemia salina* Leach, is restricted to highly saline lakes and evaporation basins used for the commercial production of salt.

Except for the immature stages in some families of insects, this is the only major taxonomic category found exclusively in fresh waters in the United States. All others have marine representatives, terrestrial representatives, or both.

**General characteristics.** All members of this primitive division are distinctly segmented and have ten to 71 pairs of delicate, flat, lobate, swimming and respiratory appendages. Because of the leaflike appearance of these appendages, the members of this division are collectively known as phyllopods. The last body segment bears a pair of short to long cercopods. Body length, exclusive of cercopods, ranges between 2 and 100 mm. Females are usually more abundant than males in natural populations, and sometimes males are rare.

The Division Eubranchiopoda consists of three sharply defined orders (Figs. 203, 205). The Anostraca (fairy shrimps) have stalked compound eyes, 11 pairs of swimming legs (in American species), and no caparace. The Notostraca (tadpole shrimps) have sessile compound eyes, a large, shieldlike carapace covering most of the body, and 35 to 71 pairs of legs. Neither the number of legs nor the number of segments is constant within a species. The Conchostraca (clam shrimps) are laterally compressed, have sessile compound eyes, ten to 32 pairs of legs, and are enclosed in a carapace consisting of two lateral valves. This carapace is flexible along the middorsal line, but rarely is there a well-defined hinge line. Many species have concentric growth lines that are important in taxonomy. Opening and closing of the valves are governed by a short transverse adductor muscle.

Coloration ranges from translucent or whitish through gray, blue, green, orange, and reddish. Coloration of some species is highly variable and probably governed to a large extent by the type of food being ingested. All of the individuals in a particular pond usually have the same general coloration at any one time, although some species exhibit progressive color changes during the adult instars.

The first antennae are small, uniramous, and often unsegmented (Figs. 205, 206). In female Anostraca the second antennae are cylindrical and somewhat elongated, but in the males they are greatly enlarged and specialized for clasping the females during copulation (Figs. 206, 215). The

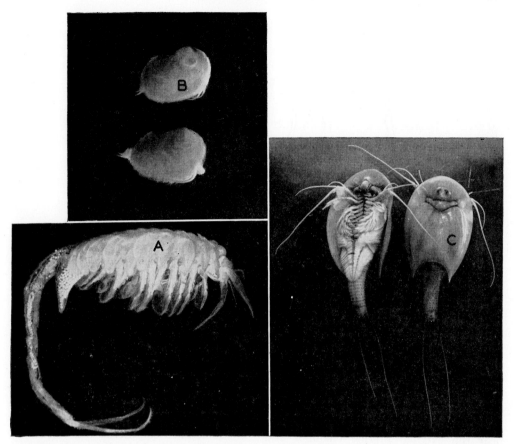

FIG. 203.—Typical Eubranchiopoda. A, female *Branchinecta gigas* Lynch, ×1; B, large clam shrimps, ×25; C, *Apus longicaudatus* LeConte, ×1.5.

males of some species of Anostraca have a median frontal appendage on the head (Fig. 216B), or an antennal appendage arising near the base of each second antenna (Figs. 206, 216E). In the Notostraca the second antennae are minute or absent in both sexes, but in the Conchostraca they are long, biramous, and setose (Fig. 205C).

In ventral view the mouth parts are largely concealed by the labrum. The mandibles have undivided molar surfaces and no palp, the first maxillae are triangular plates with setose biting edges, and the second maxillae are small simple plates which are of little importance in feeding (Fig. 204).

According to prevailing usage, the boundary between head and trunk of phyllopods lies immediately behind the segment that bears the second maxillae, the first trunk segment being the one that bears the first pair of legs. Although the head forms a well-defined body region, the trunk is not clearly divisible into thorax and abdomen as it is in most entomostraca. The trunk segments are all similar morphologically and vary widely in number from one genus to another. Furthermore, the number of pairs of legs and the proportion of trunk segments bearing them also vary widely. The location of the genital pores, however, is sometimes used as a basis for loosely designating a

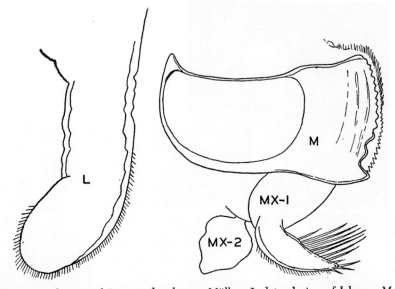

Fig. 204.—Mouth parts of *Lynceus brachyurus* Müller. L, lateral view of labrum; M, MX-1, and MX-2, right mandible, first maxilla, and second maxilla as seen from below. (Modified from Sars.)

"thorax" (pregenital segments) and an "abdomen" (postgenital segments) in some families. In the Anostraca the first two abdominal segments (collectively the genital segment) are partially fused and bear the external uterine chamber and base of the ovisac in the female, and penes in the male.

All Anostraca of the United States have 20 trunk segments, including 11 which bear legs, the two genital segments, and seven other posterior segments, the last of which is the telson. The Conchostraca have ten to 32 trunk segments and ten to 32 pairs of legs.

The body divisions, segmentation, and leg arrangement of the Notostraca represent a peculiar situation among fresh-water crustaceans. Posterior to the second maxillae there are 25 to 44 so-called "segments," not counting the terminal telson. Unlike typical segments, however, many of them have two or more pairs of legs, and especially posteriorly some of them bear five, ten, or more pairs of legs per segment (Figs. 203C, 207). The total number of pairs of legs ranges from 35 to 71

among the American species of Notostraca. Following the suggestions of Linder (1952), it therefore seems preferable to refer to "body rings" in the Notostraca rather than "segments." The first 11 rings are sometimes considered the thorax, the remainder being the abdomen. In general, all body rings are of comparable length. A variable number of posterior abdominal rings are without legs. A single species usually shows considerable variation with respect to: number of body rings, total number of legs, number of legs on a particular body ring, number of leg-bearing abdominal rings, and number of legless abdominal rings. In *Apus longicaudatus* LeConte, for example, the number of legless abdominal rings varies from four to 16. The number of body rings is usually more constant in a parthenogenetic population than in one containing males.

Tadpole shrimps sometimes have an incomplete body ring just anterior to the telson. Only the dorsal or ventral part of the ring may be present. About one per cent of the specimens in many collections show "spiral rings" (Fig. 208), usually

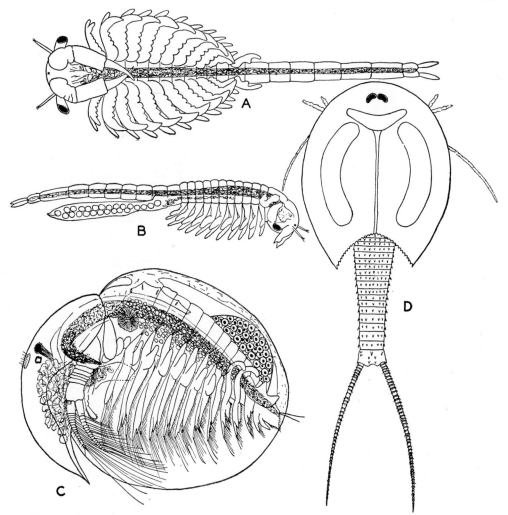

Fig. 205.—Typical Eubranchiopoda. A, ventral view of male *Branchinecta paludosa* (O. F. M.), ×8, (setation omitted); B, lateral view of female *B. paludosa*, ×6 (setation omitted) showing brood sac; C, female *Lynceus brachyurus*, ×25, with left valve removed (diagrammatic); D, dorsal view of *Apus*, ×3. (A to C modified from Sars.)

near the telson. These consist of one to four spirals, running either to the left or to the right.

The telson of the fairy shrimps bears two terminal platelike plumose cercopods (caudal rami, furcal rami). In the tadpole shrimps the cercopods are very long, filamentous, segmented, and spiny. In the clam shrimps the telson is laterally compressed and bears two flattened upward curved processes and two stout anal spines (Fig. 218F).

Most phyllopod trunk appendages, or swimming legs, are basically similar (Fig. 209). They are biramous, flat, translucent, lobed, and setose. The median margin bears a series of small lobes, or endites, the basal endite of the Notostraca and Conchostraca being a more robust gnathobase. Near the base of the lateral margin

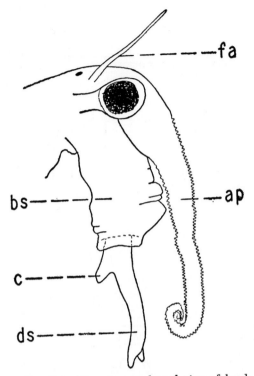

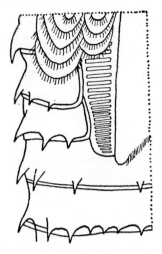

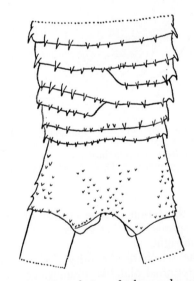

Fig. 206.—Diagrammatic lateral view of head of male *Chirocephalopsis bundyi* (Forbes). *ap*, antennal appendage; *bs*, basal segment of second antenna; *c*, calcar of distal segment of second antenna; *ds*, distal segment of second antenna; *fa*, first antenna.

Fig. 207.—Ventral view of a portion of the right side of a female *Lepidurus lynchi* Linder from which the last 25 legs have been removed. The small rectangles represent the attachment areas of the removed legs. (Redrawn from Linder, 1952.)

Fig. 208.—Ventral view of telson and a portion of the abdomen of *Apus longicaudatus* LeConte showing a spiral of two rounds located between normal body rings and beginning and ending in the midventral line. (Modified from Linder, 1952.)

are one or two large lobes, the proepipodites, and more distally is the thin, oval or elongated, nonsetose branchia (epipodite). The two large distal lobes are the exopodite (flabellum) and endopodite.

A few of the legs of all phyllopods are modified from this basic plan. In the Anostraca the more posterior pairs are definitely smaller and less lobate than preceding pairs. In the Notostraca the first one or two pairs of legs have elongated filamentous rami which probably serve as tactile structures (Fig. 210A). The flabellum of the eleventh pair of legs of the female is modified into a cuplike brood pouch which carries the eggs after they leave the reproductive tract (Fig. 210C). The more posterior legs of the Notostraca taper progressively to a very small size.

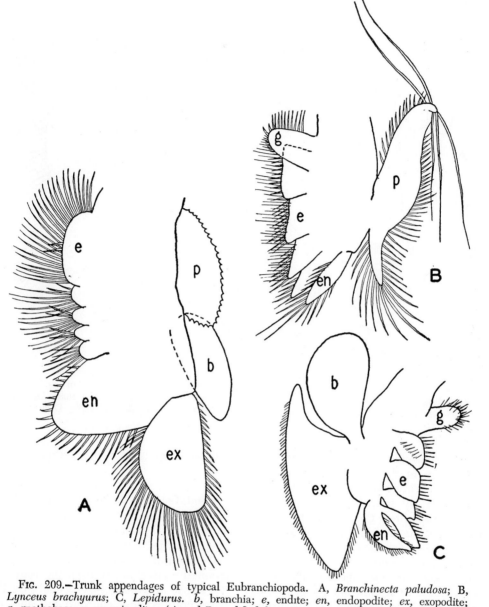

FIG. 209.—Trunk appendages of typical Eubranchiopoda. A, *Branchinecta paludosa*; B, *Lynceus brachyurus*; C, *Lepidurus*. *b*, branchia; *e*, endite; *en*, endopodite; *ex*, exopodite; *g*, gnathobase; *p*, proepipodite. (A and B modified from Sars; C modified from Packard.)

The first one or two pairs of legs of male Conchostraca are hooked and prehensile (Fig. 210D), and in the female elongated flabella of two or three pairs of posterior legs aid in keeping the developing eggs in place between body and carapace (Fig. 205C).

**Locomotion.** Fairy shrimps and tadpole shrimps glide or swim gracefully by means of complex beating movements of the legs which pass in a wavelike anterior-posterior direction. Sometimes they drift along slowly; other times they dart rapidly or come to rest on the bottom. Lowndes

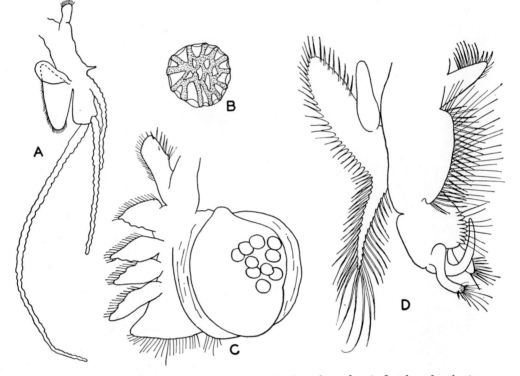

Fig. 210.—Specialized reproductive structures of Eubranchiopoda. A, first leg of male *Apus*; B, resting egg of *Eulimnadia*; C, eleventh leg of female *Apus*; D, first leg of male *Lynceus brachyurus*. (A and C modified from Packard; B redrawn from Mattox, 1939; D modified from Sars.)

(1933) presents evidence to show that locomotion in the Anostraca is not produced by beating of the legs as a whole, but rather by propeller-like movements of the exopodites, the speed of the animal being determined by the angle at which the exopodites are held. In the clam shrimps locomotion is accomplished mainly by "rowing" movements of the large biramous second antennae, the legs being of little importance. Fairy shrimps habitually swim with the ventral side upward, but members of the other two orders are often seen swimming with the ventral side downward. Tadpole shrimps creep or burrow superficially in soft substrates much of the time. Clam shrimps also burrow or move along the surface of the substrate in a clumsy manner. When the antennae stop beating they fall on their side.

**Food, feeding.** Food consists mostly of algae, bacteria, Protozoa, rotifers, and bits of detritus. Movements of the legs serve as a food-getting mechanism, plankton and materials from the substrate being strained nonselectively from the water by the setose appendages (especially by the basal endites) and concentrated and agglutinated in a median ventral groove running most of the length of the body. This stream of food moves forward, activated chiefly by the gnathobases, and is further agglutinated at the anterior end by a sticky secretion produced by labral glands. Mastication occurs outside the digestive tract in an atrium formed by the overhanging labrum. It is probable that phyllopods feed continuously, but all of the food reaching the mouth is not necessarily ingested, the excess being sloughed off. Although microscopic organisms and detritus constitute the sole food of Anostraca and Conchostraca, the Notostraca also utilize larger particles and have even been observed gnawing on dead tadpoles, earthworms, mollusks, and frog eggs. Anostraca often feed on the bottom detritus with the ventral side downward.

**Internal anatomy, physiology.** The digestive tract consists of a vertical esophagus, a small lobate stomach lying in the head, a long intestine, a short rectum, and anus. Two digestive glands in the head empty into the stomach.

A dorsal tubular heart extends throughout most or all of the body segments in the Anostraca, but in the Notostraca and Conchostraca it is much shorter, sometimes extending through only four segments. A variable number of paired, lateral, slitlike ostia bring blood from the hemocoel into the heart, and blood is forced anteriorly and out of the opening at the anterior end of the heart by peristaltic contractions. Colorless amoebocytes occur in phyllopod blood, and an erythrocruorin is known to be dissolved in the plasma of some species.

The exchange of oxygen and carbon dioxide probably takes place through all exposed surfaces of the body but especially through the surfaces of the legs and their branchiae.

The chief excretory organs are the two coiled shell glands which empty their contents at the base of the second maxillae. It is possible that the paired antennal glands and mandibular glands also function in excretion during the early instars of some species. Osmotic regulation presumably occurs through the wall of the digestive tract.

The ladder-like nervous system is diagrammatic and primitive (Fig. 211). The two widely separated nerve cords run the

Fig. 211.—Nervous system of *Branchinecta*. (Modified from Sars.)

full length of the body, and except for the more posterior segments, there are two ganglia and two transverse commissures per segment.

In the Anostraca the compound eyes are stalked and far apart, but in the other two orders they are quite close together, sometimes touching or partially fused. A small median ocellus of the nauplius persists in the adult. Experiments have shown that the upside down swimming position of some species is a phototropic response governed by stimuli received by both the ocellus and compound eyes, and if the

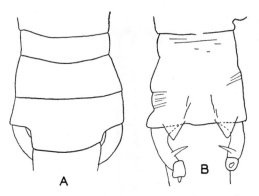

FIG. 212.—Genital segments of male *Branchinecta paludosa*. A, dorsal view; B, ventral view showing penes. (Redrawn from Linder.)

upper side of the container is covered and weak illumination is supplied from below, many of the animals will turn over and swim with the ventral side downward. Swimming on the back is normal in darkness. Immature individuals usually react more strongly to a light source than do the mature animals. Taste areas appear to be concentrated in the region of the mouth parts, and touch is distributed over the whole body. The "dorsal organ" is a small patch of modified cephalic epithelium of unknown function, but it is probably sensory.

**Reproduction.** None of the Eubranchiopoda are known to be hermaphroditic. Testes and ovaries are two posterior tubules, one on each side of the digestive tract; in the Notostraca the gonads are ramified. Males have two short vasa deferentia and two small seminal vesicles in the genital segment; sperm leave the body through two simple genital pores in the Notostraca and Conchostraca, but through penes in the Anostraca (Fig. 212).

Many of the reproductive phenomena in the phyllopods are poorly understood. The occurrence of males, for example, cannot usually be correlated with any seasonal, ecological, or reproductive events. In many species males are not abundant in natural populations. Parthenogenesis is therefore common, and, in a few species of Notostraca, sometimes the rule. Even in a mixed population, however, both parthenogenetic and syngamic reproduction may occur at the same time.

Clasping, paired males and females may swim about firmly united together for several days at a time. In the Anostraca the male assumes a dorsal position with the second antennae clasped around the female in the region of the genital segment. The actual processes of copulation and transfer of sperm are completed in a few seconds or minutes. In the fairy shrimps the male turns the body at an angle to that of the female and recurves the posterior end so that the genital segment is brought into contact with the external uterine chamber of the female. The process is somewhat similar in the tadpole shrimps, and in the clam shrimps the body of the male is placed at a right angle and vertical to that of the female before sperm can be transferred. Males usually die a few hours after copulation.

Both fertilized and parthenogenetic eggs are retained externally for one to several days on the body of the female before being released. The eggs of Anostraca are carried in an oval or elongated ventral brood sac. In the Notostraca they are carried in a curious receptacle formed by modified and overlapping flabellum and branchia on each eleventh trunk appendage. In the Conchostraca the eggs are held together in a mucous mass between body and shell (Fig. 205C).

The number of eggs produced by a single female varies widely. They are released in a series of fertilized or unfertilized clutches at intervals of two to six or more days. Usually there are one to six clutches per female and ten to 250 eggs per clutch, depending on the species. In syngamic reproduction, each clutch of eggs is fertilized by a separate copulation. The female carries the eggs for one to several days during which time they undergo early development. Thereafter they may be dropped to the bottom or remain attached until the female dies and sinks to the bottom.

From the available evidence, it appears that some phyllopods produce two distinct types of eggs: (1) thin-shelled "summer" eggs which hatch almost immediately, and (2) thick-shelled, brown "resting," or "winter" eggs which are capable of withstanding unusual heat, cold, and prolonged desiccation (Fig. 210B). Both types are produced in either the presence or absence of males in the population. There is some evidence to indicate that the type of egg depends on the nature and amount of secretion coming out of the shell glands at the time of egg formation. A copious brown secretion results in thick-shelled resting eggs; slightly less secretion produces thinner shells, and the eggs hatch within several days after deposition; if the secretion is scanty and colorless, the shell is thin and transparent, and development is so rapid that the larva may hatch before the egg is released from the body of the female. It is thought that both thin- and thick-shelled eggs may produce either males or females; the genetic and physiological mechanisms involved are not clear.

**Resting eggs.** When it is recalled that phyllopods are chiefly inhabitants of vernal pools and ponds which dry up completely in the dry, warm months, it becomes obvious that resting eggs constitute the sole device for tiding a population over from one season to another. It is probable that resting eggs of all species are capable of withstanding desiccation. During the summer the resting eggs become dried in the bottom mud, and during the winter they are frozen for varying periods. Until rather recently it was commonly believed that *both* drying and freezing were necessary prerequisites for further development and hatching of these eggs, but experimental evidence has been accumulated to show that this is sometimes not the case. Resting eggs have been hatched in the laboratory after drying without freezing and freezing without drying as well as after both freezing and drying. Groups of eggs subjected to rapid or slow freezing and thawing all showed hatching. There is also some evidence to show that resting eggs of a few species will hatch without either drying or freezing.

The observation is sometimes made that phyllopods occur in ponds that never dry up completely during the summer months. This is unquestionably true, but it must be borne in mind that the active phyllopod population completely disappears with the onset of warm or cool weather and that the animals appearing in the following spring have undoubtedly hatched from resting eggs which overwintered on the bottom or in the dried mud along the pond margin above the lowered water level.

Although freezing and drying usually occur naturally, neither is indispensable. The resting period usually lasts from six to ten months in temperate latitudes, but such a long interval is neither necessary nor inhibitory; dry eggs of certain species may be placed in water and hatched at any time of the year in the laboratory. The viability of resting eggs is very striking. Some species have been described from adults reared from eggs in dried mud sent from distant parts of the world. Viable eggs have been kept in dried pond mud on the laboratory shelf for as long as 15 years. Viable eggs of *Artemia* have withstood a temperature of 81°C. for one hour, −190°C. for 24 hours, and an air pressure of 0.000001 mm. of mercury for six months.

**Development, life cycle.** Depending on the species, the eggs hatch into typical nauplius or the more advanced metanauplius larvae with three pairs of appendages representing the first antennae, second antennae, and mandibles of the adults (Fig. 213). A metanauplius usually shows the faint beginning of two or three trunk segments. Although summer eggs hatch while they are still held on the body of the female or on the bottom shortly after their release, development of resting eggs is

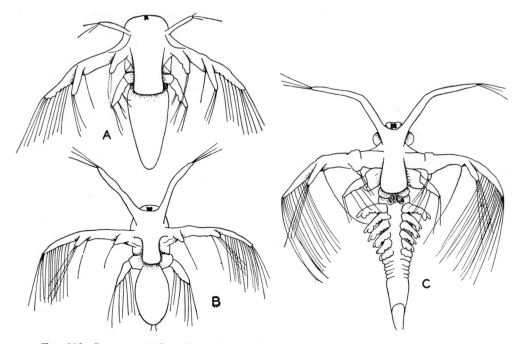

Fig. 213.—Immature Eubranchiopoda. A, first instar (nauplius) of *Artemia salina* Leach, ×110; B, first instar (nauplius) of *Eubranchipus occidentalis* (Dodds), ×80; C, third instar of *E. occidentalis*, ×30. (Modified from Heath.)

much slower. It is thought that early segmentation begins soon after the eggs reach the bottom of the drying pond and before the water temperature gets too low. Development ceases or is greatly retarded by desiccation and low temperatures, however, and is not resumed until early the following spring when water is available and temperatures become favorable. Hatching of resting eggs in temperate latitudes therefore normally occurs sometime between late January and early May. Development proceeds comparatively rapidly in the early spring, and phyllopods may often be collected immediately after the ice melts. They have even been seen swimming about under ice, especially after an early thaw and subsequent freeze, or in the winter months in deep pools.

Beginning with the newly-hatched nauplius, there is a long series of instars, each following a complete ecdysis, or shedding of the exoskeleton. Changes in size from one instar to the next are gradual, and there is progressive appearance of more segments, more appendages, and increasing complexity of appendages. *Eubranchipus occidentalis* (Dodds), for example, has 17 instars in the life history. By the third instar the length averages 1.1 mm. and all appendages through the fifth or sixth trunk segments are represented to some degree. By the sixth instar the average length is 2.1 mm., and all appendages are present though most of the more posterior ones are incompletely developed. Complete development, sexual maturity, and copulation are attained in the 16th instar. *Artemia salina* probably has 14 instars, sexual maturity being attained in the 12th instar. Some investigators are convinced that the number of instars is variable for each species, depending on temperatures and food conditions.

The active portion of the life cycle may be completed in a surprisingly short time.

Mattox (1937), for example, found that the life history of *Eulimnadia diversa* Mattox from hatching until death was completed during the 15 days that a small pond had water in it. He also found (1939) that *Lynceus brachyurus* Müller lived about 26 days and *Cyzicus mexicanus* (Claus) about two months. *Artemia salina,* on the other hand, reaches sexual maturity in 18 to 21 days after hatching and has a normal life span of four months, although specimens have been kept alive for nine months in the laboratory. *Eubranchipus oregonus* Creaser has an exceptionally long natural life span, sometimes up to 25 weeks.

In small ponds which contain water for only a few weeks during the spring and early summer, phyllopods usually have one generation per year. The resting eggs hatch early in the spring, and the animals mature rapidly and produce resting eggs which fall to the bottom and do not hatch until the following spring. Some summer eggs are usually produced during the short period of activity, and although they may hatch, there is not sufficient time for the second generation to mature, and such immature individuals and any remaining summer eggs are presumably destroyed by the adverse conditions accompanying the disappearance of water from the pond.

In Great Salt Lake, in permanent ponds, and in ponds that persist for several months, however, there are usually two or more complete generations per year, the summer generations being completed in a short time by virtue of the fact that the summer eggs hatch almost immediately.

**Ecology.** It seems quite clear that the development of phyllopod populations in the spring and their sudden disappearance in summer or early autumn are governed largely by temperature conditions. Most species do not appear until water temperatures exceed 4°, and 13° to 30°, depending on the species, is the upper limit beyond which individuals die quickly. In Great Salt Lake, *Artemia salina* disappears in the

autumn when the water temperature drops below 6°; *Chirocephalopsis bundyi* (Forbes) and *Eubranchipus serratus* Forbes are seldom found in water warmer than 15°.

Most species exhibit little in the way of specific habitat preferences. The widely distributed *Eubranchipus vernalis* (Verrill), for example, occurs in roadside ditches, grassy vernal ponds, cattail marshes, and woodland pools. Some species, however, appear to be generally restricted to clear or muddy waters. *Chirocephalopsis bundyi,* *Eubranchipus oregonus* Creaser, and *Branchinecta shantzi* Mackin occur only in clear ponds and pools, while many clam shrimps, *Apus,* *Branchinecta gigas* Lynch, and *Thamnocephalus platyurus* Packard are almost invariably found in muddy, alkaline waters.

A curious feature about phyllopod ecology is their absence from lakes. Seldom are they collected from bodies of water having areas exceeding one acre. Phyllopods are almost defenseless, and it is also notable that they are not often abundant in ponds containing carnivorous insects, and are never present along with carnivorous fishes. In fact they attain greatest densities in vernal ponds and prairie pools that are generally lacking in other macrometazoans.

In keeping with widely fluctuating water levels and the consequent rapid changes in the dissolved salt content of pond waters, phyllopods have highly efficient but poorly known means of making physiological adjustments to varying osmotic pressures. In prairie pools, for example, the total salt or alkali content may vary between 0.05 and 1.00 per cent within several weeks, yet their phyllopod populations maintain themselves successfully. Similarly, prairie phyllopods are usually capable of tolerating wide ranges in hydrogen ion concentration. *Eubranchipus serratus* has been found in a pH range of 6.6 to 9.5, *E. vernalis* from 5.2 to 7.4, and *Streptocephalus seali* Ryder in 5.2 to 10.0. As a whole, however, phyllopods have alkaline affinities; pH 6.8 seems to be about the usual lower limit for most species.

Excellent cultures of *Artemia salina* can be maintained in the laboratory, using natural or synthetic sea water, and much experimental work has been done on this species. Mature specimens will tolerate salinities ranging from the saturation point of sodium chloride down to about 3 per cent sea water, though they will not reproduce in salinities below 3 per cent sodium chloride. Adults reared in high salt concentrations reach a larger size than those reared in lower salt concentrations, and sexual maturity is attained more rapidly in populations reared at low salt concentrations. Europeans have found that the pregenital : postgenital body-length ratio and relative development of the cercopods and their setation are correlated with salinity, but these results have not been duplicated with American strains.

Year-to-year field notes on the occurrence of phyllopods in particular ponds present a puzzling problem. Sometimes a species is abundant for several successive years, and then one year it is unaccountably absent. Other ponds may have populations present or absent from year to year in a completely sporadic manner. Furthermore, where there is a group of small ponds and pools in a restricted area, phyllopods are usually present only in certain scattered pools and absent from most or all of the bodies of water immediately surrounding each inhabited one. With few exceptions, a pond never contains more than one species of a particular genus at a time.

The bodies and appendages of phyllopods sometimes become so completely covered with sessile ciliates and green algae that they swim sluggishly and with difficulty.

**Geographical distribution.** A few genera and species of Eubranchiopoda are truly cosmopolitan. *Artemia salina* is found on all continents, and in the United States is best known from Great Salt Lake and man-made California salterns. *Lepidurus* occurs everywhere except in South America. The species of *Streptocephalus* are quite restricted; there are two species in Asia, 21 in Africa and Madagascar, one in Europe, two in the West Indies, and three in continental North America. The seven known species of *Eubranchipus* are all restricted to North America, and, as extreme examples of endemism, *Eulimnadia diversa* Mattox is known only from a single Illinois pond and *E. stoningtonensis* Berry was found year after year in a single small pool in Connecticut. Similar examples are evident from the key which follows. Temporary ponds and pools of the Great Plains constitute a rich collecting ground, the majority of the species reported from the United States occurring in this area.

Phyllopods are probably effectively distributed through their resting eggs, which may be blown about as dust or transported by birds and insects. The presence of populations of *Branchinecta shantzi* above timberline in rock pools having a volume of only a few gallons may be easily attributed to both of these agencies.

**Enemies.** Amphibia, dytiscid larvae, caddis larvae, and perhaps a few other insects are the chief predators of phyllopods. They are of no importance in the diet of fish since they occur in bodies of water too alkaline, too small, or too temporary to support fish.

**Economic importance.** Years ago, the Indians in the vicinity of Great Salt Lake are said to have used dried *Artemia* extensively as food, and *Apus* is at present said to be used as food by a few natives of the Federal District, Mexico. A recent report describes the depredations of *Apus* in California rice fields; these phyllopods chew on the leaves of the young plants and keep the silt stirred up so that photosynthesis is greatly decreased.

**Collection, preparation.** A coarse dip-net is the only necessary implement for collecting adults, but a plankton net is required for the early immature stages. Either 4 per cent formalin or 70 to 80 per cent alcohol is a satisfactory killing agent and preservative.

With the exception of *Artemia* (Galtsoff *et al.*, 1937), phyllopods are usually difficult to maintain and rear in the laboratory.

Dissection is not often necessary for identification, but specimens being studied for any length of time should be manipulated in glycerin. Conchostraca and isolated appendages may be permanently mounted in glycerin jelly.

**Taxonomy.** The Anostraca, Notostraca, Conchostraca, and Cladocera constitute the Subclass Branchiopoda and have the following characters in common: leafy trunk appendages, compound eyes, reduced mouth parts, and usually parthenogenesis, fertilized eggs, and a carapace. The Anostraca, Notostraca, and Conchostraca, however, form a convenient taxonomic group, the Division Eubranchiopoda, having several fundamental characters in common and differing from the Cladocera (Division Oligobranchiopoda) in some important features. The bodies of Eubranchiopoda are elongated, distinctly segmented, and have ten or more pairs of trunk appendages, while the Cladocera are short and compact, with no sign of segmentation, and have only five or six pairs of trunk appendages. The abdomen of Cladocera is greatly reduced, but in Eubranchiopoda the abdomen (postgenital region) is prominent. It is also significant that the phyllopods have nauplius stages, while the Cladocera have direct development. Other less important differences are the occurrence of ephippia in the Cladocera and a single compound eye in Cladocera as compared with two in phyllopods.

Instead of Branchiopoda, the name Phyllopoda is occasionally used for the whole subclass; other references use Phyllopoda to include all Branchiopoda exclusive of Cladocera. Preuss uses Phyllopoda to include all Branchiopoda except Anostraca. Because of this ambiguity "Phyllopoda" is best not used in systematic nomenclature to designate a definite taxonomic category. On the other hand, there is no such serious objection to using "phyllopod" as a common, descriptive, inclusive term for Anostraca, Notostraca, and Conchostraca.

Because of too brief descriptions, inadequate figures, and a reluctance to recognize wide variations within a species as to size, color, and the number and arrangement of spines and spinules, many phyllopods have an uncertain and controversial taxonomy. Until rather recently, for example, most investigators maintained that there were four to six species of *Apus* in the United States. These presumed species are represented by surprisingly few collections and specimens, and furthermore their differentiation was based on size, the number of exposed trunk segments behind the carapace, and the number and disposition of spinules on the telson. The revision of Linder (1952), however, has shown that none of these characters are reliable taxonomically, and that it is quite likely that there is only a single highly variable species of *Apus* in the United States, *A. longicaudatus*. *Lepidurus*, the only other American notostracan genus, is represented by five recognizable species.

Morphological variations within single species of Notostraca are so pronounced that Linder has been led to make the following statement: "A new species should never be described from less than 100 specimens from the same district, preferably taken at varying times of the year."

Unfortunately the general outline of the conchostracan shell is somewhat variable and does not have the taxonomic importance formerly attributed to it. Furthermore, the original descriptions of many American conchostracans are too generalized to be used for critical work. Hence this section of the following key is subject to considerable revision

The taxonomic status of *Artemia* has long been controversial, especially in Europe where *Artemia* shows much greater variability than it does in the United States. The reproductive habits of different populations vary markedly. In parts of Europe parthenogenesis is the rule, males being rare or absent; some such populations are diploid, but others are tetraploid and octoploid. *Artemia* in Great Salt Lake is diploid and males are common. Kuenen (1939) maintains that there are at least two species of *Artemia*, but other workers have found that his anatomical criteria are often not valid. The present consensus is that there is a single cosmopolitan species, *Artemia salina*, which has numerous intergrading physiological and morphological varieties.

In order to use the following key effectively, mature males and females should be used. The scanty and spotty distribution records are usually the result of inadequate collecting; undoubtedly such ranges will eventually be greatly extended.

## KEY TO SPECIES OF EUBRANCHIOPODA

1. Eyes stalked; no carapace; body elongated; 11 pairs of swimming legs; second antennae uniramous, greatly enlarged and used as clasping organs in male; some genera with one frontal appendage or two antennal appendages in male (Figs. 214–217)................Order **ANOSTRACA** (fairy shrimps), **3**
   Eyes sessile; with a large carapace.......................................**2**
2. With a low, arched, univalve carapace covering head and much of trunk; 35 to 71 pairs of trunk appendages; second antennae minute or absent; two long cercopods (Figs. 203C, 205D); total length 11 to 58 mm., not including supra-anal plate; not known east of the Mississippi River.

   Order **NOTOSTRACA** (tadpole shrimps), **40**
   Body compressed laterally and completely enclosed in a carapace composed of two lateral, shell-like valves; ten to 32 pairs of legs; second antennae large and biramous (Fig. 205C)....Order **CONCHOSTRACA** (clam shrimps), **21**
3. Second antennae of male long and with a long folded cheliform outgrowth on the basal segment (Fig. 214C); with a small median frontal appendage between the bases of the second antennae.

   STREPTOCEPHALIDAE, Streptocephalus, **5**
   Second antennae of male shorter and more simply constructed................**4**
4. Frontal and antennal appendages small or absent (Fig. 215)................**7**
   With one median frontal appendage or two large antennal appendages (Figs. 216, 217)....................................................**13**
5. Male cercopods setose along proximal half and with short, curved spines along distal half (Fig. 214A); up to 45 mm. long; widely distributed in pools and ponds....................................**Streptocephalus seali** Ryder
   Male cercopods uniformly setose along entire margin (Fig. 214B).............**6**
6. Inner branch of male second antenna with a process on posterolateral margin near distal end (Fig. 214C); up to 23 mm. long; in pools and ponds of the plains in the southwestern quarter of U. S........**Streptocephalus texanus** Packard
   Inner branch of male second antenna without a process near distal end (Fig. 214D); 10 to 18 mm. long; Okla., Texas, and N. M.

   **Streptocephalus dorothae** Mackin
7. Male second antennae somewhat fused basally and with a laminate terminal segment (Fig. 215A); average length 10 mm.; in saline lakes and salterns of Utah, Nev., Calif., Ore., Wash., N. D., and Conn.

   ARTEMIIDAE, **Artemia salina** Leach
   Male second antennae not fused basally and terminal segment not laminate (Figs. 215B–G); common and widely distributed west of the Mississippi River....**8**

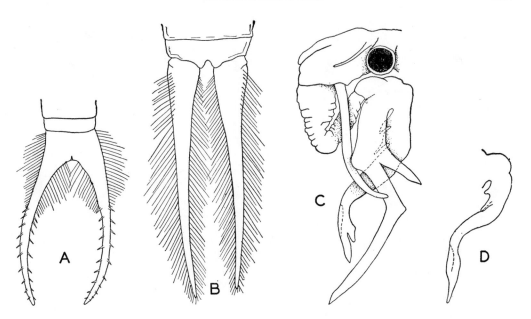

Fig. 214.—Structure of *Streptocephalus*. A, cercopods of *Streptocephalus seali* Ryder; B, cercopods of *S. texanus* Packard; C, lateral view of anterior part of head and appendages of male *S. texanus*; D, inner branch of male second antenna of *S. dorothae* Mackin. (B to D modified from Mackin, 1942.)

8. Length 50 to 100 mm. (Fig. 203A); male second antennae completely without protuberances and outgrowths; known only from a few temporary alkali ponds in Wash., Nev., Utah, and Mont.

BRANCHINECTIDAE, **Branchinecta gigas** Lynch

Usually between 8 and 25 mm. long. . . . . . . . . . . . . . . . . . . . . . . . . . . . . . . . .9

9. Basal segment of male second antenna serrate on inner margin (Fig. 215B); a subarctic species, in U. S. known only from mountains of Wyo.

BRANCHINECTIDAE, **Branchinecta paludosa** (O. F. M.)

Basal segment of male second antenna not serrate on inner margin. . . . . . . . . . . .10

10. With one or two prominent processes, tubercles, or reduced antennal appendages at base of male second antenna (Figs. 215D, F, G). . . . . . . . . . . . . . . . . . . . .11

Without prominent basal tubercles or processes on male second antenna but with a slightly raised basal toothed area (Fig. 215C); Iowa, Kan., Nebr., N. D., Wyo., Colo., Ariz., and N. M.

BRANCHINECTIDAE, **Branchinecta coloradensis** Packard

11. Inner margin of basal segment of male second antenna with an elevated spiny area at about mid-length (Figs. 215F, G).

BRANCHINECTIDAE, **Branchinecta, 12**

Inner margin of basal segment of male second antenna without such a spiny area, but each antenna with a reduced basal antennal appendage (Fig. 215D); Palo Alto, Calif.

CHIROCEPHALIDAE, **Eubranchipus occidentalis** (Dodds)*

* This species is placed in *Eubranchipus* provisionally; Linder (1941) includes it in *Pristicephalus.*

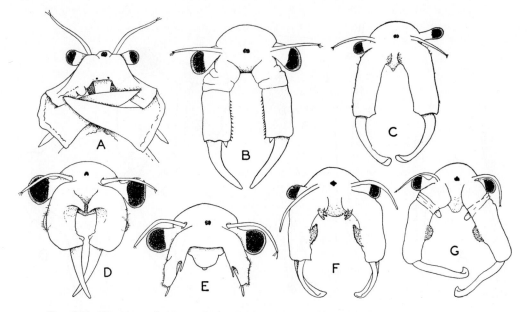

Fig. 215.—Structure of Artemiidae and Branchinectidae. A, head of male *Artemia salina*; B, head of male *Branchinecta paludosa*; C, head of male *B. coloradensis* Packard; D, head of male *Eubranchipus occidentalis*; E, head of female *E. occidentalis*; F, head of male *B. lindahli* Packard; G, head of male *B. shantzi* Mackin. (A modified from Heath; B modified from Sars; C modified from Shantz; D and E modified from Dodds.)

12. With two short, finger-like processes near base of each male second antenna; elevated spiny area spurlike (Fig. 215F); plains areas of Wyo., Colo., Kan., Nebr., N. M., Ariz., Texas, and Okla........**Branchinecta lindahli** Packard
   With a single tubercle near base of each male second antenna; elevated spiny area not spurlike (Fig. 215G); usually in ponds and pools at elevations of 7,000 to 12,800 feet; Calif., Texas, Utah, Colo., Wyo., Okla., and Ore.

   **Branchinecta shantzi** Mackin

13. Posterior end with a flangelike expansion on each side, cercopods apparently absent (Fig. 216A); male with a long, branched, frontal appendage (Fig. 216B); female with a long, unbranched frontal appendage (Fig. 216C); up to 50 mm. long; central and southwestern states.

   THAMNOCEPHALIDAE, **Thamnocephalus platyurus** Packard
   Cercopods distinct (Fig. 205A)....................................**14**

14. With a single, median, branched frontal appendage; 8 to 11 mm. long; known only from rock pools in DeKalb Co., Ga.

   THAMNOCEPHALIDAE, **Branchinella lithaca** (Creaser)
   With a laminar appendage arising from the base of each second antenna (Figs. 216F; 217A, B)............................CHIROCEPHALIDAE, **15**

15. Antennal appendages very long, usually coiled (Figs. 216D–F)............**16**
   Antennal appendages not particularly long (Figs. 217A, B).....**Eubranchipus, 17**

16. Antennal appendages with very small serrations (Fig. 216D); 10 to 18 mm. long; widely distributed and common in northern states.

   **Chirocephalopsis bundyi** (Forbes)
   Antennal appendages with lamelliform and digitiform processes (Fig. 216E); 8 to 17 mm. long; Conn., N. J., Long Island, Va., N. C., Ga., Tenn., Ohio, and La.

   **Eubranchipus holmani** (Ryder)

**17.** Antennal appendage of male short, never extending beyond basal segment of second antenna (Fig. 217A) . . . . . . . . . . . . . . . . . . . . . . . . . . . . . . . . . . . . . . . . . . . . . . . . . **18**

Antennal appendage of male extending beyond basal segment of second antenna (Fig. 217B) . . . . . . . . . . . . . . . . . . . . . . . . . . . . . . . . . . . . . . . . . . . . . . . . . . . . . . . . . **20**

**18.** Teeth on either side of male antennal appendage not greatly different in size (Figs. 217D, E) . . . . . . . . . . . . . . . . . . . . . . . . . . . . . . . . . . . . . . . . . . . . . . . . . . . . **19**

Teeth on one side of male antennal appendage much longer than those on other side (Fig. 217C); average length about 23 mm.; known only from one locality near Lexington, Ky. . . . . . . . . . . . . . . . . . . . . **Eubranchipus neglectus** Garman

**19.** Antennal appendage of male with small teeth (Fig. 217D); 20 to 26 mm. long; widely distributed and common in northern states.

**Eubranchipus vernalis** (Verrill)

Antennal appendage of male with large, separate teeth (Fig. 217E); 12 to 18 mm. long; Wash., Ore., and Okla. . . . . . . . . . . . . . . **Eubranchipus oregonus** Creaser

**20.** Terminal segment of male second antenna with a calcar half as long as the segment (Fig. 217B); 10 to 35 mm. long; Wis., Ill., Ind., Mo., Nebr., Kan., Okla., Mont., Wash., and Ore. . . . . . . . . . . . . . . . . . . . . **Eubranchipus serratus** Forbes

Terminal segment of male second antenna with a calcar about one-eighth or less as long as the segment (Fig. 217F); average length 12 mm.; Wis. and Minn.

**Eubranchipus ornatus** Holmes

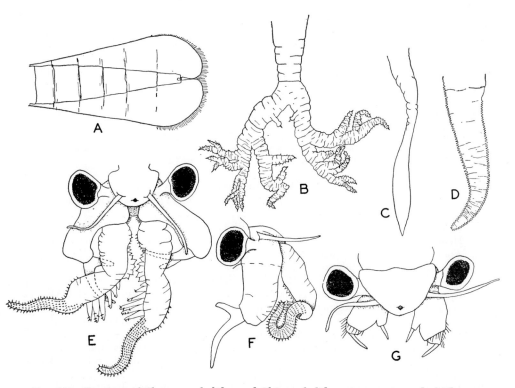

Fig. 216.—Structure of Thamnocephalidae and Chirocephalidae. A, posterior end of *Thamnocephalus platyurus* Packard; B, frontal appendage of male *T. platyurus*; C, frontal appendage of female *T. platyurus*; D, antennal appendage of *Chirocephalopsis bundyi*; E, anterior view of head of male *Eubranchipus holmani* (Ryder); F, lateral view of head of male *E. holmani*; G, anterior view of head of female *E. holmani*. (C redrawn from Packard; E to G modified from Mattox, 1936.)

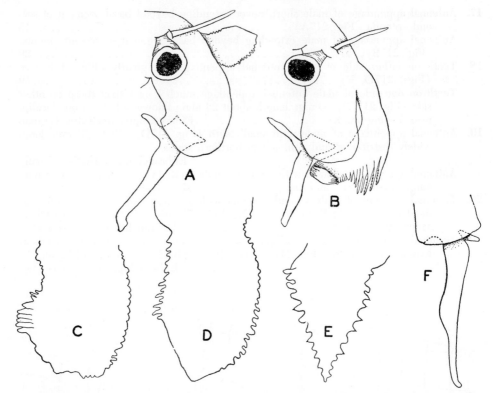

Fig. 217.—Structure of *Eubranchipus*. A, lateral view of head of *Eubranchipus vernalis* (Verrill); B, lateral view of head of *E. serratus* Forbes (antennal appendage partly coiled); C, antennal appendage of *E. neglectus* Garman; D, antennal appendage of *E. vernalis*; E, antennal appendage of *E. oregonus* Creaser; F, male second antenna of *E. ornatus* Holmes. (A and B modified from Mattox, 1939; C to F redrawn from Creaser, 1930.)

**21.** Shell without growth lines; head not entirely covered by carapace.

LYNCEIDAE, **Lynceus,** 24

Shell with growth lines.............................................22
**22.** Head with a frontal appendage (Fig. 218E)..............LIMNADIIDAE, 27
Head without a frontal appendage......................................23
**23.** Apex of rostrum armed with a heavy spine (Fig. 218C); about 11 mm. long; Kan., Texas, Colo., Utah, and Calif.

LEPTESTHERIIDAE, **Leptestheria compleximanus** (Packard)

Apex of rostrum unarmed........................CAENESTHERIIDAE, 34
**24.** Second antennae 29-segmented; 4 to 6 mm. long; Kan. and Colo.

**Lynceus brevifrons** (Packard)

Second antennae with 20 or less segments............................25
**25.** Second antennae 20-segmented; 4.2 mm. long; rare; reported only from Texas.

**Lynceus gracilicornis** (Packard)

Second antennae with less than 20 segments...........................26
**26.** Front of head of male narrow (Fig. 218B); second antennae 16-segmented; 2 to 6 mm. long; the only common species in this genus; often in permanent ponds; widely distributed in the northeastern quarter of U. S., but reported as far west as Colo. and Ore...................**Lynceus brachyurus** Müller

Front of head of male broad and square; rami of second antennae 14- to 17-segmented; 4 mm. long; Mont. and Kan........**Lynceus mucronatus** (Packard)

27. Shell with about seven to 18 growth lines, broadly oval, and about 10 to 17
    mm. long; Mass.............................**Limnadia lenticularis** (L.)
    Shell with two to 11 growth lines (Fig. 218D); narrow, oval, 3 to 11 mm. long.
                                                            **Eulimnadia, 28**
28. With an average of ten growth lines; 14 spinules on telson; forked filament of telson
    between fifth and sixth spinules; rare; Conn.
                                            **Eulimnadia stoningtonensis** Berry
    Usually less than ten growth lines....................................**29**
29. With an average of seven growth lines (range of five to 11), telson with about 15
    spinules; forked filament between third and fourth spinules; Ill.
                                            **Eulimnadia thompsoni** Mattox
    With less than seven growth lines.....................................**30**
30. With two or three growth lines (Fig. 218D); telson with about 12 spinules; forked
    filament between third and fourth spinules; Ill....**Eulimnadia diversa** Mattox
    Usually with four to six growth lines, rarely with two or three...............**31**

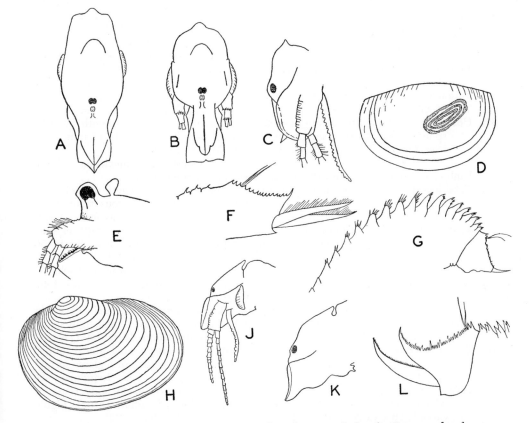

Fig. 218.—Structure of Conchostraca. A, frontal view of female *Lynceus brachyurus*;
B, frontal view of male *L. brachyurus*; C, lateral view of head of *Leptestheria compleximanus*
(Packard); D, lateral view of male shell of *Eulimnadia diversa* Mattox, ×9; E, head of
female *E. diversa*; F, telson of *E. texana* Packard; G, telson and dorsal portion of abdomen of
*Caenestheriella mexicana* (Claus); H, lateral view of *C. belfragei*, ×3.5; J, head of male
*C. mexicana*; K, head of female *C. mexicana*; L, telson of *C. mexicana*. (A, B, D, G, H, J,
and K redrawn from Mattox, 1939; C, F, and L modified from Packard.)

**31.** With forked filament between sixth and seventh spinules of telson; three to four growth lines; about 16 spinules on telson; Ill.....**Eulimnadia inflecta** Mattox
Forked filament located more basally.................................**32**

**32.** With about seven to nine spinules on telson; forked filament between second and third or third and fourth spinules; four to six growth lines; Okla.
**Eulimnadia antlei** Mackin
With more than ten spinules on telson................................**33**

**33.** With about 16 spinules on telson; forked filament between third and fourth spinules (Fig. 218F); two to six growth lines; Texas, Kan., Nebr., and Colo.
**Eulimnadia texana** Packard
With about 12 spinules on telson; forked filament between first and second spinules; four growth lines; rare; reported only from Penikese Island, Mass.
**Eulimnadia agassizi** Packard

**34.** Rostrum like hatchet blade; with large, smooth spine on the middorsal line of most trunk segments; rare, poorly known; Okla........**Eocyzicus concava** Mattox
Rostrum not hatchet-shaped (Figs. 218J, K); most trunk segments armed with a large subspined process in the middorsal line (Fig. 218G); 5 to 16 mm. long.
**Caenestheriella, 35**

**35.** Lines of growth on lowest third or fourth of shell crowded together and indistinct, but total number more than 35; shell globose, 5 to 6 mm. thick and 9 to 13 mm. long; with more than 17 small spines on telson; S. D., Nebr., Iowa., Colo., and Okla. .........................**Caenestheriella morsei** (Packard)
Lines of growth more symmetrically arranged, less than 35 present; shell not especially globose............................................**36**

**36.** Telson with 30 or more spinules (Fig. 218L)...........................**37**
Telson with 25 or fewer spines......................................**39**

**37.** Umbo about one-eighth the length of shell from anterior edge; telson with 45 to 52 spinules (Fig. 218L); shell with 24 to 33 growth lines and 9 to 12 mm. long; from Ohio to the Rockies and Canada to Mexico.
**Caenestheriella mexicana** (Claus)
Umbo more than one-eighth the length of shell from anterior edge............**38**

**38.** Total length 7 to 11 mm.; umbo prominent, about one-fifth the length of shell from anterior edge; shell with 15 to 25 growth lines; with numerous spinules on telson; reported only from Ohio............**Caenestheriella gynecia** Mattox
Total length usually 12 to 16 mm.; umbo small, about one-sixth the length of shell from anterior edge; shell averaging about 17 growth lines; with 30 to 50 spinules on telson; rare and poorly known; reported only from Calif.
**Caenestheriella californica** (Packard)

**39.** Shell with 23 to 25 growth lines (Fig. 218H); telson with 17 to 25 spines; total length up to 11 mm.; Kan., Texas, and Okla.
**Caenestheriella belfragei** (Packard)
Shell with 13 to 18 growth lines; telson with 11 to 15 spines; total length up to 7 mm.; Nebr., Okla., and Ore............**Caenestheriella setosa** (Pearse)

**40.** Telson extended as a flat, paddle-shaped protuberance (supra-anal plate) (Figs. 219 A–D); 25 to 34 body rings, of which three to eight are legless; second maxillae well developed................................**Lepidurus, 41**
Telson not extended as a supra-anal plate (Fig. 205D); 34 to 44 body rings, of which nine to 15 are legless; second maxillae reduced in adult; a single highly variable species generally distributed west of meridian 99 or 100.
**Apus longicaudatus** LeConte

**41.** Anterior part of nuchal organ between posterior part of eye tubercles, not far from hind margin of eyes (Figs. 219F–H)..............................**42**
Nuchal organ considerably behind eye tubercles (Fig. 219E); 30 to 34 body rings; 60 to 71 pairs of legs; supra-anal plate simple or bilobed; ponds in Lake and Grand counties, Wash., and Esmeralda Co., Nev.....**Lepidurus lynchi** Linder

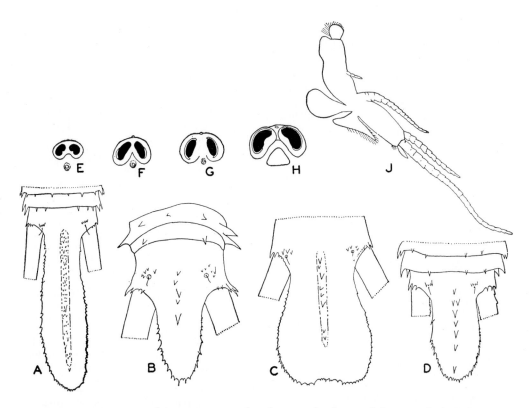

Fig. 219.—Structure of Notostraca. A, dorsal view of telson and last two body rings of *Lepidurus couesi* Packard; B, dorsal view of telson and last two body rings of *L. lynchi*; C, dorsal view of telson of *L. bilobatus* Packard; D, dorsal view of telson and last two body rings of *L. packardi* Simon; E, eyes and nuchal organ of *L. lynchi*; F, eyes and nuchal organ of *L. packardi*; G, eyes and nuchal organ of *L. couesi*; H, eyes and nuchal organ of *Apus longicaudatus*; J, first leg of *Lepidurus couesi* (note long fifth endite). (A to H modified from Linder, 1952.)

**42.** With 9.5 to 13 leg-bearing abdominal rings; usually 25 to 28 body rings.......**43**
　　With 16 or 17 leg-bearing abdominal rings; 32 body rings; supra-anal plate slightly
　　　bilobed (Fig. 219C); about 62 pairs of legs; a poorly known species reported
　　　from Colo., Ariz., and Utah.................**Lepidurus bilobatus** Packard
**43.** Third to fifth endites of first leg rather similar in size, projecting very little or not
　　　at all beyond edge of carapace; 41 to 46 pairs of legs; reported from subarctic
　　　America and not known from the U. S...........**Lepidurus arcticus** (Pallas)
　　Third to fifth endites of first leg dissimilar in size, the fifth endite projecting well
　　　beyond the carapace margin (Fig. 219J)..........................**44**
**44.** Median spines of supra-anal plate similar in size, few in number, and not placed on
　　　a keel (Fig. 219D); about 35 pairs of legs; a poorly known species reported
　　　from only two Calif. localities.................**Lepidurus packardi** Simon
　　Median spines of supra-anal plate dissimilar in size, numerous, and placed on a
　　　keel (Fig. 219A); about 35 to 40 pairs of legs; reported from Mont., Idaho,
　　　N. D., Ore., and Utah.......................**Lepidurus couesi** Packard

# EUBRANCHIOPODA REFERENCES

BERRY, E. W. 1926. Description and notes on the life-history of a new species of Eulimnadia. *Amer. Jour. Sci.* 11:429–433.

BOND, R. M. 1932. Observations on Artemia "franciscana" Kellogg, especially on the relation of environment to morphology. *Int. Rev.* 28:117–125.

CANNON, H. G., and F. M. C. LEAK. 1933. On the feeding mechanism of the Branchiopoda. *Philos. Trans. Roy. Soc. London, B,* **222**:267–352.

CREASER, E. P. 1930. Revision of the phyllopod genus Eubranchipus with description of a new species. *Occ. Pap. Mus. Zool. Univ. Mich.* **208**:1–13.

———. 1930a. The North American phyllopods of the genus Streptocephalus. *Ibid.* **217**:1–10.

———. 1940. A new species of phyllopod crustacean from Stone Mountain, Georgia. *Jour. Wash. Acad. Sci.* 30:435–437.

DADAY DE DEÉS, E. 1910. Monographie systématique des phyllopodes anostracés. *Ann. Sci. Nat. Zool.* (9) 11:91–492.

———. 1915. Monographie systématique des phyllopodes conchostracés. *Ibid.* **20**:39–330.

———. 1923. Monographie systématique des phyllopodes conchostracés (2ᵉ partie). *Ibid.* (10) 6:255–390.

———. 1925. Monographie systématique des phyllopodes conchostracés. Troisième partie. *Ibid.* 8: 143–184.

———. 1926. Monographie systématique phyllopodes conchostracés. Troisième partie (suite). *Ibid.* 9:1–81.

———. 1927. Monographie systématique des phyllopodes conchostracés. Troisième partie (fin.). *Ibid.* **10**:1–112.

DEXTER, R. W. 1946. Further studies on the life history and distribution of Eubranchipus vernalis (Verrill). *Ohio Jour. Sci.* 46:31–44.

DEXTER, R. W., and M. S. FERGUSON, 1943. Life history and distributional studies on Eubranchipus serratus Forbes (1876). *Amer. Midl. Nat.* 29:210–222.

DEXTER, R. W., and C. H. KUEHNLE. 1951. Further studies on the fairy shrimp populations of northeastern Ohio. *Ohio Jour. Sci.* 51:73–86.

DODDS, G. S. 1923. A new species of phyllopod. *Occ. Pap. Mus. Zool. Univ. Mich.* 141:1–3.

ERIKSSON, S. 1936. Studien über die Fangapparate der Branchiopoden nebst einigen phylogenetischen Bemerkungen. *Zool. Bidr. Uppsala* 15:23–287.

HEATH, H. 1924. The external development of certain phyllopods. *Jour. Morph.* 38:453–483.

JENNINGS, R. H., and D. M. WHITAKER. 1941. The effect of salinity upon the rate of excystment of Artemia. *Biol. Bull.* 80:194–201.

JENSEN, A. C. 1918. Some observations on Artemia gracilis, the brine shrimp of Great Salt Lake. *Ibid.* 34:18–32.

KUENEN, D. J. 1939. Systematical and physiological notes on the brine shrimp, Artemia. *Arch. Neerland. Zool.* 3:365–449.

LINDER, F. 1941. Contributions to the morphology and the taxonomy of the Branchiopoda Anostraca. *Zool. Bidr. Uppsala* 20:101–302.

———. 1952. Contributions to the morphology and taxonomy of the Branchiopoda Notostraca, with special reference to the North American species. *Proc. U. S. Nat. Mus.* 102:1–69.

LOCHHEAD, J. H. 1941. Artemia, the "brine shrimp." *Turtox News* 19:41–45.

LOCHHEAD, J. H., and M. S. LOCHHEAD. 1941. Studies on the blood and related tissues in Artemia (Crustacea, Anostraca). *Jour. Morph.* 68:593–632.

LOWNDES, A. G. 1933. The feeding mechanism of Chirocephalus diaphanus Prévost, the fairy shrimp. *Proc. Zool. Soc. London* (B) (1933): 1093–1118.

LYNCH, J. E. 1937. A giant new species of fairy shrimp of the genus Branchinecta from the State of Washington. *Proc. U. S. Nat. Mus.* 84:555–562.

MACKIN, J. G. 1939. Key to the species of Phyllopoda of Oklahoma and neighboring states. *Proc. Okla. Acad. Sci.* 19:45–47.

———. 1940. A new species of conchostracan phyllopod, Eulimnadia antlei, from Oklahoma. *Amer. Midl. Nat.* 23:219–221.

———. 1942. A new species of phyllopod crustacean from the southwestern short-grass prairies. *Proc. U. S. Nat. Mus.* 92:33–39.

———. 1952. On the correct specific names of several North American species of Branchinecta Verrill. *Amer. Midl. Nat.* 47:61–65.

MATHIAS, P. 1937. Biologie des Crustacés Phyllopodes. *Actualités Scientifiques et Industrielles* 447:1–107.

MATTOX, N. T. 1937. Studies on the life history of a new species of fairy shrimp, Eulimnadia diversa. *Trans. Amer. Micros. Soc.* 56:249–255.

———. 1939. Descriptions of two new species of the genus Eulimnadia and notes on the other Phyllopoda of Illinois. *Amer. Midl. Nat.* 22:642–653.

———. 1950. Notes on the life history and description of a new species of conchostracan phyllopod, Caenestheriella gynecia. *Trans. Amer. Micros. Soc.* 69:50–53.

MOORE, W. G. 1951. Observations on the biology of Streptocephalus seali. *Proc. La. Acad. Sci.* **14**:57–65.

PACKARD, A. 1883. A monograph of the phyllopod Crustacea of North America, with remarks on the Order Phyllocarida. *12th Ann. Rept. U. S. Geol. and Geog. Surv. of the Terr. 1878 (Hayden Survey), Part I*:295–592.

PEARSE, A. S. 1913. Notes on phyllopod crustacea. *14th Rept. Mich. Acad. Sci.*, 191–197.

PREUSS, G. 1951. Die Verwandtschaft der Anostraca und Phyllopoda. *Zool. Anz.* **147**:49–64.

RELYEA, G. M. 1937. The brine shrimp of Great Salt Lake. *Amer. Nat.* **71**:612–616.

ROSENBERG, L. E. 1946. Fairy shrimps in California rice fields. *Science* **104**:111–112.

———. New species of Apus from California. *Trans. Amer. Micros. Soc.* **66**:70–73.

SARS, G. O. 1896. Phyllocarida og Phyllopoda. *Fauna Norvegiae* **1**:1–140.

SHANTZ, H. L. 1905. Notes on North American species of Branchinecta and their habits. *Biol. Bull.* **9**:249–264.

WARREN, H. S. 1938. The segmental excretory glands of Artemia salina Linn. var. principalis Simon. (The brine shrimp.) *Jour. Morph.* **62**:263–298.

WEAVER, C. R. 1943. Observations on the life cycle of the fairy shrimp, Eubranchipus vernalis. *Ecology* **24**:500–502.

WHITAKER, D. M. 1940. The tolerance of Artemia for cold and high vacuum. *Jour. Exp. Zool.* **83**:391–399.

# Chapter 16

# CLADOCERA (WATER FLEAS)

BECAUSE of their interesting habits, their availability in nearly all types of freshwater habitats, and their complex but easily studied anatomy, the water fleas have been favorite objects of observation by both amateur and professional biologists ever since the invention of the microscope.

**General characteristics.** Most members of the Order Cladocera are between 0.2 and 3.0 mm. long. The body is not clearly segmented, and in the great majority of species the thoracic and abdominal regions are covered by a secreted shell or carapace which has a general bivalved appearance but is actually a single folded piece which gapes ventrally. In lateral view the shell is variously shaped; it may be oval, round, elongated, or angular. There are often surfaces reticulations, striations, or other types of markings. In many species the posterior end has a spinule or spine, and the ventral edges of the valves usually bear setae. The inner surface of the valves is lined with the delicate body wall.

The head is a compact structure and does not open ventrally as the valves do. It is bent downwards and dorsally it is sometimes indistinctly set off from the body by a cervical sinus or notch. The most conspicuous internal structure of the head is the large compound eye. It consists of a few to many small hyaline lenses surrounding a mass of pigment granules. It is rotated constantly and jerkily by three pairs of small muscles. A single small ocellus lies posterior to the compound eye. The first antennae (antennules) are inserted on the ventral side of the head near its posterior margin. They are usually inconspicuous, unsegmented, and bear olfactory setae. The second antennae, however, are very large and are inserted laterally near the posterior margin of the head. Each consists of a stout basal segment, a segmented dorsal ramus, and a segmented ventral ramus. The two rami bear a variable number of plumose setae. Setation formulas are often used as a means of identifying genera and species. Thus, the setation formula for *Daphnia* is 0–0–1–3/1–1–3; it indicates that the dorsal ramus of the antenna is four-segmented and that the basal, second, third, and fourth segments bear 0, 0, 1, and 3 setae, respectively; it also indicates a three-segmented ventral ramus of which the basal, second, and third segments bear 1, 1, and 3 setae, respectively. The antennae are activated by a set of powerful muscles which originate dorsally in the "neck" region. Externally, there is a strengthening ridge, or fornix, above the base of each antenna. The beak, or rostrum, is a more or less well defined projection of the head between or in front of the antennules. The vertex of the head is that part which lies anterior to the compound eye.

The small mouth parts are situated near the junction of head and body. Beginning at the anterior end, they consist of (1) a median labrum, (2) a pair of stout, sclerotized, toothed or ridged grinding man-

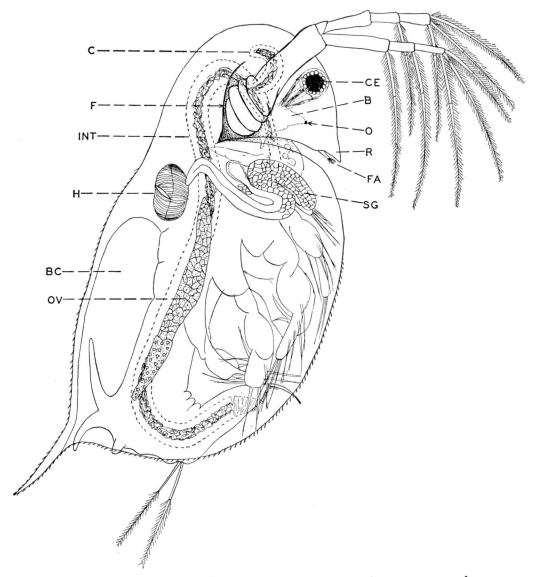

Fig. 220.—Anatomy of female *Daphnia pulex* (De Geer), ×70; diagrammatic; muscles not shown. *B*, brain; *BC*, brood chamber; *C*, digestive caecum; *CE*, compound eye; *F*, fornix; *FA*, first antenna (antennule); *H*, heart; *INT*, intestine; *O*, ocellus; *OV*, ovary; *R*, rostrum or beak; *SG*, shell gland. (Greatly modified from Storch, 1925.)

dibles, (3) a pair of small, pointed maxillae, used in pushing food between the mandibles, and (4) a single median labium. In some of the Macrothricidae and Chydoridae the labium bears a median keel which is of systematic value.

There are five or six pairs of lobed, leaf-like thoracic legs, bearing numerous hairs and setae (Fig. 222). Although the legs are fundamentally biramous, this condition is not clearly evident because of their considerable modification. In the Sididae and Holopedidae all legs are similar, but in the other families the first two pairs are

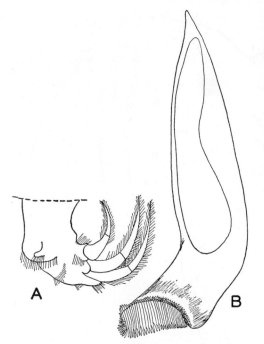

FIG. 221.—Mouth parts of *Daphnia pulex*. A, maxilla; B, mandible. (Redrawn from Lilljeborg.)

more or less prehensile and may aid in clinging to a substrate.

The true abdomen is suppressed, but there is a large postabdomen at the posterior end of the body. It is usually bent forward so that the dorsal side is downward. It bears two long abdominal setae, two terminal claws, and usually a series of marginal or lateral teeth or denticles. The postabdomen seems to be used chiefly for cleaning debris from the thoracic legs, although it may aid in locomotion.

During the greater part of the year Cladocera populations consist almost exclusively of females, the males being abundant only in the autumn or spring. In many species, however, males are rare or unknown. Anatomically, males are distinguished from females by their smaller size, larger antennules, modified postabdomen, and first legs armed with a stout hook used in clasping (Fig. 223E).

Limnetic species are usually light-colored and translucent. Pond, littoral, and bottom species are darker in color, ranging from light yellowish-brown to reddish-brown, grayish, or almost black. Pigmentation occurs in both the carapace and general body tissues.

**Locomotion.** For the most part, Cladocera keep intermittenly in motion, the antennae being the chief organs of locomotion. In some genera, such as *Latona*, single vigorous strokes of the antennae produce powerful leaps. *Daphnia* and its relatives move by a series of "hops," produced by more rapid and less vigorous strokes. In some other genera the swimming movements have been characterized as "uncertain" and "tottering." A few genera, including *Holopedium* and *Scapholeberis*, habitually swim upside down. Species occurring on a substrate have less frequent periods of active swimming and often use the antennae incidentally for obtaining a purchase on vegetation and bottom debris. The postabdomen is also useful for locomotion in bottom-inhabiting species. A cladoceran may literally kick itself along, sometimes by quite respectable hops.

**Feeding.** Complex movements of the highly setose thoracic legs produce a constant current of water between the valves. These movements further serve to filter food particles from the water and collect them in a median ventral groove at the base of the legs. This stream of food is fed forward to the mouth parts where the particles may be ground between the surfaces of the mandibles before being taken into the mouth.

Algae and Protozoa have often been assumed to be the chief foods, to the exclusion of other materials, but it is now well known that organic detritus of all kinds, as well as bacteria, are very important and commonly form the great bulk of material ingested. It has also been successfully demonstrated that the feeding movements of the legs of plankton species are so efficient that they separate some colloidal organic particles from the water. Although

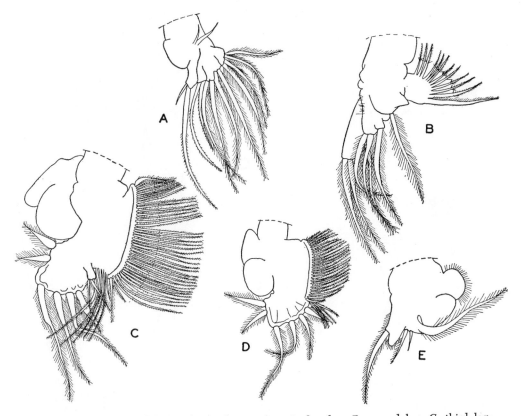

FIG. 222.—Legs of adult female *Daphnia pulex*. A, first leg; B, second leg; C, third leg; D, fourth; E, fifth. (Modified from Uéno.)

there is a little evidence that certain types of food, such as particular groups of algae, Protozoa, or bacteria may be selected by some species, it is generally believed that all organic particles of suitable size are ingested without any selective mechanism. When undesirable material or large tangled masses are introduced between the mandibles, they may be removed by spines at the base of the first legs and then kicked out of the shell by the post-abdomen. Although the food stream in the median groove is continuous, ingestion may cease for varying periods. Minute amounts of dissolved organic materials may be absorbed by the general body surface, but they are of no metabolic significance.

A few genera, such as *Polyphemus* and *Leptodora*, are predaceous and have the legs modified for seizing. Their prey consists mostly of other entomostraca and rotifers.

The finely divided food is passed from the mouth parts to the esophagus in small masses of definite size. The time required to fill the digestive tract varies considerably, depending on the species, temperature, concentration of food, and other factors. Laboratory observations show a range of 10 to 240 minutes. Hasler (1937) demonstrated the presence of fat, carbohydrate, and protein digesting enzymes in *Daphnia* and *Polyphemus*. He found the pH of the digestive tract of *Daphnia* to range between 6.8 and 7.2. The indigestible residue leaves the body through the anus which is usually situated on the lower (dorsal) border of the post-abdomen.

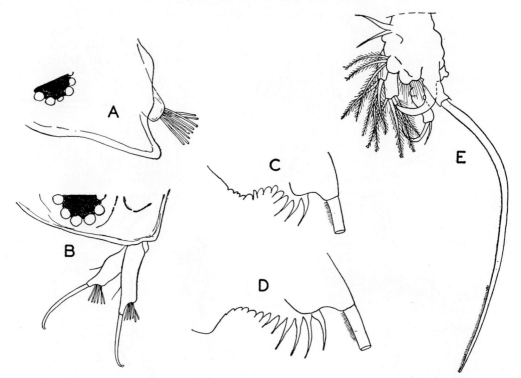

Fig. 223.—Sex characters of Cladocera. A, rostrum region of female *Daphnia pulex*; B, rostrum region of male *D. pulex*; C, postabdomen of male *Simocephalus exspinosus* (Koch); D, postabdomen of female *S. exspinosus*; E, first leg of male *D. pulex*. (C and D redrawn from Banta; E modified from Uéno.)

**Internal anatomy.** Although the complex muscular system obscures some of the smaller anatomical features, the essential parts of most of the organ systems can be easily distinguished. The digestive system is relatively unspecialized. In the head region the narrow esophagus opens into a stomach which, however, is often indistinguishable from the remainder of the tubular digestive tract, the intestine. In some genera there are one or two digestive caeca which open into the anterior part of the intestine. The course of the intestine may be relatively straight or convoluted. It can always be distinguished in both living and preserved specimens because of its contained dark food mass. In some of the Chydoridae there is a posterior ventral caecum. The posterior part of the digestive tract is somewhat specialized as a rectum.

The simple oval or football-shaped heart lies behind the head on the dorsal side. Blood enters the heart through two lateral ostia and leaves through an anterior opening. At room temperature the heart beats about as rapidly as one can open and close his fist. There are no blood vessels, the blood being roughly guided about in the hemocoel by a series of thin mesenteries. The blood plasma is usually colorless or has a faint yellowish cast; it contains numerous colorless corpuscles.

Some pond species, however, are pinkish in color owing to dissolved erythrocruorin which may be formed when dissolved oxygen concentrations are low. It is of no respiratory significance to the adult but may be concentrated in the eggs just before their release to the brood pouch. Presumably it functions in the respiration of embyros that are retained in a more or less closed brood pouch with little access to the outside water.

The exchange of oxygen and carbon dioxide occurs through the general body surface but especially along the inner surfaces of the valves and through the surfaces of the legs.

Irregular or looped shell glands, situated near the anterior end of the valves, are thought to function as excretory organs.

The nervous system consists of the usual ventral double nerve cord, relatively few ganglia, paired nerves, and a brain just anterior (dorsal) to the esophagus. Both the compound eye and the ocellus appear to be important in orientation to light

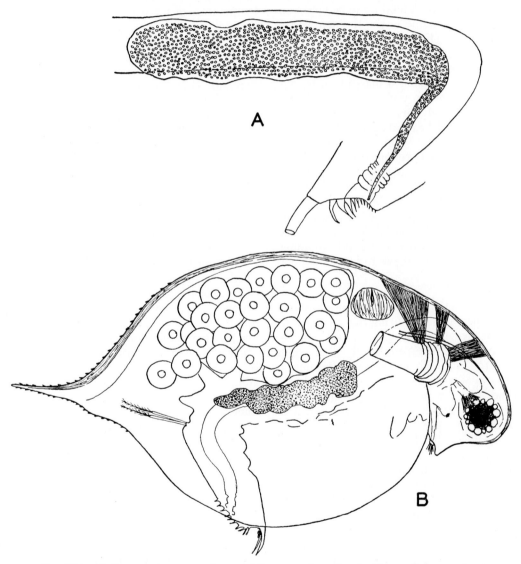

FIG. 224.—Cladoceran structures. A, postabdomen region of male *Simocephalus exspinosus,* showing testis, sperm duct, intestine, and rectum; B, mature female *Daphnia pulex* (×70), showing ovary, parthenogenetic eggs in brood chamber, heart, antennal muscles, and compound eye. (A modified from Banta; B modified from Uéno.)

sources and light intensity. Olfactory stimuli are thought to be received by the setae at the edges of the valves, by the antennules, and by areas around the mouth. The sense of touch is centered particularly in the abdominal setae and sensory hairs on the basal segment of the antennae.

Gonads are easily distinguished only in sexually mature specimens. The two elongated ovaries lie lateral or somewhat ventral to the intestine in the thoracic region of the body (Fig. 224B). Depending on the stage in reproduction, an ovary is densely granular, with large oogonial nuclei, or it contains a mass of large, pigmented, granular, yolky eggs. Each oviduct is located dorsally at the posterior end; it is so delicate that it cannot be distinguished except when an egg is passing through it. The testes are smaller and contain small, semitransparent, granule-like sperm (Fig. 224A). The sperm ducts are posterior continuations of the testes which pass laterally to the intestine and rectum and open on the postabdomen near the anus or claws. A part of the postabdomen is sometimes specialized to form a copulatory organ.

**Reproduction in general.** Reproduction is parthenogenetic during the greater part of the year in most habitats, and only female young are produced. The eggs undergo a single maturation division in the ovary and a number are released at a time via the oviducts into the brood chamber. The latter is a cavity dorsal to the body proper and between the valves; it is effectively closed posteriorly by the abdominal processes. Depending on the species and environmental conditions, the number of eggs per clutch varies considerably; usually there are between two and 40, and most frequently between ten and 20. The parthenogenetic eggs undergo further development in the brood chamber and hatch into young similar in form to the adult. The parent then liberates them to the outside by moving the postabdomen downward. Normally, one clutch of eggs is released into the brood chamber during each adult instar.

**Seasonal abundance.** In early spring relatively few cladocerans are to be found in lakes and ponds. Such populations consist of females which survived over the winter or recently hatched from winter (resting) eggs. As the water reaches a temperature of 6° to 12°, active reproduction begins and subsequently speeds up tremendously so that large populations result (in exceptional cases as high as 200 to 500 individuals per liter of water). Populations in ponds then soon begin to wane, so that few individuals can be found during the summer months. In the autumn there may or may not be a second population pulse, but during the winter the population is invariably low, with little or no reproduction. Thus, in a pond where the common species is *Daphnia pulex* (de Geer) or *D. magna* Straus, the population may be monocyclic or dicyclic, that is, having one or two population maxima during the year.

In larger bodies of water, however, seasonal variations in the abundance of Cladocera are not usually so pronounced. There is commonly a spring maximum and sometimes a less well defined fall maximum, but summer and winter populations are large compared with those of ponds. In some lakes *D. pulex* is monocyclic, in others dicyclic. *Daphnia longispina* (O. F. M.) may be monocyclic, dicyclic, and in some cold lakes, acyclic, that is, without any pronounced population maxima during the entire year. Other common forms exhibiting monocycly or dicycly are *Simocephalus* and *Ceriodaphnia*. Occasionally, as in *Sida crystallina* (O. F. M.) in some lakes, there may be a single autumn pulse. There are also many Cladocera that exhibit single long population pulses during the warmer months in certain lakes. Examples are *Diaphanosoma brachyurum* (Liévin), *Chydorus sphaericus* (O. F. M.), *Bosmina longirostris* (O. F. M.), and *Moina*.

It is useless to predict or formulate any preconceived notions concerning the seasonal abundance of Cladocera in a particular lake or pond. Species differ greatly from one another in their seasonal abundance; a single species may have quite different population curves in two adjacent bodies of water; furthermore, relative abundance and the specific time of maximum and minimum populations may vary considerably within a single species in the same lake from one year to the next.

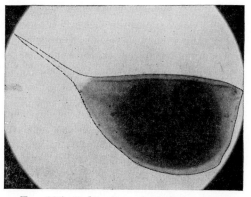

FIG. 225.—Ephippium of *Daphnia pulex.*

**Male production, resting eggs.** Numbers of males begin to appear in ponds in the spring, late in the intensive reproductive cycle. Sometimes only 5 per cent of the population may consist of males; sometimes more than half are males. The factors responsible for the appearance of males in cladoceran populations have been the object of long and intensive studies by many investigators. We do not as yet have a detailed explanation of the phenomenon. By way of partial explanation, however, it is probable that a complex interplay of factors is responsible. Production of male eggs seems to be induced mostly by: (1) crowding of the females and the subsequent accumulation of excretory products, (2) a decrease in available food, and (3) a water temperature of 14° to 17°. These conditions (and probably others also), by altering the metabolism, appear to affect the chromosome mechanism in such a way that parthenogenetic male eggs rather than parthenogenetic female eggs are released into the brood chamber.

The same conditions responsible for male production, if continued for a longer time, appear to induce the appearance of sexual eggs. Females producing such eggs are morphologically similar to parthenogenetic females, but they produce only one, two, or sometimes several large opaque "resting" eggs, and, unlike the parthenogenetic females, they are capable of copulation with males. The fertilized eggs pass into the brood chamber, the walls of which then become thickened and darkened to form an ephippium (Fig. 225). In the Daphnidae the ephippium separates from the rest of the shell at the subsequent molt. In the Chydoridae it remains attached to the shell at the molt. Sometimes as many as a third or half of the females in a population may bear ephippia.

Upon being released, the ephippia sink to the bottom or float upon the surface. In the latter event, they may be blown ashore and accumulated in diminutive windrows. Ephippia and their contained eggs are capable of withstanding drying and freezing, and their production is clearly an adaptation to adverse environmental conditions. They are of special value in small ponds which dry up during the summer months. When such basins become filled with water in the early autumn, a large percentage of the ephippial eggs hatch into parthenogenetic females. Then there may be an autumn pulse followed by the appearance of males, sexual females, and ephippia which winter over and give rise to at least a part of the small seed population in the following spring.

Thus it is seen that during most of the year the population consists entirely of parthenogenetic females, but for short periods the population may be complex, consisting of parthenogenetic females, males, unfertilized sexual females, and fertilized sexual females.

In bodies of water larger than ponds,

ephippia are produced by smaller percentages of the populations, and in limnetic populations in large lakes it is thought that reproduction may be entirely parthenogenetic the year round, especially in *Daphnia longispina.*

The expressions "monocyclic" and "dicyclic" are really used in two different ways in the literature. They may refer to an annual population curve having one or two pronounced maxima, without reference to types of reproduction, or they may be used to designate populations having one or two periods of syngamic reproduction during the year.

The older idea of internal genetic or physiological "rhythms" being responsible for the periodic occurrence of syngamic reproduction has been discarded. The experimental work of Banta and others has demonstrated conclusively that the mode of reproduction is influenced by environmental factors. By changing the culture solutions frequently, Banta reared several common Cladocera for 800 to 1,600 successive parthenogenetic generations (more than 27 years). Males, sexual females, and subsequent ephippia may be easily produced by crowding the mothers in a small amount of culture solution or by chilling the culture.

Laboratory observations have shown that under appropriate conditions a mature parthenogenetic female may begin to produce sexual eggs, or a sexual female may change over and produce parthenogenetic eggs. Males usually appear in both natural and controlled populations before females begin the formation of sexual eggs in the ovary. When a female passes an unfertilized sexual egg into the developing ephippium it disintegrates. There are, however, a few records in the literature of such eggs developing into parthenogenetic females.

Wood (1938) has contributed much to our understanding of the induction of hatching of ephippial eggs. Working with *Daphnia longispina*, she found that (1) the considerable majority of eggs died when stored either wet or dry for one to many weeks; (2) the longer the period of storage, the greater the mortality; (3) a few eggs stored wet for seven years were viable; (4) exposure to low temperatures decreased the percentage of hatch; (5) placing eggs in fresh culture medium or allowing them to dry out only a day or two gave the highest percentage of hatch, usually 35 to 45 per cent; and (6) aeration and changing the culture solution frequently induced hatching of a comparable percentage of eggs which had not been allowed to dry out.

**Development, life cycle.** Length of life, from release of the egg into the brood chamber until the death of the adult, is highly variable, depending on the species and environmental conditions. *Daphnia longispina* usually lives for 28 to 33 days in laboratory cultures. MacArthur and Baillie (1929) found that *D. magna* lived an average of 26, 42, and 108 days at 28°, 18°, and 8°, respectively. Limnetic individuals undoubtedly live through the entire winter at low temperatures. Poor food supply also increases length of life.

Four distinct periods may be recognized in the life history of a cladoceran: egg, juvenile, adolescent, and adult. When a clutch of eggs is released into the brood chamber, segmentation begins promptly; the young, in the first juvenile instar and similar in form to the adult, are released from the brood chamber in about two days. There are but few juvenile instars, although greatest growth occurs during these stages. *Moina macrocopa* has two juvenile instars, *Daphnia longispina* has three, *D. pulex* has three or four, and *D. magna* three to five. The adolescent period is a single instar between the last juvenile instar and the first adult instar; during this instar the first clutch of eggs reaches full development in the ovary. As soon as the animal molts at the end of the adolescent instar and enters the first adult instar, the first clutch of parthenogenetic eggs is released into the brood chamber. During the first adult instar the second clutch of eggs is developing in the ovary. Successive adult instars and new clutches of young are produced in a similar manner. However, there is often a sterile period during the last few instars of life.

As in all other Crustacea, growth, in terms of increase in size, becomes apparent only immediately after each molt. During juvenile instars there may be almost a doubling of size after each molt, the increase in volume occurring within a few seconds or minutes and before the new exoskeleton hardens and loses its elasticity.

The number of adult instars is much more variable than the number of juvenile instars. *Daphnia pulex* usually has 18 to 25 adult instars, *D. longispina* ten to 19, and *D. magna* six to 22. As already inferred, the duration of a single adult instar is highly variable, from a day to several weeks, though about two days under favorable conditions. At the close of each adult instar four events follow one another in rapid succession, usually in a few minutes to a few hours. These are: the release of young from the brood chamber to the outside, molting, increase in size, and the release of a new clutch of eggs to the brood chamber.

**Cyclomorphosis.** One of the most intriguing and puzzling of all cladoceran problems is the matter of cyclomorphosis, or seasonal changes in morphology, especially in females of limnetic species such as *Daphnia pulex* and *D. longispina*. A population of a cyclomorphic species has a homogeneous "normal," or round-headed, form during the late fall, winter, and early spring. As the water becomes warmer and the population develops, however, there is commonly a progressive increase in the longitudinal axis produced by a general elongation of the head and the appearance of a "helmet" (Figs. 226E, P, Q). Characteristically, the helmets become fully developed by midsummer, when they may be quite bizarre (Figs. 226G, H, Q). Beginning in the late summer or early

autumn, the morphology of the head progressively reverts so that the "normal" head condition prevails by late autumn. In addition to changes in the shape of the head, cyclomorphosis may also involve changes in size of eye and length of the posterior spine.

The problem is greatly complicated by the fact that the degree of summer helmet development differs widely in the same species, even in two neighboring lakes. Cyclomorphosis is less pronounced in ponds and shallow lakes, and the degree of helmet development is relatively consistent from one individual to another at any one time, but in larger and deeper lakes cyclomorphosis and the degree of helmet development in a population is much more variable, and both strongly developed and poorly developed helmets, as well as intergrades, may be found in the same townet sample.

Explanations of these seasonal changes in form have naturally long been sought for in the changing seasonal ecological conditions in bodies of water. Between 1900 and 1910 Wessenberg-Lund and Ostwald elaborated their "Buoyance Theory" which attempted to explain the occurrence of helmets as a flotation adaptation to decreased viscosities of water at summer temperatures. Subsequent observations and experimental work by Woltereck and many others, however, have discredited this viewpoint. Other more recent proposals have centered around nutrition, internal cycles, and the accumulation of waste products, but none of these now receives favorable consideration by investigators in this field.

At present, one of the most logical explanations of cyclomorphosis appears to center around temperature, and particularly the temperature during the early stages of development. The controlled experiments of Coker and Addlestone (1938) are illuminating. These investigators found that the last one-third of the period of development of the first juvenile instar in the brood chamber was the critical

Fig. 226.—Some variations in head form in *Daphnia pulex* (A to H) and *D. longispina* (J to Q). A, *typica*; B, *obtusa*; C, *pulicoides*; D, *parapulex*; E to H, *retrocurva*; J and K, *typica*; L and M, *mendotae*; N, *galeata*; O, laboratory culture descendant of *galeata*; P and Q, *apicata*.

period. *Daphnia longispina* raised at a temperature of 10° or below during this period all had round heads; 15 per cent of those raised at 12° has pointed heads; 33 per cent of those raised at 13° had pointed heads; 87 per cent at 14° had pointed heads; and all of those raised at 16° or more had pointed heads. In general, the higher temperatures produced more prom-

inent helmets. Brooks (1946) found comparable temperature relationships for helmet formation in *Daphnia retrocurva* (= *pulex*?) and head spine formation in *D. galeata* (= *longispina*?). Kiang (1942) demonstrated a relation between mean temperature of a lake and relative head length in *D. longispina*.

Nevertheless, the work of Banta (1938)

indicates that temperature is by no means the whole story and that genetic factors probably play an important role. He collected ten distinct morphological types of *Daphnia pulex* in the field and cultured them in the laboratory. Under such circumstances the pronounced helmets were lost or minimized, but each of the ten types remained recognizable and peculiar to itself. Other workers have shown that turbulence may increase the degree of helmet formation.

In the words of Coker (1939), "The changes in form are not simple functions of external conditions or of any inherent cycle, but rather of a combination of internal and external conditions in a way that becomes exceedingly baffling the more we know about it."

One aspect of the study of cyclomorphosis which appears to have been overlooked is the fact that plankton Cladocera show considerable vertical migrations with the 24-hour changes of subsurface illumination. Since the degree of helmet formation may be at least partially dependent upon temperature during a short period while the young are in the brood chamber, and since individual Cladocera are known to vary greatly in the amplitude of their daily vertical movements, it seems quite likely that in some cases the degree of helmet development in the released young may have been determined by the migration behavior of the mother during the previous 24-hour period; that is, whether she migrated only a short distance out of the cold bottom water at night or whether she migrated a much greater distance up into the warm epilimnion for the greater portion of the night.

**General ecology.** Cladocera are primarily fresh-water organisms, the several American marine species belonging to *Evadne* and *Podon* (Polyphemidae). Aside from rapid streams, brooks, and grossly polluted waters, they are abundant everywhere. Common open water and limnetic forms are *Daphnia longi-*

*spina, D. pulex, Bosmina, Diaphanosoma, Chydorus sphaericus, Ceriodaphnia,* and *Holopedium.* The greatest abundance of species may be collected in the vegetation at margins of lakes and rivers, including *D. pulex, Sida crystallina, Ophryoxus gracilis* Sars, most Chydoridae, and most Macrothricidae. The two most common inhabitants of ponds, permanent pools, and temporary pools are *D. pulex* and *D. magna. Alona quadrangularis* (O. F. M.), *Drepanothrix, Ilyocryptus,* and *Monospilus* are among the most common forms to be found on or near the bottom in weedy littoral areas. Specific affinities are indicated for most species in the key at the end of this chapter.

The great majority of species and nearly all of the common ones are eurythermal. Only a few appear to have distributions limited by temperature. *Latona, Holopedium gibberum* Zad., and *Daphnia longiremis* Sars are cold stenotherms, and *Pseudosida bidentata* Herrick, *Ceriodaphnia rigaudi* Richard, and *Euryalona occidentalis* Sars are restricted to warm waters of southern states.

Little information is available concerning chemical limiting factors. Dissolved oxygen is seldom of any significance except in the hypolimnion of lakes during summer and winter periods of complete oxygen exhaustion. Many species are known to be able to withstand oxygen concentrations of less than one part per million. Most Cladocera occur in waters containing a wide range of concentrations of calcium. *Holopedium,* however, is widely distributed and confined to calcium-poor waters. Hutchinson (1932) found that magnesium may act as a limiting factor by inhibiting reproduction; critical concentrations for *Daphnia magna, D. pulex,* and *D. longispina* were found to be 240, 120, and 30 to 60 milligrams per liter. Although a few species are restricted to acid and bog waters, most Cladocera occur over a wide range in pH, nearly all species being found in the range 6.5 to 8.5.

TABLE VII.  General Geographic Distribution of Some Common Species of Cladocera.

Cosmopolitan
>   Alona guttata, A. rectangula
>   Ceriodaphnia laticaudata
>   Chydorus sphaericus
>   Daphnia magna, D. pulex

North America, Europe, Asia, and South America
>   Alona affinis
>   Bosmina longirostris
>   Ceriodaphnia quadrangula
>   Macrothrix laticornis
>   Simocephalus vetulus

North America, Europe, and Asia
>   Acroperus harpae
>   Bosmina coregoni
>   Camptocercus rectirostris
>   Daphnia longispina
>   Diaphanosoma brachyurum
>   Eurycercus lamellatus
>   Holopedium gibberum
>   Leptodora kindti
>   Moina macrocopa
>   Pleuroxus strictus
>   Polyphemus pediculus
>   Scapholeberis mucronata
>   Sida crystallina

**Geographical distribution.** Because of their resistant ephippial eggs, Cladocera are easily transported overland to new habitats. As a result, the great majority of species are very widely distributed, some being truly cosmopolitan. The general occurrence of a few common species is indicated in Table VII. Less than 20 species are known only from the United States, and most of these have been collected in only one or two localities. Intensive collecting has been done in relatively few areas, however, and our knowledge of the geographical limits of many species in the United States is decidedly incomplete.

**Economic significance.** The great importance of Cladocera in the aquatic food chain as food for both young and adult fish was emphasized first by Forbes in 1883, and since then by innumerable investigators. Various studies of the stomach contents of young fish show from one to 95 per cent Cladocera by volume, and very few studies show less than 10 per cent. Other groups of less importance which utilize Cladocera in the diet are *Hydra* and immature and mature insects.

**Collecting, preserving.** An ordinary plankton townet is suitable for limnetic species but is of little use for collecting in littoral vegetation. For such habitats the Birge cone net does an excellent job. Bottom forms may be taken by bringing the top centimeter of mud and debris into the laboratory and allowing it to settle. By looking horizontally along the surface toward a light source, the Cladocera may be located and picked up with a long pipette. In small ponds and pools, and to some extent in vegetation, a small dipnet is convenient.

The best general killing agent is undoubtedly 95 per cent ethyl alcohol. Because of their delicate body and strong muscles, however, *Moina* and most of the

Sididae are badly distorted when placed in alcohol. These forms should first be narcotized with chloral hydrate or a similar deadening agent. Seventy per cent alcohol is the standard preservative. The writer always adds 5 per cent glycerin to his storage vials so that specimens will not be destroyed through evaporation if the corks dry out or the vials break.

Fortunately, little or no dissection is necessary for identification purposes, but permanent slide mounts in glycerin or glycerin jelly are highly desirable. Cover slips should be supported by bits of cardboard of appropriate thickness so that specimens will not be crushed.

**Taxonomy.** Any account of the Cladocera of the United States must necessarily rely heavily on the masterful treatment by E. A. Birge in Ward and Whipple's *Freshwater Biology* (1918). Surprisingly little has since been added to our knowledge of cladoceran taxonomy and distribution.

The long-continued and vexing problem of the taxonomic relationships of the various forms of *Daphnia pulex* and *D. longispina* is still a controversial matter. Depending chiefly on the shape of the head, the former exhibits a multitude of summer "species," "subspecies," "varieties," and "forms" in North America but not in Europe. Some of the more common variants, cyclomorphic and otherwise, have been designated as *pulicaria, minnehaha, curvirostris, obtusa, retrocurva,* and *arcuata* (Figs. 226A–H). *D. longispina,* on the other hand, exhibits a comparable complex condition on both sides of the Atlantic. Common variants are *hyalina, typica, mendotae,* and *galeata* (Figs. 226J–Q). As emphasized earlier in this chapter, it is extremely difficult to distinguish the relative significance of seasonal, environmental, and genetic factors in the determination of these variants.

Although there is some value in designating some of the more distinctive forms by name (Kiser, 1950), the majority of investigators now appear to be convinced that there is no advantage to be gained in attempting to define and give nomenclatorial designations to the endless number of intergrading forms of these two species. In accordance with this opinion, therefore, *D. pulex* and its close relatives are here included in a single highly variable species, and *D. longispina* and its relatives are included in another single highly variable species.

A few investigators take the opposite viewpoint. Mackin (1931) favors the concept that *D. longispina* and *D. pulex* are two complex groups of species. Scourfield (1942) separates *D. obtusa* Kurz from *D. pulex* on the basis of a row of medially projecting setae on the ventral margin of each valve. Brooks (1946) believes that *D. retrocurva* is specifically distinct from *D. pulex,* and *D. galeata* from *D. longispina* on the basis of the appearance of a summer retrocurved helmet and spiked head, respectively, in some lakes.

A fundamental difficulty in attempting to establish numerous distinct species in the *longispina* and *pulex* complexes is the fact that no morphological criteria have yet been found by which the various forms can be distinguished from each other during the colder months (October to March), when all the individuals in each species constitute what is apparently a single morphological type.

Aside from the *Daphnia* problem, certain other genera are in need of revision and clarification, notably *Ceriodaphnia, Moina, Alona, Alonella,* and *Pleuroxus.*

In the key which follows, lengths refer only to females and do not include spines or antennae. Some species appear in two different places in the key because of variable anatomical characters.

## KEY TO SPECIES OF CLADOCERA

1. Body and legs covered with a bivalve shell; legs foliaceous, not clearly segmented.
   Suborder **CALYPTOMERA, 2**

   Body and legs not covered with a shell; legs subcylindrical or somewhat flattened, clearly segmented, and prehensile; northern states.
   Suborder **GYMNOMERA, 121**

2. With six pairs of foliaceous legs; first and second pairs not prehensile (Fig. 227C).
   Tribe CTENOPODA, 3

   With five or six pairs of legs; first and second pairs more or less prehensile (Figs. 222A, B) . . . . . . . . . . . . . . . . . . . . . . . . . . . . . . . . . . .Tribe ANOMOPODA, **11**

3. Shell of the usual type; antennae of female biramous and flattened (Figs. 227E–G).
   SIDIDAE, 5

   Animal enclosed in a large gelatinous case, open ventrally and forming two valves (Fig. 227A); antennae of female simple and cylindrical; 1 to 2 mm. long.
   HOLOPEDIDAE, **Holopedium, 4**

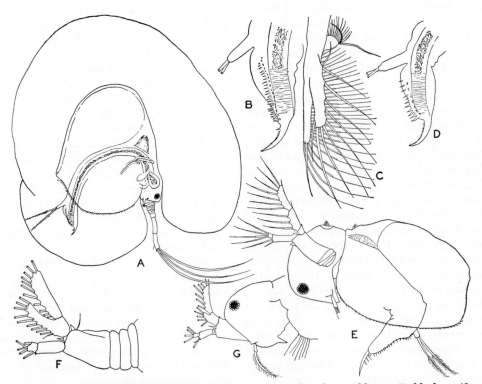

FIG. 227.—Structure of Holopedidae and Sididae. A, *Holopedium gibberum* Zaddach, ×40; B, postabdomen of *H. gibberum*; C, first leg of *H. gibberum*; D, postabdomen of *H. amazonicum* Stingelin; E, *Sida crystallina* (O. F. M.), ×14; F, antenna of *Latona setifera* (O. F. M.); G, anterior end of *L. parviremis* Birge. (B and D modified from Ward and Whipple, 1918; C modified from Sars; E and F modified from Lilljeborg.)

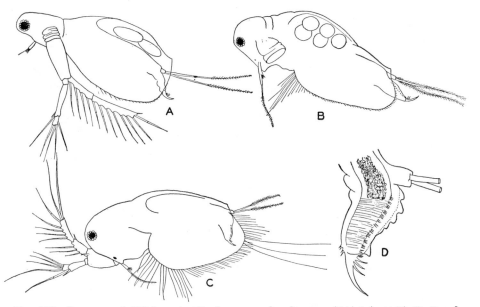

Fɪɢ. 228.—Structure of Sididae. A, *Diaphanosoma brachyurum* (Liévin), ×45; B, *Pseudosida bidentata* Herrick, ×27; C, *Latonopsis occidentalis* Birge, ×22; D, *L. fasciculata* Daday. (A modified from Lilljeborg, 1900; B modified from Birge, 1910; C and D modified from Ward and Whipple.)

4. Ventral margins of valves with fine spines; up to 25 anal spines and spinules; anal claws with a basal spine (Fig. 227B); common in open waters of northern states..............................**Holopedium gibberum** Zaddach *
   Ventral margins of valves smooth; seven to 12 anal spines and spinules; anal claws without basal spine (Fig. 227D); east of La. and south of northern tier of states.........................**Holopedium amazonicum** Stingelin *
5. Dorsal ramus of antenna three-segmented (Fig. 227E); 3 to 4 mm. long; common among aquatic plants in lakes and ponds........**Sida crystallina** (O. F. M.)
   Dorsal ramus of antenna two-segmented..................................6
6. With a lateral expansion on basal segment of dorsal ramus of antenna; with a tonguelike projection on ventral surface of head (Figs. 227F, G); 2 to 3 mm. long; in littoral vegetation; chiefly in northern states and mountainous areas.
                                                                **Latona, 7**
   Without lateral expansion on antenna.....................................8
7. Antennal expansion very large (Fig. 227F)..........**Latona setifera** (O. F. M.)
   Antennal expansion small (Fig. 227G)................**Latona parviremis** Birge
8. Without spines on postabdomen; ocellus absent; 0.8 to 1.2 mm. long; littoral and limnetic; common and widely distributed (Fig. 228A).
                                               **Diaphanosoma brachyurum** (Liévin)
   With spines on postabdomen (Fig. 228D); ocellus present; about 2 mm. long...9
9. Rostrum present (Fig. 228B); southern states......**Pseudosida bidentata** Herrick
   Rostrum absent (Fig. 228C); usually in aquatic vegetation.......**Latonopsis, 10**
10. Postabdomen with about nine small spines; common in Gulf states, sporadic farther north (Fig. 228C)................**Latonopsis occidentalis** Birge
    Postabdomen with 12 to 14 small clusters of lancet-shaped anal spines (Fig. 228D); Gulf states..............................**Latonopsis fasciculata** Daday

* Several workers have collected specimens which form intermediate series between these two species. It is possible that they should be combined into a single variable species.

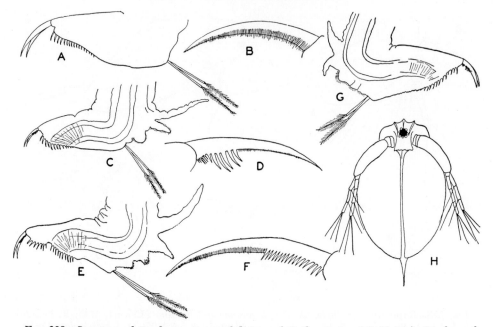

FIG. 229.—Structure of *Daphnia*. A, postabdomen of *D. longispina* (O. F. M.); B, claw of same; C, postabdomen of *D. pulex*; D, claw of same; E, postabdomen of *D. magna* Straus; F, claw of same; G, postabdomen of *D. carinata* King; H, ventral view of *D. magna*, diagrammatic, ×11.

**11.** Antennules attached to ventral side of head, not covered by fornices (Figs. 230–234). . . . . . . . . . . . . . . . . . . . . . . . . . . . . . . . . . . . . . . . . . . . . . . . . . . . . . . . . . . . .12
   Fornices extended so as to cover antennules more or less, and united with rostrum into a beak which projects ventrally in front of antennules (Figs. 235–238).
CHYDORIDAE, 55
**12.** Antennules of female small, often rudimentary; if large, then never inserted at anterior end of ventral edge of head (Figs. 230, 231) . . . . .DAPHNIDAE, 14
   Antennules of female large, inserted at anterior end of ventral edge of head (Figs. 232–234). . . . . . . . . . . . . . . . . . . . . . . . . . . . . . . . . . . . . . . . . . . . . . . . . . .13
**13.** Antennules of female fixed (Figs. 232A–D); intestine simple; 0.3 to 0.5 mm. long.
BOSMINIDAE, 37
   Antennules of female freely movable (Figs. 233, 234); intestine simple or convoluted. . . . . . . . . . . . . . . . . . . . . . . . . . . . . . . . . . . . .MACROTHRICIDAE, 39
**14.** Rostrum present. . . . . . . . . . . . . . . . . . . . . . . . . . . . . . . . . . . . . . . . . . . . . . . . . . . . . .15
   Rostrum absent. . . . . . . . . . . . . . . . . . . . . . . . . . . . . . . . . . . . . . . . . . . . . . . . . . . . . . .24
**15.** Without cervical sinus; the species in this genus are badly confused and in need of revision. . . . . . . . . . . . . . . . . . . . . . . . . . . . . . . . . . . . . . . . . . . . . . .**Daphnia**, 16
   With cervical sinus (Fig. 230). . . . . . . . . . . . . . . . . . . . . . . . . . . . . . . . . . . . . . . . . .20
**16.** Claws with pecten (Figs. 229D, F). . . . . . . . . . . . . . . . . . . . . . . . . . . . . . . . . . . . . .17
   Claws without pecten (Fig. 229B). . . . . . . . . . . . . . . . . . . . . . . . . . . . . . . . . . . . . . .19
**17.** Distal pecten usually with 12 or more teeth (Fig. 229F); heavy, thick-bodied forms. . . . . . . . . . . . . . . . . . . . . . . . . . . . . . . . . . . . . . . . . . . . . . . . . . . . . . . . .18
   Distal pecten usually with less than 12 teeth (Fig. 229D); not heavy and thick-bodied; up to 3.8 mm. long; highly variable and polymorphic (Figs. 226A–H); widely distributed and common in many types of habitats.
**Daphnia pulex** (de Geer)

18. Postabdomen with a sinuate margin (Fig. 229E); up to 5 mm. long; widely dis-
tributed but uncommon in shallow ponds containing much organic matter.
**Daphnia magna** Straus
Margin of postabdomen not sinuate (Fig. 229G); up to 2.8 mm. long; pools and
ponds; rare, reported only from Nebr. and Colo.....**Daphnia carinata** King
19. Ocellus present, though small; up to 2 mm. long; highly variable and polymorphic
(Figs. 226J–Q); common everywhere in open waters.
**Daphnia longispina** (O. F. M.)
Ocellus absent; up to 1.5 mm. long; in cold waters, sometimes confined to the
hypolimnion; uncommon......................**Daphnia longiremis** Sars
20. Valves transversely striated (Fig. 230B); up to 3 mm. long.....**Simocephalus, 21**
Valves not transversely striated; up to 1 mm. long; usually in aquatic vegetation.
**Scapholeberis, 23**
21. Claws with a pecten (Fig. 230A); uncommon; reported from scattered localities in
the eastern half of the U. S..............**Simocephalus exspinosus** (Koch)
Claws without a pecten...........................................22
22. Vertex evenly rounded about the eye and without serrations or spinules (Fig.
230B); widely distributed but not common..**Simocephalus vetulus** (O. F. M.)
With serrations or spinules in front of or below eye; vertex more or less angulate
(Fig. 230C); common everywhere........**Simocephalus serrulatus** (Koch)

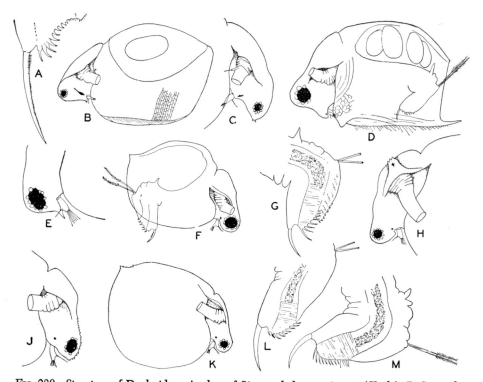

FIG. 230.—Structure of Daphnidae. A, claw of *Simocephalus exspinosus* (Koch); B, *S. vetulus*
(O. F. M.) showing a portion of transverse striations, ×15; C, head of *S. serrulatus* (Koch);
D, *Scapholeberis mucronata* (O. F. M.), ×50; E, head of *Ceriodaphnia rigaudi* Richard; F,
*C. reticulata* (Jurine), ×25; G, postabdomen of *C. megalops* Sars; H, head of *C. lacustris*
Birge; J, head of *C. rotunda* Sars; K, *C. laticaudata* P. E. Müller, ×50; L, postabdomen of
*C. quadrangula* (O. F. M.); M, postabdomen of *C. pulchella* Sars. (B to H, and L modified
from Ward and Whipple; J and M modified from Lilljeborg.)

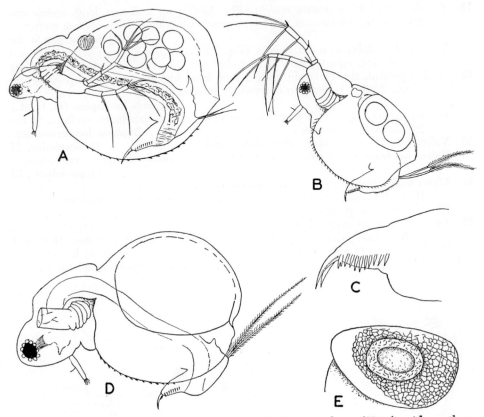

FIG. 231.—Structure of Daphnidae. A, *Moinodaphnia macleayi* (King) with parthenogenetic eggs, ×60; B, *Moina macrocopa* Straus with ephippium, ×24; C, postabdomen of same;
D, *M. brachiata* (Jurine), ×40; E, ephippium of *M. rectirostris* (Leydig). (A, D, and E
modified from Ward and Whipple; B and C modified from Uéno.)

23. Color usually dark, often nearly black; common and widely distributed (Fig.
    230D); a variety with a frontal horn is rare in the U. S.
                                            **Scapholeberis mucronata** (O. F. M.)
    Color whitish or greenish, translucent or opaque; uncommon; northern states.
                                              **Scapholeberis aurita** (Fischer)
24. Antennules small; head small and depressed (Figs. 230E, F, H–K); up to 1.4
    mm. long...................................................**Ceriodaphnia, 25**
    Antennules large; head large and extended (Fig. 231A, B, D)..............32
25. Head with a short spine (Fig. 230E); 0.4 to 0.5 mm. long; pools; in southern states.
                                            **Ceriodaphnia rigaudi** Richard
    Head without spine........................................................26
26. Claws with pecten (Fig. 230F); up to 1.4 mm. long; common and widely dis-
    tributed.............................**Ceriodaphnia reticulata** (Jurine)
    Claws without pecten......................................................27
27. Postabdomen abruptly incised (Fig. 230G); widely distributed but uncommon.
                                            **Ceriodaphnia megalops** Sars
    Postabdomen not incised...................................................28
28. Fornices projecting to form spinous processes (Fig. 230H); 0.8 to 0.9 mm. long;
    limnetic; scattered east of the Mississippi R......**Ceriodaphnia lacustris** Birge
    Fornices of the usual form; up to 1 mm. long..............................29

29. Vertex with spines (Fig. 230J); in aquatic vegetation; reported only from Wis.

$\qquad$ **Ceriodaphnia rotunda** Sars

Vertex without spines; widely distributed. . . . . . . . . . . . . . . . . . . . . . . . . . . . . . .**30**

30. General form round (Fig. 230K); up to 1 mm. long; in aquatic vegetation.

$\qquad$ **Ceriodaphnia laticaudata** P. E. Müller

General form not especially round; littoral and limnetic. . . . . . . . . . . . . . . . . . .**31**

31. With seven to nine anal spines (Fig. 230L); up to 1 mm. long.

$\qquad$ **Ceriodaphnia quadrangula** (O. F. M.)

With seven to ten anal spines plus three to five anal setae (Fig. 230M); up to 0.7 mm. long. . . . . . . . . . . . . . . . . . . . . . . . . . . . .**Ceriodaphnia pulchella** Sars

32. Body laterally compressed; valves completely covering body (Fig. 231A); up to 1 mm. long; in aquatic vegetation; reported only from La.

$\qquad$ **Moinodaphnia macleayi** (King)

Body thick and heavy; valves not completely covering body (Figs. 231B, D); usually in pools and ponds. . . . . . . . . . . . . . . . . . . . . . . . . . . . . . . . . . .**Moina,**\* **33**

33. With less than eight postanal spines; 0.5 mm. long; central states.

$\qquad$ **Moina micrura** Kurz

With eight or more postanal spines (Fig. 231C); 1 mm. or more long; widely distributed. . . . . . . . . . . . . . . . . . . . . . . . . . . . . . . . . . . . . . . . . . . . . . . . . . . . . .**34**

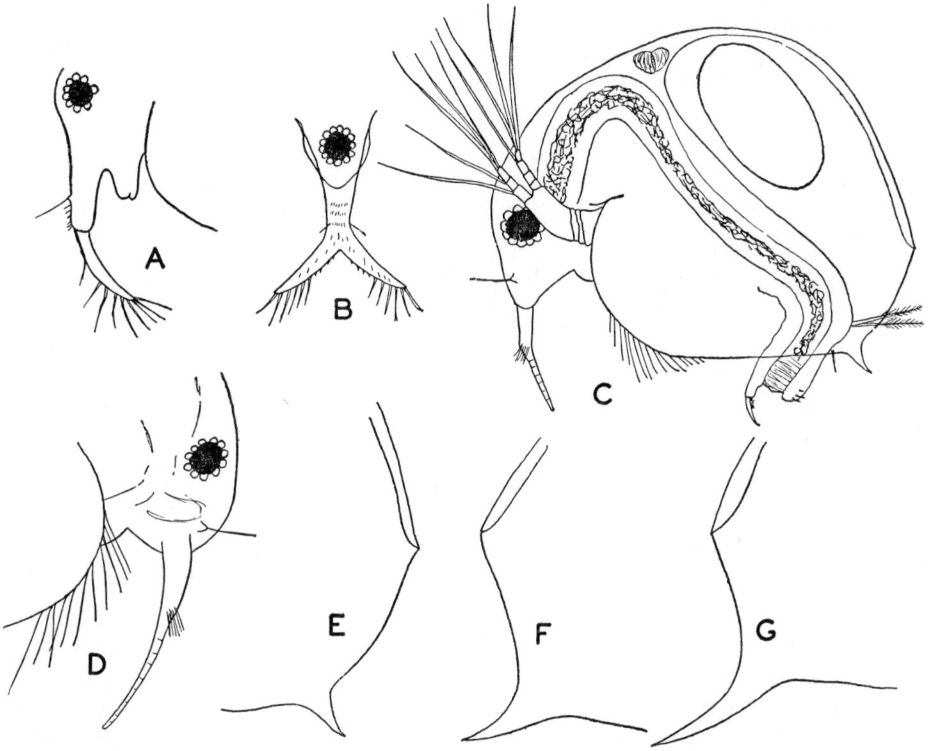

FIG. 232.—Structure of Bosminidae. A, lateral view of antennules of *Bosminopsis dietersi* Richard; B, dorsal view of same; C, *Bosmina longirostris* (O. F. M.), ×140; D, anterior end of *B. coregoni* Baird; E, mucro of *B. longirostris*; F and G, mucrones of *B. coregoni*. (B modified from Ward and Whipple.)

\* Several rare forms, known only from highly alkaline Nevada lakes, are not included in this key. See Brehm (1937) for descriptions.

34. With supraocular depression (Fig. 231D); claws pectinate..................35
    Without supraocular depression (Fig. 231B); claws not pectinate.
                                                      **Moina macrocopa** Straus
35. With two ephippial eggs; body greenish; valves faintly reticulated.
                                                      **Moina brachiata** (Jurine)
    With one ephippial egg; body colorless or with a bluish cast.................36
36. Valves smooth; 1 to 2 mm. long; ephippium reticulated around edges and smooth
    in middle (Fig. 231E).....................**Moina rectirostris** (Leydig)
    Valves striated; 0.8 to 1.0 mm. long; ephippium reticulated over entire surface.
                                                      **Moina affinis** Birge
37. Antennules united at base and diverging at apex (Fig. 232B); widely distributed
    in southern states; uncommon...............**Bosminopsis deitersi** Richard
    Antennules not united at base, parallel; highly variable; littoral and limnetic;
    widely distributed and common..........................**Bosmina, 38**
38. With a small sensory hair near the center of the space between the eye and the
    base of the antennule (Fig. 232C); mucrones short (Fig. 232E).
                                                      **Bosmina longirostris** (O. F. M.)
    With a small sensory hair near the base of the antennule; mucrones long (Figs.
    232D, F, G)..............................**Bosmina coregoni** Baird
39. Intestine convoluted (Fig. 233A)....................................**40**
    Intestine simple.................................................**45**
40. Valves with spine at posterior dorsal angle (Fig. 233A); up to 2 mm. long; in
    aquatic vegetation............................**Ophryoxus gracilis** Sars
    Valves without such a spine......................................**41**

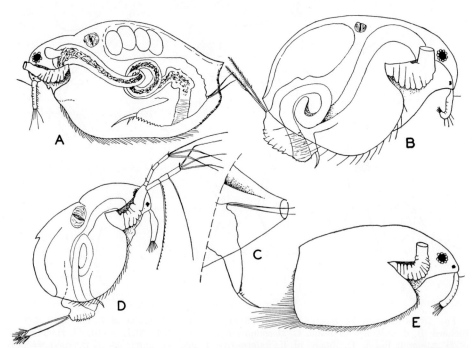

Fig. 233.—Structure of Macrothricidae. A, *Ophryoxus gracilis* Sars, ×30; B, *Streblocerus serricaudatus* (Fischer), ×100; C, posterior end of *Parophryoxus tubulatus* Doolittle; D, *Drepanothrix dentata* Eurén, ×60; E, *Acantholeberis curvirostris* (O. F. M.), ×26. (Modified from Ward and Whipple.)

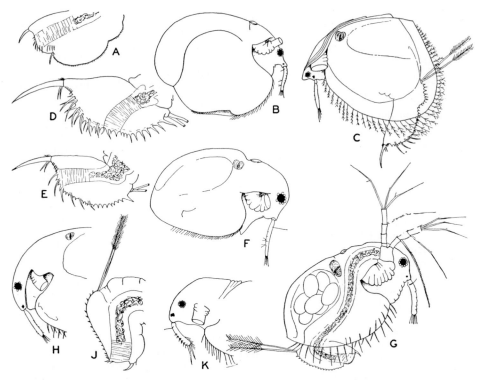

FIG. 234.—Structure of Macrothricidae. A, postabdomen of *Grimaldina brazzai* Richard; B, *Bunops serricaudata* (Daday), ×35; C, *Ilyocryptus spinifer* Herrick, ×40; D, postabdomen of *I. sordidus* (Liéven); E, postabdomen of *I. acutifrons* Sars; F, *Lathonura rectirostris* (O. F. M.), ×38; G, *Macrothrix rosea* (Jurine), ×55; H, anterior end of *M. borysthenica* Matile; J, postabdomen of *M. laticornis* (Jurine); K, anterior end of *M. montana* Birge. (B to H and K modified from Ward and Whipple; J modified from Lilljeborg.)

41. Antennal setae 0–0–1–3/1–1–3; 0.2 to 0.5 mm. long . . . . . . . . . . . **Streblocerus, 42**
    With another antennal setae formula; more than 0.5 mm. long . . . . . . . . . . . . . .**43**
42. Dorsal margin of valves smooth (Fig. 233B); uncommon but widely distributed in littoral zones . . . . . . . . . . . . . . . . . . . . . . .**Streblocerus serricaudatus** (Fischer)
    Dorsal margin of valves serrate; in vegetation in pools; La.
                                                    **Streblocerus pygmaeus** Sars
43. Valves narrowed posteriorly and prolonged into a short tube (Fig. 233C); up to 1.2 mm. long; in vegetation; New England states.
                                                    **Parophryoxus tubulatus** Doolittle
    Valves not narrowed posteriorly; widely distributed . . . . . . . . . . . . . . . . . . . . . . .**44**
44. Dorsal and posterior margin arched; with a conspicuous dorsal tooth (Fig. 233D); up to 0.7 mm. long; in littoral zones; uncommon.
                                                    **Drepanothrix dentata** (Eurén)
    Animal more angular; without a dorsal tooth (Fig. 233E); up to 1.8 mm. long; in littoral, especially in *Sphagnum* bogs. .**Acantholeberis curvirostris** (O. F. M.)
45. With a wide crest on dorsal margin of valves (Fig. 234B); up to 1 mm. long; reported from Maine and Wis. . . . . . . . . . . . . . . .**Bunops serricaudata** (Daday)
    Without such a crest . . . . . . . . . . . . . . . . . . . . . . . . . . . . . . . . . . . . . . . . . . . . . .**46**

46. Postabdomen with numerous long spines (Figs. 234D, E); antennal setae 0–0–0–3/1–1–3; often more or less covered with detritus; usually found creeping about on the substrate..........................**Ilyocryptus, 48**

    Postabdomen without numerous long spines; with another setae formula......47

47. Hepatic caeca present; 0.9 mm. long; in vegetation in shallow water.
                                                          **Grimaldina brazzai** Richard

    Hepatic caeca absent...............................................50

48. Anus on dorsal margin of postabdomen (Fig. 234D); molting imperfect; widely distributed. ......................................................49

    Anus terminal (Fig. 234E); molting perfect; reported from R. I. and Colo.
                                                          **Ilyocryptus acutifrons** Sars

49. With eight or more preanal spines (Fig. 234D); uncommon.
                                                          **Ilyocryptus sordidus** (Liéven)

    With five to seven preanal spines (Fig. 234C); common.
                                                          **Ilyocryptus spinifer** Herrick

50. Antennal setae 0–0–1–3/1–1–3; setae of basal segment of lower ramus stout (Fig. 234G).........................................**Macrothrix, 51**

    Antennal setae 0–1–1–3/1–1–3; all setae slender; 1 mm. long (Fig. 234F); widely distributed in vegetation of littoral........**Lathonura rectirostris** (O. F. M.)

51. Dorsal margin of head evenly rounded.................................52

    Dorsal margin of head not evenly rounded (Fig. 234G); 0.7 mm. long; in aquatic vegetation; widely distributed..................**Macrothrix rosea** (Jurine)

52. Head depressed, rostrum close to margin of valves (Fig. 234H); up to 1.1 mm. long; N. M......................................**Macrothrix borysthenica** Matile

    Head extended, rostrum far from margin of valves (Fig. 234K)..............53

53. Postabdomen not bilobed (Fig. 234J); up to 0.7 mm. long; widely distributed.
                                                          **Macrothrix laticornis** (Jurine)

    Postabdomen bilobed; 0.55 mm. long.................................54

54. With conspicuous folds at cervical sinus (Fig. 234K); Colo. and Calif.
                                                          **Macrothrix montana** Birge

    Without such folds; New England to Colo.
                                                          **Macrothrix hirsuticornis** Norman and Brady

55. Anus terminal; 3 mm. long (Fig. 235A); common everywhere in shallows.
                                                  EURYCERCINAE, **Eurycercus lamellatus** (O. F. M.)

    Anus on dorsal side of abdomen (Fig. 235B)..................CHYDORINAE, 56

56. Compound eye present..............................................57

    Compound eye absent; 0.5 mm. long; rare; northern states.
                                                          **Monospilus dispar** Sars

57. Eye and ocellus of usual size........................................58

    Compound eye and ocellus extremely large and of similar size; known only from a single specimen from a pool at Smithville, Tex.....**Dadaya macrops** (Daday)

58. Posterior margin of valves not greatly less than maximum height (Figs. 235D–F). ......................................................59

    Posterior margin of valves considerably less than maximum height (Fig. 238)...84

59. Claws with secondary tooth in the middle (Fig. 235B); secondary tooth sometimes very small.................................................60

    Claws without secondary tooth in the middle.............................68

60. Postabdomen with both marginal and lateral denticles (Fig. 235C)..........62

    Postabdomen without both marginal and lateral denticles...................61

61. Postabdomen with lateral denticles only, sometimes inconspicuous (Fig. 235H); 0.8 to 0.9 mm. long; common everywhere in aquatic vegetation.
                                                          **Acroperus, 67**

    Postabdomen with marginal denticles only (Fig. 235B); up to 1.9 mm. long; in littoral vegetation; known only from Maine......**Alonopsis aureola** Doolittle

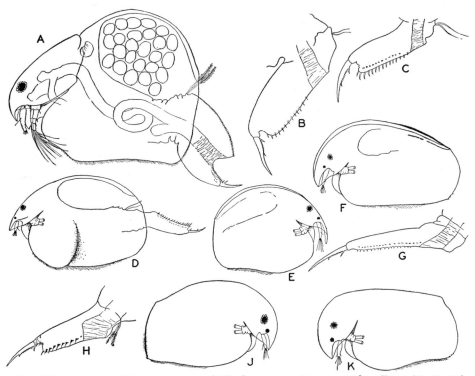

Fig. 235.—Structure of Eurycercinae and Chydorinae. A, *Eurycercus lamellatus* (O. F. M.), ×17; B, postabdomen of *Alonopsis aureola* Doolittle; C, postabdomen of *A. elongata* Sars; D, *Euryalona occidentalis* Sars, ×38; E, *Kurzia latissima* (Kurz), ×48; F, *Camptocercus rectirostris* Schödler, ×40; G, postabdomen of same; H, postabdomen of *Acroperus harpae* Baird; J, *A. harpae*, ×42; K, *A. angustatus* Sars, ×46. (A modified from Lilljeborg; B and C modified from Doolittle; D, E, F, J, and K modified from Ward and Whipple; G and H modified from Uéno.)

**62.** Postabdomen relatively broad (Fig. 235C); 0.8 mm. long.

**Alonopsis elongata** Sars

Postabdomen relatively narrow (Figs. 235D, G)..........................**63**

**63.** Anterior portion of valves swollen (Fig. 235D); 1 mm. long; in aquatic vegetation; southern states..........................**Euryalona occidentalis** Sars

Anterior portion of valves not swollen; usually in aquatic vegetation in shallows. .**64**

**64.** Crest on head and valves (Fig. 235F); about 1 mm. long......**Camptocercus, 65**

Crest on valves only (Fig. 235E); 0.6 mm. long; common everywhere.

**Kurzia latissima** (Kurz)

**65.** Postabdomen with 15 to 17 marginal denticles (Fig. 235G); common everywhere.

**Camptocercus rectirostris** Schödler

Postabdomen with 20 or more marginal denticles..........................**66**

**66.** Postabdomen with 20 to 30 marginal denticles; widely distributed but rare.

**Camptocercus macrurus** (O. F. M.)

Postabdomen with 45 to 65 minute marginal denticles; in temporary ponds in Okla..........................**Camptocercus oklahomensis** Mackin

67. Dorsal margin arched (Fig. 235J)..................**Acroperus harpae** Baird °
    Dorsal margin not arched (Fig. 235K)............**Acroperus angustatus** Sars °
68. Rostrum not greatly exceeding antennules (Fig. 236).....................69
    Rostrum much longer than antennules (Fig. 239D)......................83
69. Rostrum abruptly narrowed and pointed near tip (Figs. 236C, G, H).........70
    Rostrum not abruptly narrowed near tip (Fig. 236A); 0.5 to 0.7 mm. long;
        usually on bottom in shallows; common and widely distributed.
                                    **Graptoleberis testudinaria** (Fischer)
70. Ventroposterior angle without teeth.....................................71
    Ventroposterior angle with one to four small teeth.........................77
71. Postabdomen with clusters of large spines (Fig. 236B); about 1 mm. long; un-
        common.......................................................**Leydigia**, 72
    Postabdomen without clusters of large spines...........................73
72. Valves without markings (Fig. 236C); widely distributed but uncommon.
                                    **Leydigia quadrangularis** (Leydig)
    Valves with longitudinal striations; La.......**Leydigia acanthocercoides** (Fischer)
73. Postabdomen with marginal and lateral denticles (Figs. 236D, K, L)........74
    Postabdomen with marginal denticles only (Figs. 236E, F)................76
74. Marginal denticles longer distally (Fig. 236D); about 0.5 mm. long.
                                    **Oxyurella**, 75
    Marginal denticles not longer distally..........................**Alona**, 78

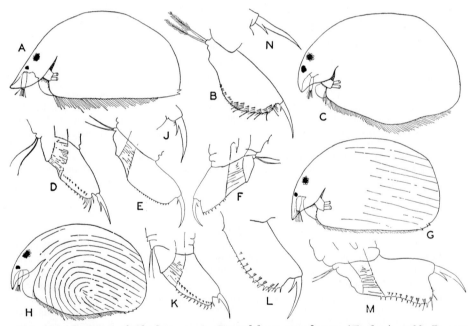

Fig. 236.—Structure of Chydorinae. A, *Graptoleberis testudinaria* (Fischer), ×80; B, post-abdomen of *Leydigia quadrangularis* (Leydig); C, *L. quadrangularis*, ×45; D, postabdomen of *Oxyurella tenuicaudis* (Sars); E, postabdomen of *Alonella diaphana* (King); F, postabdomen of *Alona guttata* Sars; G, *A. monacantha* Sars, ×100; H, *Alonella karua* (King), ×75; J, claw of *Alona affinis* (Leydig); K, postabdomen of *A. costata* Sars; L, postabdomen of *A. rectangula* Sars; M, postabdomen of *A. intermedia* Sars; N, claw of *A. quadrangularis* (O. F. M.). (A, E, G, and H modified from Ward and Whipple; B and L modified from Volterra D'Ancona; C, F, K, and M modified from Lilljeborg; D modified from Birge, 1910.)

* Intermediate forms between these two species indicate that they might belong to a single variable species.

75. Penultimate marginal denticle largest (Fig. 236D); widely distributed.
      **Oxyurella tenuicaudis** (Sars)
      Ultimate marginal denticle largest, serrate; rare; La.
      **Oxyurella longicaudis** (Birge)
76. Denticles minute (Fig. 236E); 0.5 mm. long; rare; southern states.
      **Alonella diaphana** (King)
      Denticles of usual size (Fig. 236F); 0.4 mm. long; common everywhere.
      **Alona guttata** Sars
77. Valves with longitudinal striae (Fig. 236G); 0.4 mm. long; in vegetation in pools;
      La...........................................**Alona monacantha** Sars
      Valves with oblique striae (Fig. 236H); about 0.5 mm. long; La., Texas, and Ark.
      **Alonella karua** (King)
78. Postabdomen with marginal denticles only (Fig. 236F); 0.4 mm. long; common
      everywhere.........................................**Alona guttata** Sars
      Postabdomen with both marginal and lateral denticles (Figs. 236K–M).......79
79. With 14 or more marginal denticles; up to 1 mm. long....................80
      With less than 14 marginal denticles; up to 0.5 mm. long..................81
80. With a cluster of fine spinules at base of claw (Fig. 236J); abundant everywhere
      in vegetation of littoral regions...................**Alona affinis** (Leydig)
      Without spinules at base of claw (Fig. 236N); in vegetation of littoral and on
      bottom in deeper water; common everywhere.
      **Alona quadrangularis** (O. F. M.)
81. Lateral denticles not extending beyond dorsal margin of postabdomen; abundant
      everywhere (Fig. 236K)...........................**Alona costata** Sars
      Lateral denticles long, extending beyond dorsal margin of postabdomen (Figs.
      236L, M)...............................................82
82. Postabdomen not broadened near apex (Fig. 236L); common everywhere.
      **Alona rectangula** Sars
      Postabdomen broadened near apex (Fig. 236M); rare......**Alona intermedia** Sars
83. Postabdomen with marginal denticles only (Fig. 236E)...........**Alonella**, 93
      Postabdomen with numerous lateral denticles, only two to four marginal denticles
      (Fig. 237A); 0.5 mm. long; northern states....**Rhynchotalona falcata** (Sars)
84. Body elongated.......................................85
      Body spherical or broadly ellipsoidal.................................102
85. Posterior margin with teeth along entire length (Fig. 237B); 0.5 mm. long.
      **Pleuroxus**, 86
      Posterior margin without teeth along entire length.......................87
86. Rostrum bent sharply into a hook (Fig. 237B); common in vegetation in northern
      states.................................**Pleuroxus procurvatus** Birge
      Rostrum not bent; Nebr....................**Pleuroxus truncatus** (O. F. M.)
87. Without teeth at the ventroposterior angle............................88
      With one or more teeth at the ventroposterior angle......................94
88. Claws with two basal spines (Figs. 237E, L, M)...............**Pleuroxus**, 89
      Claws with one basal spine (Fig. 236E).....................**Alonella**, 92
89. Postabdomen long and slender; ventroposterior angle rounded (Fig. 237D); 0.8
      mm. long; common in aquatic vegetation........**Pleuroxus striatus** Schödler
      Postabdomen of moderate length (Figs. 237L, M); 0.5 to 0.6 mm. long........90
90. Angle of postabdomen sharp; in pools and aquatic vegetation; probably generally
      distributed; more common in northern states......**Pleuroxus hamulatus** Birge
      Angle of postabdomen rounded (Figs. 237L, M)........................91
91. With row of marginal denticles longer than anal emargination (Fig. 237L); widely
      distributed but uncommon..............**Pleuroxus trigonellus** (O. F. M.)
      With row of marginal denticles about equal to anal emargination (Fig. 237M);
      in aquatic vegetation; reported from several northern and western states.
      **Pleuroxus aduncus** (Jurine)

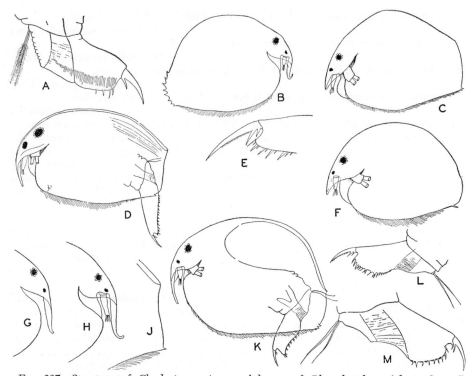

Fig. 237.—Structure of Chydorinae. A, postabdomen of *Rhynchotalona falcata* Sars; B, *Pleuroxus procurvatus* Birge, ×70; C, *Alonella dentifera* Sars, ×95; D, *Pleuroxus striatus* Schödler, ×55; E, claw of *P. striatus*; F, *Dunhevedia crassa* King, ×75; G and H, anterior end of *Pleuroxus uncinatus* Baird; J, posterior end of *P. hastatus* Sars; K, *P. denticulatus* Birge, ×85; L, postabdomen of *P. trigonellus* (O. F. M.); M, postabdomen of *P. aduncus* (Jurine). (A modified from Lilljeborg; B, C, and F through M modified from Ward and Whipple; D and E redrawn from Uéno.)

92. Postabdomen with marginal and lateral denticles; La....**Alonella globulosa** Daday
    Postabdomen with marginal denticles only (Fig. 236E).....................93
93. Marginal denticles minute (Fig. 236E); rostrum reaching not more than two-
        thirds the distance to the ventral margin; rare; southern states.

                                        **Alonella diaphana** (King)
    Marginal denticles of usual size; rostrum long, recurved, and reaching the ventral
        margin (Fig. 239D).........................**Alonella rostrata** (Koch)
94. Claws with two basal spines...........................................95
    Claws with one basal spine.........................................115
95. Rostrum long, extending well beyond the tips of the terminal olfactory setae
        (Figs. 237D, G, H, K); teeth on ventroposterior angle variable.

                                                    **Pleuroxus, 97**

    Rostrum shorter, extending only slightly, if at all, beyond the tips of the olfactory
        setae; lowermost part of posterior margin excised or notched, or ventro-
        posterior angle with one or two prominent teeth (Figs. 239J, K).

                                                    **Alonella, 96**

96. Postabdomen angled at apex (Fig. 239F); common everywhere in aquatic
        vegetation.................................**Alonella excisa** (Fischer)
    Postabdomen rounded at apex (Fig. 239G); rare; northern states.

                                        **Alonella exigua** (Lillj.)

97. Rostrum curved forward (Figs. 237G, H); two to four long, curved teeth at infero-posterior angle; 0.7 to 0.9 mm. long; rare; northern states.

Pleuroxus uncinatus Baird

Rostrum not curved forward.........................................98

98. Postabdomen long and slender (Fig. 237D)............................99

Postabdomen of moderate length (Figs. 237K–M); 0.5 to 0.6 mm. long......100

99. Ventroposterior angle a sharp point, with a very small tooth (Fig. 237J); 0.6 mm. long; rare but widely distributed.................Pleuroxus hastatus Sars

Ventroposterior angle rounded, with a small tooth anterior to it (Fig. 237D); 0.8 mm. long; common everywhere in aquatic vegetation.

Pleuroxus striatus Schödler

100. Angle of postabdomen sharp; ventroposterior angle with teeth (Fig. 237K); common everywhere in aquatic vegetation....Pleuroxus denticulatus Birge

Angle of postabdomen rounded (Figs. 237L, M).......................101

101. With row of marginal denticles longer than anal emargination (Fig. 237L); two to three small teeth on inferoposterior angle; widely distributed but uncommon..........................Pleuroxus trigonellus (O. F. M.)

With row of marginal denticles about equal to anal emargination (Fig. 237M); occasionally two or three small teeth on inferoposterior angle; in aquatic vegetation; reported from several northern and western states.

Pleuroxus aduncus (Jurine)

102. With a small to large spine at ventroposterior angle (Fig. 238A)..........103

Without a spine at ventroposterior angle............................104

103. Valves conspicuously striated (Fig. 238A); 0.2 to 0.3 mm. long; rare; northern states.......................................Alonella nana (Baird)

Valves not striated............................................Chydorus, 114

104. Valves with conspicuous projection at anteroventral margin (Fig. 238B); 0.35 mm. long; widely distributed.................Anchistropus minor Birge

Valves without such a projection...................................105

105. Animal spherical or ovate; postabdomen with prominent preanal angle (Fig. 238G); 0.3 to 0.8 mm. long...........................Chydorus, 106

Animal more elongated; postabdomen without prominent preanal angle; 0.2 to 0.5 mm. long............................................115

106. Postabdomen long, narrow (Fig. 238C); widely distributed; in aquatic vegetation.

Chydorus globosus Baird

Postabdomen short, broad (Fig. 238G)...............................107

107. Shell deeply sculptured..........................................108

Shell not deeply sculptured.......................................109

108. Shell covered with deep polygonal cells; widely distributed but uncommon.

Chydorus faviformis Birge

Shell covered with deep polygonal cells and ridges (Fig. 238D); Maine, N. H., and N. J.......................................Chydorus bicornutus Doolittle

109. Ventral edge of keel of labrum smooth..............................110

Ventral edge of keel of labrum toothed (Figs. 239A–C); rare...............113

110. Dorsoanterior surface of head and valves somewhat flattened (Fig. 238E); rare; northern states.................................Chydorus gibbus Lillj.

Dorsoanterior surface of head and valves not flattened...................111

111. All olfactory setae inserted at end of antennule (Fig. 238H); 0.3 to 0.5 mm. long; one of the most common of all Cladocera; widely distributed.

Chydorus sphaericus (O. F. M.)

All olfactory setae not inserted at end of antennule; rare..................112

112. With two olfactory setae on side of antennule (Fig. 238J); 0.4 mm. long; Maine.

Chydorus piger Sars

With one olfactory seta on side of antennule (Fig. 238K); 0.5 mm. long; Nebr.

Chydorus ovalis Kurz

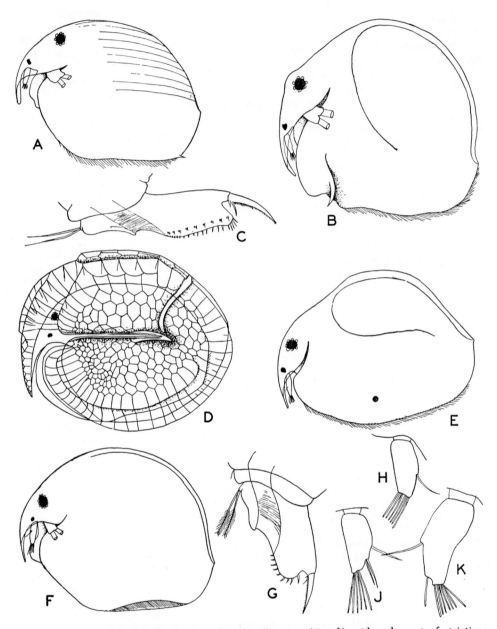

FIG. 238.—Structure of Chydorinae. A, *Alonella nana* (Baird) with only part of striations shown, ×200; B, *Anchistropus minor* Birge, ×160; C, postabdomen of *Chydorus globosus* Baird; D, *C. bicornutus* Doolittle, ×120; E, *C. gibbus* Lillj., ×110; F, *C. sphaericus* (O. F. M.), ×130; G, postabdomen of *C. sphaericus*; H, antennule of *C. sphaericus*; J, antennule of *C. piger* Sars; K, antennule of *C. ovalis* Kurz. (A to E modified from Ward and Whipple; G to K modified from Lilljeborg.)

113.  Without a spine at the ventroposterior angle; one tooth on labrum (Fig. 239A); La. and Calif.................................**Chydorus poppei** Richard

With a spine at the ventroposterior angle; one or several teeth on labrum....**114**

114.  With several teeth on keel of labrum (Fig. 239B); La.

**Chydorus barroisi** (Richard)

With one tooth on keel of labrum (Fig. 239C); widely distributed.

**Chydorus hybridus** Daday

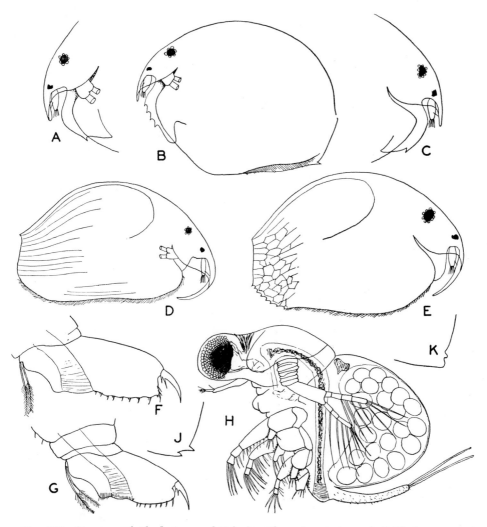

FIG. 239.—Structure of Chydorinae and Polyphemidae. A, anterior end of *Chydorus poppei* Richard; B, *C. barroisi* (Richard), ×140; C, anterior end of *C. hybridus*, Daday; D, *Alonella rostrata* (Koch) with only a portion of valve striations shown, ×110; E, *A. dadayi* Birge with only a portion of valve reticulations shown, ×200; F, postabdomen of *Alonella excisa* (Fischer); G, postabdomen of *A. exigua* (Lillj.); H, *Polyphemus pediculus* (L.), ×50; J and K, ventroposterior angle of *Alonella excisa*. (A to E modified from Ward and Whipple; F to H modified from Lilljeborg.)

115. Rostrum short, extending only slightly, if at all, beyond the tips of the terminal olfactory setae (Figs. 236H; 237C, F); lateral denticles present on post-abdomen. ....................................................................116
Rostrum long, extending well beyond the tips of the terminal olfactory setae (Figs. 238A; 239D, E); lateral denticles absent....................**Alonella, 119**

116. Postabdomen bent abruptly behind anus; one or two teeth at inferoposterior angle.
**Dunhevedia, 117**
Postabdomen not bent abruptly behind anus.....................**Alonella, 118**

117. Ventral margin of keel of labrum smooth; dorsal margin of body arched (Fig. 237F); up to 0.5 mm. long; widely distributed....**Dunhevedia crassa** King
Ventral margin of keel of labrum toothed; dorsal margin of body only slightly arched; up to 0.7 mm. long; La., Texas..........**Dunhevedia serrata** King

118. Valves striated; one to four (usually three) small teeth at inferoposterior angle (Fig. 236H); La., Texas, and Ark................**Alonella karua** (King)
Valves reticulated; one to three larger teeth at inferoposterior angle (Fig. 237C); La. and Texas................................**Alonella dentifera** Sars

119. Rostrum very long and strongly recurved (Figs. 239D, E)................120
Rostrum shorter and only slightly recurved; one small tooth at inferoposterior angle (Fig. 238A); up to 0.3 mm. long; rare; northern states.
**Alonella nana** Baird

120. Valves striated; one minute tooth at inferoposterior angle (Fig. 239D); up to 0.5 mm. long; rare but widely distributed..........**Alonella rostrata** (Koch)
Valves reticulated; inferoposterior angle rounded, with several minute teeth (Fig. 239E); up to 0.3 mm. long; in pools in aquatic vegetation; La. and Texas.......................................**Alonella dadayi** Birge

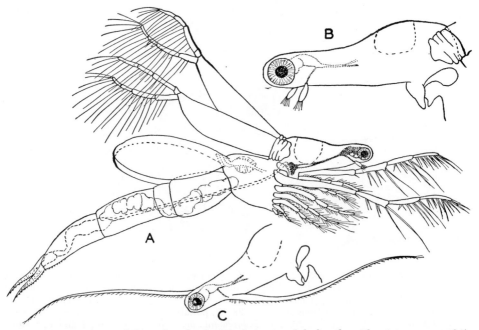

Fig. 240.—Structure of *Leptodora kindti* (Focke). A, adult female with winter eggs, ×8.5; B, anterior end of female; C, anterior end of male. (Modified from Sebestyén.)

**121.** Body short; with four pairs of stout legs, bearing branchial appendages (Fig. 239H); up to 1.5 mm. long; common in lakes, ponds, and marshes.

Tribe ONYCHOPODA, POLYPHEMIDAE, **Polyphemus pediculus** (L.)

Body long; with six pairs of legs; branchial appendages absent; up to 18 mm. long (Fig. 240); limnetic; common.

Tribe HAPLOPODA, LEPTODORIDAE, **Leptodora kindti** (Focke)

# CLADOCERA REFERENCES

ANDERSON, B. G., and J. C. JENKINS. 1942. A time study of events in the life span of Daphnia magna. *Biol. Bull.* **83**:260–272.

ANDERSON, B. G., H. LUMER, and L. J. ZUPANCIC, JR. 1937. Growth and variability in Daphnia pulex. *Ibid.* **73**:444–463.

AUSTIN, T. S. 1942. The fossil species of Bosmina. (Appendix I. Studies on Connecticut lake sediments. III. The biostratonomy of Linsley Pond. Part II., by E. S. Deevey, Jr.) *Amer. Jour. Sci.* **240**:325–331.

BANTA, A. M. 1939. Studies on the physiology, genetics, and evolution of some Cladocera. *Publ. Carnegie Inst. Wash.* **513**:1–285.

BERG, K. 1931. Studies on the genus Daphnia O. F. Müller with especial reference to the mode of reproduction. *Vidensk. Medd. Dansk. naturhist. Foren.* **92**:1–222.

———. 1934. Cyclic reproduction, sex determination and depression in the Cladocera. *Biol. Rev.* **9**:139–174.

BIRGE, E. A. 1893. Notes on Cladocera III. Descriptions of new and rare species. *Trans. Wis. Acad. Sci. Arts and Lett.* **9**:275–317.

———. 1910. Notes on Cladocera. IV. *Ibid.* **16**:1017–1066.

BREHM, V. 1937. Zwei neue Moina-Formen aus Nevada, U. S. A. *Zool. Anz.* **117**:91–96.

BROOKS, J. L. 1946. Cyclomorphosis in Daphnia. I. An analysis of D. retrocurva and D. galeata. *Ecol. Monogr.* **16**:409–447.

BROWN, L. A. 1929. The natural history of cladocerans in relation to temperature. I. Distribution and the temperature limits for vital activities. *Amer. Nat.* **68**:248–264.

CANNON, H. G., and F. M. C. LEAK. 1933. On the feeding mechanism of the Branchiopoda. *Philos. Trans. Roy. Soc. London, B*, **222**:267–352.

CARPENTER, K. E. 1931. Variations in Holopedium species. *Science* **74**:550–551.

COKER, R. E. 1939. The problem of cyclomorphosis in Daphnia. *Quart. Rev. Biol.* **14**:137–148.

COKER, R. E., and H. H. ADDLESTONE. 1938. Influence of temperature on cyclomorphosis of D. longispina. *Jour. Elisha Mitchell Sci. Soc.* **54**:45–75.

ERIKSSON, S. 1936. Studien über die Fangapparate der Branchiopoden nebst einigen phylogenetischen Bemerkungen. *Zool. Bidrag Uppsala* **15**:23–287.

GELLIS, S. S., and G. L. CLARKE. 1935. Organic matter in dissolved and in colloidal form as food for Daphnia magna. *Physiol. Zool.* **8**:127–137.

HASLER, A. D. 1937. The physiology of digestion in plankton Crustacea. II. Further studies on the digestive enzymes of (A) Daphnia and Polyphemus; (B) Diaptomus and Calanus. *Biol. Bull.* **72**:290–298.

HERRICK, C. L., and C. H. TURNER. 1895. A synopsis of the Entomostraca of Minnesota. *Geol. and Nat. Hist. Surv. Minn., Second Rept. State Zoologist*, 1–337.

INGLE, L., T. R. WOOD, and A. M. BANTA. 1937. A study of longevity, growth, reproduction, and heart rate in Daphnia longispina as influenced by limitations in quantity of food. *Jour. Exp. Zool.* **76**:325–352.

KIANG, H.-M. 1942. Über die Cyclomorphose der Daphnien einiger Voralpenseen. *Int. Rev.* **41**:345–408.

KISER, R. W. 1950. *A revision of the North American species of the cladoceran genus Daphnia.* 65 pp. Seattle, Wash.

KLUGH, A. B. 1927. The ecology, food-relations and culture of fresh-water Entomostraca. *Trans. Roy. Canad. Inst.* **16**:15–98.

LILLJEBORG, W. 1900. Cladocera sueciae. *Nova Acta Regiae Soc. Scient. Upsaliensis, Ser. 3*, **19**:1–701.

MACKIN, J. G. 1930. Studies on the Crustacea of Oklahoma. I. Camptocercus oklahomensis n. sp. *Trans. Amer. Micros. Soc.* **49**:46–53.

———. 1931. Studies on the Crustacea of Oklahoma: notes on the cladoceran fauna. *Proc. Okla. Acad. Sci.* **11**:22–28.

PACAUD, A. 1939. Contribution à l'écologie des Cladocères. *Bull. biol. France et de Belg., Suppl.* **25**:1–260.

PARENZAN, P. 1932. Cladocera. Sistematica e corologia dei Cladoceri limnicoli italiani ed appendice sui Cladoceri in generale. *Boll. Pesca, Piscicolt. Idrobiologia, Mem. Sci. (Ser. B), Suppl.* **8**:1–340.

PRATT, D. M. 1943. Analysis of population development in Daphnia at different temperatures. *Biol. Bull.* **85**:116–140.

RYLOV, W. M. 1935. Die Cladoceren. *Die Binnengewässer* **15**:97–157.

SCOURFIELD, D. J. 1942. The "pulex" forms of Daphnia and their separation into two distinct series represented by D. pulex (De Geer) and D. obtusa Kurz. *Ann. Mag. Nat. Hist.* **9**:202–219.

SEBESTYÉN, O. 1931. Contribution to the biology and morphology of Leptodora kindtii (Focke) (Crustacea, Cladocera). *Arb. Ungar. Biol. Forsch.-Inst.* **4**:151–170.

STORCH, O. 1924. Morphologie und Physiologie des Fangapparates der Daphniden. *Ergeb. Fortschritte der Zool.* **6**:125–234.

———. 1925. Cladocera. *Biologie der Tiere Deutschlands* **15**:23–102.

UÉNO, M. 1927. The freshwater Branchiopoda of Japan. I. *Mem. Coll. Sci. Kyoto Imp. Univ. Ser. B*, **2**:259–311.

VOLTERRA D'ANCONA, L. 1933. Contributo allo studio dei Cladoceri dell' Italia centrale. I Cladoceri di un Laghetto dei dintorni di Siena. *Int. Rev.* **29**:33–83.

VON SAALFELD, E. 1936. Untersuchungen über den Blutkreislauf bei Leptodora hyalina. *Zeitschr. vergl. Physiol.* **24**:58–70.

WAGLER, E. 1936. Die Systematik und geographische Verbreitung des Genus Daphnia O. F. Müller besonderer Berücksichtigung der südafrikanischen Arten. *Arch. Hydrobiol.* **30**:505–556.

WESENBERG-LUND, C. 1926. Contributions to the biology and morphology of the genus Daphnia with some remarks on heredity. *Mem. Acad. Roy. Sci. Lett. Danemark, Sect. Sci., Ser. 8*, **11**:89–251.

WOLTERECK, R. 1913. Über Funktion, Herkunft und Entstehungsursachen der sogen. "Schwebe-Fortsätze" pelagischer Cladoceren. *Zoologica* **26**:474–550.

———. 1932. Races, associations and stratification of pelagic daphnids in some lakes of Wisconsin and other regions of the United States and Canada. *Trans. Wis. Acad. Sci. Arts and Lett.* **27**:487–522.

WOOD, T. R. 1938. *Activation of the dormant form of freshwater animals, with special reference to Cladocera.* Ph.D. thesis, Library of Brown University; 87 pp., typewritten.

WOOD, T. R., and A. M. BANTA. 1937. Hatchability of Daphnia and Moina sexual eggs without drying. *Int. Rev.* **35**:229–242.

# Chapter 17

## COPEPODA

LIKE THE Cladocera, the Copepoda are almost universally distributed in the plankton, benthic, and littoral regions of fresh waters. They are either absent or present in small numbers in rapid head-water brooks and streams.

**General characteristics.** The body length of the American species ranges from 0.3 to 3.2 mm., but the great majority are less than 2.0 mm. long. Most species are drab grayish or brownish in color, but others, especially littoral species in the spring of the year and at high altitudes, are brilliant orange, purple, or red. As a group, the members of the Subclass Copepoda are much more homogeneous in their general structure than the Cladocera, and accurate identification is based largely on anatomical details of the appendages.

The American fresh-water copepods comprise two orders, Eucopepoda and Branchiura, and six suborders: Caligoida, Lernaeopodoida, Arguloida, Calanoida, Cyclopoida, and Harpacticoida. The first three of these suborders are exclusively parasitic, and the morphology is greatly modified and specialized. In the three free-living suborders, however, the body is clearly segmented, more or less elongated, cylindrical, and is divided into a head, thorax, and abdomen. The thoracic region is here considered to be composed of seven segments, but the first one or two are fused with the head to form a cephalothorax, which is covered with a carapace. In addition the fourth and fifth or fifth and sixth thoracic segments are also occasionally fused. The abdomen consists of three to five segments, typically four. Commonly the last thoracic (genital) segment and the first abdominal segment are fused together. Conversely, there is subdivision of some segments in a few species.

Each segment is a rigid, sclerotized cylinder which is attached to adjacent segments by a short, flexible, annular portion. One of the articulations is particularly movable, and, for convenience, the copepod body is often divided into metasome and urosome, the former being that part anterior to this articulation and the latter posterior (Fig. 241). The urosome includes all of the abdomen, the seventh thoracic (genital) segment, and sometimes the sixth thoracic segment.

**Appendages.** The true head is considered to have five pairs of appendages: first antennae, second antennae, mandibles, first maxillae, and second maxillae. The first thoracic segment (fused with the head) bears a pair of maxillipeds, and each of the five subsequent thoracic segments bears one pair of swimming legs. In a few species the seventh thoracic (genital) segment bears a pair of vestigial swimming legs. There are no abdominal appendages.

In Figs. 241A and C the first two thoracic segments are fused with the head; the metasome therefore consists of cephalothorax and free thoracic segments III to V; the urosome consists of thoracic segment

383

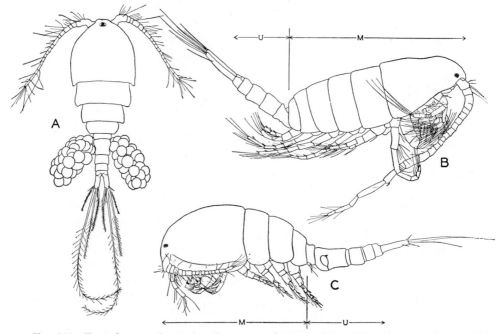

Fig. 241.—Typical copepods. A, female *Macrocyclops ater* (Herrick) with egg masses, ×18; B, male *Limnocalanus macrurus* Sars, ×33; C, female *Cyclops*, ×42. *M*, metasome; *U*, urosome. (A modified from Coker, 1938; B modified from Gurney.)

VI, thoracic segment VII (fused with abdominal segment I), and free abdominal segments II to IV. In Fig. 241B only the first thoracic segment is fused with the head; the metasome therefore consists of the cephalothorax and free thoracic segments II to VI; the urosome consists of thoracic segment VII (genital segment) and abdominal segments I to IV.

Some investigators consider the maxillipeds to be a part of the true head, so that there are only six thoracic segments. Others consider the genital segment to be a part of the abdomen.

In studying species with confusing fusion or subdivision of the thoracic segments, it is easy to orient oneself by locating the first and subsequent swimming legs. They correspond to thoracic segments II to VI. Fundamentally, all head and thoracic appendages are biramous, and a primitive copepod swimming leg consists of a three-segmented basipod having attached at its distal end a median three-segmented endopod and a lateral three-segmented exopod. A typical and relatively unmodified swimming leg of *Cyclops* is shown in Fig. 242.

The appendages of the head are highly modified for various special functions. The first antennae are uniramous and long, consisting of as many as 25 segments; they are sensory appendages but are used also for locomotion. In male cyclopoids and harpacticoids both first antennae are geniculate and modified for copulation (Fig. 243A). In male calanoids only the right is geniculate (Fig. 241B).

The second antennae (Fig. 243C) are much shorter, either biramous or uniramous, and are probably most important as sensory structures, although they are prehensile in male harpacticoids. The mandibles, first maxillae, second maxillae, and maxillipeds (occurring in that order) are highly modified for food getting and handling (Figs. 243D–G).

The segmentation of the legs varies considerably from the primitive condition, and the modifications are most pronounced in the last two pairs. In the free-living species the sixth legs are always lacking in the female and are either rudimentary or lacking in the male. The fifth legs are reduced or vestigial in both sexes in the Cyclopoida and Harpacticoida, but in the Calanoida they are well developed and symmetrical in the female and asymmetrical and modified for clasping in the male (Figs. 250–254).

The last abdominal (anal) segment bears two posteriorly directed caudal rami. These are simple, more or less cylindrical structures which are neither biramous nor serially homologous with the head and thoracic appendages.

In general, there are four types of slender outgrowths from the exoskeleton. One type, the aesthetasks, presumably function as sensory receptors. They are delicate, elongated, blunt tipped, and occur on the

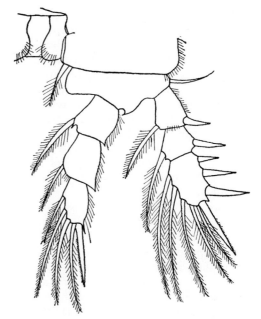

Fig. 242.—Typical swimming leg (right, second) of *Cyclops*, showing two-segmented basipod, three-segmented exopod (right), and three-segmented endopod (left). (Redrawn from Gurney.)

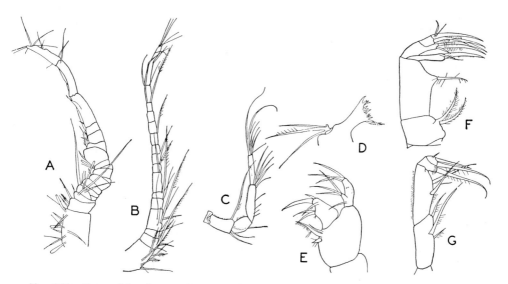

Fig. 243.—Copepod head appendages. A, first antenna of male *Mesocyclops leuckarti* Claus; B, first antenna of female *Macrocyclops fuscus* (Jurine); C, second antenna of same; D, mandible of same; E, first maxilla of same; F, second maxilla of same; G, maxilliped of same. (Redrawn from Gurney.)

first and second antennae. Aesthetasks are shown in Fig. 243A. The other three types of outgrowths occur on all copepod appendages and less commonly on the body segments; they form a morphological series: spines—setae—hairs. Spines are generally short, stout, strong, and inflexible. Setae, on the other hand, are relatively long, flexible, and thin. Hairs are the very finest outgrowths and they usually occur as fringes or rows on setae and spines. None of the categories spines, setae, and hairs can be precisely defined to the exclusion of the others, and there are wide variations in size and all possible and imperceptible intergrades. All of them, however, may have one or several functions, depending on their location. Generally they aid in swimming, crawling, and feeding, but some are sensory, and it is possible that the long setae of the caudal rami may act as balancers or stabilizers during locomotion.

**Feeding.** Harpacticoid mouth parts are adapted for raking, seizing, and scraping food from the bottom. Calanoids feed chiefly by filtration of plankton, the antennae being used as screws to produce a current, from which the particles are filtered by the mouth parts, chiefly the maxillae. There is considerable evidence to show that calanoids exhibit some selectivity in the size and kind of algae ingested. Cyclopoids have the mouth parts modified for seizing and biting. The food consists mostly of unicellular plant and animal organisms as well as organic debris, and it has now been well established that debris may, under some circumstances, form the majority of material ingested. The course of the food through the digestive tract can easily be seen in the living animal under the microscope. The anus is on the last abdominal segment between the bases of the caudal rami. The accumulation of reserve food in the form of oil globules is usually chiefly responsible for the brilliant red coloration of some species of *Diaptomus*.

**Locomotion.** Harpacticoids crawl or run on, and to some extent in, the substrate, and although some cyclopoids and calanoids also occur in close association with the substrate, they are characteristically swimmers. The swimming mechanisms of *Diaptomus* have been carefully analyzed by Storch (1929). A constant, smooth, and relatively slow type of locomotion is produced by the feeding movements of the mouth parts and second antennae. This is punctuated at frequent intervals by a jerky type of locomotion caused by rapid backward movements of the legs. Between beats of the legs the first antennae are kept thrust out stiffly and laterally; they are thus thought to act chiefly as parachutes which greatly retard sinking. A small fraction of a second before each beat of the legs, however, the first antennae are bent medially into the general longitudinal plane of the body, the beat of the legs thereby being much more effective. Immediately following each beat of the legs, the antennae are again extended laterally. According to Storch, a single beat of the legs and the accompanying antennal movements are completed in less than one-twelfth of a second. Cyclopoid mouth parts are of little importance, locomotion being brought about by relatively frequent beats of the legs. The accompanying antennal movements are similar to those of *Diaptomus*. In both cyclopoids and calanoids the abdomen is thought to function as a rudder.

**Internal anatomy.** Internal details are generally difficult to study because of the fact that they are largely obscured by the very complicated system of muscles. A saccular heart occurs only in the Calanoida, and in the other suborders the blood simply circulates about in the hemocoel as the result of the movements of muscles, appendages, and the digestive tract. The oxygen and carbon dioxide exchange occurs through the general body surface and probably to some extent through the posterior part of the digestive tract where water is drawn in and out by extrinsic muscles. Excretion is thought to occur through the maxillary glands near the anterior end, but it is possible that the general body surface and the posterior part of the digestive tract may function in excretion also. The nervous system exhibits considerable fusion and cephalization. Aside from tactile structures, the only recognizable sensory area is the eyespot. In free-living species this is a small, median dorsal, clear or pigmented area at the anterior end of the cephalothorax.

**Reproduction.** Although reproductive habits are generally similar throughout the free-living copepods, the various species differ widely in their detailed behavior and breeding periods. Some species, such as *Cyclops vernalis* Fischer and *Eucyclops agilis* (Koch), reproduce throughout the year; *E. prasinus* (Fischer) breeds between July and October. Other species are monocyclic and breed for only short periods. *Macrocyclops fuscus* (Jurine) and *M. ater* (Herrick), for example, reproduce only during the summer months, and some species of *Diaptomus* and *Limnocalanus macrurus* Sars have only one generation per year.

The antennae and, in some genera, the modified fifth legs of the male are used in clasping the female. The period of clasping may last only a few minutes or it may persist for several days. Sometimes the male clasps the female before she has had her final molt, and such clasping pairs have been observed over periods of as long as ten days.

Male calanoids have a single pore located asymmetrically on the genital segment, but female calanoids and both sexes in the other free-living suborders have paired genital pores. During clasping, the male transfers the sperm to the female in small, packet-like spermatophores, usually with the aid of the legs. The sperm are stored in a special ventral area of the female genital segment which serves as a seminal receptacle.

Actual fertilization occurs sometime after the two sexes have separated and as the eggs leave the female reproductive tract. This process may be completed within a few minutes or as long as two months after copulation. Fertilized eggs are carried by the female in one or two ovisacs (Fig. 241A). Ovisacs usually contain from five to 40 eggs each and are attached to the genital segment ventrally, laterally, or subdorsally. In some species the clutch size varies seasonally, with the largest numbers of eggs being produced in the spring months. Possibly this variation is correlated with temperature or food conditions.

In *Cyclops* the approximate incubation period ranges from 12 hours to five days, and when the newly hatched larvae leave the disintegrating ovisacs the female releases another group of eggs from the reproductive tract; these, in turn, are fertilized and retained in a new pair of ovisacs. In this way from seven to 13 pairs of ovisacs full of eggs may be produced successively at intervals of one to six days, all resulting from the sperm retained from a single copulation. Sometimes unfertilized females release sterile, nonhatching eggs, and a single European species of *Attheyella* is known to reproduce by parthenogenesis.

Although it is believed that ordinary fertilized eggs may occasionally overwinter in an extended incubation period, adverse environmental conditions are usually withstood by special thick-walled "resting" eggs. Such eggs do not occur in the cyclopoids, but they are known to be produced by several species of *Diaptomus* and some harpacticoids, and it is the only type of egg produced by *Limnocalanus macrurus*.

**Metamorphosis.** The copepod egg hatches into a small, compact, active larva called a nauplius which has three pairs of abbreviated appendages representing the first antennae, second antennae, and mandibles (Fig. 244A). After a

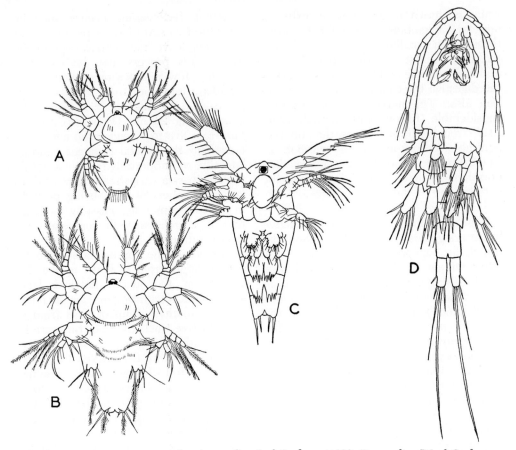

Fig. 244.—Immature copepods. A, nauplius I of *Cyclops,* ×100; B, nauplius IV of *Cyclops,* ×100; C, nauplius VI of *Diaptomus,* ×80; D, diagram of *Cyclops* copepodid, ×90 (only alternate legs shown on each side). (A and B redrawn from Gurney; C modified from Gurney.)

period of feeding, it molts and becomes the nauplius II stage which usually has the first maxillae in addition. In a similar manner there are four additional nauplius stages and five copepodid stages before the last molt which results in the sexually mature adult. As metamorphosis proceeds, the larvae become progressively larger and more elongated, and acquire additional appendages (Figs. 244B–D). Nauplius VI, for example, usually has all appendages through the second pair of legs, and copepodid I has four distinct thoracic segments and all appendages through the fourth legs. In summary, the typical life cycle consists of the egg, six

nauplius stages, five copepodid stages, and the adult. However, in all parasitic species and many free-living species this series is abbreviated. Thus, there are five nauplius stages in some Cyclopoida, and only four or five in certain Harpacticoida.

The time necessary for the complete life cycle from egg to egg is highly variable, depending on the species and environmental conditions. In *Cyclops* it lasts from seven to about 180 days, while some species of *Diaptomus* and *Limnocalanus macrurus* have a one-year cycle.

**Parasitic copepods.** Copepod parasites are known to occur on most common species of American fish and they are among the most highly modified and bizarre of all fresh-water animals. They are found on the general body surface, fins, and gills, and obtain nourishment from the tissues of the host.

Only a single genus, *Ergasilus*, of the Suborder Cyclopoida is parasitic and, incidentally, it is the least specialized for its parasitic existence. Only the adult female is parasitic, the immature females and all stages of males being free living. Superficially, the female looks like a *Cyclops* but may be easily distinguished by the greatly enlarged three-segmented clawlike second antennae (Fig. 246) which are used for clinging to the gills of fish.

The Caligoida is a relatively large suborder composed entirely of parasites. Only one species in one genus and about a dozen species in a second genus occur in American fresh waters, all others being parasitic on marine fishes. The former, *Lepeophtheirus salmonis* (Kröyer) (the sea louse) is scarcely recognizable as a copepod in the adult stage (Fig. 245B); there is a large, broad, flat cephalothorax, and most of the segments are fused, and the legs reduced. This species is only an incidental one in fresh waters; it is found attached to the surface of the body near the anus of salmon which have recently migrated from the sea, and may live only a week or two in fresh water. The males are very rare.

The other genus of the Suborder Caligoida occurring in the United States is *Lernaea*. The nauplii are free-living plankters, but the copepodids seek out a temporary host fish, cling to the gills, and copulate in this immature stage. Soon thereafter the male copepodid dies, but the female leaves the host and is free living for a short time. She then attaches to the

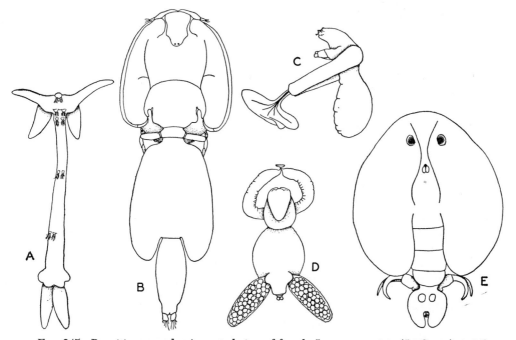

FIG. 245.—Parasitic copepods. A, ventral view of female *Lernaea cruciata* (Le Seuer), ×6.5; B, dorsal view of female *Lepeophtheirus salmonis* (Kröyer), ×6; C, lateral view of female *Salmincola inermis* (Wilson), ×6; D, dorsal view of female *Achtheres micropteri* Wright, ×8; E, dorsal view of female *Argulus flavescens* Wilson, ×10. (A and E modified from Wilson, 1914; B modified from Gurney; C and D modified from Wilson, 1915.)

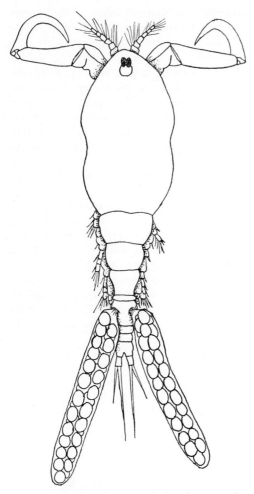

FIG. 246.—Dorsal view of female *Ergasilus versicolor* Wilson, ×70. (Modified from Wilson, 1911.)

are found attached in the branchial chamber or on the general body surface. Fish lice (Figs. 245E, 247) are greatly flattened dorsoventrally, and the head and thorax are covered with an expanded carapace whose lateral areas have a respiratory function. The abdominal segments are fused. The mouth parts are greatly modified or reduced; the second maxillae are completely transformed into curious suction cups; and the region of the mouth has a piercing organ used in obtaining the host blood. The first four pairs of legs are well developed and used for swimming, but the fifth and sixth legs are absent. Dorsally, there are two large movable compound eyes. *Argulus* often leaves its host and swims about freely, especially during the breeding season when the eggs are attached to stones and sticks of the substrate.

Of the parasitic Suborder Lernaeopodoida, only *Achtheres* and *Salmincola* occur in American fresh waters. These two genera are found in the gills and fins of many fishes and are perhaps the ultimate among Copepoda in modification for the parasitic mode of life. The soft-bellied adult females (Figs. 245C, D) have no legs, little evidence of segmentation, and greatly reduced mouth parts. The second maxillae, however, are large cylindrical structures which have a single saucer- or umbrella-shaped organ at their distal end. The latter is imbedded in the host tissues and functions in absorbing nutriment. Very little is known about the males; they are dwarfed, attached to the host fish during the immature stages, but cling to the body of the female before and after copulation. The nauplii stages are passed within the egg, but the first copepodid is a free-swimming plankter for a brief period before becoming attached to a fish.

**Economic significance.** Under natural conditions parasitic copepods are rarely present in sufficient numbers to cause serious injury to the host. In hatchery ponds, however, where fish are crowded in a limited area, there is much greater oppor-

general body surface of any one of a great variety of fresh-water fishes and becomes completely altered morphologically into a long wormlike creature. The anterior half of the body is buried in the superficial host tissues and produces several large anchoring processes (Fig. 245A).

The genus *Argulus* of the parasitic Suborder Arguloida is the only one occurring in the United States. There are about 15 species parasitizing many fresh-water fishes. The adults, familiarly known as fish lice, range from 5 to 25 mm. in length and

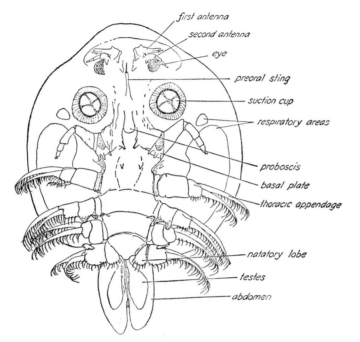

first antenna

second antenna

eye

preoral sting

suction cup

respiratory areas

proboscis

basal plate

thoracic appendage

natatory lobe

testes

abdomen

FIG. 247.—Ventral view of male *Argulus*, ×23. (Modified from Meehean.)

tunity for the free-swimming immature stages to find a host, and, as a result, heavy and serious infections may break out. When firmly established, copepod parasites are difficult to control, chiefly because the sclerotized exoskeleton of the adult is resistant to chemical solutions. Newly attached larval parasites are relatively delicate, however, and sometimes it is feasible to combat infections by giving the fish frequent salt or acid baths. In extreme cases there is no alternative but to get rid of the parasitized fish, clean the hatchery ponds, and start anew.

Free-living copepods constitute an essential link in the aquatic food chain. They are on an intermediate trophic level between bacteria, algae, and protozoans on the one hand and small and large plankton predators (chiefly fish) on the other. In general, however, fresh-water copepods are not as important an element in the fish diet as Cladocera.

Copepods are of further importance as intermediate hosts of parasites of higher animals, particularly some tapeworms of fish, waterfowl, and carnivores, some flukes of fish, amphibians, and birds, and a few nematodes of fish and birds. In Africa, southern Asia, the West Indies, and parts of the Guianas and Brazil, *Cyclops* is of great importance in the transmission of the nematode parasite of man, *Dracunculus medinensis* (the Guinea worm), and some species of both *Cyclops* and *Diaptomus* are intermediate hosts of the broad or fish tapeworm of man and numerous carnivores.

**Ecology.** Of the free-living copepods, the limnetic cyclopoid and calanoid species are by far the best known and most frequently collected. Sometimes they have been found in almost unbelievable numbers, up to 1,000 individuals per liter having been recorded. In most lakes the limnetic copepod plankton is rather monotonous; usually it is composed of only one, two, or three species, very often *Cyclops bicuspidatus* Claus, *C. vernalis*,

*Mesocyclops leuckarti* (Claus), *Diaptomus oregonensis* Lillj., or *D. siciloides* Lillj. Perhaps because of the greater variety of ecological niches afforded, the shallow littoral, especially in aquatic vegetation, is much richer in cyclopoid and calanoid species, but the population density is not usually high. Common littoral species are *Orthocyclops modestus* (Herrick), *Macrocyclops fuscus,* and *M. albidus* (Jurine).

In rivers and lakes the Harpacticoida are restricted to bottom debris of both littoral and benthic regions. In addition, however, there are many Cyclopoida and Calanoida that have become adapted to this habitat. Common bottom forms are *Paracyclops fimbriatus* (Fischer), *Eucyclops agilis* (Koch), *Macrocyclops fuscus, M. albidus,* and species of *Canthocamptus, Bryocamptus,* and *Attheyella.* Very few copepods are found in rapid streams.

As ecological groups, the deep water and limnetic species are somewhat distinct from those occurring in the shallow littoral. The former are generally smaller, slender, and more translucent, while the latter are larger, stout, more deeply pigmented, and have more robust appendages.

Harpacticoid copepods have been reported from some unusual habitats. Large numbers (up to 277 per 10 cubic centimeters of sand) have been found in the interstitial waters of sandy lake beaches, with greatest concentrations at depths of 1 to 6 centimeters, and at distances of 1.0 to 2.5 meters from the water's edge (Pennak, 1940). European workers have described unusual endemic species from springs, underground streams, and cave systems, but little collecting has been done in such habitats in this country. Harpacticoids have also been reported from damp moss in forests far from any body of water.

It is thought that temperature plays an exceedingly important role in copepod distribution and activity. Some species, such as *Limnocalanus macrurus, Senecella calanoides* Juday, *Epischura lacustris* Forbes, *Diaptomus minutus* Lillj., *D. sicilis* Forbes,

and *D. oregonensis* are definitely cold-water forms occurring only in the northern states and in deep lakes. Others, such as *Diaptomus mississippiensis* Marsh and *D. dorsalis* Marsh, are restricted to the southern states. The rare species *Cyclops crassicaudis* Sars occurs only in small, temporary, warm pools.

In some interesting experiments, Coker (1933) and Aycock (1942) reared *Cyclops vernalis, C. agilis,* and *C. viridis* (Jurine) under controlled conditions and found that at low temperatures (7.7° to 8.0°) adults were as much as 50 per cent longer than adults that had been reared at high temperatures (28.0° to 30.0°). These workers believe that such size variations with temperature are internally controlled and are not dependent upon the available food supply.

In general, copepods are much more tolerant of a deficiency of oxygen than are Cladocera. *Cyclops* and *Canthocamptus* have been collected many times from the surface of bottom muds in stratified lakes during summer and winter periods of stagnation and oxygen depletion. Although it is possible that *Cyclops* may swim up into the upper oxygenated layers intermittently, *Canthocamptus,* not being a swimmer, is necessarily restricted to the substrate. The whole problem of the metabolism of copepods and other organisms in anaerobic benthic regions deserves much more attention.

*Canthocamptus* and *Cyclops* may form cysts or cocoons during unfavorable environmental conditions, and the fact that cysts have been found in abundance on lake bottoms in midsummer is an indication that they may be formed as a response to anaerobic conditions. In *Cyclops,* but not in *Canthocamptus,* the cysts also constitute an aestivation mechanism and are resistant to drying. The cyst wall is composed of a secreted organic membrane and an enveloping mass of detritus. *Cyclops* encysts in the copepodid stages rather than as an adult.

Like the Cladocera, some common species of plankton copepods show a daily rhythmic cycle of vertical migrations in lakes, with a greater concentration of individuals in the upper waters during the hours of darkness and correspondingly large numbers in the bottom waters during the hours of daylight. Individuals of some species may move upward at dusk and downward at dawn a vertical distance of as much as 10 or 20 meters. It is believed that the primary stimulus for vertical migrations is the daily cycle of subsurface illumination.

**Geographical distribution.** The Copepoda undoubtedly originated in the ocean, and in this environment they have undergone much greater evolutionary specialization and speciation than in fresh water. The accompanying physiological divergence has been quite complete, and only a very few American species found in fresh water are known also to inhabit brackish or salt water. Some of these are *Limnocalanus macrurus*, *Eurytemora affinis* (Poppe), *Harpacticus gracilis* Claus, *Nitocra spinipes* Boeck, and *Marshia*.

*Limnocalanus macrurus* is generally considered to be a relict species, that is, a salt-water form which has gradually become acclimated to fresh water. It is found only in the deep waters of larger lakes such as Green Lake (Wisconsin), the Finger Lakes, and the Great Lakes. It is also widely distributed in similar European lakes and in salt water. *Eurytemora* has close relatives in salt water and is probably a recent migrant. *Senecella* is thought to be of postglacial origin; it has been recently reported from several localities in Siberia, including some saline lakes. *Epischura* is confined to North America except for two Asiatic species.

*Cyclops* and its relatives have a world-wide distribution in fresh waters, some species, such as *C. bicuspidatus*, being essentially cosmopolitan. The closest marine and brackish relative is probably *Halicyclops*.

The Diaptomidae are confined to fresh waters, and there are no near marine relatives. Unlike the cyclopoids, they show much evidence of recent speciation, and the species of *Diaptomus* occurring on this continent are all apparently endemic. Furthermore, many of them seem to be confined to small geographic areas; numerous examples are given in the key which follows.

Nearly all fresh-water harpacticoids belong to the family Canthocamptidae, a group which has a world-wide distribution in salt, brackish, and fresh waters. Many species occur in both North American and European fresh waters, but so little systematic collecting has been done on the other continents that there are insufficient records to warrant the use of the term "cosmopolitan" for them.

Unquestionably, active migration is responsible for the geographic dispersal of species throughout a single drainage system, but overland transport to adjacent systems presents some difficult questions. Calanoida and Harpacticoida are probably dispersed as resting eggs, and although cysts are produced by some of the latter, they are not resistant to drying. The Cyclopoida, on the other hand, are not known to produce resting eggs, but resistant copepodid cysts are presumably of common occurrence, and it is likely that passive dispersal is brought about in this stage. It is significant that the first cyclopoids to appear in dried mud cultures are in the copepodid stages. Many copepods are found year after year in vernal ponds which are completely dried up during the greater part of the year, and we may safely assume that resting eggs and cysts in the dry mud and debris tide the species over.

While passive transfer by waterfowl, aquatic insects, and in wind-blown dust explains the extensive distribution of some species, it is difficult to account for the fact that others are restricted to very small geographic areas, sometimes a single lake.

**Collecting.** Littoral and plankton copepods are easily collected with a fine townet or dipnet. An abundance of species may often be obtained by drawing nets through rooted aquatic vegetation and by lightly skimming the bottom. Collecting harpacticoids is a more tedious procedure. The top centimeter or two of mud and debris should be scooped up, brought into the laboratory, and allowed to settle. If the material is examined by looking toward a light source along the surface of the settled mud, the harpacticoids can be seen moving about at the mud–water interface and can be removed with a long pipette. Sometimes washings of aquatic mosses produce surprising numbers of specimens.

**Preservation.** The best specimens are obtained by killing in 95 per cent alcohol. Seventy per cent alcohol is a suitable preservative and is much superior to formalin solutions.

**Identification.** It is unfortunate that the identification of species is usually based on minute anatomical details. Some characters, such as the structure of the antennae, first legs, and caudal rami, may be studied from the whole animal, but it is often necessary to dissect the animal in order to study the mouth parts and legs, and it is an imperative procedure in formulating descriptions of new species. Harpacticoids must be dissected more frequently because of their general opacity and smaller appendages. Specimens to be dissected should be placed in a solution of 20 per cent glycerin in 95 per cent alcohol in a partially covered watch glass. After one to several days, most of the alcohol and water will have evaporated, leaving the undistorted specimens in glycerin. Then they may be easily picked up and trans-

ferred on the tip of a fine, flat, toothbrush bristle mounted at the end of a matchstick. The animals should be dissected, one at a time, in a drop of glycerin on a slide on the stage of a high power Greenough type binocular microscope. The necessary appendages are removed with a pair of sharp, mounted "minuten nadeln." As a fair warning, it should be said that requisite skill and patience in dissection come only with considerable practice! Appendages and whole animals are conveniently and permanently mounted for examination in glycerin jelly under a cover slip ringed with Murrayite. Mounting in fluid glycerin is more of a nuisance and less permanent. Immature forms of the great majority of species cannot be identified.

If an abundance of specimens is available, the writer has found that all of the necessary anatomical details can usually be seen, even in difficult species, if five to ten whole specimens are mounted, ventral side up, on the same slide. The appendages will become spread out sufficiently in a variety of ways so that all structures can be observed by studying several specimens under the high powers of the compound microscope.

Sometimes it is helpful if the animals are stained before dissection and mounting. From 70 per cent alcohol they should be transferred to alum cochineal over night, washed in 70 per cent alcohol for five minutes, and then transferred to the glycerin-alcohol mixture.

Accurate measurements of body length are of limited use as a taxonomic character because of the fact that the trunk segments may be more or less retracted into each other.

## KEY TO GENERA AND SPECIES OF COPEPODA

1. With a movable articulation between the fifth and sixth thoracic segments (Fig. 241C); depressed or cylindrical; parasitic, commensal, free-swimming, or benthic. .................................................................6

   Without a movable articulation between fifth and sixth thoracic segments; free-living or fixed parasites........................Order **EUCOPEPODA, 2**

2. With a movable articulation between sixth and seventh thoracic segments (Fig. 241B); segmentation well defined; first antennae long, composed of 22 to 25 segments; male left antenna geniculate in *Senecella*, male right antenna geniculate in all other genera; free-living......Suborder **CALANOIDA, 39**
   Body rigidly fused, without movable articulations, often without segmentation; fixed parasites of fishes.....................................................**3**
3. Adults long and wormlike (Fig. 245A); on gills and general external surface of many common fresh-water fishes; copepodid clings to gills of temporary host fish, then leaves and is free swimming for a short time before becoming attached to final host; adult females 7 to 15 mm. long; about a dozen species.
   Suborder **CALIGOIDA, LERNAEIDAE, Lernaea**
   Adults not long and wormlike; males rare......................................**4**
4. Cephalothorax forming a broad flat disc (Fig. 245B); first to fourth legs well developed; males not reduced in size, rare; attached to surface of body near anus of salmon which have recently migrated from the sea; may live for a week or more in fresh water; 6 to 16 mm. long; sea lice.
   Suborder **CALIGOIDA, CALIGIDAE, Lepeophtheirus salmonis** (Kröyer)
   Cephalothorax not forming a broad flat disc; legs absent; males small to minute pygmies clinging to females; early immature stages passed in egg; first copepodid free living for a brief period before seeking host; attached to gills and fins of host by greatly enlarged second maxillae; adult females 3 to 8 mm. long without egg sacs.
   Suborder **LERNAEOPODOIDA, LERNAEOPODIDAE, 5**
5. Without dorsal carapace on cephalothorax; abdomen absent; without segmentation (Fig. 245C); about a dozen American species parasitic on Salmonidae and Coregonidae. ............................................................**Salmincola**
   With a partial dorsal carapace; abdomen present; segmentation present or absent (Fig. 245D); about ten American species parasitic on a few species of Coregonidae, Centrarchidae, and Ameiuridae..................**Achtheres**
6. Body greatly flattened dorsoventrally; abdominal segments fused; no fifth or sixth legs (Fig. 245E); fixed parasites in branchial chamber or on general body surface of many species of fish; from 5 to 25 mm. long but usually less than 10 mm.; fish lice; a single American genus and about 15 species parasitizing many species of fresh-water fish.
   Order **BRANCHIURA,** Suborder **ARGULOIDA, ARGULIDAE, Argulus**
   Body not greatly flattened dorsoventrally; abdominal segments not fused; fifth and often sixth legs present; less than 3 mm. long; all genera free living except *Ergasilus*....................................Order **EUCOPEPODA, 7**
7. Metasome much wider than urosome; basal segment of fifth legs without inner expansion; first antennae with no more than 17 segments.
   Suborder **CYCLOPOIDA, 8**
   Urosome about as wide as metasome and both more or less cylindrical; basal segment of fifth legs with inner expansion; 0.3 to 1.0 mm. long.
   Suborder **HARPACTICOIDA, 90**
8. Second antennae large, three-segmented, and with a large apical claw used for prehension (Fig. 246); adult females parasitic on gills of many common species of fresh-water fishes; 0.6 to 1.0 mm. long; males and immature females free-living; about a dozen species in U. S..**ERGASILIDAE, Ergasilus**
   Second antennae small, without a large apical claw; 0.6 to 3.0 mm. long.
   **CYCLOPIDAE, 9**
9. Both rami of fourth legs three-segmented....................................**10**
   Both rami of fourth legs two-segmented...........................**Cyclops, 25**
10. Rami of first legs two-segmented; very rare; N. C..........**Cyclops nanus Sars**
    Rami of first legs three-segmented.........................................**11**

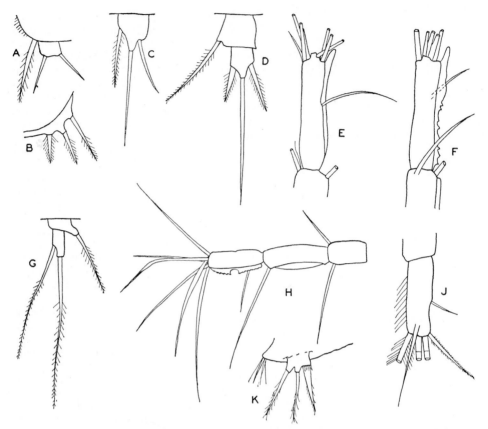

Fig. 248.—Structure of cyclopoid copepods. A, fifth leg of male *Ectocyclops phaleratus* (Koch); B, fifth leg of female *E. phaleratus*; C, fifth leg of female *Eucyclops prasinus* (Fischer); D, fifth leg of male *Macrocyclops albidus* (Jurine); E, last segment of female first antenna of same; F, last segment of female first antenna of *M. fuscus* (Jurine); G, fifth leg of *Mesocyclops leuckarti* (Claus); H, terminal segments of first antenna of same; J, dorsal view of right caudal ramus of *M. edax* (Forbes); K, fifth leg of male *Paracyclops fimbriatus* (Fischer). (A to D modified from Wilson, 1932; E modified from Gurney; F modified from Ward and Whipple; G and H modified from Coker, 1943.)

11. Fifth leg represented by a plate armed with three stout setae (Figs. 248A, B);
     widely distributed but not abundant........**Ectocyclops phaleratus** (Koch)
     Fifth leg otherwise...................................................**12**
12. Fifth leg made up of a single distinct segment (Fig. 248C)................**13**
     Fifth leg made up of two or three segments............................**16**
13. First antennae 17-segmented; rare but widely distributed; usually in the shallows.
                                          **Macrocyclops ater** (Herrick)
     First antennae with no more than 12 segments; bottom debris in both shallow and
     deep water; widely distributed...................................**14**
14. First antennae eight-segmented; widely distributed.
                                   **Paracyclops fimbriatus** (Fischer)
     First antennae 12-segmented.................................**Eucyclops, 15**
15. Outer margin of caudal rami toothed; a variable species; common everywhere on
     the bottom in many types of habitats.............**Eucyclops agilis** (Koch)
     Outer margin of caudal rami smooth; widely distributed but not common; usually
     in limnetic habitats......................**Eucyclops prasinus** (Fischer)

16. Fifth leg composed of two segments (Fig. 248D)..........................17
Fifth leg composed of three segments; usually among aquatic vegetation; widely distributed..........................**Orthocyclops modestus** (Herrick)

17. Last segment of fifth leg with three setae (Fig. 248D)........**Macrocyclops, 18**
Last segment of fifth leg with two setae or one seta and a spine or spur; common everywhere...........................................20

18. Lamella on last segment of antenna of female notched (Fig. 248F); in shallows among vegetation or on bottom; widely distributed.....**Macrocyclops fuscus** (Jurine)
Lamella on last segment of antenna of female smooth or lacking.............19

19. Lamella on last segment of antenna of female smooth and forming a lappet at tip of segment (Fig. 248E); in shallows among vegetation or on bottom; widely distributed.............................**Macrocyclops albidus** (Jurine)
Lamella lacking on last segment of antenna of female; rare.
**Macrocyclops distinctus** (Koch)

20. Setae of terminal segment of fifth leg approximately equal in length (Fig. 248G). .........................................................21
Inner seta of terminal segment of fifth leg spinelike, much shorter than outer (Fig. 249B).......................................**Cyclops, 27**

21. With a hyaline membrane on each of the last two segments of first antennae (Fig. 248H)........................................**Mesocyclops, 22**
Without a hyaline membrane on each of the last two segments of the first antennae; a few rare varieties of one species of *Cyclops*.
**Cyclops bicuspidatus** Claus

22. Fifth leg with inner seta on median side of second segment (Fig. 248G); common and widely distributed............................................23
Fifth leg with inner seta apical or subapical; rare.........................24

23. Caudal rami without hairs on inner margins......**Mesocyclops leuckarti** (Claus)
Caudal rami with hairs on inner margins (Fig. 248J).
**Mesocyclops edax** (Forbes)

24. Plate connecting bases of fourth legs with rounded unarmored prominence; Ariz.
**Mesocyclops tenuis** (Marsh)
Plate connecting bases of fourth legs without process; Wyo. and Ill.
**Mesocyclops dybowski** Lande

25. Caudal rami about six times as long as broad; Salton Sea, Calif.
**Cyclops dimorphus** Kiefer
Caudal rami two and one-half to five times as long as broad...............26

26. Longest terminal seta of caudal ramus longer than abdomen and ramus combined; widely distributed.............................**Cyclops varicans** Sars
Longest terminal seta of caudal ramus much shorter than abdomen and ramus combined; eastern states; scattered and rare..........**Cyclops bicolor** Sars

27. Each caudal ramus with a longitudinal dorsal ridge (Fig. 249A); N. Y.
**Cyclops scutifer** Sars
Caudal rami without longitudinal dorsal ridges............................28

28. Second segment of fifth leg with an apical seta and a very small spine or spur (Fig. 249B).......................................................29
Second segment of fifth leg with an apical seta and a long slender spine (Fig. 249D). ......................................................36

29. Small spur of fifth leg situated at about mid-length of the inner margin of the segment. .............................................................30
Small spur of fifth leg more distally situated (Fig. 249B)...............32

30. Setae of terminal segment of fourth endopod not extending to the distal end of the inner terminal spine (Fig. 249C); very rare; scattered distribution.
**Cyclops viridis** (Jurine)
Setae of terminal segment of fourth endopod extending beyond distal end of terminal spine...........................................................31

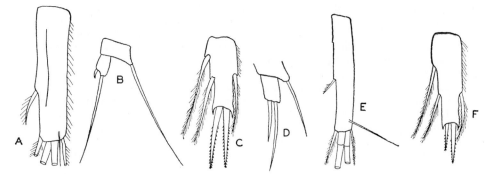

Fig. 249.—Structure of *Cyclops*. A, dorsal view of left caudal ramus of *Cyclops scutifer* Sars; B, fifth leg of *C. vernalis* Fischer; C, terminal segment of fourth endopod of *C. viridis* (Jurine); D, fifth leg of *C. bicuspidatus* Claus; E, dorsal view of left caudal ramus of same; F, terminal segment of fourth endopod of same. (A, B, C, E, and F modified from Yeatman.)

31. Innermost terminal seta of caudal ramus not quite twice as long as outermost; known only from Chapel Hill, N. C., and Ann Arbor, Mich., but probably widely distributed.............................**Cyclops gigas** Lowndes
    Innermost terminal seta of caudal ramus about three times as long as outermost; known only from Donnaldson Cave, Ind......**Cyclops donnaldsoni** Chappuis
32. First antennae with 17 segments (occasionally 18).......................**33**
    First antennae with less than 17 segments.................................**35**
33. Inner margins of caudal rami without hairs; common and widely distributed.
                                                      **Cyclops vernalis** Fischer
    Inner margins of caudal rami with hairs..................................**34**
34. Inner margins of caudal rami with tufts of fine hairs; outer margins without hairs; known only from Chapel Hill, N. C...........**Cyclops carolinianus** Yeatman
    Both inner and outer margins of caudal rami with fine hairs, not tufted; N. C. and Conn....................................**Cyclops venustoides** Coker
35. First antennae 11-segmented; N. C. and N. Y...............**Cyclops exilis** Coker
    First antennae 12-segmented; N. C. and Conn........**Cyclops venustoides** Coker
36. First antennae 17-segmented........................................**37**
    First antennae 12-segmented; very rare; usually in small pools; N. C. and N. Y.
                                                      **Cyclops crassicaudis** Sars
37. Terminal segment of fourth endopod about one to one and one-half times as long as broad; very rare.......................................**38**
    Terminal segment of fourth endopod about three or four times as long as broad (Fig. 249F); common and widely distributed....**Cyclops bicuspidatus** Claus
38. Terminal segment of fourth endopod with three stout spines and two setae; Mass. and N. C.....................................**Cyclops nearcticus** Kiefer
    Terminal segment of fourth endopod with one stout spine and four setae; N. C. and Morengo Cave, Ind.....................**Cyclops jeanneli** Chappuis
39. Endopod of first leg two-segmented; 0.9 to 4.5 mm. long but usually 1.2 to 2.5 mm. long..................................DIAPTOMIDAE, **Diaptomus, 46**
    Endopod of first leg with one or three segments; limnetic...................**40**
40. Endopod of first leg one-segmented.....................................**41**
    Endopod of first leg three-segmented.................CENTROPAGIDAE, **43**
41. Endopods of second to fourth legs one-segmented; abdomen of male asymmetrical (Figs. 250D, F); 1.1 to 2.9 mm. long........TEMORIDAE, **Epischura, 44**
    Endopods of second to fourth legs two- or three-segmented; abdomen of male symmetrical ..................................................**42**

**42.** Endopods of second to fourth legs two-segmented; male right antenna geniculate; 1.0 to 1.5 mm. long; in salt and brackish waters, as well as fresh-water ponds and lakes, along Atlantic and Gulf coasts.

TEMORIDAE, **Eurytemora affinis** (Poppe)*

Endopod of second leg two-segmented, those of third and fourth legs three-segmented; male left antenna not geniculate; 2.4 to 2.9 mm. long (Fig. 250A); deep cold lakes of Great Lakes region.

SENECELLIDAE, **Senecella calanoides** Juday

**43.** Caudal rami short (Fig. 250B); 1.5 to 2.5 mm. long; uncommon and erratically distributed over most of the U. S.........**Osphranticum labronectum** Forbes

Caudal rami long (Fig. 250C); 2.0 to 3.2 mm. long; occurs only in deep cold lakes, such as Great Lakes, Finger Lakes, and Green L., Wis.; usually considered a relict marine species in Great Lakes...**Limnocalanus macrurus** Sars

**44.** Female abdomen bent to the right (Fig. 250G); deep cold waters of Great Lakes region..................................**Epischura lacustris** Forbes

Female abdomen straight.............................................**45**

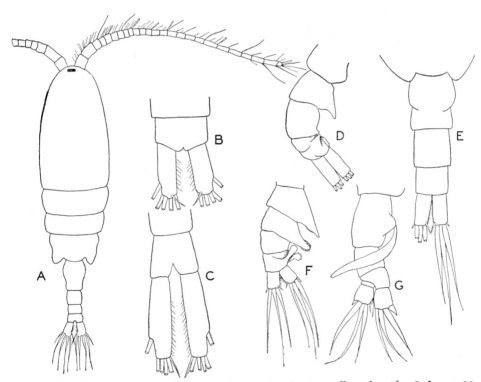

Fɪɢ. 250.—Structure of calanoid copepods. A, female *Senecella calanoides* Juday, ×26; B, caudal rami of female *Osphranticum labronectum* Forbes; C, caudal rami of male *Limnocalanus*; D, abdomen of male *Epischura nordenskiöldi* Lillj.; E, female abdomen of same; F, abdomen of male *Epischura lacustris* Forbes; G, female abdomen of same. (A modified from Juday; D to G modified from Marsh, 1933.)

* Several other species of *Eurytemora* are occasionally found in brackish and fresh waters in the immediate vicinity of the coasts.

**45.** Last abdominal segment of male with two projecting processes, one dorsal and one ventral; terminal segment of female fifth leg armed with six spines; Mass. and mountainous areas of western states, especially Wash. to Calif.

**Epischura nevadensis** Lillj.

Last abdominal segment of male with one dorsal projecting process (Fig. 250D); terminal segment of female fifth leg armed with five spines; Atlantic coast from Me. to N. C..........................**Epischura nordenskiöldi** Lillj.

**46.** Antepenultimate segment of male right first antenna without distinct appendage..**47**

Antepenultimate segment of male right first antenna with lateral lamella or terminal process (Figs. 252E, G).....................................................**54**

**47.** Male right and left fifth legs nearly equal in length, terminal hook of right leg symmetrical (Fig. 251A); common and widely distributed, especially in northern states.........................**Diaptomus oregonensis** Lillj.

Male left fifth leg shorter than right......................................**48**

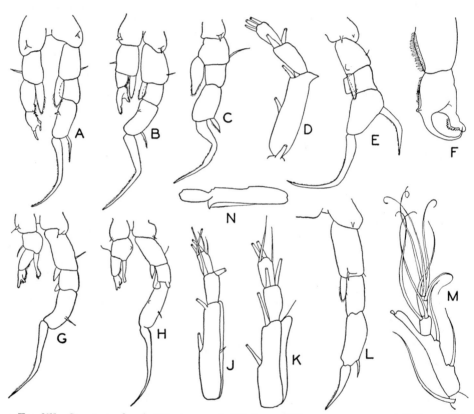

Fig. 251.—Structure of male *Diaptomus*. A, fifth legs of *Diaptomus oregonensis* Lillj.; B, fifth legs of *D. reighardi* Marsh; C, right fifth leg of *D. mississippiensis* Marsh; D, terminal right antennal segments of *D. birgei* Marsh; E, right fifth leg of same; F, left fifth exopod of *D. pallidus* Herrick; G, fifth legs of *D. tyrelli* Poppe; H, fifth legs of *D. coloradensis* Marsh; J, terminal right antennal segments of *D. clavipes* Schacht; K, terminal right antennal segments of *D. leptopus* Forbes; L, right fifth leg of same; M, terminal right antennal segments of *D. natriophilus* Light; N, antepenultimate and penultimate segments of right first antenna of *D. hesperus* Wilson and Light. (A to E, G, and J to L modified from Marsh, 1907; F modified from Light, 1939; H modified from Dodds; M modified from Light, 1938.)

**62.** First segment of male right fifth exopod produced as a rounded lobe on its lateral
distal margin, its inner margin bearing a rounded hyaline lamella (Fig. 252B);
Kern Co., Calif.............................**Diaptomus connexus** Light
First segment of male right fifth exopod not produced on its lateral distal margin,
its inner margin bearing a triangular hyaline lamella (Fig. 252C); Twin
Lakes, Colo.................................**Diaptomus judayi** Marsh
**63.** Process about as long as the penultimate segment (Fig. 252E)...............64
Process longer than the penultimate segment (Figs. 252G, K)...............66
**64.** Male right fifth endopod about as long as first exopod segment (Fig. 252D); Utah
Lake....................................**Diaptomus tenuicaudatus** Marsh
Male right fifth endopod longer than first exopod segment...................65
**65.** Inner process of terminal segment of male left fifth leg falciform; Colo.
**Diaptomus bacillifer** Kölbel
Inner process of terminal segment of male left fifth leg digitate (Fig. 252F); com-
mon in northern states, usually in larger lakes.... ..**Diaptomus sicilis** Forbes
**66.** Antennae at most reaching the proximal end of the caudal rami..............67
Antennae reaching beyond the distal end of the caudal rami.................71

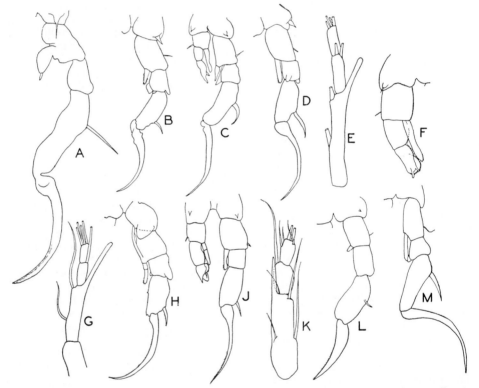

Fig. 252.—Structure of male *Diaptomus*. A, right fifth leg of *Diaptomus trybomi* Lillj.; B, right fifth leg of *D. connexus* Light; C, fifth legs of *D. judayi* Marsh; D, right fifth leg of *D. tenuicaudatus* Marsh; E, terminal antennal segments of *D. sicilis* Forbes; F, left fifth leg of same; G, terminal antennal segments of *D. wardi* Pearse; H, right fifth leg of *D. caducus* Light; J, fifth legs of *D. shoshone* Forbes; K, terminal antennal segments of same; L, right fifth leg of *D. minutus* Lillj.; M, right fifth leg of *D. ashlandi* Marsh. (A, D, E, F, and K to M modified from Marsh, 1907; B and H modified from Light, 1938; C modified from Ward and Whipple.)

**67.** Process of antepenultimate segment of male right antenna not extending beyond
 the distal end of the terminal segment (Fig. 252K)....................**68**
 Process of antepenultimate segment of male right antenna extending beyond the
 distal end of the terminal segment (Fig. 252G); Wash.
                                                  **Diaptomus wardi** Pearse
**68.** Animal 1.0 to 1.5 mm. long; northeastern Nev.......**Diaptomus spinicornis** Light
 Animal 2.2 to 3.3 mm. long.........................................**69**
**69.** Male left fifth endopod a rudimentary triangular prominence; Ga. and N. C.
                                              **Diaptomus augustaensis** Turner
 Male left fifth endopod not rudimentary (Figs. 252H, J)....................**70**
**70.** First segment of male right fifth exopod with thick projection on distal lateral corner (Fig. 252H); Pacific Coast ponds .........**Diaptomus caducus** Light
 First segment of male right fifth exopod without such a projection (Fig. 252J);
 at altitudes above 6,000 feet in western states....**Diaptomus shoshone** Forbes
**71.** Lateral spine of second segment of male right fifth exopod short; right endopod
 rudimentary (Fig. 252L); common in cold waters in northeastern states, very
 rare west of Mississippi R.......................**Diaptomus minutus** Lillj.
 Lateral spine of second segment of male right fifth exopod long; right endopod as
 long as first exopod segment (Fig. 252M); scattered in northern states.
                                              **Diaptomus ashlandi** Marsh

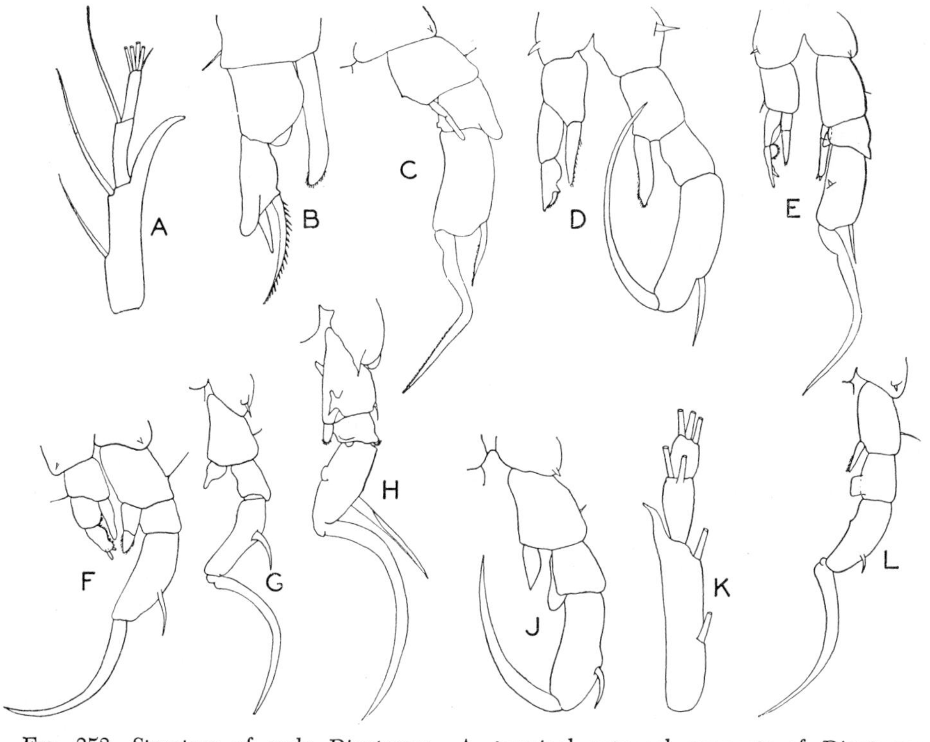

FIG. 253.—Structure of male *Diaptomus.* A, terminal antennal segments of *Diaptomus franciscanus* Lillj.; B, left fifth leg of *D. forbesi* Light; C, right fifth leg of *D. eiseni* Lillj.; D, fifth legs of *D. novamexicanus* Herrick; E, fifth legs of *D. bakeri* Marsh; F, fifth legs of *D. washingtonensis* Marsh; G, right fifth leg of *D. nudus* Marsh; H, right fifth leg of *D. albuquerquensis* Herrick; J, right fifth leg of *D. signicauda* Lillj.; K, terminal antennal segments of *D. siciloides* Lillj.; L, right fifth leg of same. (A modified from De Guerne and Richard, 1889; B modified from Light, 1938; C, E, F, G, H, J, and L modified from Marsh, 1907; D modified from Herrick and Turner; K modified from Dodds.)

**72.** Process equal to or exceeding the length of the penultimate segment.........73

Process shorter than the penultimate segment (Fig. 253K)................76

**73.** Process about as long as the last two segments..........................74

Process only slightly longer than the penultimate segment (Fig. 253A); San Francisco area..............................**Diaptomus franciscanus** Lillj.

**74.** Male left fifth exopod with a long stiff pinnate terminal seta (Fig. 253B); Orange Co., Calif.................................**Diaptomus forbesi** Light

Male left fifth exopod without such a seta...............................75

**75.** Terminal hook of male right fifth leg abruptly angled (Fig. 253C); rare; Calif. and Nebr.........................................**Diaptomus eiseni** Lillj.

Terminal hook of male right fifth leg curved, not angled; rare; Calif., Nev., and N. D.
**Diaptomus nevadensis** Light

**76.** Both terminal processes of male left fifth exopod digitiform and blunt..........77

Both terminal processes of male left fifth exopod not digitiform and blunt......83

**77.** Male right fifth endopod as long as or longer than the first segment of the exopod (Figs. 253D–F).............................................78

Male right fifth endopod shorter than the first segment of the exopod (Figs. 253G, H, J, L).............................................80

**78.** Endopods of both male fifth legs one-segmented (Fig. 253D); rare; N. M. and Utah...............................**Diaptomus novamexicanus** Herrick

Endopods of either or both male fifth legs two-segmented...................79

**79.** Endopods of both male fifth legs two-segmented (Fig. 253E); Calif.
**Diaptomus bakeri** Marsh

Endopod of male right fifth leg two-segmented, left one-segmented (Fig. 253F); Wash. and Colo......................**Diaptomus washingtonensis** Marsh

**80.** With hyaline appendages on either the second basal segment of male right fifth leg or first segment of male right fifth exopod.........................81

Without such appendages (Fig. 253G); Rocky Mountain states, rare elsewhere.
**Diaptomus nudus** Marsh

**81.** With hyaline appendages on second basal segment of male right fifth leg (Fig. 253H); Ga., Colo., and N. M..........**Diaptomus albuquerquensis** Herrick

With a hyaline appendage on first segment of male right fifth exopod..........82

**82.** Male right fifth endopod about as long as first segment of exopod (Fig. 253J); occasional in western states....................**Diaptomus signicauda** Lillj.

Male right fifth endopod much shorter than first segment of exopod (Fig. 253L); common and widely distributed................**Diaptomus siciloides** Lillj.

**83.** Male left fifth endopod marked with transverse striae (Fig. 254E); 3.5 to 4.5 mm. long; eastern states........................**Diaptomus stagnalis** Forbes

Male left fifth endopod not marked with transverse striae...................84

**84.** Male right fifth endopod rudimentary (Fig. 254D).........................85

Male right fifth endopod not rudimentary................................86

**85.** Both terminal processes of male left fifth exopod about the same length (Fig. 254B); La.................................**Diaptomus conipedatus** Marsh

Terminal processes of male left fifth exopod of very unequal length (Fig. 254D); west of Great Plains.........................**Diaptomus lintoni** Forbes

**86.** One of the terminal processes of the male left fifth exopod in the form of a straight sharp spine (Fig. 254F); Fla.................**Diaptomus floridanus** Marsh

One of the terminal processes of the male left fifth exopod distinctly falciform..87

**87.** Male right fifth endopod shorter than first segment of exopod................88

Male right fifth endopod distinctly longer than first segment of exopod (Fig. 254G); uncommon; states bordering Gulf of Mexico......**Diaptomus dorsalis** Marsh

**88.** Terminal segment of male right fifth exopod slender and elongated (Fig. 254A); Me. and Mass......................**Diaptomus spatulocrenatus** Pearse

Terminal segment of male right fifth exopod of the usual proportions..........89

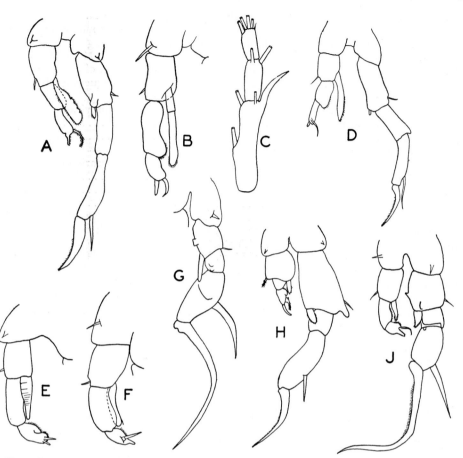

FIG. 254.—Structure of male *Diaptomus*. A, fifth legs of *Diaptomus spatulocrenatus* Pearse; B, left fifth leg of *D. conipedatus* Marsh; C, terminal antennal segments of *D. lintoni* Forbes; D, fifth legs of same; E, left fifth leg of *D. stagnalis* Forbes; F, left fifth leg of *D. floridanus* Marsh; G, right fifth leg of *D. dorsalis* Marsh; H, fifth legs of *D. sanguineus* Forbes; J, fifth legs of *D. saltillinus* Brewer. (A and E modified from Marsh, 1929; B, G, H, and J modified from Marsh, 1907; C and D modified from Dodds; F modified from Marsh, 1926.)

89. Male left fifth leg not attaining the end of the first exopod segment of the right
     leg (Fig. 254H); common in eastern states, rare elsewhere.
                                        **Diaptomus sanguineus** Forbes
     Male left fifth leg extending beyond the end of the first exopod segment of the right
     leg (Fig. 254J); Nebr. and Texas...........**Diaptomus saltillinus** Brewer
90. Endopod of fourth leg one-segmented...................................**91**
     Endopod of fourth leg two- or three-segmented.........................**95**
91. Endopod of third leg one-segmented..CYLINDROPSYLLIDAE, **Parastenocaris, 92**
     Endopod of third leg with two or more segments.....CANTHOCAMPTIDAE, **93**
92. With two setae at about mid-length of the caudal rami (Fig. 255A); known only
          from the sandy beach of a single Wis. lake....**Parastenocaris starretti** Pennak
     With four or more large setae at about mid-length of the caudal rami; known from
          sandy beaches of many Mass. and Wis. lakes..**Parastenocaris brevipes** Kessler

93. Segments of second and third endopods about equal in length; N. Y.

**Epactophanes muscicola** Richters

Distal segments of second and third endopods three times as long as the proximal; in fresh, brackish, and alkaline waters; Mass., Colo., and N. M....**Marshia, 94**

94. Caudal rami of female two and one-half times as long as wide, of male four times as long as wide......................**Marshia albuquerquensis** Herrick

Caudal rami of female and male about twice as long as wide.

**Marshia brevicaudata** Herrick

95. Fourth endopod two-segmented........................................96

Fourth endopod three-segmented.....................................117

96. Third endopod one-segmented; female; Mass.

CYLINDROPSYLLIDAE, **Stenocaris minor** (Scott)

Third endopod two- or three-segmented................................97

97. Third endopod three-segmented......................................98

Third endopod two-segmented.......................................111

98. Third, and often second, endopod modified for prehension; males............99

Neither second nor third endopods modified for prehension; both sexes........109

99. First endopod stout and tipped with stout claw for prehension (Fig. 255B); two species from sandy beaches of Mass. lakes....LAOPHONTIDAE, **Laophonte**

First endopod slender and natatory...............CANTHOCAMPTIDAE, **100**

100. Both second and third endopods modified for prehension (Fig. 255F).......**101**

Second endopod unmodified, third endopod modified for prehension (Fig. 256A).

**Attheyella,\* 105**

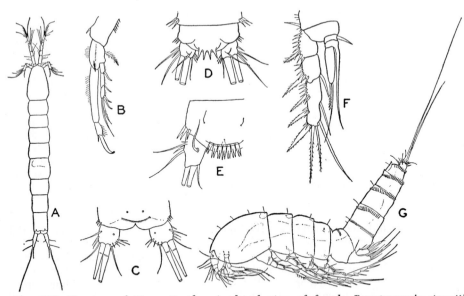

Fig. 255.—Structure of Harpacticoida. A, dorsal view of female *Parastenocaris starretti* Pennak, ×100; B, female first leg of *Laophonte proxima* Sars; C, posterior end of *Bryocamptus hiemalis* (Pearse); D, posterior end of *B. zschokkei* (Schmeil); E, left caudal ramus of *B. minutus* Claus; F, male third leg of *B. hiemalis*; G, female *B. hiemalis*, ×85. (A from Pennak, 1939; B modified from Wilson, 1932; C, D, F, and G modified from Coker, 1934; E redrawn from Gurney.)

\* Three rare species in this genus, known mostly from single localities, are not included in this key. These are *A. pilosa* Chappuis (Ind., Ken.), *A. bicolor* Wilson (Mass.), and *A. wierzejski* Mrázek (N. Y.).

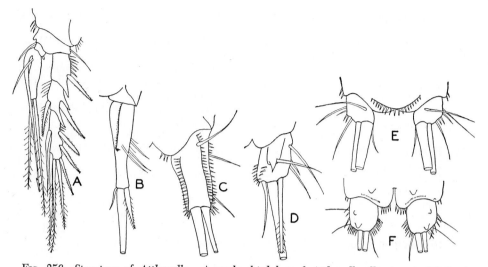

Fig. 256.—Structure of *Attheyella*. A, male third leg of *Attheyella illinoisensis* (Forbes);
B, right caudal ramus of *A. idahoensis* (Marsh); C, right caudal ramus of *A. carolinensis*
Chappuis; D, right caudal ramus of *A. bidens* (Schmeil); E, posterior end of *A. northumbrica*
Brady; F, posterior end of *A. illinoisensis*. (Modified from Coker, 1934.)

**101.** First endopod exceeding exopod by length of distal segment or more; common and
    widely distributed in northern states in pools, ponds, and marshes.
                                              **Canthocamptus staphylinoides** Pearse
    First endopod shorter than exopod or exceeding it only slightly.
                                                            **Bryocamptus,** * 102
**102.** Anal plate with many fine spinules (Fig. 255C); widely distributed.
                                                    **Bryocamptus hiemalis** (Pearse)
    Anal plate with few large spines....................................**103**
**103.** With three to five large spines on anal plate (Fig. 255D); streams, brooks, and
    springs, often in moss; widely distributed..**Bryocamptus zschokkei** (Schmeil)
    With more than five large spines on anal plate.........................**104**
**104.** With six to nine simple spines on anal plate; Va. and Conn.
                                                    **Bryocamptus hutchinsoni** Kiefer
    With six to ten bifid spines on anal plate (Fig. 255E); common and widely dis-
    tributed, especially in moss at water's edge.....**Bryocamptus minutus** Claus
**105.** Caudal rami at least one and one-half times as long as wide..............**106**
    Caudal rami less than one and one-half times as long as wide............**107**
**106.** Caudal rami very long, without longitudinal rows of spinules (Fig. 256B); Idaho
    and Mont............................**Attheyella idahoensis** (Marsh)
    Caudal rami shorter, with longitudinal rows of spinules (Fig. 256C); Va. and
    N. C.................................**Attheyella carolinensis** Chappuis
**107.** Caudal ramus with a dorsal hooked projection (Fig. 256D); reported from N. C.
    and Pa., but probably widely distributed......**Attheyella bidens** (Schmeil)
    Caudal ramus without a dorsal hooked projection........................**108**
**108.** Caudal rami set far apart and bent toward mid-line (Fig. 256E); common and
    widely distributed......................**Attheyella northumbrica** Brady
    Caudal rami not set far apart and bent toward mid-line (Fig. 256F); common and
    widely distributed in a great variety of habitats.
                                                    **Attheyella illinoisensis** (Forbes)

* Five rare species in this genus, known mostly from single localities, are not included in this
key. These are *B. newyorkensis* Chappuis (N. Y.), *B. minusculus* Willey (N. Y.), *B. pygmaeus* Sars
(N. Y.), *B. australis* Coker (N. C.), and *B. morrisoni* Chappuis (Ind., Ken.).

109. First endopod shorter than exopod; known only from sandy beach of a single Wis. lake.

PHYLLOGNATHOPODIDAE, **Phyllognathopus paludosus** Mrázek

First endopod longer than exopod; females.

CANTHOCAMPTIDAE, **Canthocamptus, 110**

110. With spinules along median borders of caudal rami; common and widely distributed in northern states in pools, ponds, and marshes.

**Canthocamptus staphylinoides** Pearse

Median borders of caudal rami unarmed; Conn., N. Y., and N. C.

**Canthocamptus sinuus** Coker

111. First endopod three-segmented.......CANTHOCAMPTIDAE, **Attheyella, 105**

First endopod two-segmented...................................112

112. First exopod two-segmented; females; two species from sandy beaches of Mass. lakes...............................LAOPHONTIDAE, **Laophonte**

First exopod three-segmented...................CANTHOCAMPTIDAE, 113

113. Distal segments of second, third, and fourth endopods longer than proximal.

**Attheyella, 105**

Segments of second, third, and fourth endopods subequal; uncommon.

**Moraria, 114**

114. First antennae seven-segmented...................................115

First antennae eight-segmented...................................116

115. Abdominal segments with posterior margin dentate; Donnaldson Cave, Ind.

**Moraria cristata** Chappuis

Abdominal segments with posterior margin smooth; N. J.

**Moraria laurentica** Willey

116. Anal plate rounded; N. Y.......................**Moraria affinis** Chappuis

Anal plate triangular; Va.......................**Moraria virginiana** Carter

117. First exopod two-segmented; fresh, brackish, and salt water; Mass.

HARPACTICIDAE, **Harpacticus gracilis** Claus

First exopod three-segmented; generally in brackish water, but reported from fresh-water ponds along Mass. coast.

CANTHOCAMPTIDAE, **Nitocra spinipes** Boeck

# COPEPODA REFERENCES

AYCOCK, D. 1942. Influence of temperature on size and form of Cyclops vernalis Fischer. *Jour. Elisha Mitchell Sci. Soc.* **58**:84–93.

BYRNES, E. F. 1909. The fresh water Cyclops of Long Island. *Cold Spring Harbor Monogr.* **7**:1–43.

CARTER, M. E. 1944. Harpacticoid copepods of the region of Mountain Lake, Virginia. *Jour. Elisha Mitchell Sci. Soc.* **60**:158–166.

CHAPPUIS, P. A. 1927. Freilebende Süsswasser-Copepoden aus Nordamerika. 2. Harpacticiden. *Zool. Anz.* **74**:302–313.

———. 1929. Die Unterfamilie der Canthocamptinae. *Arch. f. Hydrobiol.* **20**:471–516.

———. 1929a. Copépodes cavernicoles de l'Amérique du Nord. *Bull. Soc. Sci. Cluj* **4**:51–58.

———. 1933. Copépodes (première série). Avec l'énumération de tous les copépodes cavernicoles connus en 1931. *Arch. Zool. exp. et gén.* **76**:1–57.

———. 1944. Die harpacticoiden Copepoden der europäischen Binnengewässer. *Arch. Naturgesch.* **12**:351–433.

COKER, R. E. 1933. Influence of temperature on size of freshwater copepods (Cyclops). *Int. Rev.* **29**:406–436.

———. 1934. Contribution to knowledge of North American freshwater harpacticoid copepod Crustacea. *Jour. Elisha Mitchell Sci. Soc.* **50**:75–141.

———. 1943. Mesocyclops edax (S. A. Forbes), M. leuckarti (Claus) and related species in America. *Ibid.* **59**:181–200.

DEEVEY, E. S. 1941. Notes on the encystment of the harpacticoid copepod Canthocamptus staphylinoides Pearse. *Ecology* **22**:197–200.

DODDS, G. S. 1915. A key to the Entomostraca of Colorado. *Univ. Colo. Studies* **11**:265–298.

ELTON, C. 1929. The ecological relationships of certain freshwater copepods. *Jour. Ecology* **17**:383–391.

EWERS, L. A. 1930. The larval development of freshwater Copepoda. *Ohio State Univ., Contrib. Franz Theodore Stone Lab.* 3:1–43.

———. 1936. Propagation and rate of reproduction of some freshwater Copepoda. *Trans. Amer. Micros. Soc.* 55:230–238.

FORBES, S. A. 1897. A contribution to a knowledge of North American fresh-water Cyclopidae. *Bull. Ill. State Lab.* 5:27–83.

GURNEY, R. 1931–1933. *British Fresh-water Copepoda.* 3 vols. 958 pp. Ray Society, London.

HERRICK, C. L., and C. H. TURNER. 1895. A synopsis of the Entomostraca of Minnesota. *2d Rept. State Zoologist, Geol. and Nat. Hist. Surv. Minn.* 1–337.

HILL, L. I., and R. E. COKER. 1930. Observations on mating habits of Cyclops. *Jour. Elisha Mitchell Sci. Soc.* 45:206–220.

JUDAY, C. 1925. Senecella calanoides, a recently described fresh-water copepod. *Proc. U. S. Nat. Mus.* 66:1–6.

KIEFER, F. 1927. Freilebende Süsswasser-Copepoden aus Nordamerika. *Zool. Anz.* 72:262–268.

———. 1934. Neue Ruderfusskrebse aus Nordamerika. *Ibid.* 107:269–271.

LIGHT, S. F. 1938. New subgenera and species of diaptomid copepods from the inland waters of California and Nevada. *Univ. Calif. Publ. Zool.* 43:67–78.

———. 1939. New American subgenera of Diaptomus Westwood (Copepoda, Calanoida). *Trans. Amer. Micros. Soc.* 58:473–484.

MARSH, C. D. 1907. A revision of the North American species of Diaptomus. *Trans. Wis. Acad. Sci. Arts and Lett.* 15:381–516.

———. 1926. On a collection of copepods from Florida with a description of Diaptomus floridanus, new species. *Proc. U. S. Nat. Mus.* 70:1–4.

———. 1929. Distribution and key to the North American copepods of the genus Diaptomus, with the description of a new species. *Ibid.* 75:1–27.

———. 1933. Synopsis of the calanoid crustaceans, exclusive of the Diaptomidae, found in fresh and brackish waters, chiefly of North America. *Ibid.* 82:1–58.

MEEHEAN, O. L. 1940. A review of the parasitic Crustacea of the genus Argulus in the collections of the United States National Museum. *Ibid.* 88:459–522.

PENNAK, R. W. 1939. A new copepod from the sandy beaches of a Wisconsin lake. *Trans. Amer. Micros. Soc.* 58:224–227.

———. 1940. Ecology of the microscopic metazoa inhabiting the sandy beaches of some Wisconsin lakes. *Ecol. Monogr.* 10:537–615.

SPANDL, H. 1926. Copepoda. *Biol. Tiere Deutschlands,* 19:1–82.

STORCH, O. 1929. Die Schwimmbewegung der Copepoden, auf Grund von Mikro-Zeitlupenaufnahmen analysiert. *Zool. Anz., Suppl. Bd.* 4:118–129.

WALTER, E. 1922. Über die Lebensdauer der freilebenden Süsswasser-Cyclopiden und andere Fragen ihrer Biologie. *Zool. Jahrb. Abt. Syst.* 44:375–420.

WILSON, C. B. 1911. North American parasitic copepods.—Part. 9. The Lernaeopodidae. *Proc. U. S. Nat. Mus.* 39:189–226.

———. 1911a. North American parasitic copepods belonging to the family Ergasilidae. *Ibid.* 263–400.

———. 1915. North American parasitic copepods belonging to the Lernaeopodidae, with a revision of the entire family. *Ibid.* 47:565–729.

———. 1916. Copepod parasites of fresh-water fishes and their economic relations to mussel glochidia. *Bull. U. S. Bur. Fish.* 34:333–374.

———. 1917. North American parasitic copepods belonging to the Lernaeidae with a revision of the entire family. *Proc. U. S. Nat. Mus.* 53:1–150.

———. 1918. The economic relations, anatomy, and life history of the genus Lernaea. *Bull. U. S. Bur. Fish.* 35:163–198.

———. 1932. The copepods of the Woods Hole region, Massachusetts. *Bull. U. S. Nat. Mus.* 158:1–635.

———. 1944. Parasitic copepods in the United States National Museum. *Proc. U. S. Nat. Mus.* 94:529–582.

WILSON, M. S. 1941. New species and distribution records of diaptomid copepods from the Marsh collection in the United States National Museum. *Jour. Wash. Acad. Sci.* 31:509–515.

YEATMAN, H. C. 1944. American cyclopoid copepods of the viridis-vernalis group (including a description of Cyclops carolinianus n. sp.). *Amer. Midl. Nat.* 32:1–90.

# Chapter 18

## OSTRACODA (SEED SHRIMPS)

ALTHOUGH ostracods are abundant and widely distributed, they have received much less attention than the Cladocera and Copepoda. They inhabit all types of substrates in both standing and running waters, including rooted vegetation, algal mats, debris, mud, sand, and rubble. A few species swim about actively above the substrate. Representatives of one genus occur only as commensals on the gills of crayfish. Ostracods are comparatively difficult to study, chiefly because of their somewhat opaque bivalve shell, and identification usually involves dissection.

Superficially, the members of the Subclass Ostracoda resemble miniature mussels, and "mussel shrimps" is an old European vernacular name. However, this name is so easily confused with "clam shrimps," which is used for the Conchostraca, that it does not seem advisable to adopt it. "Seed shrimps" is suggested as an appropriate alternative, for indeed, without a lens ostracods do look much like small seeds.

**General characteristics.** The American fresh-water species are seldom more than 3 mm. long and usually less than 1 mm. long. A South African fresh-water species reaches a length of nearly 8 mm., and the largest marine species is 21 mm. long.

Coloration ranges from white through yellow, green, gray, red, brown, and blackish. Light-colored valves are often blotched with darker colors, and species occurring among algae and rooted aquatics are usually gray, green, or brown.

Each sclerotized lime-impregnated valve consists of an inner and an outer plate which are fused along the anterior, posterior, and ventral margins. The space between the two plates is occupied by a thin skin fold which secretes the valve material. Dorsally, the skin folds are continuous with the main body of the animal. The valves are connected on the dorsal margin by an elastic band and may be tightly closed by a group of adductor muscle fibers passing transversely through the body of the ostracod and attached to the inner surfaces of the valves (Figs. 262–264). When the animal is active, however, the valves gape and the locomotor appendages protrude. The outer surface of the valves may be smooth, pitted, papillate, or setose, and the margins are often tuberculate, crenulate, or lipped. There are no concentric growth lines as in some Conchostraca.

All traces of body segmentation are lost, but the region corresponding to the head bears four paired appendages: first antennae (antennules), second antennae (antennae), mandibles, and maxillae. The five- to seven-segmented first antennae are uniramous, the exopod being lost; they bear short, stiff, clawlike bristles for digging and climbing or long setae for swimming. The four- to six-segmented second antennae are also uniramous, the exopod being reduced to a scale or seta; these appendages are used in locomotion and feeding, and in the male they are modified for clasping the female during copulation. The mouth is surrounded by an up-

410

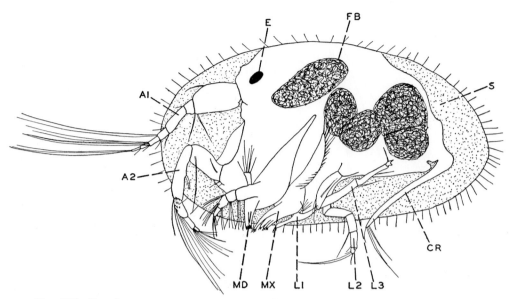

Fig. 257.–Female *Cypricercus reticulatus* (Zadd.), ×80, with left valve removed, semi-diagrammatic. *A1*, first antenna; *A2*, second antenna; *CR*, caudal ramus; *E*, eye; *FB*, food ball in digestive tract; *L1*, first leg; *L2*, second leg; *L3*, third leg; *MD*, mandible; *MX*, maxilla; *S*, right valve of shell. (Modified from Hoff, 1942.)

per and a lower lip and two lateral mandibles. Each mandible consists of a strongly toothed and sclerotized base, a branchial plate, and a three-segmented palp. Each maxilla has a large branchial plate and four basal processes, the outermost of which is largest and palplike.

The thoracic region bears three pairs of legs. In the Cytheridae all pairs are morphologically similar, in the Darwinulidae the second and third are similar, and in the Cypridae all legs are different. The first legs may be modified for mastication, prehension, copulation, or respiration (respiratory plate). The second legs usually have a long terminal claw. The third legs of the Cypridae are bent dorsally and used in keeping the body and inner surface of the shell free of foreign material.

The abdomen is represented only by two long caudal rami (furcal rami), which are articulated to the body. Each ramus usually has two terminal claws and two terminal setae. In some species the rami are reduced or lacking.

**Locomotion.** The great majority of individuals are found moving about on the substrate by means of beating movements of the first and second antennae, and to some extent by kicking of the caudal rami. Such locomotion ranges from creeping and uncertain, weak, tottering movements to rapid bouncing or scurrying. Some of the Candoninae burrow superficially in soft substrates. Those species which leave the bottom and swim about actively are characterized by long, plumose antennules and antennae.

**Food, feeding.** Food consists mostly of bacteria, molds, algae, and fine detritus, but some of the larger Cyprinae have been observed feeding on dead animals. Ecologically, ostracods are omnivorous scavengers. Beating movements of the setose mandibular palps, maxillary processes, and the branchial plates of the first legs create a current of water between the valves. The current picks up fine particles from the substrate which are strained out by the setae and brought to the mouth.

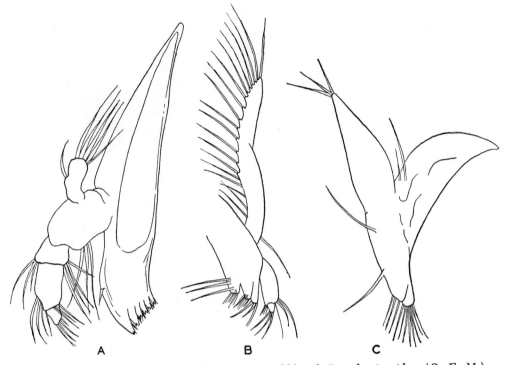

**A**          **B**          **C**

Fig. 258.—Some ostracod appendages. A, mandible of *Cypridopsis vidua* (O. F. M.), showing the long, sclerotized, toothed basal portion, the single-segmented branchial plate, and the larger segmented palp; B, maxilla of *Candona acuta* Hoff, showing the four basal processes and the long branchial plate; C, first leg of *Candona fluviatilis* Hoff. (A modified from Sars; B and C redrawn from Hoff, 1942.)

Inedible particles are mostly rejected and removed by the respiratory plates of the maxillae. Large edible bits of food are pulled or pushed toward the mouth by the antennae, mandibles, and first legs. The mandibles are used to rasp and break up the larger pieces. Small balls of finely divided food are swept into the mouth by the mandibular palps.

**Internal anatomy.** The digestive tract consists of a short esophagus, a secretory and absorptive midgut, and a hindgut. One digestive gland on each side between the lamellae of the valves empties into the midgut. The anus lies at the base of the caudal rami.

Respiration occurs through the general body surface, and a constant supply of oxygenated water is ensured by the movements of the branchial plates.

The hemocoel is filled with a circulating fluid, but no heart has ever been described for fresh-water species.

Three distinct, paired glands are found in ostracods, but for no one of them has a definite function been assigned. The large convoluted shell glands lie between the shell lamellae and in the hemocoel; they open near the base of the second antennae and have an unknown function. The small antennal glands open near the base of the first antennae; presumably they have an excretory function, especially during immature stages. The small maxillary glands are imbedded in the tissues just posterior to the lower lip; some investigators believe that they have an excretory function.

The nervous system consists of a large supraesophageal ganglion (brain), two esophageal connectives, a subesophageal ganglion, and a ventral chain of two paired ganglia.

Two or three prominent eyespots, each with a small lens, and fused in varying degrees, are mounted on a protuberance near the bases of the first antennae. In a few species the eyespots are absent. Many setae of the appendages undoubtedly have a tactile function. In the Cypridae the second antenna bears a small clublike sensory structure similar to the aesthetasks of copepods (Figs. 257, 261M).

**Reproduction.** A superficial examination of any field collection of ostracods usually reveals a great majority of females. The various species differ widely in their reproductive habits, depending on the relative occurrence of males, and Hoff (1942) has accordingly recognized four general groups of ostracods. One group,

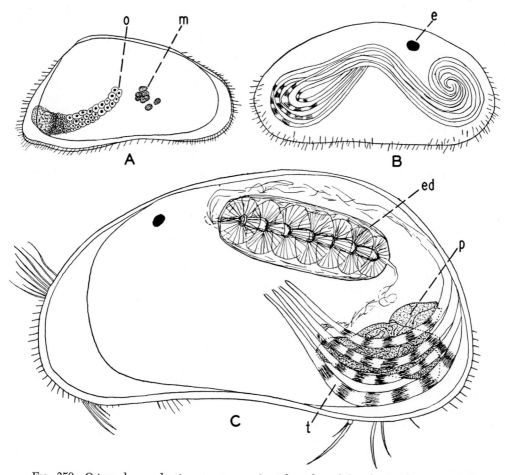

Fig. 259.—Ostracod reproductive structures. A, right valve of female *Candona intermedia* Furtos, ×40, showing chief reproductive structures; B, right valve of male *Cypricercus columbiensis* Dobbin, ×33, showing convoluted testes; C, male reproductive system of *Candona*, ×80, as seen from the left side, diagrammatic. *e*, eye; *ed*, ejaculatory duct; *m*, adductor muscle attachment scars; *o*, mature ovum; *p*, penis (shaded, and mostly hidden by testis); *t*, one of four branches of testis. (A modified from Furtos, 1933; B redrawn from Dobbin.)

including some species of *Candona* and *Cypricercus*, always reproduces by parthenogenesis, the males being unknown. In some species of *Candona*, *Cyprinotus*, *Darwinula*, and *Ilyocypris* males are rare and reproduction is usually parthenogenetic. In some *Cypricercus* and *Potamocypris* males occur in small numbers, and reproduction is both syngamic and parthenogenetic. A fourth group includes species in which males are always present and reproduction is usually syngamic: *Candona*, *Cyclocypris*, *Cypria*, *Cypricercus*, *Cyprois*, *Limnocythere*, *Notodromas*, and *Physocypria*.

The female reproductive system is rather simple, consisting of paired tubular ovaries, oviducts, seminal receptacles, and genital openings. In the Cypridae the ovaries lie between the valve lamellae, but in the Cytheridae they are lateral to the midgut. The genital openings are located between the bases of the third legs and the caudal rami.

The paired male reproductive system is more complicated, especially in the Cypridae. Each testis consists of four long, tubular branches lying between the valve lamellae. In the body proper these unite to form a vas deferens which enters the dorsal and posterior ejaculatory duct, a spiny, sclerotized cylinder which forces sperm into the penis during copulation. The two penes are large, irregular, lobed, complex, sclerotized structures located near the posterior end of the animal. In the Cytheridae there is no ejaculatory duct, and the testes are lateral to the midgut in the body proper. The detailed anatomy of the penis is of importance in separating species taxonomically.

Copulation involves the attachment of the male to the dorsal and posterior margin of the female shell. The second antennae of the male aid in this attachment, and the penes are inserted between the valves and into the female genital pores. Fertilization occurs in the seminal receptacles.

The careful investigations of Lowndes (1935) have led to some interesting conclusions. He maintains that fertilization of the egg does not actually occur in spite of copulation and highly specialized copulatory apparatus, that all ostracod reproduction is parthenogenetic, and that copulation is merely an instinctive behavior pattern which is a relic of past times when the union of sperm and egg was probably the sole means of reproduction.

*Darwinula stevensoni* (B. and R.) retains the fertilized eggs in the dorsal part of the shell cavity until embryonic development is completed, but all other American fresh-water species are thought to be oviparous. The spherical eggs have a delicate, double-walled, limy shell, and are usually white, yellow, orange, red, or green in color. They are deposited singly or in clumps or rows on rocks, twigs, other bits of debris, or aquatic vegetation.

**Development, life history.** Egg development is usually suspended during the cold months and unfavorable moisture conditions, and there are numerous records of ostracods hatching from eggs kept in dried pond mud in the laboratory for many weeks and months. One report indicates that viable eggs may be kept for more than 20 years in the desiccated condition.

In normal habitats, however, the eggs usually hatch in a few days to several months. The liberated larva (Fig. 260) is a shelled nauplius with three pairs of appendages, representing the first antennae, second antennae, and mandibles of the adult. Eight molts and eight additional instars occur during the life history. Other appendages and increased structural complexity develop with each successive molt. The caudal rami, for example, first appear as two small bristles in the fourth instar. The copulatory organs appear in the eighth instar, but sexual maturity and copulation do not occur until the ninth and last instar.

Many species exhibit a definite seasonal periodicity. Ferguson (1944), working in Missouri, found that *Cypridopsis vidua* (O. F. M.) was active between February and December, *Potamocypris smaragdina* (Vavra) between March and October, and *Physocypria pustulosa* (Sharpe) between March and September. Many species of *Candona* may be collected only in the spring. A few species occur only in the autumn. Aside from eggs and some adults that winter over, the usual life span is completed in several weeks to seven or eight months, depending on the species and environmental conditions. Sometimes the adult instar may last as long as six months. A single generation per year is the common condition in vernal ponds; the three species mentioned above have two or three generations per year.

**Ecology.** The nature of the substrate and the general type of environment seem to have little influence on the distribution of most seed shrimps. In many cases the same species may be found on algae, decaying vegetation, rooted aquatics, mud, and gravel. *Cyprinotus incongruens* (Ramdohr), for example, may be found in swift streams, ponds, and puddles. Only a minority of species are restricted to such places as vernal ponds, permanent lakes, and temporary streams. Out of 31 species collected in Illinois by Hoff (1942), four were restricted to temporary still waters, six were restricted to permanent still waters, two were found only in temporary running waters, and one in permanent running waters. The other 18 species were collected in two or more of these habitats. The largest numbers of species may be collected on mud bottoms where there is little or no current; few species occur on bare rocks. Many forms, especially clamberers and active swimmers, such as *Cyprinotus* and *Cypricercus*, are more active on lighted than on shaded bottoms. Most species occur in water less than one meter deep, but some are found regularly as

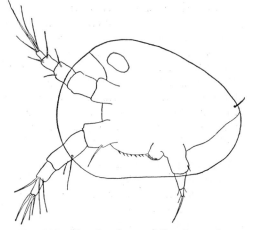

FIG. 260.—Nauplius larva of *Cyprinotus incongruens* Ramdohr, ×260. (Redrawn from Schreiber.)

deep as 15 meters. *Cypridopsis vidua* has been found in depths ranging from one centimeter to 300 meters. *Notodromas monacha* (O. F. M.) is unusual in that it clings to the surface film with the dorsal surface downward.

In general, ostracods tolerate wide ranges of ecological factors usually regarded as limiting for entomostracans. The normal ranges of temperature and water chemistry are of little significance. Though they do not occur in grossly polluted waters, such genera as *Candona* and *Cypris* survive long periods of stagnation and oxygen exhaustion on lake bottoms. Aquaria and old protozoan cultures sometimes become thick with them.

**Geographical distribution.** Most genera and many species are cosmopolitan or Holarctic, *Chlamydotheca* and *Entocythere* being the only important North American genera not found in the Palearctic Region. Because of the fact that little intensive collecting has been done in the United States, however, about half of the reported species are known from only a single state or collecting locality. Active and passive distribution are brought about much as in the Cladocera and Copepoda.

**Economic significance.** With occasional exceptions, ostracods are only a minor element in the diet of young and adult fish. A few are the intermediate hosts of Acanthocephala parasitizing fish. Hoff (1942) estimates that 1.0 to 1.5 per cent of the ostracods in permanent waters are infected. Ostracods are also the intermediate hosts of some tapeworms of waterfowl.

**Collection, preparation.** Perhaps the chief reason for the general neglect of the American Ostracoda lies in the fact that they are nearly always necessarily collected in masses of debris from which they must be laboriously separated. Surface debris of the bottom and its contained ostracods may be scooped up with a dipnet, but the Birge cone net towed along the bottom, or better, the Birge cone net mounted on a toboggan-like piece of sheet metal is most useful. By washing the debris thoroughly through a fine net, the smaller particles may be removed, and if the remaining mass is allowed to stand quietly in jars of water, the ostracods soon become active at the debris–water interface where, with a little patience, they may be picked up with a long pipette. Also, by stirring the contents well, some of the ostracods get a small bubble of air caught between the valves and rise to the surface where they may be easily removed.

Specimens should be killed in 50 per cent alcohol and preserved in 85 per cent alcohol. Formaldehyde makes the animals brittle and may decalcify the valves.

Stained or unstained whole animals may be mounted in balsam or glycerin jelly, but cover-glass supports should be used to avoid crushing. Dissections of adult specimens are usually necessary for accurate identification, and the operation is best carried out in glycerin with fine needles. The valves should be removed first, leaving the body intact, and then the appendages should be carefully dissected off. Valves and appendages are conveniently mounted on separate slides.

**Taxonomy.** The Subclass Ostracoda is divided into four orders: Myodocopa, Cladocopa, Platycopa, and Podocopa. The first three of these are confined to marine waters and are not considered here. The Podocopa are found in both marine and fresh-water environments; the family Bairdiidae is exclusively marine, the Cytheridae contains only a few fresh-water genera, Cypridae are well represented in both environments, and the Darwinulidae are confined to fresh waters.

In the United States, seed shrimps have received more than casual consideration only in Ohio, Massachusetts, Illinois, Florida, and Washington, and each new comprehensive study reveals many undescribed species. Ward and Whipple (1918) listed 54 species from the entire United States, but in 1933 Furtos listed 57 species from Ohio alone. Dobbin (1941) collected 33 species in Washington, of which 14 were new, and Hoff (1942) collected 39 in Illinois, of which ten were new. Obviously, it is fruitless to include here a key to the known American species, since such a key would be obsolete in a few years. The key given below therefore goes only as far as genera. It should be borne in mind that it can be used successfully only for specimens in the late instars, preferably the last.

## KEY TO GENERA OF OSTRACODA

1. Exopod of second antenna in the form of a long, hollow seta carrying the secretion from a gland located at the base of the antenna (Fig. 264E); all legs morphologically similar..................................CYTHERIDAE, 25

   Exopod otherwise; all legs not morphologically similar......................2

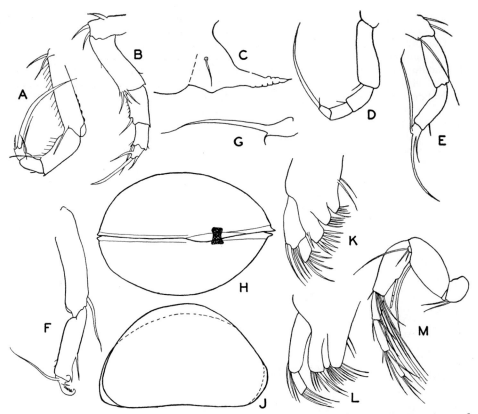

FIG. 261.—Structure of Ostracoda. A, second leg of female *Darwinula stevensoni* (B. and R.); B, third leg of same; C, end of thorax of same; D, second leg of female *Candona punctata* Furtos; E, third leg of same; F, third leg of female *Cypridopsis vidua*; G, caudal ramus of female *Potamocypris smaragdina* Vavra; H, dorsal view of female *Cypridopsis vidua*, ×70; J, lateral view of female *Potamocypris hyboforma* Dobbin, ×40; K, maxilla of *Cyprois marginata* (Straus); L, maxilla of female *Cyprinotus incongruens* (Ramdohr); M, second antenna of female *Notodromas monacha* (O. F. M.). (A, B, F, and G redrawn from Furtos, 1933; C, D, and E redrawn from Hoff, 1942; H modified from Furtos, 1933; J and L modified from Dobbin.)

2. Second and third legs similar (Figs. 261A, B); caudal rami lacking, body terminating in a single process (Fig. 261C); 0.70 to 0.80 mm. long; on mud bottoms of larger bodies of water; widely distributed but rare.

DARWINULIDAE, **Darwinula stevensoni** (B. and R.)

Second and third legs not similar (Figs. 261D, E); caudal rami present but sometimes reduced.....................................CYPRIDAE, **3**

3. Terminal segment of third leg short, usually armed with beaklike claw and reflexed seta (Fig. 263H).....................................**4**

Terminal segment of third leg more or less cylindrical (rarely spherical), armed with three setae and no claw (Fig. 261E).........................**16**

4. Caudal rami well developed, usually with two claws and two setae (Figs. 262C, D).....................................CYPRINAE, **6**

Caudal rami rudimentary, terminating in a simple flagellum (Fig. 261G); 0.50 to 0.80 mm. long.....................................CYPRIDOPSINAE, **5**

5. Tumid (Fig. 261H); valves nearly equal in size; widely distributed and very common in many types of habitats.............................**Cypridopsis**
   Compressed; right valve higher than left (Fig. 261J); common in both standing and running waters............................**Potamocypris**
6. Natatory setae of second antenna well developed, extending beyond mid-length of claws (Figs. 262A, B)............................7
   Natatory setae of second antenna greatly reduced, not attaining mid-length of claws (Figs. 262H, J)............................14
7. Caudal ramus with three claws and one seta (Fig. 262C); shell with reticulate patterns anteriorly and posteriorly; 1.10 to 1.20 mm. long; ponds and slow streams; rare............................**Ilyodromus pectinatus** Sharpe
   Caudal ramus with two claws and two setae (Fig. 262D)............................8

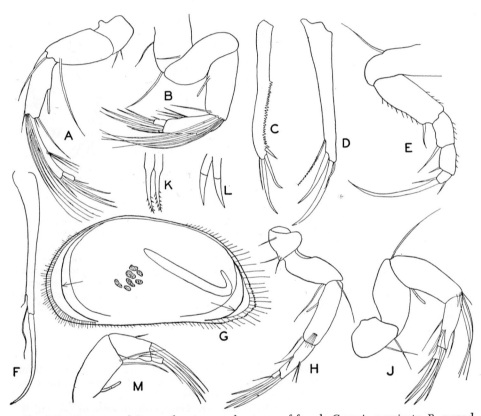

Fig. 262.—Structure of Ostracoda. A, second antenna of female *Cyprois marginata*; B, second antenna of female *Cyprinotus incongruens*; C, caudal ramus of *Ilyodromus pectinatus* Sharpe; D, caudal ramus of female *Cyprinotus incongruens*; E, second leg of female *Eucypris virens* (Jurine); F, caudal ramus of *Cypretta turgida* (Sars); G, lateral view of female *Candonocypris pugionis* Furtos, ×15 (anterior and posterior ridges indicated by arrows); H, second antenna of female *Prionocypris longiforma* Dobbin; J, second antenna of female *Herpetocypris repetans* (Baird); K, spines of third maxillary process of *H. repetans*; L, spines of third maxillary process of *Cypriconcha gigantea* Dobbin; M, end of female second antenna of *Candona caudata* Kaufmann. (B, H, J, and M modified from Dobbin, 1941; C redrawn from Ward and Whipple, 1918; D redrawn from Furtos, 1933; E modified from Sars; F redrawn from Furtos, 1936; G modified from Furtos, 1936; K and L redrawn from Dobbin.)

8. Second segment of second leg with two large setae; 2.60 to 3.30 mm. long; several uncommon species in southern half of U. S.................Chlamydotheca
   Second segment of second leg with a single large seta (Fig. 262E); 0.50 to 4.20 mm. long........................................................9
9. Caudal ramus usually less than one-half as long as valves; males usually absent; common and widely distributed................................10
   Caudal ramus usually at least one-half as long as valves; males present; 0.80 to 4.20 mm. long..........................................................13
10. Subterminal claw of caudal ramus stout, usually nearly as long as terminal claw (Fig. 262D); 1.00 to 2.30 mm. long; very common; many species........11
    Subterminal claw of caudal ramus seta-like, usually much shorter than terminal claw (Fig. 262F); 0.50 to 0.95 mm. long.....................Cypretta
11. Second leg four-segmented, third and fourth segments fused..........Cypris *
    Second leg five-segmented (Fig. 262E)......................................12
12. Margins of both valves smooth........................................Eucypris *
    At least the anterior edge of one valve tuberculate................Cyprinotus *
13. Anterior and posterior extremity of each valve with distinct ridge between inner duplicature and submarginal line (Fig. 262G); several scattered and rare species. ..............................................Candonocypris
    Anterior and posterior extremity of each valve without such a ridge; ten species; widely distributed and common..........................Cypricercus

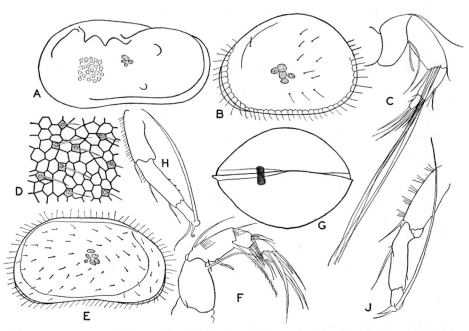

Fig. 263.—Structure of Ostracoda. A, left valve of *Ilyocypris gibba* (Ramdohr), ×47, showing a small portion of sculpturing; B, left valve of *Cyclocypris sharpei* Furtos, ×75; C, second antenna of female *Cypria elegantula* (Lillj.); D, valve sculpturing of *Paracandona euplectella* (B. and N.); E, right valve of female *Candona parallela* Müller, ×55; F, second antenna of male *Candocypria osburni* Furtos; G, dorsal view of female *Cyclocypris sharpei*, ×75; H, third leg of female *C. sharpei*; J, third leg of female *Cypria elegantula*. (A, B, D, E, and G modified from Furtos, 1933; F, H and J redrawn from Furtos, 1933; C modified from Dobbin.)

* Some authorities unite these three genera under *Cypris*.

**14.** Natatory setae of second antenna very small (Fig. 262H); 1.25 mm. long; rare; Wash.....................................**Prionocypris longiforma** Dobbin
    Natatory setae of second antenna longer, reaching nearly halfway to tip of terminal claws (Fig. 262J); 2.0 to 4.0 mm. long; several widely distributed but uncommon species................................................................15
**15.** Spines of third maxillary process distinctly denticulate (Fig. 262K)..**Herpetocypris**
    Spines of third maxillary process smooth (Fig. 262L)...............**Cypriconcha**
**16.** Natatory setae of second antenna lacking (Fig. 262M); shell white when dry; creeping and burrowing forms.........................CANDONINAE, **18**
    Natatory setae of second antenna present; shell not white when dry.........**17**
**17.** Shell usually short and rounded (Figs. 263B, G); except in one species, natatory setae of second antenna extending well beyond tips of terminal claws (Fig. 261M). .............................................................**19**
    Shell elliptical to subrectangular (Fig. 263A); natatory setae of second antenna short or extending only slightly beyond tips of terminal claws; 0.80 to 1.20 mm. long; more abundant in running than in standing waters; widely distributed and common.............................ILYOCYPRINAE, **Ilyocypris**
**18.** Shell ornamented with polygonal areas and tubercles (Fig. 263D); 0.50 to 0.60 mm. long; scattered distribution; rare...**Paracandona euplectella** (B. and N.)
    Shell plain (Fig. 263E); 0.60 to 2.00 mm. long; widely distributed and common; about 20 species...................................................**Candona**
**19.** Third maxillary process with six prominent spines (Fig. 261K).
                                                            NOTODROMINAE, **20**

    Third maxillary process with only two or three prominent spines plus some setae.
                                                            CYCLOCYPRINAE, **21**

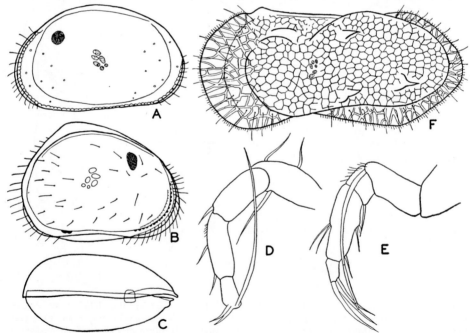

FIG. 264.—Structure of Ostracoda. A, left view of male *Cypria obesa* Sharpe, ×60; B, right view of female *Physocypria pustulosa* Sharpe, ×70; C, dorsal view of same, ×70; D, third leg of female *Cyclocypria kincaidia* Dobbin; E, second antenna of female *Limnocythere verrucosa* Hoff; F, left valve of male *Limnocythere ornata* Furtos, ×80. (A, C, and F redrawn from Furtos, 1933; B modified from Furtos, 1933; D redrawn from Dobbin; E redrawn from Hoff, 1942.)

20. Second antenna six-segmented (Fig. 261M); 1.10 to 1.20 mm. long; active swimmers; usually in aquatic vegetation; rare....**Notodromas monacha** (O. F. M.)
Second antenna five-segmented (Fig. 262A); 1.10 to 1.70 mm. long; creeks and vernal ponds; widely distributed.............................**Cyprois**

21. Natatory setae of second antenna rudimentary (Fig. 263F); 0.80 to 1.00 mm. long; a burrower and creeper; reported from brooks in Ohio.
                                                                **Candocypria osburni** Furtos
Natatory setae of second antenna well developed.........................**22**

22. Shell tumid (Fig. 263G); last segment of third leg at least twice as long as wide (Fig. 263H); 0.40 to 0.80 mm. long; widely distributed........**Cyclocypris**
Shell compressed; last segment of third leg less than twice as long as wide (Fig. 263J). ...............................................................**23**

23. Valves nearly equal in size; margin of both valves smooth (Fig. 264A).......**24**
Valves unequal in height or length or both; margin of either valve more or less tuberculate (Figs. 264B, C); 0.40 to 0.70 mm. long; widely distributed.
                                                                **Physocypria**

24. With a single large seta on the penultimate segment of third leg (Fig. 263J); 0.40 to 1.00 mm. long; numerous widely distributed species.............**Cypria**
With two large setae on the penultimate segment of third leg (Fig. 264D); 0.45 mm. long; Wash......................**Cyclocypria kincaidia** Dobbin

25. Free margins of valves flattened, with many long pore-canals (Fig. 264F); free living; 0.50 to 0.90 mm. long; eight species in a variety of habitats.
                                                LIMNOCYTHERINAE, **Limnocythere**
Free margins of valves not flattened, without conspicuous pore-canals; commensals on gills of crayfish; 0.30 to 0.70 mm. long; numerous species.
                                                ENTOCYTHERINAE, **Entocythere**

## OSTRACODA REFERENCES

DOBBIN, C. N. 1941. Fresh-water Ostracoda from Washington and other western localities. *Univ. Wash. Publ. Biol.* **4**:175–245.

FERGUSON, E. 1944. Studies of the seasonal life history of three species of freshwater Ostracoda. *Amer. Midl. Nat.* **32**:713–727.

FURTOS, N. C. 1933. The Ostracoda of Ohio. *Bull. Ohio Biol. Surv.* **29**:413–524.

———. 1935. Fresh-water Ostracoda from Massachusetts. *Jour. Wash. Acad. Sci.* **25**:530–544.

———. 1936. Freshwater Ostracoda from Florida and North Carolina. *Amer. Midl. Nat.* **17**:491–522.

HERRICK, C. L., and C. H. TURNER. 1895. A synopsis of the Entomostraca of Minnesota. *Second Rept. State Zoologist, Geol. and Nat. Hist. Surv. Minn.* 1–337.

HOFF, C. C. 1942. The ostracods of Illinois. *Univ. Ill. Biol. Monogr.* **19**:1–196.

———. 1942a. The subfamily Entocytherinae, a new subfamily of fresh-water cytherid Ostracoda, with descriptions of two new species of the genus Entocythere. *Amer. Midl. Nat.* **27**:63–73.

———. 1943. Seasonal changes in the ostracod fauna of temporary ponds. *Ecology* **24**:116–118.

———. 1944. The origin of Nearctic fresh-water ostracods. *Ibid.* **25**:369–372.

———. 1944a. New American species of the ostracod genus Entocythere. *Amer. Midl. Nat.* **32**:327–357.

KESLING, R. V. 1951. The morphology of ostracod molt stages. *Ill. Biol. Monogr.* **21**:1–324.

KLIE, W. 1926. Ostracoda. *Biol. Tiere Deutschlands,* **16**(22):1–56.

LOWNDES, A. G. 1935. The sperms of freshwater ostracods. *Proc. Zool. Soc. London* (1935) **1**:35–48.

SARS, G. O. 1928. Ostracoda. An *Account of the Crustacea of Norway* **9**:1–277.

SCHEERER-OSTERMEYER, E. 1940. Beitrag zur Entwicklungsgeschichte der Süsswasserostrakoden. *Zool. Jahrb., Abt. Anat. Ontog. Tiere* **66**:349–370.

SCHREIBER, E. 1922. Beiträge zur Kenntnis der Morphologie, Entwicklung und Lebensweise der Süsswasser-Ostrakoden. *Ibid.* **43**:485–538.

SHARPE, R. W. 1897. Contributions to a knowledge of the North American freshwater Ostracoda including the families Cytheridae and Cyprididae. *Bull. Ill. State Lab. Nat. Hist.* **4**:414–484.

TRESSLER, W. L. 1947. A check list of the known species of North American freshwater Ostracoda. *Amer. Midl. Nat.* **38**:698–707.

# Chapter 19

# MYSIDACEA (OPOSSUM SHRIMPS)

THE OPOSSUM shrimps form a large order which is almost exclusively marine, only two species having become adapted to fresh waters in the United States. *Mysis oculata* var. *relicta* (Lovén) (formerly called *M. relicta*) is a plankter in deep, cold, oligotrophic lakes of the northern states east of the Great Plains, and *Neomysis mercedis* Holmes occurs in lakes, rivers, and brackish estuaries of the Washington, Oregon, and California coasts.

Superficially, mysids resemble miniature crayfish. A closer examination, however, reveals some striking differences. The carapace, for example, is thin and does not completely cover the thorax, the last two segments being exposed dorsally and, to some degree, laterally. In place of the five pairs of walking legs of decapods, mysids have long, thin, setose, biramous, many-segmented appendages. The first thoracic segment bears a pair of maxillipeds and is fused with the head, but the other seven thoracic segments are distinct. The second thoracic segment bears the second maxillipeds, and each of the remaining six segments has a pair of swimming legs. The stalked compound eyes are extremely large, the scale of the second antenna is large, but the pleopods are proportionately much more reduced than those of decapods. *Mysis oculata relicta* reaches a length of 30 mm. and *Neomysis mercedis* reaches 15 mm.

Mature male mysids may be distinguished from females by their long and specialized fourth pleopods which may extend as far as the posterior end of the telson, while females are characterized by a marsupium consisting of four ventral oostegites originating at the bases of the last two pairs of legs (hence the name "opossum shrimps"). Females are generally larger and more abundant than males.

The exopods of the six pairs of legs project laterally somewhat and their beating produces smooth, rapid swimming. The endopods of these appendages extend more medially, and their movements create a current of water which passes anteriorly over the mouth parts. The two pairs of maxillipeds are particularly efficient in straining zooplankton, phytoplankton, and particulate debris from this current. Such food is then passed on toward the second maxillae, first maxillae, mandibles, and mouth.

Internal anatomy and physiology are generally comparable to conditions found in the crayfish. There are no gills, however, most respiration occurring through the thin lining of the carapace. A current of water is drawn under the carapace by the action of the epipodites of the first maxillipeds. A unique feature is the occurrence of a statocyst in the basal portion of the endopod of each uropod.

Reproduction is restricted to the colder months, and females are gravid between October and May, although a few gravid specimens may sometimes be found as late as June. A female may produce up to

40 eggs per clutch, depending on her size. Developing eggs and young are carried in the marsupium for one to three months, the young leaving the mother when three or four millimeters long. Development is direct and the life cycle is thought to extend through two years. Little is known about the number of clutches of eggs which may be produced by a female during her life cycle.

Fresh-water mysids, and especially *Mysis oculata relicta*, are cold water forms. During the warm months this species is almost restricted to the hypolimnion where temperatures range as low as 4°. It is thought that 14° is the maximum temperature that can be tolerated for any length of time, and certainly *Mysis* has never been reported from lakes where the hypolimnial maximum exceeds this figure.

Of all the fresh-water Crustacea known to exhibit daily vertical migrations, *Mysis* has the most extensive and rapid migrations. Populations are confined to the meter of water just above the bottom during the middle of the day and no amount of sampling above that depth will take specimens. At dusk, however, most of the individuals, especially the older ones, migrate into the surface waters where temperatures as high as 20° may be tolerated for a few hours. Reverse downward movements begin at dawn.

*M. oculata relicta* has been recorded a few times from water that was only about 20 per cent saturated with oxygen, but the great majority of investigations show that 40 or 50 per cent saturation is the usual lower limit. In exceptional years the oxygen content of the water just above the bottom of oligotrophic lakes falls below this limit, and populations are then confined to strata above the deepest waters during the daytime.

*M. oculata relicta* has been reported from the Great Lakes (as deep as 270 meters in Lake Superior); Geneva, Trout, and Green lakes in Wisconsin; some of the Finger Lakes in New York; a few other lakes in the northern states; and in many

Fig. 265.—Male *Mysis oculata* var. *relicta* (Lovén), ×2.

deep Canadian lakes. It is especially abundant in Waterton Lake on the border between Montana and Canada. Undoubtedly it is much more common and widely distributed in the United States than the published literature indicates. This variety is circumpolar and occurs also in the British Isles, the Scandinavian countries, northern Germany, and northern Russia. A few zoogeographers contend that it is a marine relict from glacial times when many northern lake basins were presumably connected with the sea and filled with salt water, but a more acceptable theory, postulating postglacial migration from the sea, is now favored. In addition to being found in fresh waters, *M. oculata relicta* has been reported from northern brackish waters and estuaries.

Variety *relicta* is closely related to *Mysis oculata* (Fabr.), a circumpolar, arctic and subarctic, sublittoral, marine species, from which it is undoubtedly derived. Adults of the two forms differ slightly in the detailed structure of the telson and antennal scale. The immature stages are almost indistinguishable, however.

*Neomysis mercedis* is a species that has apparently evolved from marine ancestry very recently. It occurs in brackish bays and estuaries on the west coast where the salinity is usually less than 20.0 and in strictly fresh waters of rivers and lakes near the coast.

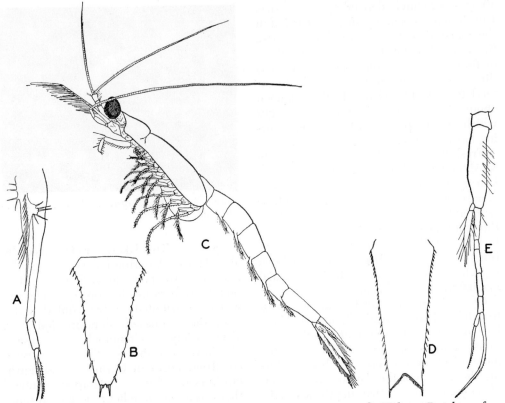

FIG. 266.—Mysidacea. A, male fourth pleopod of *Neomysis mercedis* Holmes; B, telson of
*N. mercedis*; C, female *Mysis oculata* var. *relicta*, ×6; D, telson of same; E, male fourth
pleopod of same. (A and B modified from Tattersall; D and E modified from Ekman.)

Fresh-water mysids are an extremely important food source for a group of commercially important fishes inhabiting deep, cold waters, namely lake trout and coregonids. Food studies show that often 80 to 100 per cent of the stomach contents of these fishes may be *Mysis*.

Both of the American species belong to the Subfamily Mysinae in the Family Mysidae. Aside from their distinctive geographic ranges, they are easily distinguished morphologically. The telson of *Mysis oculata relicta* has a wide bifurcated tip, but that of *Neomysis mercedis* has a narrow truncated tip. Also, the exopod of the fourth pleopod of the mature male of the former species is six-segmented, while that of *N. mercedis* is two-segmented.

## MYSIDACEA REFERENCES

JUDAY, C., and E. A. BIRGE. 1927. Pontoporeia and Mysis in Wisconsin lakes. *Ecology* 7:445–452.

SCHULZE, P. 1926. Schizopoda. *Biol. Tiere Deutschlands* 17:1–18.

TATTERSALL, W. M. 1932. Contributions to a knowledge of the Mysidacea of California. II. The Mysidacea collected during the survey of San Francisco Bay by the U. S. S. "Albatross" in 1914. *Univ. Calif. Publ. Zool.* 37:315–347.

———. 1951. A review of the Mysidacea of the United States National Museum. *Bull. U. S. Nat. Mus.* 201:1–292.

THIENEMANN, A. 1925. Mysis relicta. *Zeitschr. Morph. Ökol. Tiere* 3:389–440.

ZIMMER, C. 1915. Die Systematik der Tribus Mysini H. J. Hansen. *Zool. Anz.* 46:202–216.

# Chapter 20

# ISOPODA (AQUATIC SOW BUGS)

PILL BUGS and sow bugs are chiefly terrestrial and marine, only about five per cent of the total known North American species being found in fresh waters. Approximately 50 fresh-water species occur in the United States, and for the most part these are restricted to springs, spring brooks, streams, and subterranean waters. A decided minority are found in ponds and the shallows of lakes. The biology of *Asellus aquaticus* L. and of several other European species has been thoroughly investigated, but relatively little is known about our American species.

**General characteristics.** Unlike amphipods, the members of the Order Isopoda are strongly flattened dorsoventrally. The "head" of an isopod is actually a cephalothorax since it represents the fusion of the true head and the first thoracic segment. The seven remaining thoracic segments are all similar and are expanded laterally in the form of eavelike lamellae over the basal portions of the thoracic appendages. In all American fresh-water species the last four abdominal segments and true telson are completely fused into a large shieldlike region, often incorrectly referred to as a "telson." The first two abdominal segments are greatly reduced and scarcely visible at the anterior end of the abdomen. In the Sphaeromidae the abdomen consists of two segments, and in *Cirolanides* there are six distinct segments.

Total length, from the anterior margin of the cephalothorax to the posterior margin of the abdomen, usually ranges between 5 and 20 mm.

Coloration may be blackish, brown, dusky, reddish, or yellowish. Some species are variously marked or mottled. Subterranean species are generally whitish or creamy.

The first antennae arise near the median line and anterior margin of the cephalothorax. Each consists of a three-segmented peduncle and a many-segmented flagellum. The second antennae are much longer than the first; they arise ventral and lateral to the first antennae and have five-segmented peduncles.

The eyes are dorsal, unstalked, compound, and usually reduced or absent in subterranean species.

In typical, common species the mouth parts form a compact buccal mass which is covered anteriorly by an upper lip. The sclerotized mandibles are strong, toothed, and may or may not have a palp. Each first maxilla has a basal portion and two, elongated, toothed and setose palps. The second maxillae are smaller, weaker, more platelike, and with three short, terminal divisions. The maxillipeds, representing the appendages of the fused thoracic segment, are flattened, palped, and fit closely together at the median line, thus effectively forming the lower and posterior surfaces of the buccal mass.

Each of the seven free thoracic segments bears a pair of long walking legs, all of which are similar except the first pair (gnathopods) which are subchelate and

425

Fig. 267.—*Asellus*, ×6.5. (Setation omitted.)

used for grasping. In general, the more posterior legs are the largest. The coxae are completely fused with the body, but the basis, ischium, merus, carpus, propodus, and dactylus are distinct in all of the legs. Mature females have large plate-like oostegites attached at the inner bases of several of the anterior pairs of legs. These oostegites extend inward and collectively form a shallow chamber, or marsupium, on the ventral side of the thorax in which incubating eggs and young are

carried. A similar device occurs in the amphipods.

The first five pairs of abdominal appendages (pleopods) are considerably modified and hidden beneath the abdomen. The sixth pair of appendages (uropods), however, are unmodified and project well beyond the posterior end of the body.

In the female the first pleopods are reduced and one-segmented, and the second pleopods are absent. The third, fourth, and fifth pleopods, however, are large, flattened, and biramous. The exopod of the third pleopod forms a sclerotized protective operculum, but the third endopod and both rami of the fourth and fifth pleopods are delicate and respiratory.

The male first pleopods are small, elongated, uniramous, and two-segmented. The second are biramous and greatly specialized for copulation and the transfer of sperm to the female. The third to sixth abdominal appendages are similar to those of the female.

Males may be distinguished from females by their larger body size, larger and more specialized gnathopods, absence of oostegites, and the structure of the first and second pleopods.

Locomotion is restricted to slow crawling. Only the Sphaeromidae are capable of rolling up into a ball as are some of the land isopods.

Species inhabiting subterranean waters are notable for their more elongated body, long weak legs, and long antennae, as well as for their great abundance of tactile hairs.

**Food, feeding.** Isopods are perhaps best characterized as scavengers since they have been observed eating dead and injured aquatic animals of all kinds, and both green and decaying leaves, grass, and aquatic vegetation.

**Internal anatomy, physiology.** The digestive system consists of a short esophagus, a stomach containing a gastric mill, and a long intestine. Four long caeca arise at the junction of the stomach and intestine.

The large heart is located in the posterior part of the thorax. It receives blood from the pericardial chamber via one to

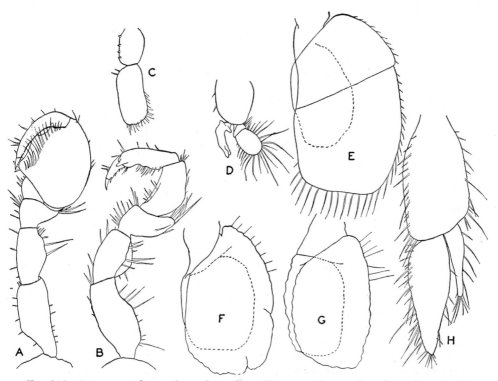

FIG. 268.—Some appendages of a male *Asellus*; all in ventral view, from left side, and all to same magnification. A, first leg (gnathopod); B, fourth leg; C, first pleopod; D, second pleopod; E, third pleopod; F, fourth pleopod; G, fifth pleopod; H, uropod.

three pairs of ostia and sends it out to the hemocoel through a surprisingly large number of arteries (up to 11 in some species). Most of the carbon dioxide–oxygen exchange occurs through the thin-walled third to fifth pleopods, although it is also possible that the general body surface may be of some respiratory significance.

Two coiled maxillary glands, probably excretory, open at the base of the second maxillae. In addition, other small paired glands in the cephalothorax have sometimes been interpreted as excretory devices.

The nervous system is quite simple in structure; it consists of a brain, circumesophageal connectives, subesophageal ganglia, a double ventral nerve cord with double segmental ganglia in the thorax, and a group of fused ganglia in the anterior portion of the abdomen.

**Reproduction.** Males have three pairs of ovoid testes in the middle of the thorax and dorsal to the intestine. The vasa deferentia open at the tips of two finger-like projections on the ventral surface of the seventh thoracic segment. (These structures should not be mistaken for the first pleopods, which immediately follow.) The two ovaries are dorsal, long, and bag-like, and the oviducts open through two slitlike genital pores on the ventral surface of the fifth thoracic segment. Just beneath the surface of the body each oviduct is swollen to form a seminal receptacle.

Reproductive habits have been observed for only a few species. In general, breeding may occur throughout the year, but very few gravid females can be found between October and February.

When ready for copulation, a mature male seizes a female and carries her, ventral side down, beneath his body with his second to fourth legs. Such females may be in either the preadult instar or they may already have shed the posterior half of their exoskeleton in the preadult molt. If a male seizes an immature female or one that has already been impregnated, he releases her almost immediately.

Little is known about the duration of the clasping and copulatory period, but in *Lirceus*, the American genus whose reproductive habits have been most carefully studied, it lasts up to 24 hours.

The female genital pores are not exposed until the preadult exoskeleton has been shed, and if the female has not already lost the posterior half of her exoskeleton, the clasping male usually aids in pulling it off. The male then assumes a copulatory position by sliding sideways so that his ventral surface is pressed against the side of the body of the female. This places the male genital pores and the first and second pleopods in the vicinity of the female genital pore on that side. As sperm are released, the male first and second pleopods undergo rapid vibratory movements which probably aid in transmitting the sperm into the female genital pore and into a seminal receptacle. The process is then repeated on the other side of the female's body, the entire bilateral copulation being completed in less than two hours.

The two individuals then separate, and the female promptly sheds the anterior half of her preadult exoskeleton, the oostegites thereby being transformed from small buds to large functional plates.

After an interval of as long as several days, the mature eggs pass down the oviducts through the seminal receptacles where they are fertilized, out the genital pores, and into the marsupium. Depending on the species and size of the female, the number of eggs per brood ranges between 40 and 250. Incubating eggs and newly hatched young are retained in the marsupium for 20 to 30 days. They are aerated by slow up-and-down movements of the oostegites and maxilliped movements which produce an anterior–posterior current of water through the marsupium. The young eventually find their way out of the posterior end of the marsupium by trial and error.

**Development, life cycle.** First instar young have the general characteristics of adults. Little is known about the total number of instars during the isopod life cycle. Presumably there may be at least 15, of which the first five to eight are probably preadult. Casting of the exoskeleton is completed in a few minutes to as much as three days. The process is initiated by a transverse split on the fourth thoracic segment. The posterior half of the exoskeleton is lost first, then, after a variable interval, the anterior half. The life span is thought to be about one year or less. Little specific information is available concerning the number of broods which may be produced during the female life cycle.

**Ecology.** Fresh-water isopods seldom come into open waters but remain secreted under rocks, vegetation, and debris. They are primarily inhabitants of the unpolluted shallows, rarely being found in water more than a meter deep. *Lirceus lineatus* (Say) is a notable exception in having been collected at depths up to 55 meters.

A single brook or a single pond almost invariably contains only one species, and it is very unusual to find two or more species in the same habitat.

A few species, such as *Asellus militaris* Hay and *A. spatulata* (Mackin and Hubricht), may occur in temporary ponds where they burrow into the substrate during periods of drought, but adaptations for withstanding adverse environmental conditions are not generally developed in this order.

Striking masses, or aggregations, of *Asellus*, consisting of scores to thousands of individuals have been observed in small streams. Such aggregations are thought to be formed chiefly as the result of reactions to current velocity. The migration of some individuals upstream as far as possible or, if the current is too swift, being washed downstream until they are able to maintain a footing, have the net result of concentrating the isopods in a segment of the stream where the current is neither too fast nor too slow.

Except for *Sphaeroma terebrans* Bate, all of our species of fresh-water isopods are restricted to North America. Furthermore, aside from about ten species which are widely distributed in this country, they are known mostly from single localities (especially caves and springs) or single states. The specific distributions for the common species are given in the key which follows.

Though the loss of sight is generally characteristic of species confined to subterranean waters, and functional eyes are characteristic of surface water species, there are some interesting exceptions and variations. *Asellus oculata* (Mackin and Hubricht) is found in springs and streams, yet the eyes are reduced. *Lirceus hoppinae* (Faxon), with functional eyes, occurs in both caves and surface waters. *Asellus hobbsi* (Maloney) is subterranean and has eyes present or absent. *A. spatulata* (Mackin and Hubricht) is a surface form, but the eyes may be present or absent.

**Economic significance.** With few exceptions, isopods are restricted to small lakes and streams and consequently they are of little importance in the diet of fishes. Economically, *Sphaeroma terebrans* is perhaps the most important species. It is a borer in salt and brackish waters, as well as in fresh-water estuaries of the Gulf coast, and causes extensive damage to wharves and piling. This species has numerous important relatives restricted to salt water. *Lirceus brachyurus* (Harger) sometimes becomes a pest in commercial beds of water cress. Some isopods serve as intermediate hosts for parasitic nematodes and Acanthocephala of birds and fishes and Acanthocephala of amphibians.

**Collection, preparation.** Isopods are easily collected by hand-picking, washing out aquatic vegetation, or with a small net. Seventy per cent alcohol is a suitable killing agent and preservative. Appendages may be dissected off under the binoculars and permanently mounted in glycerin jelly.

**Taxonomy.** Many of the older descriptions of isopods are useless because they stress highly variable characters such as the number of segments in the antennae and the body length : width ratio. In recent years greater emphasis has been placed on the detailed structure of the mature male second pleopods and gnathopods. These features are constant within each species and there are considerable differences from one genus and species to another.

Most studies in the United States have been scattered and uncorrelated. In 1918 only 21 species were known; now there are about 50, and the several active American investigators in this group have specimens of many more undescribed species in their collections. There are still differences of opinion as to which characters are of generic and specific rank. The status of *Caecidotea* and *Asellus* has been the object of a long controversy; some workers contend that the two should be united under *Asellus*, and this policy has been followed in this manual.

By far the most common American species is *Asellus militaris* Hay, which is widely distributed everywhere east of the Rockies. This is the species usually incorrectly referred to as *A. communis* Say.

## KEY TO COMMON SPECIES OF ISOPODA

1. Free-living; morphologically unmodified.....................................2
   Parasitic in branchial chambers of Palaemonidae (*Macrobrachium* and *Palaemonetes*); greatly modified for parasitic existence, appendages reduced, female asymmetrical (Fig. 269); two species.
   Suborder EPICARIDEA, BOPYRIDAE, Probopyrus
2. Uropods terminal (Fig. 267)...........Suborder **ASELLOTA**, ASELLIDAE, **5**
   Uropods broad and inserted laterally on abdomen, forming with it a large horizontally expanded fanlike structure (Fig. 270B)..Suborder **FLABELLIFERA, 3**

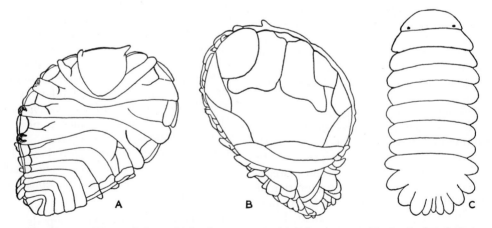

Fɪɢ. 269.—*Probopyrus bithynis* Richardson, parasitic on *Palaemonetes ohionis.* A, dorsal view of female, ×16; B, ventral view of female, ×16; C, dorsal view of male, ×40. (Modified from Richardson, 1904.)

3. Abdomen with two distinct segments (Fig. 270B); eyes present; up to 10 mm. long......................................................SPHAEROMIDAE, **4**
   Abdomen with six distinct segments (Fig. 270A); eyes absent; up to 17 mm. long; known only from artesian wells near San Marcos, Texas.

   CIROLANIDAE, *Cirolanides texensis* Benedict

4. Second, third, and fourth segments of palp of maxilliped not produced into lobes (Fig. 270D); a borer in timbers, roots, and mangroves in fresh, brackish, and salt waters; Fla. to Texas......................*Sphaeroma terebrans* Bate
   Second, third, and fourth segments of palp of maxilliped produced into lobes (Fig. 270C); one rare species known from warm springs at Socorro, N. M.; a second rare species known from San Nicholas Island, Calif.; a third species, *E. oregonensis* (Dana), is common in fresh-water ponds and pools near the Pacific coast, but it occurs also in the ocean.................*Exosphaeroma*

5. Anterior margin of cephalothorax with a low but distinct carina (Figs. 271A–C); suture between exopod segments of third pleopod running from the median posterior angle very obliquely toward the lateral margin (Fig. 271H); up to 25 mm. long; eyes present; eastern U. S. as far west as the Great Plains; seven local species, usually common but with restricted ranges; five additional and common species that are more widely distributed are keyed below.. **Lirceus, 6**
   Without a carina on the anterior margin of cephalothorax (Fig. 272F); suture between exopod segments of third pleopod running from the median margin less obliquely toward the lateral margin (Fig. 268E); up to 20 mm. long; eyes present or absent; about 25 species reported mostly from springs, streams, or cave systems; six common species keyed below................**Asellus, 13**

6. Mandible with a one- to three-segmented palp, often quite small and stumplike...**7**
   Mandible without a palp.............................................................**8**

7. Abdomen distinctly broader than long (Fig. 271D); reported from streams and springs in Mo., Ark., and Okla.................*Lirceus hoppinae* (Faxon)
   Abdomen only slightly wider than long (Fig. 271F); ponds, springs, and spring brooks in Ohio, Ind., Ill., Ky., and Tenn............*Lirceus fontinalis* Raf.

8. Middle and distal propodal processes absent (Fig. 271G); usually in water cress; Penn. and Va.............................*Lirceus brachyurus* (Harger)
   Middle process and usually also the distal process of the propodus present (Figs. 271J, L).............................................................**9**

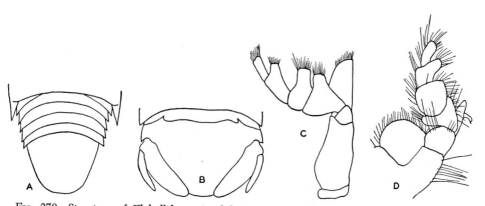

Fig. 270.—Structure of Flabellifera. A, abdomen of *Cirolanides texensis* Benedict; B, posterior end of *Exosphaeroma*; C, palp of maxilliped of *Exosphaeroma*; D, palp of maxilliped of *Sphaeroma terebrans* Bate. (A to C modified from Richardson, 1905; D modified from Van Name, 1936.)

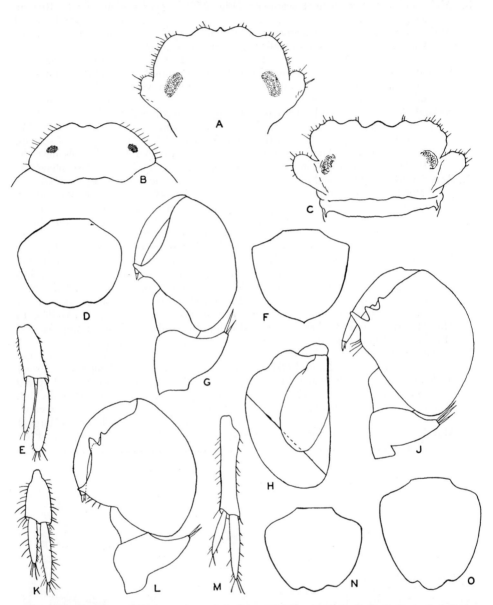

Fig. 271.—Structure of *Lirceus*. A, cephalothorax of *Lirceus fontinalis* Raf.; B, cephalothorax of *L. brachyurus* (Harger); C, cephalothorax of *L. lineatus* (Say); D, abdomen of *L. hoppinae* (Faxon); E, uropod of *L. hoppinae*; F, abdomen of *L. fontinalis*; G, gnathopod of *L. brachyurus*; H, third pleopod of *L. brachyurus*; J, gnathopod of *L. garmani* Hubricht and Mackin; K, uropod of *L. garmani*; L, gnathopod of *L. lineatus*; M, uropod of *L. lineatus*; N, abdomen of *L. lineatus*; O, abdomen of *L. louisianae* (Mackin and Hubricht). (A and C modified from Racovitza, 1920a; D, E, G, and J to O modified from Hubricht and Mackin.)

9.  Endopod of each uropod about as long or longer than the basal segment (Fig.
    271K). . . . . . . . . . . . . . . . . . . . . . . . . . . . . . . . . . . . . . . . . . . . . . . . . . . . . . . .10
    Endopod of each uropod shorter than the basal segment (Fig. 271M). . . . . . . . .12
10. Proximal process of propodus as large or larger than the middle process (Fig.
    271J); wells and permanent or temporary streams in Mo., Ark., Kan., and
    Okla. . . . . . . . . . . . . . . . . . . . . . . . . **Lirceus garmani** Hubricht and Mackin
    Proximal process of propodus smaller than middle process (Fig. 271L). . . . . . . .11
11. Uropods flattened (Fig. 271E) . . . . . . . . . . . . . . . . . . . . . . . . . . . . . . . . . . . . . . .7
    Uropods cylindrical (Fig. 271M); the most common and widely distributed species
    in this genus; Great Lakes region, and southeastern U. S. from Va. to Fla. and
    Ala. . . . . . . . . . . . . . . . . . . . . . . . . . . . . . . . . . . . .**Lirceus lineatus** (Say)
12. Abdomen longer than broad (Fig. 271O); streams, sloughs, ditches, and marshes
    in Ill., Mo., Ark., and La. . . . . . . .**Lirceus louisianae** (Mackin and Hubricht)
    Abdomen as broad as long or distinctly broader (Figs. 271D, F). . . . . . . . . . . . .11
13. Eyes present; abdomen broader than long (Fig. 272E); up to 16 mm. long; not
    subterranean. . . . . . . . . . . . . . . . . . . . . . . . . . . . . . . . . . . . . . . . . . . . . . . . . .15
    Eyes absent; abdomen longer than broad (Fig. 272A); subterranean springs, wells,
    and caves; rarely in surface waters . . . . . . . . . . . . . . . . . . . . . . . . . . . . . . . . .14

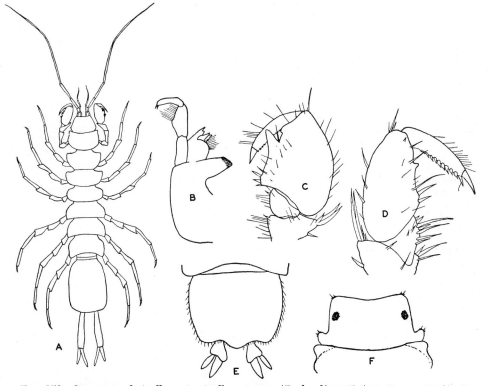

FIG. 272.—Structure of *Asellus*. A, *Asellus stygius* (Packard), ×7 (setation omitted); B, mandible of *Asellus*; C, gnathopod of male *A. militaris* (Hay); D, gnathopod of female *A. militaris*; E, posterior end of *A. brevicaudus* Forbes; F, anterior end of *A. intermedius* Forbes. (A modified from Hay, 1903; B modified from Huntsman, 1915; C and D modified from Racovitza, 1920.)

**14.** Length of male third pleopod twice or less than the width; Mo., Ind., and Ky.

**Asellus stygius** (Packard)

Length of male third pleopod more than twice the width; northern fringes of the Ozarks..............................**Asellus tridentatus** (Hungerford)

**15.** Propodus of first leg armed with two triangular processes, one or both of which are sometimes replaced by a strong spine (Figs. 268A; 272C, D)........**16**

Propodus of first leg with setae only; streams and lakes along West Coast.

**Asellus tomalensis** Harford

**16.** Uropods about as long as abdomen (Fig. 267)............................**17**

Uropods about half as long as abdomen (Fig. 272E); reported from streams in Ill., Tenn., Mo., and Ark.; occasional in caves....**Asellus brevicaudus** Forbes

**17.** Male with one process on the palmar margin of gnathopod; cephalothorax with a small but distinct lobe at each posterolateral corner (Fig. 272F); up to 10 mm. long; uncommon but generally distributed in streams, springs, and lakes of central U. S. as far west as Nebr............**Asellus intermedius** Forbes

Male with two processes on the palmar margin of gnathopod (Fig. 272C); cephalothorax with posterolateral lobes less distinct or absent; up to 20 mm. long; by far the most common American species........**Asellus militaris** Hay

# ISOPODA REFERENCES

ALLEE, W. C. 1929. Studies in animal aggregations: natural aggregations of the isopod, Asellus communis. *Ecology* **10**:14–36.

COLLINGE, W. E. 1944. On the freshwater isopod genus Caecidotea Packard. *Ann. Mag. Nat. Hist.* (11) **11**:815–817.

HATCHETT, S. P. 1947. Biology of the Isopoda of Michigan. *Ecol. Monogr.* **17**:47–79.

HOFFMAN, C. H. 1933. The biology of Caecidotea tridentata Hungerford (Isopoda-Crustacca). *Jour. Kan. Ent. Soc.* **6**:26–33.

HUBRICHT, L., and J. G. MACKIN. 1949. The freshwater isopods of the genus Lirceus (Asellota, Asellidae). *Amer. Midl. Nat.* **42**:334–349.

KUNKEL, B. W. 1918. The Arthrostraca of Connecticut. *Bull. Conn. Geol. and Nat. Hist. Surv.* **26**:1–261.

LEVI, H. W. 1949. Two new species of cave isopods from Pennsylvania. *Notulae Nat.* **220**:1–6.

MACKIN, J. G., and L. HUBRICHT. 1938. Records of the distribution of species of isopods in Central and Southern United States, with descriptions of four new species of Mancasellus and Asellus (Asellota, Asellidae). *Amer. Midl. Nat.* **19**:628–637.

———. 1940. Descriptions of seven new species of Caecidotea (Isopoda, Asellidae) from central United States. *Trans. Amer. Micros. Soc.* **59**:383–397.

MARKUS, H. C. 1930. Studies on the morphology and life history of the isopod, Mancasellus macrourus. *Ibid.* **49**:220–237.

MILLER, M. A. 1933. A new blind isopod, Asellus californicus, and a revision of the subterranean asellids. *Univ. Calif. Publ. Zool.* **39**:97–110.

NEEDHAM, A. E. 1941. Abdominal appendages of Asellus, II. *Quart. Jour. Micros. Sci.* **83**:61–89.

RACOVITZA, E. G. 1920. Notes sur les isopodes. 6. Asellus communis Say. 7. Les pléopodes I and II dés asellides; morphologie et développement. *Arch. Zool. Exp. Gen.* **58**:79–115.

———. 1920a. Notes sur les isopodes. 8. Mancasellus tenax (Smith). 9. Mancasellus macrourus (Garman). *Ibid.* **59**:28–66.

RICHARDSON, H. 1904. Contributions to the natural history of the Isopoda. *Proc. U. S. Nat. Mus.* **27**:1–89.

———. 1905. A monograph of the isopods of North America. *Bull. U. S. Nat. Mus.* **54**:1–727.

TSCHETWERIKOFF, S. 1911. Beiträge zur Anatomie der Wasserassel (Asellus aquaticus L.). *Bull. Soc. Imp. Nat. Moscou* **24**:377–509.

UNWIN, E. E. 1921. Note upon the reproduction of Asellus aquaticus. *Jour. Linn. Soc.* **34**:335–343.

VAN NAME, W. G. 1936. The American land and fresh-water isopod Crustacea. *Bull. Amer. Mus. Nat. Hist.* **71**:1–535.

———. 1940. A supplement to the American land and fresh-water Isopoda. *Ibid.* **77**:109–142.

———. 1942. A second supplement to the American land and fresh-water isopod Crustacea. *Ibid.* **80**:299–329.

# Chapter 21

# AMPHIPODA (SCUDS, SIDESWIMMERS)

LIKE THE Decapoda, the Amphipoda are chiefly marine, only about 50 American species being confined to fresh waters. They occur in a wide variety of unpolluted lakes, ponds, streams, brooks, springs, and subterranean waters. With the exception of one species which may swim about as a plankter in lakes, they are all more or less confined to the substrate.

**General characteristics.** The great majority of species are from 5 to 20 mm. long. The body is laterally compressed and consists of a cephalothorax (first thoracic segment fused with the head), seven free thoracic segments, a six-segmented abdomen, and a small, terminal telson. The pleura of the first three abdominal segments are prolonged ventrally so that these segments are deeper than any of the other body segments. In some species the last three abdominal segments are more or less fused.

Eyes are usually well developed in species living above ground, but subterranean species show varying degrees of degeneration or complete absence of eyes. They are unstalked, compound, and round, oval, reniform, or elongated.

Both pairs of antennae range from short to long. Each first antenna consists of a three-segmented peduncle and a long flagellum; sometimes there is a very small accessory flagellum (Figs. 274A, B). Each second antenna has a flagellum and a five-segmented peduncle, but the basal segment of the peduncle is fused with the

head, and the second and third segments are very short; only the last two segments are well developed.

The mouth parts are relatively small, compactly arranged, and hidden by the basal segments of the appendages of the first thoracic segment. They include an upper lip, a pair of tearing and cutting mandibles, a pair of laminar and spinous first maxillae, a pair of small, flexible second maxillae, a lower lip, and a pair of maxillipeds. The maxillipeds are homologues of the first maxillipeds of decapods; each consists of an inner plate, outer plate, and palp.

The seven pairs of thoracic legs all have seven segments corresponding to the segments of crayfish legs. Beginning proximally, these are: coxa, basis, ischium, merus, carpus, propodus, and dactylus. The coxae are usually called coxal plates; they are greatly enlarged, flattened, relatively immovable, and project ventrally at the edges of the body.

The first two pairs of legs, known as gnathopods, are subchelate and adapted for grasping (Fig. 275D), but the third to seventh legs are relatively unspecialized pereiopods. The first two pereiopods are usually flexed forward, the last three backward.

The coxal gills are flattened, oval sacs extending downward from the inner surface of the upper posterior corner of the coxal plates. They occur on the second to seventh or second to sixth legs. In addition, there are sometimes very small

435

Fig. 273.—*Gammarus limnaeus* Smith, ×4.

lateral sternal gills on some of the thoracic segments (Fig. 276B).

The first three abdominal segments bear paired pleopods. Each consists of a basal peduncle and two flexible, many-segmented rami. The last three abdominal segments bear paired uropods. These appendages are never very movable, always directed posteriorly, and closely approximated. The peduncles are unsegmented, but the rami are sometimes composed of two segments, the terminal one being small.

Coloration in living amphipods is frequently brilliant, but preserved specimens bleach out so that they are whitish, gray, or cream-colored. Some common species show a wide range in color from one place or time to another. *Hyalella azteca* (Saussure), for example, is usually light brown or greenish, but bluish, purple, dark brown, or reddish populations are often found. *Synurella dentata* Hubricht is usually gray-blue but sometimes lavender, brown, or greenish. *Gammarus fasciatus* Say is whitish, with the body and proximal segments of the appendages banded with green or brown. Very little is known about the causes of color variations within single species. Subterranean amphipods are almost invariably whitish, cream-colored, gray, or translucent.

The sexes are most readily separated on the basis of large marsupial plates, or oostegites, on the inner surface of the coxal plates of some of the legs (usually second to fifth) of the female. Males often have the larger gnathopods.

**Locomotion.** In general, amphipods are much more active at night than during the hours of daylight. The pereiopods are used in crawling and walking but are aided by pushing with the uropods and grasping and pulling with the gnathopods. The last two pereiopods are flexed outward somewhat and are important in a clumsy, skittering sort of locomotion when the animal is on its side. Flexing and extending movements of the entire body aid in crawling and walking. The pleopods are the chief locomotor appendages for rapid undulatory swimming above the substrate, the body being kept well straightened and the pereiopods directed backward. As an amphipod swims it often rolls over on its side or back (hence the name sideswimmer).

**Food, feeding.** Amphipods are voracious feeders, all kinds of animal and plant matter being consumed. Only rarely do they attack and feed on living animals, but freshly killed animals are consumed readily. Species occurring in aquatic vegetation may often be seen browsing on the film of microscopic plants, animals, and organic debris covering the leaves and stems. Like the decapods, then, scuds are omnivorous, general scavengers.

The food mass is held by the gnathopods and anterior pereiopods and chewed directly without being first torn into smaller pieces.

**Internal anatomy, physiology.** Food passes through a short esophagus and into a small stomach containing a gastric mill. The long, undifferentiated intestine opens via the anus just below the telson. Six caeca are usually associated with the digestive tract. One is anterior, dorsal, and long; a second is very small and near the posterior end; and the other four are very long, lateral, and ventral.

The tubular heart is in the dorsal portion of the thorax. It has three pairs of ostia and an anterior and posterior aorta.

Although it is possible that some respiration occurs through the general body surface, the thin-walled coxal gills are undoubtedly the chief organs for the oxygen–carbon dioxide exchange. The beating of the pleopods creates a current of water over the gills.

Antennal glands, probably excretory, open at the base of the second antennae.

The typical nervous system consists of two ventral nerve cords united at intervals by large segmental ganglia, two circumesophageal connectives, and a supraesophageal mass, or "brain."

Both pairs of antennae are olfactory and highly sensitive to touch. They sometimes bear minute, stalked, clublike, or wineglass-shaped sensory appendages (Figs. 275H, J), presumably comparable to the aesthetasks of copepods.

**Reproduction.** Testes and ovaries are paired, elongated strands ventral to the heart. The oviducts open at the base of the fifth coxal plates, and the male genital pores open on papillae on the ventral side of the last thoracic segment.

With the exception of *Hyalella azteca* and two or three other species, our knowledge of the details of reproductive behavior is rather sketchy. Syngamic reproduction is the rule, although the rarity of males in *Stygobromus* indicates the possibility of parthenogenetic reproduction. Most common species breed some time between February and October, depending largely on water temperatures. Mature males pair for the first time when they are in their ninth instar, females in their eighth (nuptial) instar. When two males meet both are active and fail to pair and soon separate, but a female is passive when seized by a male.

In *Gammarus*, *Hyalella azteca*, and one species of *Synurella*, pairing consists of the males carrying the females on their backs and keeping them in place with their gnathopods. Paired individuals feed and swim about for one to as much as seven days, or until the female is ready to molt to the first adult instar. The two animals then separate for a few minutes to several hours while the female loses her old exoskeleton. A male then returns, the two individuals pair again, and copulation usually occurs within the subsequent 24 hours.

Copulation and transfer of sperm are completed in less than a minute. The male extends the posterior part of his body around and to the ventral side of the female until the tips of his uropods touch the marsupium which is formed by the marsupial plates, or oostegites. Ejected sperm are then swept into the marsupium by movements of the female pleopods. This process of sperm transfer may be repeated several times at intervals of a few minutes, the male holding on to the female all the time.

The animals finally separate, and the female promptly releases her eggs from the oviducts into the marsupium where they are fertilized. The number of eggs released by the female depends on her size and age as well as the particular species. In general, the larger and older females release the larger numbers of eggs. One species of *Stygobromus* releases only one or two eggs at a time, but the more common species usually average from 15 to 50 eggs per brood. *Hyalella azteca* averages about 18 eggs per brood.

**Development, life cycle.** The oostegites are bordered with stiff hairs which are hooked distally and entangled somewhat, and the developing eggs are therefore retained securely within the marsupium. In the few species that have been carefully studied, the incubation period ranges from one to three weeks. Newly hatched young are retained in the marsupium an additional one to eight days and are released to the outside when the mother has her first molt following copulation.

Judging from the limited observations that have been made, the females of most species produce only a single brood during the life cycle, but in a few species each female customarily produces a series of broods during the breeding months. *Hyalella azteca*, for example, averages 15 broods in 152 days (Embody, 1911). Copulation is necessary for the production of each brood, so that females pair for the second or subsequent time while they are still carrying their previous brood of eggs or young in the marsupium. These events therefore closely follow each other within a few hours: (1) male leaves female, (2) female molts and releases young, (3) male and female pair again, (4) release of eggs to marsupium, (5) repeated copulation and fertilization, and (6) male leaves female.

*Hyalella azteca* has a minimum of nine instars in its life history (Geisler). As in all other species, development is direct, and the newly hatched young have all of the adult appendages. The first five instars form the juvenile period, during which the sexes are indistinguishable. In the sixth and seventh instars, or adolescent period, the sexes can be differentiated; the female has small oostegites and a few small eggs in the ovaries, and the male has slightly enlarged gnathopods. Pairing occurs for the first time in the eighth, or nuptial, instar, and the ninth and subsequent instars form the adult period. The number of molts which may occur during the adult period is variable but may be as high as 15 or 20.

When the old exoskeleton is ready to be cast, a dorsal, transverse split appears halfway around the body between the first and second thoracic segments or occasionally between the cephalothorax and first thoracic segment. Sometimes there are accessory longitudinal splits along the upper margins of the coxal plates. The cephalothorax is withdrawn first and then the rest of the body. Molting is completed in less than an hour.

The interval between molts ranges from a minimum of three to a maximum of 40 days, depending on food conditions, temperature, and the species. Immature amphipods molt at much shorter intervals than adults.

Most species complete the life cycle in a year or less. *Pontoporeia affinis* (Lindström) is unusual in that it is thought to have a life cycle of 30 months or more. This species breeds between December and April, and the young are released from the marsupium in the spring.

**Ecology.** *Hyalella azteca, Gammarus limnaeus* Smith, *G. fasciatus* Say, and *Crangonyx gracilis* Smith constitute the great majority of specimens taken by casual collectors. These species are widely distributed and common in unpolluted clear waters, including springs, spring brooks, streams, pools, ponds, and lakes. Less common species are more restricted to certain types of environments. *Pontoporeia affinis*, for example, occurs only in deep, cold, oligotrophic, northern lakes. *Gammarus minus* Say occurs only in caves, springs, and small streams in the Appalachian and Ozark uplifts. Many species are restricted to seeps, springs, and subterranean waters in one or a few states.

As a group, amphipods are strongly thigmotactic and react negatively to light. Consequently, during the daytime they are in vegetation or hidden under and between debris and stones. They usually congregate in the corners of culture jars in the laboratory. The true burrowing habit has not evolved in fresh-water species.

Amphipods are sometimes unbelievably abundant. The writer has collected *Gammarus* from spring brooks rich in rooted vegetation where populations have exceeded 10,000 per square meter. Juday and Birge (1927) reported an average population of 4,553 *Pontoporeia affinis* per square meter at a depth of 50 to 60 meters on the bottom of Green Lake, Wisconsin.

Except for *P. affinis*, which is both a benthic and plankton organism and which has been found as deep as 300 meters in Lake Superior, amphipods are restricted to shallow waters. *Hyalella azteca* is about the only other species ever found at depths exceeding one meter.

Although it is generally true that the majority of species appear to be restricted to waters of low or medium carbonate content, there are a few notable exceptions. *Gammarus limnaeus* is common in hard waters, and *Hyalella azteca* is sometimes found in alkaline and brackish waters.

An abundance of dissolved oxygen appears to be an environmental necessity. The only reported notable exception is *Pontoporeia affinis*, which has been collected from the bottom waters of lakes where the concentration of dissolved oxygen was less than 7 per cent saturation.

The restriction of many species to subterranean waters and springs strongly suggests that they are cold stenotherms.

**Geographic distribution, dispersal.** Most of the scuds of the United States are restricted to this continent. In the Gammaridae, all genera except *Crangonyx*, *Synurella*, and *Gammarus* are restricted to North America. *Hyalella azteca* occurs also in South America, and *Pontoporeia affinis* is common in cold lakes of northern Europe.

Very little is known about the passive transport of amphipods from one drainage system to another. Unlike the entomostraca, amphipods are not generally adapted for withstanding drought and other adverse environmental conditions. *Crangonyx gracilis*, *C. shoemakeri* (Hubricht and Mackin), and *Synurella bifurca* (Hay), however, are inhabitants of temporary as well as permanent ponds and streams, and it has been suggested that these species tide over unfavorable conditions by burrowing into the substrate.

*C. forbesi* (Hubricht and Mackin) un-dergoes interesting seasonal migrations. In the spring, populations move upstream into spring brooks and springs. There the populations often become so dense that cannibalism results. In the autumn the remnants of the population migrate back downstream. Breeding occurs during the winter months.

*Pontoporeia affinis* occurs in the brackish Baltic Sea and has very close marine relatives. This species is presumably a marine relict, and two theories have been advanced to account for its presence in fresh waters. First, *P. affinis* may have inhabited certain lake basins when they were well below sea level, connected with the sea, and filled with salt water. During the subsequent elevation of the land and gradual replacement of the salt water by fresh they have slowly become adapted to the new environment. Second, it may have migrated from the sea into fresh waters at the close of the last glacial period.

**Subterranean amphipods.** The central and south-central states, from eastern Kansas and Oklahoma to Indiana, Kentucky, and Tennessee is a region abundant in large caves and cave systems, most of which contain brooks, streams, and pools. It is in such bodies of water that interesting subterranean amphipods are found. Although the cave habit has evolved in many genera, the species, as a group, are similarly modified. They are generally whitish, creamy, or straw-colored, the antennae and tactile hairs are well developed, the body is often relatively fragile, and the eyes are usually reduced, vestigial, or absent. Their food consists of bits of dead vegetation washed into the caves and the thin bacterial scum covering submerged surfaces. Some subterranean species are generally distributed throughout large areas, but others are rare and have been reported only from single or a few localities.

Subterranean amphipods are often collected just outside of caves and underground streams where the water forms surface seeps, wells, and springs. Some species are represented by two distinct varieties, one subterranean and the other a surface form. The cave variety of *Crangonyx gracilis*, for example, has degenerate eyes and no pigmentation, while its pond and stream counterpart has functional eyes and good pigmentation. Comparable differences occur in the varieties of *C. forbesi* and *Gammarus troglophilus* Hubricht and Mackin. *G. minus* is unusual in having three varieties. The one occurring in springs has large eyes, short antennae, and brown coloration. A cave variety has slightly reduced eyes, long antennae, and bluish coloration. Another rare cave variety has a fragile body, greatly reduced eyes, long antennae, and bluish coloration.

**Enemies, commensals, parasites.** Fishes are the chief predators, although few species of amphipods occur in streams and ponds large enough to support natural fish populations. The planting of amphipods in small Rocky Mountain lakes has, in a few instances, been at least temporarily successful in augmenting the natural food supply of trout. Birds, predaceous aquatic insects, and amphibians probably take an appreciable toll.

Like crayfish, amphipods support an amazing population of algae and sessile Protozoa on all of the external body surfaces.

Scuds serve as intermediate hosts for a wide variety of parasites, including tapeworms of waterfowl and fishes, and a few nematodes, trematodes, and Acanthocephala of birds, fishes, and amphibians.

**Collection, preparation.** Where specimens are abundant they may be easily taken with a dipnet and by rinsing out masses of aquatic vegetation and bottom debris. Stony bottoms require hand picking with forceps or a small aquarium net. Seventy per cent alcohol is a satisfactory killing agent and preservative.

Live specimens may be maintained in aquaria, especially if they are well supplied with aquatic vegetation.

**Taxonomy.** Of the three suborders of the Order Amphipoda, only one, the Gammaroidea, is represented in American fresh waters. The list of species has grown from 16 in 1907 (Weckel) to about 50 at the present time. Of these, all but two belong in the Gammaridae, *Hyalella azteca* belonging in the Talitridae and *Pontoporeia affinis* in the Haustoriidae.

For accurate identification it is important that mature males and females be used, since the keys below are based largely on structures which are best differentiated in the later instars.

*Pontoporeia* has been a particularly puzzling genus, and several species have been described from the United States. A recent critical study (Segerstråle, 1937), however, has shown that there is only one valid species, *P. affinis*, which is identical with one occurring in Europe. The previous confusion resulted from the fact that this species shows marked changes in the later instars, especially with respect to length of the antennae and structure of the uropods.

## KEY TO GENERA AND SPECIES OF AMPHIPODA

1. First antenna with accessory flagellum (Figs. 274A, B) and either longer or shorter than second antenna; third uropod with or without rami; telson cleft or entire. .................................................................2
   First antenna without accessory flagellum (Fig. 274D) and shorter than second antenna; third uropod uniramous (Fig. 274E); telson entire; 4 to 8 mm. long; springs, spring brooks, pools, and lakes; widely distributed and common.
   TALITRIDAE, **Hyalella azteca** (Saussure)

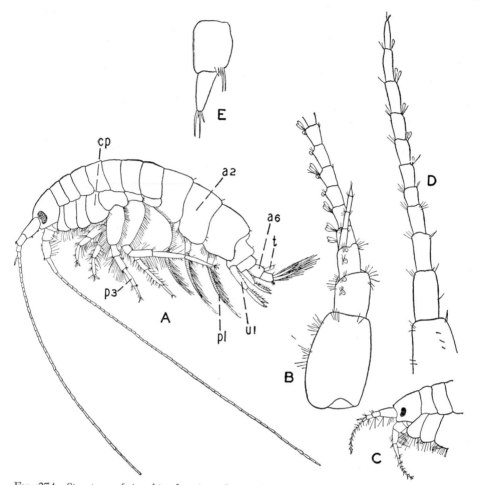

Fig. 274.—Structure of Amphipoda. A, male *Pontoporeia affinis* (Lindström), ×9; B, basal portion of first antenna of male *P. affinis*; C, anterior end of female *P. affinis*; D, first antenna of female *Hyalella azteca* (Saussure); E, third uropod of *H. azteca*. *a2*, second abdominal segment; *a6*, sixth abdominal segment; *cp*, coxal plate; *p3*, third pereiopod; *pl*, third pleopod; *t*, telson; *u1*, first uropod. (A to C modified from Segerstråle; D, redrawn from Geisler; E redrawn from Weckel, 1907.)

2. First antenna slightly shorter than second antenna, very short in female (Fig. 274C) and very long in mature male (Fig. 274A); accessory flagellum of first antenna consisting of three or four segments (Fig. 274B); fifth pereiopod much shorter than fourth and with second segment greatly expanded; up to 9 mm. long; on the bottom and in the plankton of deep, cold lakes, including Great Lakes, L. Nipigon, Green L., Wis., Lake Washington, Seattle, some Finger Lakes, N. Y., and others. Mature male of variety *typica* has 31 to 57 segments in the flagellum of the first antenna and 42 to 72 segments in the flagellum of the second antenna; mature male of variety *brevicornis* has 14 to 19 and 19 to 24 segments, respectively.

HAUSTORIIDAE, **Pontoporeia affinis** (Lindström)

First antenna either longer or shorter than second, but both antennae long and
slender; accessory flagellum very short, consisting of two short segments, or
well developed and consisting of from three to seven segments; fifth pereiopod
longer or slightly shorter than fourth, and with the second segment only moderately expanded (Fig. 275A)........................GAMMARIDAE, 3

3. Accessory flagellum of first antenna three- to seven-segmented (Fig. 275G); third
uropod well developed (Fig. 275E)................................4

Accessory flagellum of first antenna small, rudimentary, or consisting of one short
and one long segment (Fig. 276D); third uropod usually reduced (Fig.
276G) .................................................9

4. Coxal gills with cylindrical appendages (Figs. 275B, C); up to 11 mm. long; two
uncommon species known from streams in Wash., Ore., and Calif.
                                                    **Anisogammarus**

Coxal gills without cylindrical appendages; up to 25 mm. long; common and
widely distributed....................................**Gammarus, 5**

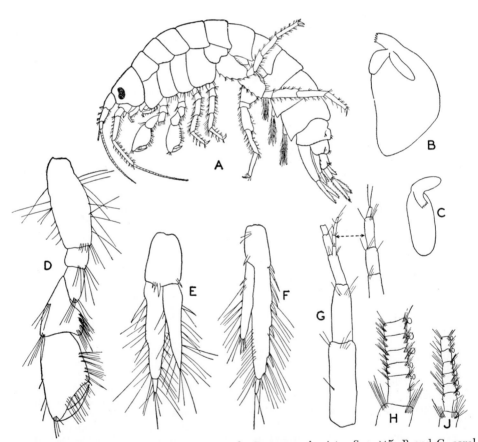

Fig. 275.—Structure of Gammaridae. A, male *Gammarus fasciatus* Say, ×5; B and C, coxal
gills of *Anisogammarus oregonensis* Shoemaker; D, second gnathopod of male *Gammarus
limnaeus*; E, third uropod of *G. limnaeus*; F, third uropod of *G. minus* Say; G, basal portion of
first antenna of *G. limnaeus*; H, basal segments of flagellum of second antenna of male *G.
troglophilus* Hubricht and Mackin; J, basal segments of flagellum of second antenna of female
*G. troglophilus*. (A modified from Kunkel; B and C modified from Shoemaker, 1944; D to G
modified from Weckel; H and J modified from Hubricht and Mackin.)

5. Flagellum of male second antenna armed with sense organs (Fig. 275H)........6
   Flagellum of second antenna not armed with sense organs in either sex........8
6. Flagellum of second antenna armed with sense organs in both sexes (Figs. 275H,
   J); palmar margin of male second gnathopod straight or convex; eyes of
   medium size; caves, springs, and streams in Ill. and Mo.
   
   **Gammarus troglophilus** Hubricht and Mackin
   
   Flagellum of second antenna of female not armed with sense organs; palmar margin of male second gnathopod slightly concave (Fig. 275D)............7
7. Inner ramus of third uropod about three-fourths as long as outer ramus (Fig.
   275E); eyes large; common and widely distributed in springs, spring brooks,
   and small spring-fed lakes....................**Gammarus limnaeus** Smith
   Inner ramus of third uropod less than two-thirds as long as outer ramus (Fig.
   275F); eyes reduced or large; caves, springs, and small streams; eastern and
   central states.................................**Gammarus minus** Say

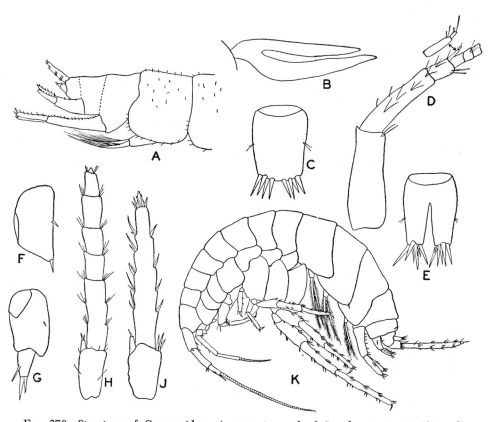

Fig. 276.—Structure of Gammaridae. A, posterior end of *Synpleonia pizzini* Shoemaker;
B, lateral sternal gill of sixth thoracic segment of *S. pizzini*; C, telson of *Stygonectes balconis*
Hubricht; D, basal portion of first antenna of *S. flagellatus* (Benedict); E, telson of *Synurella
dentata* Hubricht; F, third uropod of *Apocrangonyx subtilis* Hubricht; G, third uropod of
*Stygobromus mackini* Hubricht; H, third uropod of male *Allocrangonyx pellucidus* (Mackin);
J, third uropod of female *A. pellucidus*; K, *A. pellucidus*, ×3. (A and B modified from Shoe-
maker, 1942; C, E, F, and G modified from Hubricht; D redrawn from Weckel; H to J redrawn
from Mackin.)

8. Eyes small and degenerate; streams in caves; rare; reported only from several localities in Ill..............**Gammarus acherondytes** Hubricht and Mackin
   Eyes large and well developed (Fig. 275A); common in lakes, ponds, streams, and springs in the Atlantic drainage, sporadic farther west and southwest as far as N. M.........................................**Gammarus fasciatus** Say
9. Third uropod with two rami, the inner ramus being short or scale-like (Figs. 276H, J; 277A, E, F).................................................10
   Third uropod with one or no rami (Figs. 276A, F).......................12
10. Outer ramus of third uropod of mature male composed of three to 12 segments (Fig. 276H); one-segmented in mature female (Fig. 276J); blind; 5 to 25 mm. long; springs, caves, and seeps in Mo. and Okla.
   **Allocrangonyx pellucidus** (Mackin)
   Outer ramus of third uropod one-segmented in both sexes at all stages (Figs. 277A, E, F).................................................11
11. Outer ramus of third uropod much longer than peduncle (Figs. 277E, F); second antennae of mature male with sense organs; eyes present or absent; up to 22 mm. long; about ten uncommon species reported from wells, springs, and ponds in widely scattered localities; four other more generally distributed species keyed below...............................**Crangonyx, 16**
   Outer ramus of third uropod not appreciably longer than peduncle (Fig. 277A); second antennae of male without sense organs; eyes absent; up to 25 mm. long; three species known from caves, pools, seeps, springs, and spring brooks in Mich., Ill., Kan., Mo., Ohio, and Okla.....................**Bactrurus**

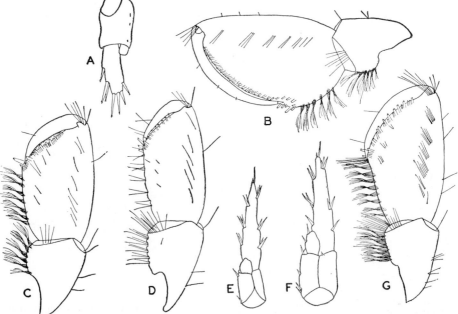

Fig. 277.—Structure of Gammaridae. A, third uropod of *Bactrurus brachycaudus* Hubricht and Mackin; B, second gnathopod of female *Crangonyx obliquus* (Hubricht and Mackin); C, second gnathopod of female *C. shoemakeri* (Hubricht and Mackin); D, second gnathopod of female *C. gracilis* Smith; E, third uropod of male *C. gracilis*; F, third uropod of female *C. gracilis*; G, second gnathopod of male *C. forbesi* (Hubricht and Mackin). (All modified from Hubricht and Mackin.)

**12.** Eyes well developed; telson cleft (Fig. 276E); three species known from ponds, streams, and springs; as far north as Ind. and Ohio and as far west as Ark.

**Synurella**

Without eyes................................................................13

**13.** Sixth and seventh thoracic segments bearing bifurcated lateral sternal gills (Fig. 276B). ..........................................................15

Sternal gills simple or absent...............................................14

**14.** Last three abdominal segments completely fused; more than 10 mm. long; two species known from caves and wells in Texas...............**Stygonectes** *

Last three abdominal segments not fused or indistinctly so; less than 10 mm. long; about ten species known from scattered wells, seeps, springs, and caves; as far north as Wis. and as far west as Okla. and Kan..........**Stygobromus** *

**15.** Third uropod with a distinct ramus (Fig. 276A); up to 20 mm. long; about six uncommon species in wells, seeps, caves, and springs; as far north as Mo. and Conn. and as far west as Kan. and Okla.................**Synpleonia** *

Third uropod without a ramus (Fig. 276F); up to 6 mm. long; two species known from wells, caves, and seeps in Ill......................**Apocrangonyx** *

**16.** Superior lateral setae of propodi of gnathopods in short transverse rows of two to seven (Figs. 277B, G)..........................................17

Superior lateral setae of propodi of gnathopods single (Figs. 277C, D).......18

**17.** Palmar margin of propodus of gnathopod one and one-half to two times as long as posterior margin and armed with more than 25 notched spines of uniform size on each side (Fig. 277B); sloughs, ponds, and springs in eastern U. S.

**Crangonyx obliquus** (Hubricht and Mackin)

Palmar margin of propodus of gnathopod less than one and one-half times as long as posterior margin and armed on each side with less than 25 notched spines of unequal size (Fig. 277G); caves, springs, spring brooks, streams, and permanent ponds in Ill., Mo., Okla., and Ark.

**Crangonyx forbesi** (Hubricht and Mackin)

**18.** Palmar margin of propodus of gnathopod concave and armed with heavy notched spines in female (Fig. 277C); pools, ponds, springs, and streams in Mich., Ill., Ind., Ohio, Okla., Mo., and Ky. and in the extreme east from Md. south to Fla....................**Crangonyx shoemakeri** (Hubricht and Mackin)

Palmar margin of propodus of gnathopod convex and armed with weak spines except at heel in female (Fig. 277D); the most common species in this genus; generally distributed in caves, pools, ponds, springs, and brooks east of the Mississippi R., but reported as far west as Okla. and Kan.

**Crangonyx gracilis** Smith

# AMPHIPODA REFERENCES

ADAMSTONE, F. B. 1928. Relict amphipods of the genus Pontoporeia. *Trans. Amer. Micros. Soc.* 47:366–371.

CREASER, E. P. 1934. A new genus and species of blind amphipod with notes on parallel evolution in certain amphipod genera. *Mus. Zool. Univ. Mich. Occ. Pap.* 282:1–6.

EMBODY, G. C. 1910. A new fresh-water amphipod from Virginia, with some notes on its biology. *Proc. U. S. Nat. Mus.* 38:299–305.

———. 1912. A preliminary study of the distribution, food and reproductive capacity of some fresh-water amphipods. *Int. Rev.* (*Suppl.*) 4:1–33.

GAYLOR, D. 1922. A study of the life history and productivity of Hyalella knickerbockeri Bate. *Proc. Ind. Acad. Sci.* (1921):239–250.

GEISLER, SISTER F. S. 1944. Studies on the postembryonic development of Hyalella azteca (Saussure). *Biol. Bull.* 86:6–22.

* These four genera are poorly defined, and it may be necessary to unite them. The characters on which they were originally based have broken down as more species have become known. Nevertheless, they are distinct groups and a careful study may reveal new characters upon which the genera may be based.

HAY, W. P. 1903. Observations on the crustacean fauna of the region about the Mammoth Cave, Kentucky. *Proc. U. S. Nat. Mus.* **25**:223–226.

HUBRICHT, L. 1943. Studies in the Nearctic freshwater Amphipoda, III. Notes on the freshwater Amphipoda of eastern United States, with descriptions of ten new species. *Amer. Midl. Nat.* **29**:683–712.

HUBRICHT, L., and C. H. HARRISON. 1941. The fresh-water amphipoda of Island County, Washington. *Amer. Midl. Nat.* **26**:330–333.

HUBRICHT, L., and J. G. MACKIN. 1940. Descriptions of nine new species of fresh-water amphipod Crustaceans with notes and new localities for other species. *Ibid.* **23**:187–218.

JUDAY, C., and E. A. BIRGE. 1927. Pontoporeia and Mysis in Wisconsin lakes. *Ecology* **7**:445–452.

KUNKEL, B. W. 1918. The Arthrostraca of Connecticut. *Bull. Conn. Geol. and Nat. Hist. Surv.* **26**:1–261.

MACKIN, J. G. 1935. Studies on the Crustacea of Oklahoma, III. Subterranean amphipods of the genera Niphargus and Boruta. *Trans. Amer. Micros. Soc.* **54**:41–51.

SEGERSTRÅLE, S. G. 1937. Studien über die Bodentierwelt in südfinnländischen Küstengewässern III. Zur Morphologie und Biologie des Amphipoden Pontoporeia affinis, nebst einer Revision der Pontoporeia-Systematik. *Soc. Sci. Fenn. Comment. Biol.* **7**:1–183.

SHOEMAKER, C. R. 1938. A new species of fresh-water amphipod of the genus Synpleonia, with remarks on related genera. *Proc. Biol. Soc. Wash.* **51**:137–142.

——. 1942. Notes on some American fresh-water amphipod crustaceans and descriptions of a new genus and two new species. *Smithson. Misc. Coll.* **101**:1–31.

——. 1944. Description of a new species of Amphipoda of the genus Anisogammarus from Oregon. *Jour. Wash. Acad. Sci.* **34**:89–93.

TITCOMB, J. W. 1927. The fresh-water shrimp for replenishing food in trout streams. *Trans. Amer. Fish. Soc.* **57**:150–161.

WECKEL, A. L. 1907. The fresh-water Amphipoda of North America. *Proc. U. S. Nat. Mus.* **32**:25–58

WILDER, J. 1940. The effects of population density upon growth, reproduction, and survival of Hyalella azteca. *Physiol. Zool.* **13**:439–462.

# Chapter 22

# DECAPODA (CRAYFISHES, SHRIMPS)

OF THE great array of species constituting the Order Decapoda, the vast majority are marine. In the United States only the Astacidae (crayfishes), about 11 species of Palaemonidae (fresh-water prawns and river shrimps), and four species of Atyidae are found in fresh waters.* These representatives, totaling about 160 species, are characteristic and common inhabitants of a wide variety of environments, including most types of running waters, shallows of lakes, ponds, sloughs, swamps, underground waters, and even wet meadows where there is no open water. They are absent from the greater portion of the Rocky Mountain region, although one species occurring in Pacific slope drainages has migrated as far eastward as the Great Basin and the headwaters of the Snake, Yellowstone, and Missouri rivers.

**General characteristics.** Crayfish, crawfish, crawdads, or crabs, as they are locally and variously known, are all more or less cylindrical, and the body and appendages are strongly sclerotized. The compound eyes are large, stalked, and movable. Total length, not including the antennae, ranges from 15 to 130 mm. The six abdominal segments are all distinct, but the head and thoracic segments are fused to form a large cephalothorax. A carapace

* To this list should be added at least one grapsoid crab, *Platychirograpsus typicus* Rathbun, which has become well established in the Hillsboro River, Florida. Possibly this river crab occurs also in Gulf coast streams of other states since it is common along the east coast of Mexico.

covers the cephalothorax, and there is a large gill chamber on each side between the body and the downward extensions of the carapace. The cervical groove of the carapace roughly delimits the head and thoracic regions, and the areola is a narrow more or less hourglass-shaped median area of the carapace just posterior to the cervical groove. The anterior end of the carapace forms an elongated rostrum which bears a short spine (acumen) at its extremity.

The 19 pairs of serially homologous appendages are basically biramous but modified for a wide variety of functions. Detailed accounts of their morphology may be found in most zoology texts and they will be only briefly discussed here. Beginning at the anterior end, each of the first antennae (antennules) has two, slender, segmented, sensory flagella. The dorsal surface of the basal segment of the first antenna bears the opening of the statocyst, an organ of balance. The second antenna has a flattened basal scale and a single long flagellum.

The next five pairs of appendages greatly overlap one another and are used chiefly for handling and mincing the food. The heavy, crushing mandibles lie on either side of the mouth. The first maxillae, which follow, are small, flattened, and delicate. Each of the second maxillae has a long, flat extension projecting laterally beyond the point of attachment of this appendage. This is the "bailer"; its rapid beating creates a posterior-anterior cur-

447

Fig. 278.—A, dorsal view of female *Procambarus*, ×0.7; B, dorsal view of male *Procambarus*, ×0.7.

rent of water through the gill chamber, thereby ensuring a continuous supply of oxygenated water for the gills in the gill chamber. The first, second, and third maxillipeds are progressively more robust and clearly biramous. The third maxillipeds are used for cleaning the antennae.

The last five pairs of appendages of the cephalothorax are large walking legs, or pereiopods (hence the name Decapoda). Each consists of seven segments. Beginning at the base, these are: coxa, basis, ischium, merus, carpus, propodus, and dactylus. Sometimes the suffix "podite" is used for each segment; thus coxopodite, basiopodite, etc. The coxa and basis are always short and compact. The first three pereiopods are clawed, or chelate, the dactylus being the movable "finger" of the claw, and the propodus constituting the "hand" and immovable finger. The first leg, or chela, is greatly enlarged in the crayfish and is used for crushing the food and as an offensive and defensive weapon. It is of little use in locomotion, walking being chiefly a function of the last four pairs of legs. The second and third legs are also used in handling and mincing the food.

Near the base of the ischium of each walking leg and marked by a double crease is a "breaking joint." When a crayfish leg is seized or irritated, reflex action causes strong contraction of special muscles at the breaking joint, and the whole leg breaks off at this point. Consequently the collector must exercise care if he is to secure suitable specimens. Perfect specimens are uncommon since appendages are often lost as the result of crayfish fighting among themselves. Missing legs are regenerated in miniature at the subsequent molt but later become larger.

The first five abdominal segments bear pleopods, or swimmerets. In the female they are all more or less biramous and are used as places of attachment for the incubating eggs, but in the male the first two pairs are modified and used during copulation. The last abdominal segment bears a flat terminal telson and a pair of flat biramous uropods. The telson and two uropods collectively form the broad tail fan.

Mature crayfish exhibit such sexual dimorphism that there is no difficulty in distinguishing the two sexes. Males usually have the larger chelae and narrower abdomen. In the Cambarinae the third segment of some of the male pereiopods bears a small hook used during copulation (Fig. 288E). In the female the genital pores are on the basal segments of the third pereiopods, but in the male they are on the fifth pereiopods. The annulus ventralis, or seminal receptacle, is a grooved, elliptical, calcified area in the mid-line between the bases of the fourth and fifth pereiopods of the female (Fig. 282). The first pleopods of the female are usually similar to the others, but in the male they have lost their biramous character and are heavily sclerotized, grooved, and specialized at the tip for sperm transfer. The male second pleopods are also somewhat specialized, and both pairs are bent forward so that they lie against the median ventral surface of the body between the bases of the pereiopods.

General body coloration ranges from

Fig. 279.—A, ventral view of female *Procambarus,* ×0.7; B, ventral view of male *Procambarus,* ×0.7.

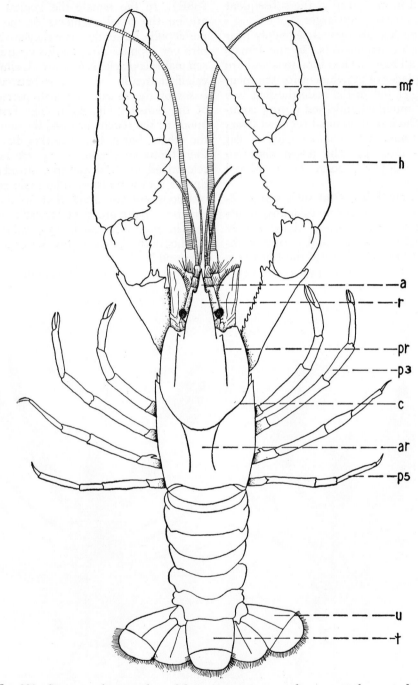

Fig. 280.—Structure of a typical crayfish. *a*, acumen; *ar*, areola; *c*, cervical groove; *h*, hand; *mf*, movable finger of chela; *p3*, third leg (pereiopod); *p5*, fifth leg (pereiopod); *pr*, postorbital ridge; *r*, rostrum; *t*, telson; *u*, uropod. (Modified from Hobbs, 1942a.)

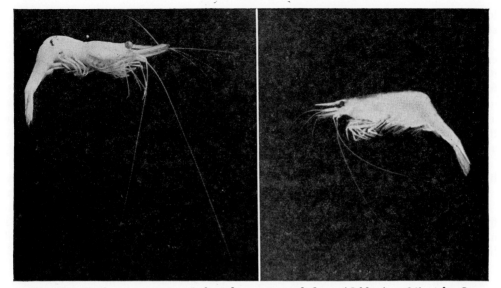

Fig. 281.—Fresh-water prawns. Left, *Palaemonetes paludosus* (Gibbes), ×2.5; right, *Syncaris pacifica* (Holmes), ×1.2.

blackish through brown, red, orange, green, and occasionally blue, with innumerable intermediate shades. Mottling is common, and the pereiopods are often tipped or banded with brighter colors than the rest of the animal. Many species show a wide range of color. *Orconectes immunis* (Hagen), for example, may be bluish, blackish, brown, greenish, or red. In general, newly molted specimens are more brightly colored than older specimens, especially since the latter usually have an accumulated coat of dirt, debris, and algae.

The coloration of a species often varies in accordance with the coloration of the substrate. In most crayfish such color adaptations are decidedly limited and occur only over a period of weeks or months. In *Palaemonetes paludosus* (Gibbes), however, variable coloration and background resemblance have become developed to a striking degree. This species has four types of chromatophores containing white, red, yellow, and blue pigment granules, respectively, and general body coloration is determined by the relative concentration or dispersion of these gran-

ules in various combinations. Color adaptation is completed in less than 24 hours after being placed on a new substrate.

**Locomotion.** Undisturbed crayfish walk or climb about slowly with the pereiopods; they may move forward, backward, or sideways. When alarmed, however, they quickly dart backward by ventrally doubling up the tail fan and the posterior end of the abdomen. They may also leave the substrate and move through the water for short distances by such abdominal contractions. In addition to these two modes of locomotion, the Palaemonidae are distinct swimmers and may move continuously forward through the water by movements of the pleopods.

**Food, feeding.** In general, crayfish are omnivorous but seldom predaceous. They eat all kinds of succulent aquatic vegetation, and animal food is usually a minor part of the diet when there is abundant vegetation. They also prefer fresh to stale meat, and in the laboratory they have been fed raw and cooked meats of all kinds, prepared fish foods, hay, whole seeds, cottonseed meal, and soybean meal. Ecologically, they are usually considered scavengers.

The chelate appendages are used for crushing, picking up the food, and tearing it into pieces. The pieces are then passed forward where they are further cut and masticated by the maxillipeds. The maxillae strain out larger particles and mince the smaller ones further. The mandibles are of limited use in grinding and chewing; mostly they hold food while the maxillipeds tear off fragments.

**Internal anatomy, physiology.** These topics are treated rather completely in most zoology texts and will only be outlined here.

A short esophagus enters a large cardiac chamber of the stomach which, in turn, enters the smaller pyloric chamber. These chambers contain the gastric mill, which is composed of heavy ossicles for grinding the food and rows of stiff setae for straining out larger particles. The long intestine extends to the anus on the ventral side of the telson. Two large glands are associated with the digestive tract in the cephalothorax; they function in digestion, absorption, and food storage.

The pentagonal heart lies in the dorsal portion of the cephalothorax. It receives blood from the surrounding pericardial sinus through three pairs of ostia and sends it out anteriorly, posteriorly, and ventrally through arteries. The blood passes out of the fine terminal endings of the blood vessels and into the various organs and hemocoel. It then circulates back to the sternal sinus, thence to the gills, and back to the pericardial sinus. The blood is almost colorless and contains amoebocytes and a dissolved hemocyanin.

Seventeen or 18 feather-like gills lie within the branchial chamber on each side. They are attached on or near the bases of the maxillipeds and walking legs and extend dorsally. Blood circulates along definite channels through the central stalk and minute lateral processes of each gill.

Excretion and osmotic control are main-tained by two complicated, compact green glands which are situated in the anterior end of the cephalothorax and open ventrally at the base of the second antennae. A crayfish does not drink, but quantities of water are continuously diffusing into the blood through the gill surfaces. Blood (minus its proteins) is absorbed by the distal coelomic sac and labyrinth of the green-gland apparatus. As it moves on through the nephridial canal, the useful materials, such as salts, carbohydrates, and some water, are reabsorbed back into the surrounding blood. The material remaining in the canal is a very dilute urine; it passes into the urinary bladder from which it is periodically voided to the outside through a small pore.

The nervous system is of the usual crustacean plan, with a ventral nerve cord and chain of ganglia, two circumesophageal connectives, and dorsal brain. The basal segment of each first antenna contains a statocyst, or organ of balance. Taste receptors are especially abundant on the mouth parts and antennae. The antennae are also sensitive tactile organs. The compound eyes are large and consist of hundreds of ommatidia.

In addition to the optic nerve and ganglia, each eyestalk contains a minute sinus gland, an endocrine gland whose secretions influence many important aspects of crayfish behavior and physiology. Among other things, the sinus gland, to a greater or lesser extent, governs: chromatophore contraction, frequency of molting, metabolic rate, growth, viability, and light adaptation of the eyes.

**Reproduction.** With reference to the structure of the first pleopods, there are two distinct types of adult male Cambarinae, first form and second form. The first pleopods of a first form male are corneous, hard, and distinctly sculptured at the tip. In a second form male they are soft and generally lacking in sculpturing. These differences are shown in Figs. 288A, B. Only a first form male is capable of

Fɪɢ. 282.—Annulus ventralis of female *Procambarus blandingi* (Girard). (Redrawn from Hobbs, 1942a.)

copulating and transferring sperm to the body of a female. Though the instar which precedes the adult first form male is a juvenile instar, the first pleopods are almost indistinguishable from those of a true second form male and for all practical purposes this stage is considered second form. The true second form male, however, is the instar immediately following the first form. Depending on the species and ecological conditions, a true second form male may undergo a further molt to become a first form male again before death. *Orconectes immunis,* for example, is commonly first form during the spring, when copulation occurs, second form during the summer, and first form again beginning in the autumn; copulation may also occur in the autumn. *Astacus* males do not have first and second forms.

Careful work has been done on less than half a dozen species in regard to breeding habits, but the available data indicate that time of copulation is variable and occurs between early spring and autumn. In *Orconectes immunis* copulation begins as early as July. *Cambarus diogenes* Girard copulates in the spring. *Palaemonetes paludosus* is thought to copulate in both spring and autumn. *Cambarus bartoni* (Fabr.), *Orconectes propinquus* (Girard), and a few other species probably copulate during spring, summer, and autumn, though spring copulation presumably does not occur in the more northern states.

Copulation seems to be more or less a matter of chance. The male has no power of sex discrimination, and during the mating season he seizes and turns over every crayfish coming his way. Another male will always resist strongly, but a female will either resist or remain passive and receptive.

The actual process of copulation and sperm transfer has been described most carefully for *Orconectes limosus* Raf. The male seizes the female and turns her over on her back. He mounts on her ventral side and holds all her clawed appendages securely with his two chelae. The tips of the first two pleopods are then inserted into the chink of the annulus ventralis, and the tips of the two vasa deferentia are extruded into the bases of the grooves which extend along the first pleopods. Sperm move along these grooves in macaroni-like cords and are deposited in the chink. The animals then separate, and either the male or female may copulate later with additional individuals. A single copulation may take from a few minutes to as much as ten hours. The second pleopods are closely applied to the first during sperm transfer, but their exact function is unknown. After copulation a white waxy plug projects from the chink of the annulus ventralis. In *Astacus* there is no annulus, and the spermatophores are deposited at random on the ventral surface of the female.

The female lays her eggs several weeks to several months after copulation, depending on the season of the year, but before laying them she cleans the ventral side of the abdomen thoroughly with the tips of the pereiopods. Immediately preceding egg extrusion she secretes a sticky, cement-like substance (glair) from ventral glands. The glair covers the ventral surface of the abdomen, tail fan, and pleopods. The sperm plug breaks and sperm are released into the glair. She then lies on her back, curls the abdomen, and releases the eggs from the genital pores. By curious turning movements of the entire body, the eggs become dispersed through the glair, fertilized, and securely attached to the pleopods by a short stalk and surrounding capsule. The female is then said to be "in berry." Most females of nearly all species are seen carrying eggs between March and June. A female may carry as few as ten eggs and as many as 800. In general, within a species, the larger the female, the greater the number of eggs. Rhythmic movements of the pleopods effectively aerate the developing eggs. Few eggs die.

**Development, life cycle.** The incubation period usually ranges from two to 20 weeks, depending largely on temperature, and during this interval the eggs change from dark and opaque to pale and translucent. Hatching involves the rupture and shedding of the embryonic skin and egg membrane, both of which, however, remain attached to the parent pleopod. A newly hatched first instar young clings to the egg stalk with the chelae, and the posterior end remains attached to the cast exoskeleton by a membrane (Fig. 283). Although clearly recognizable as a crayfish, the first instar differs markedly from advanced instars and adults. The cephalothorax is proportionately very large, the rostrum is large, pointed, and bent downward, the eyes are large, the chelae are slender, and there are no first

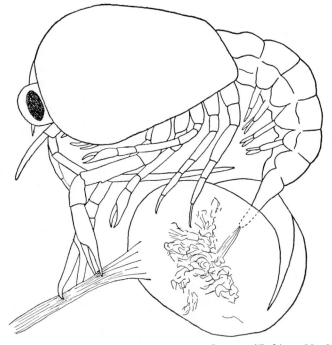

Fig. 283.—Newly hatched first instar of *Orconectes limosus* (Raf.), ×28. Note claws fastened to stalk of egg shell and abdomen attached to cast skin inside of egg shell. (Modified from Andrews, 1904.)

and sixth abdominal appendages. The first instar usually persists for two to seven days, and when it molts the posterior connection with the remains of the egg is lost. The second instar lasts for about four to 12 days and remains attached to the pleopods of the mother with its chelae and pereiopods. Third instar crayfish leave the parent pleopods intermittently and then permanently. The young of burrowing species leave the burrow of the mother when they have a body length of about 8 to 20 mm. Individuals hatching in the spring usually have a total of six to ten molts by autumn, when growth and molting cease. During these early instars the body and its appendages gradually assume adult proportions and anatomical details.

Great differences in growth rate may be found within a single pond or stream, the larger specimens being twice or more as long as the smaller ones by autumn. Such differential growth rates are probably due mainly to varying activity and amounts of food consumed.

By autumn many females are sexually mature and many males are first form, so that copulation commonly occurs in the first autumn of life. Some females, however, do not become sexually mature until after a molt early the following spring; similarly, some males do not become first form until after one or two spring molts. Such individuals copulate in the spring, and the female is in berry after a very short interval. Some females which copulate in the autumn are not in berry until the following spring. Other species, especially burrowers, copulate and are in berry in the autumn. The young leave the burrow some time during the following spring or summer.

Subsequent to the first mating season, most crayfish have only two to four molts before they die. Following copulation, a female does not molt until after her third-instar young have left her. If a male is first form in its first autumn, it usually remains first form during the winter, molts to second form early in the following spring,

and after a very short interval molts back again to first form. Such males may therefore copulate again during their second summer or autumn. Among the few species on which life history studies have been made, the normal life span of both male and female crayfish is usually less than 20 months, although a few survive their second winter. Females that pass through a second winter may be in berry for the second time the following spring. Lyle (1938) reports an exceptional longevity for *Procambarus hagenianus* (Faxon) in Mississippi and Alabama, the species attaining an age of six or seven years.

**Ecology.** Adults remain hidden in their burrows, under stones or debris, or half buried in small depressions in the substrate during the daytime, but between dusk and dawn they feed and move about, even to the extent of coming out on banks of streams and ponds. In shaded streams, however, and especially on cloudy days, adults may venture into open water in daylight. Immature specimens of most species, on the other hand, regularly crawl about actively on the bottom and in vegetation during the daytime.

Many crayfish have specific habitat requirements. Some are burrowers in wet meadows and do not enter bodies of water; some occur only in muddy ponds and ditches; some are found only in lakes or slow rivers; others are restricted to swift, stony streams. The preferences of representative species are included in the key which follows.

Crayfish are generally inhabitants of shallow waters, seldom being found deeper than three to five feet. An exceptional record is the occurrence of *Orconectes virilis* (Hagen) at a depth of 104 feet in Lake Michigan. Most species tolerate normal but wide ranges in temperature, hydrogen ion concentration, and free and bound carbon dioxide, though stream species are usually less tolerant than lake and pond species.

Population densities vary greatly, de-

Fig. 284.—A typical crayfish chimney.

pending on the species and habitat. Pond populations usually amount to less than 100 pounds per acre, but in exceptional cases may attain 500, 1,000, or even 1,500 pounds per acre. In general, stream populations are less dense, although there is one record of 1,176 pounds of crayfish per acre.

**Burrows.** Some species, such as *Procambarus gracilis* (Bundy) and *Cambarus carolinus* (Erichson), habitually burrow in wet pastures and marshy areas where there is no open water. Species in a second group live in bodies of water during the greater part of the year, but when streams or ponds dry up in late summer or when the temperature drops in the autumn they construct burrows along the margins and live in them until the water level rises and the weather becomes warmer. *Procambarus simulans* (Faxon), *P. blandingi* (Girard), and *Orconectes immunis* are included in this group. Species of a third group live continuously in permanent waters and do not make burrows.

Burrows differ widely in construction, depending on the species, the soil, and the depth of the water table (Fig. 285). Usually there is only one entrance, though there may be as many as three. The tunnel leading from the entrance may proceed vertically, at an angle, or almost laterally in a sloping bank. Sometimes the tunnels are branched or irregular, but there is always a chamber at the lower end where the crayfish remains during the hours of daylight. Occasionally a burrow has a lateral chamber. The depth of a burrow ranges from a few inches to as much as eight or ten feet and is partially determined by the level of the water table since the chamber must contain water to keep the gills wet. Burrows close to the edge of a pond or stream are shallow, those farther away are deeper.

Except during the breeding season, each burrow houses a single crayfish. Burrows are constructed only at night, and the crayfish brings up pellets of mud and deposits them at the entrance to form a chimney. Such chimneys are usually about six inches high, but a few as high as 18 inches have been reported. They do not serve any particular purpose, but are simply the result of the safest and most convenient method of disposing of the mud pellets.

**Geographic distribution, dispersal.** The Cambarinae are restricted to North

America, and Ortmann (1905) postulated the origin of this subfamily between Cretaceous and Tertiary times in central Mexico. From this area there was a general spread into the southern United States where several centers of dispersal arose.

Ancestors of the present species of *Procambarus* are thought to have originated in Mexico and migrated to the general region of Kansas, Oklahoma, Texas, Arkansas, and Louisiana. From there, one group of species migrated northward as far as Wisconsin. A second group migrated eastward to the southern Appalachians where a new large center of dispersal later expanded out extensively up and down the Atlantic coast, as far north as Michigan and Ohio, and eventually as far west as Texas and Oklahoma.

*Orconectes* is thought to have arisen at the junctions of the Ohio, Mississippi, and Missouri rivers and radiated out in all directions as far as Colorado, Wyoming, southern Canada, Lake Superior, the St. Lawrence valley, and the Gulf states. A few species even crossed the divide and reached Atlantic coast drainages.

*Cambarus* is thought to have arisen in the Ozarks and southern Appalachians. Early migration occurred mainly in a northeasterly direction at high altitudes, but later some species invaded the lowlands, spread out in all directions, and attained a very wide distribution.

*Cambarellus* originated in Mexico or extreme southern United States and migrated eastward through the Gulf states.

The five American species of *Astacus* are restricted to Pacific slope drainages, although one has migrated over to the Great Basin and headwaters of the Missouri River. The genus probably origi-

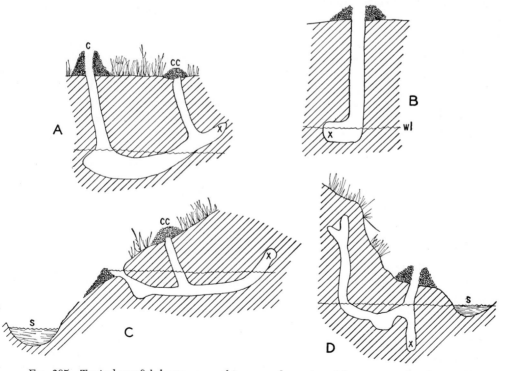

Fig. 285.—Typical crayfish burrows. *c*, chimney and opening of burrow; *cc*, closed chimney; *s*, stream; *wl*, ground water level; *x*, place where crayfish was taken. (A, C, and D modified from Ortmann, 1906.)

nated in the Old World where about ten species occur in northern Europe and Asia.

In general, speciation has proceeded most rapidly in the southern states. Colorado, Nebraska, and Wisconsin, for example, each has only six species of Cambarinae. Oklahoma has ten species, Ohio has 17, Mississippi 18, Kentucky 22, and Florida 39.

Dry land forms an effective barrier to the migration and geographical spread of lake and stream species, but burrowers such as *Cambarus diogenes* have migrated rapidly and are now found commonly in wet meadows east of the Rocky Mountains.

Male first form *Procambarus clarki* (Girard) spawn in the autumn and then migrate overland by the thousands. Such exhausted males are weak and soon die; it is doubtful whether they contribute appreciably to the spread of the species.

Restriction to specific aquatic habitats forms a partial barrier for many species. *Procambarus blandingi*, for example, is restricted to sluggish streams and stagnant waters and cannot migrate upstream into rapid water drainage areas.

*Orconectes virilis* (Hagen) and *O. immunis* form an interesting example of ecological isolation. The two species are very closely related and are often in the same general geographic areas. Yet the former occurs only in clear, running waters with stony bottoms, while the latter is restricted to stagnant waters and mud bottoms. Very little is known about interspecific competition among crayfishes.

Many species, especially in the southern states, are known only from a single state or single collecting locality. Twenty-five species and subspecies reported from Florida, for example, are known only from that state.

**Cave crayfish.** Perhaps some of the most interesting examples of ecological isolation are to be found among those subterranean crayfish and shrimp which are restricted to the waters of single caves,

cave systems, large springs, and sinks. Below is a list of such species known from the United States.

*Palaemonias ganteri* Hay—Mammoth Cave, Ky.

*Palaemonetes antrorum* Benedict—artesian wells near San Marcos, Texas

*Troglocambarus maclanei* Hobbs—Florida caves

*Procambarus lucifugus* (Hobbs)—Florida cave

*P. pallidus* (Hobbs)—Florida caves

*P. acherontis* (Lönnberg)—Florida underground sinks and springs

*Cambarus cahni* Rhoades—Alabama caves

*C. cryptodytes* Hobbs—Florida well

*C. hamulatus* Packard and Cope—Nickajack Cave, Tenn.

*C. setosus* Faxon—several Missouri caves

*C. ayersi* Steele—Fisher's Cave, Mo.

*Orconectes pellucidus* (Tellkampf)—Alabama, Kentucky, and Indiana caves

Cave species are strikingly modified for that environment (Fig. 286). They are mostly small, the body length ranging from 14 to 80 mm. The body is slender, the chelae are not well developed, and the antennae and other appendages are very long and highly specialized as tactile organs. Pigmentation is absent, and the body is translucent or whitish. All are blind, the eyes being atrophied and the eyestalks reduced or rudimentary.

In addition to the species listed above, there are some which are normally found above ground but have migrated into caves where they have successfully persisted. With the exception of one or two species which have become differentiated into subspecies, these forms are identical with individuals occurring above ground.

**Parasites, commensals, enemies.** The external surfaces of crayfish form a convenient and favorable habitat for microorganisms, and when the exoskeleton has not been shed for a long time it is often

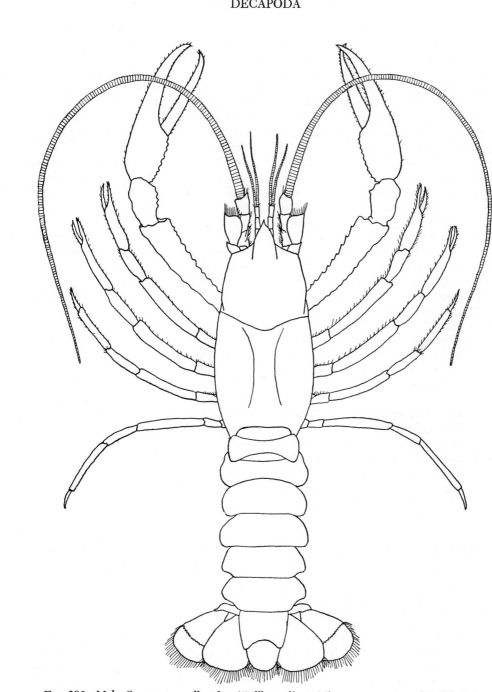

Fig. 286.—Male *Orconectes pellucidus* (Tellkampf), ×1.7, a cave species. (Modified from Hay, 1893.)

covered with debris and a dense growth of algae and sessile Protozoa, especially at winter's end.

The Branchiobdellidae (see page 284) are small, leechlike, parasitic or commensal oligochaetes that live on the gills, in the gill chambers, on the general body surface, and at the bases of the legs, antennae, and mouth parts. A genus of ostracods, *Entocythere*, is commensal on the gills (see page 421).

Many species of crayfish east of the Mississippi River may act as the second intermediate host of *Paragonimus westermani*, a lung fluke parasitic in man and many carnivores. The metacercariae of this parasite become imbedded in the muscles and viscera of the crayfish from which they may be transmitted to the definitive host when the raw or poorly cooked crayfish are used as food.

Fish are the most important enemies of crayfish, although wading birds, frogs, turtles, raccoons, otter, and mink consume appreciable numbers.

**Economic importance.** In poorly drained clay agricultural lands of West Virginia, Mississippi, Alabama, and a few other southern states burrowing crayfish become so abundant (as many as 30,000 burrows per acre) that crops cannot be raised because of the fact that the crayfish denude the land of the young grain, sugarcane, and cotton seedlings. Also, their chimneys clog farm machinery. If the land cannot be drained, the best control is the application of some poison to the burrows. Pyrethrum, creosote, cyanide, carbon disulphide, and unslaked lime are some of the more useful poisons. They are most effective when the water table is high. Bait poisoned with DDT and spread over infested areas is a more recent and successful control measure.

Occasionally crayfish become a nuisance in small reservoirs when their lateral burrows through earthen dams and dikes drain the reservoirs.

Europeans use crayfish for the table to a much greater extent than do Americans. Most of the edible crayfish in this country come from the Great Lakes, certain parts of the Mississippi River system, Louisiana, and Oregon. The harvest has greatly declined during the past 30 or 40 years, although in 1938 and 1949 Oregon produced 93,700 and 46,000 pounds, respectively.

Small species of crayfish have been raised experimentally at hatcheries for use as fish food, but the practice has not attained any importance.

**Collection, preparation.** Stream and pond species may be collected with long-handled dipnets, minnow seines, and minnow traps. When crayfish are not abundant, however, it is often necessary to collect by hand and examine overhanging banks, masses of vegetation, and the undersides of submerged logs and stones.

A skillful collector with a headlamp may find it profitable to collect burrowers (as well as open water species) at night when they usually leave the burrow and roam about, but often there is no alternative but to dig up the burrow carefully with a spade or trowel until the specimen can be taken in its chamber.

Crayfish should be killed and stored in 80 per cent alcohol. This preservative keeps the joints pliable. Some workers remove the male first pleopods and the female annulus ventralis, dehydrate in absolute alcohol, clear in xylol, and mount on insect pins.

**Taxonomy.** In 1902 only 66 species of North American Cambarinae were known, but now there are about 130 from the United States alone, most of the additional species having been described from southern states. In addition, some of the common and widely distributed species are represented by long series of well-defined subspecies. *Cambarus bartoni* is a striking example of subspeciation, five subspecies having been reported from Kentucky alone.

Characters which are useful for identifying both males and females of certain genera and species include the structure of the rostrum, shape of the areola, structure of the chelae, spines on the cephalothorax, and general body proportions. Unfortunately, however, most species can be identified only from first form males, particularly by the copulatory hooks on some of the legs and the detailed morphology of the first pleopods. In making collections in the field it is therefore essential to get first form males whenever possible.

Beginning with the publication of Hagen's monograph in 1870, various classification schemes for the Cambarinae have been suggested. Most of these publications recognized only a single genus, *Cambarus*, with a series of subgenera or "groups." In 1942, however, Hobbs proposed a more logical and revised classification in which the Subfamily Cambarinae is divided into six full genera. His proposals are followed in this manual.

The formulation of an accurate key to all species and subspecies known from the United States does not appear to be feasible at the present time, especially since many forms have not been adequately described and since many species differences are difficult to set up in key couplets. The key given below, however, includes all genera, all species in the smaller genera, and the more common species in the larger genera. Total lengths extend from the tip of the acumen to the posterior edge of the telson.

## KEY TO GENERA AND SPECIES OF DECAPODA

1. First three pairs of legs chelate; cephalothorax subcylindrical; abdomen more or less flattened dorsoventrally (Figs. 278, 279)..............ASTACIDAE, **2**
    First two pairs of legs chelate; cephalothorax and abdomen laterally compressed (Figs. 281, 292)................................................**24**
2. Male first pleopods simply rolled at tips; pereiopods of male without any basal hooks; female without first pleopods; up to 110 mm. long; except in the Upper Missouri, found west of the Continental Divide.
                                    ASTACINAE, **Astacus, 3** *
    Male first pleopods bifid or toothed at tips (Figs. 288B–D); some of pereiopods of male with hooks on the ischiopodite (Fig. 288E); female with first pleopods; found east of the Continental Divide......................CAMBARINAE, **7**

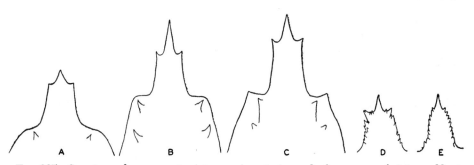

FIG. 287.—Structure of carapace in *Astacus*. A, anterior end of carapace of *Astacus klamathensis* Stimpson; B, anterior end of carapace of *A. leniusculus* Dana; C, anterior end of carapace of *A. trowbridgi* Stimpson; D, rostrum of *A. nigrescens* Stimpson; E, rostrum of *A. gambeli* Girard.

* The taxonomy of the genus *Astacus* is in a confused state, almost no work having been done recently. The separation characters here used for the various species are admittedly indistinct and variable. Nevertheless, judging from the published literature, they appear to be the best criteria available.

**3.** Margins of rostrum not denticulated (Figs. 287A–C)......................4
Margins of rostrum denticulated (Figs. 287D, E)........................**6**
**4.** One spine on postorbital ridge; rostrum with short acumen (Fig. 287A); in lakes
and mountain streams of Idaho, Wash., Ore., and Calif.
**Astacus klamathensis** Stimpson
Two spines on postorbital ridge; rostrum with long acumen..................**5**
**5.** Posterior spine of postorbital ridge long and acute (Fig. 287B); Wash., Ore., and
Calif......................................**Astacus leniusculus** Dana
Posterior spine of postorbital ridge small, sometimes reduced to a tubercle (Fig.
287C); lower Columbia River system in Ore. and Wash.
**Astacus trowbridgi** Stimpson
**6.** Sides of rostrum nearly parallel, with five or more spines (Fig. 287D); hand of
chela without a beard; Wash., Ore., and the northern half of Calif.; uncommon.
**Astacus nigrescens** Stimpson
Sides of rostrum converging, with a row of minute conical tubercles (Fig. 287E);
hand of chela with a long lateral beard; Wash., Ore., Idaho., Utah, and a
small area of the headwaters of the Missouri River in Mont. and Wyo.
**Astacus gambeli** Girard
**7.** First pleopod of first form male terminating in three or more distinct parts (Fig.
288B), or two distinct parts plus a strong shoulder on the cephalic margin
near the tip (Figs. 288C, D)......................................**8**
First pleopod of first form male terminating in only two distinct parts; never with
a well-developed shoulder on the cephalic margin near the tip (Figs. 289A, B);
usually from 50 to 130 mm. long; widely distributed from Canada to the
Gulf. ......................................**13**
**8.** Ischiopodite of third maxilliped with teeth along inner margin; usually 50 to 130
mm. long......................................**9**
Ischiopodite of third maxilliped without teeth along inner margin; eyes reduced
and without pigment; almost transparent; first pereiopod long and slender;
about 30 mm. long; known only from a few Florida caves.
**Troglocambarus maclanei** Hobbs
**9.** Hooks present on ischiopodites of male third or third and fourth pereiopods (Fig.
288E); large species; about 50 species known from the U. S., mostly from
southern and southeastern states; (four common and widely distributed
species keyed below)......................................**Procambarus, 10**
Hooks present on ischiopodites of male second and third pereiopods; small species,
15 to 30 mm. long......................................**Cambarellus**
*C. shufeldti* (Faxon), the "dwarf crayfish" in La., Miss., and Tenn.; *C.
schmitti* Hobbs in Fla. springs, streams, and seepage areas; *C. diminutus*
Hobbs in Ala. and Miss.; *C. puer* Hobbs in Texas and La.
**10.** Hooks present only on ischiopodites of male third pereiopods................**11**
Hooks present on ischiopodites of male third and fourth pereiopods; body generally reddish in color......................................**12**
**11.** Areola obliterated; a burrower in marshy and seepage areas; Wis., Iowa, Kan.,
Okla., Mo., Ill., and Ind......................**Procambarus gracilis** (Bundy)
Areola present (Fig. 288F); in muddy streams and ponds; burrows when water
level falls or water dries up; Ark., Kan., Okla., Texas, N. M., and Colo.
**Procambarus simulans** (Faxon)
**12.** Opposable margins of chela of first form male with a few large basal tubercles
(Fig. 288G); first form male first pleopod with four distinct elongated
terminal processes (Fig. 288B); swift streams, sluggish streams, and
permanent and temporary ponds; burrows when water level falls; the "pond
crayfish"; Mississippi River and Great Lakes drainages and occasional in
southeastern states as far as Fla.........**Procambarus blandingi** (Girard)

Opposable margins of chela of first form male with numerous large tubercles (Fig. 288H); first form male first pleopod without four distinct elongated terminal processes; marshes, sluggish streams, and sloughs; the "swamp crayfish"; Fla. to Texas and as far north as Ark.; introduced into southern Calif. and Nev....................................**Procambarus clarki** (Girard)

13. Two terminals on first pleopod short and strongly recurved; entire appendage short and heavy (Fig. 289A); about 24 species; (four common and widely distributed species keyed below).........................**Cambarus, 14**

Terminals on first pleopod short or long, never strongly recurved; if slightly recurved they are slender and setiform (Fig. 289B); about 42 species, mostly in large interior river systems; (eight common and widely distributed species keyed below)..................................**Orconectes, 18**

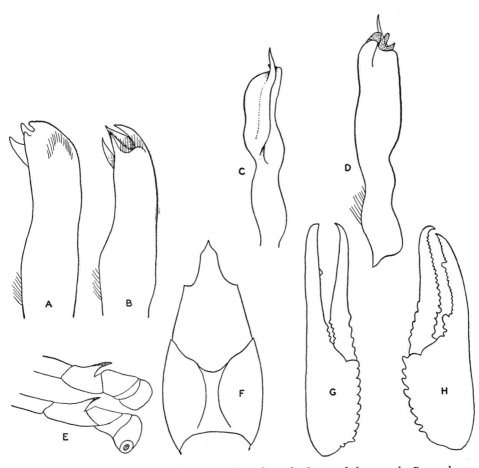

Fig. 288.—Structure of *Procambarus*. A, first pleopod of second form male *Procambarus blandingi*; B, first pleopod of first form male *P. blandingi*; C, first pleopod of first form male *P. barbatus* (Faxon); D, first pleopod of first form male *P. simulans* (Faxon); E, basal portions of third and fourth legs of male *P. blandingi*; F, carapace of *P. simulans* (Faxon); G, chela of *P. blandingi*; H, chela of *P. clarki* (Girard). (A to C modified from Hobbs, 1942a; D redrawn from Creaser and Ortenburger; E modified from Turner, 1926; G redrawn from Hobbs, 1942a.)

14. Areola wide (Fig. 289C); general color green to brownish; burrows only rarely..**15**
    Areola narrow, linear, or obliterated in middle (Figs. 289F, G)..............**16**
15. Inner margin of hand with a single row of tubercles (Fig. 289D); in springs and
        small streams, occasional in large streams; common and generally distributed
        east of Mississippi R......................**Cambarus bartoni** (Fabr.)
    Inner margin of hand with a double row of tubercles (Fig. 289E); swift, stony
        streams; N. Y. to W. Va. and westward to Mich. and Ill.
                                       **Cambarus bartoni robustus** Girard
16. Areola narrow but not linear (Fig. 289F); the red crayfish; burrows in swampy
        pastures and fields; mountains of Pa. to S. C., occasional as far west as Tenn.
                                        **Cambarus carolinus** (Erichson)
    Areola linear or obliterated (Fig. 289G)...............................**17**
17. Movable finger of chela with a straight cutting edge (Fig. 289H); general color
        greenish to brownish; burrows in wet fields and marshy areas; resorts to
        ponds and streams only during breeding season; the solitary crayfish; common
        and generally distributed east of the Continental Divide.
                                         **Cambarus diogenes** Girard
    Movable finger of chela with an incision near base of inner margin (Fig. 289J);
        permanent ponds, temporary ponds, and burrows in poorly drained areas;
        Mich., Ill., Ind., and Ohio....................**Cambarus fodiens** (Cottle)

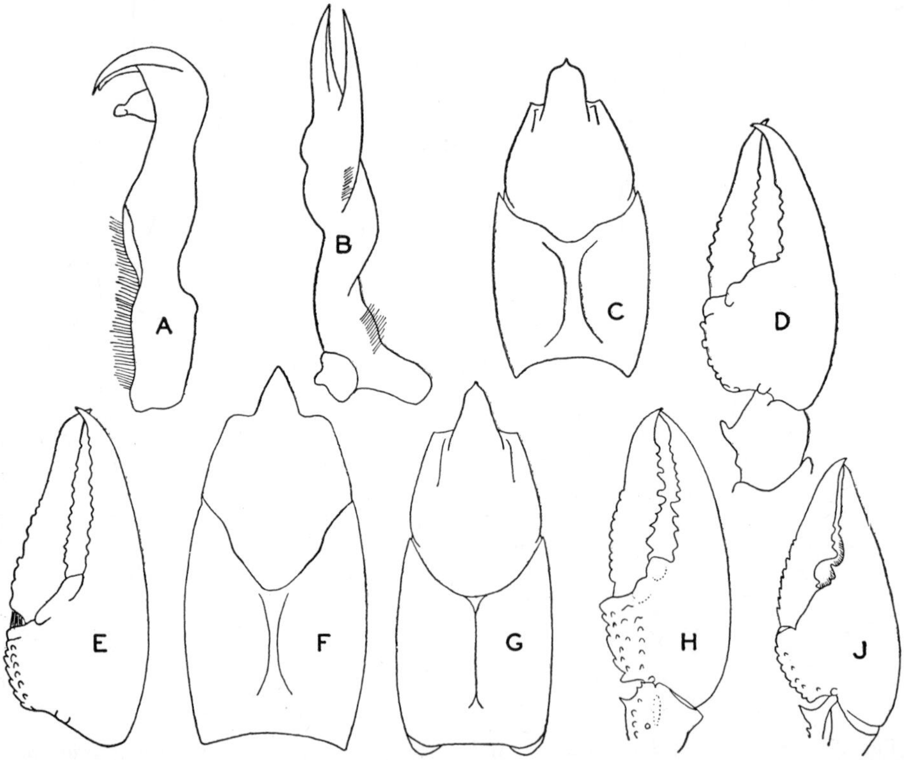

Fig. 289.—Structure of *Cambarus* and *Orconectes*. A, first pleopod of first form male *Cambarus bartoni* (Fabr.); B, first pleopod of first form male *Orconectes propinquus* (Girard); C, carapace of *Cambarus bartoni*; D, chela of *C. bartoni*; E, chela of *C. bartoni robustus* Girard; F, carapace of *C. carolinus* (Erichson); G, carapace of *C. diogenes* Girard; H, chela of *C. diogenes*; J, chela of *C. fodiens* (Cottle). (A to C redrawn from Turner, 1926; D and E modified from Ortmann, 1906; G redrawn from Hobbs, 1942a; H and J redrawn from Huntsman, 1915.)

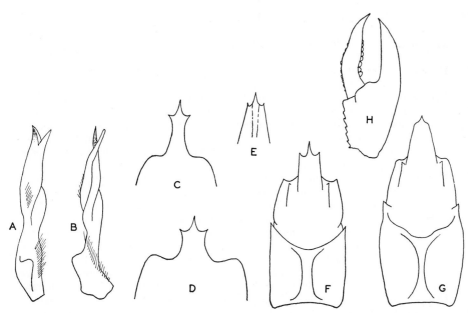

Fig. 290.—Structure of *Orconectes*. A and B, first pleopod of first form male *Orconectes limosus*; C and D, rostrum of *O. rusticus* (Girard); E, rostrum of *O. propinquus*; F, carapace of *O. virilis* (Hagen); G, carapace of *O. immunis* (Hagen); H, chela of *O. immunis*. (A and B redrawn from Ortmann, 1906; F and G redrawn from Turner, 1926.)

18. Tips of male first pleopods short, straight, and divergent (Figs. 290A, B); general color olive-green to olive-yellow; seldom burrows; common in larger rivers of Atlantic coastal plain from Mass., Pa., and N. J. to Va.

**Orconectes limosus (Raf.)**

Tips of male first pleopods not divergent (Fig. 289B).......................19

19. Sides of rostrum concave (Figs. 290C, D); streams and lakes; Ill., Mich., and Ohio south to Mo. and Ala..................**Orconectes rusticus (Girard)**

Sides of rostrum not concave (Figs. 290E–G)............................20

20. Rostrum with median keel (Fig. 290E)...................................21

Rostrum without median keel (Figs. 290F, G).............................22

21. Male first pleopods reaching base of third pereiopods; general color gray to olive-green; streams, rivers, and lakes, especially on stony bottoms; Great Lakes crayfish, gray rock crayfish; northeastern quarter of U.S., especially the Mississippi, Ohio, and Great Lakes drainages......**Orconectes propinquus (Girard)**

Male first pleopods reaching base of first pereiopods; body generally yellow; in streams and rivers with clear water and a current; Mo., Kan., Colo., Ark., Okla., and Texas.........................**Orconectes neglectus (Faxon)**

22. Movable finger of chela with a straight cutting edge.......................23

Movable finger of chela with an excision at base (Fig. 290H); mud crayfish; in sluggish streams and ponds; burrows when water level falls; common in Mississippi R. and Great Lakes drainages......**Orconectes immunis (Hagen)**

23. Male first pleopods reaching base of chelae when flexed; northern crayfish; lakes, streams, and rivers with permanent water supply; usually on stony bottoms; northern crayfish; common in Mississippi R. and Great Lakes drainages.

**Orconectes virilis (Hagen)**

Male first pleopods reaching only to base of second or third pereiopods when flexed; general color olive green; Allegheny crayfish; large streams of upper Ohio drainage in N. Y., Pa., Md., and W. Va........**Orconectes obscurus (Hagen)**

24. Second chelae larger than first; chelae without terminal hair tufts (Figs. 292H, J).
                                                                    PALAEMONIDAE, 28
     First and second chelae subequal, with terminal hair tufts (Fig. 292K).
                                                                          ATYIDAE, 25
25. Eyestalks rudimentary, no trace of facets or pigments; translucent; 14 to 23 mm.
     long; Mammoth Cave, Ky......................Palaemonias ganteri Hay
     Eyes well developed; usually 20 to 50 mm. long.................Syncaris, 26
26. Upper margin of rostrum with one or two spines, lower margin with five to nine
     spines; supraorbital spine present (Fig. 292L); coastal streams north of
     San Francisco Bay...........................Syncaris pacifica (Holmes)
     Upper margin of rostrum without spines, lower margin with few spines; supra-
     orbital spine present or absent....................................27
27. Lower margin of rostrum with three to five spines; supraorbital spine present;
     described in 1900 from several specimens collected in a small stream near
     San Gabriel, Calif., but probably now extinct........Syncaris trewi Holmes
     Lower margin of rostrum without spines, or occasionally with one spine; supra-
     orbital spine absent; reported many years ago from coastal streams near Los
     Angeles, Calif., but probably now extinct....Syncaris pasadenae (Holmes)
28. Second legs only slightly longer than first (Fig. 292A); usually 25 to 45 mm.
     long; fresh-water prawns, glass shrimps................Palaemonetes, 29 *
     Second legs much longer than first (Fig. 292F); river shrimps..Macrobrachium, 35
29. Eyes pigmented, cornea well developed; second legs longer and stouter than first;
     not subterranean...................................................30
     Eyes unpigmented, cornea degenerate; first and second legs subequal; up to 18
     mm. long; known only from subterranean waters near San Marcos, Texas.
                                                        Palaemonetes antrorum Benedict

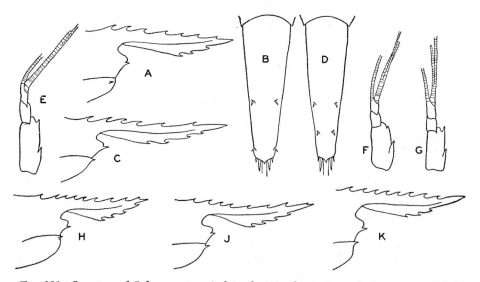

Fig. 291.—Structure of *Palaemonetes*. A, lateral view of anterior end of carapace of *Palaemonetes kadiakensis* Rathbun; B, dorsal view of telson of *P. kadiakensis*; C, lateral view of anterior end of carapace of *P. paludosus*; D, dorsal view of telson of *P. paludosus*; E, basal portion of first antenna of *P. paludosus*; F, basal portion of first antenna of *P. hiltoni* Schmitt; G, basal portion of first antenna of *P. vulgaris* (Say); H, lateral view of anterior end of *P. vulgaris*; J, lateral view of anterior end of *P. intermedius* Holthuis; K, lateral view of anterior end of *P. pugio* Holthuis. (All modified from Holthuis.)

* Key to species of *Palaemonetes* modified from Holthuis.

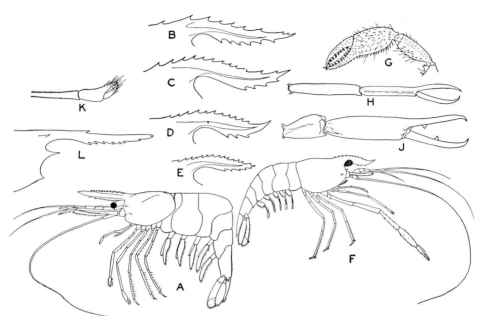

Fig. 292.—Structure of Palaemonidae. A, *Palaemonetes paludosus,* ×1.6; B, rostrum of *Macrobrachium acanthurus* (Wiegmann); C, rostrum of *M. carcinus* (L.); D, rostrum of *M. ohione* (Smith); E, rostrum of *M. olfersi* (Wiegmann); F, *M. ohione,* ×.6; G, large chela of male *M. olfersi;* H, chela of *M. acanthurus* (spines and setae omitted); J, chela of *M. carcinus* (spines and setae omitted); K, second chela of *Syncaris pacifica;* L, anterior end of carapace of *S. pacifica.* (A modified from Creaser, 1939; B to F redrawn from Hedgpeth, 1947; G to J modified from Hedgpeth, 1949.)

**30.** Fused portion of the two rami of upper flagellum of first antenna longer than free portion of the shorter ramus (Fig. 291E); carpopodite of second leg longer than claw; fresh waters...........................................**31**

Fused portion of the two rami of upper flagellum of first antenna shorter than free portion of the shorter ramus (Figs. 291F, G); carpopodite of second leg shorter than claw; brackish or salt water.............................**32**

**31.** Branchiostegal spine on anterior margin of carapace, just below branchiostegal groove (Fig. 291C); posterior pair of dorsal spines of telson situated midway between anterior pair and posterior margin of telson (Fig. 291D); up to 46 mm. long; common in Atlantic coast drainages, rare in central U. S.

**Palaemonetes paludosus** (Gibbes)

Branchiostegal spine removed from anterior margin of carapace, below branchiostegal groove (Fig. 291A); posterior pair of dorsal spines of telson placed close to posterior margin of telson (Fig. 291B); up to 53 mm. long; sporadic in central third of U. S., west of Alleghenies, and from Canada to Gulf.

**Palaemonetes kadiakensis** Rathbun

**32.** Anterior margin of basal segment of first antenna extending farther forward than anterolateral spine of this segment (Fig. 291F); body up to 24 mm. long; probably in brackish water; southern Calif......**Palaemonetes hiltoni** (Schmitt)

Anterior margin of basal segment of first antenna not extending farther forward than anterolateral spine of this segment (Fig. 291G); Mass. to Texas......**33**

**33.** Rostrum with first two teeth of dorsal margin posterior to orbit; lower margin of rostrum with three to five teeth (Fig. 291H); body up to 42 mm. long; salt and brackish waters.......................**Palaemonetes vulgaris** (Say)

Rostrum with only one dorsal tooth behind orbit (Figs. 291J, K).............**34**

34. Dorsal teeth of rostrum reaching apex, which is often bifid; lower margin of rostrum with four or five, seldom three teeth (Fig. 291J); up to 37 mm. long; brackish waters..................................**Palaemonetes intermedius** Holthuis

     Dorsal teeth of rostrum not reaching apex; lower margin of rostrum with two to four, generally three teeth (Fig. 291K); up to 50 mm. long; brackish to nearly fresh waters......................**Palaemonetes pugio** Holthuis

35. Carpopodite of second leg shorter than claw; rostrum with about three teeth posterior to margin of orbit and three to five ventral teeth (Figs. 292C, E).....**36**

     Carpopodite of second leg about as long as claw (Fig. 292H); rostrum usually with a single tooth posterior to margin of orbit and about six ventral teeth (Fig. 292B); body up to 170 mm. long; rivers of Fla. to Texas.

                                **Macrobrachium acanthurus** (Wiegmann)

36. Claw of second leg without prominent teeth or hairy covering (Fig. 292F); up to 95 mm. long; N. C. to Texas, and Mississippi and Ohio rivers and their main tributaries as far north as Okla., Mo., Ill., Ind., and Ohio.

                                **Macrobrachium ohione** (Smith)

     Claw of second leg with hair or teeth.................................**37**

37. Claw of second leg similar in both sexes, with a broad triangular tooth on each finger (Fig. 292J); body up to 240 mm. long; rivers, spring brooks, and springs in Fla. and Texas.................**Macrobrachium carcinus** (L.)

     Claw of second leg on one side in male greatly enlarged, armed with spines and tufts of bristles (Fig. 292G); body up to 90 mm. long; St. Augustine, Fla.

                                **Macrobrachium olfersi** (Wiegmann)

# DECAPODA REFERENCES

ANDREWS, E. A. 1904. Breeding habits of crayfish. *Amer. Nat.* 38:165–206.

——. 1910. The young of the crayfishes Astacus and Cambarus. *Smithson. Contrib. Knowledge* 35:5–79.

——. 1910a. Conjugation in the crayfish, Cambarus affinis. *Jour. Exp. Zool.* 9:235–264.

BOVBJERG, R. V. 1952. Comparative ecology and physiology of the crayfish Orconectes propinquus and Cambarus fodiens. *Physiol. Zool.* 25:34–56.

BROWN, F. A. 1935. Color changes in Palaemonetes. *Jour. Morph.* 57:317–334.

——. 1939. Background selection in crayfishes. *Ecology* 20:507–516.

CHIDESTER, F. E. 1912. The biology of the crayfish. *Amer. Nat.* 46:279–293.

CREASER, E. P. 1931. The Michigan decapod crustaceans. *Pap. Mich. Acad. Sci. Arts and Lett.* 13:257–276.

——. 1933. Seasonal changes in the male population of Faxonius propinquus (Girard). *Mus. Zool. Univ. Mich. Occ. Pap.* 253:1–9.

——. 1933a. Descriptions of some new and poorly known species of North American crayfishes. *Ibid.* 275:1–21.

——. 1934. A faunistic area of five isolated species of crayfish in southeastern Missouri. *Ibid.* 278:1–8.

——. 1934a. Age, growth, and sex ratios in the crayfish, Faxonius propinquus. *Pap. Mich. Acad. Sci. Arts and Lett.* 19:581–585.

CREASER, E. P., and A. I. ORTENBURGER. 1933. The decapod crustaceans of Oklahoma. *Publ. Univ. Okla. Biol. Surv.* 5:14–80.

ENGLE, E. T. 1926. Crayfishes of the genus Cambarus in Nebraska and eastern Colorado. *Bull. U. S. Bur. Fish.* 42:87–104.

FAXON, W. 1885. Revision of the Astacidae, Part I. The genera Cambarus and Astacus. *Mem. Mus. Comp. Zool.* 10:1–186.

——. 1898. Observations on the Astacidae in the United States National Museum and in the Museum of Comparative Zoology, with descriptions of new species. *Proc. U. S. Nat. Mus.* 20:643–694.

——. 1914. Notes on the crayfishes in the United States National Museum and the Museum of Comparative Zoology with descriptions of new species and subspecies to which is appended a catalogue of the known species and subspecies. *Mem. Mus. Comp. Zool. Harvard Coll.* 40:347–427.

FISHER, A. K. 1912. Crawfish as crop destroyers. *U. S. Dept. Agric. Yearbook for 1911*, 321–324.

GUNTER, G. 1937. Observations on the river shrimp, Macrobrachium ohionis (Smith). *Amer. Midl. Nat.* 18:1038–1042.

HAGEN, H. A. 1870. Monograph of the North American Astacidae. *Illus. Cat. Mus. Comp. Zool. Harvard Coll.* 3:1–109.

HARRIS, J. A. 1903. An ecological catalogue of the crayfishes belonging to the genus Cambarus. *Kan. Univ. Sci. Bull.* 2:51–187.

Hay, W. P. 1903. Observations on the crustacean fauna of the region about the Mammoth Cave, Kentucky. *Proc. U. S. Nat. Mus.* **25**:223–226.

Hedgpeth, J. W. 1947. River shrimps. *Prog. Fish-Cult.* **9**:181–184.

———. 1949. The North American species of Macrobrachium (river shrimp). *Tex. Jour. Sci.* **1**:28–38.

Hobbs, H. H., Jr. 1942. A generic revision of the crayfishes of the Subfamily Cambarinae (Decapoda, Astacidae) with the description of a new genus and species. *Amer. Midl. Nat.* **28**:334–357.

———. 1942a. The crayfishes of Florida. *Univ. Fla. Publ. Biol. Sci. Ser.* **3**:1–179.

———. 1945. Two new species of crayfishes of the genus Cambarellus from the Gulf Coast states, with a key to the species of the genus (Decapoda, Astacidae). *Amer. Midl. Nat.* **34**:466–474.

———. 1945a. Notes on the first pleopod of the male Cambarinae (Decapoda, Astacidae). *Quart. Jour. Fla. Acad. Sci.* **8**:67–70.

———. 1948. On the crayfishes of the Limosus section of the genus Orconectes (Decapoda, Astacidae). *Jour. Wash. Acad. Sci.* **38**:14–21.

———. 1948a. Two new crayfishes of the genus Orconectes from Arkansas, with a key to the species of the Hylas group (Decapoda, Astacidae). *Amer. Midl. Nat.* **39**:139–150.

Holmes, S. J. 1900. Synopsis of California stalk-eyed Crustacea. *Occ. Pap. Calif. Acad. Sci.* **7**:1–255.

Holthuis, L. B. 1949. Note on the species of Palaemonetes (Crustacea Decapoda) found in the United States of America. *Proc. Konink. Nederland. Akad. Wetensch.* **52**:87–95.

———. 1952. A general revision of the Palaemonidae (Crustacea Decapoda Natantia) of the Americas. II. The Subfamily Palaemoninae. *Occ. Pap. Allan Hancock Found.* **12**:1–396.

Huxley, T. H. 1906. *The crayfish.* 2d ed. 371 pp. London.

Kent, W. J. 1901. The colors of the crayfish. *Amer. Nat.* **35**:933–936.

Lagler, K. F., and M. J. Lagler. 1944. Natural enemies of crayfishes in Michigan. *Pap. Mich. Acad. Sci. Arts and Lett.* **29**:293–303.

Lyle, C. 1938. The crawfishes of Mississippi, with special reference to the biology and control of destructive species. *Iowa State Coll. Jour. Sci.* **13**:75–77.

Maluf, N. S. R. 1939. On the anatomy of the kidney of the crayfish and on the absorption of chlorid from freshwater by this animal. *Zool. Jahrb. Abt. allg. Zool. u. Physiol. Tiere* **59**:515–534.

Meehean, O. L. 1936. Notes on the freshwater

shrimp Palaemonetes paludosa (Gibbes). *Trans. Amer. Micros. Soc.* **55**:433–441.

Ortmann, A. E. 1902. The geographical distribution of the freshwater decapods and its bearing upon ancient geography. *Proc. Amer. Philos. Soc.* **41**:267–400.

———. 1905. The mutual affinities of the species of the genus Cambarus, and their dispersal over the United States. *Ibid.* **44**:91–136.

———. 1906. The crawfishes of the state of Pennsylvania. *Mem. Carnegie Mus.* **2**:343–521.

———. 1931. Crawfishes of the southern Appalachians and the Cumberland Plateau. *Ann. Carnegie Mus.* **20**:61–160.

Park, T. 1945. A further report on toleration experiments by ecology classes. *Ecology* **26**:305–308.

Pearse, A. S. 1909. Observations on copulation among crayfishes. *Amer. Nat.* **43**:746–753.

Penn, G. H. 1942. Observations on the biology of the dwarf crawfish, Cambarellus shufeldtii (Faxon). *Amer. Midl. Nat.* **28**:644–647.

———. 1943. A study of the life history of the Louisiana red-crawfish, Cambarus clarkii Girard. *Ecology* **24**:1–18.

Rhoades, R. 1944. The crayfishes of Kentucky, with notes on variation, distribution and descriptions of new species and subspecies. *Amer. Midl. Nat.* **31**:111–149.

———. 1944a. Further studies on distribution and taxonomy of Ohio crayfishes, with the description of a new subspecies. *Ohio Jour. Sci.* **44**:95–99.

Roberts, T. W. 1944. Light, eyestalk chemical, and certain other factors as regulators of community activity for the crayfish, Cambarus virilis Hagen. *Ecol. Monogr.* **14**:359–392.

Schmitt, W. L. 1933. Notes on shrimps of the genus Macrobrachium found in the United States. *Jour. Wash. Acad. Sci.* **23**:312–317.

Scudamore, H. H. 1947. The influence of the sinus glands upon molting and associated changes in the crayfish. *Physiol. Zool.* **20**:187–208.

———. 1948. Factors influencing molting and the sexual cycles in the crayfish. *Biol. Bull.* **95**:229–237.

Steele, M. 1902. The crayfish of Missouri. *Univ. Cincinnati Bull.* **10**:1–53.

Tack, P. I. 1941. The life history and ecology of the crayfish Cambarus immunis Hagen. *Amer. Midl. Nat.* **25**:420–446.

Turner, C. L. 1926. The crayfish of Ohio. *Bull. Ohio Biol. Surv.* **13**:145–195.

———. 1935. The aberrant secondary sex characters of the crayfishes of the genus Cambarus. *Amer. Midl. Nat.* **16**:863–882.

Van Deventer, W. C. 1937. Studies on the biology of the crayfish, Cambarus propinquus Girard. *Ill. Biol. Monogr.* **15**:1–67.

# Chapter 23

# HYDRACARINA (WATER MITES)

The class Arachnoidea consists chiefly of terrestrial and parasitic members, including such familiar arthropods as spiders, scorpions, ticks, and mites. Only the water mites, forming the Order Hydracarina (or Hydrachnellae), have become generally adapted to fresh waters. Furthermore, considering the animal kingdom as a whole, the Order Hydracarina is one of the few characteristic fresh-water groups, being almost restricted to fresh waters; only a few species are found in brackish and salt waters, and none are terrestrial.

Although Hydracarina are found in almost all types of fresh-water habitats, they are most abundant and characteristic of ponds and the littoral region of lakes, especially where there are quantities of rooted aquatic vegetation. Their bright colors, globular to ovoid shape, and clambering and swimming habits identify them unmistakably.

**General characteristics.** Superficially, water mites appear to be minute spiders, but they differ most significantly from the true spiders in having the cephalothorax and abdomen completely fused into a single mass, all evident segmentation being lost. A decided minority of genera depart from the usual globular or ovoid shape and are dorsoventrally or laterally compressed. Most Hydracarina, and especially the more primitive genera, are soft bodied, but in many forms the cuticle is leathery or thickened to form a series of heavily sclerotized plates. Sometimes the body is almost completely enclosed by two plates, one dorsal and one ventral, while in other genera there are numerous smaller plates. The surface of the body is smooth, finely marked, granular, striated, or papillated. A variable number of setae are borne on the body. Total length usually ranges between 0.4 and 3.0 mm.

The six pairs of arachnid appendages are always present, the most conspicuous being the last four pairs, or legs. Each leg is long and consists of six segments which are variously supplied with spines, setae, and long hairs. The last segment usually bears two terminal movable claws. Each of the eight legs originates from a sclerotized ventral plate called a coxal plate, or epimera. At least some of the epimera are adjacent and more or less fused.

The first two pairs of appendages are borne on an anterior and ventral headlike structure called the capitulum, or maxillary organ. The mouth is located at the anterior end of the capitulum, often at the extremity of a straight or curved rostrum of variable length. The ventral surface of the capitulum is termed the maxillary shield. The chelicerae (usually called mandibles in the Hydracarina) are small and, except during feeding, are kept withdrawn into the capitulum. In a few genera they are stiletto-like or saber-like (Fig. 297E), but usually there is a separate, terminal, curved, clawlike segment (Fig. 297G). The five-segmented pedipalps (or

470

"palps") are inserted laterally or at the anterolateral angles of the maxillary shield and are customarily curved ventrally.

The only other conspicuous external feature is the genital field, a group of closely associated structures located on the ventral median line between or behind the epimera and sometimes at the extreme posterior end of the body. The genital pore is a small longitudinal slit in the center of the field; it is flanked by two plates which bear few to many curious knoblike or cuplike acetabula of unknown function. Sometimes there is a pair of longitudinal movable or immovable genital flaps which may or may not cover the acetabula (Figs. 293B, 297J).

The two pigmented eyes are near the anterior margin of the body and are usually widely separated, but in a few genera they lie close together along the median line. Each eye is characteristically paired.

The so-called "anus" is an inconspicuous pore near the posterior end; sometimes it is borne on a special small plate.

The two minute spiracles are located on the dorsal surface of the capitulum near its base and are therefore hidden from view by the body and can be seen only when the capitulum is dissected off.

In contrast to fresh-water invertebrates in general, water mites are particularly striking because of their coloration. The majority of species are some shade of red or green, but there are many others that are blue, yellow, tan, or brown. The basic body coloration is caused by pigmentation of the body wall, but yellow, brown, or blackish markings and patterns, especially in dorsal view, are produced by the coloration of internal organs, especially the digestive tract and excretory gland (Fig. 293A). *Axonopsis complanata* (Müller) is one of the most spectacular species; the appendages and general ventral surface are green; the epimera and much of the dorsal surface are blue; the capitulum, genital field, and central part of the dorsal surface are yellowish; and the large excretory gland produces a brown dorsal Y-shaped area. Some species of *Arrenurus* have equally striking combinations of green, blue, and orange. Stream species of water mites are characteristically brownish. Coloration of some species is somewhat variable, especially in *Limnesia,*

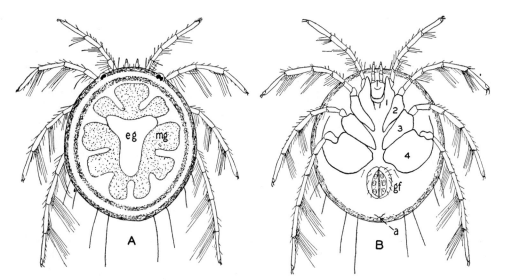

FIG. 293.—*Mideopsis orbicularis* (Müller) female, ×40. A, dorsal; B, ventral. 1, 2, 3, and 4, first, second, third, and fourth epimera; *a*, anus; *eg*, excretory gland; *gf*, genital field; *mg*, midgut. (Modified from Soar and Williamson.)

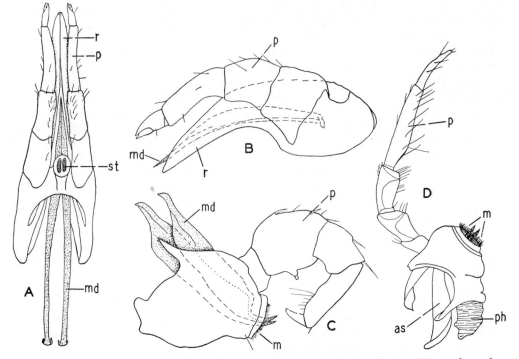

FIG. 294.—Hydracarina capitulum and associated structures. A, dorsal view of capitulum of *Hydrachna*; B, lateral view of capitulum of *Hydrachna* (only left palp shown); C, lateral view of capitulum of *Tyrellia* (only right palp shown); D, lateral view of capitulum of *Eylais* (only right palp shown). *as*, air sac; *m*, mouth (with projecting mandibles); *md*, mandibles (shaded); *p*, palp; *ph*, pharynx; *r*, rostrum; *st*, stigma (cross hatched). A and D modified from Viets; C modified from Marshall, 1940.)

and different specimens of the same species taken at the same place and time may exhibit different shades of red or green. These variations can be at least partially ascribed to differences in age and varying contents of the digestive tract and excretory gland.

**Locomotion.** Swimming is effected by relatively uncoordinated flailing movements of the legs, and the ability to swim is variously developed from one genus to another. The best swimmers have rows of long swimming hairs on the legs, especially the more posterior pairs (Fig. 293). At the other extreme are many species that are strictly creepers and crawlers on the bottom or among vegetation; their legs are supplied with only short spines and setae.

Swimming ability is lost in many swift stream forms.

Irrespective of the degree of swimming development, Hydracarina are clearly associated with the substrate and rarely stray far from it. Specific gravity of the body is usually high, and unless they cling to some object, they quickly fall to the bottom when not in motion. *Unionicola crassipes* Müller is probably the only American species that strays far enough from vegetation and a substrate to be considered an accidental plankton organism.

In addition to locomotion, the legs are used periodically for cleaning debris from the body and from each other.

**Food, feeding.** The great majority of water mites are carnivorous or parasitic, their food consisting chiefly of entomostraca, small insects, various kinds of worms, or host tissues. Sometimes the more active and voracious species are cannibalistic. Sluggish species usually feed on dead animals, and a few investigators claim that they may utilize vegetable material.

The prey is seized and held with the palps, with or without the aid of the legs, and the body is quickly pierced with the mandibles. Only fluids are ingested, and it it probable that secretions of the several pairs of salivary glands are injected into the prey where they predigest some of the more solid tissues so that they may be sucked up along with the body fluids. The exoskeleton and indigestible remnants of the prey are then discarded.

**Internal anatomy, physiology.** Ingested fluids pass through the small cavity of the suctorial pharynx and into the midgut, the latter being a capacious, lobed, digestive and absorptive organ filling one-third to one-half of the hemocoel. The midgut usually has about 12 caeca, although there may be as many as 30 in some species. In all of the Hydracarina whose anatomy has been carefully studied, it has been found that the midgut and its caeca end blindly, and there is no connection with the "anus."

A heart and blood vessels are lacking, but the blood is circulated about freely in the hemocoel by the movements of the muscles and digestive tract.

Each of the two minute spiracles opens into an elongated air sac (Fig. 294). At the posterior end of this sac is a single, short tracheal trunk which branches into many fine threadlike tracheae ramifying to all parts of the body.

Although the tracheal system is always filled with a gas (air), no adult water mite has ever been observed taking air at the surface film in the manner of many aquatic insects. When larvae or developing nymphs parasitize insects that leave the water and become aerial, however, it

is probable that they take in air through the spiracles. There is also the possibility that air could be taken into the tracheal system when the mandibles and a good portion of the capitulum are thrust into the air-containing tissues of aquatic plants. Nymphs have been observed in this attitude, but it is doubtful whether adults do it, with the possible exception of females of a few species that may assume the attitude as a preliminary to oviposition. Furthermore, mites are found in many habitats where there are no rooted aquatics.

Aside from the question of the physiological significance of the water mite tracheal system and the source of its contained gas, all investigators seem to agree that most of the oxygen utilized in metabolism is absorbed through the general body surface and that carbon dioxide diffuses outward through it. Those species with a thick body wall usually have scattered thin porous areas which presumably facilitate the gaseous exchange.

The excretory gland is a large dorsal T- or Y-shaped organ (Fig. 293A) which connects with the ventral "anus," or "excretory pore," by a duct. Many typical mites have seven pairs of oval or pear-shaped epidermal glands opening over the dorsal and lateral surfaces of the body, and it is possible that these structures have an accessory excretory function.

The nervous system consists of a large central ganglionic mass with little indication of the method of fusion. It is perforated by the pharynx and has radiating nerves. Each of the two lateral eyes consists of two elements which may be clearly separated or more or less fused. An element consists of a pigmented bulb and cuticular lens. Many species have an additional fifth, or median, eye (Fig. 297D). Other senses are poorly developed; the palps are tactile and probably detect substances in solution, and most of the body setae are probably tactile.

In the male there are two testes, two vasa deferentia, and a single penis, which

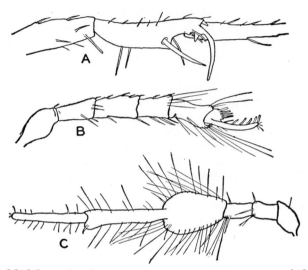

Fig. 295.—Modified legs of male Hydracarina. A, middle segments of third leg of male *Hydrochoreutes ungulatus* (Koch); B, fourth leg of male *Forelia*; C, fourth leg of male *Acercus*. (A modified from Marshall, 1927; B modified from Marshall, 1935; C modified from Marshall, 1937.)

can be extruded through the genital pore. The female has two fused ovaries, two oviducts, and a single vagina, or uterus.

**Reproduction.** Sometimes the two sexes can be distinguished only by slight differences in the anatomy of the genital field, palps, third legs, and fourth legs, but more commonly sexual dimorphism is pronounced. Males frequently have much larger fourth epimera, and genital fields that differ considerably from those of females. The third and fourth legs of males are sometimes specialized for copulation and the transfer of spermatophores; often the fourth legs are elongated, and in a few genera the fourth segment is flattened and platelike (Fig. 295C) or the terminal segment is roughly sickle-shaped (Fig. 295B). The third legs may be modified for clasping the female (Fig. 295A), and sometimes the distal segments form a club for sperm transfer. In *Arrenurus* sexual dimorphism is extreme, the males being characterized by a large posterior prolongation, or cauda (Fig. 298B, C). Unfortunately there is no single general

anatomical character or several characters which may be used in distinguishing the sexes throughout the order.

Judging from the few species whose reproductive habits have been carefully described, it appears that Hydracarina exhibit a wide variety of clasping and spermatophore transfer habits. Occasionally the male is carried on the back of the female for a varying time. The males of a few species drag the female about in a haphazard manner. In some genera the genital pores of the two copulating individuals are almost in direct contact during spermatophore transfer, but more commonly the bodies are placed at various angles to each other (often at right angles), while the male securely holds the first two pairs of female legs with his fourth legs. Regardless of the specific copulatory position, the male picks up the packet-like spermatophores from the tip of his extruded penis with his third legs and transfers them to the region of the female genital pore. Spermatophore transfer takes from less than a minute to as long as an hour.

Statements concerning the breeding season vary widely. Some authorities state that breeding and egg deposition may occur at any time during the year; others maintain that eggs are usually deposited in May, June, and July. It therefore seems logical to assume that the breeding season may vary widely from one species to another and also that it may vary within a single species according to latitude, temperature, and season.

As the female releases the eggs from her genital pore they are fertilized by the sperm contained in the spermatophores previously placed there by the male. Fertilized eggs are rarely deposited singly; usually they are extruded in groups of 20 to 200 onto stones, vegetation, and debris. Each egg may have its own individual gelatinous covering, or the whole group of eggs may be imbedded in a common gelatinous mass. Eggs are usually red in color. *Hydrachna* oviposits in the tissues of aquatic plants.

**Development, life history.** Depending on temperatures and the particular species, the eggs hatch in one to six weeks. The larvae have functional mouth parts, small epimera, three pairs of legs, and no genital field (Figs. 296A, B). After a short free-swimming period, the larvae become attached to aquatic insects with their capitulum and assume a parasitic exist-

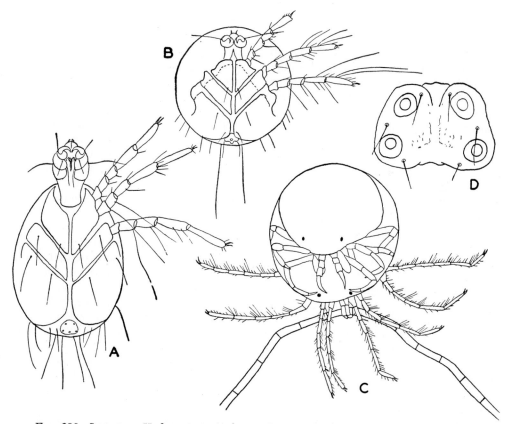

Fig. 296.—Immature Hydracarina. A, larva of *Arrenurus*, ×260; B, larva of *Mideopsis*, ×130; C, adult *Piona* developing within nymphal exoskeleton, attached to filamentous alga, ×40; D, genital field of *Limnesia* nymph. (A and B modified from Soar and Williamson, 1925; C modified from Uchida; D redrawn from Viets.)

ence. Wesenberg-Lund (1919) favors the theory of some broad preference by larvae for certain insect hosts; thus, he states that the Limnocharidae usually parasitize hydrometrids, that Eylaidae mostly parasitize aerial insects, that Hydryphantidae usually occur on culicids, and that several other families appear to be almost restricted to insects that do not leave the water. In view of more recent ecological observations, it is possible that his conclusions may be a reflection of restricted mite and insect faunas in the ponds he studied. It would be highly desirable to test this question experimentally in order to find out definitely whether or not a particular larval mite has any specific host preference. It is significant that Ephemeroptera and hydrophilid and dytiscid beetles are rarely parasitized, and that Trichoptera are uncommon hosts. The usual hosts are Plecoptera, Odonata, Diptera, and Hemiptera. The larval mite may come in contact with its host on the substrate or at the surface film. Often a single insect may carry ten or 20 mite parasites.

After a variable feeding period on the host, the larva begins to metamorphose to the nymphal stage. Feeding ceases, and the larva shrinks from its exoskeleton which then becomes a loose baglike puparium (still attached to the host). The contained larva loses its definitive features and becomes more or less reconstituted to form the nymph stage. Soon the nymph ruptures the puparium and escapes into the water. The period of inactivity between cessation of feeding by the larva and the escape of the nymph is comparable to a pupal stage and is called the nymphophan. The nymphophan stage lasts for periods ranging from five days to six months.

The nymph is considerably larger than the larva and almost as large as the adult. It has the same general structures and proportions as the adult, but there is no genital opening in the genital field. Unlike the larva, the nymph is free living and has the same carnivorous food habits as the adult.

At the end of a variable period of activity, the nymph attaches itself to an algal filament, rooted aquatic, or bottom debris with its mouth parts and enters a second pupal stage, or teleiophan. Again, the nymphal exoskeleton becomes a baglike puparium with the developing adult within (Fig. 296C). This quiescent period usually lasts only seven to ten days after which the nymphal exoskeleton ruptures and the sexually mature adult emerges.

By way of recapitulation, the stages in the life history of a typical water mite may be outlined as follows: Egg—active larva—parasitic larva—quiescent nymphophan—active nymph—quiescent teleiophan—active adult. The active larval and parasitic larval stages are morphologically indistinguishable.

If the larva attaches to an insect that is aquatic until the termination of the nymphophan, the developed nymph simply breaks out of its puparium into the water. If the insect host is an adult beetle or hemipteran, however, it may leave the water intermittently with its attached larval parasite exposed to the air. Furthermore, the host may metamorphose to an adult that leaves the water and is aerial for the rest of its life (Odonata, Diptera, and Plecoptera, for example). In such instances the fully developed nymph breaks out of the puparium and may fall into the water fortuitously, or it may re-enter the water when its host oviposits in the water. Nymphs that fall to the ground from an aerial host are presumed to die very shortly.

There are many exceptions to the generalized type of life history outlined in the above paragraphs. A few water mites deposit their eggs in the tissues of sponges or the gelatinous matrix of colonial Protozoa. Others are thought to leave the insect host while still in the larval stage and attach to the substrate for the transformation to the nymph. Certain stream species of *Piona* and *Limnesia* do not have a parasitic stage but remain in the gelatinous egg mass until they become nymphs.

The species of *Unionicola* have unusual life histories. The majority pass their entire lives in the tissues or cavities of mussels, but in a few species the adults are found either in mussels or free swimming, and one or two are parasitic in sponges. It is thought that eggs are produced the year round; they are inserted into the tissues of the mussel gills by means of a special ovipositor. The larvae are parasitic on the gills, but the nymphs and adults clamber about actively in the gill or mantle cavities. The parasitic adults have short legs and no swimming hairs. Sometimes the great majority of mussels in a bed are infected, and although infestations may be heavy, the mites appear to do little damage to the hosts. It is possible that the nymphs and adults are commensals rather than true parasites. In addition to *Unionicola*, *Najadicola ingens* Koen., an uncommon species, also occurs in mussels.

Complete life histories are known for relatively few water mites, and it is likely that many additional variations, exceptions, and complications will appear as further studies are made.

Almost nothing is known about the duration of the life cycle or number of generations per year, but it is thought that the great majority of species have a life span of less than one year. Overwintering probably occurs most frequently in the adult stage, although parasitic larvae, teleiophans, and nymphs have also been reported.

**Ecology.** Unlike most groups of freshwater invertebrates, water mites may be collected in all seasons, even under ice, but the greatest numbers of adults are to be found in late spring and early autumn.

They are invariably most abundant in species and individuals among the heaviest growths of rooted aquatics where the water is only a meter or two deep. Populations in excess of 2,000 mites per square meter of bottom have been reported from such habitats. Acid, dystrophic lakes, though superficially an ideal collecting ground, contain very few Hydracarina. Wave-beaten sand and gravel shores are also poor places to collect. Many species are capable of clambering and swimming about with surprising agility, while others, devoid of swimming hairs, are sluggish creepers of the bottom. Between these two extremes are all gradations in crawling, swimming, and clambering ability. Mites are active only during the hours of daylight, and sometimes they remain fixed in the same position all night long.

As the water deepens offshore, the fauna becomes progressively depauperate, and even though Hydracarina may be collected from the bottom at depths of ten to 100 meters, such populations are usually scanty and composed of only one to several species. There is some evidence for migration into the weedy shallows in the late spring and back to deeper waters in the autumn when vegetation disappears, but this problem needs further investigation.

Some genera, notably *Thyas*, *Hydryphantes*, *Acercus*, *Piona*, and *Limnesia*, are characteristic of temporary ponds and are capable of withstanding periods of drought by being buried in wet mud and debris of the substrate.

Brook and stream species are often conspicuously modified for withstanding the force of the current. Dorsoventral flattening, small size, strong claws, and the absence of swimming hairs are the usual adaptations. Stream species produce comparatively small numbers of eggs.

Coloration is sometimes correlated with the background, though there is little evidence that the resemblance has any protective value. Elton (1923) found that hungry sticklebacks refused to eat bright scarlet mites, and he postulated possible Müllerian mimicry and warning coloration.

**Geographical distribution, dispersal.** Although the geographical distribution and ecological affinities are well known for many species in Europe, collecting in the United States has been so highly regional and generally neglected that we have little reliable information on the distribution of most species. In view of this fact, it has been largely necessary to omit distributional data for the genera and species included in the key beginning on page 480. The majority of species reported from the United States appear to be restricted to this country, and many are known only from a single locality or two or three widely separated localities. However, only a single rare genus, *Najadicola*, appears to be restricted to North America. On the other hand, a surprising number of American species are cosmopolitan and widely distributed throughout the northern and even the southern hemispheres. Furthermore, it is rather striking that in each of about half of the genera occurring in the United States one species (and only one) is widely distributed and common in both North America and Europe. Some of these species are: *Piona rotunda* (Koen.), *Unionicola crassipes* (Müller), *Hydryphantes ruber* (DeGeer), *Diplodontus despiciens* (Müller), *Lebertia porosa* Thor, *Hygrobates longipalpis* (Herm.), *Hydrochoreutes ungulatus* (Koch), and *Mideopsis orbicularis* (Müller).

Dispersal is both active and passive, and those species that are parasitic on insects are undoubtedly easily distributed overland to new drainage systems.

**Enemies.** Hydracarina are preyed upon by a wide variety of aquatic invertebrates, especially coelenterates and carnivorous insects. They are not ordinarily an important element in the diet of fishes, but occasionally a fish stomach is found in which mites predominate. Several new species have been described from the stomach contents of Wyoming trout.

**Collection, preparation.** A successful way to collect quantities of mites is to draw a Birge cone net through vegetation or along the bottom. Hand picking, dip-netting, and washing out quantities of vege-

tation in an enameled pan are also very useful techniques. Living specimens may be kept in the laboratory and fed entomostraca or nonpredatory aquatic insects, but crowding is disastrous since they are often cannibalistic.

Because they are so active, it is best to examine living specimens in a compression slide or by anesthetizing and relaxing them with chloretone or in water saturated with chloroform vapor. Binoculars, an opaque white background, and a bright spotlight are essential.

Five per cent formalin is a suitable killing agent, but specimens should not be preserved in this fluid as it makes the appendages extremely brittle. A good killing and preserving agent can be made up as follows: 5 parts by volume of glycerin, 4 parts water, and 1 part glacial acetic acid. Wolcott recommends the following solution: 2 parts glycerin, 3 parts water, 2 parts glacial acetic acid, and 1 part absolute alcohol.

Suitably translucent whole mounts may sometimes be made by cutting a small incision in the dorsal body wall and pressing out the contents, but it is first necessary to treat dense and hard species with 5 per cent potassium hydroxide in order to render them sufficiently translucent for work with the compound microscope. Acetic corrosive is a superior clearing agent. It consists of equal parts (by weight) of glacial acetic acid, chloral hydrate, and water. For critical study and accurate identification, the mouth parts, capitulum, and legs should be dissected off and mounted separately. Some workers prefer permanent euparal or similar mounting media (see Lavers, 1945); others use glycerin or glycerin jelly.

**Taxonomy.** More than 90 per cent of all published information on our American species is based on the work of two careful investigators—Robert Wolcott, whose publications extend from 1899 to 1918, and Ruth Marshall, whose numerous papers appeared between 1903 and 1944. The potential number of species in the United States must be large, Marshall having reported 140 species and varieties from Wisconsin alone. Viets (1936) lists 444 species from Germany, and Soar and Williamson (1925–1929) list 247 for the British Isles. Very little is known about the Hydracarina of rapid streams, high altitudes, states west of the Great Plains, and southeastern states.

Identification to genus and species is based primarily on the detailed adult anatomy of the epimera, genital field, capitulum, and palps. The taxonomic status and limits of several families and genera are still controversial, but the following classification of American fresh-water genera used in this manual is only slightly modified from the widely accepted one proposed by Viets (1936).

Superfamily Hydrachnae
  Hydrachnidae—*Hydrachna*
Superfamily Limnocharae
  Protziidae—*Calonyx*
  Limnocharidae—*Limnochares* (including *Cyclothrix*)
  Eylaidae—*Eylais*
Superfamily Hydryphantae
  Hydryphantidae—*Hydryphantes*
  Thyasidae—*Thyas*
  Diplodontidae—*Diplodontus* (= *Hydrodroma*)
  Thermacaridae—*Thermacarus*
Superfamily Lebertiae
  Sperchonidae—*Sperchon, Sperchonopsis* (= *Pseudosperchon*)
  Lebertiidae—*Lebertia, Frontipoda, Gnaphiscus, Oxus*
  Atractideidae—*Atractides, Testudacarus*
Superfamily Pionae
  Limnesiidae—*Limnesia* (including *Limnesiopsis*)
  Tyrelliidae—*Tyrellia*
  Hygrobatidae—*Hygrobates, Megapus*
  Unionicolidae—*Huitfeldtia, Koenikea, Najadicola, Neumania, Unionicola* (= *Atax*)
  Pionidae—*Acercus, Forelia, Hydrochoreutes, Piona*

Superfamily Axonopsae
  Axonopsidae—*Albia, Axonopsis*
Superfamily Mideopsae
  Mideidae—*Midea*
  Mideopsidae—*Mideopsis* (including *Xystonotus*)
Superfamily Arrenurae
  Athienemanniidae—*Geayia, Krendowskia*
  Arrenuridae—*Arrenurus*

**Other fresh-water arachnids.** A single family of Hydracarina, the Halacaridae, is primarily marine but contains a few fresh-water species. It can be most easily distinguished from all other families by the fact that the palps are only three- or four-segmented. In addition, the mouth parts are usually on a large rostrum projecting well beyond the anterior margin of the body. The exoskeleton is leathery and reinforced with four dorsal plates and four ventral plates. The legs are attached laterally. These mites do not swim but creep about sluggishly in algae and debris of the littoral. Except for the work of Newell (1947), this family has been almost ignored in the United States but has been carefully studied in Europe. In addition to the marine species, about a dozen widely distributed fresh-water species have been described from ponds, pools, and springs. *Porolohmannella, Soldanellonyx, Halacarus, Copidognathus,* and *Porohalacarus* are known to occur in North American fresh waters. Some free-living species occur also as commensals in the gill chambers of European fresh-water crayfish (Astacinae). There appear to be no American records of such commensal halacarid mites, but it should be interesting to look for them in the gill chambers of the American Astacinae, which are confined to the west coast states.

Mites belonging to the large Order Oribatoidea feed principally on vegetable or decaying animal matter and live in moss, grass, crevices of bark, and duff. *Oribatella aquatica* Banks and several other rare and poorly known species, however, are found in ponds where they crawl about sluggishly on submerged vegetation. The body is coriaceous, eyes are absent, and there is a specialized seta arising from a pore near the two posterior corners of the cephalothorax.

Among the true spiders, or Araneae, there are no American species that are strictly aquatic, although a European species, *Argyroneta aquatica*, has become curiously adapted to the aquatic environment; it spins a dense, flat, underwater web in vegetation and brings small air bubbles down from the surface film and releases them beneath the web, thus forming a large bell-shaped bubble held in place by the web; the spider spends most of its time within the bubble. Many American species, however, are semiaquatic. They

run about along the beach or among shore vegetation and often skitter out over the surface of ponds and marshes where they may feed on Hemiptera and other insects supported on the surface film. Some even dive beneath the surface when alarmed. Many build their webs on emergent vegetation. Some of the genera having common semiaquatic species are *Dolomedes*, *Lycosa*, *Pirata*, *Pachygnatha*, and *Tetragnatha*. *Dolomedes* is a colorful and spectacular genus, often reaching a diameter of five centimeters. It dives with difficulty and remains submerged by hanging on to objects, but may remain below the surface as long as 45 minutes. Oxygen is probably obtained from air bubbles adhering to the body near the respiratory openings.

## KEY TO GENERA OF HYDRACARINA

1. Lateral eyes of the two sides close together at the median line and borne on a common plate (Figs. 297B, C); simple, red, soft-bodied species; up to 5 mm. long. .................................................................5
Lateral eyes widely separated (Figs. 298–300) ............................2
2. Distal extremity of the fourth palp segment produced into a point well beyond the point of insertion of segment five, the two segments together usually resembling a pair of shears (Figs. 297F, H)...............................3
Distal extremity of fourth palp segment not pointed and produced, or only slightly produced and blunt (Figs. 301D–F); segment five free, tapered, and with the tip pointed, clawed, or toothed....................................8
3. Mandible one-segmented, the terminal portion straight and stiletto-like (Fig. 297E); globular, soft, and papillated; capitulum produced as a rostrum well beyond anterior end of body (Fig. 297D); with swimming hairs; usually red, orange, or brown; 1 to 6 mm. long; common everywhere in standing waters; numerous species.......................HYDRACHNIDAE, **Hydrachna**
Mandible two-segmented, the terminal segment curved, clawlike, and often very small (Figs. 297F, H); capitulum only slightly or not at all produced beyond anterior end of body..................................................4
4. Last two epimera widely separated from first two epimera (Fig. 297K); bottom forms; no swimming hairs; soft-bodied; cold waters; two species.
PROTZIIDAE, **Calonyx**
Last two epimera not so widely separated from first two epimera (Fig. 297J)....6
5. Eye capsules on either side of an elongated plate in the mid-line (Fig. 297B); mouth at the tip of a protruding rostrum; usually creepers; several common and widely distributed species..........LIMNOCHARIDAE, **Limnochares**
Eye capsules connected by a narrow bridge (Fig. 297C); mouth not at the tip of a protruding rostrum; swimmers in quiet waters; about ten described species.
EYLAIDAE, **Eylais**

**6.** Distal extremity of fourth segment of palp short (Fig. 297H); median eye present; 1.0 to 2.5 mm. long; red.............................................7

Distal extremity of fourth segment of palp long (Fig. 297F); median eye absent; with swimming hairs; soft red body; 2.0 mm. long; widely distributed and common............DIPLODONTIDAE, **Diplodontus despiciens** (Müller)

**7.** Swimming hairs present; several widely distributed species.

HYDRYPHANTIDAE, **Hydryphantes**

Swimming hairs absent, only short spines on legs; several uncommon species in northern states.............................................THYASIDAE, **Thyas**

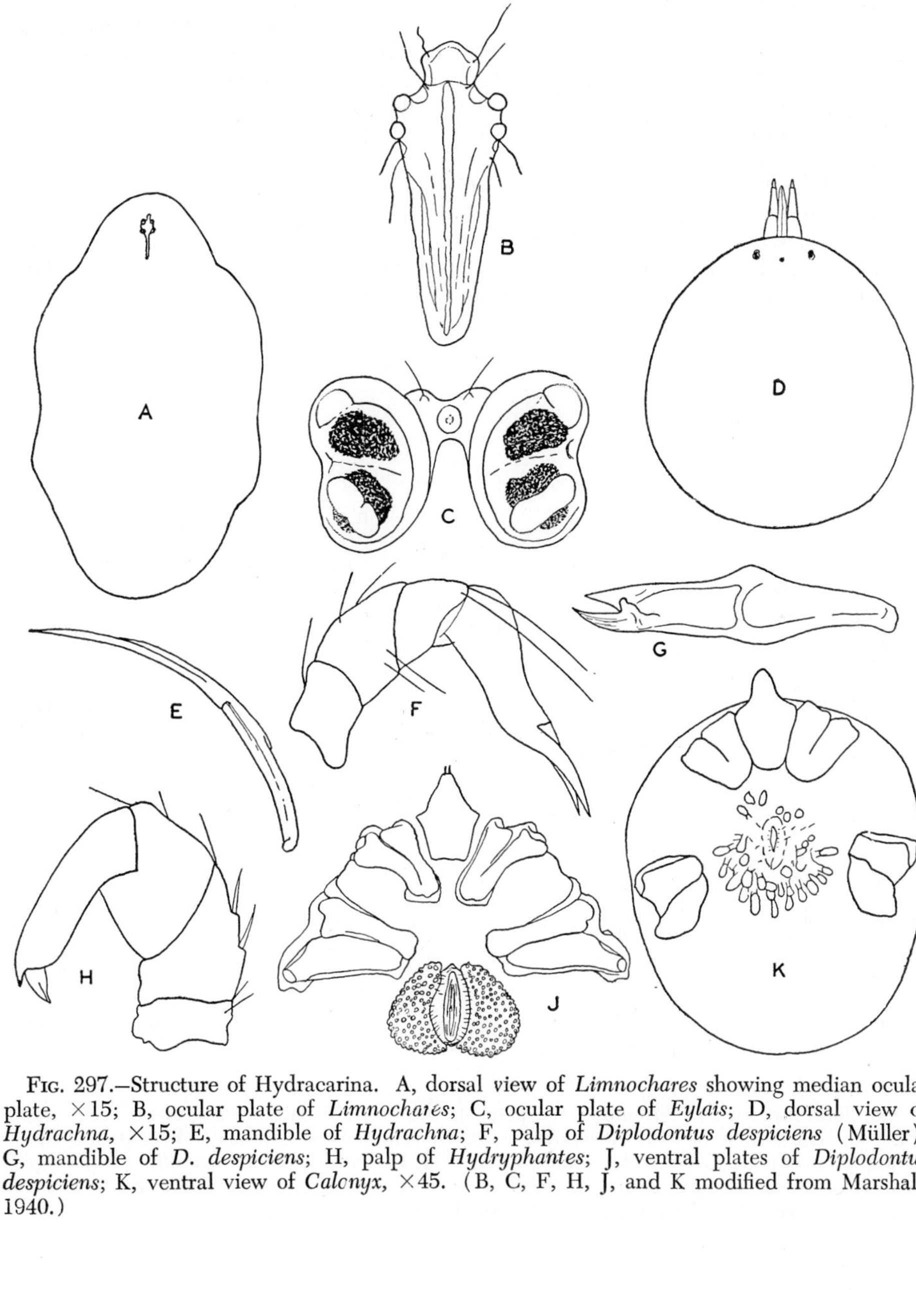

FIG. 297.—Structure of Hydracarina. A, dorsal view of *Limnochares* showing median ocular plate, ×15; B, ocular plate of *Limnochares*; C, ocular plate of *Eylais*; D, dorsal view of *Hydrachna*, ×15; E, mandible of *Hydrachna*; F, palp of *Diplodontus despiciens* (Müller); G, mandible of *D. despiciens*; H, palp of *Hydryphantes*; J, ventral plates of *Diplodontus despiciens*; K, ventral view of *Calonyx*, ×45. (B, C, F, H, J, and K modified from Marshall, 1940.)

**8.** Fifth segment of palp pointed, clawlike, and opposable to the projecting margin of segment four (Fig. 298A)..................................................9

Fifth segment of palp not opposable to fourth, and bearing small distal claws or teeth. ...................................................................11

**9.** Genital field lying posterior to fourth epimera; males usually with a large posterior prolongation, or cauda (Figs. 298B, C); body wall heavily sclerotized; common everywhere, especially in vegetation; usually red or greenish; the largest American genus; about 80 species and varieties in North America.

ARRENURIDAE, **Arrenurus**

Genital field lying between fourth epimera (Fig. 298E).

ATHIENEMANNIIDAE, **10**

**10.** With six genital acetabula (Fig. 298E); dorsal shield large (Fig. 298F); reported from Wis., Ill., Ind., and Mich...................**Krendowskia similis** Viets

With eight genital acetabula (Fig. 298G); dorsal shield smaller (Fig. 298H); uncommon; reported from Wis., Minn., and Mich......**Geayia ovata** (Wolcott)

**11.** Legs crowded together and inserted at anterior end of body; epimera united; body laterally compressed (Fig. 299A–C); uncommon........LEBERTIIDAE, **12**

Legs not crowded together at anterior end of body; body not laterally compressed. ...................................................................14

**12.** Without a longitudinal furrow on the dorsal surface; several species.........**Oxus**

Dorsal surface of body with a narrow to wide longitudinal furrow (Fig. 299C)..**13**

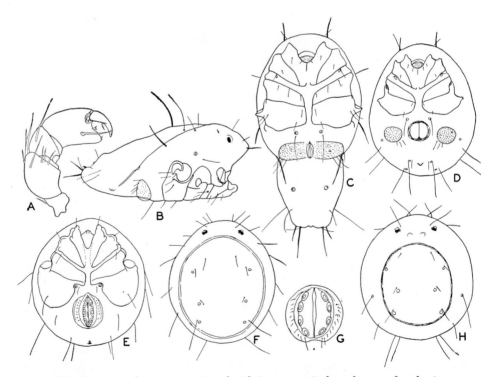

Fig. 298.—Structure of Arrenurae. A, palp of *Arrenurus*; B, lateral view of male *Arrenurus*, ×37; C, ventral view of male *Arrenurus*, ×40; D, ventral view of female *Arrenurus*, ×27; E, ventral view of male *Krendowskia similis* Viets, ×33; F, dorsal view of *K. similis*, ×33; G, genital field of female *Geayia ovata* (Wolcott); H, dorsal view of *G. ovata*, ×37. (A to D modified from Lavers; E to H modified from Marshall, 1940.)

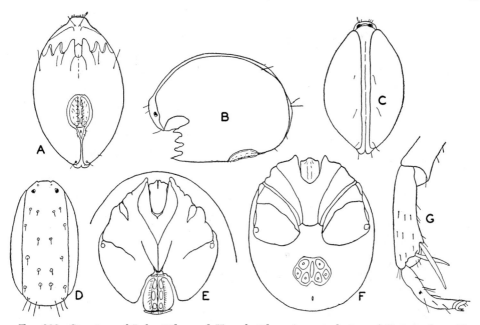

FIG. 299.—Structure of Lebertiidae and Hygrobatidae. A, ventral view of *Frontipoda*, ×80; B, lateral view of *Frontipoda*, ×80; C, dorsal view of *Frontipoda*, ×70; D, dorsal view of *Gnaphiscus*, ×47; E, ventral plates of *Lebertia*; F, ventral view of *Megapus*, ×45; G, terminal portion of first leg of *Megapus*. (A and C modified from Marshall, 1914; E modified from Marshall, 1932; F and G modified from Marshall, 1943.)

13. Anal plate present (Fig. 299A); two species....................**Frontipoda**
    Anal plate absent; one very rare species.........................**Gnaphiscus**
14. First epimera completely fused along the median line (Figs. 299E, F)........**15**
    First epimera not fused along the median line (Figs. 301, 302)..............**25**
15. With a large sclerotized dorsal plate (Fig. 300B)........................**18**
    Without a dorsal plate...............................................**16**
16. Genital field between fourth epimera (Fig. 299E); widely distributed in many
    habitats, especially cold waters; about 12 species.

                                    LEBERTIIDAE, **Lebertia**
    Genital field posterior to fourth epimera (Fig. 299F); common and widely distrib-
    uted......................................HYGROBATIDAE, **17**
17. Fifth segment of first leg with two special conspicuous setae (Fig. 299G); several
    species. ................................................**Megapus**
    Fifth segment of first leg without such setae; about five species.......**Hygrobates**
18. Anterior ends of first epimera projecting well beyond the anterior margin of body,
    leaving a large bay for the capitulum (Figs. 300A, 301C).

                                    ATRACTIDEIDAE, **19**
    Anterior ends of first epimera not projecting beyond anterior margin of body (Fig.
    300F)...........................................................**20**
19. With four small anterior dorsal plates (Fig. 300C); without swimming hairs;
    usually in cold streams; widely distributed; about 20 species......**Atractides**
    With three small anterior dorsal plates (Fig. 300B); two rare species reported from
    California streams..................................................**Testudacarus**
20. Occurring only in hot springs; one species reported from Nev.

                                    THERMACARIDAE, **Thermacarus**
    Not in hot springs...............................................**21**

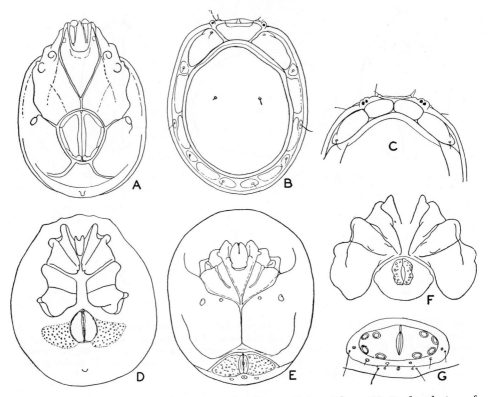

FIG. 300.—Structure of Hydracarina. A, ventral view of *Atractides*, ×80; B, dorsal view of *Testudacarus*, ×60; C, dorsal anterior region of *Atractides*; D, ventral view of *Koenikea*, ×65; E, ventral view of *Albia*, ×60; F, ventral plates of *Midea*; G, genital field of *Axonopsis complanata* (Müller). (A to C modified from Marshall, 1943; D and E modified from Marshall, 1935; G modified from Viets.)

21. Genital field lying in a bay bounded by all of the epimera (Fig. 300F); one rare
     species reported from Wis.........................MIDEIDAE, **Midea**
     Genital field not lying in a bay bounded by all of the epimera................22
22. With numerous genital acetabula (Figs. 300E, 302A).....................23
     With three or four pairs of genital acetabula (Fig. 300G)..................24
23. Genital field near posterior margin of body; fourth epimera large (Fig. 300E); sev-
     eral widely distributed species...................AXONOPSIDAE, **Albia**
     Genital field not near posterior margin of body; fourth epimera not especially large
     (Fig. 300D); about six widely distributed species.
                                                   UNIONICOLIDAE, **Koenikea**
24. Four pairs of genital acetabula; genital field at extreme posterior end of body (Fig.
     300G); 0.45 mm. long; brightly colored in green, blue, and yellow; rare; north-
     ern lakes...............AXONOPSIDAE, **Axonopsis complanata** (Müller)
     Three pairs of genital acetabula; genital field not at extreme posterior end of body;
     about ten species, of which only one is common and widely distributed.
                                           MIDEOPSIDAE, **Mideopsis**
25. Genital field anterior, at least between fourth epimera; no ancoral process on capit-
     ulum (Figs. 301C, G).........................................26
     Genital field posterior to fourth epimera; ancoral process present on capitulum
     (Fig. 302).................................................29

26. Genital acetabula borne on uncovered plates, genital flaps absent (Fig. 301C)..**27**
    Genital acetabula more or less covered by genital flaps (Fig. 301G); swimming
    hairs absent; sluggish bottom forms..............SPERCHONIDAE, **28**
27. Fourth leg with two terminal claws (Fig. 301A); swimming hairs absent; sluggish;
    two uncommon species......................TYRELLIIDAE, **Tyrellia**
    Fourth leg without terminal claws (Fig. 301B); swimming hairs usually present; in
    a variety of habitats but most common in standing waters; about 15
    species.................................LIMNESIIDAE, **Limnesia**
28. Fourth segment of palp with two small processes on flexor surface, or processes
    absent (Figs. 301D, E); in northern states and mountainous areas; several
    uncommon species.........................................**Sperchon**
    Fourth segment of palp with one large process on proximal end of flexor surface
    (Fig. 301F); common and widely distributed.
                                              **Sperchonopsis verrucosa** (Protz)

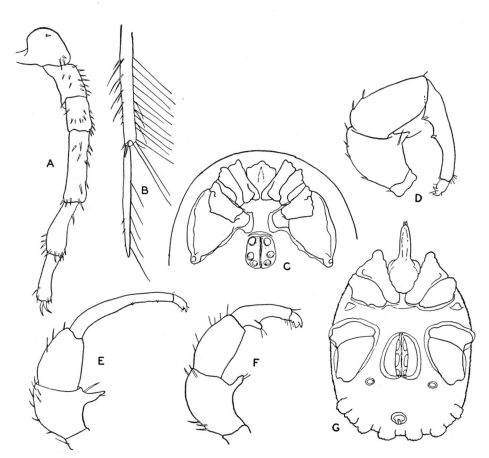

Fig. 301.—Structure of Hydracarina. A, fourth leg of *Tyrellia*; B, fifth and sixth segments of fourth leg of *Limnesia*; C, ventral plates of *Limnesia*; D, palp of female *Sperchon*; E, palp of male *Sperchon*; F, palp of *Sperchonopsis verrucosa* (Protz); G, ventral view of male *S. verrucosa*, ×115. (A modified from Marshall, 1940a; B modified from Viets; C modified from Marshall, 1932; D to G modified from Marshall, 1943.)

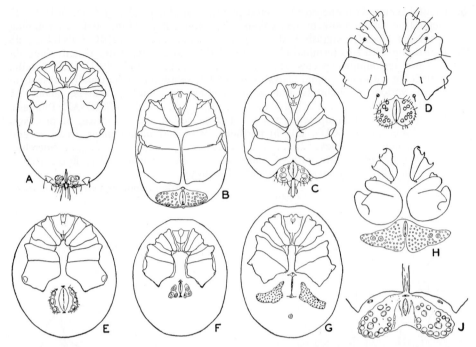

Fig. 302.—Structure of Hydracarina. A, ventral view of *Unionicola,* ×36; B, ventral view of *Neumania,* ×35; C, ventral view of male *Hydrochoreutes ungulatus,* ×65; D, ventral plates of *Huitfeldtia rectipes* Thor; E, ventral view of female *Hydrochoreutes ungulatus,* ×40; F, ventral view of female *Acercus torris* (Müller), ×25; G, ventral view of *Forelia,* ×44; H, ventral plates of *Najadicola ingens* Koen.; J, genital field of *Piona.* (All modified as follows: A and B from Marshall, 1933; C and E from Marshall, 1927; D from Viets; F from Marshall, 1937; G and J from Marshall, 1935; H from Wolcott, 1904.)

**29.** Genital field usually near posterior margin of body and separated from epimera; posterior margin of fourth epimera transverse (Figs. 302A, B).

UNIONICOLIDAE, **30**

Genital field not near posterior margin of body; posterior median corners or posterior margins of fourth epimera more or less excavated to receive genital field (Figs. 302G–J)..............................................................**31**

**30.** Suture between third and fourth epimera present only laterally (Fig. 302A); most species parasitic or commensal throughout life in gills or mantle cavity of mussels; several species free-living as adults; about 15 widely distributed American species...........................................................**Unionicola**

Suture between third and fourth epimera complete (Fig. 302B); usually red or bluish with lighter patterns; active swimmers; widely distributed and common; about 20 species................................................**Neumania**

**31.** With eight or nine genital acetabula on each side (Fig. 302D); third leg with a long lateral seta; with swimming hairs; uncommon in northern lakes.

UNIONICOLIDAE, **Huitfeldtia rectipes** Thor

With three or many genital acetabula on each side; third leg without long lateral seta. ...........................................................................**32**

**32.** With three pairs of genital acetabula (Figs. 302C, E, F); widely distributed.

PIONIDAE, **33**

With many pairs of genital acetabula (Figs. 302G–J)......................**34**

33. Palps and legs very long; male with a petiole (Fig. 302C); posterior end of female fourth epimera blunt (Fig. 302E). ..... **Hydrochoreutes ungulatus** (Koch)
   Palps and legs not especially long; male without a petiole; posterior end of female fourth epimera pointed (Fig. 302F)..............**Acercus torris** (Müller)
34. Fourth epimera pointed medially (Fig. 302G); several widely distributed species.
   PIONIDAE, **Forelia**
   Fourth epimera with longitudinal median margin (Figs. 302H, J)............**35**
35. Posterior margin of fourth epimera convexly rounded (Fig. 302H); parasitic or commensal in gills or mantle cavities of mussels; generally distributed but not common....................UNIONICOLIDAE, **Najadicola ingens** Koen.
   Posterior margin of fourth epimera not convexly rounded (Fig. 302J); with swimming hairs; brightly colored; common and widely distributed; about 20 species.
   PIONIDAE, **Piona**

## HYDRACARINA REFERENCES

ARNDT, W., and K. VIETS. 1938. Die biologischen (parasitologischen) Beziehungen zwischen Arachnoideen und Spongien. *Zeitschr. Parasitenk.* 10:67–93.

BAKER, E. W., and G. W. WHARTON. 1952. *An introduction to acarology.* 465 pp. New York.

ELTON, C. S. 1923. On the colours of water-mites. *Proc. Zool. Soc. London* (1922):1231–1239.

HOFF, C. C. 1944. A preliminary study of the Hydracarina of Reelfoot Lake, Tennessee. *Jour. Tenn. Acad. Sci.* 19:45–69.

LAVERS, C. H., JR. 1945. The species of Arrenurus of the state of Washington. *Trans. Amer. Micros. Soc.* 44:228–264.

LUNDBLAD, O. 1935. Die nordamerikanischen Arten der Gattung Hydrachna. *Ark. f. Zool.* 28:1–44.

———. 1941. Eine Übersicht des Hydrachnellensystems und der bis jetzt bekannten Verbreitung der Gattungen dieser Gruppe. *Zool. Bidr.* 20:359–379.

MARSHALL, R. 1908. The Arrhenuri of the United States. *Trans. Amer. Micros. Soc.* 28:85–140.

———. 1914. Some new American water mites. *Trans. Wis. Acad. Sci. Arts and Lett.* 17:1300–1304.

———. 1927. Hydracarina of the Douglas Lake region. *Trans. Amer. Micros. Soc.* 46:268–285.

———. 1928. A new species of water mite from thermal springs. *Psyche* 35:92–95.

———. 1931. Preliminary list of the Hydracarina of Wisconsin. I. The red mites. *Trans. Wis. Acad. Sci., Arts and Lett.* 26:311–319.

———. 1932. Preliminary list of the Hydracarina of Wisconsin. Part II. *Ibid.* 27:339–358.

———. 1933. Preliminary list of the Hydracarina of Wisconsin. Part III. *Ibid.* 28:37–61.

———. 1935. Preliminary list of the Hydracarina of Wisconsin. IV. *Ibid.* 29:273–298.

———. 1937. Preliminary list of the Hydracarina of Wisconsin. V. *Ibid.* 30:225–252.

———. 1940. Preliminary list of the Hydracarina of Wisconsin. VI. *Ibid.* 32:135–165.

———. 1940a. The water mite genus Tyrellia. *Ibid.* 383–389.

———. 1943. Hydracarina from California. Part I. *Trans. Amer. Micros. Soc.* 62:306–324.

———. 1943a. Hydracarina from California. Part II. *Ibid.* 404–415.

———. 1944. Preliminary list of the Hydracarina of Wisconsin. Revision of Part I. *Trans. Wis. Acad. Sci., Arts and Lett.* 36:349–373.

NEWELL, I. M. 1947. A systematic and ecological study of the Halacaridae of eastern North America. *Bull. Bingham Oceanogr. Coll.* 10:1–232.

SCHMIDT, U. 1935. Beiträge zur Anatomie und Histologie der Hydracarinen, besonders von Diplodontus despiciens O. F. Müller. *Zeitschr. Morph. Ökol. Tiere* 30:99–176.

SOAR, C. D., and W. WILLIAMSON. 1925–1929. *British Hydracarina.* 3 vols. 612 pp. Ray Society, London.

SOKOLOW, I. 1924. Untersuchungen über die Eiablage und den Laich der Hydracarina. I. *Arch. Hydrobiol.* 15:383–405.

———. 1925. Untersuchungen über die Eiablage und den Laich der Hydracarina. II. *Zeitschr. Morph. Ökol. Tiere* 4:301–332.

SZALAY, L. 1949. Ueber die Hydracarinen der unterirdischen Gewässer. *Hydrobiologia* 2:141–179.

UCHIDA, T. 1932. Some ecological observations on water mites. *Jour. Fac. Sci. Hokkaido Imp. Univ. Ser. VI. Zool.* 1:143–165.

VIETS, K. 1936. Wassermilben oder Hydracarina. *Die Tierwelt Deutschlands* 31 and 32:1–574.

WESENBERG-LUND, C. 1919. Contributions to the knowledge of the postembryonal development of the Hydracarina. *Videnskab. Medd. Dansk Naturhist. For.* 70:5–57.

WOLCOTT, R. H. 1899. On the North American species of the genus Atax (Fabr.) Bruz. *Trans. Amer. Micros. Soc.* 20:193–259.

———. 1905. A review of the genera of water mites. *Ibid.* 26:161–243.

# Chapter 24

## GENERAL INTRODUCTION TO THE INSECTA

FROM A BIOLOGICAL standpoint, insects undoubtedly form the most successful group in the animal kingdom. It is estimated that more than 1,000,000 species have been described. Insects vary widely in their habits, they occur in tremendous numbers, and many have become highly specialized and adapted to almost every conceivable habitat. Nevertheless, as a group, insects have not been particularly successful in colonizing aquatic environments. Certainly less than 4 per cent of the total number of species occur in or on water at some time during their life histories. Although all of the species of Plecoptera, Ephemeroptera, Odonata, and Trichoptera have aquatic stages, these orders are relatively small and are of little numerical significance when compared with the large orders Hemiptera, Lepidoptera, Coleoptera, Hymenoptera, and Diptera where only a small percentage of the species are aquatic.

Eleven of the 30 to 35 orders of insects contain species that are aquatic or semi-aquatic. Among the primitive insects which have no metamorphosis the order Collembola (springtails) is the only one in which there are aquatic species. A few occur on the surface of ponds and pools.

The Hemiptera (bugs) is the only paurometabolous order containing aquatic forms. In this group the metamorphosis is gradual, and the series of immature forms (nymphs) resemble the adults somewhat except in size, body proportions, and wing development. Many species of Hemiptera occur below the surface in both the nymphal and adult stages; others move about on the surface film.

The Ephemeroptera (mayflies), Odonata (dragonflies and damselflies), and Plecoptera (stoneflies) are hemimetabolous insects. The adults are terrestrial, but there is a series of aquatic nymphs (naiads) which usually possess accessory gills.

The other six orders are holometabolous, the stages in development being egg, active larva, quiescent pupa, and adult. A very few Neuroptera (lacewings) and Lepidoptera (moths and butterflies), many Coleoptera (beetles) and Diptera (true flies), and all Megaloptera and Trichoptera (caddis flies) have aquatic larvae. All Trichoptera and many Diptera have aquatic pupae. A very few Hymenoptera, not considered in this volume, are egg parasites which enter the water only long enough to find and oviposit on the eggs of their aquatic victims.

The major problem in becoming adapted to an aquatic environment seems to be centered around the respiratory mechanisms of insects. The air-filled tracheal system is, of course, capable of functioning only when the spiracles are in contact with air, and it is significant that in Hemiptera and Coleoptera, the only orders having aquatic adults, the tracheal system is essentially unmodified. Some adult beetles and nymphal and adult bugs come to the surface at intervals where the spiracles are placed in contact with the

Fig. 303.—Immature aquatic insects. A, dytiscid beetle pupae, ×1.7; B, pupae of the dobson fly, *Corydalus cornutus* L., ×1; C, larva of the caddis fly, *Phryganea*, ×1; D, larva of the caddis fly, *Hydropsyche*, ×1; E, larva of the dobson fly, ×1; F, larva of the midge, *Tendipes*, ×1; G, rat-tailed maggot larva, *Tubifera tenax* (L), ×1; H, larva of the horse fly, *Tabanus*, ×1; J, larva of the crane fly, *Tipula*, ×1; K, predaceous diving beetle larva, *Dytiscus*, ×0.8.

air, and the supply in the tracheal system is renewed.

The occurrence of bubble-like "air stores" under the wings or on various parts of the body is common among adult aquatic hemipterans and beetles. Such air stores invariably are in direct contact with certain of the spiracles. The air and water interface of an air store acts as a diffusion membrane or gill, with oxygen entering and carbon dioxide diffusing outward into the water. Carbon dioxide never accumulates in such air stores because of its high solubility in water. However, such air bubbles get smaller the longer the insect remains submerged, chiefly because of the diffusion of nitrogen outward, and it is therefore necessary for the insect to come to the surface periodically to renew the bubble. The renewal interval is highly variable. Sometimes it is only a minute or two, sometimes as long as several hours, depending on temperature, the amount of oxygen in the water, the particular species involved, and presumably certain physiological variables.

Although similar in function, a plastron differs from an ordinary air store in several

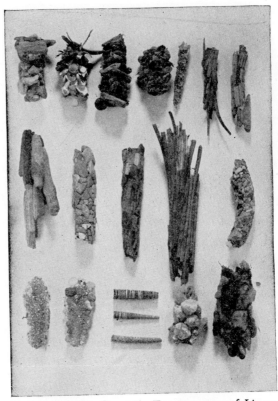

FIG. 304.—Cases of immature caddis flies, ×1. Top row, cases of *Limnephilus* larvae; second row, cases of larvae: *Pycnopsyche, Pycnopsyche, Phryganea, Phryganea, Glyphopsyche*; bottom row: two larval cases of *Molanna*, three larval cases of *Brachycentrus*, two pupal cases of *Hydropsyche*.

ways. The former is a very thin layer of air in direct contact with large portions of the body surface in certain small aquatic hemipterans and beetles, especially those species that habitually creep about on submerged substrates. The film of air is held in place by "pile," which is an extremely thick growth of fine short hairs. Sometimes there may be more than 2,000,000 such hairs per square millimeter of body surface. Pile hairs are curved at the tip and resist the tendency of water to compress and invade the air space, up to a water pressure of four or five atmospheres. The volume of the air film therefore remains essentially constant, and pile-bearing insects are capable of remaining submerged indefinitely, especially if the water is more than 80 per cent saturated

with air. In addition to the uptake of oxygen via the spiracles, it has been shown that some oxygen diffuses from the plastron through the cuticle to the internal tissues.

Bubbles of oxygen emitted by aquatic plants and air bubbles in turbulent waters presumably fuse incidentally with air stores and plastrons and thus aid in their maintenance.

In some immature forms, particularly beetle and fly larvae, the aerial mode of respiration has been retained, and functional spiracles persist, usually at the posterior end of the body. From an evolutionary standpoint, however, most larvae have shown more plasticity. They have no spiracles, and most of the oxygen absorption occurs from the water itself through the specialized or unspecialized body surface. Thus they are independent of aerial respiration. Most nymphs of the hemimetabolous orders and larvae of the holometabolous orders have tracheal gills of very diverse location and structure. Fundamentally, however, such gills are simply thin-walled projections from the body containing tracheae.

The occurrence of blood gills among immature insects presents some interesting questions. Strictly speaking, a blood gill is a small, thin-walled projection from the body which is devoid of tracheation but

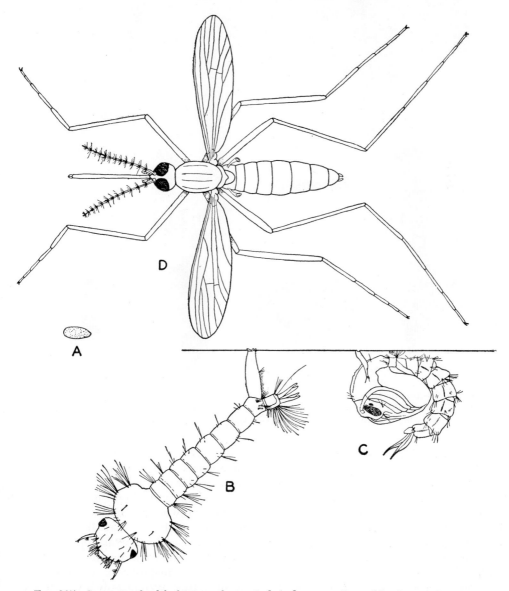

Fig. 305.—Stages in the life history of a typical *Aedes* mosquito, ×10. A, egg; B, mature larva with respiratory opening at surface film; C, pupa with respiratory opening at surface film; D, adult female (setation omitted).

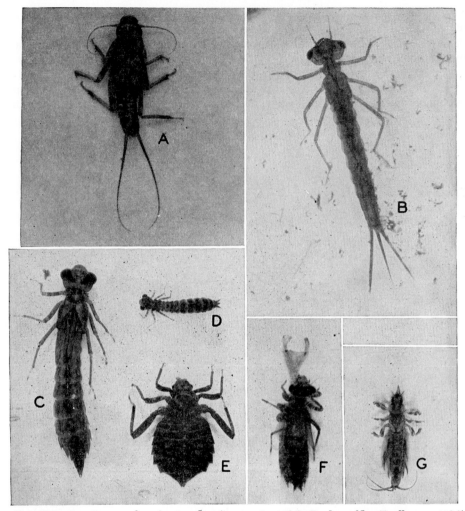

FIG. 306.—Aquatic nymphs. A, stonefly, *Acroneuria,* ×1.3; B, damselfly, *Enallagma,* ×3.5; C to F, dragonflies; C, *Anax,* ×1; D, *Boyeria,* ×1; E, *Hagenius brevistylus* Selys, ×1; F, *Libellula,* showing extended labium, ×1.6; G, mayfly, *Hexagenia,* ×1.

contains circulating blood and supposedly functions efficiently in oxygen absorption. Such structures occur in the larvae of some Diptera, Coleoptera, and Lepidoptera. Recent investigations, however, seem to indicate that blood gills are probably of more importance as devices for maintaining the appropriate osmotic relationships within the animal.

There is an increasing tendency among insect physiologists to ascribe considerable respiratory significance to the general body surface in immature aquatic hemimetabolous and holometabolous insects. Compared with adults, the cuticle is relatively thin, and there is often a rich tracheal network just under it. In addition, it seems probable that the blood just below the cuticle may take up appreciable quantities of oxygen directly.

The vast majority of aquatic insects occur in fresh waters, only a very few species having invaded marine and brackish waters. They have become adapted to nearly all types of fresh-water habitats, from the smallest brooks to mountain torrents and sluggish rivers, and from puddles to the largest lakes. With few excep-

tions, aquatic insects are found near shores, in the shallows, and where there is an adequate supply of oxygen. Only a few Diptera are consistently found in deep

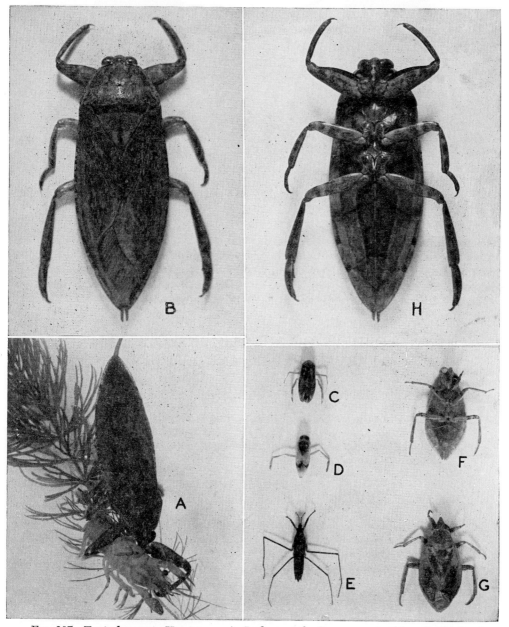

FIG. 307.—Typical aquatic Hemiptera. A, *Lethocerus* feeding on a crayfish, ×1; B, dorsal view of *Lethocerus*, ×1.4; C, *Sigara*, ×1; D, *Notonecta*, ×1; E, *Gerris*, ×1; F, *Belostoma*, ventral, ×1; G, *Belostoma*, dorsal, ×1; H, ventral view of *Lethocerus*, ×1.4.

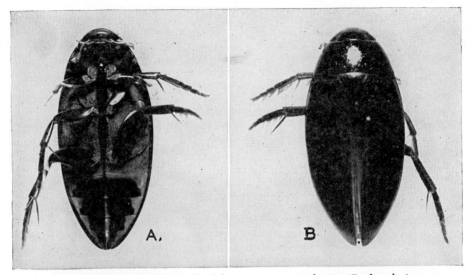

Fig. 308.—Large aquatic beetle, *Hydrophilus*, ×2. A, ventral view; B, dorsal view.

lakes and in waters containing a reduced supply of oxygen. The free-swimming plankton habit has been evolved only in some of the midge larvae.

The key below is admittedly an artificial one. An effort has been made, however, to utilize the most obvious characteristics for the determination of the various orders. Each order is dealt with individually on subsequent pages.

## KEY TO ORDERS OF AQUATIC INSECTS; NYMPHS, LARVAE, PUPAE, AND ADULTS

1. Usually inactive; pupae.................................................2
   Active; nymphs, larvae, and adults....................................4
2. Maggot-like, but the body shorter, hard, and dark-colored.
                         Pupae of **DIPTERA** (flies), p. 628
   Mummy-like, with the future adult appendages more or less concealed in translucent cases and held close to the body in a fixed position................3
3. Within a case composed of bits of vegetation or mineral matter.
                         Pupae of **TRICHOPTERA** (caddis flies), p. 565
   Without a case, but sometimes in a silken tube or fibrous cocoon.
                         Pupae of **DIPTERA** (flies), p. 628
4.. Without jointed thoracic legs; maggot-like....Larvae of **DIPTERA** (flies), p. 628
   Jointed thoracic legs present.....................................5
5. With long, segmented, filamentous appendages at the posterior end............6
   Posterior filamentous appendages absent, or, if present, then not long and segmented. .......................................................7
6. With two posterior filamentous appendages; two tarsal claws; usually with finger-like tracheal gills on ventral side of thorax.
                         Nymphs of **PLECOPTERA** (stoneflies), p. 500
   Usually with three, sometimes two, filamentous posterior appendages; one tarsal claw; with tracheal gills on lateral margins of abdominal segments.
                         Nymphs of **EPHEMEROPTERA** (mayflies), p. 509

7. With large hard or leathery forewings covering the abdomen; biting mouth parts.
    Adult **COLEOPTERA** (beetles), p. 588
    Wings, if present, of another structure. . . . . . . . . . . . . . . . . . . . . . . . . . . . . . . . . . . . . . . **8**
8. Small insects, usually less than 3 mm. long; wingless; with a long forked appendage
    beneath the abdomen used in springing; on the surface of quiet waters.
    Immature and adult **COLLEMBOLA** (springtails), p. 497
    Usually more than 3 mm. long; wings present or absent; no abdominal appendage
    for springing; usually submerged. . . . . . . . . . . . . . . . . . . . . . . . . . . . . . . . . . . . . **9**
9. With wing rudiments (pads) or functional wings; nymphs and adults. . . . . . . . .**10**
    Without wing rudiments or functional wings; larvae. . . . . . . . . . . . . . . . . . . . . . .**11**
10. Sucking mouth parts in the form of a long jointed beak.
    Nymphs and adults of **HEMIPTERA** (bugs), p. 541
    Chewing mouth parts; labium, when extended, long and scooplike, and when folded
    serving as a mask covering the other mouth parts; with or without platelike
    caudal gills. . . . .Nymphs of **ODONATA** (dragonflies and damselflies), p. 522
11. With slender, decurved, piercing and sucking mouth parts about half as long as the
    body; small larvae living in or on sponges.
    **NEUROPTERA** (spongilla fly larvae), p. 563
    With biting mouth parts. . . . . . . . . . . . . . . . . . . . . . . . . . . . . . . . . . . . . . . . . . . .**12**
12. With five pairs of abdominal prolegs.
    **LEPIDOPTERA** (aquatic caterpillars), p. 585
    Prolegs absent, or confined to the last abdominal segment. . . . . . . . . . . . . . . . . .**13**
13. Each abdominal segment with one pair of stout lateral processes.
    **MEGALOPTERA** (hellgrammites, alderfly and fishfly larvae), p. 560
    No stout lateral abdominal processes, but sometimes with long, thin, lateral fila-
    mentous processes; a few beetle larvae with four stout hornlike processes on
    each body segment. . . . . . . . . . . . . . . . . . . . . . . . . . . . . . . . . . . . . . . . . . . . . . .**14**
14. With a pair of terminal abdominal prolegs; usually with small, finger-like, abdomi-
    nal tracheal gills; usually in fixed or portable cases.
    **TRICHOPTERA** (caddis fly larvae), p. 565
    Without terminal prolegs; rarely with long, thin, filamentous, abdominal tracheal
    gills; without cases. . . . . . . . . . . . . . . .**COLEOPTERA** (beetle larvae), p. 588

# INSECTA, GENERAL REFERENCES

ALEXANDER, C. P. 1925. An entomological survey of the Salt Fork of the Vermilion River
in 1921, with a bibliography of aquatic insects.
*Bull. Ill. Nat. Hist. Surv.* 15:439–535.

BALDUF, W. V. 1939. *The bionomics of ento-
mophagous insects. Part II.* 384 pp. St. Louis.
(Trichoptera, Megaloptera, and Neuroptera
only.)

BRUES, C. T. 1932. Further studies on the fauna
of North American hot springs. *Proc. Amer.
Acad. Arts and Sci.* 67:185–303.

BRUES, C. T., and A. L. MELANDER. 1932.
Classification of insects. *Bull. Mus. Comp.
Zool.* 73:1–672.

COLE, A. C. 1942. Collecting and preserving
immature insects. *Jour. Tenn. Acad. Sci.*
17:166–172.

ESSIG, E. O. 1942. *College entomology.* 900 pp.
New York.

HAYES, W. P. 1941. Some recent works on the

classification of immature insects. *Jour. Kan.
Ent. Soc.* 14:3–11.

IMMS, A. D. 1934. *A general textbook of entomology.* 3d ed. 727 pp. New York.

KARNY, H. H. 1934. *Biologie der Wasserinsek-
ten.* 311 pp. Vienna.

MIALL, L. C. 1895. *The natural history of
aquatic insects.* 395 pp. New York.

MUTTKOWSKI, R. A. 1918. The fauna of Lake
Mendota—a qualitative and quantitative survey
with special reference to insects.
*Trans. Wis. Acad. Sci., Arts and Lett.* 19:374–
482.

———. 1920. The respiration of aquatic insects.
*Bull. Brooklyn Ent. Soc.* 15:89–96.

NEEDHAM, J. G., and C. BETTEN. 1901. Aquatic
insects in the Adirondacks. *Bull. N. Y. State
Mus.* 47:382–612.

NEEDHAM, J. G., A. D. MacGILLIVRAY, A. O.
JOHANNSEN, and K. C. DAVIS. 1903. Aquatic

insects in New York State. *Ibid.* **68**:199–517. (Odonata, Diptera, Coleoptera, and Megaloptera only.)

PETERSON, A. 1939. Keys to the orders of immature stages (exclusive of eggs and pronymphs) of North American insects. *Ann. Ent. Soc. Amer.* **32**:267–278.

PORTIER, P. 1911. Recherches physiologiques sur les insects aquatiques. *Arch. Zool. exp. et gén.,* Ser. 5, **8**:89–379.

ROUSSEAU, E. 1921. *Les larves et nymphes aquatiques des insectes d'Europe (morphologie biologie, systematique).* Vol. I. 967 pp. Brussels. (Hemiptera, Odonata, Ephemeroptera, Plecoptera, Megaloptera, and Neuroptera only.)

THORPE, W. H. 1950. Plastron respiration in aquatic insects. *Biol. Rev.* **25**:344–390.

USINGER, R. L., *et al.* 1948. *Biology of aquatic and littoral insects.* 244 pp. (mimeographed). Univ. of California Press, Berkeley and Los Angeles.

WESENBERG-LUND, C. 1943. *Biologie der Süsswasserinsekten.* 682 pp. Copenhagen, Denmark.

WIGGLESWORTH, V. B. 1931. The respiration of insects. *Biol. Rev.* **6**:181–220.

———. 1939. *The principles of insect physiology.* 434 pp. New York.

# Chapter 25

# COLLEMBOLA (SPRINGTAILS)

STRICTLY speaking, none of the Collembola are aquatic since the few species associated with water remain suspended on the surface film and submerge only accidentally. They are small to minute, grotesque insects with primitive metamorphosis. Coloration ranges from whitish and bright metallic hues to drab grayish or blackish. The mouth parts are largely hidden and overgrown by the genae; usually they are adapted for biting, but in some species they are drawn out into stylets enclosed in a cone. The eyes are composed of no more than eight ocelli. There are no wings. The abdomen consists of only six segments and these are sometimes indistinctly separated from each other. The first abdominal segment has a curious ventral tubule which is presumably used for anchorage. The most characteristic abdominal structure is the furcula; it consists of a pair of springlike partially fused appendages attached to the ventral side of the fourth abdominal segment. On the ventral side of the third segment is a catchlike spring holder. When the furcula is released from the holder and suddenly moved downward and backward, the animal is thrown into the air, sometimes as high as several inches.

All springtails occur in damp surroundings, and the great majority are found in such places as moss, humus, fallen trees, litter of the forest floor, and lake beaches. On the surface of marshes, pools, and the quiet backwaters of lakes and ponds, however, springtails may be found on the surface film in blackish patches composed of thousands of individuals. If disturbed, they leap into the air like flying spray, scattering in all directions and coming down a foot or more away. In many aquatic species the two mucrones at the end of the furcula are broadly spoon-shaped and lamellate at the edges and thus exert more force on the water during leaping. The small size and water-repellent body surface prevent collembolans from breaking through the surface film.

Aquatic collembolans are most common in the early spring or late autumn, but some may be found throughout the year and even in the middle of the winter. Miall believes that they may hibernate on the bottom, although other investigators doubt this. They feed chiefly on algae, other plant tissues, and vegetable debris of all kinds, but occasionally they are found feeding on dead worms, mollusks, and crustaceans.

Usually where springtails occur on the water they may be found in even greater abundance in the debris and vegetation on the adjacent shore. *Podura aquatica* L. and *Sminthurides* are the forms most commonly found on the water. The other species indicated in the key below, as well as a few additional rare forms, are encountered on water less frequently by the casual collector.

Although published records indicate a spotty distribution, it is probable that the common species occur all over the United States. Collembola may be collected with

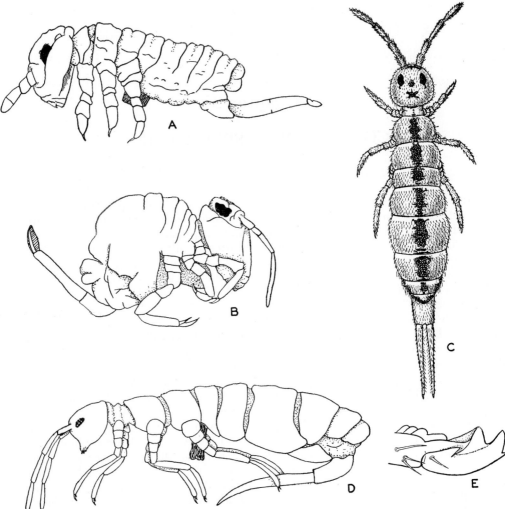

FIG. 309.—Aquatic and semiaquatic Collembola. A, *Podura aquatica* L., ×55; B, *Sminthurides aquaticus* (Bour.), ×75; C and D, *Isotomurus palustris* (Müller), ×40; E, mucro of furcula of same. (A modified from Willem, 1911; C and E from Folsom, 1937; D modified from Miall.)

a glass sucking tube, Berlese funnel, or pipette, and transported alive in small vials containing moist earth or filter paper. Hot 95 per cent alcohol is a suitable fixative, and 80 per cent alcohol is a satisfactory preservative. Specimens may be mounted in glycerin or glycerin jelly, but clearing in creosote and mounting in euparal is also a good procedure. For distinguishing minute details it is best to clear in 5 per cent potassium hydroxide before mounting.

# KEY TO COMMON AQUATIC AND SEMIAQUATIC COLLEMBOLA

1. Body elongated; thorax and abdomen distinctly segmented.
   Suborder **ARTHROPLEONA, 3**
   Body somewhat globular; thorax and abdomen indistinctly segmented (Fig. 309B).
   Suborder **SYMPHYPLEONA**, SMINTHURIDAE, 2
2. Ventral tube without tubercles; 0.5 to 1.0 mm. long (Fig. 309B); several aquatic and semiaquatic species.........................................**Sminthurides**
   Ventral tube with tubercles; up to 2.2 mm. long; olive, yellow, purple, or brown color.................................**Bourletiella spinata** (MacG.)
3. Pronotum well developed, with bristles (Fig. 309A); cuticle granular.
   PODURIDAE, 4
   Pronotum poorly developed, naked (Fig. 309C); cuticle smooth..ISOTOMIDAE, 5
4. Furcula long, extending beyond the ventral tube when projecting forward (Fig. 309A); 1.0 to 1.5 mm. long; reddish-brown to bluish-black..**Podura aquatica** L.
   Furcula shorter, not extending beyond the ventral tube when projecting forward; 1.2 to 1.8 mm. long; coloration bluish or greenish gray; several semiaquatic species.
   **Hypogastrura**
5. Body without sensory hairs; 2 to 7 mm. long; coloration variable; several semi-aquatic species..................................................**Isotoma**
   Body with fine sensory hairs arising from cuplike pits in the integument; 1.5 to 2.7 mm. long (Figs. 309C, D); coloration yellowish or greenish, with blue, purple, or blackish markings.....................**Isotomurus palustris** (Müller)

# COLLEMBOLA REFERENCES

BACON, G. A. 1914. The distribution of Collembola in the Claremont-Laguna region of California. *Jour. Ent. and Zool.* 6:137–179.

BRITT, N. W. 1951. Observations on the life history of the collembolan Achorutes armatus. *Trans. Amer. Micros. Soc.* 70:119–132.

FOLSOM, J. W. 1916. North American collembolous insects of the subfamilies Achorutinae, Neanurinae, and Podurinae. *Proc. U. S. Nat. Mus.* 50:477–525.

———. 1937. Nearctic Collembola or springtails, of the family Isotomidae. *Bull. U. S. Nat. Mus.* 168:1–144.

FOLSOM, J. W., and H. B. MILLS. 1938. Contribution to the knowledge of the genus Sminthurides Börner. *Bull. Mus. Comp. Zool.* 82:229–274.

GUTHRIE, J. E. 1903. The Collembola of Minnesota. *Rept. Geol. Nat. Hist. Surv. Minn., Zool. Ser.* 4:1–110.

JAMES, D. G. 1933. Collembola of the Toronto region with notes on the biology of Isotoma palustris Mueller. *Trans. Roy. Canad. Inst.* 19:77–116.

MAYNARD, E. A. 1951. *A monograph of the Collembola or springtail insects of New York State.* 339 pp. Ithaca, N. Y.

MILLS, H. B. 1934. A monograph of the Collembola of Iowa. *Monogr. Iowa State Coll.* 3:1–143.

MILLS, H. B., and A. R. ROLFS. 1933. Collembola from the state of Washington. *Pan-Pacific Ent.* 9:77–83.

# Chapter 26

# PLECOPTERA (STONEFLIES)

STONEFLIES are terrestrial insects, but they are seldom found very far from running water, the habitat of the immature stages. The adults are somber-colored, elongated, somewhat flattened, medium to large, and decidedly primitive in structure. At the posterior end there are two cerci; in the North American forms these are usually long and composed of many segments. The legs are well developed. The two pairs of long wings are folded over the back when at rest. In some genera the wings are reduced or rudimentary, especially in the males, and different individuals within the same species may show considerable variation in the degree of wing development. The broad head bears long filiform antennae. Although the mouth parts are of the biting type, they are rather weak, and in some cases the mandibles are reduced, especially in the more northern forms.

Stoneflies have a world-wide distribution, and North America has an especially rich fauna. In mountainous areas of the western states many species are found in rather definite altitudinal zones. They are poor fliers and are usually found resting on objects along the shores of streams or rocky, wave-swept shoals of lakes. Some species are decidedly nocturnal in their activities. In temperate climates the great majority of adults are found between November and August. Some species of Nemouridae are unique in the insect world in that they emerge during the late fall and winter. It is striking to see them moving about on snow or ice in the sunshine of midwinter days. Each species is rather definite in the time of its appearance in the adult stage. As such, they probably do not live more than several weeks.

Oviposition habits vary considerably. Some females drop masses of eggs while flying above the surface of the water; others alight at the surface momentarily and release the eggs; a few have been seen depositing on objects immediately above the surface or actually crawling about beneath the surface.

The nymphs are all strictly aquatic, and, as a group, are remarkably homogeneous in structure. They resemble the adults but may be distinguished from them by the structure of the mouth parts, lack of genitalia, and often by the presence of filamentous tracheal gills, and wing pads instead of wings. The length of mature nymphs, exclusive of antennae and cerci, ranges from about 6 to 50 mm. Coloration is yellow, tan, brown, or blackish. Some of the nymphs, such as *Isoperla* and *Acroneuria*, are brilliantly decorated with contrasting yellow and black areas on the dorsal surface. Others are quite dull and inconspicuous.

For the most part, stonefly nymphs are sluggish. They occur in debris, masses of leaves and algae, and under stones in every kind of lotic environment. A few species occur on the wave-swept shoals of lakes. In general, they are found only where there is an abundance of oxygen.

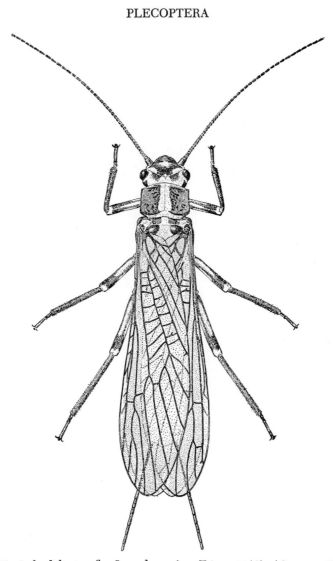

Fig. 310.—Typical adult stonefly, *Isoperla confusa* Frison, ×4.5. (Courtesy Illinois Natural History Survey.)

Many species are quite specific in their ecological preferences. Some occur only in small brooks; others, especially the largest forms, occur in the larger rivers. Some are found only where the current is swiftest, others in pools. The nymphs may be collected by hand-picking on the undersides of stones or by sorting over masses of debris and dead leaves in a large shallow pan. If the former method is used, it is wise to place a net or piece of screening downstream in order to catch individuals floating away in the current. Eighty per cent alcohol is the best preservative. Pinned specimens are of limited value.

The Perlidae, Perlodidae, and some Chloroperlidae are carnivorous and feed on other aquatic insects including mayfly nymphs and Diptera larvae. The other forms feed on algae and vegetable debris.

The great majority of large nymphs possess filamentous tracheal gills. These cus-

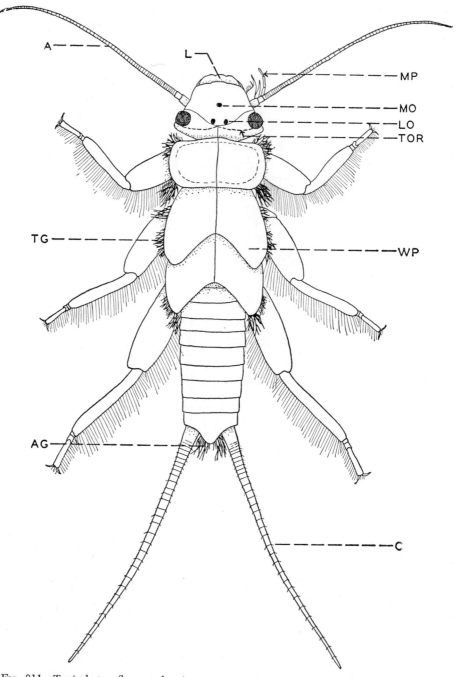

FIG. 311.—Typical stonefly nymph. *A*, antenna; *AG*, anal gills; *C*, cercus; *L*, labrum; *LO*, lateral ocellus; *MO*, median ocellus; *MP*, maxillary palp; *TG*, thoracic gills; *TOR*, transverse occipital ridge; *WP*, wing pad. (Modified from Frison, 1935.)

tomarily occur in tufts and are most abundant on the lateral and ventral surfaces of the thorax, but may also be on the coxae, submentum, and first few abdominal segments. Many species have very delicate, retractile, branched anal "gills." In those without gills the respiratory exchange occurs through the general body surface. It is probable that some cutaneous respiration occurs in the gilled forms also.

Relatively little accurate information is available concerning the number of instars and the duration of nymphal stages. In the few species that have been carefully studied the number of instars ranges from 12 to 36. Under natural conditions the great majority of species are thought to spend from one to three years as nymphs.

Just before emergence the nymphs crawl out of the water onto stones, brush, or debris. A dorsal split appears in the exoskeleton, and the adult makes its way out. After a short wait while the wings and body structures harden and dry they fly or crawl away. As indicated above, most species emerge during the fall, winter, and spring. Sometimes cast skins may be found by the hundreds along the edges of streams.

Nymphs may be artificially reared to the adult stage by keeping them in wire cages in a stream, provided they are supplied with the appropriate debris and food. The

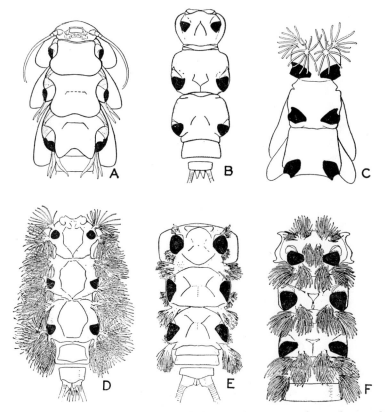

FIG. 312.—Ventral views of thorax and several abdominal segments of stonefly nymphs showing arrangements and types of gills. Black spots indicate leg attachments. A, *Peltoperla*; B, *Isoperla*; C, *Nemoura*; D, *Perlinella*; E, *Acroneuria*; F, *Pteronarcys*. (Courtesy Ill. Nat. Hist. Surv.)

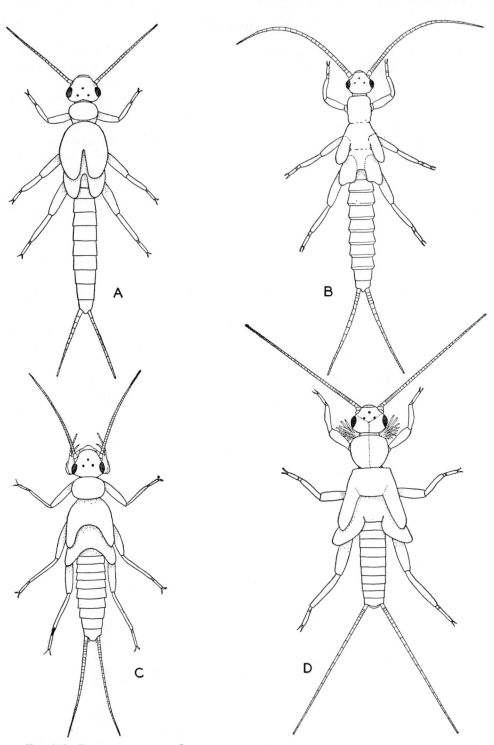

FIG. 313.—Representative stonefly nymphs. A, *Hastaperla brevis* (Banks), ×12; B, *Allocapnia vivipara* (Claassen), ×8.5; C, *Isogenus modesta* (Banks), ×3.3; D, *Nemoura venosa* Banks, ×9. (A, B, and D modified from Frison, 1935; C modified from Frison, 1942.)

cages should project above the surface of the water so that emergence may occur. When kept in ordinary aquaria in the laboratory they die very shortly, presumably because of a lack of oxygen. Under such conditions they exhibit curious rhythmic up-and-down movements of the bodies. If aquaria are supplied with aerators and kept at suitable temperatures, however, many species may be successfully reared indoors.

Numerous investigations of the food habits of stream fishes, especially trout, have shown that stonefly nymphs form an important portion of the diet.

Authorities are by no means agreed on the taxonomy of this order, even with respect to certain family designations. This situation is undoubtedly largely due to a general neglect of the stoneflies by entomologists. Recently, however, much progress has been made, chiefly through the efforts of W. E. Ricker and the late T. H. Frison. The generic and family relationships indicated in Table VIII follow Ricker's (1950) arrangement. There are over 250 species known as adults from North America, and less than half of these are definitely known in the immature stages. Most of the genera found in the United States are quite small, some being monotypic. Relatively few species in each genus are known in the immature stages. Indeed, the nymphs of several genera are rare or unknown, and Table VIII includes several genera that have not yet been reported from the United States, but are known in Canada. Only in *Isogenus, Isoperla,* and *Acroneuria* are more than ten species known in the immature stages.

Formerly many American species were placed in the genus *Perla.* Recently, however, many of these species have been shown to belong to other genera. Moreover, as indicated by Frison (1942), *Perla,* if valid at all, is strictly a European genus. American species which were formerly placed in *Perla* are now included in *Isogenus, Claassenia, Paragnetina, Neophasganophora, Isoperla,* and *Acroneuria.*

TABLE VIII. CLASSIFICATION OF THE PLECOPTERA OF NORTH AMERICA.

Genera encountered most commonly in the United States are indicated by asterisks.

---

Pteronarcidae— *Pteronarcella*
  *Pteronarcys*

Peltoperlidae—*Peltoperla*

Nemouridae
  Taeniopteryginae— *Brachyptera*
    *Taeniopteryx*
  Nemourinae—*Nemoura*
  Leuctrinae— *Leuctra*
    *Megaleuctra*
    *Perlomyia*
  Capniinae— *Allocapnia*
    *Capnia*
    *Eucapnopsis*
    *Isocapnia*
    *Nemocapnia*

Perlidae
  Perlinae— *Neoperla*
    *Neophasganophora*
  Acroneuriinae— *Acroneuria*
    *Atoperla*
    *Claassenia*
    *Paragnetina*
    *Perlesta*
    *Perlinella*

Perlodidae
  Perlodinae— *Dictyopterygella*
  Isoperlinae— *Isoperla*
  Isogeninae— *Arcynopteryx*
    *Isogenus*

Chloroperlidae
  Chloroperlinae— *Alloperla*
    *Chloroperla*
    *Hastaperla*
  Paraperlinae— *Kathroperla*
    *Paraperla*

---

The key which follows has been greatly modified from keys published by Frison (1935, 1942). The approximate size of mature nymphs, exclusive of antennae and cerci, as well as the general geographic distribution in the United States, are included. This key leaves much to be desired, but on the basis of our incomplete knowledge of the nymphs in certain genera it is the best that can be devised.

# KEY TO FAMILIES AND GENERA OF PLECOPTERA NYMPHS

1. Gills present on the ventral surface of some of the basal abdominal segments (Fig. 312F)..................................................PTERONARCIDAE, 11
   Without abdominal gills.................................................................2
2. Ventral surface of thorax covered by large, overlapping, shieldlike plates (Fig. 312A); flat, broad, and roachlike; less than 10 mm. long; widely distributed.
   PELTOPERLIDAE, **Peltoperla**
   Ventral surface of thorax without overlapping, shieldlike plates...............3
3. Labium with paraglossae and glossae extending forward about the same distance (Fig. 314E).....................................................NEMOURIDAE, 4
   Labium with paraglossae extending forward much farther than the glossae (Figs. 314F, G)............................................................................7
4. Second tarsal segment as long as or longer than the first (Fig. 314A); widely distributed.......................................................TAENIOPTERYGINAE, 12
   Second tarsal segment shorter than the first.....................................5
5. Small and robust nymphs, less than 10 mm. long; hairy; hind wing pads extending out from the body at an angle; ventral cervical gills present or absent; widely distributed.......................................................NEMOURINAE, **Nemoura**
   Small and slender nymphs; hairs few, fine, or lacking; hind wing pads approximately longitudinal; no cervical gills............................................6
6. Lateral margins of abdominal segments somewhat rounded; segments widest at posterior margin; wing pads present, rudimentary, or absent....CAPNIINAE, 13
   Lateral margins of abdominal segments almost straight; abdomen appearing more cylindrical; wing pads always present; 10 mm. or less long; widely distributed....................................................................LEUCTRINAE, **Leuctra**
7. Branched filamentous gills on lateral and ventral surfaces of thorax (Figs. 312D, E).
   PERLIDAE, 18
   Without branched filamentous gills on lateral and ventral surfaces of thorax......8
8. With a small, membranous, finger-like gill located near each side of the outer base of the submentum (Fig. 314G); 14 to 23 mm. long.
   PERLODIDAE, ISOGENINAE, 30
   Without such gills on the submentum..............................................9
9. Lateral margins of forewing pads approximately straight; tip of lacinia with one or more teeth; diameter of fourth segment of maxillary palp not much greater than base of fifth segment...........................................PERLODIDAE, 10
   Lateral margins of forewing pads rounded (Fig. 313A); tip of lacinia never with more than one tooth; diameter of fourth segment of maxillary palp often much greater than base of fifth segment...............CHLOROPERLIDAE, 26
10. Maxillae bulging out from sides of head in a conspicuous manner (Fig. 313C); diameter of lacinia tapering rapidly and forming a long single claw or a long claw plus a secondary one; 14 to 23 mm. long...................................29
    Maxillae not or but slightly bulging out from sides of head; lacinia more robust and with smaller tooth or teeth at apex (Fig. 314H); 10 to 14 mm. long; widely distributed and common............PERLODIDAE, ISOPERLINAE, **Isoperla**
11. With gills on third abdominal segment; less than 25 mm. long; western.
    **Pteronarcella**
    Without gills on third abdominal segment; 35 to 50 mm. long; generally distributed. .............................................................**Pteronarcys**
12. With coxal gills (Fig. 314A)....................................**Taeniopteryx**
    Without coxal gills..............................................**Brachyptera**
13. Wing pads rudimentary or absent.....................................17
    Wing pads well developed............................................14

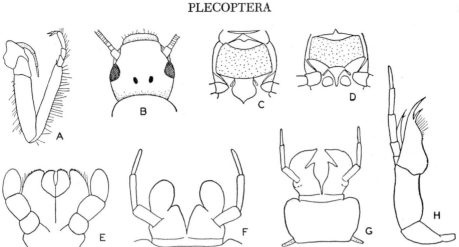

Fig. 314.—Taxonomic characters of stonefly nymphs. A, hind leg of *Taeniopteryx nivalis* (Fitch) showing coxal gill; B, head of *Atoperla ephyre* (Newman); C, ventral view of portion of thorax of *Nemocapnia carolina* Banks showing median area of mesosternum (shaded); D, same for *Capnia*; E, ventral view of labium of *Taeniopteryx nivalis* showing similar length of glossae and paraglossae; F, ventral view of labium of *Perlesta placida* (Hagen) showing paraglossae extending farther forward than glossae; G, labium of *Isogenus frontalis* (Newman) showing gills at base of submentum; H, maxilla of *Isoperla holochlora* (Klap.). (A and F modified from Frison, 1935; E redrawn from Frison, 1935; C modified from Frison, 1942; G and H redrawn from Frison, 1942.)

14. Anal lobe of hind wing extending to about middle of wing length.............15
    Anal lobe of hind wing large and extending nearly to length of wing (Fig. 313B); widely distributed and common..........................**Allocapnia**
15. Mature nymph 15 mm. or more long; confined to the extreme northwestern states; rare. ...............................................**Isocapnia**
    Mature nymph usually less than 12 mm. long; widely distributed.............16
16. Posterior margin of second basisternal sclerite but slightly produced backward (Fig. 314C); rare; eastern......................**Nemocapnia carolina** Banks
    Posterior margin of second basisternal sclerite strongly produced backward (Fig. 314D); widely distributed and common........................**Capnia**
17. Confined to eastern and central states; common....................**Allocapnia**
    Mostly in the western states...............................**Capnia**
18. Compound eyes situated far forward on sides of head (Fig. 314B); widely distributed east of Rockies.............................Acroneuriinae, 19
    Compound eyes situated near posterior margin of head....................20
19. Anterior ocellus absent (Fig. 314B); less than 12 mm. long.
                                                    **Atoperla ephyre** (Newman)
    Anterior ocellus present; up to 22 mm. long.........**Perlinella drymo** (Newman)
20. Anterior ocellus absent; up to 13 mm. long; common and widely distributed.
                                            Perlinae, **Neoperla clymene** (Newman)
    Anterior ocellus present..................................................21
21. Dorsal surface of abdomen with conspicuous freckle-like spots; up to 10 mm. long; common and widely distributed..Acroneuriinae, **Perlesta placida** (Hagen)
    Dorsal surface of abdomen without freckle-like spots......................22
22. Transverse occipital ridge present (Fig. 311)............................23
    Transverse occipital ridge absent; 20 to 30 mm. long; common and widely distributed......................................Acroneuriinae, **Acroneuria**

23. Anal gills present (Fig. 311).........................................24
    Anal gills absent...................................ACRONEURIINAE, 25
24. With yellow mark between posterior ocelli; abdomen not yellow and black banded;
    up to 31 mm. long; uncommon; western.

ACRONEURIINAE, **Claassenia arctica** (Klap.)

    Without yellow mark between posterior ocelli; abdomen with conspicuous trans-
    verse yellow and black bands; up to 23 mm. long; common; eastern.

PERLINAE, **Neophasganophora capitata** (Pictet)

25. Dorsal surface of head and thorax uniformly light brown; from 20 to 30 mm. long;
    common and widely distributed.............................**Acroneuria**
    Dorsal surface of head and thorax with some light areas distinct from brown back-
    ground; up to 22 mm. long; common; eastern.................**Paragnetina**
26. Mostly confined to the states east of the Rockies; common....CHLOROPERLINAE, 27
    Confined to the western states; up to 18 mm. long; rare........PARAPERLINAE, 28
27. Mature nymph about 6 mm. long; two species, one of which is very common.

**Hastaperla brevis** (Banks)

    Mature nymph 7 to 13 mm. long.................................**Alloperla**
28. Head about as long as wide.....................**Paraperla frontalis** Banks
    Head longer than wide.........................**Kathroperla perdita** Banks
29. Rare; 20 mm. long; western......PERLODINAE, **Dictyopterygella knowltoni** Frison
    Common; 12 to 20 mm. long; widely distributed..........ISOGENINAE, **Isogenus**
30. With large, finger-like, tapered gills on lateral parts of thorax and abdominal seg-
    ments; rare; California.....................................**Arcynopteryx**
    Without such gills..............................................31
31. Without thoracic gills...........................................32
    With two or three pairs of thoracic gills; cervical gills present or absent; confined
    to the Rocky Mountain area...............................**Arcynopteryx**
32. Common; western and northern.................................**Isogenus**
    Uncommon; confined mostly to the Rocky Mountain area.........**Arcynopteryx**

## PLECOPTERA REFERENCES

CLAASSEN, P. W. 1928. Additions and corrections to the monograph on the Plecoptera of North America. *Ann. Ent. Soc. Amer.* 21:667–668.

———. 1931. Plecoptera nymphs of North America (north of Mexico). *Publ. Thomas Say Found.* 3:1–199.

———. 1940. A catalog of the Plecoptera of the world. *Cornell Univ. Agric. Exp. Sta. Mem.* 232:1–235.

FRISON, T. H. 1929. Fall and winter stoneflies, or Plecoptera, of Illinois. *Bull. Ill. Nat. Hist. Surv.* 18:343–409.

———. 1935. The stoneflies, or Plecoptera, of Illinois. *Ibid.* 20:281–371.

———. 1937. Studies of Nearctic aquatic insects. II. Descriptions of Plecoptera. *Ibid.* 21:78–98.

———. 1942. Studies of North American Plecoptera, with special reference to the fauna of Illinois. *Ibid.* 22:235–356.

HANSON, J. F. 1946. Comparative morphology and taxonomy of the Capniidae (Plecoptera). *Amer. Midl. Nat.* 35:193–249.

HARDEN, P. H. 1942. The immature stages of some Minnesota Plecoptera. *Ann. Ent. Soc. Amer.* 35:318–331.

HYNES, H. B. N. 1941. The taxonomy and ecology of the nymphs of British Plecoptera with notes on the adults and eggs. *Trans. Roy. Ent. Soc. London* 91:459–557.

NEEDHAM, J. G., and P. W. CLAASSEN. 1925. A monograph of the Plecoptera or stoneflies of America north of Mexico. *Publ. Thomas Say Found.* 2:1–397.

RICKER, W. E. 1943. Stoneflies of southwestern British Columbia. *Univ. Indiana Publ. Sci. Ser.* 12:1–145.

———. 1949. The North American species of Paragnetina. *Ann. Ent. Soc. Amer.* 42:279–288.

———. 1950. Some evolutionary trends in Plecoptera. *Proc. Indiana Acad. Sci.* 59:197–209.

WU, C. F. 1923. Morphology, anatomy and ethology of Nemoura. *Bull. Lloyd Library* 23:1–81.

# Chapter 27

# EPHEMEROPTERA (MAYFLIES)

THESE ARE small to medium-sized terrestrial insects with delicate, many-veined, transparent wings which are held together vertically when at rest. Sometimes the hind wings may be greatly reduced or lacking. The head bears inconspicuous antennae, large compound eyes, and vestigial mouth parts. No food is taken during the adult stage. The mesothorax is large, the legs are slender and weak, and at the posterior end of the abdomen there are two or three, long, segmented filaments.

Mayflies have a world-wide distribution but are found only in the vicinity of bodies of fresh water in which the immature stages are passed. Much of the time, and always when a wind is blowing, the adults remain clinging to vegetation, but on calm, sunny, spring and summer days or in the evening they take to the air in great hovering swarms. Such swarms are composed almost entirely of males. Each individual flies quickly upward in the swarm and then, spreading out the wings horizontally, it floats downward to the lower part of the swarm "like a bit of thistledown." These movements are repeated over and over. Females enter the swarm singly and emerge almost immediately accompanied by a male. Mating then occurs during flight. Many species are attracted to lights at night, and sometimes mayflies may be present in such tremendous numbers as to form dense clouds around lights, and in the morning their bodies may be found piled literally more than a foot deep on the ground below. Numerous newspaper accounts tell how the millions of dead mayflies make bridges and roads near lakes and streams so slippery as to stop traffic. Such accounts refer particularly to *Ephemera, Hexagenia,* and *Ephoron.* On the shores of large lakes their bodies may be washed up in windrows.

Oviposition habits vary considerably. The eggs may be washed off a few at a time as the female dips her abdomen into the water, or they may be released in large masses. In some species the female actually crawls below the surface and oviposits on submerged objects. The eggs, which are produced in great numbers, are usually oval, extremely small, and of a great variety of colors. They are commonly sculptured and viscid, and are sometimes imbedded in a gelatinous material. They often have some additional means of anchorage in the form of knobs or long coiled filaments which become entangled in the debris of the substrate. Depending on the species and water temperature, the eggs hatch in a few days to a few months. Some species of *Callibaetis* are known to be ovoviviparous.

Usually the fully developed aquatic nymph (naiad) merely comes to the surface when it is ready to transform, but in some cases it may crawl out of the water on rocks or emergent vegetation. The nymphal exoskeleton is shed in a few seconds or minutes. The winged insect which appears, however, is not the final adult but a unique "dun," or subimago, which differs

509

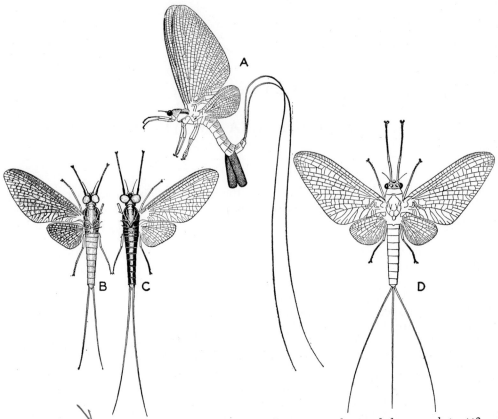

Fig. 315.—Adult mayflies. A, female *Ephoron album* Say with extruded egg packets, ×2; B, female subimago of *Isonychia sicca* (Walsh), ×2.5; C, adult female of *I. sicca*, ×2.5; D, *Potamanthus*, ×2.5. (From Needham, 1920.)

slightly from the imago, having a duller appearance and translucent wings. The subimago very soon flies upward and alights on vegetation where it remains quietly unless disturbed. Some subimagoes are active on warm summer nights. This stage may last only a few minutes, but in the more common species it persists for 24 hours or more. Then a very delicate exocuticle is cast from the whole body, including the wings, and the fully formed imago, or "spinner," is revealed. In this condition the wings are usually transparent and the body has a more shiny appearance. In general, the sexually mature adult is notably short-lived. Some species live only a few hours and others a

day to a week or more, especially if the weather is cool and moist.

In contrast to the uniform structure of the adults, the nymphs show considerable variations and adaptations to their specific habitats. Mature nymphs, however, are all characterized by an elongated body, large head, well-developed mandibulate mouthparts, stout legs, long filiform antennae, large compound eyes, and three rather prominent ocelli. Large, paired tracheal gills on the lateral or dorsal surface of most of the abdominal segments constitute the most characteristic feature and serve to distinguish mayfly nymphs from all other aquatic insects. At the tip of the abdomen are usually three, and sometimes two, long, segmented, fringed, caudal filaments. One or two pairs of wing pads are visible in the great majority of species, but in a few nymphs they are hidden by the pronotum. Coloration varies greatly; some forms are dull brown, gray, or blackish; others are pale, greenish, reddish, and variously marked. Many are protectively colored. Without the caudal filaments, the length range of mature nymphs is about 3 to 28 mm. In general, the burrowers are the larger species.

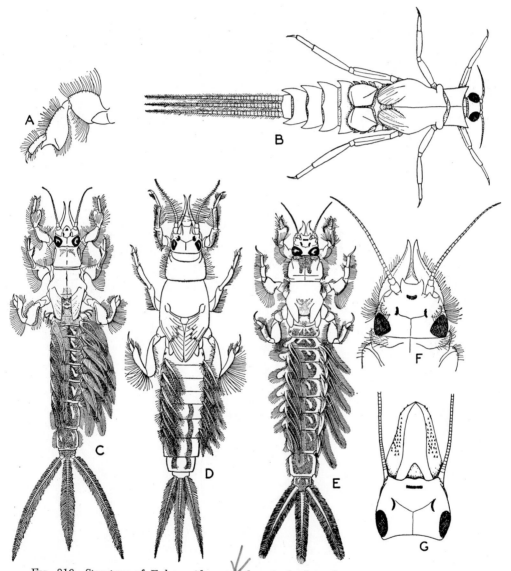

FIG. 316.—Structure of Ephemeridae nymphs. A, foreleg of *Hexagenia bilineata* Say; B, *Oreianthus purpureus* Traver, ×3.5; C, *Hexagenia bilineata*, ×2; D, *Ephemera varia* Eaton, ×4; E, *Pentagenia vittigera* Walsh, ×3; F, head of *P. vittigera*; G, head of *Ephoron*. (A and C to E from Needham, 1920; B modified from Traver, 1931; F modified from Needham, 1920; G modified from Ide, 1935.)

The tracheal gills show almost endless morphological variations (Fig. 317). Typically, they are leaflike and richly supplied with tracheae connecting with the main tracheal trunks of the abdomen. Most genera have gills on abdominal segments one to seven, but sometimes one or more pairs may be vestigial or absent. Internal muscles vibrate the gills in a rapid shuttle-like manner, either intermittently or for long periods. Undoubtedly the water currents thus set up ensure an adequate oxygen supply. The relative significance of gills and general body surface

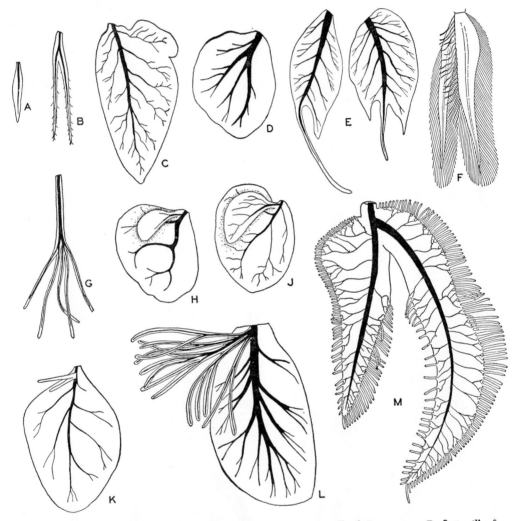

Fig. 317.—Tracheal gills of mayfly nymphs. A, seventh gill of *Stenonema*; B, first gill of *Blasturus*; C, third gill of *Callibaetis*; D, fourth gill of *Neocloeon alamance* Traver; E, third pair of gills of *Blasturus intermedius* Traver; F, second gill of *Hexagenia bilineata*; G, first gill of *Habrophlebia*; H, fourth gill of *Cloeon simplex* McD.; J, fourth gill of *Cloeon*; K, second gill of *Cinygmula*; L, second gill of *Cinygma*; M, fourth gill of *Ephoron*. (C and J redrawn from McDunnough, 1930; G modified from Needham, Traver, and Hsu by permission of the Comstock Publishing Co.; F from Needham, 1920; H modified from Ide, 1937; K and L redrawn from McDunnough, 1933; M modified from Ide, 1935.)

in respiration is still a matter of debate. Recent experimental evidence, however, indicates that a greater percentage of oxygen is absorbed through the general integument in the nonburrowers than in the burrowers. Gills are regenerated after being broken off.

Mayfly nymphs occur in all types of fresh waters, wherever there is an abundance of oxygen. Although they may be found as deep as 15 meters, they are most characteristic of the shallows. Those species inhabiting a particular lake, pond, or stream seem to be determined to a large extent by the specific nature of the substrate. Some occur only in vegetation; some only on mud, debris, gravel, or rock bottoms; some are found only between or under rocks; many burrow in mud or debris. Water movements are apparently a further significant ecological factor since many species are confined to quiet ponds and lakes, wave-swept shores, slow streams, rapid streams, or mountain torrents.

The three families of mayfly nymphs are somewhat distinctive in their habitats. Most of the Ephemeridae burrow in mud and debris; a few genera are sprawlers. The Baetidae clamber and sprawl on many kinds of substrates in both standing and running waters but do not burrow. The Heptageniidae are flattened sprawlers occurring mostly in streams. A more precise ecological classification, however, as suggested by Needham, Traver, and Hsu (1935), is given below:

A. Nymphs restricted to the quiet waters of ponds, lakes, and backwaters of streams.

   1. Climbers. These nymphs climb, dart, run, or jump about, usually in submerged vegetation. Their rapid locomotion is due to sudden strong movements of the caudal filaments and gills. Such nymphs are smooth-bodied, not especially streamlined, and have heavily fringed caudal filaments and platelike gills. Typi-cal genera are *Blasturus, Cloeon, Siphlonurus,* and *Callibaetis* (Fig. 319G).

   2. Bottom sprawlers. These nymphs crawl about slowly on all types of bottoms. They are stiff-legged, hairy, and covered with debris. The legs are spread out laterally, the body is more or less depressed, and the caudal filaments are thinly fringed. The first pair of gills are often differentiated into gill covers which overlap and protect the other gills from silt. Common genera are *Caenis, Ephemerella,* and *Potamanthus* (Figs. 318A, B; 319H).

   3. Burrowers. These are among the most interesting of all mayfly nymphs. Molelike, they literally plow their way through mud, muddy sand, or debris. The burrow has two openings and is constructed with the flattened front legs and undulations of the long abdomen. In addition, in most species there is a large tusklike projection from the outer side of each mandible (Fig. 316), and these are probably of some use in digging the burrow.* The plumose gills are dorsal in position and their movements maintain a constant current through the burrow which brings in oxygenated water and removes debris. It is also thought that the presence of the current prevents the collapse of the burrow. Usually burrowers are found in the top 5 centimeters of mud, but they have been observed as deep as 15 centimeters. Except for *Potamanthus,* all of the Ephemeridae are burrowers.

B. Nymphs in running waters and on wave-swept shores. Compound eyes dorsal.

--------

* It is interesting to note that a somewhat similar tusk has been developed in some species of *Paraleptophlebia* which are sprawlers rather than burrowers.

1. Free-ranging species of rapid waters. When at rest, these attractively colored nymphs maintain themselves in the current by clinging to pebbles, but they are able to move about in spite of the current with quick, minnow-like darts. Typical genera are *Isonychia*, *Ameletus*, *Paraleptophlebia*, and *Baetis* (Figs. 319E, F).

2. Clinging species. Unlike the foregoing, these nymphs move about slowly and deliberately. They cling tightly to stones and other objects and may be found in greatest abundance in crevices and on the undersides of stones. The body is very flat and broad anteriorly, and the legs are characteristically flattened. Common genera are *Iron*, *Stenonema*, *Heptagenia*, *Rhithrogena*, and *Ephemerella* (Figs. 318A, B; 320F, G). In *Iron*, *Ironopsis*, and *Rhithrogena* there is, in effect, a ventral sucker-like holdfast. This is composed of the gills which have thick spiny margins and which are laterally outspread on the substrate, the whole forming a kind of oval ring around the abdomen (Fig. 320E). In some species of *Ephemerella* the ventral surface of the abdominal segments is modified to form a sucker.

3. Species inhabiting trash, silt, and moss. These stream-inhabiting nymphs do not occur in swift currents. They are stiff-legged and spiny. Some species of *Ephemerella* and *Oreianthus* are typical representatives.

Mayfly nymphs are almost entirely herbivorous, although a few have been observed feeding on exuviae, the bodies of dead nymphs, and small invertebrates. In general, they browse on the substrate, feeding, with a grinding action of the mandibles, on algae or the tissues of higher aquatic plants. In *Isonychia* there are rows of long stiff bristles set at an angle on the anterior surface of the first legs. These constitute a sieve which strains small particles of food from the water.

The first nymphal stage which hatches from the egg is a minute creature usually less than a millimeter long and resembling similar stages of the Plecoptera and Zygoptera (Fig. 320A). In some species all of the gills appear in the second instar, but usually they appear one pair at a time or irregularly with successive molts. As growth proceeds there is an increase in the number of antennal segments and in the relative size of the compound eyes and wing pads. Just before emergence the body has a silvery appearance owing to gas between the nymphal integument and that of the developing subimago. Very few life histories are completely known. There are numerous nymphal ecdyses, with more than 40 having been recorded for one species. Unlike the adult, then, the nymphal stages constitute a relatively long period in the life history. Most species have an annual life cycle, although a few live two and possibly three years.

Species occurring in vegetation may be collected by sweeping with a net or by washing out the vegetation in a suitable container. A sieve net is essential for separating burrowers from the surrounding mud. For stream work a large screen held in the current while rocks and debris upstream are agitated will retain many dislodged specimens. Hand-picking may be used for the species which cling to stones, and in some instances a knife blade is necessary to dislodge the nymphs without injuring them. Seventy or 80 per cent alcohol is a suitable preservative.

In view of their very slow growth, rearing the immature stages to the imago is a matter of great patience. It is essential, of course, that the nymphs be kept at a suitable temperature in aerated or running water. The burrowing forms may be kept in pans of mud submerged in running water. Some kind of a wire or cloth cage should be arranged to retain the imago at emergence.

As shown by many food studies, mayfly nymphs are often the most abundant and typical trout stream insects. In the riffles especially they form an important item of the trout diet. In many lakes and ponds the nymphs are almost equally important to other types of fishes.

Nearly 500 species of mayflies are known from the United States. *Ephemerella* is by far the largest genus with about 70 species having been described as adults. *Baetis, Stenonema, Heptagenia, Paraleptophlebia,* and *Isonychia* are also rather large genera. In more than half of the American genera, however, less than ten species are known. Imagoes are far better known than the nymphs, and in several genera the immature stages are entirely unknown. The key below includes all except a few very rare and poorly-known genera. In general, it can be used for any of the late nymphal stages.

## KEY TO FAMILIES AND GENERA OF EPHEMEROPTERA NYMPHS *

1. Mandible with an external projecting tusk visible dorsally (Fig. 316)..........2
   Mandible without such a tusk........................................4
2. Gills dorsal, curving up over abdomen; first tibiae somewhat flattened (Fig. 316); fossorial......................................EPHEMERIDAE, 7
   Gills lateral; first tibiae slender; mostly sprawlers..........................3
3. Gills on first abdominal segment rudimentary; fossorial; common; southern and eastern...............................EPHEMERIDAE, **Potamanthus**
   Gills on first abdominal segment normal in size; rare; western.
                                    BAETIDAE, **Paraleptophlebia**
4. Gills on second abdominal segment in the form of a protecting plate covering all following gills (Fig. 316B).........................................5
   Gills not so arranged..........................................6
5. With two pairs of wing buds; sprawlers; uncommon; southeastern.
                                    EPHEMERIDAE, **Oreianthus**
   Hind wing buds lacking; sprawlers..........................BAETIDAE, 11
6. Head strongly depressed and held parallel to the substrate; eyes dorsal (Fig. 320); upper member of each gill pair platelike, the lower member fibrillate and often very much reduced (Figs. 317K, L)..............HEPTAGENIIDAE, 37
   Head usually not strongly depressed, held at an angle to the substrate; eyes lateral (Figs. 318, 319); if head is depressed, then gills not as above.
                                    BAETIDAE, 13
7. Head with a conspicuous frontal process (Fig. 316).......................8
   Front of head rounded, lacking frontal process; uncommon; generally distributed.
                                    **Campsurus**
8. Frontal process of head round, truncate, or conical (Figs. 316C, G)...........9
   Frontal process of head bifid (Figs. 316D–F)............................10
9. Mandibular tusks with toothlike tubercles (Fig. 316G); widely distributed except in southern states......................................**Ephoron**
   Mandibular tusks smooth......................................**Hexagenia**
10. Mandibular tusks crenate on outer (upper) margins (Fig. 316F); central and southern. .........................................**Pentagenia**
   Mandibular tusks with smooth margins; generally distributed.........**Ephemera**

* Greatly modified and rearranged from Needham, Traver, and Hsu (1935), the Comstock Publishing Co.

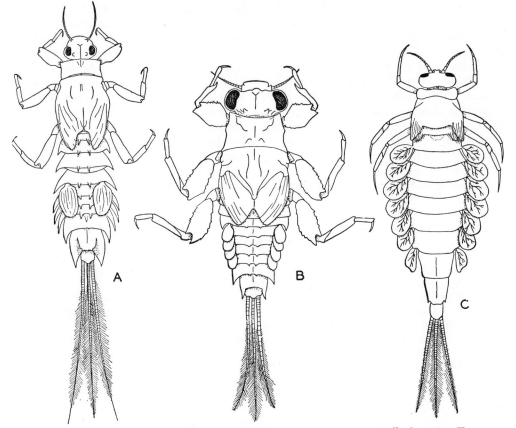

Fig. 318.—Baetidae nymphs. A, *Ephemerella doris* Traver, ×8; B, *E. allegheniensis* Traver, ×7; C, *Ametropus*, ×4. (Modified from Needham, Traver, and Hsu by permission of the Comstock Publishing Co.)

11. Gills on abdominal segments two to six single; in mud and silt.............. **12**
    Gills on abdominal segments two to six double; in sand or gravel stream beds or in plant growths on stones, etc.; widely distributed............**Tricorythodes**
12. With three prominent tubercles on head; eastern................. **Brachycercus**
    No tubercles on head; widely distributed........................... **Caenis**
13. Gills completely concealed beneath an enormously enlarged thoracic carapace (Fig. 319A); eastern........................................**Baetisca**
    No such carapace..................................................**14**
14. Lateral caudal filaments fringed on both sides (Figs. 318A, B; 320F)........**15**
    Lateral caudal filaments with heavy fringes on inner side only (Figs. 318C, 319D)...................................................**22**
15. Gills present on abdominal segments one to seven........................**16**
    Gills absent from one or more of segments one to seven; generally distributed.
                                                              **Ephemerella**
16. First pair of gills different in form from the others........................**17**
    First pair of gills similar to the others.................................**19**
17. Gills filamentous and branched (Fig. 317G); eastern and southeastern.
                                                              **Habrophlebia**
    Gills broad; generally distributed.......................................**18**

18. Gill on first abdominal segment single and unbranched..............**Choroterpes**
    Gill on first abdominal segment definitely bifid (Fig. 317B); gills two to six notched
    and with a terminal filament (Fig. 317E).....................**Blasturus**

19. Entire inner and outer margins of each gill on the middle abdominal segments finely
    dissected and forming a fringe; rare; western...................**Traverella**
    Inner and outer margins of gills on middle abdominal segments not as above....**20**

20. Lateral spines present on abdominal segments two to nine; gills diminishing in size
    posteriorly; rare; southwestern............................**Thraulodes**
    Lateral spines present on abdominal segments eight and nine, or nine only (Fig.
    319F); gills not diminishing in size posteriorly.......................**21**

21. Hind dorsal margin of segments one to ten finely spinulose; generally distributed.
                                          **Paraleptophlebia**
    Hind dorsal margin of segments seven to ten finely spinulose; eastern and south-
    eastern. ........................................**Habrophlebiodes**

22. Claws of middle and hind legs long and slender, about as long as the short
    tibiae. ...............................................**23**
    Claws on all legs similar, much shorter than tibiae.......................**24**

23. Claw of foreleg bifid (Fig. 319C); eastern......................**Siphloplecton**
    Claw of foreleg not bifid; slender, curved, and bearing several long spines (Fig.
    319B); rare; western.......................................**Ametropus**

24. Posterolateral angles of apical abdominal segments prolonged into thin flat lateral
    spines. ................................................**34**
    Posterolateral angles of apical abdominal segments hardly more than acute, not
    prolonged into thin flat lateral spines............................**25**

25. With a series of pectinate spines on crown of maxilla (Fig. 319J); generally dis-
    tributed. ..............................................**Ameletus**
    Without pectinate spines on crown of maxilla..........................**26**

26. Gill lamellae double on abdominal segments one to six, often with only a small
    recurved flap on dorsal or ventral surface (Figs. 317C, J)..............**27**
    Gill lamellae all single......................................**29**

27. Tracheae of gill lamellae pinnately branched (Fig. 317C); second pair of wing
    buds present; generally distributed................................**28**
    Tracheae of gill lamellae more or less palmately branched (Figs. 317H, J); second
    pair of wing buds absent; mostly eastern and northern...............**Cloeon**

28. Double portion of gill a small flap on the ventral surface (Fig. 317C); maxillary
    palp two-segmented......................................**Callibaetis**
    Double portion of gill a small flap on the dorsal surface; maxillary palp three-seg-
    mented. ............................................**Centroptilum**

29. With two caudal filaments.....................................**30**
    With three caudal filaments....................................**32**

30. Second pair of wing buds present (very minute in *Heterocloeon*).............**31**
    Second pair of wing buds absent; widely distributed..............**Pseudocloeon**

31. Gills blackish, with a narrow pale border; rare; eastern............**Heterocloeon**
    Gills not as above; common and widely distributed....................**Baetis**

32. Middle caudal filament shorter and weaker than the lateral ones; common; widely
    distributed. ...........................................**Baetis**
    All caudal filaments similar; middle filament sometimes slightly shorter but never
    weaker than lateral filaments.................................**33**

33. Second pair of wing buds present; gills symmetrical; generally distributed.
                                            **Centroptilum**
    Second pair of wing buds absent; gills asymmetrical (Fig. 317D); uncommon;
    eastern. ............................................**Neocloeon**

34. Forelegs with conspicuous fringes of long hairs (Fig. 319E); widely distributed.
                                            **Isonychia**
    Forelegs without such fringes....................................**35**

**35.** All gill lamellae single. . . . . . . . . . . . . . . . . . . . . . . . . . . . . . . . . . . . . . . . . . . . . . . . . . .**36**
Gill lamellae double on abdominal segments one and two, and sometimes on others
also; generally distributed. . . . . . . . . . . . . . . . . . . . . . . . . . . . . . . . . . .**Siphlonurus**

**36.** Abdominal segments five to nine greatly expanded laterally; rare; northeastern.
**Siphlonisca**

Abdominal segments five to nine not greatly expanded laterally; generally distrib-
uted. . . . . . . . . . . . . . . . . . . . . . . . . . . . . . . . . . . . . . . . . . . . . . . . . . . . .**Ameletus**

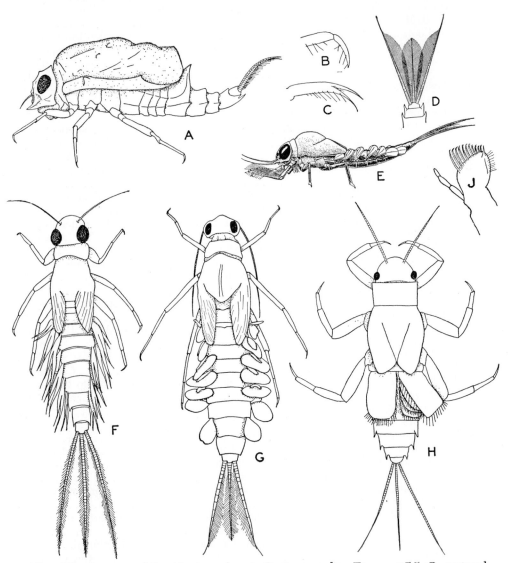

Fig. 319.—Structure of Baetidae nymphs. A, *Baetisca carolina* Traver, ×7.5; B, protarsal
claw of *Ametropus*; C, protarsal claw of *Siphloplecton basale* Walker; D, posterior end of
*Isonychia sicca*; E, *I. sicca*, ×2.5; F, *Paraleptophlebia volitans* McD., ×9; G, *Cloeon mendax*
Walsh, ×9; H, *Caenis*, ×5.5; J, maxilla of *Ameletus*. (A to C, H, and J modified from Needham,
Traver, and Hsu by permission of the Comstock Publishing Co.; D and E from Needham,
1920; F and G modified from Ide, 1930.)

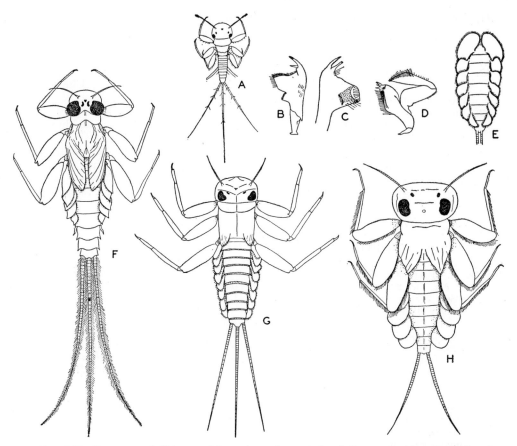

FIG. 320.—Structure of Heptageniidae. A, early nymph of *Stenonema*; B, mandible of *Cinygma integrum* Eaton; C, mandible of *Heptagenia*; D, maxilla of *Iron*; E, ventral view of abdomen of *Iron*; F, *Stenonema frontale* Banks, ×4.5; G, *Rhithrogena*, ×4; H, *Iron humeralis* Morgan, ×4.5. (A and F modified from Needham, Traver, and Hsu; B redrawn from McDunnough, 1933; C redrawn from Needham and Needham, 1938; D modified from Ide, 1930; G modified from Needham, 1940. A, C, F, and G by permission of the Comstock Publishing Co.)

37.  Fibrillar portion of each pair of gills lacking; uncommon; northeastern.
                                                                **Arthroplea**
     Fibrillar portion of each pair of gills present (Figs. 317K, L), sometimes vestigial. .......................................................................38
38.  With two caudal filaments (Fig. 320H)...................................39
     With three caudal filaments...........................................41
39.  With three stout spines at tip of galea-lacinia (Fig. 320D); usually with each gill
        overlapping the one behind it, the outer margins of all gills being pressed
        against the substrate, and the whole forming a large sucker-like structure
        (Fig. 320E)........................................................40
     Without three such spines; gills arranged normally; western...........**Ironodes**
40.  With a median row of long hairs on abdominal tergites; uncommon; western.
                                                                **Ironopsis**
     Without such hairs; common; generally distributed.....................**Iron**

**41.** Gills of seventh abdominal segment reduced to a single slender tapered filament or spine (Fig. 317A), sometimes apparently absent; generally distributed east of the Rockies..............................................................**Stenonema**

Gills of seventh abdominal segment flat and platelike, similar to preceding pairs..**42**

**42.** Fibrillar portion of first few gills reduced to one to four tiny threads (Fig. 317K); western and rarely northeastern..............................................**Cinygmula**

Fibrillar portion of gills well developed (Fig. 317L)...........................**43**

**43.** First and last pairs of gills much enlarged, converging beneath body (Fig. 320G); generally distributed..................................................**Rhithrogena**

First and last pairs of gills not modified as above, directed laterally...........**44**

**44.** With a sclerotized area projecting inward from the molar surface of each mandible; inner canine about one-half as long as outer (Fig. 320B); western...**Cinygma**

Without such a sclerotized area on mandible; inner canine at least three-quarters as long as outer (Fig. 320C); generally distributed.............**Heptagenia**

# EPHEMEROPTERA REFERENCES *

BERNER, L. 1941. Ovoviviparous mayflies in Florida. *Fla. Ent.* 24:32–34.

———. 1950. The mayflies of Florida. *Univ. Fla. Studies, Biol. Sci. Ser.* 4:1–267.

DAGGY, R. H. 1941. *Taxonomic and biological investigations on Minnesota mayflies (Ephemeroptera).* Ph.D. thesis. Typewritten. 331 pp. Univ. of Minnesota Library.

DODDS, G. S., and F. L. HISAW. 1924. Ecological studies of aquatic insects. I. Adaptations of mayfly nymphs to swift streams. *Ecology* 5:137–148.

———. 1924. Ecological studies of aquatic insects. II. Size of respiratory organs in relation to environmental conditions. *Ibid.* 262–271.

———. 1925. Ecological studies on aquatic insects. IV. Altitudinal range and zonation of mayflies, stoneflies, and caddisflies in the Colorado Rockies. *Ibid.* 6:380–390.

FOX, H. M., C. A. WINGFIELD, and B. G. SIMMONDS. 1937. The oxygen consumption of ephemerid nymphs from flowing and from still waters in relation to the concentration of oxygen in the water. *Jour. Exp. Biol.* 14:210–218.

IDE, F. P. 1930. Contribution to the biology of Ontario mayflies with descriptions of new species. *Canad. Ent.* 62:204–213, 218–231.

———. 1935. Life history notes on Ephoron, Potamanthus, Leptophlebia, and Blasturus with descriptions (Ephemeroptera). *Ibid.* 67:113–125.

———. 1935. The effect of temperature on the distribution of the mayfly fauna of a stream. *Univ. Toronto Studies, Biol. Ser.* 39:3–76.

———. 1935. Post embryological development of Ephemeroptera (Mayflies). External characters only. *Canad. Jour. Res.* 12:433–478.

———. 1937. Descriptions of eastern North American species of mayflies with particular reference to nymphal stages. *Canad. Ent.* 69:219–231, 235–243.

LINDUSKA, J. P. 1942. Bottom type as a factor influencing the local distribution of mayfly nymphs. *Ibid.* 74:26–30.

LYMAN, F. E. 1943. Swimming and burrowing activities of mayfly nymphs of the genus Hexagenia. *Ann. Ent. Soc. Amer.* 36:250–256.

McDUNNOUGH, J. 1932. New species of North American Ephemeroptera. II. *Canad. Ent.* 64:209–215.

———. 1933. The nymph of Cinygma integrum and description of a new heptagenine genus. *Ibid.* 65:73–76.

MORGAN, A. H. 1913. A contribution to the biology of may-flies. *Ann. Ent. Soc. Amer.* 6:371–413.

MORGAN, A. H., and M. C. GRIERSON. 1932. The functions of the gills in burrowing may flies (Hexagenia recurvata). *Physiol. Zool.* 5:230–245.

NEEDHAM, J. G. 1920. Burrowing mayflies of our larger lakes and streams. *Bull. U. S. Bur. Fish.* 36:265–292.

———. 1927. A baetine mayfly with tusked mandibles. *Canad. Ent.* 59:44–47.

NEEDHAM, J. G., J. R. TRAVER, and Y. HSU. 1935. *The biology of mayflies.* 759 pp. Ithaca, N. Y.

SEEMAN, T. M. 1927. Dragonflies, stoneflies and mayflies of Southern California. *Jour. Ent. and Zool.* 19:1–69.

* The standard reference on American mayflies is the volume by Needham, Traver, and Hsu (1935), and the serious student will find this book indispensable. Since it contains a complete bibliography, the present list consists only of some of the more important publications, especially those which have appeared since 1935.

SPIETH, H. T. 1936. The life history of Ephemera simulans in Lake Wawasee. *Canad. Ent.* **68**:263–266.

——. 1938. A method of rearing Hexagenia nymphs (Ephemerida). *Ent. News* **49**:29–32.

——. 1941. Taxonomic studies on the Ephemeroptera II. The genus Hexagenia. *Amer. Midl. Nat.* **26**:233–280.

——. 1947. Taxonomic studies on the Ephemeroptera. IV. The genus Stenonema. *Ann Ent. Soc. Amer.* **40**:87–122.

TRAVER, J. R. 1931. A new mayfly genus from North Carolina. *Canad. Ent.* **63**:103–109.

——. 1931a. The ephemerid genus Baetisca. *Jour. N. Y. Ent. Soc.* **39**:45–66.

——. 1932. Neocloeon, a new mayfly genus (Ephemerida). *Ibid.* **40**:365–371.

——. 1932a. Mayflies in North Carolina. *Jour. Elisha Mitchell Sci. Soc.* **47**:85–236.

——. 1933. Mayflies of North Carolina, Pt. III. The Heptageninae. *Ibid.* **48**:141–206.

——. 1935. Two new genera of North American Heptageniidae (Ephemerida). *Canad. Ent.* **67**:31–38.

——. 1937. Notes on mayflies of the southeastern states (Ephemeroptera). *Jour. Elisha Mitchell Sci. Soc.* **53**:27–86.

WINGFIELD, C. A. 1939. The functions of the gills of mayfly nymphs from different habitats. *Jour. Exp. Biol.* **16**:363–373.

# Chapter 28

# ODONATA (DRAGONFLIES, DAMSELFLIES)

WITH THE exception of the mosquitoes, the Odonata are perhaps the best-known insects having aquatic larvae. The adults are often called darning needles or mosquito hawks because of their size, shape, and habits. They are medium to large insects, often handsomely colored, and have a long, slender abdomen. The two pairs of wings are long, narrow, and net-veined, and the legs are rather short and used for perching. The head is mobile and bears very large compound eyes. From early morning until late evening dragonflies may be found flying back and forth or darting about erratically, especially along the shores and over the waters of marshes, ponds, rivers, and lakes. The mouth parts are constructed for biting, and the food, consisting of small flying insects, is caught on the wing.

The group is divided into two distinct suborders, the Anisoptera (true dragonflies) and the Zygoptera (damselflies). Dragonflies and damselflies differ in several important ways. The latter are smaller, more slender and delicate, and slower and apparently more uncertain in flight. In the dragonflies the hind wings are broader at the base than the forewings, while the two pairs of wings are similar in the damselflies. Also, dragonflies hold the wings horizontally outward when at rest, and damselflies hold them folded parallel with the abdomen or tilted upward.

It is only the series of nymphal stages, or naiads, which are aquatic. These are grotesque creatures, robust or elongated, and gray, greenish, or somber-colored. The body may be smooth or rough and bearing small spines; it is often covered with a dense growth of filamentous algae and debris. The naiads are commonly found on submerged vegetation and the bottoms of ponds, marshes, streams, and in the shallows of lakes, but are rare in polluted waters. One of their most striking features is the labium, which is greatly modified as a food-getting device (Figs. 323, 332, 335). It is very long, sometimes nearly one-fourth of the body length. Normally it lies folded backward at the base of the submentum and also folded upon itself at the base of the mentum; the whole structure lies beneath the head and thorax with the middle hinge resting between the bases of the legs. The distal end of the mentum is more or less enlarged and bears two lateral labial lobes which are usually armed with stout teeth and setae. Damselfly nymphs can always be distinguished from dragonflies by the fact that they have three leaflike tracheal gills at the tip of the abdomen: also damselflies are much more slender than dragonflies.

Depending on the species, there is a wide range in size. Mature dragonfly nymphs of the more common species usually range between 15 and 45 mm. in length; common mature damselfly nymphs range from about 10 to 22 mm. in length, exclusive of the gills.

Adult Odonata are often seen mating. This process may occur while at rest or

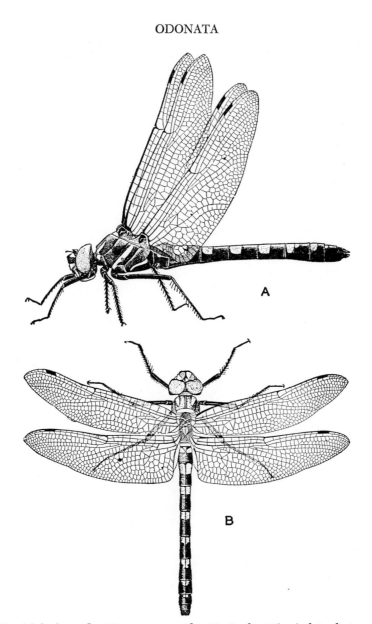

Fɪɢ. 321.—Adult dragonfly, *Macromia magnifica* MacLach., ×1. A, lateral view; B, dorsal view. (From Kennedy, 1915.)

during flight. After fertilization, egg deposition occurs in a variety of ways. In some species the female flies along a short distance above the water and scatters eggs by touching the tip of the abdomen to the surface or by actually dipping much of the abdomen now and then. A few species deposit their eggs in gelatinous masses. Some forms deposit eggs in floating mats of algae, others in sand, mud, or moss near the water's edge (Fig. 325). All female Zygoptera and some Anisoptera have specialized ovipositors with which holes are usually cut in stems of submerged or emergent plants to receive the eggs (Fig. 326). Some damselflies have been seen crawling down along a stem submerged as much as 30 cm., systematically depositing their eggs as they go down.

The newly-hatched young is enclosed in a thin, membranous, shroudlike covering, the pronymphal sheath. This is shed within a few seconds or minutes after leaving the egg, and the nymph which emerges is thus in the second instar. At this stage the nymph is a tiny, long-legged, spidery creature usually less than 1 mm. long (Fig. 327). The complete life history has been worked out for only a very few species, but it is probable that the great majority of species have from 11 to 14 nymphal instars. The length of each instar varies greatly, depending on the particular species, as well as on the prevailing temperature and food conditions. Sometimes an instar may last only three days; sometimes it may persist for as long as six

months. It has been said that a one-year life cycle is the prevailing condition, but there are many exceptions. In some of the Zygoptera, especially *Enallagma* and *Ischnura*, there is more than one generation per year. At the other extreme, it has been estimated that some of the large aeschnids may require more than four years for the complete life cycle.

Many important morphological changes occur during the series of nymphal instars. In addition to changes in size and body proportions, there are significant changes in the structure of the labium, a great increase in the relative size of the compound eyes, an increase in the number of antennal segments, and many minor changes in the setation and spines of the body. Wing covers appear after three to five molts and then grow progressively larger. For a short time after each shedding of the exo-

Fig. 322.—Typical adult damselfly, ×2.5. (Courtesy of Walker Van Riper.)

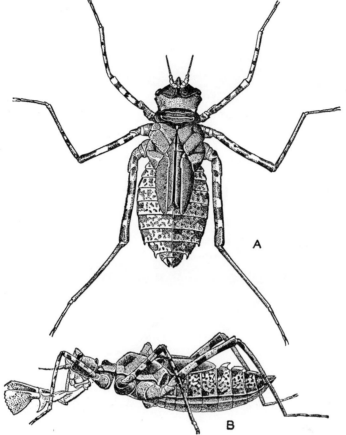

FIG. 323.—Nymph of *Macromia magnifica,* ×1.6. A, dorsal view; B, lateral view with labium extended. (From Kennedy, 1915.)

skeleton the nymphs are gray or light green and quite translucent, but thereafter the cuticle becomes more opaque.

Odonata nymphs may be roughly classified into climbers, sprawlers, and burrowers. The climbers move about slowly in dense vegetation or trash in still waters. To this group belong the Coenagrionidae and the Aeschnidae. Most of the sprawlers are long-legged, sluggish, dull-colored creatures occurring on many types of bottoms. To this group belong the Agrionidae and the Libellulidae. Although not true burrowers, the Cordulegasteridae lie almost hidden in sand or silt bottoms. This is accomplished by raking the sand out

from beneath the body so that they sink downward. The Petaluridae and the Gomphidae burrow into silt, mud, and sand so that usually only the tip of the abdomen and the eyes are above the surface. The members of the latter family are easily distinguished by their wedge-shaped head and the more or less flattened scraper-like anterior tibiae. Some of these nymphs are capable of burrowing out of sight in a few seconds.

Although all odonate nymphs are carnivorous, the food-getting habits vary. Some species cautiously stalk their prey; some remain motionless until the food comes within reach. The burrowing forms

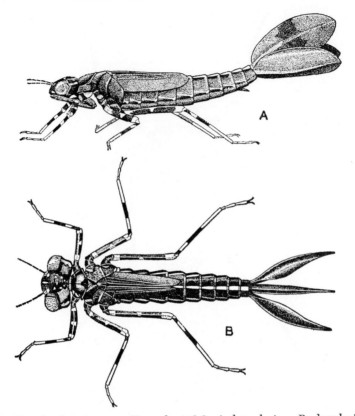

Fig. 324.—Nymph of *Argia emma* Kennedy, ×3.6. A, lateral view; B, dorsal view. (From Kennedy, 1915.)

lie almost completely concealed and may remain immobile for days at a time. In any case, when the prey is within reach it is seized suddenly and effectively by a lightning-like extension and contraction of the labium. Very large nymphs are said to be able to seize prey as much as 25 mm. away as the result of the combined action of the labium and the forward lurching movement of the whole body. The labium, with its two lateral lobes, serves as a clamp to hold the food in position at the mouth where it is crushed with the mandibles. The real process of mastication, however, occurs in the gizzard which is supplied with longitudinal, toothed, chitinous ridges. Food consists chiefly of other aquatic insects, annelids, and small Crustacea and mollusks. Very young nymphs are said to consume Protozoa. Although

large dragonfly nymphs may be induced to feed on small fish in the laboratory when the normal food is absent, it is doubtful whether they ever attack fish in the normal environment. When crowded under laboratory conditions cannibalism may result. Very little food of any kind is taken during the winter months in the northern states.

The rectal chamber of dragonfly nymphs is one of the most highly specialized respiratory devices to be found among aquatic insects. This barrel-shaped organ fills much of the abdomen and is set off from the rest of the digestive tract by a constriction. It contains longitudinal rows of minute thin tracheal gills which project into the cavity. Each gill contains an abundance of tracheoles which absorb oxygen from the water in the rectum. The walls of the rectum are provided with muscles which produce regular expansion and contraction movements. In this way water is taken into and expelled from the chamber vigorously by way of the anus. The anus is guarded by three minute valves surrounded by five spinous anal appendages (Fig. 331). The respiratory pulsations of the abdomen can easily be observed.

Damselfly nymphs have one median and two lateral flat caudal tracheal gills which are supplied with large tracheal trunks.

These gills vary somewhat in shape and color. They are easily broken off at their bases but may be regenerated. Unlike the condition in the dragonflies, the rectum is unspecialized, and although small quantities of water may be taken into the rectal chamber at frequent intervals in young nymphs, it is thought that this organ is of negligible respiratory significance, especially in older individuals. In addition to the gills, the general body surface undoubtedly absorbs large quantities of oxygen.

Fig. 325.—*Cordulegaster dorsalis* Hagen. A, female ovipositing in stream bed; B, nymph; C, exuvia. (From Kennedy, 1917.)

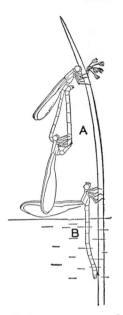

Climbing nymphs may be collected by rinsing out masses of vegetation in a suitable container. Sprawling and burrowing forms are found by raking up bottom trash or by pulling a wire sieve net through the surface layers of mud, sand, and debris. When the material is sorted on shore the awkward movements of the

FIG. 326.—*Ischnura perparva* Selys. A, in copulation; B, female ovipositing in aquatic plant. (From Kennedy, 1915.)

Just before the transformation to the imago, the nymph crawls out of the water, usually on emergent aquatic vegetation. The smaller damselflies crawl only a few centimeters above the surface, but other species crawl up higher. Some species, especially sprawlers and burrowers, leave the water on broader objects such as logs, rocks, and trees. Others simply crawl out onto the adjacent shore, and a few individuals have been found wandering more than ten meters from the water. Most Odonata emerge in the early morning or late afternoon; a very few emerge during midday or the hours of darkness.

The actual process of emergence of the imago is heralded by a split in the exoskeleton along the middorsal surface of the thorax. As this rupture becomes longer, the thorax, head, legs, wings, and lastly the abdomen are slowly withdrawn through it (Figs. 329, 330). Before flying off, the newly-emerged adult clings to the nymph skeleton for an hour or so while the wings and body become dry and stiff.

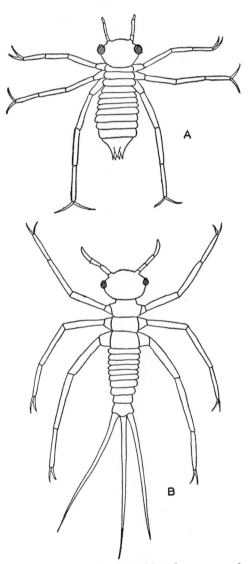

FIG. 327.—Newly hatched Odonata nymphs. A, *Libellula*, ×33, B, *Enallagma,* ×38. (Modified from Wilson.)

TABLE IX. Relative Number of Species in the Genera of Odonata of the United States for Which the Nymph Stages Have Been Reported.

Genera indicated by asterisks are those which are most common and widely distributed.

| Suborder | Family | Subfamily | Number of species of nymphs reported | | | |
|---|---|---|---|---|---|---|
| | | | None | One | Two to ten | More than ten |
| Anisoptera | Petaluridae | | Tanypteryx | Tachopteryx | | |
| | Gomphidae | | Cyclophylla | *Hagenius<br>Octogomphus | Dromogomphus<br>Erpetogomphus<br>Gomphoides<br>Lanthus<br>Ophiogomphus<br>Progomphus | *Gomphus |
| | Aeschnidae | | Oplonaeschna<br>Triacanthagyna | *Basiaeschna<br>Coryphaeschna<br>*Epiaeschna<br>Gynacantha<br>*Nasiaeschna | *Anax<br>Boyeria<br>Gomphaeschna | *Aeschna |
| | Cordulegasteridae | | | Taeniogaster | *Cordulegaster | |
| | Libellulidae | Cordulinae | Williamsonia | Cordulia<br>Dorocordulia<br>Platycordulia | Didymops<br>*Epicordulia<br>Helocordulia<br>Macromia<br>Neurocordulia<br>*Tetragoneuria | *Somatochlora |
| | | Libellulinae | | Brechmorrhoga<br>Cannacria<br>Lepthemis<br>Macrodiplax<br>Nannothemis<br>Orthemis<br>*Pachydiplax<br>Paltothemis<br>*Plathemis<br>Pseudoleon | *Celithemis<br>Dythemis<br>*Erythemis<br>Erythrodiplax<br>Ladona<br>*Leucorrhinia<br>Miathyria<br>*Pantala<br>*Perithemis<br>Tarnetrum<br>*Trapezostigma | *Libellula<br>*Sympetrum |
| Zygoptera | Agrionidae | | | | *Agrion<br>*Hetaerina | |
| | Coenagrionidae | Lestinae | | | Archilestes | *Lestes |
| | | Coenagrioninae | Argiallagma<br>Neonura | *Amphiagrion<br>Anomalagrion<br>Chromagrion<br>*Coenagrion<br>Hesperagrion<br>Hyponeura<br>Teleallagma<br>Telebasis<br>Zoniagrion | *Ischnura<br>Nehallenia | *Argia<br>*Enallagma |

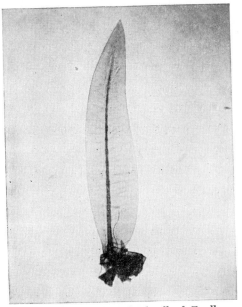

FIG. 328.—Typical tracheal gill of *Enallagma*, ×10. Note primary and secondary tracheae.

nymphs render them easily visible. Seventy or 80 per cent alcohol is a satisfactory preservative.

Unfortunately many species of Odonata are known only in the adult stage. It has been estimated that more than a third of the North American forms are unknown as nymphs. As indicated in Table IX, most of the genera reported in the nymphal stages from the United States are represented by only a few species. The identification of a nymph, even to genus, is often no easy matter because of the fact that morphological differences are so slight. Keys must therefore be used with great care. Furthermore, key characters usually apply only to the more advanced instars. The standard work for American species is the manual of Needham and Heywood (1929), and it may be used for identifying nymphs and adults to species. Identification is more reliable in the case of ques-

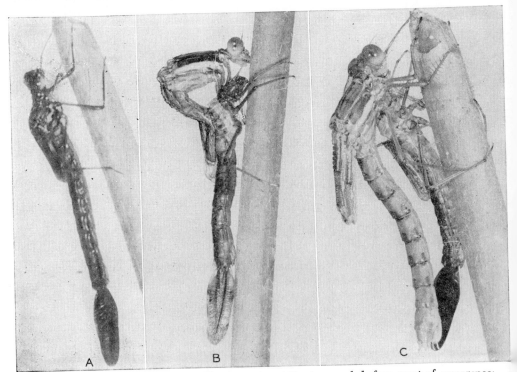

FIG. 329.—Early stages in damselfly emergence, ×3. A, nymph before onset of emergence; B, adult about half way out of nymphal exoskeleton; C, adult completely emerged. (Courtesy of Walker Van Riper.)

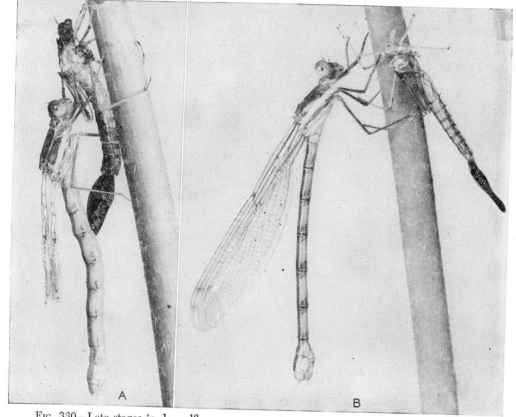

FIG. 330.—Late stages in damselfly emergence, ×3. A, wings of adult beginning to unfold; B, wings of adult completely extended and nearly dry. (Courtesy of Walker Van Riper.)

tionable nymphs if the nymphs can be reared to the adult stage. Needham recommends simple cylindrical window-screen rearing cages for use in the laboratory. They should be kept in an upright position about half way out of the water.

In the key below the general geographic range in the United States is given for each genus. Lengths refer to the last nymphal instars.

## KEY TO GENERA OF ODONATA NYMPHS *

1. Gills within the posterior part of the digestive tract; head not wider than thorax and abdomen; dragonfly nymphs..............Suborder **ANISOPTERA, 2**
   Gills consisting of three flat external plates at posterior end of abdomen; damselfly nymphs..................................Suborder **ZYGOPTERA, 60**
2. Labium flat (Fig. 332C); true burrowers and climbers....................40
   Labium spoon-shaped, covering lower part of face like a mask as far as the base of the antennae (Fig. 332G)..........................................3

* Greatly modified and rearranged from keys given by Needham and Heywood (1929) (by permission), and Byers (1936).

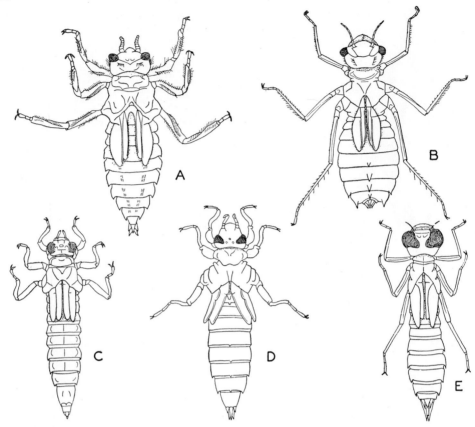

FIG. 331.—Typical dragonfly nymphs. A, *Tachopteryx thoreyi* Hagen, ×1.3; B, *Helocordulia uhleri* Selys, ×2.2; C, *Gomphus,* ×1.5; D, *Progomphus obscurus* (Rambur), ×2; E, *Aeschna,* ×1.3. (A redrawn from Kennedy, 1917; B redrawn from Kennedy, 1924; D redrawn from Kennedy, 1921.)

3. Inner edge of lateral lobe of labium coarsely and irregularly toothed (Fig. 332B); usually lying hidden in debris, sand, and silt, but not true burrowers.

CORDULEGASTERIDAE, 4

Inner edge of lateral lobe of labium evenly and regularly toothed, or without teeth (Fig. 332A); bottom sprawlers, not climbers or burrowers.

LIBELLULIDAE, 5

4. Mental setae 12 or 13; * Fla., Ga., and northeastern..............**Taeniogaster**
   Less than 12 mental setae; eastern..........................**Cordulegaster**
5. Frontal projection between bases of antennae produced into a prominent median pyramidal horn (Fig. 323)..........................................6
   No such frontal projection...................................................8
6. Antennae about one and one-half times as long as frontal horn; legs short; rare; central states.........................**Platycordulia xanthosoma** Williamson
   Antennae more than twice as long as frontal horn; legs long; more common......7

* The number of mental setae, as used in this key, refers to the number on one side of the mid-line.

7. Head widest across the eyes (Fig. 323A); widely distributed..........Macromia
   Head hardly as wide across the eyes as across the hind angles; eastern..Didymops
8. Abdomen with dorsal hooks (Figs. 334E, F)................................9
   Abdomen without dorsal hooks.......................................27
9. Dorsal hook present on ninth abdominal segment (Figs. 334D, G)...........10
   No dorsal hook on ninth abdominal segment............................20
10. Lateral spines of ninth abdominal segment reaching or surpassing the tips of the
    anal appendages (Fig. 334D)....................................11
    Lateral spines of ninth abdominal segment not attaining the tips of the anal
    appendages. ...............................................13

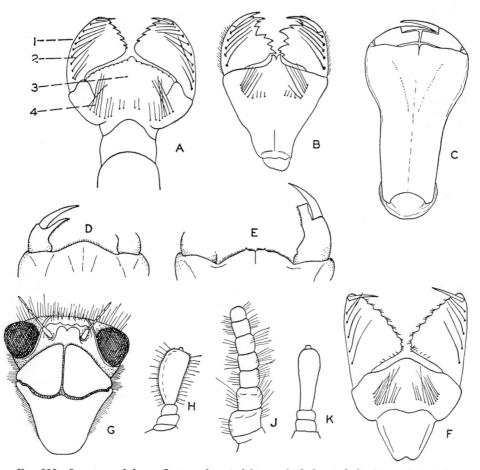

FIG. 332.—Structure of dragonfly nymphs. A, labium of *Plathemis lydia* (Drury); B, labium of *Cordulegaster*; C, labium of *Aeschna*; D, lateral labial lobe of *Basiaeschna janata* (Say); E, lateral labial lobe of *Boyeria*; F, labium of *Perithemis domtia* (Drury); G, anterior view of head of *Erythemis simplicollis* (Say), showing masklike labium; H, antenna of *Octogomphus*; J, antenna of *Tachopteryx thoreyi*; K, antenna of *Ophiogomphus*. 1, lateral labial lobe; 2, lateral labial setae; 3, mentum; 4, mental setae. (A, B, and F redrawn from Garman, 1927; D and E redrawn from Howe, 1922; G redrawn from Wilson, 1920; H and J redrawn from Kennedy, 1917.)

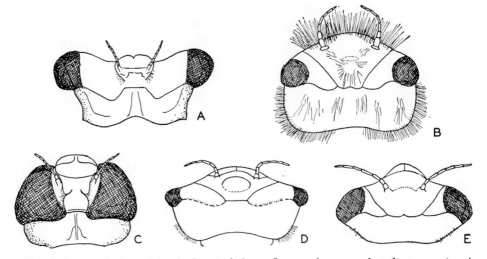

Fig. 333.—Dorsal view of head of typical dragonfly nymphs, somewhat diagrammatic. A, *Nasiaeschna, Basiaeschna,* and *Boyeria;* B, *Plathemis;* C, *Aeschna* and *Epiaeschna;* D, *Somatochlora;* E, *Leucorrhinia.* (A and C modified from Howe, 1922; B and E modified from Wright and Peterson; D modified from Walker, 1925.)

11.  Lateral spines of eighth abdominal segment set at an angle to the long axis of the body and not parallel to those of segment nine (Fig. 334G); eastern.
                                                                    **Neurocordulia**
     Lateral spines of eighth abdominal segment not set at an angle, parallel to those of segment nine............................................12
12.  Four or five lateral labial setae; about 27 mm. long; eastern........**Epicordulia**
     Six to eight lateral labial setae; about 16 to 20 mm. long; widely distributed.
                                                                    **Tetragoneuria**
13.  Superior and inferior anal appendages as long as the middorsal length of abdominal segments eight plus nine.........................................14
     Superior and inferior anal appendages shorter than the middorsal length of abdominal segments eight plus nine (Fig. 334N)............................16
14.  Lateral spines of segment nine long and strongly incurved (Fig. 334H); rare; Gulf coast states...............................**Macrodiplax balteata** (Hagen)
     Lateral spines of segment nine not strongly incurved.......................15
15.  Eight lateral labial setae; Fla...................................**Miathyria**
     Six or ten lateral labial setae; southern............**Cannacria gravida** (Calvert)
16.  Dorsal hooks blunt and broad; rare; Calif. and Texas.
                                                       **Brechmorrhoga mendax** (Hagen)
     Dorsal hooks sharp and slender......................................17
17.  Lateral anal appendages nearly as long as the superior (Fig. 334N)..........18
     Lateral anal appendages not more than half as long as the superior...........19
18.  Dorsal hooks absent on abdominal segments three and four; eastern (Fig. 331B).
                                                                    **Helocordulia**
     Dorsal hooks present on abdominal segments three and four; widely distributed.
                                                                    **Somatochlora**
19.  With five lateral labial setae (Fig. 332F); eastern and southern.
                                                          **Perithemis domitia** Drury
     With six to ten lateral labial setae; southern.......................**Dythemis**

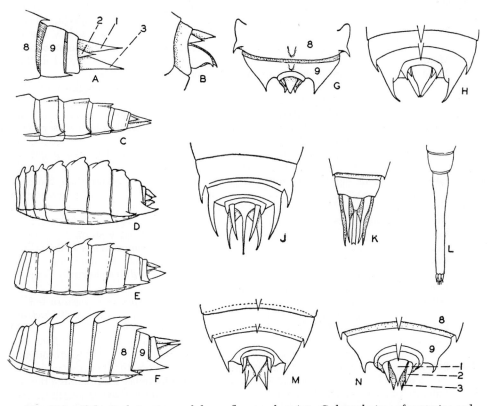

Fig. 334.—Abdominal structures of dragonfly nymphs. A to C, lateral view of posterior end; A, *Libellula*; B, *Erythemis*; C, *Nasiaeschna*; D to F, lateral view of abdomen; D, *Neurocordulia yamaskanensis* (Prov.); E, *Sympetrum*; F, *Leucorrhinia*; G to N, dorsal view of posterior end; G, *Neurocordulia yamaskanensis*; H, *Macrodiplax balteata* (Hagen); J, *Pantala hymenea* (Say); K, *Coryphaeschna*; L, *Gomphoides williamsoni* Gloyd; M, *Sympetrum*; N, *Somatochlora minor*. 1, superior anal appendage; 2, lateral; 3, inferior; 8, eighth abdominal segment; 9, ninth abdominal segment. (B modified from Needham and Needham, 1938, by permission of the Comstock Publishing Co.; C, E, and F modified from Howe, 1922; D and G modified from Byers, 1937; H modified from Needham and Fisher, 1936; J modified from Kennedy, 1923; L modified from Byers, 1930; N modified from Walker, 1925.)

24. With none or four mental setae; eastern...........................Ladona *
    With eight to 15 mental setae.......................................25
25. Body smooth; southwestern...................................Paltothemis
    Body hairy..........................................................26
26. Median lobe of labium evenly contoured; widely distributed............Libellula
    Median lobe of labium crenulate on front border (Fig. 332A); widely distributed.
                                        Plathemis lydia Drury *
27. Inferior anal appendages strongly decurved (Fig. 334B)..................28
    Inferior anal appendages not decurved...............................29
28. Eleven or 12 lateral labial setae; Gulf coast states....Lepthemis vesiculosa Hagen
    Seven to nine lateral labial setae; widely distributed................Erythemis
29. Eyes capping the anterolateral angles of head, usually small (Fig. 333D)......30
    Eyes lateral, usually large (Fig. 333E)..............................33
30. Lateral anal appendages nearly as long as the superior (Fig. 334N).........31
    Lateral anal appendages one-third to one-half as long as the superior (Fig.
        334A)..........................................................32
31. With obsolete crenulations on distal margin of lateral lobe of labium; extreme
        southwest.............................................Pseudoleon superbus Hagen
    With deep crenulations on distal margin of lateral lobe of labium; widely distrib-
        uted. ...............................................Somatochlora
32. Median lobe of labium evenly contoured; widely distributed...........Libellula
    Median lobe of labium crenulate on front border; Gulf coast states.
                                        Orthemis ferruginea (Fabr.)
33. Anal appendages long, slender, and needle-pointed; lateral spines of segments eight
        and nine long and incurved (Fig. 334J); widely distributed...............34
    Anal appendages short and heavy, not needle-pointed; lateral spines of segments
        eight and nine flat and straight...................................35
34. Lateral spines of eighth abdominal segment one-third to one-half the length of
        those of segment nine (Fig. 334J)............................Pantala
    Lateral spines of eighth abdominal segment only slightly shorter than those of
        segment nine.......................................Trapezostigma
35. Six or seven lateral labial setae....................................36
    Nine to 14 lateral labial setae......................................37
36. Inferior anal appendages as long as the superior; 10 mm. long; eastern.
                                        Nannothemis bella (Uhl.)
    Inferior anal appendages longer than the superior; more than 15 mm. long; north-
        eastern.........................................Cordulia shurtleffi Scudder
37. Lateral spines present on eighth abdominal segment.......................38
    Lateral spines lacking on eighth abdominal segment; one species in eastern half of
        U. S., one species in far west.................................Tarnetrum
38. Lateral spines of eighth abdominal segment short, of ninth long..............39
    Lateral spines of eighth and ninth segments about the same length; southern and
        southeastern states; some species in brackish waters..........Erythrodiplax
39. Lateral spines of ninth abdominal segment equal to or greater than the middorsal
        length of segment nine; widely distributed..Pachydiplax longipennis (Burm.)
    Lateral spines of ninth abdominal segment less than the middorsal length of seg-
        ment nine; northern states...................................Leucorrhinia
40. Tarsi 2–2–3 segmented; antennae with four segments.........GOMPHIDAE, 42
    Tarsi 3–3–3 or 2–3–3 segmented; antennae with seven segments............41
41. Antennae thick (Fig. 332J); eastern.
                                PETALURIDAE, Tachopteryx thoreyi (Hagen)
    Antennae slender...................................AESCHNIDAE, 52

----

* Borror (1945) considers these as subgenera of Libellula.

42. Abdomen circular; legs not fossorial; eastern and southern.

**Hagenius brevistylus** Selys

Abdomen much longer than wide; legs fossorial (Figs. 331C, D)...........43

43. Tenth abdominal segment one-third to one-half the total length of the abdomen and no wider than the anal appendages are long; Fla. and La.

**Gomphoides williamsoni** Gloyd

Tenth abdominal segment of normal size................................44

44. Wing cases divergent (Fig. 331D)....................................45

Wing cases not divergent..........................................47

45. Fourth antennal segment cylindrical; one species in Fla., one in east and south, and one in west........................................**Progomphus**

Fourth antennal segment a spherical rudiment (Fig. 332K)................46

46. Dorsal hooks present on abdominal segments two or three to nine; widely distributed. ................................................**Ophiogomphus**

Dorsal hooks present only on abdominal segments two to four; south and west.

**Erpetogomphus**

47. Third antennal segment flat and oval (Fig. 332H)......................48

Third antennal segment elongated or linear............................49

48. Short lateral spines present on abdominal segments eight and nine; eastern.

**Lanthus**

Short lateral spines present on abdominal segments seven to nine; far western.

**Octogomphus specularis** Hagen

49. Ninth abdominal segment with sharp middorsal ridge ending in apical spine....50

Ninth abdominal segment otherwise; widely distributed..............**Gomphus**

50. Without lateral spines on sixth abdominal segment..................**Gomphus**

With lateral spines on sixth abdominal segment........................51

51. Lateral anal appendages as long as the inferiors; southern Texas.

**Gomphoides stigmata** Say

Lateral anal appendages shorter than the inferiors; eastern and southern.

**Dromogomphus**

52. Lateral lobes of labium armed with strong raptorial setae; Fla. and Calif.

**Gynacantha nervosa** Rambur

Lateral lobes of labium lacking raptorial setae (Fig. 332C)..................53

53. First tarsi with two segments; eastern......................**Gomphaeschna**

First tarsi with three segments.....................................54

54. Hind angle of head strongly angular (Fig. 333A).........................55

Hind angle of head broadly rounded (Fig. 333C).........................57

55. Superior anal appendage as long as the inferiors (Fig. 334K); southeastern coastal states................................**Coryphaeschna ingens** Rambur

Superior anal appendage much shorter than the inferiors...................56

56. Lateral lobe of labium squarely truncate at tip (Fig. 332E); eastern......**Boyeria**

Lateral lobe of labium with tapered, pointed tip (Fig. 332D); eastern and central.

**Basiaeschna janata** (Say)

57. Lateral spines on abdominal segments four or five to nine; eastern half of U. S...58

Lateral spines otherwise; generally distributed............................59

58. Low dorsal hooks on segments seven to nine (Fig. 334C).

**Nasiaeschna pentacantha** (Rambur)

No dorsal hooks on abdomen......................**Epiaeschna heros** (Fabr.)

59. Lateral spines on abdominal segments seven to nine......................**Anax**

Lateral spines on abdominal segments six to nine (Fig. 331E)..........**Aeschna**

60. First segment of antenna longer than the remaining segments combined.

**AGRIONIDAE, 61**

First segment of antenna shorter than the remaining segments combined.

**COENAGRIONIDAE, 62**

**61.** Middle lobe of labium cleft far below base of lateral lobes (Fig. 335C); mostly in
eastern half of U. S.............................................**Agrion**
Middle lobe of labium cleft only to base of lateral lobes; widely distributed.
                                                                        **Hetaerina**

**62.** Gills somewhat parallel-sided and blunt (Fig. 335F); middle lobe of labium with
median cleft (Figs. 335D, E)......................................63
Gills with curved margins and pointed tips; middle lobe of labium entire......64

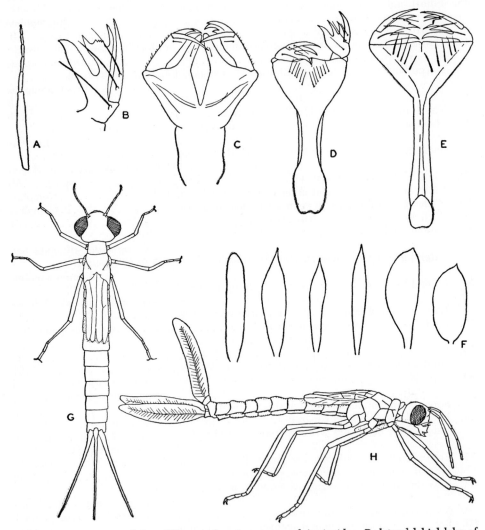

Fig. 335.—Structure of damselfly nymphs. A, antenna of Agrionidae; B, lateral labial lobe of
*Lestes stultus* Hagen; C, labium of *Agrion*; D, labium of *Archilestes californica* McLach.;
E, labium of *Lestes*; F, tracheal gills, left to right: *Lestes, Ischnura, Chromagrion, Enallagma,
Enallagma,* and *Argia*; G, dorsal view of *Coenagrion,* ×4; H, lateral view of *Lestes stultus,*
×3. (B redrawn from Kennedy, 1917; C and E redrawn from Garman, 1927; D and G modified from Kennedy, 1915; H modified from Essig, *College Entomology,* 1942, by permission of
the Macmillan Co.)

63. With a simple upper notch in the trifid lateral lobe of the labium (Fig. 335D); 20 to 30 mm. long not including gills; chiefly on the west coast......**Archilestes**

With a serrated upper notch in the trifid lateral lobe of the labium (Fig. 335B); 17 to 25 mm. long not including gills; generally distributed..........**Lestes**

64. Gills about half as broad as long (Fig. 335F).........................**65**

Gills not more than one-third as broad as long...........................**66**

65. With one to four lateral labial setae; widely distributed.................**Argia**

Lateral labial setae absent (rarely one); far southwestern states.

**Hyponeura lugens** (Hagen)

66. Head angular at posterolateral margins................................**67**

Head rounded at posterolateral margins.................................**68**

67. Gills widest in middle, one-third as broad as long; widely distributed except in far south................................**Amphiagrion saucium** (Burm.)

Gills widest distally, one-sixth as broad as long (Fig. 335F); northeastern.

**Chromagrion conditum** (Hagen)

68. One or two mental setae...........................................**69**

Three or more mental setae.........................................**70**

69. One mental seta; eastern..........................................**Nehallenia**

Two mental setae..................................................**72**

70. Six or seven lateral labial setae; total length 14 mm.; rare; far southwest but occasional as far east as Fla....................................**Telebasis**

Four to six lateral labial setae; common and widely distributed...............**71**

71. Gills tapering to a fine point (Fig. 335F); length without gills 10 to 15 mm.; three to five mental setae; five or six lateral labial setae.................**Ischnura**

Gills not tapering to a fine point (Figs. 328, 335F); length without gills 16 to 23 mm.; three or four mental setae; four to six lateral labial setae.....**Enallagma**

72. Six or seven lateral labial setae.......................................**73**

Four or five lateral labial setae.......................................**75**

73. Gills tapering to a slender point; length without gills about 18 mm.; east coast states.

**Teleallagma daecki** Calvert

Gills bluntly pointed.............................................**74**

74. Tip of gills obtusely angled; extreme northern states.

**Coenagrion resolutum** (Hagen)

Tip of gills rounded; extreme southwest........**Hesperagrion heterodoxum** Selys

75. Without lateral spines on terminal abdominal segment; eastern half of U. S.

**Anomalagrion hastatum** Say

With lateral spines on terminal abdominal segment; Calif.

**Zoniagrion exclamationis** Selys

## ODONATA REFERENCES *

BICK, G. H. 1941. Life-history of the dragonfly Erythemis simplicollis. *Ann. Ent. Soc. Amer.* 34:215–230.

BORROR, D. J. 1945. A key to the New World genera of Libellulidae (Odonata). *Ibid.* 38:168–194.

\* Entomological journals contain a great abundance of papers giving species lists of Odonata from various areas and descriptions of nymphs and adults. The papers cited here represent only a few selected titles. These include such works as monographs, comprehensive treatises, and ecological studies, especially those which have appeared since 1929. Complete lists of older citations may be found in Muttkowski (1910) and Needham and Heywood (1929).

BYERS, C. F. 1930. A contribution to the knowledge of Florida Odonata. *Univ. Fla. Publ., Biol. Sci. Ser.* 1:9–327.

———. 1936. The immature form of Brachymesia gravida, with notes on the taxonomy of the group (Libellulidae). *Ent. News* 47:35–37, 60–64.

———. 1937. A review of the dragon-flies of the genera Neurocordulia and Platycordulia. *Univ. Mich., Misc. Publ. Mus. Zool.* 36:1–36.

———. 1939. A study of the dragonflies of the genus Progomphus (Gomphoides), with a description of a new species. *Proc. Fla. Acad. Sci.* 4:19–85.

CALVERT, P. P. 1893. Catalogue of the Odonata (dragonflies) of the vicinity of Philadelphia, with an introduction to the study of this group of insects. *Trans. Amer. Ent. Soc.* **20**:152a–272.

——. 1934. The rates of growth, larval development and seasonal distribution of dragon-flies of the genus Anax (Odonata: Aeshnidae). *Proc. Amer. Philos. Soc.* **73**:1–70.

GARMAN, P. 1917. The Zygoptera, or damsel-flies, of Illinois. *Bull. Ill. State Lab. Nat. Hist.* **12**:411–587.

——. 1927. The Odonata or dragonflies of Connecticut. *Bull. State Geol. Nat. Hist. Surv. Conn.* **39**:1–331.

GROSS, F. 1930. Odonata. *Biol. Tiere Deutschlands*, **30**:1–78.

HAYES, W. P. 1941. A bibliography of keys for the identification of immature insects. Part II. Odonata. *Ent. News* **52**:52–55, 66–69, 93–98.

KENNEDY, C. H. 1915. Notes on the life history and ecology of the dragonflies (Odonata) of Washington and Oregon. *Proc. U. S. Nat. Mus.* **49**:259–345.

——. 1917. Notes on the life history and ecology of the dragonflies (Odonata) of Central California and Nevada. *Ibid.* **52**:483–635.

——. 1921. Some interesting dragon-fly naiads from Texas. *Ibid.* **59**:595–598.

——. 1922. The ecological relationships of the dragonflies of the Bass Islands of Lake Erie. *Ecology* **3**:325–336.

——. 1938. The present status of work on the ecology of aquatic insects as shown by the work on the Odonata. *Ohio Jour. Sci.* **38**:267–276.

MARTIN, R. D. C. 1939. Life histories of Agrion aequabile and Agrion maculatum (Agriidae: Odonata). *Ann. Ent. Soc. Amer.* **32**:601–620.

MUTTKOWSKI, R. A. 1910. Catalogue of the Odonata of North America. *Bull. Publ. Mus. Milwaukee* **1**:1–207.

NEEDHAM, J. G. 1941. Life history studies on Progomphus and its nearest allies (Odonata: Aeshnidae). *Trans. Amer. Ent. Soc.* **67**:221–245.

——. 1948. Studies on the North American species of the genus Gomphus (Odonata). *Ibid.* **73**:307–339.

NEEDHAM, J. G., and E. FISHER. 1936. The nymphs of North American Libelluline dragonflies (Odonata). *Trans. Amer. Ent. Soc.* **67**:107–116.

NEEDHAM, J. G., and C. H. HART. 1901. The dragonflies (Odonata) of Illinois. Part I. Petaluridae, Aeschnidae, and Gomphidae. *Bull. Ill. State Lab. Nat. Hist.* **6**:1–94.

NEEDHAM, J. G., and H. B. HEYWOOD. 1929. A handbook of the dragonflies of North America. 378 pp. Springfield, Ill.

PENNAK, R. W., and C. M. McCOLL. 1944. An experimental study of oxygen absorption in some damselfly naiads. *Jour. Cell. and Comp. Physiol.* **23**:1–10.

TILLYARD, R. J. 1917. *The biology of dragonflies (Odonata or Paraneuroptera).* 396 pp. Cambridge.

WALKER, E. M. 1912. The North American dragonflies of the genus Aeshna. *Univ. Toronto Studies, Biol. Ser.* **11**:1–213.

——. 1925. The North American dragonflies of the genus Somatochlora. *Ibid.* **26**:1–202.

WHITEHOUSE, F. C. 1941. British Columbia dragonflies (Odonata), with notes on distribution and habits (with descriptions of two new nymphs by E. M. Walker). *Amer. Midl. Nat.* **26**:488–557.

WILSON, C. B. 1920. Dragonflies and damselflies in relation to pond-fish culture, with a list of those found near Fairport, Iowa. *Bull. U. S. Bur. Fish.* **36**:182–264.

WRIGHT, M. 1943. A comparison of the dragonfly fauna of the lower delta of the Mississippi River with that of the marshes of the Central Gulf Coast. *Ecol. Monogr.* **13**:481–497.

——. 1943a. The effect of certain ecological factors on dragonfly nymphs. *Jour. Tenn. Acad. Sci.* **18**:172–196.

WRIGHT, M., and A. PETERSON. 1944. A key to the genera of anisopterous dragonfly nymphs of the United States and Canada (Odonata, suborder Anisoptera). *Ohio Jour. Sci.* **44**:151–166.

# Chapter 29

# HEMIPTERA (BUGS)

THE TRUE "bugs" may be distinguished from other orders of insects by three outstanding features: (1) the mouth parts are greatly modified to form a jointed, piercing and sucking "beak" inserted near the anterior end of the head; (2) the anterior pair of wings are leathery at the base and membranous apically, while the second pair are entirely membranous; and (3) metamorphosis is simple and gradual.

In size, they range from minute to very large. Shape varies from oval to very long and cylindrical; many genera are considerably flattened. The prothorax is large and free, and the meso- and metathorax are united. The scutellum is usually prominent. The antennae have only four or five segments. With few exceptions, there are five nymphal instars; these immature forms look and act much like the adults, but are smaller and sexually immature. Wing buds usually appear in the second or third nymphal instar. In some species considerable variations occur in the degree of wing development in the adult, and the condition may be macropterous, brachypterous, vestigial, or apterous. Apterous and macropterous individuals may be found in the same aggregation.

Although this is a large and important order of insects, relatively few species have become adapted to aquatic environments. There is, however, a series of semiaquatic and aquatic families which show a gradual transition in their habitats from the damp shores of ponds, swamps, and lakes to the subsurface waters. The Saldidae, Ochteri-dae, and Gelastocoridae, for example, live on the shore; they run and jump in varying degrees, make short flights, but usually light on the water only by accident. The Hebridae run about at the water's edge on floating vegetation, surface of the water, and the adjacent damp ground. The Hydrometridae, Mesoveliidae, and some Veliidae venture farther out and are almost always found on floating algae and plant rafts. Certain other Veliidae and the Gerridae skate rapidly over the surface of the water. In the Hebridae the body is covered with a velvety pile which effectively sheds water, but in the other surface-living families usually only the legs and especially the tarsi are covered with pile. Six families are truly aquatic and normally found below the surface. Of these, the Nepidae and Belostomatidae usually cling to the substrate but remain more or less in contact with the surface film. The former are modified very little for an aquatic existence, and although the latter have the second and third legs flattened and fringed with hairs, they do not swim a great deal. Both the Pleidae and the Naucoridae clamber about in tangled submerged vegetation, and although they are both swimmers, they are not particularly specialized for such locomotion. The Corixidae and the Notonectidae are the swimmers *par excellence*. In both groups the long, flattened, hairy hind legs are used as oars. In the former family the middle legs are long and thin for clinging to the substrate.

541

Those forms occurring above the surface of the water have the usual unspecialized tracheal respiration characteristic of terrestrial insects. Those that swim below the surface come to the surface at intervals and renew the air in the tracheae. In some Corixidae the pronotum breaks the surface film, but in all other families the tip of the abdomen is brought into contact with the air. In some families, such as the Corixidae, Naucoridae, and Belostomatidae, there is a dorsal reservoir of air between the wings and the body. Also, there may be portions of the general body surface where a film of air is carried by a hydrofuge pubescence; this is especially noticeable in the Corixidae. No tracheal gills are known in the entire order.

Nearly all aquatic Hemiptera are strict predators, the particular prey, depending on the specific habits of the various genera, being chiefly small terrestrial and aquatic insects and entomostraca. The majority have the forelegs more or less specialized for seizing and holding the prey while body fluids are sucked up through the mouth parts with the muscular pharynx.

Although some of the semiaquatic Hemiptera oviposit on sphagnum and shore grasses, the eggs of the aquatic families are customarily laid on the surface or within the tissues of submerged plants. A few Corixidae oviposit on crayfish, snails, and dragonfly nymphs. All ecdyses of the aquatic forms occur under water. The great majority of species winter over as adults hidden in mud, trash, or vegetation at the edges and bottom of their habitat. They may often be seen swimming about under the ice, however.

Aside from the usual nets, no special equipment is necessary for collecting aquatic Hemiptera. They may be reared in aquaria provided they are supplied with suitable food. Either alcoholic or pinned specimens are suitable for identification.

## KEY TO SEMIAQUATIC AND AQUATIC FAMILIES OF ADULT HEMIPTERA *

1. Antennae shorter than head...........................................2
   Antennae as long or longer than head................................9
2. Ocelli present; semiaquatic, shore-living...........................3
   Ocelli absent; aquatic..............................................4
3. Antennae concealed; front legs raptorial; eyes protuberant; squat, toad-shaped, mottled bugs found on moist shores of streams, marshes, and ponds; three small but widely distributed genera in U. S.; toadbugs......GELASTOCORIDAE
   Antennae exposed; front and middle legs similar; resemble Gelastocoridae in appearance and habits; only one small genus in U. S..............OCHTERIDAE
4. Front tarsi consisting of a single spatulate segment.........CORIXIDAE, p. 554
   Front tarsi of the usual form.......................................5
5. Front coxae inserted at or near the front margin of the prosternum; front legs modified for grasping.......................................................7
   Front coxae inserted at the hind margin of the short prosternum; legs modified for swimming. .........................................................6
6. Hind tibiae and tarsi ciliate; beak four-segmented; eyes very large; body elongated.
   NOTONECTIDAE, p. 548

   Hind tibiae and tarsi simple, beak three-segmented; eyes not especially large; body oval........................................................PLEIDAE, p. 549
7. Membrane of upper wings reticulately veined............................8
   Membrane of upper wings without veins...............NAUCORIDAE, p. 550
8. Apical appendages of abdomen long and slender; tarsi one-segmented.
   NEPIDAE, p. 551

* Greatly modified from Hungerford (1919).

Apical appendages of abdomen short, flat, and retractile; tarsi two-segmented.

BELOSTOMATIDAE, p. 552

9.  Head as long as entire thorax; both elongated......HYDROMETRIDAE, p. 544
    Head shorter than thorax, including scutellum..........................10
10. Tarsal claws preapical............................................11
    Tarsal claws apical..............................................12
11. Hind femur extending much beyond apex of abdomen; beak four-segmented.

GERRIDAE, p. 545

    Hind femur not extending much beyond apex of abdomen; beak three-segmented.

VELIIDAE, p. 547

12. Antennae of five prominent segments (except *Merragata* which has four); first and
    second segments of antennae thicker than the others....HEBRIDAE, p. 543
    Antennae four-segmented; two basal segments not swollen..................13
13. Scutellum distinct behind posterior margin of pronotum; widely distributed....14
    Pronotum elongated posteriorly; no distinct scutellum; in vegetation and debris close
    to edges of streams; does not venture out onto water; western states.

MACROVELIIDAE, **Macrovelia horni** Uhler

14. Membrane of upper wings without cells; on floating vegetation.

MESOVELIIDAE, p. 545

    Membrane of upper wings with four or five long closed cells; on shore near water's
    edge; active, erratic bugs somewhat similar to the Ochteridae and Gelasto-
    coridae in their habits; eight small but widely distributed genera in U. S.;
    shore bugs..................................................SALDIDAE

## HEBRIDAE (VELVET WATER BUGS)

These bugs are minute, the usual length being only 1.5 to 2.5 mm.; as a result they are usually overlooked by the casual collector. Aside from the fact that the body is covered with a dense, velvety, water-resistant pile, they are similar in their morphology to terrestrial hemipterans. There are two genera in the United States, *Naeogeus* (= *Hebrus*) and *Merragata*, and only a few species have been recorded for each. The former is common over most of the country, but *Merragata* is mostly confined to the Midwest. They are found along the margins of bodies of water. *Naeogeus* usually occurs on shore or on plant rafts and is seldom found on the water. *Merragata*, however, is found on the shore less often and runs about on the surface of the water; occasionally it crawls on submerged surfaces at which times it is covered with a film of air. The velvet water bugs are said to feed on other small insects.

The two genera may be best distinguished on the basis of the structure of the antennae. The antennae of *Naeogeus* are composed of five large segments; those of *Merragata* are composed of four large segments.

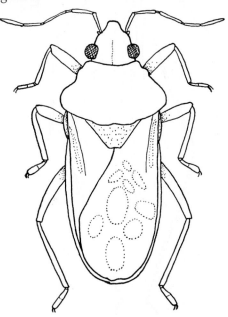

Fig. 336.—Dorsal view of adult female *Naeogeus*, ×35. (Redrawn from Hungerford, 1919.)

## HYDROMETRIDAE (MARSH TREADERS, WATER MEASURERS)

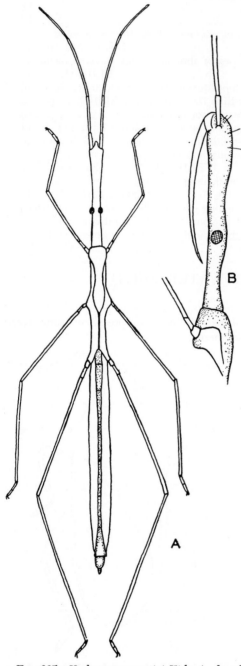

The marsh treaders are exceedingly slender brownish or greenish hemipterans with rather long thin legs and antennae. The usual length of the body is 8 to 11 mm. in adults. They are not rare, but are seldom noticed because of their inconspicuous color and shape and because of their slow, deliberate manner of walking about on shore, floating vegetation, or on the surface of the water of puddles and ponds. They feed on all kinds of small aquatic metazoans at or near the surface film. The prey is slowly stalked and literally "harpooned" with the tip of the beak and held thus while a pair of thin, flexible stylets are protruded farther into the body where they are moved about rapidly in the tissues like reamers while the fluids are sucked up. The spindle-shaped eggs are deposited on objects, especially rushes, a little above the surface of the water. Development may occur very rapidly, and under most favorable conditions the entire life cycle may be completed in 15 days, and there may be several broods per summer. In southern states marsh treaders are active the year round, but in the more northern states the adult hibernates during the winter and becomes active soon after the ice melts in the spring. These hemipterans are easily reared in aquaria if they are supplied with appropriate food organisms. Apterous adults are much more common than the winged forms. *Hydrometra* is the only North American genus and *H. martini* Kirk. is by far the most common species, being found from coast to coast. Several other species have been reported from scattered localities, mostly in the southern states, although one of these forms occurs as far north as Kansas.

Fig. 337.—*Hydrometra martini* Kirk. A, dorsal view of adult, ×12; B, lateral view of head.

## MESOVELIIDAE (WATER TREADERS)

These small hemipterans occur at the edges of ponds and on floating vegetation and other objects. When disturbed, they run rapidly and often take to the surface of the open water. The adults are usually apterous and a green or yellowish-green color, but the silvery winged forms are quite conspicuous. Winged and wingless forms occur together. Food consists of small living and dead insects which fall to the surface and small aquatic organisms which are caught just beneath the surface film. The female oviposits the fertilized eggs in the tissues of emergent or shore plants. Presumably it is the adult that hibernates during the winter. *Mesovelia mulsanti* White is common over most of the United States; the length of the adult is 4 to 5 mm. Two other species have been described from the eastern states, but they are uncommon and only about half as large as *M. mulsanti*.

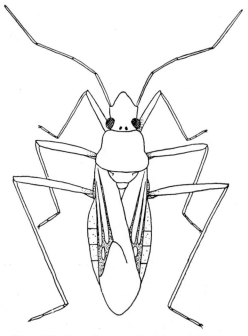

Fig. 338.—Dorsal view of adult female *Mesovelia mulsanti* White, ×13. (Redrawn from Hungerford, 1919.)

## GERRIDAE (WATER STRIDERS, POND SKATERS, WHERRYMEN)

From early spring until late autumn these semiaquatic long-legged hemipterans may be found skating or leaping about on the surface film of ponds and streams everywhere. Many species are gregarious and occur in large blackish masses, especially under overhanging banks or in other shade. When disturbed, they scatter nervously in all directions. The forelegs are relatively short, raptorial, and of little use in locomotion. Water striders feed upon a variety of entomostracans and aquatic insects which they catch just below the surface, or upon such terrestrial insects as may fall to the water. When food is scarce, however, they are known to be cannibalistic upon nymphs and weaker adults of their own species. Wings are usually absent. The length range is about 2 to 15 mm.

Of the five genera found in the United States, *Gerris* is everywhere the most common; it is represented by about 20 species, of which *G. remigis* Say and *G. marginatus* Say are most widely distributed. The usual length is 8 to 15 mm.

Two species of *Limnogonus* are known from the United States; *L. hesione* (Kirk.) seems to be widely distributed east of the Rockies, while *L. franciscanus* Stål is a Central American and West Indies form which has been reported from Texas and California. *Limnogonus* is smaller than *Gerris*, being only 4.5 to 8 mm. long; it has an abdomen which is proportionately much shorter and a shiny upper surface on

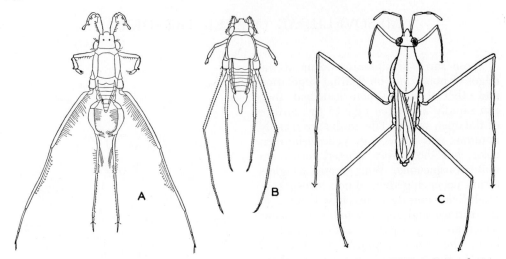

Fig. 339.—Gerridae. A, adult male *Rheumatobates rileyi* Berg, ×7; B, adult female *R. rileyi*, ×7; C, adult *Gerris*, ×3. (A and B from Silvey.)

the head and thorax; in *Gerris* these areas are dull and pubescent.

Although three species of the genus *Metrobates* have been reported, two of these have been found only rarely in some of the western states. The other species, *Metrobates hesperius* Uhl., however, has been found in scattered localities in most of the states east of the Rockies. The body is black, robust, and 3 to 5 mm. long. *Metrobates* is said to be able to jump several inches into the air and catch mosquitoes in flight.

The members of the genus *Trepobates* are also very small, the body length being only 3 to 4 mm. Coloration is usually yellow and black. Seven species have been reported, and the range seems to

be east of the Rocky Mountains. *T. inermis* Esaki and *T. pictus* (H. S.) are the most common and widely distributed.

Since none of the species of *Rheumatobates* are much over 3 mm. in length, they are often mistaken for immature stages of larger striders and are usually taken only by the few collectors particularly interested in this group. The males are bizarre creatures; they have curiously curved, spiny antennae, and in many species have curved or deformed hind legs. Judging from the published records, the several American species seem to have a spotty distribution. The most common one, *Rheumatobates rileyi* Berg, occurs east of the Rockies.

## KEY TO GENERA OF GERRIDAE

1. Median margin of eye sinuate or concave behind the middle; body long and narrow. . . . . . . . . . . . . . . . . . . . . . . . . . . . . . . . . . . . . . . . . . . . . . . . . . . . . . .2
  Median margin of eye convexly rounded; body short and broad. . . . . . . . . . . . . .3
2. Basal tarsal subsegment of forelegs about half as long as second. . . . . . **Limnogonus**
  Basal tarsal subsegment of forelegs subequal to second. . . . . . . . . . . . . . . . . . **Gerris**
3. First antennal segment much shorter than the other three taken together. . . . . . . . .4
  First antennal segment nearly equal to the remaining three taken together.
                                                       **Metrobates**
4. Abdomen much shorter than remainder of body. . . . . . . . . . . . . . . . . . . **Trepobates**
  Abdomen as long as remainder of body. . . . . . . . . . . . . . . . . . . . . . . **Rheumatobates**

## VELIIDAE (BROAD-SHOULDERED WATER STRIDERS)

This is a small family of gregarious, plump-bodied surface dwellers. The usual length range is only 1.6 to 5.5 mm., and the color is brown or black, often with silvery markings. The legs are not particularly long and are modified for running and walking rather than rowing. These insects are called broad-shouldered water striders because of the fact that the body is broadest in the region of the attachment of the second and third legs. The appropriate name of "ripple bugs" has also been

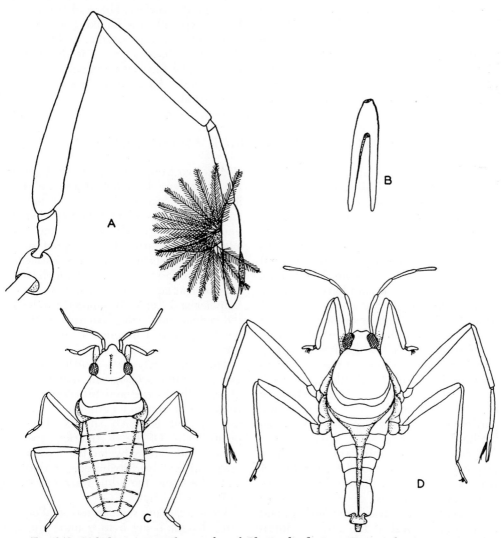

Fig. 340.—Veliidae. A, mesothoracic leg of *Rhagovelia flavicinta* Bueno, showing swimming plume and claws; B, notched second tarsus of *R. flavicinta* from which claws and swimming plume have been removed; C, apterous female *Microvelia borealis* Bueno, ×30; D, apterous female *Rhagovelia obesa* Uhl., ×13. (A and B modified from Coker, Millsaps, and Rice, 1936; C and D redrawn from Hungerford, 1919.)

suggested since they occur chiefly in or near the ripples and rapids of small streams where they await food brought by the current. Such food consists of small insects and aquatic Metazoa on or just below the surface. Many species are excellent divers and can swim readily below the surface.

*Microvelia* is said to be the most abundant and widely distributed of all American aquatic Hemiptera. At the same time the numerous species in this genus are among the smallest of such forms, the usual length being only 1.6 to 3.7 mm. The hind tarsi have only two segments. *Microvelia* occurs on the rock, sand, and mud borders of streams and ponds as well as on the surface of the water. About five species of *Velia* and a dozen of *Rhagovelia* have been recorded. Both of these genera have three segments in the hind tarsi. The latter genus is easily identified, however, by a curious tuft of long, feather-like hairs accompanied by long, flat, bladelike, chitinous structures in a deep cleft of the terminal segment of the second tarsus. In locomotion the middle tarsus is thrust through the surface film and the tuft of hairs is spread in a fanlike manner, presulmably acting as a paddle. In *Microvelia* the last antennal segment is the longest, but in *Velia* the first antennal segment is the longest. All three genera are widely distributed.

## NOTONECTIDAE (BACK SWIMMERS)

The back swimmers are among the best known water bugs. Unlike all of the preceding families in this chapter, they are aquatic rather than semiaquatic and remain submerged except when in flight. The fact that they swim on their backs readily distinguishes them in their natural environment. They are more deep-bodied than other Hemiptera and have unusually large eyes. The general dorsal surface of head and thorax is often strikingly colored and patterned with various combinations of white, pearly, yellow, golden, gray, tan, brown, and black. Some of the more common species show considerable color variations, especially in the relative amounts of white and black. The antennae are partly concealed in a depression between the head and thorax.

Notonectids are abundant everywhere in ponds, small lakes, and backwaters of streams. They swim powerfully for short distances by means of rapid, oarlike strokes of the densely setose hind legs and often come to rest at the surface, dorsal side downward, with the tip of the abdomen in contact with the air, and the body at an angle. Otherwise they may be found clinging to submerged objects. Air is carried in two troughs on the ventral side of the abdomen. It is held there by three longitudinal fringes of hairs, one median and two lateral. Additional air is carried under the wings and between the head and thorax. During the nymphal stages the food consists mostly of entomostracans, but mature forms may feed on much larger prey such as aquatic insects and even small tadpoles and fishes. If handled carelessly, the notonectids "sting" sharply with the mouth parts and produce a burning sensation.

There are only two North American genera in this widespread family. *Notonecta* is the longer and broader, ranging from 8 to 17 mm. in length; the last antennal segment is much shorter than the penultimate. Of the 15 American species, *N. undulata* Say is by far the most common and widely distributed. It is black and white, and the adult ranges from 10 to 13 mm. in length.

*Buenoa* is more slender and smaller, the usual length being 5 to 9 mm.; the last antennal segment is longer than the penultimate. It differs from *Notonecta* also in that it seldom comes to the surface. The males of this genus can stridulate by rub-

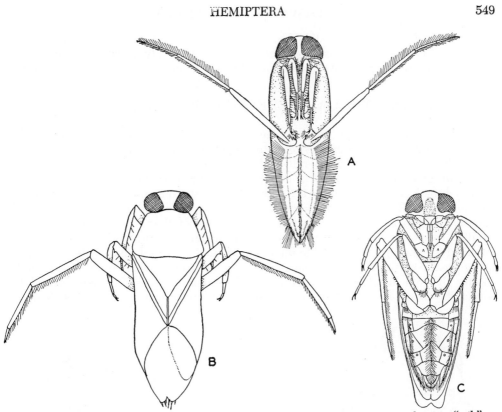

Fig. 341.—Notonectidae. A, ventral view of *Buenoa margaritacea* Bueno showing "crib" formed by first two pairs of legs, ×8; B, dorsal view of *Notonecta*, ×4.5; C, ventral view of *Notonecta*, ×4.5. (A and C modified from Hungerford, 1919; B modified from Britton.)

bing roughened patches on the front legs against the basal segment of the beak, and in both sexes the four anterior legs are margined with long spines which, when folded against the body, form a "crib" to hold the prey. Like the similar Old World genus *Anisops*, *Buenoa* possesses erythrocruorin-containing cells in the abdomen. *B. margaritacea* Torre-Bueno and *B. elegans* (Fieb.) are the most common of the half dozen American species.

## PLEIDAE (PIGMY BACKSWIMMERS)

These water bugs are among the smallest aquatic Hemiptera, the adult being only 1.6 to 2.3 mm. long. The body is strongly arched, and the color is grayish-yellow. They are found only in dense, tangled vegetation, such as *Chara, Anacharis,* and *Myriophyllum,* where they spend most of their time clinging to the leaves and stems. They swim only for short distances and seem to dodge from stem to stem. Such locomotion is an even, rapid gait, rather than the jerky motion of the

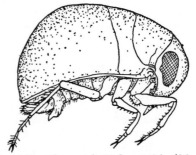

Fig. 342.—*Plea striola* Fieber, ×24. (Modified from Hungerford, 1919.)

notonectids. Food consists mostly of small entomostracans. The eggs are deposited in stems. The single North American spe-

cies known in this family, *Plea striola* Fieber, is widely distributed and common. It has several intergrading color variants.

## NAUCORIDAE (CREEPING WATER BUGS)

Creeping water bugs are broad, somewhat flattened, and of moderate size (5 to 16 mm. long). Coloration is generally dull brown or greenish. The head is exceptionally broad, and the antennae are short and concealed. They feed on a variety of aquatic Metazoa, and sting viciously when handled carelessly. The anterior legs are modified for grasping the prey, the femora being greatly enlarged. The antennae are shorter than the head and lie concealed. Although these hemipterans are truly

aquatic, the legs are but little modified for that habitat. Locomotion consists of a rapid, half-creeping, half-swimming gait in the dense cover of tangled vegetation of ponds, streams, and small lakes. Some species are common on gravel and pebble bottoms of slow streams, and a few occur in warm or cold spring brooks. A supply of air is carried under the wings. Although naucorids are numerous in the Old World and tropics of the New World, they are not common in the United States.

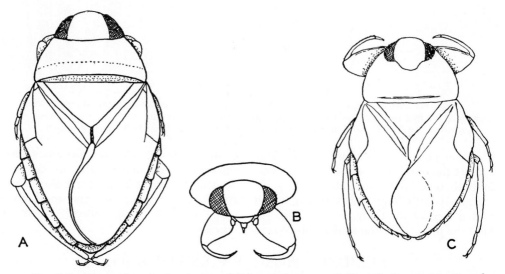

Fig. 343.—Naucoridae. A, dorsal view of *Pelocoris femoratus* P. B., ×6; B, anterior view of head of *P. femoratus*; C, dorsal view of *Ambrysus mormon* Montd., ×5. (A and B modified from Britton; C modified from Usinger, 1946.)

## KEY TO GENERA OF NAUCORIDAE

1. Anterior margin of pronotum deeply excavated for reception of head (Fig. 343C)..2
   Anterior margin of pronotum straight (Fig. 343A).........................3
2. Ventral surface of abdomen densely pubescent; about 11 species known from the
   southwestern states, but an additional species occurs as far north as southern
   Idaho and Mont...............................................**Ambrysus**
   Ventral surface of abdomen naked; two rare species reported from extreme southern
   Texas......................................................**Cryphocricos**

3. Inner margins of eyes divergent anteriorly; body broadly oval and flattened; one
   species reported from Clark Co., Nev.........................Usingerina
   Inner margins of eyes convergent anteriorly (Fig. 343B); body strongly convex;
   several species common east of the Rockies, rare as far west as Texas and Nev.
                                                                      **Pelocoris**

## NEPIDAE (WATER SCORPIONS)

Although the general body shape varies greatly in this peculiar family, there are certain consistent and striking features. All of the species have two long, slender, nonretractile caudal filaments. Each of these has a groove on the median surface, and, when fitted together, the filaments constitute a respiratory tube; at intervals

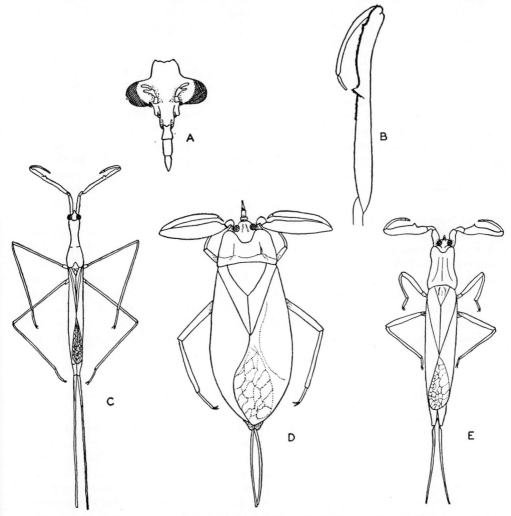

Fig. 344.—Nepidae. A, ventral view of head of *Ranatra*; B, femur, tibia, and tarsus of first leg of *Ranatra fusca* P. B.; C, *Ranatra*, ×1.5; D, *Nepa apiculata* Uhler, ×3; E, *Curicta*, ×2.5. (A, B, and E redrawn from Hungerford, 1922; C modified from Hungerford, 1919; D modified from Britton.)

its tip is placed at the surface film so that the oxygen in the tracheal system may be replenished. The Nepidae are called water scorpions because of the fact that the forelegs have a superficial resemblance to the pedipalps of scorpions. The femur of each of these raptorial appendages is long and stout, and the tibia and tarsus may be folded back against the femur, the whole thus acting as a scissors. The eyes are large, the beak is relatively short and three-segmented, and the antennae are small and concealed.

Nepids are inconspicuous owing to their protective coloration and sluggish movements. They are usually found in trash and mud in the shallows of ponds and slow, grassy streams where they lie in wait for their prey. The forelegs are held out in striking position and are capable of lashing out with great speed. All kinds of aquatic Metazoa, and especially insects, are seized and held in this way while the body fluids are sucked out. Occasional slow swimming movements are effected by alternate motions of the unspecialized second and third legs. Flight occurs at night.

On the abdomen are three pairs of peculiar sievelike openings which are in the positions normally occupied by spiracles. Their function is not definitely known, but Hamilton (1931) has shown that they are well supplied with sensory cells and believes that they have a hydrostatic function and aid in keeping the animals oriented in the water. The older theory holds that they are used in obtaining oxygen directly from the water by osmosis.

Of the three American genera, *Ranatra* is the most common and widely distributed. These insects are exceedingly slender and have a striking resemblance to small straws and grasses. The body length, without the respiratory siphon, ranges from 20 to 40 mm. They are usually found clinging to submerged vegetation with the tip of the siphon just above the surface film. *R. fusca* P. B. ( = *R. americana* Montd.) is the most common of the nine species.

The only representative of the second genus is *Nepa apiculata* Uhl. It is smaller (17 mm.), broad, flat, and brown and is found in the trash of the bottom where the water is less than 10 cm. deep.

The two species of *Curicta* are confined to several states in the extreme southwest and are seldom encountered by the casual collector. The body shape is intermediate between those of *Nepa* and *Ranatra* and ranges from 16 to 22 mm. in length without the respiratory siphon.

The three genera may be separated as follows. In *Nepa apiculata* the body is broadly oval and flat, but in *Curicta* and *Ranatra* the body is elongated. *Curicta* has the prothorax a little broader than the head, and the body is oval-elongate. *Ranatra* has the prothorax narrower than the head, and the body is greatly elongated.

## BELOSTOMATIDAE (GIANT WATER BUGS)

Unlike the preceding family, the giant water bugs are a rather homogeneous group. They constitute the largest Hemiptera, the usual length of the American species being 20 to 70 mm. The body is somewhat flat and oval and a brown or dull greenish color. The four-segmented antennae are hidden beneath the prominent eyes, and there is a pair of short, straplike, retractile appendages at the tip of the abdomen. The forelegs are raptorial, but the other legs are long, flat, and ciliated for swimming. These giant bugs are found on the bottom of shallow ponds and lakes or clinging to some support near the surface with the tip of the abdomen in contact with the air. They are fiercely predaceous and feed on all kinds of aquatic organisms, including such relatively large forms as tadpoles, small frogs, and fishes. Occasionally they become nuisances in fish hatcheries. All secrete a toxic salivary substance which kills the prey in a very short time. The layman knows the belostomatids as "electric light bugs" because of their attraction to lights at night.

In two genera, *Abedus* and *Belostoma*, the female cements the eggs to the back of the male, and he carries them about for a week or two during incubation. In some species more than 150 eggs may be carried in this manner.

The majority of species in this family are tropical and subtropical, and, as might be expected, most American forms occur in the southern states. Eight species of *Abedus*, for example, are confined to the southwest; a ninth species, only 12 to 14 mm. long, occurs in Florida and Georgia. In the genus *Belostoma* about a half dozen species are western or southern and three are of more general distribution; *B. fluminea* Say is certainly the most common. The large *Benacus griseus* (Say) has a scattered distribution in the southern and southeastern states. In the family as a whole, the most widely distributed and common form is *Lethocerus americanus* (Leidy); there are several other species in this same genus, but they are confined to the south and southwest.

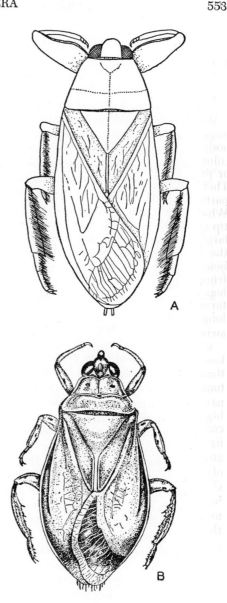

Fig. 345.—Belostomatidae. A, *Lethocerus americanus* (Leidy), ×1.5; B, *Belostoma fluminea* Say, ×3. (A modified from Britton; B from *Insects in Kansas*.)

## KEY TO GENERA OF BELOSTOMATIDAE

1. Metasternum with a strong midventral keel; membrane of first wing reduced.
   **Abedus**
   Metasternum without midventral keel; membrane of first wing not reduced......2
2. Basal segment of beak longer than the second; less than 30 mm. long.....**Belostoma**
   Basal segment of beak shorter than the second; more than 30 mm. long.........3
3. Anterior femur grooved for the reception of the tibia.................**Lethocerus**
   Anterior femur not grooved for the reception of the tibia....**Benacus griseus** (Say)

# CORIXIDAE (WATER BOATMEN)

Water boatmen are medium to small bugs, usually less than 12 mm. long. The body is somewhat flattened above, and the color is dark grayish, customarily mottled or marked with yellow, brown, or black. There is no extended beak, and the mouth parts are fused and built into the head. What corresponds to the opening at the tip of the beak in other families is a rather large opening on the anterior surface of the face. The front tarsi are peculiar, being one-segmented, flat, scooplike, and fringed with strong bristles. The middle legs are long, slender, and end in two tarsal claws. The hind legs are also long but are flattened and fringed for swimming.

Corixids occur everywhere in the shallows of ponds, lakes, and streams where they spend most of their time on the bottom; they are even found in muddy stagnant pools. Popham (1943) has found a high correlation between the range of color of any particular species and that of its natural habitat. In their favorite attitude they anchor themselves to some object near the bottom with the tarsal claws of the long second legs. They swim in a quick darting manner by oarlike movements of the hind legs; at such times the first two pairs of legs lie backwards along the sternum.

The body is almost completely enveloped in a film of air, and there is also air beneath the wings. Consequently, when not swimming or clinging to some object, they rise to the surface where the supply of oxygen is renewed. Some authorities, however, maintain that in well-aerated water they may remain submerged indefinitely, obtaining their oxygen by diffusion through the air–water interface.

Most water boatmen are strong fliers and take off easily from the surface of the water. Adults are mainly stimulated to migrate by high temperatures, overcrowding, and an unsuitably colored background. They are sometimes found around bright lights at night.

Hungerford (1919) has shown that corixids gather their food from muddy bottoms by sweeping the flocculent material into the mouth with their first tarsi. It consists of debris and a great variety of algae, Protozoa, and microscopic Metazoa characteristic of that habitat. In addition, they feed on algal filaments by piercing each cell with their protrusible stylets and sucking out the contents.

The adult males of some species are able to stridulate, or chirp, by rubbing a patch of pegs on the base of the front femur against a scraper on the side of the head. The males of most species have a curry-comb-like organ, called a strigil, near either the left or right margin on the dorsal side of the sixth abdominal segment; the function of this peculiar structure is unknown, but it may be used during copulation. The males may also be distinguished from the females by the fact that the last few abdominal segments are strongly asymmetrical; with the exception of *Neocorixa snowi* Hungerford, those of the female are perfectly regular.

In most cases the eggs are attached to the stems of aquatic plants. *Ramphocorixa acuminata* (Uhl.), however, habitually affixes its eggs to the body of a crayfish, especially on the first abdominal pleurite. Either the nymphs or adults may winter over. They hibernate in bottom mud and debris, but may sometimes be found actively swimming about, even under ice.

From a taxonomic standpoint, corixids are undoubtedly the most difficult of all of the families of aquatic and semiaquatic Hemiptera. There are several reasons for this situation, the chief ones being the great similarity in the various genera and species and the lack of distinctive, easily-observed diagnostic features. In addition, many species are quite plastic and show considerable variation in structural details.

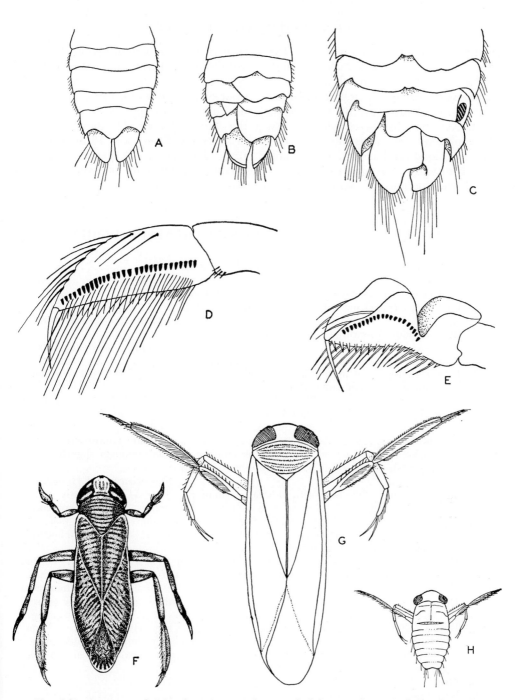

FIG. 346.—Structure of Corixidae. A, ventral view of abdomen of a typical female corixid; B, ventral view of abdomen of a typical male corixid; C, dorsal view of abdomen of male corixid showing strigil; D, first tarsus (pala) of a corixid, showing strong setae, scooplike shape, and row of chitinous pegs; E, first tarsus of *Ramphocorixa acuminata* (Uhl.); F, *Sigara alternata* (Say), ×7; G, adult corixid, diagrammatic, ×7; H, first instar nymph of a typical corixid, ×7. (A and B redrawn from Hungerford, 1919; C modified from Hungerford, 1942; D modified from Walley, 1936; F from *Insects in Kansas*.)

555

Identification is based largely on the characters of the males, the females throughout the family being so much alike that it is fruitless to attempt to include them in a key to be used primarily by the nonspecialist. Nevertheless, the females can usually be placed by their resemblance to the males in coloration and structural details.

Until recently, the generic and subgeneric designations of many American corixids were uncertain and controversial, but the recent careful monograph of Hungerford (1948) appears to have settled most of these questions in a logical manner. About 115 species are known from the United States. Of these, 45 belong in the genus *Sigara* and 18 in *Hesperocorixa*. The other 14 genera are much smaller, several being monotypic and quite rare.

## KEY TO GENERA AND SUBGENERA OF MALE CORIXIDAE

1. Last three segments asymmetrical ventrally (Fig. 346B)..............males, 2
   Last three segments symmetrical ventrally (except in *Neocorixa*)........females
2. First tarsus (pala) elongated and subcylindrical (Figs. 347B, C).............3
   First tarsus (pala) not subcylindrical (Fig. 347G).
   $\qquad$ Corixinae, Tribe Corixini, 6
3. Beak without cross ridges; 6.0 to 8.0 mm. long; northern.
   $\qquad$ Cymatiinae, **Cymatia americana** Hussey
   Beak with cross ridges (Fig. 347A)..........................Corixinae, 4
4. Palar claw long; not more than 12 to 14 lower palmar hairs; 7.6 to 9.2 mm. long; rare; known only from Minn.
   $\qquad$ Tribe Glaenocorisini, **Dasycorixa hybrida** Hungerford
   Palar claw short, and pala with 8 to 18 lower palmar hairs (Fig. 347B); or palar claw medium to long, and pala with more than 14 lower palmar hairs (Fig. 347C).......................................Tribe Graptocorixini, 5
5. Strigil absent; abdomen with sinistral asymmetry; female abdomen slightly asymmetrical; 6.9 to 8.2 mm. long; rare in Ariz. and N. M.
   $\qquad$ **Neocorixa snowi** Hungerford
   Strigil present; abdomen with dextral asymmetry (Fig. 347D); mostly southwestern, but one species reported from Ore.; six species........**Graptocorixa**
6. Abdomen with sinistral asymmetry (Fig. 347E); pala short and triangular; less than 5.6 mm. long; widely distributed and common; 11 species..**Trichocorixa**
   Abdomen with dextral asymmetry...................................7
7. Dorsal lobe of seventh abdominal segment with a projection which is clearly hooked (Fig. 347F); widely distributed from Atlantic coast to Rockies; three species.
   $\qquad$ **Palmacorixa**
   Dorsal lobe of seventh abdominal segment with or without a projection, if present then never hooklike.................................................8
8. Upper surface of pala deeply incised near middle (Fig. 346E); 5.0 to 5.7 mm. long; one rare species reported from Ariz.; another widely distributed in central and southern states.................**Ramphocorixa acuminata** (Uhler)
   Upper surface of pala not deeply incised..............................9
9. Strigil absent........................................................10
   Strigil present (Fig. 346C)..........................................12
10. Body short, broad, and more than one-third as broad as long; one or two rows of palar pegs of which one is never arranged along distal margin of pala......11
    Body less than one-third as broad as long; always with two rows of palar pegs of which one is arranged along the distal margin of the pala (Fig. 347G); 6.7 to 8.1 mm. long; northern states and at high altitudes; four species.
    $\qquad$ **Callicorixa**

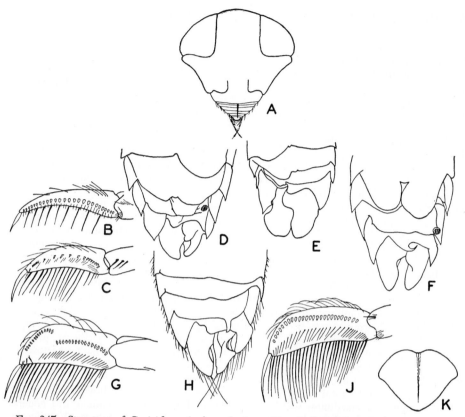

Fig. 347.—Structure of Corixidae. A, frontal view of head of male *Graptocorixa*; B and C, pala of male *Graptocorixa*; D, dorsal view of abdomen of male *Graptocorixa*; E, dorsal view of abdomen of male *Trichocorixa*; F, dorsal view of abdomen of male *Palmacorixa*; G, pala of male *Callicorixa*; H, dorsal view of abdomen of male *Morphocorixa*; J, pala of male *Hesperocorixa*; K, pronotum of *Arctocorisa*. (Modified and redrawn from Hungerford, 1948.)

11. Dorsal side of eighth abdominal segment with a slender projection (Fig. 347H); 5.8 to 7.5 mm. long; reported from Ariz., Okla., and Texas; two species.
**Morphocorixa**
Eighth abdominal segment without such a projection; 6.0 to 8.2 mm. long; one rare species reported from southern Texas......**Centrocorisa nigripennis** (Fabr.)

12. With two distinct rows of pegs on pala, or rarely one row of about 12 pegs......**13**
With a single straight to irregular row of 14 or more pegs on pala (Fig. 347J)...**14**

13. Body width more than one-third of body length; 5.3 to 6.0 mm. long; rare; reported only from Ariz....................**Pseudocorixa beameri** (Hungerford)
Body width less than one-third of body length; 4.0 to 8.0 mm. long; western states, but one species extending eastward to Penn.; five species..........**Corisella**

14. First tibia with a group of hairs near the outer apical margin (Fig. 347J); 6.3 to 11.4 mm. long; widely distributed and very common; about 18 species.
**Hesperocorixa**
First tibia without such a group of hairs................................**15**

15. With a well-defined median ridge on pronotum, usually visible for almost the entire length of the pronotum (Fig. 347K); 7.4 to 9.8 mm. long; two species in Mont., Wyo., and Colo..................................**Arctocorisa**
Median ridge absent or visible only on anterior third of pronotum............**16**

16. Wings entirely blackish, with no apparent markings; 5.3 to 6.4 mm. long; south-eastern states; two species..........................**Sigara (Pediosigara)**
    Wings not entirely blackish............................................**17**
17. Each wing with two prominent longitudinal black stripes; 3.6 to 6.0 mm. long; mostly north central states, but reported as far west as Wyo.; two species.
    **Sigara (Lasiosigara)**
    Without prominent longitudinal black stripes on wings.....................**18**
18. Palar claw serrated on basal half; 8.2 to 9.2 mm. long; northern states.
    **Sigara (Allosigara) decorata (Abbott)**
    Palar claw not serrated...............................................**19**
19. Dorsal margin of pala with a pronounced concavity about one-third of way from basal end; 8.1 to 9.2 mm. long; Maine to N. Y. and N. J., also reported from Ore..........................**Sigara (Xenosigara) ornata (Abbott)**
    Without such a concavity.............................................**20**
20. Pala wide and short, with 26 to 38 pegs; pronotum crossed by 6 to 14 more or less complete dark bands; interocular space more than one-third the maximum width of head; total length 5.2 to 7.8 mm.; widely distributed in the western half of the U. S.; nine species............................**Cenocorixa**
    With another combination of characters.........................**Sigara, 21**
21. Pala with about 26 pegs; pronotum crossed by six or seven dark bands; total length 5.3 to 5.8 mm.; inner margins of eyes parallel; Minn. to Mass. and N. J....................**Sigara (Pileosigara) douglasensis (Hungerford)**
    With another combination of characters................................**22**
22. Pala with 25 to 42 pegs; pronotum crossed by seven to nine more or less complete dark bands; total length 5.7 to 8.8 mm.; pala elongated; northeast quarter of U. S. but as far west as the Dakotas; four species......**Sigara (Arctosigara)**
    With another combination of characters................................**23**
23. Pala with 20 to 35 pegs; pronotum crossed by four to ten more or less complete dark bands; total length 4.0 to 7.1 mm.; interocular width about one-third or more the maximum width of the head (Fig. 346F); common and generally distributed; 20 species..........................**Sigara (Vermicorixa)**
    Pala with 12 to 25 pegs; pronotum crossed by four to nine more or less complete dark bands; interocular width about one-fourth the maximum width of head; total length 2.4 to 6.3 mm.; common and widely distributed in the eastern half of the U. S.; 13 species.....................**Sigara (Phaeosigara)**

# HEMIPTERA REFERENCES

ANDERSON, L. D. 1931. A monograph of the genus Metrobates (Hemiptera, Gerridae). *Univ. Kan. Sci. Bull.* **20**:297–311.

BARE, C. O. 1926. Life histories of some Kansas "backswimmers." *Ann. Ent. Soc. Amer.* **19**:93–101.

BLATCHLEY, W. S. 1926. *Heteroptera or true bugs of eastern North America.* 1116 pp. Indianapolis, Ind.

BRITTON, W. E., *et al.* 1923. Guide to the insects of Connecticut. Part IV. The Hemiptera or sucking insects of Connecticut. *State of Conn., Bull. Geol. Nat. Hist. Surv.* **34**:1–807.

CUMMINGS, C. 1933. The giant water bugs (Belostomatidae, Hemiptera). *Univ. Kan. Sci. Bull.* **21**:197–220.

DEAY, H. O., and G. E. GOULD. 1936. The Hemiptera of Indiana, I. Family Gerridae. *Amer. Midl. Nat.* **17**:753–76ɔ.

DRAKE, C. J., and H. M. HARRIS. 1932. A synopsis of the genus Metrobates Uhler. (Hemiptera: Gerridae). *Ann. Carnegie Mus.* **21**:83–88.

———. 1932a. A survey of the species of Trepobates Uhler (Hemiptera, Gerridae). *Bull. Brooklyn Ent. Soc.* **27**:113–122.

———. 1934. The Gerrinae of the Western Hemisphere (Hemiptera). *Ann. Carnegie Mus.* **23**:179–240.

EKBLOM, T. 1926. Morphological and biological studies of the Swedish families of Hemiptera-Heteroptera. Part I. The families Saldidae,

Nabidae, Lygaeidae, Hydrometridae, Veliidae, and Gerridae. *Zool. Bidrag f. Uppsala* **10**:31–180.

——. 1930. Morphological and biological studies of the Swedish families of Hemiptera-Heteroptera. Part II. The families Mesoveliidae, Corizidae, and Corixidae. *Ibid.* **12**:113–150.

ELLIS, L. L. 1950. The status of Plea striola and harnedi. *Proc. Ent. Soc. Wash.* **52**:104–105.

GOULD, G. E. 1931. The Rhagovelia of the Western Hemisphere with notes on world distribution (Hemiptera, Veliidae). *Univ. Kan. Sci. Bull.* **20**:5–61.

GRIFFITH, M. E. 1945. The environment, life history, and structure of the water boatman, Ramphocorixa acuminata (Uhler) (Hemiptera, Corixidae). *Ibid.* **30**:241–365.

HAMILTON, M. A. 1931. The morphology of the water-scorpion, Nepa cinerea Linn. (Rhynchota, Heteroptera). *Proc. Zool. Soc. London* (1931):1067–1136.

HIDALGO, J. 1935. The genus Abedus (Belostomatidae, Hemiptera). *Univ. Kan. Sci. Bull.* **22**:493–520.

HOFFMAN, C. H. 1924. The life history of three species of gerrids (Heteroptera Gerridae). *Ann. Ent. Soc. Amer.* **17**:419–430.

——. 1932. The biology of three North American species of Mesovelia (Hemiptera, Mesoveliidae). *Canad. Ent.* **64**:88–95, 113–120, 126–134.

HUNGERFORD, H. B. 1919. The biology and ecology of aquatic and semiaquatic Hemiptera. *Univ. Kan. Sci. Bull.* **11**:3–328.

——. 1922. The Nepidae of America north of Mexico (Heteroptera). *Ibid.* **14**:423–472.

——. 1927. The life history of the creeping water bug, Pelocoris carolinensis Bueno (Naucoridae). *Ibid.* **22**:77–82.

——. 1933. The genus Notonecta of the world. *Ibid.* **21**:5–196.

——. 1948. The Corixidae of the Western Hemisphere. *Ibid.* **32**:1–827.

HUNGERFORD, H. B., and N. E. EVANS. 1934. The Hydrometridae of the Hungarian National Museum and other studies in the family. *Ann. Mus. Nat. Hung.* **28**:31–112.

KUITERT, L. C. 1942. Gerrinae in University of Kansas collections. *Univ. Kan. Sci. Bull.* **28**:113–142.

LARIVERS, I. 1948. A new species of Pelocoris from Nevada, with notes on the genus in the United States (Hemiptera: Naucoridae). *Ann. Ent. Soc. Amer.* **41**:371–376.

——. 1951. A revision of the genus Ambrysus in the United States (Hemiptera: Naucoridae). *Univ. Calif. Publ. Ent.* **8**:277–338.

MCKINSTRY, A. P. 1942. A new family of Hemiptera-Heteroptera proposed for Macrovelia hornii Uhler. *Pan-Pac. Ent.* **18**:90–96.

POISSON, R. 1924. Contribution à l'Étude des Hémiptères Aquatiques. *Bull. Biol. de la France et de la Belgique* **58**:49–305.

POPHAM, E. J. 1943. Ecological studies of the common species of British Corixidae. *Jour. Anim. Ecol.* **12**:124–136.

RANKIN, K. P. 1935. Life history of Lethocerus americanus Leidy (Belostomatidae, Hemiptera). *Univ. Kan. Sci. Bull.* **22**:479–491.

SCHROEDER, H. O. 1931. The genus Rheumatobates and notes on the male genitalia of some Gerridae (Hemiptera, Gerridae). *Ibid.* **20**:63–99.

SILVEY, J. K. G. 1931. Observations on the life-history of Rheumatobates rileyi (Berg.) (Hemiptera-Gerridae). *Pap. Mich. Acad. Sci., Arts and Lett.* **13**:433–446.

DE LA TORRE-BUENO, J. R. 1924. A preliminary survey of the species of Microvelia Westwood (Veliidae, Heteroptera) of the western world, with description of a new species from the southern United States. *Bull. Brooklyn Ent. Soc.* **19**:186–194.

——. 1926. The family Hydrometridae in the western hemisphere. *Ent. Amer.* **7**:83–128.

USINGER, R. L. 1941. Key to the subfamilies of Naucoridae with a generic synopsis of the new subfamily Ambrysinae (Hemiptera). *Ann. Ent. Soc. Amer.* **34**:5–16.

——. 1946. Notes and descriptions of Ambrysus Stål with an account of the life history of Ambrysus mormon Montd. (Hemiptera, Naucoridae). *Univ. Kan. Sci. Bull.* **31**:185–210.

VAN DUZEE, E. P. 1917. Catalogue of the Hemiptera of America north of Mexico, excepting the Aphididae, Coccidae, and Aleurodidae. *Univ. Calif. Publ. Tech. Bull.* **2**:1–902.

WALTON, G. A. 1943. The natural classification of the British Corixidae (Hemiptera). *Trans. Soc. Brit. Ent.* **8**:155–168.

# Chapter 30

# MEGALOPTERA (ALDERFLIES, DOBSONFLIES, FISHFLIES)

These insects were formerly placed in the order Neuroptera, but most authorities now contend that they constitute a small separate order. They are dull-colored and medium to large in size, the length ranging from about 10 to 70 mm. The two pairs of wings are similar and are held flat or rooflike over the body when at rest. Flight is rather weak. The head bears long, slender antennae and biting mouth parts. The order is readily divisible into two families, the Sialidae (alderflies) and Corydalidae (dobsonflies and fishflies). Species belonging in the former family are small, diurnal, and have the fourth tarsal segments dilated and conspicuously bilobed. The Corydalidae, on the other hand, are about 25 to 70 mm. long, nocturnal, and have cylindrical fourth tarsal segments. Although the Megaloptera are widely distributed in the United States, they are rarely found in large numbers. Adults appear mostly in the spring and early summer near streams, ponds, and lakes in which the larval stages are spent. The imagoes live for only a few days. Pupation occurs on shore.

The minute elongated eggs are laid in rows forming masses of several thousand on vegetation and other objects overhanging the water, and upon hatching, the larvae fall into the water. In most cases the larval stages last for two or three years. Considering this long period of time, there are surprisingly few larval instars, about ten being the usual number.

Mature Megaloptera larvae are among the most striking of aquatic insects. They can be easily distinguished by the presence of a pair of lateral, cylindrical, simple or segmented gill filaments on the first seven or eight abdominal segments. These structures are supplied with tracheae and are supposedly of considerable respiratory significance. The body is stout, elongated, from 25 to 90 mm. in length, dull yellowish, brown, or dusky, and often mottled. The head bears four-segmented antennae, rather small compound eyes, and strong mouth parts. The legs are well developed. Because they possess functional abdominal spiracles, these larvae may be kept out of water for days at a time provided the surface of the body is damp. The Corydalidae have a pair of hooked anal prolegs, while the Sialidae have a terminal anal filament.

Although larvae have occasionally been collected as deep as 15 meters in lakes, they are customarily found along the margins of ponds and lakes and under and between stones in streams. *Sialis* sometimes lies buried in muddy substrates. Although the larvae typically move about by crawling on the substrate, they can swim to some extent by undulations of the body. As indicated by the structure of the mouth parts, they are active predators which feed on all kinds of aquatic organisms, especially insects.

To the fisherman, hellgrammites are one of the finest of all live baits. They can be kept for days in damp moss and are tough and hardy when placed on a hook.

Just before pupation the larvae crawl out of the water onto the shore, sometimes as much as 50 meters from the water. The pupal chamber may be constructed under stones or debris, or up to 5 or 10 cm. deep in the earth. The characteristic pupal stage is short and usually terminates in less than two weeks.

As indicated in the accompanying key, the Sialidae and the Corydalidae are easily distinguished. The former family includes only one American genus, *Sialis*.

According to Ross (1937), about 20 species are known. Some are widely distributed over most of the United States, while others are confined to the far west or Appalachian regions. In the Corydalidae, *Corydalus cornutus* L. is found throughout eastern North America. The generic affinities of the other species in this family are still unsettled, and for the present they are all regarded as belonging to a single widely distributed genus, *Chauliodes*.

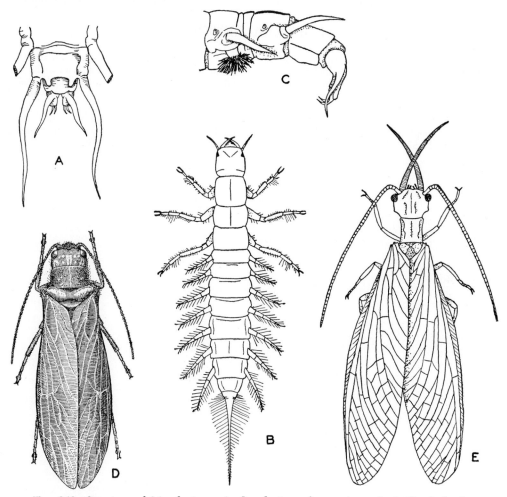

Fig. 348.—Structure of Megaloptera. A, dorsal view of posterior end of *Chauliodes* larva showing prolegs; B, dorsal view of *Sialis* larva, ×3; C, lateral view of posterior end of *Corydalus cornutus* L. showing prolegs, spiracles, and tracheal gills; D, adult *Sialis*, ×5; E, adult male *Corydalus cornutus* showing enormously developed mandibles, ×1.2. (D from Ross; B modified from Ross; A and C modified from Snodgrass, 1935.)

# KEY TO GENERA OF MEGALOPTERA LARVAE

1. With seven pairs of lateral segmented abdominal appendages and a long terminal anal filament; anal prolegs absent (Fig. 348B); total length up to 30 mm. when mature; alderfly larvae..............................SIALIDAE, **Sialis**
   With eight pairs of lateral abdominal appendages, unsegmented or imperfectly segmented; no terminal anal filament; anal prolegs present (Figs. 348A, C); total length up to 90 mm. when mature....................CORYDALIDAE, **2**
2. With a tuft of hairlike tracheal gills at the base of each lateral abdominal appendage (Figs. 303E, 348C); total length up to 90 mm. when mature; the true dobson or hellgrammite....................................**Corydalus cornutus** L.
   Without tracheal gills at the base of the abdominal appendages; total length up to 40 mm. when mature; fishfly larvae........................**Chauliodes**

## MEGALOPTERA REFERENCES

DuBois, A.-M., and R. Geigy. 1935. Beiträge zur Oekologie, Fortpflanzungsbiologie und Metamorphose von Sialis lutaria L. *Rev. Suisse de Zool.* **42**:169–248.

Ross, H. H. 1937. Studies of Nearctic aquatic insects. I. Nearctic alder flies of the genus Sialis (Megaloptera, Sialidae). *Bull. Ill. Nat. Hist. Surv.* **21**:57–78.

Seitz, W. 1940. Zur Frage des Extremitätencharakters der Tracheenkiemen von Sialis flavilatera L. im Rahmen allgemeiner biologischer Untersuchungen. *Zeitschr. Morph. u. Ökol. Tiere* **37**:214–275.

Townsend, L. H. 1935. Key to larvae of certain families and genera of Nearctic Neuroptera. *Proc. Ent. Soc. Wash.* **37**:25–30.

# Chapter 31

# NEUROPTERA, SISYRIDAE (SPONGILLA FLIES)

ALTHOUGH there are about 40 families of Neuroptera, only one, the Sisyridae, is of interest to the aquatic biologist. In this family, which is very poorly known except to the specialist, the larvae occur in the cavities and on the surface of fresh-water sponges. Hence the name "spongilla flies."

The adults appear during the summer months and probably live for only a few days. They are 6 to 8 mm. long and brown or yellow and brown in color. The head bears biting mouth parts and long antennae. The two pairs of wings are somewhat similar.

Eggs are laid in small masses on emergent vegetation and other objects overhanging the water. When the minute larvae hatch they fall into the water where they swim about in an aimless jerking manner. Although it is possible that they are attracted by the currents of water coming out of sponges, it may be that they come in contact with the sponges purely by chance.

The mature larva ranges from 4 to 6 mm. in length. The body is stout and bears long stiff bristles among which bits of sponge become entangled. This condition, in conjunction with their pale green or yellowish coloration, effectively camouflages the larvae. The mouth parts are highly modified, elongated, and grooved to form a needle-like tube which is slightly curved apically. This tube is thrust into the tissues of the sponge and the contents are sucked up into the body. The alimentary canal is closed at the junction of the mid- and hindgut, and any indigestible residue is probably retained in the stomach until the imago stage.

On the ventral side of the first seven abdominal segments in the larger larvae are curious, paired, segmented, tracheal gills. These are moved intermittently in an exceedingly rapid shuttle-like manner.

According to a recent revision there are only two species of spongilla flies known from the United States. *Sisyra vicaria* Walker is known from the eastern states and from Oregon, and *Climacia areolaris* (Hagen) occurs generally between the Atlantic states and the Great Plains. The larvae are similar in appearance and habits. In *Climacia*, however, the setae of the pronotum are pedunculate (situated on small projections), while in *Sisyra* they are sessile.

The larvae appear to be found on most of the common species of sponges. A few observers have reported them on Bryozoa and algae, but it seems likely that such occurrences are accidental.

Just before pupation the larvae climb out of the water onto the shore, emergent vegetation, or other objects. The silk which is used in constructing the cocoon emerges from the anus. In addition to a close-meshed cocoon which fits tightly around the body, there is an additional loose-fitting outer cocoon, composed of large open hexagons in *Climacia* but close-meshed in *Sisyra*. The pupal stage usually lasts less than 14 days. It is thought that wintering over occurs within the cocoon in the prepupal stage.

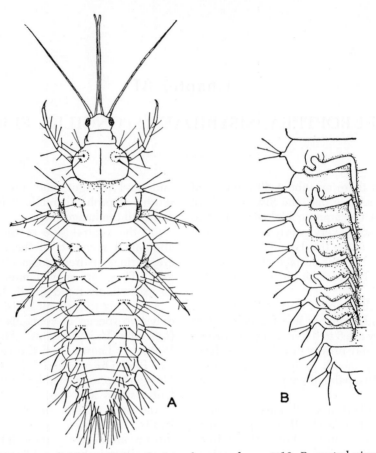

FIG. 349.—Larva of *Sisyra*. A, dorsal view of mature larva, ×16; B, ventral view of right side of abdomen showing tracheal gills, ×30. (A modified from Townsend, 1935; B modified from Rousseau, 1921.)

## SISYRIDAE REFERENCES

ANTHONY, M. H. 1902. The metamorphosis of Sisyra. *Amer. Nat.* **36**:615–631.

BROWN, H. P. 1952. The life history of Climacia areolaris (Hagen) a neuropterous "parasite" of fresh water sponges. *Amer. Midl. Nat.* **47**:130–160.

CARPENTER, F. M. 1940. A revision of the Nearctic Hemerobiidae, Berothidae, Sisyridae, Polystoechotidae and Dilaridae (Neuroptera). *Proc. Amer. Acad. Arts and Sci.* **74**:193–280.

OLD, M. C. 1932. Observations on the Sisyridae (Neuroptera). *Pap. Mich. Acad. Sci., Arts and Lett.* **17**:681–684.

WITHYCOMBE, C. L. 1922. Notes on the biology of some British Neuroptera (Planipennia). *Trans. Ent. Soc. London* **70**:501–594.

# Chapter 32

# TRICHOPTERA (CADDIS FLIES)

ADULT CADDIS flies are small to medium-sized mothlike insects found near streams, ponds, and lakes, especially between May and September. They are generally an inconspicuous gray, tan, brown, or blackish in color. The great majority are crepuscular or nocturnal. Flight in most species is rapid, with well-developed dodging movements. The wings are hairy and scaly and are folded rooflike over the body when at rest. The mouth parts are feeble and specialized for the ingestion of liquid foods, the antennae are filiform, and the compound eyes are large.

Metamorphosis is complete, and although the adults are terrestrial insects, the larvae and pupae are aquatic and may be found in all types of fresh-water habitats. Oviposition habits vary widely. In some species the eggs are dropped into the water during flight; in others they are deposited while at rest. Sometimes the eggs are deposited on objects a short distance above the water, and in such cases the newly-hatched larvae are thought to be washed into the water by rain. In the majority of instances, however, the females actually go below the surface to oviposit. The eggs may then be enclosed in gelatinous strings or masses in bottom debris or attached to submerged objects. Sometimes the eggs are simply glued to the substrate by a cement-like substance.

It is thought that caddis flies may have one or two generations per year, the former being the rule at higher latitudes. The adults are short-lived, and in most

species it is likely that this stage lasts about 30 days or less. The greater portion of the life history is spent as a larva, and it is usually this stage that winters over. The pupal stage lasts only about two weeks.

The first encounter with caddis fly larvae in the field is usually a considerable surprise. One first detects what appear to be small pieces of debris moving jerkily about on the bottom of a shallow pond or stream. On closer examination these bits of debris are found to be hollow cylindrical cases composed of sand grains, gravel, small pieces of leaves, grass, bark, or twigs. Within, and largely hidden from view, is the elongated caddis worm, or larva.

Although the larval head and thorax may be heavily sclerotized and darkly pigmented, the abdomen is soft and delicately colored, usually green, tan, gray, cream-colored, or whitish. The head bears a pair of very small antennae, chewing mouth parts, and two clumps of jet black ocelli. The three segments of the thorax are distinctly set off from each other, never fused. The prothoracic legs are generally the stoutest and shortest, and are used more for holding the prey and case building than for locomotion.

Each leg consists of the usual five segments, but some of these are subdivided. The trochanters, for example, are thought to be composed of two parts in all species, the basal portion sometimes being very short. In some species the middle and hind femora are divided, and in a few cases even the tibiae or tarsi are divided.

565

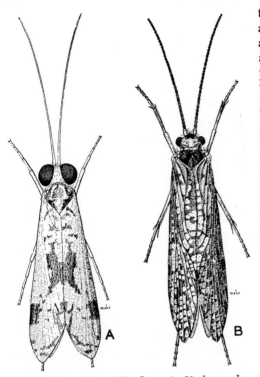

Fig. 350.—Adult caddis flies. A, *Hydropsyche aerata* Ross, ×5.5; B, *Rhyacophila fenestra* Ross, ×4.5. (From Ross, 1938, courtesy Illinois Natural History Survey.)

In most of the case-building larvae there are three tubercles or "spacing humps" on the first abdominal segment. One is mid-dorsal and the other two are lateral. Supposedly these prominences serve to maintain a space between the body and the case, so that freshly oxygenated water may come in contact with as much of the body surface as possible. At the posterior end is a pair of small to large prolegs. They bear hooks and function in anchoring the larva to the case or substrate. A lateral line is present in some caddis larvae; it consists of a fringe of hairs on each side of some of the posterior abdominal segments.

Most of the larvae that build portable cases have nonretractile tracheal gills. These occur on most of the abdominal segments, but in a few species they are also present on the thorax. In distribu-

tion, number, and morphology they show a wide range of conditions. They are arranged in more or less well defined rows along the abdomen and may be conical processes or long and filamentous. Usually they are single and simple, but in some genera they are arranged in tufts or are branched. In a few forms the gills are covered with fine hairs. Small finger-like blood gills are limited to the anal region and occur much less frequently; recent evidence indicates that they are of little or no importance in oxygen absorption, but it is possible that they may be osmoregulatory. In larvae that have no tracheal gills the respiratory exchange occurs through the general body surface. Even in the gilled forms, however, the integument is of much respiratory significance, and experimental work has shown that some larvae are able to obtain sufficient oxygen after all of the gills have been removed. In case-building forms undulatory movements of the abdomen and the hairs forming the lateral line serve to create a current of water through the case, and in this way the larvae are assured of an adequate oxygen supply. Actually, it may be said that *all* caddis larvae are surrounded by running water.

With reference to morphology and habits, two general types of larvae have long been recognized: campodeiform and eruciform. As indicated in Table X, however, this division is an unnatural one, there being many intermediate types and exceptions.

There are six or seven larval instars between the egg and pupa. The duration of these instars, and possibly their number, depends on the particular species as well as on such factors as water temperature, amount and type of available food, and current velocity. Thus a single particular larval instar may terminate in as little as fifteen days, or it may persist for several months, depending on these conditions.

The great majority of larvae that build portable cases cannot swim but simply crawl about on the substrate with the legs

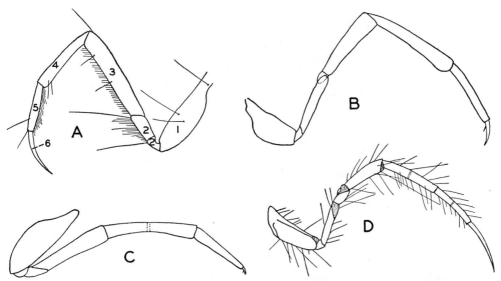

FIG. 351.—Structure of third legs of caddis larvae. A, *Ptilostomis*, showing divided trochanter; B, *Leptocella*, showing divided trochanter and femur; C, *Molanna*, showing divided trochanter and tibia; D, *Mystacides*, showing divided trochanter, femur, tibia, and tarsus. 1, coxa; 2, trochanter; 3, femur; 4, tibia; 5, tarsus; 6, tarsal claw. (C modified from Betten; D redrawn from Ross, 1944.)

when the head and thorax are protruded from the case. Some of the Phryganeidae and Leptoceridae, however, are able to swim well, provided the case is not too heavy. In these larvae the hind legs are modified for swimming. Most of the naked larvae and those that build fixed cases are able to swim, and in such species locomotion is aided considerably by powerful undulations of the body.

Caddis larvae are chiefly omnivorous, although the Limnephilidae, Hydropsychidae, and many Hydroptilidae feed on a preponderance of diatoms, other algae,

TABLE X. A COMPARISON OF THE TWO MAIN TYPES OF CADDIS LARVAE.

|  | Campodeiform | Eruciform |
|---|---|---|
| Position of head | Head held more or less straight forward, forming a continuation of the long axis of the body. | Head usually bent at a right angle to the long axis of the body. |
| Abdomen | Usually somewhat compressed; middle abdominal segments sometimes wider than the others. | Usually cylindrical; of about equal diameter throughout. |
| Tubercles on first abdominal segment | Absent. | Present in some groups. |
| Lateral line | Absent. | Usually present. |
| Case | Case, if present, not portable. | Case usually portable. |
| Habitat | More common in running water. | More common in standing water. |

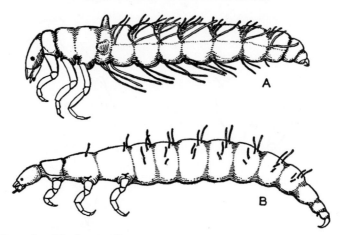

Fig. 352.—Typical caddis larvae, diagrammatic. A, eruciform larva; B, campodeiform larva. (From Dodds and Hisaw, 1925.)

and higher plants. The genus *Rhyacophila* and some Psychomyiidae, on the other hand, are thought to be generally carnivorous. Animal food consists of small crustaceans, annelids, and insect larvae. Most caddis worms move about actively in search of food, but those stream forms that build catch nets simply remove the plant and animal material that collects on the inner surface of the nets.

Larvae may be collected in shallow fresh-water habitats wherever there is an adequate supply of oxygen, sometimes in very great numbers. They occur on all types of substrates, including rock, gravel, sand, mud, debris, and vegetation. With few exceptions, the various taxonomic categories do not seem to be confined to particular types of habitats. Representatives of the same family or genus, for example, may be found in marshes, ponds, lakes, slow streams, rapid streams, and on a variety of substrates. In general, however, the naked larvae, such as *Rhyacophila*, are restricted to rapidly flowing streams and brooks. Also, those larvae that build silken catch nets (Philopotamidae, Hydropsychidae, and some Psychomyiidae) are confined to running waters. On the other hand, the numerous species that construct rough, clumsy, portable cases are restricted to lentic habi-

tats. It is also usually true that portable cases of larvae inhabiting swift waters are made of heavy materials.

Some species aestivate in debris or the substrate when ponds and streams are temporarily dry during midsummer.

Interest in caddis fly larvae has largely been maintained because of their curious habit of net and case construction. From a taxonomic standpoint, it is unfortunate that the identification of most larvae from case characters alone is very difficult and usually impossible. Only a few genera can be positively identified by their unique cases. *Helicopsyche*, for example, builds a case of sand grains in the shape of a snail shell; *Neureclipsis* is found in long, partially coiled, trumpet-shaped silken nets. In most families, and indeed in many genera, the construction of the case is variable, sometimes apparently being largely determined by the specific nature of the materials available to the larva. In the genera of the Limnephilidae the case may be triangular, circular, or flat in cross section; it may be neat and compact or clumsy and loosely constructed; it may be built of bits of leaves, twigs, grass, sand, gravel, seeds, mollusk shells, or debris of all kinds. In Table XI are indicated the chief features of larval case and net construction for the various families.

TABLE XI.  Chief Features of Larval Net and Case Construction in the Families of Trichoptera.

| | |
|---|---|
| Rhyacophilidae | No case or net in *Rhyacophila*. Elliptical, portable, gravel case shaped like a turtle shell in other genera (Fig. 356E). |
| Philopotamidae | Finger-shaped silken nets attached to rocks (Fig. 358A). |
| Psychomyiidae | Silken nets of various shapes; fastened to objects and more or less covered with algae and silt (Figs. 358J, M). Long debris-covered silken galleries on stones. Delicate branched tubes of fine sand buried in the substrate except for a small projecting turret. |
| Hydropsychidae | No case, or larva lying in a loosely made immovable case of mineral or vegetable matter, such a case opening into the apical portion of a conical silken net (Fig. 357M). |
| Hydroptilidae | Bean- or flask-shaped silken case open at both ends and usually covered with debris, sand, or algae (Figs. 355E, F). No case in early instars of some species. |
| Phryganeidae | Case a spirally wound cylinder of bits of vegetation (Figs. 360B-D) or a cylinder composed of rings of bits of vegetation placed end to end (Fig. 360E). |
| Limnephilidae | Case triangular, circular, or flat in cross section; compact or loosely constructed; composed of bits of a great variety of vegetable or mineral matter (Fig. 361). |
| Molannidae | Straight sand tubes with or without lateral winglike extensions (Fig. 353C). |
| Beraeidae | Case conical, curved, made of sand. |
| Odontoceridae | Case cylindrical, curved, made of sand (Fig. 354B). |
| Calamoceratidae | Case a bit of hollowed-out twig, or composed of bits of leaves and twigs. |
| Leptoceridae | Case conical or cylindrical; made of sand, vegetable matter, or silk (Fig. 359). |
| Goeridae | Case of small pebbles with larger stones along each side; nearly cylindrical (Fig. 354C). |
| Lepidostomatidae | Smooth conical cases of sand, or built of vegetable material and square in cross section. |
| Brachycentridae | Conical cases of sand grains, or built of vegetable material and round or square in cross section (Fig. 360F). |
| Sericostomatidae | Case conical in early instars, cylindrical later; made of fine sand. |
| Helicopsychidae | Case composed of sand grains, in the shape of a snail shell (Fig. 353B). |

Case construction is usually begun soon after hatching. Materials are selected from the substrate with the legs, and, if it is vegetable material, it may be cut to correct size with the mouth parts. There are large glands in the anterior portion of the body which produce a gluelike substance used for cementing together the particles constituting the case. As the larva grows, additional pieces are added to the case at the anterior end. A few species tear off the posterior part of the case or leave the old cases and form new ones at intervals. Under normal conditions the same species select the same materials and build cases in the same way, but when the usual materials are not available, substitutes may be utilized. Experimental work has shown that a variety of unusual objects, such as paper and egg shells, may be used. Exposed larvae are often able to distinguish their own case from those of others.

In the Hydroptilidae the gluelike substance secreted at the mouth is formed into a translucent sheet which forms the bulk of the case. In the larvae that build trapnets this material appears as a thin, tough, sticky thread which hardens on exposure to the water. As it leaves the mouth it is woven to form the meshes of the net.

In some genera, notably in the family Limnephilidae, cases may differ considerably in shape or construction according to the age of the larvae. An early case, for example, may be built of vegetable material, but a case of the same individual in a later instar may be built of mineral material. Some of the Hydroptilidae and Rhyacophilidae do not begin case construction until they are far along in the larval stage. Sometimes it is built just prior to pupation.

Numerous stream and fish food surveys have shown that caddis larvae form one of the most important items in the diet of trout. The fish pick them out of bottom debris or actually scrape them off rocks with the jaws and swallow them, case and all. Occasionally swarms of adults assume pest proportions along lake shores.

Field collections may be made by picking the larvae and cases off the substrate with fingers or forceps, or by raking or washing them out of drift, debris, or vegetation with a sieve net or large pan. Eighty per cent alcohol is the best preservative.

The larvae and pupae are not difficult to rear in the laboratory. They should be kept in running water or in an aquarium supplied with adequate oxygen by photosynthesis or by an aerator. There should also be sufficient food available.

Although more than 750 species of adult caddis flies are known from the United States, the immature stages of less than 20 per cent of these have been described. Fortunately, however, this small proportion includes practically all of the common forms. The great majority of genera are widely distributed over most of the country or over the eastern half. Fifty-nine genera and 181 species are known from Michigan. The fauna of the Rocky Mountain area has been only sketchily studied.

## KEY TO GENERA OF TRICHOPTERA LARVAE *

1. Abdomen much wider and (or) deeper than thorax (Figs. 355H, J); usually less than 3 mm. long; purse-, bean-, or flask-shaped silken cases, or sand cases, usually much larger than larvae and covered with foreign material; lotic and lentic................................HYDROPTILIDAE, 18

    Abdomen not much wider and (or) deeper than thorax; usually more than 5 mm. long; cases, when present, not much larger than larvae..................2

2. Case spiral, in the form of a snail shell, composed of sand (Fig. 353B); widely distributed and very common...........HELICOPSYCHIDAE, Helicopsyche

    Case of another design, or absent......................................3

* Modified from Ross (1944). This key includes all but a few rare and poorly known genera of larvae; most of these are restricted to the Pacific coast area.

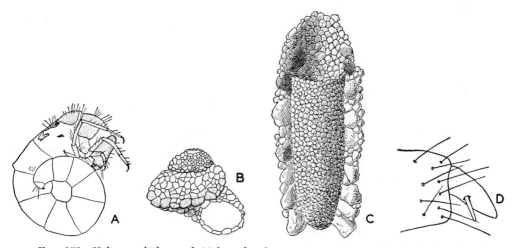

Fig. 353.—Helicopsychidae and Molannidae larvae. A, position of *Helicopsyche borealis* (Hagen) in case, ×8; B, case of *H. borealis*, ×7; C, case of *Molanna uniophila* Vorhies, ×2.4; D, tip of third leg of *Molanna cinerea* Hagen. (A and B from Elkins; C from Ross, 1944, courtesy Illinois Natural History Survey; D redrawn from Betten.)

3.  Pro-, meso-, and metanotum each with a single large sclerotized shield; with con-
    spicuous branched tracheal gills (Fig. 357O); no case, or larva in a loosely
    made case of mineral or vegetable material, such a case opening into the
    apical portion of a silken net (Fig. 357M); in swift water.
    HYDROPSYCHIDAE, 31
    Either meso- or metanotum or both without sclerites or with sclerotized shield sub-
    divided into separate plates (Figs. 356A, 354D) . . . . . . . . . . . . . . . . . . . . . . .4
4.  Anal legs projecting beyond, and free from, membranous lobes of tenth abdominal
    segment (Figs. 356B, C); no tubercles on first abdominal segment; case, if
    present, usually not movable. . . . . . . . . . . . . . . . . . . . . . . . . . . . . . . . . . . . . .5
    Anal legs appearing as lateral sclerites of membranous lobes of tenth abdominal seg-
    ment; with or without tubercles on first abdominal segment; case movable. . .7
5.  Last abdominal segment with a dorsal sclerotized shield (Fig. 356C); in swift
    water. . . . . . . . . . . . . . . . . . . . . . . . . . . . . . . . . . . .RHYACOPHILIDAE, 28
    Last abdominal segment without a dorsal sclerotized shield. . . . . . . . . . . . . . . . .6
6.  Labrum soft and expanded laterally (Fig. 358E); in finger-shaped silken nets in
    rapid streams (Fig. 358A). . . . . . . . . . . . . . . . . . . . .PHILOPOTAMIDAE, 38
    Labrum entirely sclerotized, not expanded laterally (Fig. 358F); silken nets or
    galleries fastened to substrate and more or less covered with algae and silt, or
    buried in the substrate. . . . . . . . . . . . . . . . . . . . . . . . .PSYCHOMYIIDAE, 40
7.  Claws of hind legs very small (Fig. 353D), those of first and second legs large;
    case of sand grains, with lateral extensions (Fig. 353C); lentic and lotic.
    MOLANNIDAE, **Molanna**
    Claws of hind legs as long as those of second legs. . . . . . . . . . . . . . . . . . . . . . . .8
8.  Antennae long, at least seven times as long as wide and arising at base of mandi-
    bles; case conical or cylindrical, curved or straight, made of sand, vegetable
    matter, or silk. . . . . . . . . . . . . . . . . . . . . . . . . . . . . . . . .LEPTOCERIDAE, 43
    Antennae short, not more than three or four times as long as wide, often incon-
    spicuous. . . . . . . . . . . . . . . . . . . . . . . . . . . . . . . . . . . . . . . . . . . . . . . . . . . . . .9
9.  Mesonotum submembranous except for a pair of parenthesis-like sclerotized bars.
    LEPTOCERIDAE, 43
    Mesonotum without such bars. . . . . . . . . . . . . . . . . . . . . . . . . . . . . . . . . . . . . .10

10. Meso- and metanotum entirely membranous or with only minute sclerites; case a spiral cylinder or rings of vegetation placed end to end; large; usually in quiet waters..................................................PHRYGANEIDAE, **49**

 Meso- and usually metanotum with conspicuous sclerotized plates............**11**

11. Labrum with a row of about 20 stout setae across the middle (Fig. 354A); case a bit of hollowed-out twig, or composed of bits of leaves and twigs; two uncommon eastern species.................CALAMOCERATIDAE, **Ganonema**

 Labrum without such a row of setae, usually with six to eight long setae, not in a row, and other small scattered setae................................**12**

12. Metanotum with a wide transverse straplike anterior sclerite, a pair of oblong lateral sclerites, and a thin posterior transverse sclerite; case curved, made of sand (Fig. 354B); eastern states...........ODONTOCERIDAE, **Psilotreta**

 Metanotum with another grouping of small sclerites........................**13**

13. Anal hooks formed of two or three long overlapping teeth; case conical or cylindrical and made of fine sand; mountainous areas of east and west; uncommon.

 SERICOSTOMATIDAE, **Sericostoma**

 Anal hooks formed of a single large tooth with one or more small teeth along its dorsal edge........................................................**14**

14. Pronotum with a deep furrow or crease running almost the full width of the sclerite, the posterior margin of the furrow forming a sharp and slightly overhanging carina; case of sand grains or bits of vegetation.

 BRACHYCENTRIDAE, **54**

 Pronotum without a furrow, or with a concave depression..................**15**

15. Hind tarsal claw slender and extremely long, as long as tibia; case conical, made of sand........................................................BERAEIDAE, **Beraea** *

 Hind tarsal claw much stouter and shorter...............................**16**

16. First abdominal segment without dorsal tubercle; either curved tapering tubes of sand, or square in cross section, made of vegetable material, and tapered very little.............................LEPIDOSTOMATIDAE, **Lepidostoma**

 First abdominal segment with dorsal tubercle.............................**17**

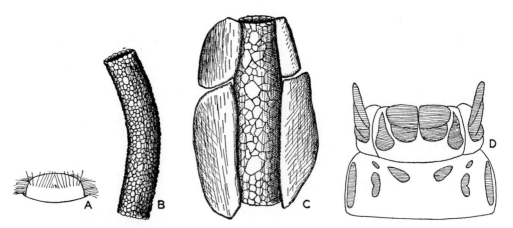

Fig. 354.—Larvae of Calamoceratidae, Odontoceridae, and Goeridae. A, labrum of *Ganonema*; B, case of *Psilotreta frontalis* Banks, ×3; C, case of *Goera calcarata* Banks, ×4; D, meso- and metanotum of *G. calcarata*. (A redrawn from Ross, 1944; B and C from Lloyd, 1921; D modified from Lloyd, 1921.)

* Not yet recorded from the United States in the larval stage, but the imago is well known.

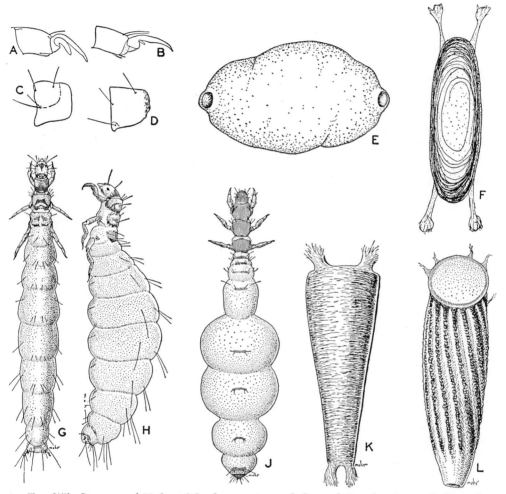

Fig. 355.—Structure of Hydroptilidae larvae. A, tarsal claws of *Tascobia*; B, tarsal claws of *Ochrotrichia*; C, metanotum of *Ochrotrichia*; D, metanotum of *Hydroptila*; E, case of *Leucotrichia pictipes* (Banks), ×10; F, case of *Agraylea multipunctata* Curtis, ×7; G, dorsal view of *Hydroptila waubesiana* Betten, ×17; H, lateral view of same; J, *Leucotrichia pictipes*, ×17; K, case of *Oxyethira serrata* Ross, ×13; L, case of *Mayatrichia ayama* Mosely, ×20. (A to C and G to L from Ross, 1944, courtesy Illinois Natural History Survey; D redrawn from Ross, 1944.)

17. Mesonotum with a series of sclerotized plates (Fig. 354D); case of sand or small stones, nearly cylindrical, and with larger stones along each side (Fig. 354C); eastern..................................................GOERIDAE, **Goera**

Mesonotum with a single rectangular sclerite having only a median fracture line; case variable in shape and composition............LIMNEPHILIDAE, **55**

18. Each abdominal segment with a dark, sclerotized dorsal area (Fig. 355J)......**19**

At least abdominal segments two to seven without dark, sclerotized dorsal area..**20**

19. Case translucent, ovoid, and flat (Fig. 355E)....................**Leucotrichia**

Case covered with fine sand, purselike, rarely tortoise-shell-like......**Ochrotrichia**

20. Abdominal segments with lateral projections; rare..................**Ithytrichia**

Abdominal segments without lateral projections...........................**21**

**21.** Second and third legs almost three times as long as first legs; case flask-shaped, broadest behind (Fig. 355K)................................**Oxyethira**
Second and third legs not more than one and one-half times as long as first legs..**22**
**22.** Second and third tarsal claws much longer than tarsi; case purselike.....**Agraylea**
Second and third tarsal claws short and stout............................**23**
**23.** Anal prolegs distinctly projecting from body mass........................**24**
Anal prolegs combined with body mass and only the claws projecting.........**25**
**24.** Case of sand grains, evenly tapered; in clear streams...............**Neotrichia**
Case translucent, evenly tapered, and with dorsal side ringed or fluted (Fig. 355L); in streams.............................................**Mayatrichia**
**25.** Tarsal claws with stout inner tooth (Fig. 355A); case fibrous and purselike.
**Tascobia**
Tarsal claws without stout inner tooth.................................**26**
**26.** Second and third tibiae cylindrical and long; case long, smooth, round in cross section, and tapered at each end...........................**Orthotrichia**
Second and third tibiae stout and swollen at apex; case purselike............**27**
**27.** Metanotum with a distinct widened ventrolateral area (Fig. 355C)...**Ochrotrichia**
Metanotum without a widened lateral area (Fig. 355D)............**Hydroptila**
**28.** Anal prolegs with large hooks (Fig. 356B); case absent............**Rhyacophila**
Anal prolegs with very small hooks; in tortoise-shell-shaped cases made of gravel.
**29**
**29.** Legs attached at anterolateral angles of pronotum................**Glossosoma**
Legs attached at lateral margins of pronotum............................**30**
**30.** Anal hook divided into many teeth...............................**Protoptila**
Anal hook divided into one large and one small tooth.................**Agapetus**

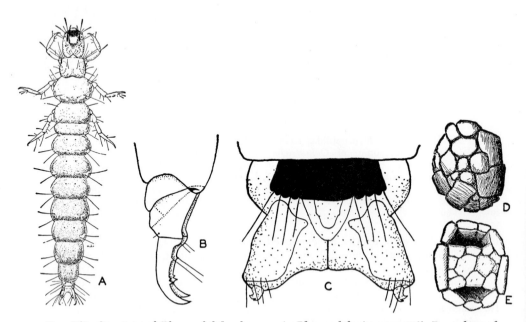

Fig. 356.—Structure of Rhyacophilidae larvae. A, *Rhyacophila fenestra*, ×5; B, prolegs of *Rhyacophila torva* Hagen; C, dorsal view of posterior end of *Glossosoma americanum* Banks; D, dorsal view of case of *G. americanum*, ×2; E, ventral view of same. (A from Ross, 1944, courtesy Illinois Natural History Survey; B modified from Lloyd, 1921; C modified from Krafka, 1924; D and E from Lloyd, 1921.)

31. Head with a broad, flat, dorsal area set off by an extensive arcuate carina; head
    greatly tapered to base of mandibles (Fig. 357J; uncommon in large swift
    rivers. ...........................................................**Macronemum**
    Head without such a broad, flat, dorsal area............................32
32. Stridulator at base of front leg forked (Fig. 357B).......................33
    Stridulator at base of front leg not forked (Fig. 357C)....................34

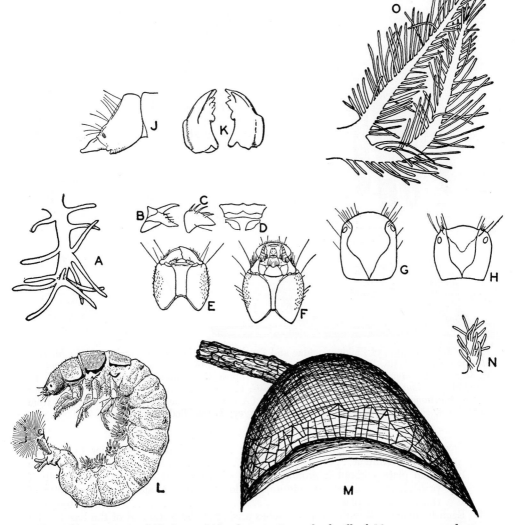

FIG. 357.—Structure of Hydropsychidae larvae. A, tracheal gill of *Macronemum zebratum*
(Hagen); B, stridulator of first leg of *Hydropsyche*; C, stridulator of first leg of *Smicridea*; D,
prosternal plates of *Hydropsyche*; E, ventral view of head of *Parapsyche*; F, ventral view of
head of *Arctopsyche*; G, dorsal view of head of *Diplectrona*; H, dorsal view of head of
*Smicridea*; J, lateral view of head of *Macronemum*; K, mandibles of *Potamyia*; L, *Hydropsyche
simulans* Ross, ×2.5; M, net and case of *Hydropsyche*; N, tracheal gill of *Diplectrona*; O,
tracheal gills of *Hydropsyche*. (A modified from Krafka, 1915; B to F and J to L from Ross,
1944, courtesy Illinois Natural History Survey; G, H, and N redrawn from Ross, 1944; M
modified from Noyes; O redrawn from Thienemann, 1905.)

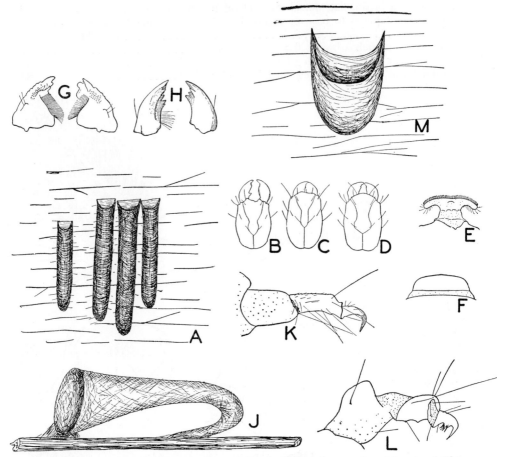

Fig. 358.—Structure of Philopotamidae and Psychomyiidae larvae. A, catch nets of *Chimarra aterrima* Hagen, ×1.3; B, head of *Chimarra*; C, head of *Dolophilodes*; D, head of *Wormaldia*; E, labrum of *Chimarra*; F, labrum of *Polycentropus*; G, mandibles of *Phylocentropus*; H, mandibles of *Neureclipsis*; J, case of *Neureclipsis*; K, posterior end of *Neureclipsis*; L, posterior end of *Psychomyia*; M, case of *Polycentropus*. (A modified from Noyes; B to H and K from Ross, 1944, courtesy Illinois Natural History Survey; L modified from Ross, 1944.)

33. Prosternal plate with a pair of prominent sclerotized plates posterior to it (Fig. 357D); common...................................**Hydropsyche**
    Prosternal plate without a prominent pair of sclerotized plates posterior to it; if present, such plates are minute and located at the lateroposterior angles of the prosternal plate...................................**Cheumatopsyche**
34. Each branched gill with all its branches arising at the distal end of the basal stalk; uncommon. ...................................**35**
    Each branched gill with its branches arising from sides as well as end of the basal stalk (Fig. 357N)...................................**36**
35. Gula roughly rectangular and of even width (Fig. 357E)............**Parapsyche**
    Gula narrowed posteriorly (Fig. 357F)...................................**Arctopsyche**
36. Mandibles with winglike dorsoventral flanges along basal half (Fig. 357K).
                                                                          **Potamyia**
    Mandibles without such flanges...................................**37**

37. Frons expanded laterally (Fig. 357G)..........................**Diplectrona**
    Frons not expanded laterally (Fig. 357H); in spring brooks..........**Smicridea**
38. Anterior margin of frons markedly asymmetrical (Fig. 358B)........**Chimarra**
    Anterior margin of frons slightly asymmetrical at most......................39
39. Frons almost perfectly symmetrical, with the posterior portion widened (Fig.
    358D). ...............................................................**Wormaldia**
    Frons slightly asymmetrical, posterior portion not widened (Fig. 358C).
                                                                    **Dolophilodes**
40. Tenth abdominal segment short, with scarcely any ventral margin (Fig. 358L).
                                                                    **Psychomyia**
    Tenth abdominal segment long and tubular (Fig. 358K)....................41
41. Mandibles short and triangular, each with a large thick brush (Fig. 358G).
                                                                **Phylocentropus**
    Mandibles longer, with a thin brush on the left mandible..................42
42. Tenth segment without hairs (Fig. 358K).....................**Neureclipsis**
    Tenth segment with numerous long hairs.....................**Polycentropus**
43. Case a translucent elongated silken cone (Fig. 359C); second tarsi bent.
                                                **Leptocerus americanus** (Banks)
    Case not translucent, of another shape; second tarsi straight.................44

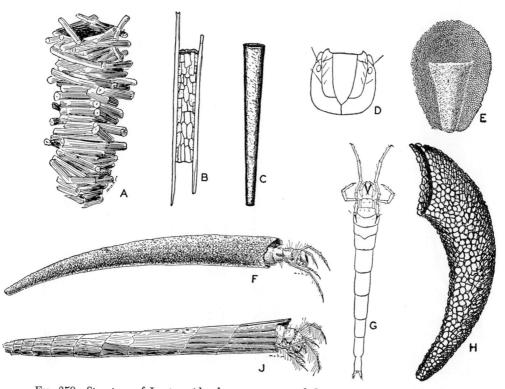

FIG. 359.—Structure of Leptoceridae larvae. A, case of *Oecetis cinerascens* (Hagen), ×6; B, case of *Mystacides sepulchralis* Walker, ×2.5; C, case of *Leptocerus americanus* (Banks), ×3.5; D, head of *Athripsodes*; E, case of *Athripsodes*, ×3.5; F, *Leptocella albida* (Walker), ×4; G, *L. albida*, ×3; H, case of *Athripsodes ancylus* (Vorhies), ×8; J, *Triaenodes tarda* Milne, ×6. (A, E, F, and J from Ross, 1944, courtesy Illinois Natural History Survey; C and H from Lloyd, 1921; D redrawn from Ross, 1944; G from Elkins.)

44. Maxillary palpi nearly as long as stipes; conical cases of sand or vegetable material.
    **Oecetis**

    Maxillary palpi about half the length of stipes..............................**45**

45. Head with two suture-like lines paralleling the epicranial arms (Fig. 359D); case
    of sand grains, with or without lateral flanges................**Athripsodes**

    Head without two suture-like lines in addition to the epicranial arms..........**46**

46. Mesonotum membranous, with a pair of sclerotized, narrow, curved or angled bars;
    case of sand grains, with or without lateral flanges (Figs. 359E, H).
    **Athripsodes**

    Mesonotum without such a pair of sclerotized bars........................**47**

47. Hind tibiae entirely sclerotized; abdomen without gills; case of sand or bits of
    vegetation. ..........................................**Leptocella**

    Hind tibiae with a fracture near the middle which appears to divide tibiae into
    two parts (Fig. 351D); abdomen with at least a few gills...............**48**

48. Hind tibiae with a regular fringe of long hairs; case usually of short bits of twigs
    or grass built into a spiral pattern (Fig. 359J)................**Triaenodes**

    Hind tibiae with only irregularly placed hairs; case cylindrical and built of irregular
    pieces of vegetation or shell fragments (Fig. 359B)............**Mystacides**

49. Frons with a median black line (Fig. 360A)..............................**50**

    Frons without a median black line........................................**51**

50. Anterior margin of pronotum black (Fig. 360A); widely distributed and common.
    **Phryganea**

    Anterior margin of pronotum mostly yellow.
    **Banksiola selina** Betten and **Agrypnia straminea** Hagen

51. Mesonotum with a pair of small sclerites near the anterior margin; northeastern
    states. ..............................................................**52**

    Mesonotum without sclerites............................................**53**

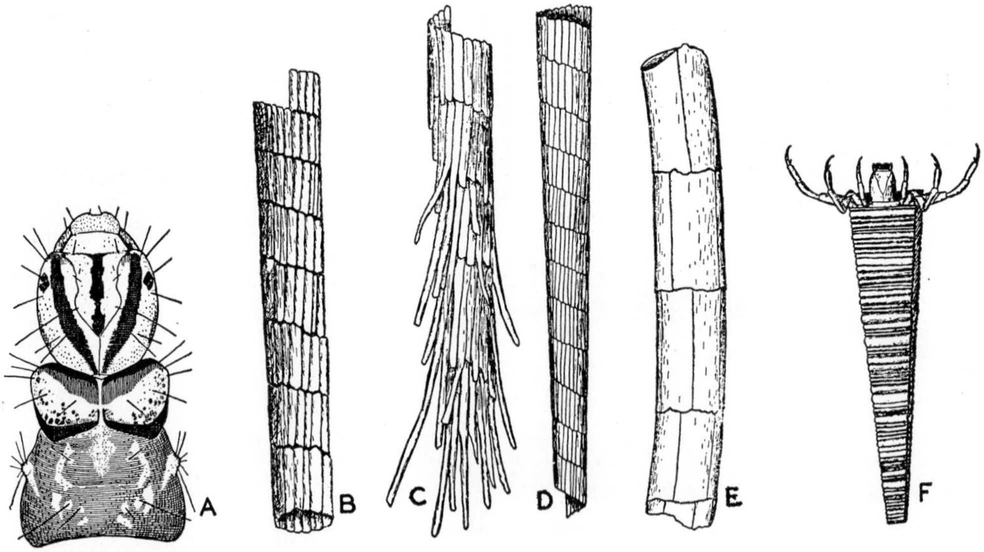

Fig. 360.—Phryganeidae and Brachycentridae. A, anterior end of larva of *Phryganea*; B, case
of *Phryganea*, ×1.3; C, case of mature larva of *Agrypnia vestita* (Walker), ×2; D, case of
young larva of *A. vestita*; E, case of *Ptilostomis postica* Walker, ×2; F, *Brachycentrus nigro-
soma* Banks, ×3. (A from Ross, 1944, courtesy Illinois Natural History Survey; B from
Wesenberg-Lund, 1911; C to F from Lloyd, 1921.)

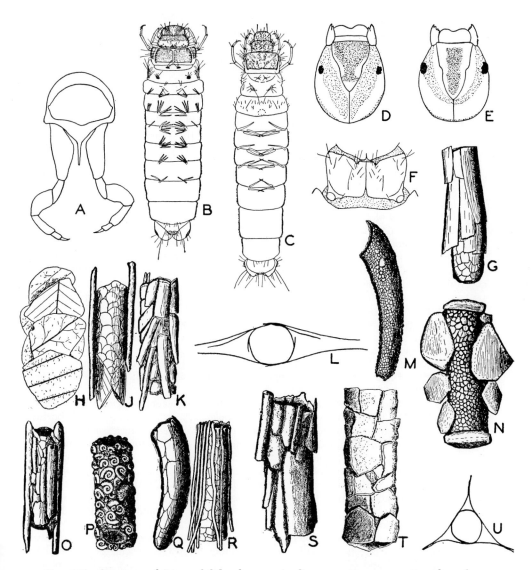

FIG. 361.—Structure of Limnephilidae larvae. A, diagrammatic cross section through prothorax of *Limnephilus*, showing prosternal horn; B, *Limnephilus combinatus* Walker, ×2.6; C, *Hesperophylax designatus* (Walker), ×2.9; D, head of *Limnephilus combinatus*; E, head of *Glyphotaelius hostilis* Hagen; F, mesonotum of *Neophylax*; G, case of *Glyphotaelius hostilis*, ×1; H, J, and K, cases of *Pycnopsyche scabripennis* Rambur, ×1; L. diagrammatic cross section of case of *P. scabripennis*; M, case of *Hesperophylax designatus*, ×2.6; N, case of *Neophylax concinnis* MacLach., ×4; O, case of *Astenophylax argus* (Harris), ×0.6; P, case of *Limnephilus*, ×1.3; Q and R, cases of *Limnephilus submonilifer* Walker, ×1.7; S and T, cases of *Limnephilus consocius* Walker, ×1.8; U, diagrammatic cross section of case of *L. consocius*. (A redrawn from Krafka, 1915; B and C from Elkins; D, E, L, and U modified from Lloyd, 1921; F modified from Ross, 1944; G to J and M to T from Lloyd, 1921.)

52. Mature larva up to 30 mm. long..................**Eubasilissa pardalis** (Walker)
    Mature larva up to 20 mm. long...............**Oligostomis ocelligera** (Hagen)
53. Anterior margin of pronotum black; eastern..........**Agrypnia vestita** (Walker)
    Anterior margin of pronotum mostly yellow; widely distributed and common.
    **Ptilostomis**
54. Second and third tibiae with an inner, apical, seta-bearing spur; case round and
    built of sand, or square, smooth, and built of bits of vegetation (Fig. 360F).
    **Brachycentrus**
    Second and third tibiae without apical spur; case built of sand grains, round and
    tapered. ...........................................................**Micrasema**
55. Anterior margin of mesonotum with a median rectangular emargination (Fig.
    361F); case of gravel with small stones along the sides (Fig. 361N).
    **Neophylax**
    Anterior margin of mesonotum evenly rounded...........................56
56. First femora slender; mostly western.........................**Dicosmoecus**
    First femora broad...................................................57
57. Gills arising singly...................................................58
    Gills in clusters of two or more......................................59
58. Seventh abdominal tergite with an anteromedian gill; case usually of bits of vege-
    tation; northeastern states..................**Astenophylax argus** (Harris)
    Seventh abdominal tergite without anteromedian gill; case highly variable (Figs.
    361H–K); mostly in northeastern states.....................**Pycnopsyche**
59. Pronotum with dense, short, black spines, especially near anterior margin; case
    irregular and cylindrical; rare...........................**Glyphopsyche**
    Pronotum with setae only.............................................60
60. Anal prolegs with a group of about ten setae on bulbous central portion; eastern;
    uncommon. ...............................................**Frenesia**
    Anal prolegs without such setae.......................................61
61. Dorsal gills of first few abdominal segments with 6 to 12 filaments per cluster...62
    Dorsal gills of first few abdominal segments with two or three filaments per cluster.
    63
62. Dorsal gills at base of abdomen with about 12 branches each; case usually of wood
    fragments; in temporary ponds and streams.....................**Caborius**
    Dorsal gills at base of abdomen with about six branches each; case cylindrical,
    straight or curved, tapered, and sometimes elongated to form a hood over the
    head (Fig. 361M), composed of sand or bits of bark; usually in springs,
    brooks, and cold waters.............................**Hesperophylax**
63. With a narrow, dark, longitudinal strip on frons (Fig. 361E); cylindrical case of
    irregular bits of leaves (Fig. 361G); northeastern.
    **Glyphotaelius hostilis** Hagen
    Frons with a wide dark area, or dark area absent........................64
64. Prosternal horn short, not projecting beyond apices of coxae (Fig. 361A); case
    highly variable, but usually roughly made; largest American genus; widely
    distributed and common.................................**Limnephilus**
    Prosternal horn projecting beyond apices of coxae; thick irregular case of frag-
    ments of vegetation.................................**Platycentropus**

In its general morphology and body proportions, the pupa is somewhat similar to the adult, the antennae, wing cases, and legs being well formed and free from the body (Fig. 362M). The larval tracheal gills are usually persistent, however, especially in the eruciform families. In those pupae that have no gills the respiratory exchange occurs through the general body surface. Some pupae are quite active in the pupal chamber, and undoubtedly their rhythmic abdominal undulations aid in obtaining oxygen by the creation of a current through the chamber.

Without exception, the transformation to the pupal stage occurs in some kind of a fixed case, and it is thought that the case-building habit may have arisen at this critical period in the life history. The portable cases of eruciform larvae are fastened to the substrate and modified in a variety of ways to form the pupal case. Frequently it is shortened, but the ends are always closed. This may be effected by loose extensions of the case, by the construction of silken nets (Phyganeidae, Limnephilidae), by silken membranes with holes or slits (Sericostomatidae, Leptoceridae), or by simply plugging the ends with small pebbles or vegetation.

The campodeiform larvae construct a special pupal case at the close of the larval period. This is usually a loosely built mound or corral-like structure of gravel and small pebbles. Within these cases most such larvae form a silken cocoon in which pupation occurs.

Although pupal cases are rather compact structures, there are always sufficient spaces between the pebbles and in the closing nets and membranes to permit the effective circulation of water over the pupa. Membranes and nets are kept free of debris by means of the sweeping action of long bristles at each end of the body.

Pupation usually occurs in the late spring and early summer. The pupal stage is of brief duration and ordinarily lasts only about two weeks. For this reason the average collector encounters relatively few pupae.

Imagoes usually emerge during the late afternoon or night. A mature pupa leaves its case by means of strong undulatory movements of the body which break the closing membranes or the case proper. Some investigators believe that the mandibles aid in this process. In most genera that inhabit swift streams the pupae swim rapidly to the surface where the adult emerges from the pupal integument in a matter of a few seconds. Of those species inhabiting quiet waters, some swim to the surface where emergence occurs more slowly, and others crawl out of the water and emerge on some exposed object.

## KEY TO FAMILIES OF TRICHOPTERA PUPAE *

1. Apex of abdomen membranous, without definite lobes except ventral membranous
   ones which contain developing genital structures......................2
   Apex of abdomen with additional projecting platelike or finger-like processes (Figs.
   362E–L). ........................................................4
2. Mandibles without teeth or serrations; pupa less than 5 mm. long.
                                          HYDROPTILIDAE
   Mandibles with teeth or serrations; pupa more than 5 mm. long...............3
3. Mandibles with teeth grouped near apex (Fig. 362D).....PHILOPOTAMIDAE
   Mandibles with teeth near middle (Fig. 362A), or mandibles only serrate (Fig.
   362B). ..............................................RHYACOPHILIDAE
4. Fifth tergite with only an anterior pair of hook-bearing plates.
                                         HYDROPSYCHIDAE
   Fifth tergite with both anterior and posterior hook-bearing plates.............5
5. Seventh abdominal tergite without a pair of sclerotized plates................6
   Seventh abdominal tergite with a pair of sclerotized hook-bearing plates.......9
6. Apical processes of abdomen short, appearing triangular in dorsal view, curved ventrally in lateral view (Figs. 362G, H).....................BERAEIDAE
   Apical processes of abdomen either much longer or not curved...............7
7. Case shaped like a snail shell........................HELICOPSYCHIDAE
   Case of another design................................................8

* Modified from Ross (1944).

8. Antennae very long, part wound around the abdominal apex...LEPTOCERIDAE
   Antennae scarcely longer than body........................MOLANNIDAE
9. Abdomen without a fringe of hairs.....................PSYCHOMYIIDAE
   Abdomen with a lateral fringe of hairs..................................10
10. Abdomen with a pair of almost linear transverse lines of hooks between fifth and
    sixth tergites.................................BRACHYCENTRIDAE
    Abdomen with these areas of hooks much wider.........................11
11. Apical processes of abdomen platelike (Fig. 362K).........PHRYGANEIDAE
    Apical processess finger-like or styliform.............................12
12. Apical processes of abdomen short, widely separated, and bearing long black spines
    (Fig. 362L)................................LEPIDOSTOMATIDAE
    Apical processes either close together or much longer.....................13

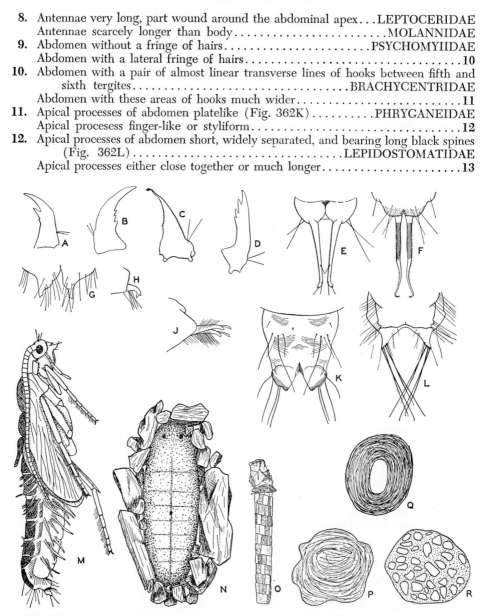

Fig. 362.—Structure of Trichoptera pupae. A, left mandible of *Glossosoma*; B, mandible of *Rhyacophila*; C, mandible of *Psilotreta*; D, mandible of *Dolophilodes*; E, apical abdominal processes of *Limnephilus*; F, apical abdominal processes of *Goera*; G, dorsal view of apical processes of *Beraea*; H, lateral view of same; J, lateral view of apical abdominal processes of *Sericostoma*; K, apical abdominal processes of *Banksiola*; L, apical abdominal processes of *Lepidostoma*; M, diagram of typical pupa; N, pupa of *Rhyacophila fuscula* Banks in cocoon in case, ×2.5; O, pupal case of *Agrypnia straminea* Hagen, ×1.3; P, anterior pupal membrane of *Helicopsyche borealis*; Q, anterior pupal membrane of *Leptocella albida*; R, anterior pupal membrane of *Limnephilus bimaculatus* Walker. (A to L from Ross, 1944, courtesy Illinois Natural History Survey; N and Q modified from Betten; O from Elkins, 1936; P and R redrawn from Denning.)

13. Mandibles produced at apex into a narrow whiplike process (Fig. 362C).
                                                                    ODONTOCERIDAE
    Mandibles pointed but not thus produced...............................14
14. Dorsal surface of abdomen with transverse patches of dense, fine hairs.
                                                                   CALAMOCERATIDAE
    Dorsal surface of abdomen with only isolated setae......................15
15. Apical processes with slender terminal appendages (Fig. 362J).
                                                                  SERICOSTOMATIDAE
    Apical processes without terminal appendages..........................16
16. Antennae about twice as long as body...................LEPTOCERIDAE
    Antennae much shorter.............................................17
17. Apical processes of abdomen extremely slender at apex (Fig. 362F)..GOERIDAE
    Apical processes of abdomen not extremely slender at apex (Fig. 362E).
                                                                    LIMNEPHILIDAE

# TRICHOPTERA REFERENCES

BETTEN, C. 1934. The caddis flies or Trichoptera of New York State. *Bull. N.Y. State Mus.* 292:1–576.

COPELAND, M., and P. S. CROWELL. 1937. Observations and experiments on the case-building instincts of two species of Trichoptera. *Psyche* 64:125–131.

DEMBOWSKI, J. 1933. Über die Plastizität der tierischen Handlungen, Beobachtungen und Versuche an Molanna-Larven. *Zool. Jahrb., Abt. Allg. Zool. u. Physiol.* 53:261–311.

DENNING, D. G. 1937. The biology of some Minnesota Trichoptera. *Trans. Amer. Ent. Soc.* 63:17–44.

DODDS, G. S. and F. L. HISAW. 1924. Ecological studies of aquatic insects. II. Size of respiratory organs in relation to environmental conditions. *Ecology* 5:262–271.

———. 1925. Ecological studies on aquatic insects. III. Adaptations of caddisfly larvae to swift streams. *Ibid.* 6:123–137.

———. 1925. Ecological studies on aquatic insects. IV. Altitudinal range and zonation of mayflies, stoneflies and caddisflies in the Colorado Rockies. *Ibid.* 380–390.

ELKINS, W. A. 1936. The immature stages of some Minnesota Trichoptera. *Ann. Ent. Soc. Amer.* 29:656–689.

FANKHAUSER, G., and L. E. REIK. 1935. Experiments on the case-building of the caddis-fly larva, Neuronia postica Walker. *Physiol. Zool.* 8:337–359.

GORTER, F. J. 1931. Köcherbauversuche an Trichopterenlarven. *Zeitschr. Morph. u. Ökol. Tiere* 20:443–532.

HICKIN, N. E. 1942. Larvae of the British Trichoptera. 1, 2, 3, 4. *Proc. Roy. Ent. Soc. Lond.* 17:9–17.

KRAFKA, J., JR. 1915. A key to the families of trichopterous larvae. *Canad. Ent.* 47:217–225.

———. 1924. Morphology of the prolegs of trichopterous larvae. *Ann. Ent. Soc. Amer.* 17:97–102.

LLOYD, J. T. 1915. Notes on the immature stages of some New York Trichoptera. *Jour. N. Y. Ent. Soc.* 23:201–212.

———. 1921. The biology of the North American caddis fly larvae. *Bull. Lloyd Libr. Bot., Pharm., Mat. Med.* 21:1–124.

MARSHALL, A. C. 1939. A qualitative and quantitative study of the Trichoptera of western Lake Erie (as indicated by trap material). *Ann. Ent. Soc. Amer.* 32:665–688.

MICKEL, C. E., and H. E. MILLIRON. 1939. Rearing the caddice fly, Limnephilus indivisus Walker and its hymenopterous parasite Hemiteles biannulatus Grav. *Ibid.* 575–580.

MILNE, D. J. 1943. The distribution and life history of the caddis flies of Waskesiu Lake, Saskatchewan. *Canad. Ent.* 75:191–198.

MILNE, L. J., and M. J. MILNE. 1938. The Arctopsychidae of continental America north of Mexico (Trichoptera). *Bull. Brooklyn Ent. Soc.* 33:97–110.

MILNE, M. J. 1938. Case building in Trichoptera as an inherited response to oxygen deficiency. *Canad. Ent.* 70:177–179.

———. 1939. Immature North American Trichoptera. *Psyche* 46:9–19.

MILNE, M. J., and L. J. MILNE. 1939. Evolutionary trends in caddis worm case construction. *Ann. Ent. Soc. Amer.* 32:533–542.

MORGAN, A. H., and H. D. O'NEIL. 1931. The function of the tracheal gills in larvae of the caddis fly Macronema zebratum Hagen. *Physiol. Zool.* 4:361–379.

NIELSEN, A. 1948. Postembryonic development and biology of the Hydroptilidae. A contribution to the phylogeny of the caddis flies and to the question of the origin of the case-building instinct. *Det. K. Danske Videnskab. Selskab, Biol. Skr.* 5:1–200.

Noyes, A. A. 1914. The biology of the net-spinning Trichoptera of Cascadilla Creek. *Ann. Ent. Soc. Amer.* **7**:251–272.

Ross, H. H. 1944. The caddis flies, or Trichoptera, of Illinois. *Bull. Ill. Nat. Hist. Surv.* **23**:1–326.

Sibley, C. K. 1926. Studies on Trichoptera. Pp. 185–221 *in*: A preliminary biological survey of the Lloyd-Cornell Reservation. *Bull. Lloyd Libr. Bot., Pharm., Mat. Med.* **27**:1–247.

Slack, H. D. 1936. The food of caddis fly (Trichoptera) larvae. *Jour. Animal Ecol.* **5**:105–116.

Sleight, C. E. 1913. Relations of Trichoptera to their environment. *Jour. N.Y. Ent. Soc.* **21**:4–8.

Ulmer, G. 1925. Trichoptera. *Biol. Tiere Deutschlands* **13**:1–113.

Vorhies, C. T. 1909. Studies on the Trichoptera of Wisconsin. *Trans. Wis. Acad. Sci., Arts and Lett.* **16**:647–738.

Wesenberg–Lund, C. 1911. Über die Biologie der Phryganea grandis und über die Mechanik ihres Gehäusebaues. *Int. Rev.* **4**:65–90.

———. 1911a. Biologischen Studien über netzspinnende, campodeoide Trichopterenlarven. *Int. Rev.* **4** (Suppl. 3):1–64.

# Chapter 33

# LEPIDOPTERA, PYRALIDIDAE (AQUATIC CATERPILLARS)

ALTHOUGH there are more than 150 families in this order, in only two American genera of a single family of moths, the Pyralididae, are the immature stages known to be truly aquatic. The larvae are true "aquatic caterpillars," having the characteristic body shape, thoracic legs, and ventral abdominal prolegs of terrestrial species. The adults are small, dull-colored, gray, brown, or blackish moths which may be found flying about on summer evenings near small ponds and streams.

Larvae of *Nymphula* are generally distributed over most of the United States in ponds which are densely overgrown with water lilies, potamogetons, and other vegetation. About a dozen species are known, of which *Nymphula maculalis* Clemens is perhaps the most common. The larvae hatch from eggs which have been deposited on the undersides of floating leaves. In most instances they construct flat ovate cases composed of two pieces of leaves fastened together at the edges with silk. With the anterior portion of the body protruding from the case, they crawl about feeding on the undersides of floating vegetation. In some southern localities they are so abundant as to be pests on water lilies. Mature larvae are 20 to 25 mm. long, yellow or whitish in color with darker head.

There are two general groups of species in the genus *Nymphula*. In one group there are no gills, and respiration occurs through functional spiracles owing to the fact that all of the body except the anterior end is situated in a large air bubble within the case. In the other group of species there are paired, lateral, filamentous tracheal gills on the thoracic and abdominal segments. In the first larval instar these gills are absent, but they appear in the second instar and subsequently become more and more abundant. In the last few instars they are branched. More than 400 separate filaments have been counted on the last instar of one species. Periodic lashing movements of the anterior end of the larvae ensure a continuous supply of oxygenated water in the case.

The larvae of *Elophila fulicalis* Clemens are found on exposed surfaces of stones in rapid streams. They are protected, however, by a silken canopy which is cemented to the substrate along most of its periphery. The canopy covering the later larval instars may be as much as 25 mm. wide and 100 mm. long. The larva moves about beneath the canopy feeding on the film of algae covering the rock. Mature larvae are 10 to 12 mm. long and straw-brown in color. A total of about 120 filamentous blood gills (apparently devoid of tracheation) are arranged in two lateral rows along the thorax and abdomen. Although the geographic distribution of this common species has not yet been accurately ascertained, it is common in the eastern states.

At least one other species of *Elophila* has habits similar to those of *E. fulicalis*, but the several other species in this genus live on *Lemna* in ponds and are air-breathing.

All species are thought to winter over as immature larvae.

## KEY TO GENERA OF MATURE PYRALIDIDAE LARVAE

1.  Gills absent....................................................3
    With filamentous lateral gills...............................2
2.  Gills simple (Fig. 363D); on stones in rapid streams...................Elophila
    Gills branched (Fig. 363A); on floating vegetation in ponds and lakes...Nymphula
3.  Case ovate; on *Lemna*......................................Elophila
    Case sharp-edged; on other types of floating vegetation...............Nymphula

Pupation habits vary. Some species of *Nymphula* remain in the water and attach the larval case to submerged vegetation, while others leave the water with the case and fasten it to emergent vegetation. In either instance, however, the larva constructs a silken cocoon within the case. Just before pupation the stream species of *Elophila* cut away the silken canopy and construct smaller, flat, oval pupal cases in their place and then spin a loose inner cocoon about themselves.

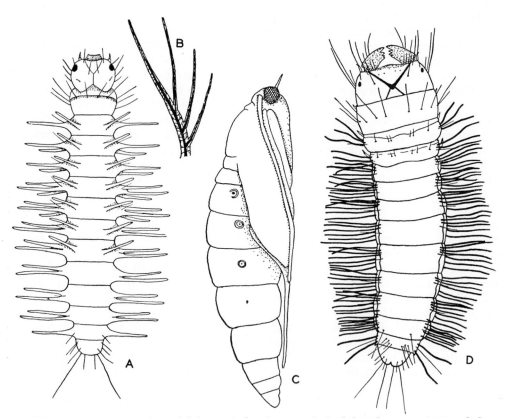

FIG. 363.—Structures of Pyralididae. A, dorsal view of third larval instar of *Nymphula maculalis* Clemens, ×20; B, branched tracheal gill of a more advanced larval instar of *Nymphula*; C, lateral view of pupa of *N. maculalis*, ×6; D, dorsal view of larva of *Elophila fulicalis* Clemens, ×8. (A and C modified from Welch, 1916; B modified from Forbes, 1910; D modified from Lloyd.)

In addition to the genera mentioned above, there are numerous other Pyralididae and a few species in other families of the Lepidoptera which are semiaquatic and are not considered in this manual. These larvae bore and mine in the emergent tissues of many different kinds of aquatic plants, particularly *Scirpus*, *Eleocharis*, and *Nelumbo*. For further information concerning these species see especially the papers of Ainslie, Chittenden, Frohne, and Welch.

## PYRALIDIDAE REFERENCES

Ainslie, G. G. 1922. Biology of the lotus borer (Pyrausta penitalis Grote). *Bull. U. S. Dept. Agric.* **1076**:1–14.

Berg, C. O. 1950. Biology of certain aquatic caterpillars (Pyralididae: Nymphula spp.) which feed on Potamogeton. *Trans. Amer. Micros. Soc.* **69**:254–266.

Chittenden, F. H. 1919. The lotus borer. *Jour. Econ. Ent.* **11**:453–457.

Forbes, W. T. M. 1910. The aquatic caterpillars of Lake Quinsigmond. *Psyche* **17**:219–228.

———. 1911. Another aquatic caterpillar (Elophila). *Ibid.* **18**:120–121.

Frohne, W. C. 1939. Biology of Chilo forbesellus Fernald, an hygrophilous crambine moth. *Trans. Amer. Micros. Soc.* **58**:304–326.

———. 1939a. Observations on the biology of three semiaquatic lacustrine moths. *Ibid.* 327–348.

Lloyd, J. T. 1914. Lepidopterous larvae from rapid streams. *Jour. N. Y. Ent. Soc.* **22**:145–152.

Welch, P. S. 1914. Habits of the larva of Bellura melanopyga Grote (Lepidoptera). *Biol. Bull.* **27**:97–114.

———. 1916. Contribution to the biology of certain aquatic Lepidoptera. *Ann. Ent. Soc. Amer.* **9**:159–187.

———. 1919. The aquatic adaptations of Pyrausta penitalis Grt. (Lepidoptera). *Ibid.* **12**:213–226.

———. 1922. The respiratory mechanism in certain aquatic Lepidoptera. *Trans. Amer. Micros. Soc.* **41**:29–50.

———. 1924. Observations on the early larval activities of Nymphula maculalis Clemens (Lepidoptera). *Ann. Ent. Soc. Amer.* **17**:395–402.

Welch, P. S., and G. L. Sehon. 1928. The periodic vibratory movements of the larva of Nymphula maculalis Clemens (Lepidoptera) and their respiratory significance. *Ibid.* **21**·243–258.

# Chapter 34

# COLEOPTERA (BEETLES)

ADULT BEETLES are familiar to everyone. They are minute to large, and the forewings are always modified into horny or leathery elytra which cover the abdomen and meet to form a straight, median, dorsal suture. The hind wings are membranous, folded beneath the elytra, and often reduced or lacking. The mouth parts are adapted for biting. Metamorphosis is complete; the larvae usually have well-developed legs and mandibulate mouth parts; the pupae have the wings and legs free from the body.

This is by far the largest order of insects, more than 250,000 species being known. Beetles are chiefly terrestrial insects, and although there are more than 150 families, only a few are wholly or partly aquatic in the adult or larval stages. Such families occurring in the United States are listed below.

Amphizoidae; very small family; all adults and larvae aquatic.

Haliplidae (crawling water beetles); small family; all adults and larvae aquatic.

Dytiscidae (predaceous diving beetles); largest aquatic family; all adults and larvae aquatic; highly adapted to aquatic habitats.

Gyrinidae (whirligig beetles); small family; all adults and larvae aquatic; well adapted to aquatic habitats.

Hydrophilidae (water scavenger beetles); large family; majority of species aquatic both as larvae and adults; some terrestrial species.

Hydroscaphidae; very small family; some larvae and adults aquatic.

Hydraenidae; very small family; most larvae and adults aquatic.

Psephenidae; very small family; all larvae and adults aquatic.

Dryopidae; small family; all larvae and adults aquatic.

Elmidae; medium-sized family; except for two genera, all adults are aquatic; all larvae aquatic.

Helodidae (=Cyphonidae); small family; adults terrestrial; larvae aquatic.

Chrysomelidae (leaf beetles); very large family; adults of three common genera found on emergent vegetation; larvae of two of these genera aquatic, the other on emergent vegetation.

Curculionidae (weevils); probably the largest family of insects; adults and immature stages of a few genera feed on emergent aquatic vegetation; adults occasionally found swimming under water.

Because of the fact that there is such diversity among the various families of aquatic beetles, the group as a whole will be considered only briefly here, more detailed material being given in the sections dealing with the individual families. In certain families, such as the Elmidae, there are no modifications of the legs for swimming, and the adults simply crawl about on the substrate. Other families, however, such as the Dytiscidae, are good swimmers, and the hind legs may be greatly flattened and hairy. In some families and

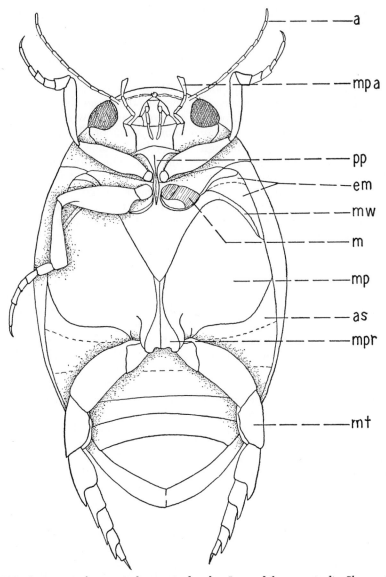

FIG. 364.—Structure of a typical aquatic beetle, *Laccophilus terminalis* Sharp, ×25. *a,* antenna; *as,* first visible abdominal sternite; *em,* episternum of metathorax; *m,* mesocoxa; *mp,* metacoxal plate; *mpa,* maxillary palp; *mpr,* metacoxal process; *mt,* metatibia; *mw,* metasternal wing; *pp,* prosternum and process. (Modified from Leech, 1948.)

even genera there is a considerable range of structural modification. Many aquatic Coleoptera are known to fly, and in this way they migrate from one body of water to another. Such flights usually occur at night, and some species are attracted to bright lights where they may be collected in large numbers. Most adult aquatic beetles are fundamentally dependent upon atmospheric oxygen. When submerged, some carry a supply of air under the elytra where oxygen diffuses into the spiracles.

This supply is renewed at the surface of the water at intervals. Others carry a quantity of air in the form of a thin film (plastron) held to various portions of the body by a hydrofuge pubescence or fine sclerotized granules. Such a film is responsible for the peculiar silvery appearance of these beetles when submerged. Although the air-water interface of a plastron may act as a diffusion membrane through which both carbon dioxide and oxygen may pass to and from the water, respectively, the plastron is usually renewed at intervals at the surface if the water does not contain an abundance of dissolved oxygen. Some species, however, have been kept submerged for several months in aerated water in the laboratory without ill effects.

Adult beetles are found everywhere in streams, rivers, ponds, and protected bays of lakes. They occur in the shallows near shore, particularly where there are quantities of debris and aquatic vegetation, but are generally absent from wave-swept shores and the deeper waters of lakes and rivers. They may be easily collected with a small dipnet or by washing out vegetation. Many common species are often overlooked by the average collector because of their small size, inconspicuous coloration, and secretive habits. It is usually the adult which winters over by burrowing into debris or mud on the bottom.

Some species, especially members of the Dryopidae and Elmidae, are often covered with tightly attached debris and require cleaning before they can be identified. Nelson (1949) recommends the following procedure. Crimp the metal tip of a small paintbrush to a diameter of about 1.5 mm. and cut the bristles down to a length of about 1 mm. Place the beetles in 5 to 10 per cent acetic acid for 20 to 30 minutes, and then place them in tap water containing a pinch of trisodium phosphate for 20 or 30 minutes. While carefully holding them in this solution, remove the loosened debris with the brush.

Food habits are quite variable, ranging from a strictly predatory (Dytiscidae) to a vegetarian diet (Haliplidae).

With few exceptions the pupal stage is terrestrial. When the mature larva leaves the water and crawls out upon the adjacent shore, some of the nonfunctional larval spiracles become perforate and begin to function. The pupal chamber is most frequently constructed within five meters of the water's edge. It may be a hollow chamber at a depth of several inches in the earth, or it may be on the surface constructed of mud pellets or bits of vegetable debris. The pupae are exarate, pale, and covered with a thin, soft cuticle.

So far as is known, all adult aquatic beetles have aquatic larvae, the eggs usually being deposited below the surface of the water. These larvae differ from the terrestrial grubs with which everyone is familiar. The former have longer, more efficient thoracic legs, and the body is more elongated and slender, or, in some cases, considerably flattened dorsoventrally. Locomotion includes rapid swimming movements (Dytiscidae), "jumping," walking, active crawling, and sluggish crawling motions (Haliplidae). Most species come to the surface at intervals to obtain a fresh supply of air in the tracheal system via a pair of spiracles at the posterior end, but a few species which have prominent lateral gills remain permanently submerged. In addition, some have delicate filamentous anal gills which may function in respiration. It also seems likely that a portion of the oxygen-carbon dioxide exchange takes place through the general body surface. As in the adults, food habits are variable, ranging from a carnivorous to an herbivorous diet. The mouth parts are well developed for biting and chewing or biting and sucking. In general, the larvae occur in the same habitats as the adults.

# KEY TO FAMILIES OF ADULT COLEOPTERA

1. Head not prolonged into a beak; common; true beetles......................2
   Head prolonged into a long beak; uncommon in aquatic habitats; weevils.
   CURCULIONIDAE, p. 623
2. Eyes completely divided by the lateral margins of the head (Fig. 372D).
   GYRINIDAE, p. 604
   Eyes not divided.......................................................3
3. Hind coxae in the form of large plates (Fig. 366B).......HALIPLIDAE, p. 593
   Hind coxae normal......................................................4
4. Tarsi with three segments; southwestern states; uncommon.
   HYDROSCAPHIDAE, p. 612
   Tarsi with more than three segments....................................5
5. Hind tarsi apparently four-segmented; third segment broadly bilobed; feeding on
   emergent aquatic vegetation.................CHRYSOMELIDAE, p. 621
   Hind tarsi five-segmented; third segment not bilobed......................6
6. Antennae clubbed......................................................7
   Antennae not clubbed..................................................9
7. Prosternum with a process which fits into a groove on the mesosternum (Fig.
   380C). ...........................................................12
   Prosternum without such a process.....................................8
8. Antennal club of five pubescent segments; not more than 2.5 mm. long.
   HYDRAENIDAE, p. 612
   Antennal club of fewer than five segments; usually more than 2.5 mm. long.
   HYDROPHILIDAE, p. 606
9. Legs much modified for swimming, flattened, with large spurs and small claws
   (Fig. 367)....................................DYTISCIDAE, p. 595
   Legs slightly or not at all modified....................................10
10. First sternite completely divided into three parts by the coxae.
    AMPHIZOIDAE, p. 593
    First sternite not divided.............................................11
11. Prosternum with a process which fits into a groove on the mesosternum (Fig.
    380C). ...........................................................12
    Prosternum without such a process; feeding on terrestrial or emergent aquatic vege-
    tation .......................................HELODIDAE, p. 620
12. Entirely aquatic......................................................13
    Not found actually in the water.
    ELMIDAE, **Lara** and **Phanocerus clavicornis** Sharp, p. 616
13. With six or seven abdominal sternites.................PSEPHENIDAE, p. 613
    With five abdominal sternites..........................................14
14. Antennae with the apical segments pectinate and forming a close club (Fig. 380A).
    DRYOPIDAE, p. 614
    Antennae usually filiform, but if clubbed, with the segments of the club never
    pectinate. ........................................................15
15. Anterior coxae rounded...............................ELMIDAE, p. 616
    Anterior coxae transverse............................DRYOPIDAE, p. 614

# KEY TO FAMILIES OF COLEOPTERA LARVAE

1. Legs six-segmented, with distinct tarsus and one or two claws..............2
   Legs either five-segmented, with tarsus and claw fused into a single segment, or
   less than five-segmented, or vestigial, or absent.......................5
2. Tenth abdominal segment armed with four apical hooks.....GYRINIDAE, p. 604
   No apical hooks.......................................................3

3. Ninth abdominal segment present......................HALIPLIDAE, p. 593
   Ninth abdominal segment rudimentary, apparently absent..................**4**
4. Edges of tergites extended laterally as flattened projections. AMPHIZOIDAE, p. 593
   Edges of tergites not extended laterally..................DYTISCIDAE, p. 595
5. Body very flat, scalelike, oval, and smooth in outline.....PSEPHENIDAE, p. 613
   Body shape otherwise...........................................**6**
6. Antennae about as long as or longer than thorax..........HELODIDAE, p. 620
   Antennae clearly shorter than thorax..............................**7**
7. Mandibles short, broad, and inconspicuous; feeding on roots and rhizomes of submerged aquatic plants or on upper surface of lily pads.
                                       CHRYSOMELIDAE, p. 621
   Mandibles prominent; food habits otherwise.............................**8**
8. Part or all of ninth sternum forming a movable operculum which usually covers a
   terminal cloacal chamber containing tufts of retractile gills...............**9**
   Movable operculum, cloacal chamber, and retractile gills absent.............**10**
9. Tracheae never with air sacs; ninth abdominal segment with or without pleural
   sclerites; with nine pairs of spiracles or with the spiracles only on the eighth
   abdominal segment.............................DRYOPIDAE, p. 614
   Tracheae with or without air sacs; ninth abdominal segment without distinct pleural
   sclerites; always with nine pairs of spiracles.............ELMIDAE, p. 616
10. With a pair of cerci-like filaments on eighth abdominal segment; true cerci absent;
    antennae very short; southwestern...........HYDROSCAPHIDAE, p. 612
    Filaments absent; cerci two-segmented and well developed; antennae rather
    long. ......................................................**11**
11. With nine complete abdominal segments, the tenth reduced but distinct.
                                       HYDRAENIDAE, p. 612
    With eight complete abdominal segments, the ninth and tenth reduced (Fig.
    375)...............................HYDROPHILIDAE, p. 606

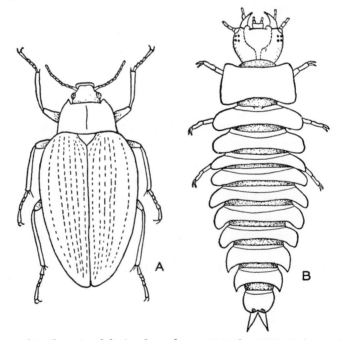

Fig. 365.—Amphizoidae. A, adult *Amphizoa lecontei* Matth., ×4.5; B, larva of same, ×6.5.
(B redrawn from Hubbard.)

# AMPHIZOIDAE

Only three species in this family, *Amphizoa insolens* Lec., *A. striata* Van Dyke, and *A. lecontei* Matth., are known from the United States. All are rare and seem to be confined to swift, clear streams in the western states. The adults are 12 to 14 mm. long, broad, and the body is rough; the antennae are glabrous. These beetles are poorly adapted to an aquatic habitat, the legs being fitted for walking.

They may be found on submerged logs and stones or in masses of floating trash; they frequently sun themselves on protruding rocks or fly about along the streamside.

The larval stages are somewhat elongated, but the edges of the tergites extend laterally as flattened lamellate projections. The tarsal claws are paired, and there are two short, spinelike cerci. Only the terminal spiracles are functional.

# HALIPLIDAE (CRAWLING WATER BEETLES)

The crawling water beetles are closely allied to the Dytiscidae. They are all small, the usual length being only 2 to 5 mm., and for this reason are frequently overlooked by collectors. The body is oval, very convex, and widest near the anterior edge of the elytra. The color is yellowish or brown, usually marked with black. The antennae are ten-segmented and threadlike, and the elytra have small punctures arranged in longitudinal rows. Of the six ventral segments of the abdomen, the first three to five are covered by the enormously enlarged platelike coxae of the hind legs. The hind femora are dumbbell-shaped and largely hidden by the coxae; they move between these plates and the abdomen. Aside from the fact that the tarsi have long hairs, the legs are unmodified for swimming. Swimming is feeble and consists of alternate movements of the legs. A supply of air is carried under the elytra and coxal plates where it is in direct contact with the thoracic and abdominal spiracles. According to Hickman (1930), these beetles normally, at intervals, take in a fresh supply of air at the surface of the water with the tip of the abdomen. Occasionally some of these beetles leave the water and fly short distances.

Four genera of this widely distributed family occur in the United States. Several species of *Brychius* are found in the western states. There are about 15 species of *Peltodytes* and 30 species of *Haliplus*, however, and these two genera are common everywhere. *Apteraliplus parvulus* Roberts is the only member of the fourth genus; it appears to be confined to the central California coastal region. Because of their inconspicuous nature, it seems likely that there may be additional, undescribed species in this genus.

Adult haliplids are usually found crawling about on and among masses of filamentous algae and other submerged vegetation in the shallows. *Brychius* is found in running water and occasionally in lakes, but *Haliplus, Apteraliplus,* and *Peltodytes* occur in pools, ponds, sluggish streams, and protected places in lakes. Apparently they feed chiefly on vegetation, although some investigators have observed them eating animal material. Many species are active throughout the winter in situations where the water does not freeze. Mating occurs early in the spring and the fertilized eggs are attached to aquatic vegetation; in some forms the eggs are deposited in the dead cells of algal filaments.

## KEY TO GENERA OF ADULT HALIPLIDAE *

**1.** Pronotum with sides of basal two-thirds nearly parallel, sometimes slightly sinuate; western states.................................................**Brychius**
Pronotum with sides widest at base and convergent anteriorly (Fig. 366A)......2

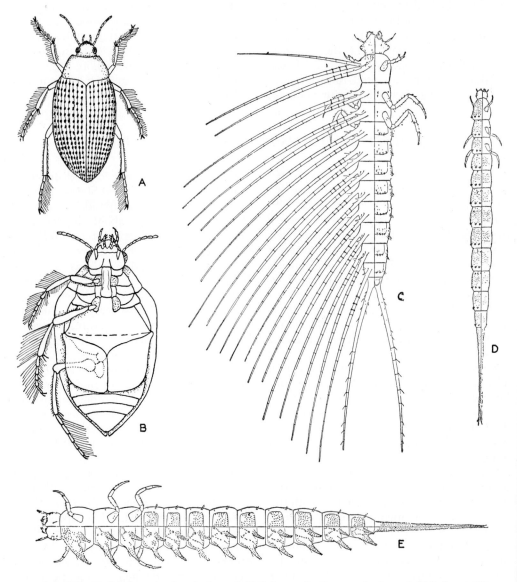

Fɪɢ. 366.—Haliplidae. A, dorsal view of *Haliplus*, ×9; B, ventral view of *Haliplus*, ×13; C, mature larva of *Peltodytes lengi* Roberts, ×4; D, mature larva of *Haliplus triopsis* Say, ×6; E, mature larva of *H. cribrarius* Le Conte, ×10. (C to E show both dorsal and ventral surfaces; from Hickman, 1930.)

* Modified from Chandler (1943).

2. Last two segments of palps about the same size; hind coxal plates margined; generally distributed.................................................................**Peltodytes**

Last segment of palps much smaller than second last; hind coxal plates not margined. ...............................................................................................**3**

3. Prosternum evenly rounded from side to side; small, 1.5 to 2.5 mm. long; confined to central California coastal region; rare.........................................**Apteraliplus**

Median portion of prosternum and prosternal process forming a plateau-like elevation (Fig. 366B); small to large; generally distributed............**Haliplus**

The larvae are sticklike, slender, and very sluggish. They are adapted only for crawling and are found in floating masses of algae, as well as in other vegetation or trash in the shallows, where they feed on filamentous algae either by chewing on the cells or by sucking out their contents. *Peltodytes* (Fig. 366C) is easily recognized because of the fact that it has two, four, or six extremely long dorsal and lateral jointed spines on each of the thoracic and first eight abdominal segments. These spines are well supplied with tracheae and are important respiratory structures. The last segment represents the fused ninth and tenth abdominal segments; it is long and widely bifurcated. *Haliplus* does not have such long spines,

but the body has numerous setigerous tubercles. Some species have four dorsal hornlike prominences on each body segment. The abdomen has ten segments of which the last is long and attenuated, with a small bifurcation at the tip (Figs. 366D, E). Very little is known about the larvae of the American species of *Brychius*, although they show a considerable resemblance to those of *Haliplus*. The larva of *Apteraliplus* has not been described. The three larval instars usually last from three to five weeks, but in cold weather they may persist much longer, even over the winter.

The pupal chamber is constructed in damp earth at edges of bodies of water. The pupal stage lasts two to three weeks.

## DYTISCIDAE (PREDACEOUS DIVING BEETLES)

Of the few families of beetles which are exclusively aquatic, the predaceous diving beetles are the most characteristic and best adapted to this environment. Although about 33 genera are known to occur in the United States, most of these are represented by relatively few species. Many species are widely distributed from coast to coast, however, and the great majority encountered by the average collector belong to genera which are indicated by asterisks in Table XII.

Adult Dytiscidae range from about 1 to 40 mm. in length. They are shiny, usually black or brownish-black, but often marked with dull yellow, green, or bronze. The antennae have 11 segments and are long and threadlike. The second and third legs are widely separated owing to

the very large hind coxae. Many species produce sounds by rubbing the abdominal segments and elytra together or by rubbing the legs against the ventral surface of the abdomen. Some genera produce an irritating substance, supposedly defensive, from prothoracic glands.

Dytiscidae may be easily collected by sweeping a net over the bottoms of pools and ponds. They are absent from waveswept shores and occur in large lakes only where there are shallow protected bays and small inlets. The presence of a clean substrate and aquatic vegetation seems to be almost indispensable. Few species occur on muddy bottoms, in rapid water, or in springs.

The first and second legs contribute little to the swimming movements, but the

TABLE XII. Relative Numbers of Species that Have Been Reported for the Various Genera of Dytiscidae in the United States. The more common genera are indicated by asterisks.

| Number of species | Genera |
|---|---|
| About 150 | * Hydroporus |
| About 50 to 75 | * Agabus<br>* Hygrotus ( = Coelambus) |
| Between 10 and 25 | * Bidessus<br>* Deronectes<br>* Ilybius<br>* Laccophilus<br>* Rhantus |
| From 5 to 10 | * Colymbetes<br>* Copelatus<br>* Desmopachria<br>* Dytiscus<br>* Hydrovatus<br>Laccornis ( = Agaporus)<br>Suphisellus ( = Canthydrus)<br>Thermonectus |
| Less than 5 | * Acilius<br>Agabetes<br>Agabinus<br>Bidessonotus<br>Celina<br>Colpius inflatus Lec.<br>* Coptotomus<br>* Cybister<br>Eretes sticticus (L.)<br>Graphoderus<br>Hoperius planatus Fall<br>Hydaticus<br>* Hydrocanthus<br>Hydrotrupes palpalis Shp.<br>Matus<br>Megadytes fraternus Shp.<br>Neoscutopterus ( = Scutopterus)<br>Notomicrus nanulus (Lec.)<br>Pachydrus princeps (Blatch.) |

hind legs are more or less flattened, elongated, and hairy; they operate together in an oarlike manner. Throughout the family there is considerable variation in the development and specialization of the hind legs. In *Bidessus* and *Hydroporus*, for example, they are only feebly developed for swimming; in *Agabus* they are more flattened and hairy; and in such genera as *Dytiscus, Acilius,* and *Cybister* they are extremely flattened and densely fringed with swimming hairs. Those genera highly developed for swimming are the most awkward on land.

Many species are known to leave the water and fly from pond to pond, some having been found flying more than six miles from any body of water. Sometimes these movements assume the proportions of mass migrations. Dytiscids may often be collected around lights at night.

The group is exclusively carnivorous and voracious. They feed on all kinds of aquatic Metazoa, the larger species commonly attacking dragonfly nymphs, tadpoles, and even small fish. When kept in aquaria, Dytiscidae must be well supplied with food. Such food need not be living organisms; almost any kind of raw or cooked meat will suffice.

There are ten pairs of spiracles; the first two pairs are on the thorax; the third through ninth pairs are on the dorsolateral portions of the abdominal segments; the last is at the tip of the abdomen. The spiracles open into the subelytral chamber so that when the beetles are submerged they utilize the oxygen of the tracheae and the subelytral chamber (Fig. 367B). It is also thought that some oxygen from the surrounding water diffuses into the subelytral chamber through the air–water interface. At intervals, however, the air supply must be renewed, and dytiscids ordinarily come to the surface every few minutes. The body is maintained head downward at an oblique angle with the tip of the abdomen penetrating the surface film (Fig. 367A). In this way the terminal spiracles are brought into contact with the atmosphere, and the air which is under the elytra is renewed.

Copulation occurs during the warm months. In the males of some genera, including *Acilius, Hydaticus, Thermonectus, Cybister, Dytiscus,* and others, the first three segments of the anterior tarsi are enormously swollen to form an acetabulum. The ventral surface of this structure is flat, edged with strong bristles, and covered with curious, small, stalked cuplets or sucker discs (Fig. 367J). A few forms have acetabula on the second tarsi also. These structures apparently act as adhesive organs for holding the two individuals together during copulation. Some authorities maintain that a sticky secretion is given off from glands on the acetabulum and that it acts in conjunction with the sucking discs. The female deposits the eggs in trash or under objects along the shore, on floating vegetation, or within the living tissues of aquatic plants by means of a specialized ovipositor. Adults of some species are known to live and reproduce for two or even three summers, and there are a few records of dytiscids which lived for five years. Only one generation is produced each year, and, depending on the species and time of oviposition and hatching, it is usually either the larva or the adult that winters over, the latter condition being more common. They ordinarily hibernate in debris or burrow into the bottom or edges of ponds. It is not uncommon, however, to see the adults swimming about under ice during the winter. Some species aestivate during a portion of the summer.

## KEY TO GENERA OF ADULT DYTISCIDAE *

1. Scutellum fully covered (Fig. 367H), or rarely with a small tip visible (in *Celina* entirely visible, but in that case the prosternal process is bent strongly downward)............................................................................2
   Scutellum entirely visible (Fig. 367G); prosternal process not deflected.......16
2. First and second tarsi distinctly five-segmented, the fourth segment approximately as long as the third (Fig. 364)................................................12
   Fourth segment of first and second tarsi minute and usually hidden between the lobes of the third; usually 2 to 6 mm. long.............HYDROPORINAE, 3
3. The broad apex of the hind coxal process divided into three parts by two oval emarginations (Fig. 368A); widely distributed...............Hydrovatus
   Hind coxal process otherwise.........................................................4

* Greatly modified from Bradley's (1930) rearrangement of Zimmerman's (1917) key, and from Leech (1942).

4. Hind coxal process short, flat, almost in a plane with the ventral segments, and without lateral wings, so that the bases of the trochanters are entirely free...5
   Hind coxal process not on a level with the first sternite, but somewhat raised, its sides divergent, and more or less produced into lobes which cover the bases of the trochanters...................................................8
5. Hind claws asymmetrical; hind tibiae straight, of almost uniform width........6
   Hind claws symmetrical; base of hind tibiae slightly arched and much more slender than the thickened apical part..............................................7
6. Middle coxae widely separated; rare; Fla........................**Pachydrus**
   Middle coxae approximate; about 2 mm. long; widely distributed...**Desmopachria**
7. Fourth segment of fore and middle tarsi reduced and hidden between lobes of the third segment; 1.5 to 2.5 mm. long; widely distributed............**Bidessus**
   Fore and middle tarsi distinctly five-segmented, the third segment rounded and not bilobed; eastern and southern; uncommon...................**Bidessonotus**
8. Elytra acuminate; widely distributed...............................**Celina**
   Elytra with apex rounded, subtruncate, or acute..........................9
9. The bent-under margin of the elytra with a basal excavation which receives the middle knee, and is marked off by a diagonal carina; widely distributed and common. ...............................................**Hygrotus**
   The bent-under margin of the elytra not excavated........................10
10. Hind femora attaining the metacoxal lobes; eastern states............**Laccornis**
    Hind femora not attaining the metacoxal lobes; widely distributed and common..11
11. Median line between lobes of metacoxal processes not abbreviated behind, the apex either truncate or more or less angularly prominent at middle (Fig. 368B).
                                                                   **Hydroporus**
    Median line between lobes of metacoxal processes triangularly excised at middle, the lobes more produced posteriorly (Fig. 368C)..............**Deronectes**
12. Hind tarsi with a single thick, straight claw (Fig. 364); usually 3 to 6 mm. long; widely distributed and common............LACCOPHILINAE, **Laccophilus**
    Hind tarsi with two slender, curved claws; usually 1 to 5 mm. long.
                                                               NOTERINAE,[*] 13
13. Laminate inner plates of the hind coxae subtruncate at apex with an arcuate emargination on each side of the depressed middle; Fla. and La.; rare....14
    Laminate inner plates of the hind coxae with a broad and deep angular excision at apex, leaving a diverging triangular process at each side; widely distributed.15
14. First tibiae without a curved apical spur; 1.25 mm. long.
                                                       **Notomicrus nanulus** (Lec.)
    First tibiae with a curved apical spur; larger.........................**Colpius**
15. Apex of posternal process about twice as broad as it is between the coxae; less than 3.5 mm. long.........................................**Suphisellus**
    Apex of prosternal process at least two and one-half or three times as broad as it is between the coxae; 4 mm. or more in length..............**Hydrocanthus**
16. Eyes emarginate (notched) above the bases of the antennae; first three segments of male first tarsi widened, but not forming a round adhesion disc; usually 4 to 16 mm. long.................................COLYMBETINAE, 17
    Eyes not emarginate; first three segments of male first tarsi forming a round or oval adhesion disc (Fig. 367J); usually 9 to 40 mm. long....DYTISCINAE, 28
17. Hind claws of equal length and usually of similar form......................18
    Hind claws of unequal length, the outer one usually more sharply bent at the tip than the inner..........................................................22
18. With a linear group of hairs near the posterior apical angles of the hind femora..19
    Without such hairs...................................................21

---

[*] Böving (1930) regards this group as a separate family, the Noteridae, on the basis of the fossorial legs of the larvae.

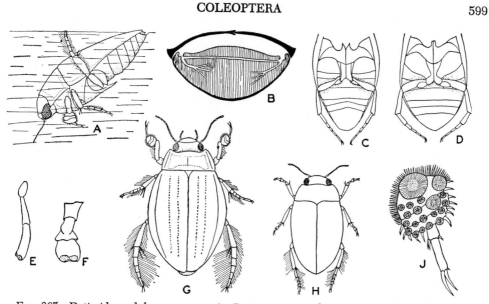

FIG. 367.—Dytiscidae adult structures. A, *Dytiscus marginalis* L. at surface film, ×1; B, diagrammatic cross section through abdomen of same showing elytra, subelytral chamber, and spiracles; C, ventral view of *Agabinus*; D, ventral view of *Agabus*; E, labial palp of *Agabus clavicornis* Sharp; F, same of *Hydrotrupes palpalis* Sharp; G, *Dytiscus*, male, ×1; H, *Hydroporus*, ×5; J, ventral view of first tarsus of male of *Thermonectus basilaris* (Harris). (A redrawn from Korshelt; C to F redrawn from Leech, 1942; J redrawn from Wilson, 1923.)

19. Hind coxal processes in the form of rounded lobes (Fig. 367D) . . . . . . . . . . . . . .**20**
    Hind coxal processes parallel-sided, lateral margins straight to the apices (Fig. 367C); western; rare . . . . . . . . . . . . . . . . . . . . . . . . . . . . . . . . . . . . . . . . . . . . . **Agabinus**
20. Labial palps very short, terminal segments subquadrate (Fig. 367F); Calif. mountain streams; rare . . . . . . . . . . . . . . . . . . . . . . . . . . . . . . . . . . . . . . . . . . . . . **Hydrotrupes**
    Labial palps approximately as long as maxillary palps, terminal segments linear, not subquadrate (Fig. 367E); widely distributed and common . . . . . . . . **Agabus** *
21. Pronotum laterally finely but sharply margined; elytra longitudinally striate in most species; widely distributed . . . . . . . . . . . . . . . . . . . . . . . . . . . . . . . . . . . . . . .**Copelatus**
    Pronotum laterally emarginate; elytral sculpture aciculate; mostly northeastern.
                                                            **Agabetes**
22. Prosternum flat, with a median longitudinal furrow; eastern and southern . . .**Matus**
    Prosternum convex or keeled, without a furrow . . . . . . . . . . . . . . . . . . . . . . . . . .**23**
23. Hind femora with a linear group of small hairs on the inner half of the apical angles (Fig. 368D); mostly east of the Rockies . . . . . . . . . . . . . . . . . . . **Ilybius**
    Hind femora without such a group of small hairs . . . . . . . . . . . . . . . . . . . . . . . . . .**24**
24. Metasternal wings narrow, linear (Fig. 368E); widely distributed . . .**Coptotomus**
    Metasternal wings broad, wedge-shaped (Figs. 368F, G) . . . . . . . . . . . . . . . . . .**25**
25. Elytra with sharply incised coarse meshwork . . . . . . . . . . . . . . . . . . . . . . . . . . . .**26**
    Elytra transversely fissured, finely impressed with transverse parallel lines, or finely and thickly reticulate; widely distributed and common . . . . . . . . . . . . . . . . . .**27**
26. Depressed; bicolored dorsal surface; Ark.; rare . . . . . . . . . . .**Hoperius planatus** Fall
    Convex; dorsal surface all black; extreme northern states . . . . . . . .**Neoscutopterus**

---

    * In accordance with the suggestions of Guignot (1936) and Leech (1942), this genus is expanded to include two American species which were formerly called *Ilybiosoma*.

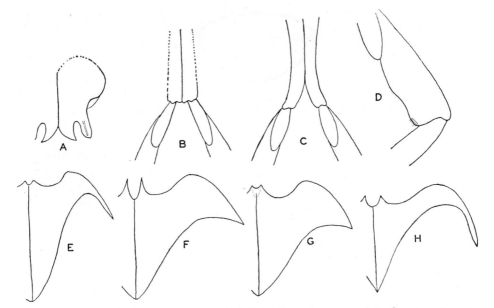

Fig. 368.—Dytiscidae adult structures. A, left hind coxal process of *Hydrovatus*; B, meta-coxal processes and base of third legs in *Hydroporus*; C, metacoxal processes and base of third legs in *Deronectes*; D, hind femur of *Ilybius* showing group of hairs on inner half of apical angle; E, left metasternum of *Coptotomus*; F, left metasternum of *Rhantus*; G, left metasternum of *Colymbetes*; H, left metasternum of *Acilius*.

27.    Metasternum with a broad and distinct pitlike depression on the anterior border between the coxae (Fig. 368F); elytral sculpture various but not of parallel transverse grooves..........................................................**Rhantus**
     Metasternum between the coxae flat or with a small, indistinct, longitudinal impression (Fig. 368G); elytral sculpture consisting of parallel transverse grooves.
                                                                     **Colymbetes**
28.    Hind margin of first four segments of the hind tarsi beset with a coarse fringe of golden, yellow, flat hairs along its entire width........................29
     Hind margin of first four segments of hind tarsi without such a fringe, or with hairs only on the outer apical angle................................33
29.    Pronotum margined laterally; Kan., Colo., Texas, Ariz., and Calif.; rare.....**Eretes**
     Pronotum not margined laterally........................................30
30.    Outer margin of wing of metasternum straight; widely distributed.....**Hydaticus**
     Outer margin of wing of metasternum arcuate (Fig. 368H)................31
31.    Elytra coarsely punctate, usually fluted in female; widely distributed and common.
                                                                     **Acilius**
     Elytra almost smooth........................................................32
32.    Hind margin of middle femora with setae as long as middle tibiae; southwest.
                                                        **Thermonectus**
     Hind margin of middle femora with setae shorter than middle tibiae; widely distributed. ...............................................**Graphoderus**
33.    Hind tibiae distinctly longer than broad; widely distributed and common..**Dytiscus**
     Hind tibiae almost as broad as long........................................34
34.    Hind legs of male with two claws, of the female with a long outer and a small rudimentary inner claw; Fla.; rare..........................**Megadytes**
     Hind legs of male always, of the female usually, with only one claw; widely distributed and common........................................**Cybister**

Most dytiscid larvae are elongated and spindle-shaped. The head is large and round, oval, elongated, or with a prominent anterior prolongation. Typically, there is a pair of cerci at the end of the last segment; these may be naked, sparsely setose, or densely setose. Most species are small and inconspicuous, and nearly all of our information is based on observations of a few large Dytiscinae larvae.

Because of their carnivorous and voracious food habits, they are often called "water tigers," and although a few forms, like *Hydroporus*, will eat pieces of animals that are already dead, this is exceptional. Food consists of all kinds of aquatic Metazoa, and some of the larger larvae, such as *Dytiscus* and *Cybister*, are of economic importance because of the fact that they may feed on fish fry in hatchery ponds. They lunge and clutch their prey with their large sickle-shaped mandibles. These mouth parts are peculiarly constructed for piercing and sucking. Each has a groovelike canal that arises near the tip and continues along the inner margin and connects with the mouth cavity at the base of the mandible (Fig. 369H). The canal is effectively, but not entirely, closed off from the outside by close-fitting ridges along the inner surface of the mandible (Fig. 369J). Food is predigested by a fluid arising in the mouth and given off from the tips of the mandibles. The resulting semifluid material (including the body fluids of the prey) is then drawn into the mouth cavity through the mandibles. The mouth itself apparently remains closed during feeding.

Some dytiscid larvae, such as *Acilius*, are efficient and graceful swimmers; the legs and posterior abdominal segments are heavily fringed with hairs. Also, some are capable of making quick darting movements by throwing the body into sudden curves. A few genera, on the other hand, are sluggish creepers which scarcely swim at all.

Only the two spiracles on the last abdominal segment are functional. Many species swim or crawl to the surface of the water and assume an angle at the surface with these spiracles in contact with the atmosphere. Such larvae as *Dytiscus, Hydaticus,* and *Acilius,* however, are usually lighter than water and float to the surface when they are not clinging to the bottom or to submerged vegetation. Many small and medium-sized larvae probably do not come to the surface at all, but obtain their oxygen by diffusion through the general body surface. *Coptotomus* has six pairs of long, lateral abdominal gills.

## KEY TO SUBFAMILIES AND SOME COMMON GENERA OF DYTISCIDAE LARVAE *

1. Legs adapted for digging....................................NOTERINAE **
   Legs adapted for swimming or crawling..................................2
2. Head with anterior prolongation (Figs. 370B, D)..............HYDROPORINAE
   Head without anterior prolongation (Figs. 370A, C, E).....................3
3. Antennae provided with accessory segments (Fig. 369G)........DYTISCINAE, 4
   Antennae without accessory segments.....................................10
4. Labium without ligula (Fig. 369B)..............................Dytiscus
   Labium with ligula (Figs. 369C–E).......................................5
5. Cerci absent or rudimentary (Fig. 369F)..........................Cybister
   Cerci well developed....................................................6
6. Ligula paired (Fig. 369A)......................................Hydaticus
   Ligula not paired.......................................................7

* Modified from Wilson (1923) and Bertrand (1928).
** Böving (1930) has placed this group in a separate family, the Noteridae, on the basis of the fossorial legs of the larvae.

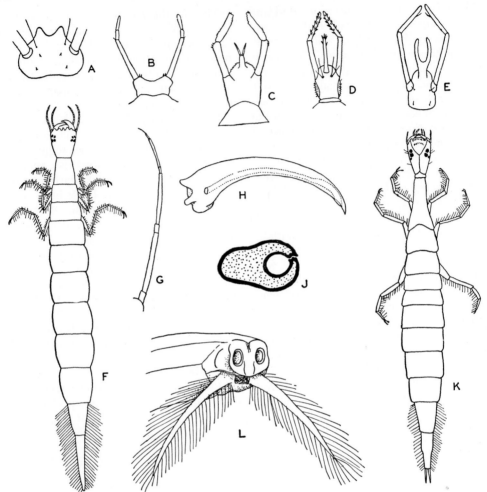

Fig. 369.—*Dytiscinae* larval structures. A, labium of *Hydaticus*; B, labium of *Dytiscus verticalis* Say; C, labium of *Thermonectus ornaticollis* (Aubé); D, labium of *Acilius semisulcatus* Aubé; E, labium of *Acilius*; F, larva of *Cybister fimbriolatus* Say, ×6.5; G, antenna of *Dytiscus verticalis* Say; H, mandible of *Dytiscus*, showing food channel; J, diagrammatic cross section of same; K, larva of *Acilius semisulcatus* Aubé, ×4; L, posterior end of *Dytiscus*, showing anus, spiracles, and cerci. (A redrawn from Bertrand, 1928; B, C, D, F, and G redrawn from Wilson, 1923; E modified from Bertrand; L modified from Portier, 1911.)

7. Ligula very short...............................................Eretes
   Ligula long.......................................................8
8. Ligula bifid, or simple and with a few very short spines (Figs. 369D, E)..Acilius
   Ligula otherwise..................................................9
9. Ligula longer than the first segment of the labial palp............Graphoderus
   Ligula shorter than the first segment of the labial palp, often tipped with two
       jointed spines (Fig. 369C).................................Thermonectus
10. Cerci with numerous hairs (Fig. 370E)...........Laccophilinae, **Laccophilus**
    Cerci with few hairs (Fig. 370B)..........................Colymbetinae, 11

11. Abdomen with slender lateral filaments which serve as tracheal gills (Fig. 370C).
................................................................**Coptotomus**
    No tracheal gills on abdomen.............................................12
12. Last abdominal segment membranous on the ventral side............**Copelatus**
    Last abdominal segment entirely sclerotized.............................13
13. Cerci densely plumose...................................................14
    Cerci with a few scattered hairs (Fig. 370A)............................15
14. Mandibles wide at base, nearly half as wide as long and with a blunt projection
    on inner face; maxillary stipes slender, with concave sides, armed on the inner
    margin with a long seta and a single spine...................**Colymbetes**
    Mandibles narrow at base, not more than one-third as wide as long and with a
    smooth inner face; maxillary stipes stout, with convex sides, armed on the
    inner margin with two or three spines and a row of setae.........**Rhantus**
15. Sides of head with a longitudinal keel or edge.........................**Ilybius**
    Sides of head lacking such a keel.................................**Agabus**

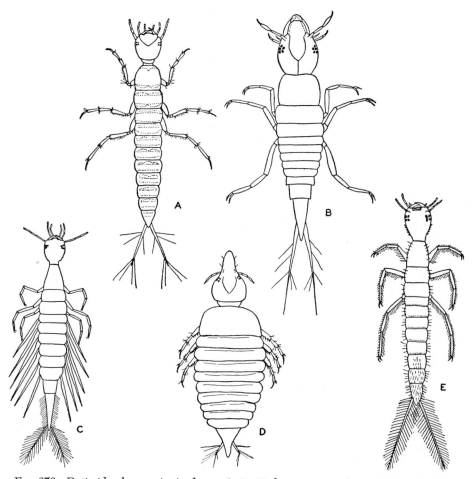

FIG. 370.—Dytiscidae larvae. A. *Agabus,* ×9; B, *Hydroporus niger* Say, ×8; C, *Coptotomus interrogatus* (Fabr.), ×4; D, *Hydrovatus,* ×11; E, *Laccophilus maculosus* Say, ×8. (A and D modified from Bertrand, 1928; B, C, and E modified from Wilson, 1923.)

Fig. 371.—Pupa of *Cybister fimbriatus* Say, ×2.3. (Redrawn from Wilson, 1923.)

When the larva leaves the water to pupate, all of the spiracles become functional. The pupal cells are formed on shore a short distance from the water, usually under stones, vegetation, or debris. They are constructed of mud pellets on the surface of the ground, or as deep as ten centimeters. The pupal stage usually lasts from a few days to two months, although a few species are thought to winter over in this stage.

As in other families of aquatic beetles with terrestrial pupae, this stage in the life history is especially susceptible to drowning. Heavy rains or melting snow may fill the pupal cells with water, resulting in a high mortality rate.

Pupae may be collected around the edges of ponds by turning over logs and masses of debris or by digging in likely areas.

## GYRINIDAE (WHIRLIGIG BEETLES)

Whirligig beetles occur in colonies of a few to a great many individuals on the surface of lakes, ponds, slow streams, and backwaters of rapid streams. They float quietly or circle and glide about each other in rapid irregular curves; when alarmed, they scatter in all directions and dive or whirl about so rapidly that they are exceedingly difficult to catch without a large dipnet. These beetles are black, shiny, oval, and somewhat depressed; the abdomen extends beyond the elytra. They are well adapted for rapid locomotion, the middle and hind legs being greatly flattened, paddle-like, and fringed (Fig. 372F). The compound eyes are divided at the edge of the head by the insertion of the antennae so that in effect there is one pair for aerial vision and another for looking down in the water (Fig. 372D). This is the most distinctive feature of the family. The third segment of the peculiar antennae is much enlarged and earlike, and the following ones form a short, spindle-shaped mass. When handled, many

species give off a milky fluid which has a peculiar odor; some authorities believe that this is a protective mechanism. Gyrinids frequently fly, but they are unable to take off from the water and must climb up on some emergent object. Although these beetles are almost always found on the surface, they are good divers. They carry an air supply under the elytra when submerged and are considerably lighter than water, but use their long hooked forelegs for clinging to the bottom. While it is likely that live insects which fall upon the surface of the water form the main portion of the diet, there are numerous observations and experiments which show that some species may feed on dead animal matter and vegetation. Balduf's (1935) conclusion that they are scavengers seems to be a logical one.

Only three genera of Gyrinidae are known from the United States. Both *Dineutus* (=*Dineutes*) and *Gyrinus* are widely distributed and common over the entire country, there being about 15 species in the former genus and 35 to 40 in the latter. The two species of *Gyretes*, however, seem to be confined chiefly to the western states.

Adult Gyrinidae hibernate in mud or trash at the bottom or edges of ponds and streams during the cold months. The eggs are laid on submerged vegetation after activity is resumed in the spring, and these hatch in a few days or weeks. During the middle or late summer the larva builds the pupal case of pellets of earth which are often mixed with sand or debris. Ordinarily it is constructed on vertical plant stems or rocks just above the water or on shore one to several inches above the surface of the ground. In those species which have been studied, the pupal stage lasts about a month. The adults are therefore most abundant in late summer and early autumn. It is thought that there is only one generation per year.

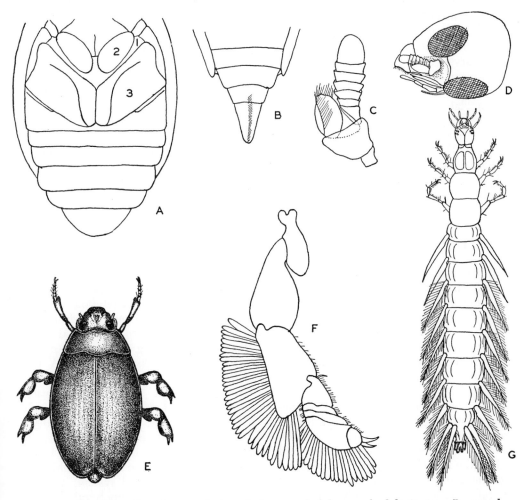

FIG. 372.—Gyrinidae. A, ventral view of thorax and abdomen of adult *Gyrinus*; B, ventral view of tip of abdomen of adult *Gyretes*; C, antenna of adult *Gyrinus*; D, lateral view of head of adult *Gyrinus*; E, adult *Dineutus assimilis* Aubé, ×4; F, mesothoracic leg of adult *Gyrinus*; G, larva of *Dineutus americanus* L., ×3.4. 1, metasternal wing; 2, mesocoxa; 3, metacoxa. (A to D modified from Hatch, 1927; E from *Insects in Kansas*; F modified from Bott; G redrawn from Wilson, 1923.)

In *Gyretes* the dorsal surface is pubescent, at least at the margins; the last abdominal segment is elongated, conical, and has a midventral row of hairs; the body is less than 9 mm. long. In *Dineutus* and *Gyrinus*, however, the dorsal surface is glabrous, and the last abdominal segment is rounded and without a midventral row of hairs. *Dineutus* is more than 10 mm. long, the metasternal wings are broadly triangular, and the elytra are smooth or with nine striae. *Gyrinus* is less than 9 mm. long, the metasternal wings are narrow, and the elytra have 11 striae, with the discal striae sometimes obsolete.

The larvae of the Gyrinidae are pale, inconspicuous, elongated, slender, and much flattened. Because of the presence of long, lateral, respiratory filaments on the abdominal segments, they have a superficial similarity to small centipedes (Fig. 372G). There is one pair of these tracheal gills on each of the first eight abdominal segments and two pairs are found on the ninth. The last abdominal segment is small and has two pairs of terminal sickle-shaped hooks which are presumably useful for clinging to the substrate and for holding the larva in place in the pupal case. Unlike the adults, they are independent of the surface for respiration. They are usually found crawling about on submerged vegetation near the shore or swimming in a characteristic sinuous manner. Gyrinid larvae are carnivorous and voracious, feeding on all types of mature and immature aquatic insects. The mandibles are large, sickle-shaped, and have a canal running their length through which the body fluids of the prey are sucked. Mature *Gyrinus* larvae average 10 to 15 mm. in length; *Dineutus* average 20 to 30 mm.

*Dineutus* larvae have a subcircular head and a distinct and narrow neck. *Gyretes* and *Gyrinus* larvae have an elongated head, and the neck is about as wide as the head and not distinct. *Gyrinus* has two to four teeth in a transverse row on the anterior median projections of the frons, but there are no such teeth in *Gyretes*.

## HYDROPHILIDAE (WATER SCAVENGER BEETLES)

Although many species in this family are terrestrial and occur in moist earth and dung, the majority are aquatic. As a group, the hydrophilids are characterized by their short, clubbed antennae which are usually concealed beneath the head; their tactile function is taken over by the long maxillary palps which are often mistaken for antennae. In addition to this feature, they may be differentiated from the somewhat similar Dytiscidae by their habit of making contact with the surface film with the edge of the body at the anterior end and by the fact that they move their hind legs alternately when swimming. Also, the ventral surface is not strongly convex as it is in the Dytiscidae. The majority of species are blackish, but some are yellow or brown. The length ranges from about 1 to 40 mm. The habits of only the larger species are well known.

Scavenger beetles are common in quiet shallow pools and ponds, especially where there is considerable vegetation. Only a few, such as *Hydrochara*, *Hydrophilus*, *Berosus*, and *Tropisternus* are good swimmers, the others being crawlers. *Laccobius* remains concealed in the mud. A few occur at the edges of streams where the current is not swift. Many leave the water and crawl about on land. Some merely "dabble in the mud at the water's edge." In the spring hydrophilids may be easily collected when they fly to electric lights.

While submerged, oxygen is obtained from air in the tracheal system, and, via the spiracles, from the subelytral chamber and from the silvery film of air (plastron) which is retained on the ventral side of the body by hydrofuge hairs. The air supply is renewed at intervals in an unusual manner. The beetle comes to the surface with the body slightly inclined to one side so as to bring the cleft between the head and prothorax in contact with the surface film. Then the antenna is introduced into this cleft and raised so that its tip breaks the surface film. The antenna and the cleft in this way form a funnel-like tube through which the ventral, subelytral, and tracheal air is renewed.

Formerly it was believed that adult hydrophilids feed exclusively on decaying vegetation (hence the name scavenger beetles), but it is now thought that they eat considerable quantities of living plant material, chiefly algae. Occasionally they eat carrion, and a few species have been known to catch and eat other aquatic insects.

Oviposition occurs in spring and early summer. Although a few species deposit uncovered eggs, the great majority enclose them in cases which are formed from a hardened silklike secretion given off from glands that open by a pair of spinnerets at the apex of the abdomen in the female. In the Hydrophilinae there may be from two to as many as 130 eggs in a single cocoon, depending on the species, but in the case-building species in the other subfamilies the eggs are enclosed singly. In *Epimetopus, Helochares,* and possibly other genera, the female may carry the cocoon on the hind legs and ventral side of the abdomen. Otherwise the cocoon may be wrapped in a leaf, free-floating, or fastened to submerged aquatic plants or surface debris. The shape of the cocoons varies greatly, but is specific for each species (Fig. 374). The eggs usually hatch in five to ten days, and the young larvae leave the cocoon a few hours after hatching. There are three larval instars. At the termination of the larval period the pupal cell is constructed on shore, either in debris on the surface of the ground or as much as seven centimeters below the surface. The pupal stage usually lasts less than three weeks. The adult winters over. In some species there may be two generations per year.

More than 160 species of aquatic Hydrophilidae occur in the United States, and in many areas they are the most abundant beetles. They are grouped in 24 genera, none of which are large. *Helophorus, Hydrochus, Berosus, Tropisternus, Paracymus, Enochrus,* and *Cymbiodyta* all contain between ten and 20 species each. Because of its large size (35 mm. long), abundance, and wide distribution, the best-known American species is probably *Hydrophilus triangularis* Say. Other common genera are *Hydrochara, Tropisternus, Berosus, Helophorus,* and *Hydrochus.*

## KEY TO GENERA OF ADULT HYDROPHILIDAE

1. Pronotum with five longitudinal sulci, or produced anteriorly at middle so as to hide much of the head................................................2
   Pronotum otherwise..............................................................3
2. Eyes nearly divided by sides of the head; southwestern; rare.
                                              EPIMETOPINAE, **Epimetopus**
   Eyes round, not divided; widely distributed........HELOPHORINAE,* **Helophorus**
3. Lateral contours of body uneven; dorsal surface with prominent tuberosities; last segment of hind tarsi as long as the four preceding segments together.
                                              HYDROCHINAE,* **Hydrochus**
   Lateral contours of body even; without prominent dorsal tuberosities; last segment of hind tarsi much shorter than the preceding segments together (except in *Helobata*)......................................HYDROPHILINAE, **4**

*According to larval structure, there is evidence that the Helophorinae and Hydrochinae should be given the status of families.

4. Scutellum usually a long triangle; antennae eight-segmented at most; pronotum narrowed posteriorly..........................................................5
Scutellum not longer, or not much longer than its basal width; antennae nine-segmented at most; pronotum not narrowed posteriorly......................6

5. Middle of emargination of fifth sternite toothless; small, narrow, strongly convex, and black species; La.; rare........................**Derallus altus** (Lec.)
Middle of emargination of fifth sternite with one or more short horny teeth; yellow or brown species; widely distributed............................**Berosus**

6. Mesosternum and metasternum raised in a common median keel, produced behind into a spine (Fig. 373D).......................................................7
Mesosternum and metasternum not raised to form a common median keel......11

7. Prosternum sulcate; metasternal spine long..............................8
Prosternum carinate; metasternal spine short; 13 to 16 mm. long.............10

8. Last segment of maxillary palps shorter than the preceding; at least 25 mm. long..9
Last segment of maxillary palps equal to or longer than the preceding; not more than 15 mm. long........................................**Tropisternus**

9. Prosternal process closed in front, hood-shaped................**Hydrophilus** †
Prosternal process not closed in front, bifurcate.....**Dibolocelus ovatus** G. and H.

10. Clypeus broadly emarginate along its anterior border, exposing the articulation of the labrum, and with its lateral angles protruding in the form of teeth.
**Neohydrophilus castus** (Say)
Clypeus more or less truncate............................**Hydrochara** **

11. The first two sternites on each side with a common excavation and covered by a peculiar bilobed hyaline plate; 1 to 2 mm. long; widely distributed; uncommon.
**Chaetarthria**
Abdomen of five or six normal segments..................................12

12. Maxillary palps stout and short, little longer or shorter than antennae.........13
Maxillary palps slender, much longer than antennae........................17

13. Elytra with sutural striae; abdomen with five visible ventral segments.........14
Elytra without sutural striae; abdomen with six visible ventral segments; widely distributed. .................................................**Laccobius**

14. More than 4.5 mm. long; widely distributed....................**Hydrobius** ††
Not more than 3.5 mm. long...............................................15

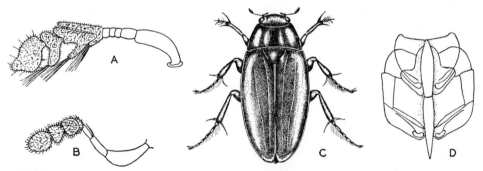

FIG. 373.—Structure of adult Hydrophilidae. A, antenna of adult *Hydrophilus triangularis* (Say); B, antenna of *Berosus striatus* (Say); C, *Hydrophilus triangularis*, ×1.2; D, ventral view of meso- and metathorax of *H. triangularis*, showing median keel. (A and B redrawn from Wilson, 1923; C from *Insects in Kansas*; D modified from Trimble.)

† In accordance with the suggestion of Mutchler (1931), this genus includes the species that were formerly included under *Hydrous,* namely *H. triangularis, H. ater,* and *H. insularis.*
** In accordance with the suggestion of Mutchler (1931), this genus includes the species that were formerly included in *Hydrophilus,* namely *H. rickseckeri, H. obtusata,* and *H. lineata.*
†† D'Orchymont (1942) believes that some of the American species of *Hydrobius* really belong in the Old World genera *Sperchopsis* and *Ametor.*

**15.** Hind femora pubescent basally, at least along the anterior margin............**16**
  Hind femora without pubescence, even along the anterior margin; widely distributed. ...............................................**Paracymus**
**16.** Hind femora not pubescent basally except for a short distance along the anterior margin; eyes protuberant; eastern; uncommon....................**Crenitis**
  Hind femora either with pubescence on their basal two-thirds or only along the trochanter and in a narrow band along the anterior border; eyes not protuberant; eastern, southern, and Calif.......................**Anacaena**
**17.** All tarsi five-segmented, though basal segment may be very small............**18**
  Middle and hind tarsi four-segmented.................................**20**
**18.** Mesosternum with a longitudinal median lamina; widely distributed.
                                         **Enochrus (=Philhydrus)**
  Mesosternum at most feebly protuberant.............................**19**
**19.** Labrum visible; eastern and southwestern........................**Helochares**
  Labrum concealed beneath clypeus; clypeus projecting laterally in front of eyes to a great extent; Fla. and La.....................**Helobata striata** Brullé
**20.** Mesosternal carina transverse or elevated at middle, forming a pyramidal or dentiform protuberance; 4 to 5.5 mm. long; widely distributed......**Cymbiodyta**
  Mesosternum with a compressed conical process; 5.5 to 7 mm. long; eastern.
                                         **Helocombus bifidus** (Lec.)

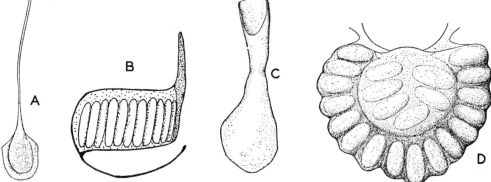

Fig. 374.—Egg cases of Hydrophilidae. A, *Berosus peregrinus* Herbst; B, longitudinal section through case of *Hydrophilus triangularis*; C, *Helophorus lacustris* Lec.; D, *Helochares maculicollis* Mulsant. (A, C, and D from Richmond, 1920; B modified from Wilson, 1923).

In general, the larvae are found in the same specific habitats as the adults. They are inconspicuous, elongated, flattened, and have well-developed mouth parts. Color is usually gray, yellowish, brown, or greenish. The great majority are crawlers, and many species are extremely sluggish. A few, such as *Tropisternus lateralis* (Fabr.) and *Hydrophilus triangularis*, swim with undulatory leechlike movements. Sometimes larvae may be found crawling about on the shore just above the water's edge.

The group is predominantly predaceous and carnivorous, even to the point of cannibalism. All types of aquatic Metazoa are eaten. After the food has been seized, the larvae usually crawl up on vegetation until the head is out of water. The prey is then crushed with the large rapacious mandibles and there may be some preoral digestion. Some species ingest only body fluids; others take in solid tissues as well. It is said that dead vegetation may form a considerable portion of the diet in certain species. Wilson (1923) observed that

*Berosus* fed only on living filamentous algae.

With few exceptions, hydrophilid larvae come to the surface at intervals to renew the air in the tracheal system. Since only the posterior pair of spiracles are functional, this renewal occurs with the tip of the abdomen at the surface film. *Berosus*, however, remains submerged since it obtains its oxygen through seven pairs of long, rigid, lateral, abdominal tracheal gills.

## KEY TO COMMON GENERA OF HYDROPHILIDAE LARVAE *

1. With nine complete abdominal segments, the tenth reduced but distinct.
    HELOPHORINAE, **Helophorus**
   With eight complete abdominal segments, the ninth and tenth reduced (Fig. 375). . . . . . . . . . . . . . . . . . . . . . . . . . . . . . . . . . . . . . . . . . . . . . . . . . . . . . .2
2. Antennae inserted farther from lateral margins of head than mandibles.
    HYDROPHILINAE, 3
   Antennae inserted nearer the lateral margins of head than mandibles.
    HYDROCHINAE, **Hydrochus**
3. With seven pairs of prominent tracheal gills on abdomen (Fig. 375D) . . . **Berosus**
   Tracheal gills reduced or absent. . . . . . . . . . . . . . . . . . . . . . . . . . . . . . . . . . . . . . . . . .4

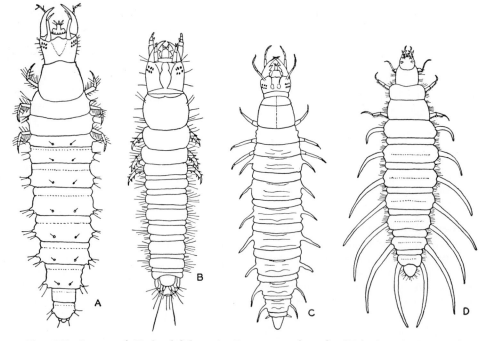

FIG. 375.—Larvae of Hydrophilidae. A, *Tropisternus lateralis* (Fabr.), ×9; B, *Enochrus nebulosus* (Say), ×10; C, *Hydrochara*, ×3; D, *Berosus striatus* (Say), ×6. (A, B, and D modified from Wilson, 1923.)

* Modified from Richmond (1920).

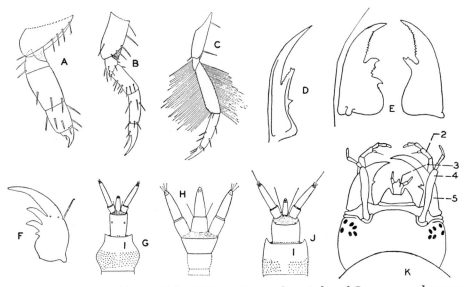

Fig. 376.—Structure of larval Hydrophilidae. A, mesothoracic leg of *Paracymus subcupreus*
Say; B, same of *Laccobius agilis* Randall; C, same of *Hydrophilus triangularis*; D, mandible of
*Tropisternus lateralis*; E, mandibles of *Enochrus diffusus* (Lec.); F, mandible of *Hydrobius
melaenum* Germ.; G, labium of *Hydrochara obtusata* (Say); H, same of *Paracymus subcupreus*;
J, same of *Tropisternus glaber* Herbst; K, head of *Hydrophilus triangularis*. 1, mentum; 2,
maxilla; 3, labium; 4, antenna; 5, mandible. (A, B, C, F, G, H, and J from Richmond, 1920;
D, E, and K modified from Wilson, 1923.)

**4.** First segment of antennae not distinctly longer than the following two taken together; femora without fringes of swimming hairs.....................**5**
   First segment of antennae distinctly longer than the following two taken together
     (Fig. 376K); femora with fringes of long swimming hairs (Fig. 376C)...**11**
**5.** Ligula absent; tarsus well developed, about as long as tibia (Fig. 376B).
                                                                    **Laccobius**
   Ligula present (Fig. 376H); tarsus usually much shorter than tibia (Figs. 376A,
     C). ..........................................................**6**
**6.** Legs reduced........................................................**7**
   Legs fairly long, not reduced........................................**8**
**7.** Each mandible with two inner teeth; legs not visible from above......**Paracymus**
   Each mandible with three inner teeth; legs barely visible from above...**Anacaena**
**8.** Mandibles symmetrical; abdomen without prolegs.......................**9**
   Mandibles asymmetrical (Fig. 376E); abdomen with prolegs on third to seventh
     segments. .............................................**Enochrus** (=**Philhydrus**)
**9.** Each mandible with three inner teeth (Fig. 376F)..................**Hydrobius**
   Each mandible with two inner teeth...................................**10**
**10.** Anterior sclerites of metathorax with caudal projections............**Helochares**
   Anterior sclerites of metathorax without caudal projections.........**Cymbiodyta**
**11.** Each mandible with a single inner tooth (Fig. 376K)..**Hydrophilus** (=**Hydrous**)
   Each mandible with more than one inner tooth, usually two (Fig. 376D)......**12**
**12.** Mentum transverse, sides only slightly rounded (Fig. 376J)........**Tropisternus**
   Mentum convex, with its sides strongly rounded (Fig. 376G); poorly developed
     tracheal gills present in some species.........**Hydrochara** (=**Hydrophilus**)

# HYDROSCAPHIDAE

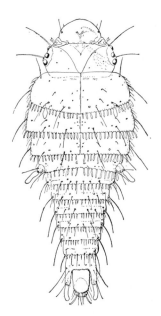

Only one aquatic species in this family, *Hydroscapha natans* Lec., is known from the United States. It is uncommon and occurs in the southwest. The adult is minute, being only 0.5 mm. or less in length. The hind coxae are widely separated and laminate, and the abdomen is conical and protrudes beyond the tip of the elytra. These beetles crawl about sluggishly on submerged stones in running waters. Presumably they feed on the algal film.

The larvae are characterized by a pair of cerci-like filaments on the eighth abdominal segment and very short, inconspicuous antennae.

Fig. 377.—Larva of *Hydroscapha natans* Lec., ×50. (From Böving, 1914.)

# HYDRAENIDAE

This small family includes a few species of aquatic beetles which are seldom encountered by the general collector. They are distinguished by a five-segmented pubescent antennal club and by their small size, the range in total length being only 1 to 2 mm. Adults of the three common genera may be distinguished as follows. In *Limnebius* the second segment of the hind tarsi is longer than the third, the base of the pronotum is as broad as the base of the elytra, total body length is about 1 mm., and the distribution is mostly southern. In *Hydraena* and *Ochthebius* the second segment of the hind tarsi is about as long as the third, the base of the pronotum is slightly or decidedly narrower than the base of the elytra, and the total length is 1 to 2 mm. *Hydraena* is widely distributed and has maxillary palpi that are much longer than the antennae, but *Ochthebius* is southern and has palpi that are shorter than the antennae

The small larvae resemble some of the Hydrophilidae but may be distinguished from the latter by the fact that they have nine complete abdominal segments instead

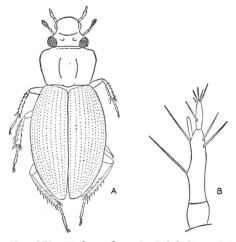

Fig. 378.—Hydraenidae. A, *Ochthebius* adult, ×25; B, larval antenna of *Hydraena pennsylvanica* Kies. (B from Richmond, 1920.)

of eight, only the tenth being reduced. In the larvae of *Ochthebius* the cerci are divergent and nearly contiguous proximally. In *Hydraena* and *Limnebius* the cerci are nearly parallel and widely separated proximally. *Hydraena*, however, has the third antennal segment without inner swellings and the second segment with a single antennal appendage. In *Limnebius* the third antennal segment has an inner swelling, and the second segment has two slender antennal appendages.

## PSEPHENIDAE (RIFFLE BEETLES)

This is a very small family of aquatic beetles represented by two genera in the United States. The most common species is *Psephenus herricki* (De Kay), formerly *P. lecontei* (Lec.), which is widely distributed in the eastern states. The four or five additional species in this genus are confined to the western states. *Eubrianax edwardsi* (Lec.) is the only other American representative of the family and it is apparently restricted to the Pacific coast states. Formerly this species was placed in a terrestrial family, the Dascillidae, but on the basis of its larval characteristics, many authorities are now inclined to place it in the Psephenidae.

The riffle beetles are most appropriately named since they commonly occur on rocky or gravel bottoms along wave-swept shores and in streams where the water is shallow and swift. Incidentally, the swift-water habit is not common among aquatic beetles. The adults are inconspicuous, small, oval, and depressed. Because of the fact that the body is clothed with hairs, these beetles retain a film of air when submerged. Clinging to logs and stones, they creep about in the swift currents, but frequently they emerge from the water to sun themselves on stones.

The adults of the two genera may be easily distinguished. In *Psephenus* the antennae are distant and inserted at the sides of the frons; the tarsal claws are large and simple; the prosternum is prolonged behind into an acute projection which fits into a narrow groove on the mesosternum; there are six or seven sternites; the color is black; and the length ranges from 3.5 to 6.0 mm. In *Eubrianax edwardsi* the antennae are situated close together on the narrow frons; the tarsal claws have a slender, membranous, basal appendage nearly as long as the claw; the prosternum has no posterior process; there are five sternites; color varies from orange to black; and the usual length is 3.5 to 5.0 mm.

The eggs, usually deposited on the undersides of stones, hatch into one of the most distinctive types of beetle larvae. Because of their curious shape and color, they are often called "water pennies." The body is broadly oval, extremely flattened, limpet-like or scalelike, and a distinct coppery color. The dorsal surface is relatively smooth, but the segments are well defined. The whole body acts in a sucker-like fashion, the larvae adhering very tightly to rocks and pebbles, where they feed on the attached algae. Because of the widely flaring margins, the mouth parts and legs are hidden and may be seen only in ventral view. There are five pairs of ventral, finely-branched, white tracheal gills in *Psephenus* and four pairs of tufts in *Eubrianax* which originate between the abdominal segments. The first thoracic tergite in *Psephenus* is triangular, and the eighth abdominal segment has no lateral expansions; in *Eubrianax* the first thoracic tergite is quadrangular, and the eighth abdominal segment has lateral expansions. *Psephenus* is about 7 mm. long.

Pupation occurs beneath the last larval integument. The larvae of *Psephenus herricki* leave the water and pupate under stones and debris in damp places beside streams and lakes. It is thought that the entire life cycle of this species takes about two years. Only the larvae winter over. *Eubrianax edwardsi* pupates in the water.

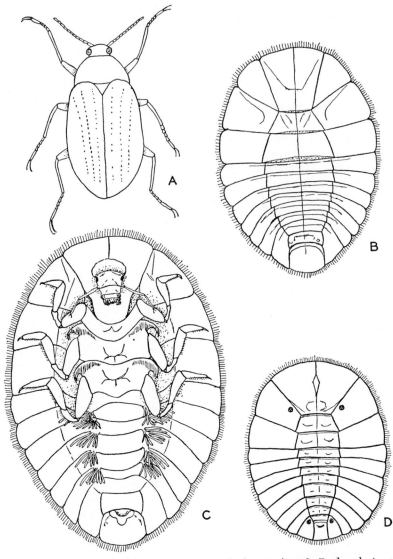

Fig. 379.—Psephenidae. A, adult *Psephenus herricki* (DeKay), ×8; B, dorsal view of larva of *P. herricki*, ×9; C, ventral view of same, ×12; D, dorsal view of larva of *Eubrianax edwardsi* Lec., ×8. (B, C, and D redrawn from Böving and Craighead.)

## DRYOPIDAE

This is a small family of aquatic beetles, there being less than 25 species in the United States. These are grouped into five genera of which *Helichus* is the largest. In their general habits and morphology they are very similar to the Elmidae. They range from 2 to 6 mm. in length, and the body is covered with a hydrofuge pubescence. In *Dryops*, *Helichus*, and *Pelonomus* the antennae form a close pectinate club beyond the second or third segment (Fig. 380A), but in *Lutrochus** and

* These two genera have been placed in the family Limnichidae by Hinton (1939).

*Throscinus* * the antennae are filiform or with the apical segments thickened but never pectinate. Much of the body is covered with a film of air (plastron) whose air-water interface acts as a diffusion membrane. Harpster (1941) has given a complete account of respiration in *Helichus striatus* Lec., including the method of re- placement of the ventral plastron at the surface of the water. Many of the Dryopidae leave the streams and fly about, especially at night. *Helichus* and *Lutrochus* are widely distributed, but the other genera seem to be confined to the south and southwest. Dryopids feed on the algal film of the stream substrate.

## KEY TO GENERA OF ADULT DRYOPIDAE

1. Antennae forming a close pectinate club beyond the second or third segment (Fig. 380A). . . . . . . . . . . . . . . . . . . . . . . . . . . . . . . . . . . . . . . . . . . . . . . . . . . . . . . . . . . . . . .3
   Antennae filiform or with the apical segments thickened but never pectinate. . . . . .2
2. Body rounded; last segment of maxillary palp hatchet-shaped. . . . . . . . . .**Lutrochus**
   Body elongated, oval; last segment of maxillary palp slender. . . . . . . . . .**Throscinus**

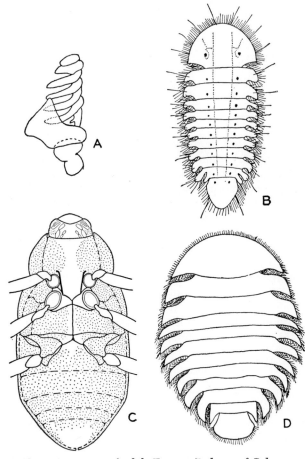

Fig. 380.—Dryopidae. A, antenna of adult *Dryops*; B, larva of *Pelonomus*, ×12; C, ventral view of adult *Helichus striatus* Lec., showing plastron (shaded area), ×5; D, larva of *Helichus*, ×11. (A and D modified from Hinton, 1939; C from Harpster.)

3. Second segment of antennae produced into an earlike process (Fig. 380A) . . . . . . 4
   Second segment of antennae not thus produced . . . . . . . . . . . . . . . . . . . . . **Pelonomus**
4. Antennae approximate; thorax with a deeply cut, sharp-edged, longitudinal line
   on each side . . . . . . . . . . . . . . . . . . . . . . . . . . . . . . . . . . . . . . . . . . . . . . . . . . . **Dryops**
   Antennae widely separated; thorax otherwise . . . . . . . . . . . . . . . . . . . . . . **Helichus**

Unfortunately, little is known about the larval stages, and we are unable to separate certain genera on the basis of consistent generic features. All larvae known from the United States are aquatic, however. Superficially, they are similar to elmid larvae, being cylindrical to onisciform; *Helichus* is so highly modified that it is sometimes mistaken for a psephenid larva (Fig. 380D). It may be distinguished from a water penny by the fact that it has deep lateral notches between the segments. Like the Elmidae, the Dryopidae have a posterior ventral operculum. Anal gills are present in all but *Dryops* and some species of *Helichus*.

## KEY TO GENERA OF MATURE DRYOPIDAE LARVAE

1. Onisciform and flattened (Figs. 380B, D) . . . . . . . . . . . . . . . . **Pelonomus, Helichus**
   Cylindrical. . . . . . . . . . . . . . . . . . . . . . . . . . . . . . . . . . . . . . . . . . . . . . . . . . . . . . . . . . 2
2. Stipes and cardo of maxilla completely fused to postmental part of labium; anal
   gills present . . . . . . . . . . . . . . . . . . . . . . . . . . . . . . . . . . . . . . **Lutrochus, Throscinus**
   Stipes and cardo of maxilla separate and not fused to postmental part of labium; anal
   gills absent . . . . . . . . . . . . . . . . . . . . . . . . . . . . . . . . . . . . . . . . . . . . . . . . . . **Dryops**

## ELMIDAE

Of the three closely related families, Elmidae, Psephenidae, and Dryopidae, the Elmidae * is by far the largest in number of species. In their general morphology, elmids are rather constant. Few species are more than 3.5 mm. long. The color is commonly an inconspicuous blackish; the head is usually partly retractile; and the antennae are filiform except in a few forms where the apical segments form a club. They do not swim but crawl about slowly, clinging to the substrate with their long tarsal claws. Although these beetles are most characteristic of running waters,

some species occur in other types of environments; *Simsonia*, *Ancyronyx*, and *Macronychus*, for example, may be found in ponds or swamps. Some species may leave the water temporarily at night, but only *Lara* and *Phanocerus* are not true aquatic forms. These two genera occur along the edges of streams; they enter the water only accidentally or when ovipositing. All Elmidae are thought to feed on vegetation and debris.

During submergence a film of air covers much of the body, and this film is in direct contact with the spiracles. Most authorities maintain that these beetles seldom come to the surface of the water for a renewal of the air supply, but that bubbles of air (or oxygen) which are released from submerged aquatic plants may come in contact with the body and fuse with the film of air. There is a strong possibility that bubbles of air being carried along in rapid streams may contribute to the oxygen supply in the same manner. How-

* During the past forty years there has been much confusion and disagreement concerning the family relationships of the psephenid, elmid, dryopid, parnid, and larid groups of aquatic beetles; for details see especially the works of Leng, West, Böving and Craighead, Bradley, Sanderson, and Hinton. Since 1930, however, these groups have been closely studied and the family characteristics more carefully distinguished. The classification here adopted, i.e., an arrangement into the families Elmidae, Psephenidae, and Dryopidae, follows in general the suggestions contained in Hinton's papers.

ever, some species are known to remain permanently submerged in environments where bubbles of air from any source are negligible, and in such cases some other mechanism must be postulated.

Largely as the result of Hinton's work, it has been found that many species in the United States which had long masqueraded under the genus *Elmis* (=*Helmis*) really belong in other genera, especially *Heterlimnius, Hexacylloepus, Microcyl-* *loepus,* and *Simsonia.* It is now believed that *Elmis* is European and is not represented in America. *Stenelmis* is the only large genus in this country, being represented by more than 25 species; a few genera, such as *Phanocerus, Zaitzevia,* and *Macronychus,* are monospecific. Most of the 16 genera are confined to the west, southwest, and south. *Stenelmis, Macronychus, Limnius,* and *Simsonia,* however, are characteristically eastern and Midwestern.

## KEY TO GENERA OF ADULT ELMIDAE *

1.  Terrestrial, rarely entering water; body without patches of tomentum........15
    Aquatic, seldom or never leaving water; body with patches of dense hairy or scale-like tomentum.........................................................2
2.  Anterior tibiae without dense pubescence (tomentum)...............**Stenelmis**
    Anterior tibiae with a patch of dense pubescence.........................3
3.  Antennae with less than ten segments.....................................4
    Antennae with ten or 11 segments........................................5
4.  Antennae seven-segmented.....................**Macronychus glabratus** (Say)
    Antennae eight-segmented.......................**Zaitzevia parvula** (Horn)

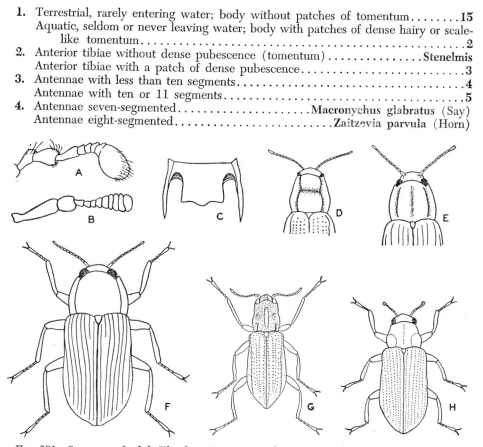

Fig. 381.—Structure of adult Elmidae. A, antenna of *Zaitzevia parvula* (Horn); B, antenna of *Phanocerus clavicornis* Sharp; C, prosternum of *Ancyronyx;* D, anterior end of *Neoelmis;* E, anterior end of *Hexacylloepus;* F, *Elsianus,* × 11; G, *Stenelmis lateralis* Sand, ×10; H, *Phanocerus clavicornis,* ×10. (A and C modified from Hinton, 1939; B and F modified from Hinton, 1940; G from Sanderson.)

* Modified from Sanderson (1938).

5. Maxillary palps three-segmented...................................**Narpus**
   Maxillary palps four-segmented...........................................6
6. Head free; prosternum not lobed in front (Fig. 381C).............**Ancyronyx**
   Head protected by prosternal lobe.......................................7
7. Second elytral stria terminating at about basal one-third of elytra (Fig. 381F).
   **Elsianus**
   Second elytral stria complete or nearly so................................8
8. Prothorax with sublateral carinae extending from base to apex (Figs. 381D, E)..9
   Prothorax without sublateral carinae or with very short ones...............14
9. Median lonigtudinal groove or impression present on prothorax (Fig. 381E)....10
   Median longitudinal groove or impression absent on prothorax..............12
10. Transverse impression on apical one-half of prothorax..........**Microcylloepus**
    Transverse impression absent on apical one-half of prothorax..............11
11. With a complete transverse belt of dense pubescence on the turned-under edge of
    the pronotum.......................................**Hexacylloepus**
    With an incomplete transverse belt of dense pubescence on the turned-under edge
    of the pronotum.........................................**Cylloepus**
12. No transverse or other impressions between sublateral carinae of prothorax.
    **Limnius**
    Transverse impression present on prothorax..............................13
13. Impression a little anterior of middle (Fig. 381D)...................**Neoelmis**
    Impression at middle..................................................**Heterelmis**
14. Sublateral carinae very short, from one-third to one-half the length of thorax.
    **Heterlimnius**
    Sublateral carinae absent.............................................**Simsonia**
15. Antennae clubbed (Fig. 381B); less than 4 mm. long.**Phanocerus clavicornis** Sharp
    Antennae not clubbed; more than 4 mm. long; along western streams......**Lara**

Relatively little is known about the larval stages of the Elmidae. They are all aquatic, however, and occur in the same specific environments as the adults. In size, they are correspondingly small, and in shape they range from parallel-sided and cylindrical to onisciform. Although much of the oxygen-carbon dioxide exchange probably occurs through the general body surface, there are three tufts of retractile anal gills. When withdrawn, these gills lie in a small cavity which is covered by an operculum. The larvae all appear to be vegetarians.

## KEY TO CERTAIN GENERA OF ELMIDAE LARVAE [*]

1. Body flattened and at least feebly onisciform (Fig. 382C)............**Phanocerus**
   Body cylindrical or subcylindrical, sometimes flattened ventrally (Fig. 382B)....2
2. Each of the first eight abdominal segments (thoracic also to a lesser degree) with
   three very large posteriorly directed processes, one on the median line and the
   the other two dorsolateral.........................................**Simsonia**
   Abdominal segments sometimes tubercular or with spinous filaments, but never with
   large processes.........................................................3
3. Propleura divided on each side into three parts............................4
   Propleura not divided, or if divided, then only into two parts on each side.......5
4. Pleura on eighth abdominal segment bounded by sutures; dorsal surface with many
   small filaments and spines.........................................**Lara**
   Eighth abdominal segment forming a complete sclerotized ring........**Limnius**

[*] The larvae in this family are very poorly known, particularly with reference to the range of morphological variations which may occur within single genera. For this reason the following genera cannot satisfactorily be included in this key: *Ancyronyx, Heterlimnius, Hexacylloepus, Limnius, Narpus, Macronychus, Stenelmis,* and *Zaitzevia.* The present key is modified from Hinton (1940).

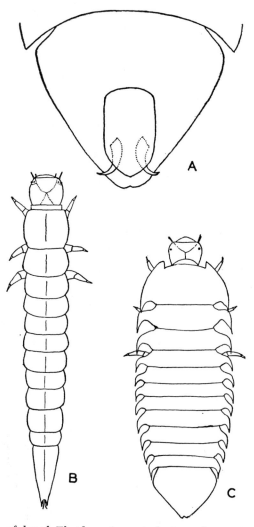

Fig. 382.—Structure of larval Elmidae. A, ventral view of posterior end of *Phanocerus clavicornis*, showing operculum; B, *Stenelmis*, ×18; C, *Phanocerus clavicornis*, ×15. (A modified from Hinton, 1939; B modified from West, 1929; C modified from Hinton, 1940.)

5. Propleura not divided, meeting on mid-line of body so that the sternum is suppressed. ...................................................................Cylloepus
   Propleura divided into an anterior and a posterior part, and only with the anterior part meeting on the mid-line of the body..............................6
6. Meso- and metapleura divided on each side into three parts...........Heterelmis
   Meso- and metapleura divided on each side into two parts....................7
7. Tubercles of terga of first eight abdominal segments arranged in parallel rows.
                                                                     Microcylloepus
   Tubercles of terga of first eight abdominal segments not arranged in parallel rows..8
8. Anterior margin of head with a large and conspicuous tooth on each side...Elsianus
   Anterior margin of head without a large and conspicuous tooth on each side.
                                                                     Neoelmis

## HELODIDAE

All of the adults in this family are terrestrial. They are less than 6 mm. long, oval or elongated, and have filiform 11-segmented antennae. The body is covered with a deciduous pubescence and is sometimes spotted. The adults occur on emergent vegetation or on the herbage along shores. There are about 30 species in the United States, including the following genera: *Cyphon, Helodes, Scirtes, Ora, Prionocyphon,* and *Microcara.*

Unfortunately, little is known of the larval stages, all of which are presumed to be aquatic. The following remarks, therefore, are subject to change when more information has been gathered on the American species. There are, however, two features by which these larvae can be distinguished from most other aquatic Coleoptera larvae. First, they have very long filiform antennae; second, they have terminal tufts of "blood gills" which can

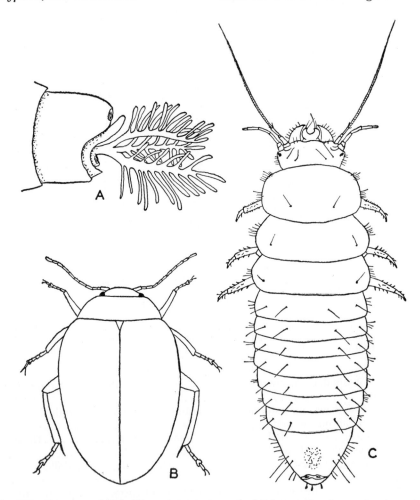

FIG. 383.—Structure of Helodidae. A, posterior end of *Prionocyphon* larva, showing extruded blood gills, anus, and left spiracle; B, *Scirtes adult,* ×1.5; C, *Prionocyphon* larva, ×16. (A and C redrawn from Böving and Craighead.)

be withdrawn into a pocket. The body is broad and somewhat flattened. There are two spiracles at the posterior end above the blood gills and these are brought into contact with the air at intervals. Some species are said to retain an air bubble at the tip of the abdomen when submerged, and, since they are lighter than water, they cling to submerged objects. Most species are found on floating or submerged vegetation in ponds, but some move through the water with awkward wriggling movements. *Helodes* may be found on the undersides of stones in swift streams. All helodid larvae are vegetarians. Pupation occurs on shore.

## CHRYSOMELIDAE (LEAF BEETLES)

In this large family of leaf beetles there are no true aquatic adults and only a few semiaquatic species. They occur above the surface of the water where they walk and fly about among the marginal, floating, and emergent vegetation of ponds and lakes. In this country there are three such genera, all of which are widely distributed. Although there are numerous species of *Donacia* and *Galerucella*, there is but one species, *Haemonia nigricornis* Kirby, in the third genus. The species of *Donacia* are elongated, have slender antennae, and are of a metallic blue, green, purple, or bronze color; they are about 6 to 13 mm. long. *H. nigricornis* resembles *Donacia* in form; the thorax, elytra, and legs are brownish-yellow, while the head and undersurfaces are black; the length ranges from 5.5 to 8 mm. The species of *Galerucella*, on the other hand, are more oval, brownish or reddish, and only 4 to 6 mm. long. The adults feed on a great variety of aquatic plants, but the floating leaves of the yellow pond lily form one of the principal foods.

## KEY TO GENERA OF ADULT CHRYSOMELIDAE

1. Head projecting from thorax, constricted or necklike behind the eyes (Fig. 384D) . 2
   Head inserted in the thorax as far as the eyes (Fig. 384C) . . . . . . . . . . .**Galerucella**
2. Tarsi slender; third segment entire, very small, and much shorter than the second; last segment nearly as long as the others united (Fig. 384B).
   Haemonia nigricornis Kirby
   Tarsi dilated; third segment deeply bilobed, never much shorter, usually as long as or longer than the second; last segment rarely as long as the two preceding segments taken together. . . . . . . . . . . . . . . . . . . . . . . . . . . . . . . . . . . . . . . . . . . . . . **Donacia**

The females of *Donacia* and *Haemonia* deposit the eggs in a variety of places. Some species eat holes in the floating leaves of the pond lily and deposit them on the undersurface near the edge of the opening. Others lay their eggs on the submerged surfaces of a great variety of other aquatic plants. A few species deposit the eggs on emergent portions of plants or in the plant tissues below the epidermis. When the eggs hatch the larvae drop to the bottom where they feed on roots and rhizomes of aquatic plants. The larvae are 8 to 16 mm. long, stout, grublike, and white or yellowish in color. The head is minute and almost hidden by the first thoracic segment. The abdomen is ten-segmented with the last three segments usually minute and curved beneath the sixth and seventh. There are nine pairs of spiracles, of which only the last pair are probably functional. These are situated on the base of two stout spines which are located on the dorsal side of the eighth abdominal segment. By pushing these caudal spines into the tissues of the underground portions of plants, the larvae obtain access to the extensive internal air

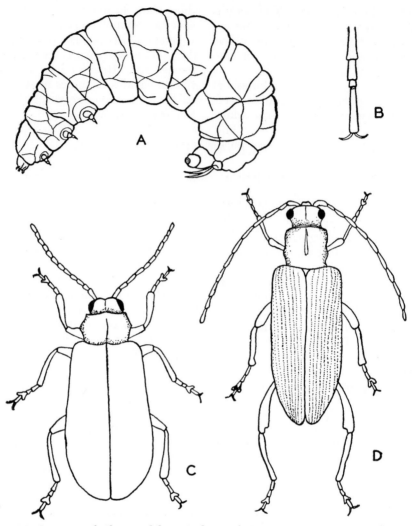

Fig. 384.—Structure of Chrysomelidae. A, larva of *Donacia*, ×6; B, tarsus of *Haemonia nigricornis* Kirby; C, *Galerucella* adult, ×10; D, *Donacia* adult, ×6. (A redrawn from Böving and Craighead.)

spaces, and by this ingenious method they obtain a continuous supply of oxygen through the posterior spiracles even though they may be in mud under a meter of water. Recently it has been shown that some species which spend a portion of the larval stage surrounded by water rather than mud or sand are capable of obtaining a sufficient quantity of oxygen through the general integument.

The larvae are rather sluggish and usu-

ally while they are feeding the body is bent into a U-shape with both the head and posterior end imbedded in the plant tissues.

Just before pupation the larva spins a cocoon which is watertight and airtight and is firmly glued to the surface of the plant. Air enters the cocoon from the plant tissues through holes or slits cut through the cocoon and epidermis of the plant where these two are in close contact.

The cocoon is completely filled with air, and the adult which breaks out is carried to the surface by the film of air which adheres to the ventral side of the body.

The habits of the immature stages of *Galerucella* differ markedly from those of the two genera described above. The adult females of *G. nymphaeae*, the only important semiaquatic species, deposit clusters of eggs on the upper surface of yellow pond lily pads. The larvae are about 7 mm. long when mature and black with fine whitish lines and spots. They remain on the upper surface of the pads, feeding on the tissues. The pupae are also found on the upper surface of the pads; they are naked, black, and about as long as mature larvae. The pupal stage persists only a few days or weeks.

## KEY TO GENERA OF CHRYSOMELIDAE LARVAE

1. Dorsal surface of eighth abdominal segment with a pair of prominent pointed spines; abdominal prolegs absent (Fig. 384A); feeding on submerged portions of aquatic plants....................................................2
   No pointed spines on dorsal surface of eighth abdominal segment; abdominal prolegs present; feeding on upper surface of leaves of water lilies and other aquatic plants. ...................................................**Galerucella**
2. White or cream-colored; legs small or moderate sized.................**Donacia**
   Green; legs large; usually on *Potamogeton natans*......**Haemonia nigricornis** Kirby

## CURCULIONIDAE (WEEVILS)

Weevils may be easily identified by the fact that the head is prolonged into a snout with the mouth parts at the tip and the antennae somewhere along its length. This is probably the largest family of insects, but only a relatively few species have developed an incidental semiaquatic habit, and their biology is comparatively unknown. About 100 species, all in the Curculioninae, are associated with a great variety of aquatic plants. The adults may usually be found feeding on the emergent tissues or in low herbage or debris on the nearby shore. Most of these weevils are a dirty brownish color and less than 5 mm. long. Aside from a scaly, gummy, waterproof coat in some species, there is little adaptation for an aquatic existence, and although some may dive and swim under water by movements of the hind legs, much the greater portion of the time is spent out of the water. The egg, larval, and pupal stages usually occur on emergent vegetation or on shore.

*Lissorhoptrus simplex* (Say), the rice water weevil, is the best-known species, chiefly because of its economic impor-

tance. The larvae feed on the roots and the adults on the emergent leaves of the rice plant as well as many species of wild aquatics. The adult swims readily on or under the surface. *Phytobius velatus* (Beck), originally a native of Europe, is unusual in that the tarsi bear swimming hairs and all of the stages in the life history are found below the surface on *Myriophyllum*, the water milfoil. *Tanysphyrus lemnae* (Fabr.), also a European importation, is thought to occur almost everywhere on *Lemna*, the duckweed. Other plants on which aquatic weevils are commonly found are arrowhead, bulrush, pickerel weed, sedges, and water lilies.

The 100 American aquatic species comprise 14 genera. Ten of these genera make up the subtribe Hydronomi; the other four are placed in tribes and subtribes that are predominantly terrestrial. The largest and most common genus is *Bagous*, with about 29 American species. Other genera which are not particularly rare are *Endalus*, *Lissorhoptrus*, *Listronotus*, and *Phytobius*.

## KEY TO GENERA OF ADULT SEMIAQUATIC CURCULIONIDAE

1.  Beak free, not received by prosternum.....................................3
    Beak received by prosternum in repose.............................2
2.  Anterior coxae contiguous........Tribe ERIRHININI, Subtribe HYDRONOMI, 5
    Anterior coxae separated.........................................Phytobius

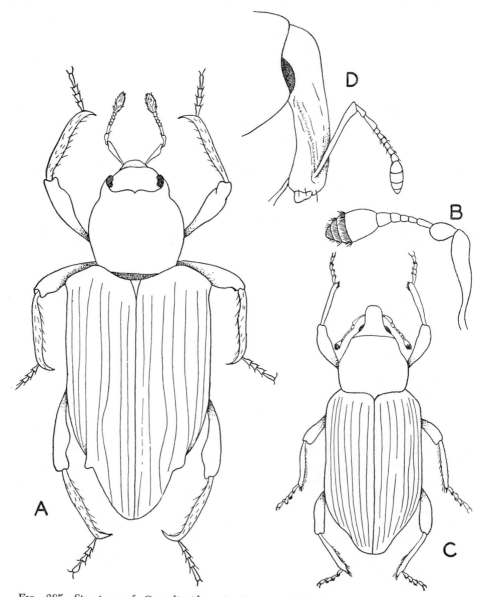

Fig. 385.—Structure of Curculionidae. A, *Bagous*, ×22; B, antenna of *Lissorhoptrus simplex* (Say); C, adult *L. simplex*, ×20; D, anterior end of *Listronotus* showing beak, antenna, and part of compound eye and pronotum. (B and C modified from Tucker.)

3. Third and fourth sternites together no longer than the second or fifth..........4
    Sternites not very unequal in size...............................Phytonomus
4. Second flagellar segment of antenna much longer than the first (Fig. 385D).
                                                                   Listronotus
    Second flagellar segment of antenna little if any longer than the first....Hyperodes
5. Beak very short and broad, shorter than head.......Stenopelmus rufinasus Gyll.
    Beak cylindrical, much longer than head.................................6
6. Third segment of hind tarsi emarginate or bilobed.....................7
    Third segment of hind tarsi simple...................................12
7. Beak curved.........................................................9
    Beak straight.......................................................8
8. First and second tibiae serrate on inner side.............Lixellus filiformis Lec.
    First and second tibiae not serrate on inner side.................Anchodemus
9. Tarsi with a single claw.......................Brachybamus electus Germ.
    Tarsi with two claws................................................10
10. Last segment of tarsi broad, claws well separated.......................11
    Last segment of tarsi narrow, projecting beyond lobes of the third.....Onychylis
11. Elytra not appreciably wider than thorax; usually 2 mm. or more long....Endalus
    Elytra much wider than thorax; usually less than 1.5 mm. long.
                                                 Tanysphyrus lemnae (Fabr.)
12. Club of antenna partly smooth and shining (Fig. 385B).
                                              Lissorhoptrus simplex (Say)
    Club of antenna entirely pubescent....................................13
13. Pronotum feebly constricted in front (Fig. 385A)....................Bagous
    Pronotum strongly constricted and tubulate in front.................Pnigodes

## COLEOPTERA REFERENCES

BALDUF, W. V. 1935. *The bionomics of ento-mophagous Coleoptera.* 220 pp. St. Louis, Mo.

BALFOUR-BROWNE, F. 1940. *British water beetles. I.* 375 pp. London.

BEERBOWER, F. V. 1943. Life history of Scirtes orbiculatus Fabius. *Ann. Ent. Soc. Amer.* 36:672–680.

BERTRAND, H. 1928. Les larves et nymphes des Dytiscides, Hygrobiides, et Haliplides. *Encycl. Entom.* 10:1–366.

BLACKWELDER, R. E. 1939. *Fourth Supplement, 1933 to 1938 (inclusive), to the Leng Catalogue of Coleoptera of America, north of Mexico.* 146 pp. Mount Vernon, N. Y.

BLATCHLEY, W. S. 1910. *An illustrated descriptive catalogue of the Coleoptera or beetles (exclusive of the Rhynchophora) known to occur in Indiana.* 1386 pp. Indianapolis.

BLATCHLEY, W. S., and C. W. LENG. 1916. *Rhynchophora or weevils of North Eastern America.* 682 pp. Indianapolis.

BÖVING, A. G. 1910. Natural history of larvae of the Donaciinae. *Int. Rev. Suppl.* 1:1–108.

———. 1914. Notes on the larva of Hydroscapha and some other aquatic larvae from Arizona. *Proc. Ent. Soc. Wash.* 16:169–174.

———. 1929. On the classification of beetles according to larval characters. *Bull. Brooklyn Ent. Soc.* 24:55–97.

BÖVING, A. G., and F. C. CRAIGHEAD. 1930–1931. An illustrated synopsis of the principal larval forms of the order Coleoptera. *Ent. Amer.* 11:1–351.

BRADLEY, J. C. 1930. *A manual of the genera of beetles of America north of Mexico.* 360 pp. Ithaca, N. Y.

CHANDLER, H. P. 1943. A new genus of Haliplidae (Coleoptera) from California. *Pan-Pac. Ent.* 19:154–158.

DARLINGTON, P. J., JR. 1929. On the dryopid beetle genus Lara. *Psyche* 36:328–331.

D'ORCHYMONT, A. 1942. Contribution a l'étude de la tribu Hydrobiini Bedel, spécialement de sa sous-tribu Hydrobiae (Palpicornia-Hydrophilidae). *Mém. Mus. roy. d'Hist. nat. Belg.,* Ser. 2, 24:1–68.

FALL, H. C. 1922. *A review of the North American species of Agabus together with a description of a new genus and species of the tribe Agabini.* 36 pp. Mount Vernon, N. Y.

———. 1922a. The North American species of Gyrinus. *Trans. Amer. Ent. Soc.* 47:269–306.

———. 1923. *A revision of the North American species of Hydroporus and Agaporus.* 129 pp.

HARPSTER, H. T. 1941. An investigation of the gaseous plastron as a respiratory mechanism in Helichus striatus Leconte (Dryopidae). *Trans. Amer. Ent. Soc.* 60:329–358.

Hatch, M. H. 1925. Phylogeny and phylogenetic tendencies of Gyrinidae. *Pap. Mich. Acad. Sci., Arts and Lett.* 5:429–467.

———. 1927. The morphology of Gyrinidae. *Ibid.* 7:311–350.

———. 1927a. A systematic index to the keys for the determination of the Nearctic Coleoptera. *Jour. N. Y. Ent. Soc.* 35:279–306.

———. 1928. A geographical index of the catalogues and local lists of Nearctic Coleoptera. *Ibid.* 36:335–354.

———. 1928a. Studies on Dytiscidae. *Bull. Brooklyn Ent. Soc.* 23:217–229.

———. 1933. Studies on Hydroporus. *Ibid.* 28:21–27.

Hickman, J. R. 1930. Life-histories of Michigan Haliplidae (Coleoptera). *Pap. Mich. Acad. Sci., Arts and Lett.* 11:399–424.

———. 1931. Respiration of the Haliplidae (Coleoptera). *Ibid.* 13:277–289.

———. 1931a. Contribution to the biology of the Haliplidae (Coleoptera). *Ann. Ent. Soc. Amer.* 24:129–142.

Hinton, H. E. 1935. Notes on the Dryopoidea, Col. *Stylops* 4:169–179.

———. 1935a. Synonymical and other notes on the Dryopidae (Coleoptera). *Ent. Month. Mag.* 72:54–58.

———. 1936. Descriptions of new genera and species of Dryopidae (Coleoptera). *Trans. Roy. Ent. Soc. Lond.* 85:415–434.

———. 1939. Notes on American Elmidae, with descriptions of new species (Coleoptera). *Ent. Month. Mag.* 75:179–185.

———. 1939a. An inquiry into the natural classification of the Dryopoidea, based partly on a study of their internal anatomy (Col.). *Trans. Roy. Ent. Soc. Lond.* 89:133–184.

———. 1940. A monographic revision of the Mexican water beetles of the family Elmidae. *Novit. Zool.* 42:217–396.

———. 1940a. A synopsis of the genus Macronychus Müller (Coleoptera, Elmidae). *Proc. Roy. Ent. Soc. Lond.* (B) 9:113–119.

Hoffman, C. E. 1940. Morphology of the immature stages of some northern Michigan Donaciini (Chrysomelidae, Coleoptera). *Pap. Mich. Acad. Sci., Arts and Lett.* 25:243–290.

———. 1940. The relation of Donacia larvae (Chrysomelidae; Coleoptera) to dissolved oxygen. *Ecology* 21:176–183.

Hubbard, H. G. 1892. Description of the larva of Amphizoa lecontei. *Proc. Ent. Soc. Wash.* 2:341–346.

Leech, H. B. 1940. Description of a new species of Laccornis, with a key to the Nearctic species (Coleoptera, Dytiscidae). *Canad. Ent.* 72:122–128.

———. 1941. The species of Matus, a genus of carnivorous water beetles (Coleoptera, Dytiscidae). *Ibid.* 73:76–83.

———. 1942. Key to the Nearctic genera of water beetles of the tribe Agabini, with some generic synonomy (Coleoptera, Dytiscidae). *Ann. Ent. Soc. Amer.* 35:355–362.

———. 1948. Contributions toward a knowledge of the insect fauna of Lower California. No. 11. Coleoptera: Haliplidae, Dytiscidae, Gyrinidae, Hydrophilidae, Limnebiidae. *Proc. Calif. Acad. Sci.* 24:375–484.

Leng, C. W. 1920. *Catalogue of the Coleoptera of America north of Mexico.* 470 pp. Mount Vernon, N. Y.

Leng, C. W., and A. J. Mutchler. 1918. Insects of Florida. V. The water beetles. *Bull. Amer. Mus. Nat. Hist.* 38:73–116.

———. 1927. *Supplement 1919 to 1924 (inclusive) to the Catalogue of the Coleoptera of America North of Mexico.* 78 pp. Mount Vernon, N. Y.

———. 1933. *Second and third supplements, 1925 to 1932 (inclusive), to Catalogue of Coleoptera of North America, North of Mexico.* 112 pp. Mount Vernon, N. Y.

Matheson, R. 1912. The Haliplidae of North America, north of Mexico. *Jour. N. Y. Ent. Soc.* 20:156–193.

Musgrave, P. N. 1935. Notes on collecting Dryopidae (Coleoptera). *Canad. Ent.* 67:61–63.

———. 1935. A synopsis of the genus Helichus Erichson in the United States and Canada, with description of a new species (Coleoptera: Dryopidae). *Proc. Ent. Soc. Wash.* 37:137–145.

Mutchler, A. J. 1931. Genotype designations of the genera Hydrophilus and Hydrochara. *Amer. Mus. Nov.* 507:1–3.

Nelson, H. G. 1949. A method of cleaning insects for study. *Coleopterists' Bull.* 6:89–92.

Richmond, E. A. 1920. Studies on the biology of the aquatic Hydrophilidae. *Bull. Amer. Mus. Nat. Hist.* 42:1–94.

———. 1931. The external morphology of Hydrophilus obtusatus Say (Coleoptera: Hydrophilidae). *Jour. N. Y. Ent. Soc.* 39:191–250.

Roberts, C. H. 1913. Critical notes on the species of Haliplidae of America north of Mexico with descriptions of new species. *Ibid.* 21:91–213.

Rymer-Roberts, A. W. 1930. A key to the principal families of Coleoptera in the larval stage. *Bull. Ent. Res.* 21:57–72.

Sanderson, M. W. 1938. A monographic revision of the North American species of Stenelmis. (Dryopidae: Coleoptera). *Kan. Univ. Sci. Bull.* 25:635–717.

Scott, H. M. 1924. Observations on the habits and life history of Galerucella nymphaea (Coleoptera). *Trans. Amer. Micros. Soc.* 43:11–16.

Segal, B. 1933. The hind wings of some Dryopidae in relation to habitat (Coleop.). *Ent. News* 44:85–88.

SHARP, D. 1882. On aquatic carnivorous Coleoptera or Dytiscidae. *Sci. Trans. Roy. Dublin Soc.* **2**:179–1003.

SHERMAN, J. D., JR. 1913. Some habits of the Dytiscidae. *Jour. N. Y. Ent. Soc.* **21**:43–54.

SUSSKIND, M. E. C. 1935. A morphological study of the respiratory system in various larval instars of Stenelmis sulcatus Blatchley (Dryopidae; Coleoptera). *Pap. Mich. Acad. Sci., Arts and Lett.* **21**:697–714.

TANNER, V. M. 1943. A study of the subtribe Hydronomi with a description of new species (Curculionidae). *Great Basin Nat.* **4**:1–38.

TRIMBLE, C. A. 1935. The external morphology of Hydrous triangularis (Hydrophilidae; Coleoptera). *Ohio Jour. Sci.* **35**:440–450.

TUCKER, E. S. 1912. The rice water-weevil and methods for its control. *U. S. Dept. Agric. Circ. No.* **152**:1–20.

VAN DYKE, E. C. 1927. The species of Amphizoa (Coleoptera). *Pan-Pac. Ent.* **3**:197–198.

WALLIS, J. B. 1933. Revision of the North American species (north of Mexico) of the genus Haliplus, Latreille. *Trans. Roy. Canad. Inst.* **19**:1–76.

––––. 1939. The genus Graphoderus Aubé in North America (north of Mexico) (Coleoptera). *Canad. Ent.* **71**:128–130.

––––. 1939a. The genus Ilybius Er. in North America (Coleoptera, Dytiscidae). *Ibid.* **71**:192–199.

WEST, L. S. 1929. Life history notes on Psephenus lecontei Lec. (Coleoptera; Dryopoidea; Psephenidae). *Battle Creek Coll. Bull.* **3**:3–20.

––––. 1929a. A preliminary study of larval structure in the Dryopidae. *Ann. Ent. Soc. Amer.* **22**:691–727.

WILSON, C. B. 1923. Life history of the scavenger water-beetle, Hydrous (Hydrophilus) triangularis, and its economic importance to fish breeding. *Bull. U. S. Bur. Fish.* **39**:9–38.

––––. 1923a. Water beetles in relation to pond-fish culture, with life histories of those found in fishponds at Fairport, Iowa. *Ibid.* **39**:231–345.

WINTERS, F. E. 1926. Notes on the Hydrobiini (Coleoptera-Hydrophilidae) of boreal America. *Pan-Pac. Ent.* **3**:49–58.

––––. 1927. Key to the subtribe Helocharae Orchym. (Coleoptera-Hydrophilidae) of boreal America. *Ibid.* **4**:19–29.

# Chapter 35

## DIPTERA (FLIES, MOSQUITOES, MIDGES)

THE DIPTERA are highly specialized two-winged flies, including such common insects as the housefly, mosquitoes, crane flies, midges, horseflies, hover flies, and botflies. They all have complete metamorphosis, large compound eyes, and mouth parts which are adapted for lapping or piercing and sucking. The hind pair of wings (halteres) are vestigial, and the thoracic segments are somewhat fused. Many species are of great economic importance.

Although the adults are never aquatic, many families have members which have aquatic immature stages. Such larvae and pupae occur in every type of fresh-water habitat, sometimes in enormous numbers. Only a few families, however, such as the Culicidae and Simuliidae, are exclusively aquatic. The egg-laying habits of aquatic Diptera are diverse. The females of some species scatter their eggs just below the surface of the water on vegetation, debris, and rocks. Others oviposit in regular or irregular gelatinous masses or strings below the surface, at the surface, or on objects just above it.

Aquatic Diptera larvae show greater variability in structure and habitat than any other order of aquatic insects. Usually, however, they are distinguished by their elongated, wormlike body, and the absence of eyes and jointed thoracic legs. In the generalized condition there are twelve body segments, that is, three thoracic and nine abdominal, but in many families there is a smaller number owing

to fusion or atrophy. The body is usually soft and flexible, and the most common colors are white, gray, yellow, reddish, brown, and black. The surface of the segments may be naked and smooth, or there may be bristles, spines, scales, or tubercles. The antennae are rarely prominent. In some families there are short, stumpy prolegs on some of the segments. In the black fly larvae, for example, there is a single stout ventral proleg on the prothorax; at the other extreme, some of the shore fly larvae have a pair of prolegs on each of the last eight segments. Many larvae swim by rapid wriggling movements of the body. Creeping on the substrate is facilitated by prolegs, spines, suckers, and sticky secretions of salivary glands. The head and mouth parts may be well developed and complex (some Orthorrapha), but in other larvae (Cyclorrapha) the head is vestigial and the mouth parts peculiarly modified, reduced, and relatively simple. In some families, such as the black flies and mosquitoes, the food consists of minute organisms and particles which are strained from the water by complex fans or mouth brushes composed of setae or bristles. In other families the mouth parts are modified for scraping debris from rocks, for feeding on aquatic plants, for predatory food habits, or simply for consuming heterogeneous plant and animal debris.

Because of the great diversity in structure and because many physiological details have not yet been established, it is difficult to characterize briefly the respiratory system of dipterous larvae. Like all other insects, however, they are fundamentally dependent upon an internal air-filled tracheal system which branches and ramifies to all of the tissues. The spiracles that open into the tracheal system are characteristically reduced in number, modified in their location, and may be entirely absent. Such families as the crane flies and mosquitoes are metapneustic, only the last pair of spiracles being open. Atmospheric air is obtained by contact of these spiracles (usually on a disc or at the end of a special respiratory siphon) with the air at the surface film. The larvae of the moth flies and the flower flies are amphipneustic, and both the prothoracic and last abdominal spiracles are open. In the families where oxygen is derived entirely from the surrounding water, there are usually thin-walled tracheal gills or blood gills which may or may not be situated in areas otherwise occupied by spiracles. During the past few years, however, several investigators have presented evidence that seems to indicate that blood gills are of little importance in respiration in some dipterous larvae. It is more likely that they are useful in the absorption of dissolved salts; the anal gills of mosquitoes, for example, are believed to be important in the absorption of chloride ions. There is also a growing tendency to attribute greater significance to the general body surface of larvae as a respiratory device. In apneustic forms particularly, such as black fly and midge larvae, the skin is supplied with a rich network of fine tracheae. A few Diptera have a specialized sharp respiratory siphon for obtaining their oxygen supply from the tissues of submerged aquatic plants.

The larval stage may last for only several weeks or it may persist for at least two years, depending on the species, temperature, and food conditions. Characteristically, the skin is cast three times during growth.

In the Stratiomyiidae (soldier flies) the exuviae persist and loosely enclose the pupae. In all other families of the Suborder Orthorrapha the skin is cast at pupation. In the Suborder Cyclorrapha the last larval skin hardens to form an immobile ovoid or barrel-shaped puparium enclosing the pupa.

The pupae of the Orthorrapha are all somewhat similar in structure. The appendages are free from the body yet more or less fused with each other and in most instances with the body surface.

The important external respiratory organs are found on the thorax and usually project anteriorly. They consist of tufts of fine filaments or a pair of respiratory tubes which range in length from very short tubercles to more than the length of the body. These respiratory structures may be either open or closed at the ends.

Although mosquito and midge pupae are capable of rapid wriggling movements, most other pupae are inactive. Some of the black fly pupae occur in loosely built cocoons. Mountain and net-winged midge pupae remain tightly fastened to the substrate by the flat ventral surface.

The pupal stage usually lasts less than two weeks, although a few types may winter over. The Orthorrapha imagoes emerge from the pupal case by means of a T-shaped dorsal split; the Cyclorrapha emerge by a caplike annular dehiscence at the anterior end.

Larvae and pupae can usually be killed and fixed in a satisfactory manner by flooding them with boiling water. Seventy-five to 85 per cent alcohol or 4 per cent formalin are suitable preservatives. Usually the detailed structure of the larval mouth parts and general integument can be more easily studied if the specimens are boiled for a few minutes or soaked for a day or two in cold 10 per cent potassium hydroxide. Such specimens must be passed through dilute acetic acid and several changes of water. Small forms may be permanently mounted on slides in glycerin jelly, balsam, or some substitute.

In accordance with the time-honored

major categories of Brauer, the following families having aquatic immature stages are included in this chapter:

Suborder Orthorrhapha
  Section Nematocera
    Family Deuterophlebiidae (mountain midges)
      Blepharoceridae (net-winged midges)
      Tipulidae (true crane flies)
      Ptychopteridae (phantom crane flies)
      Psychodidae (moth flies)
      Dixidae (dixa midges)
      Culicidae
        Culicinae (mosquitoes)
        Chaoborinae (phantom midges)
      Simuliidae (black flies)
      Tendipedidae (midges)
        Podonominae
        Pelopiinae
        Diamesinae
        Hydrobaeninae
        Tendipedinae
      Ceratopogonidae (biting midges)

Section Brachycera
    Family Stratiomyiidae (soldier flies)
      Tabanidae (horseflies)
      Rhagionidae (snipe flies)

Suborder Cyclorrhapha
  Family Syrphidae (flower flies)
    Scatophagidae (dung flies)
    Tetanoceridae (marsh flies)
    Ephydridae (shore flies)
    Anthomyiidae (anthomyiids)

In addition to the families listed above, there are about a dozen other families containing a few rare species, most of which are semiaquatic and found in or on mud and wet moss, or on wet stones. References to these species will be found in the papers of Johannsen. In the keys which follow, all of the common genera are included. Also, the great majority of forms are strictly aquatic, very few semiaquatic species being indicated. It should be borne in mind that only the last larval instars are included in the descriptions and keys. In many instances the keys will not apply to immature larvae.

## KEY TO FAMILIES OF DIPTERA LARVAE *

1. Head capsule complete, differentiated, sclerotized, and free or retractile into the first thoracic segment....................Suborder **ORTHORRHAPHA, 2**
   Head vestigial, not differentiated, membranous, and often apparently lacking.
                        Suborder **CYCLORRHAPHA, 15**
2. Head well developed, with antennae; mandibles opposed to each other horizontally or inclined obliquely downward...........Section NEMATOCERA, 3
   Head somewhat incomplete and usually retractile into the first thoracic segment; mandibles or mouth hooks parallel and moving in a vertical plane.
                        Section BRACHYCERA, 13
3. Head, thorax, and first abdominal segment fused; with a row of six ventral suckers for attachment to beds of rapid streams......BLEPHAROCERIDAE, p. 635
   Head not fused with thorax and first abdominal segment; ventral suckers usually absent (present in *Maruina*)........................................4
4. Abdomen with seven pairs of large lateral prolegs supplied with concentric rings of minute claws; antennae branched; on rocks and pebbles in rapid streams.
                        DEUTEROPHLEBIIDAE, p. 632
   With other characters.............................................5
5. Lobed respiratory disc at the posterior end of body bearing spiracles; head retractile............................................TIPULIDAE, p. 636
   No lobed disc at posterior end of body; head not retractile..................6

---

* Modified from Johannsen (1934).

6. Body terminating in a very long conspicuous respiratory tube.
PTYCHOPTERIDAE, p. 639
No long terminal respiratory tube.....................................7
7. Prolegs present...................................................**10**
Prolegs absent....................................................**8**
8. Segments secondarily divided into more or less distinct annuli; amphipneustic.
PSYCHODIDAE, p. 640
Segments not annulated; not amphipneustic............................9
9. Thoracic segments fused and distinctly thicker than rest of body.
CULICIDAE, p. 642
Thorax and abdomen about equal in diameter....CERATOPOGONIDAE, p. 654
10. With a single proleg projecting anteriorly from prothorax...SIMULIIDAE, p. 647
Prolegs otherwise................................................**11**
11. Body flattened, oval in cross section; most segments with long lateral processes; one pair of anterior prolegs.
CERATOPOGONIDAE (genus *Atrichopogon* only), p. 654
Body round in cross section; no lateral processes......................**12**
12. Two prolegs on each of the first two abdominal segments; body bent into a U-shape when at rest....................................DIXIDAE, p. 641
One pair of prolegs on prothorax and another pair at the end of the abdomen; body not U-shaped..........................TENDIPEDIDAE, p. 649
13. Integument with calcium carbonate crystals; prolegs lacking.
STRATIOMYIIDAE, p. 657
No calcium carbonate deposits in integument; prolegs present............**14**
14. Last abdominal segment ending in two long, fringed appendages.
RHAGIONIDAE, p. 659
Last abdominal segment otherwise; spiracle at extreme posterior end of body ending in a vertical slit or in a sharply compressed spine; girdle of prolegs on most segments...................................TABANIDAE, p. 658
15. Last segment elongated into a very long telescoping retractile tail.
SYRPHIDAE, p. 660
Last segment otherwise............................................**16**
16. Larva a miner in petioles of pond lilies.............SCATOPHAGIDAE, p. 661
Larva not a miner in petioles of pond lilies............................**17**
17. Spiracular disc at posterior end surrounded by several lobes.
TETANOCERIDAE, p. 661
Without such lobes...............................................**18**
18. Leaf miners in aquatic plants.......................EPHYDRIDAE, p. 662
Not leaf miners in aquatic plants....................................**19**
19. Mouth hooks sharp, slender, not dentate below........ANTHOMYIIDAE, p. 663
Mouth hooks palmate or digitate.....................EPHYDRIDAE, p. 662

## KEY TO FAMILIES OF DIPTERA PUPAE [*]

1. Pupa free, not completely covered by last larval skin; cocoon may be present.
Suborder **ORTHORRHAPHA, 2**
Pupa remaining wholly within the last larval skin (puparium)................3
2. Antennal sacs elongated, lying over compound eyes and extending to or beyond the bases of the wing sheaths; prothoracic respiratory organs usually conspicuous.
Section NEMATOCERA, 4
Antennal sacs short, not lying over compound eyes; prothoracic respiratory organs lacking or rudimentary........................Section BRACHYCERA

[*] Modified from Johannsen (1934).

3. Pupa within the last larval skin (puparium), which is unchanged in shape; larval head distinct.

  Suborder **ORTHORRHAPHA**, Section BRACHYCERA, STRATIOMYIIDAE

  Puparium without a distinct head, modified in shape; usually heavily sclerotized, shortened, ellipsoidal, or egg-shaped.........Suborder **CYCLORRHAPHA**

4. Pupa within a fibrous cocoon..........................................5

  Pupa without a cocoon, though sometimes in a silken tube..................6

5. Cocoon vase-shaped, slipper-shaped, in the form of a wall pocket, or simply a structureless mass of matted threads; respiratory organs, consisting of four to 60 coarse filaments, projecting from open end; in running water.

  SIMULIIDAE

  Cocoon conical or cylindrical; respiratory organ a slender unbranched filament.

  TENDIPEDIDAE

6. Pupa more or less convex and hard-shelled; attached limpet-like to stream bed...7

  Pupa not so attached and not limpet-like..................................9

7. Thoracic respiratory organs leaflike...................BLEPHAROCERIDAE

  Thoracic respiratory organs not leaflike; in western mountain streams..........8

8. Thoracic respiratory organs branched and filamentous..DEUTEROPHLEBIIDAE

  Thoracic respiratory organs short, simple, and unbranched......PSYCHODIDAE

9. Leg sheaths straight, projecting beyond ends of wing sheaths, in most cases far beyond; caudal end not paddle-shaped; usually more than 8 mm. long; pupation in sand or mud, rarely in open water..............................10

  Leg sheaths often curved or folded, projecting little if any beyond ends of wing sheaths; caudal end often ending in a paddle; usually less than 8 mm. long; pupation usually in open water.......................................11

10. One of breathing horns longer than the body, the other short.PTYCHOPTERIDAE

  Breathing horns less than three-fourths of the body length, subequal in length.

  TIPULIDAE

11. Wing sheaths ending about mid-length of pupa; leg sheaths short, straight, and superimposed. .....................................PSYCHODIDAE

  Wing sheaths ending distinctly before mid-length of pupa when body and leg sheaths are straight, or body arched and leg sheaths undulatory..........12

12. Caudal end with two paddles, each with a midrib...............CULICIDAE

  Paddles, if present, without a distinct midrib............................13

13. Paddles narrow, completely fused at base; each with a strong hair on outer margin beyond mid-length and several stout spines at tip; minute species.

  CULICIDAE

  With other characters................................................14

14. Caudal paddles long and pointed, fused basally; pupa normally lying on its side in an arched position.....................................DIXIDAE

  Caudal paddles absent, or, if present, the pupa differing in other characters....15

15. Thoracic respiratory organs with open stigmata.........................16

  Thoracic respiratory organs without open stigmata, or composed of numerous filaments, or lacking................................TENDIPEDIDAE

16. Anal segment ending in a pair of pointed processes.......CERATOPOGONIDAE

  Anal segment with a two-lobed swimming paddle............TENDIPEDIDAE

# DEUTEROPHLEBIIDAE (MOUNTAIN MIDGES)

These curious and poorly known flies have been collected in widely separated mountainous areas of Japan, the Asiatic mainland, and the United States. The adults of only four species are known, but the immature stages of five species have been adequately described. There is only one genus in the family, *Deuterophlebia*. The adults are small, the mouth parts are completely absent, the immense wings have elaborate secondary and concentric transverse folds, and the male has extremely long antennae.

The larvae, which creep about slowly on rocky bottoms of clear mountain streams, are reminiscent of blepharocerids.

The head, thoracic segments, and all eight abdominal segments are distinct and separated from each other, however. Among the most striking features are the large, blunt, lateral prolegs of the first seven abdominal segments. Each of these

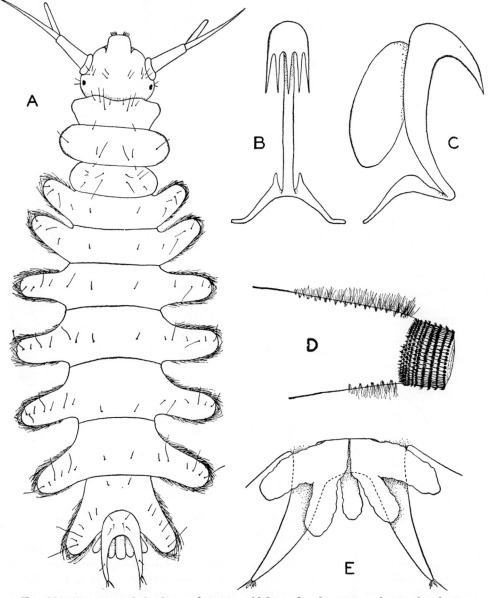

FIG. 386.—Structure of the larva of *Deuterophlebia coloradensis* Pennak. A, dorsal view, ×37; B, frontal view of claw of proleg; C, lateral view of claw of proleg; D, ventral view of proleg which has been straightened to show rings of claws; E, ventral view of posterior end, showing the five anal gills. (From Pennak.)

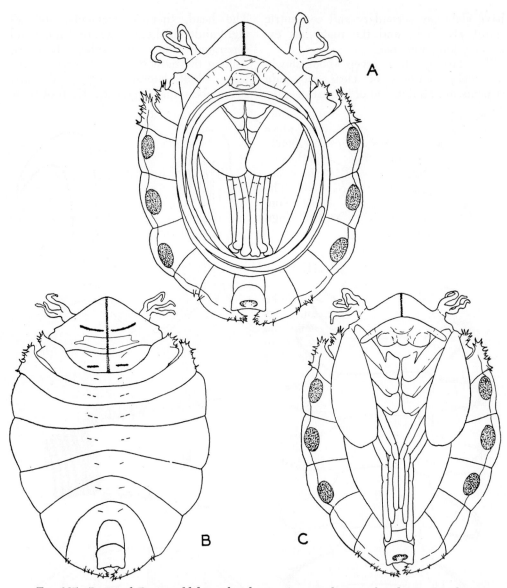

FIG. 387.—Pupae of *Deuterophlebia coloradensis*. A, ventral view of male; B, dorsal view of female; C, ventral view of female; all ×35. (From Pennak.)

has a series of rings of minute sclerotized claws, and the claws, together with the blunt ends of the prolegs, act as imperfect sucking discs for clinging to the substrate. The head is rather flat, and the unique branched antennae are long and originate on stout tubercles. The peculiar mouth parts are specialized for scraping diatoms and other algae from rock surfaces. The

last abdominal segment is comparatively small and is provided with two long, tapering, sclerotized processes and five delicate blood-gill-like structures originating around the anus. It is thought that there are four larval instars, the average length of the last being about 4 mm.

The pupae adhere tightly to the substrate. They are broadly oval, only slightly convex dorsally, and flat ventrally. The dorsal surface is strongly sclerotized and dark brown or blackish in color. On the anterior lateral margins of the thorax are two respiratory processes consisting of several slender filaments. The first, second, and seventh abdominal segments are supplied with stout thornlike spines along their lateral margins. The eighth and ninth abdominal segments are almost completely enclosed by the projecting seventh segment. On the ventral surface there are three pairs of lateral adhesive pads. The antennae of the male are enormously elongated, being coiled in large elliptical rings.

The larval and pupal stages of only two American species have been adequately described. *Deuterophlebia coloradensis* Pennak is common in mountain streams in Colorado and also is known from several other western states. *D. shasta* Wirth is known only from California and Oregon. Unfortunately, no larval characters have been found by which species may be identified. The pupae, however, do show distinguishing morphological differences.

Undoubtedly careful collecting in mountain streams of the West will show that the Deuterophlebiidae are widely distributed and not uncommon.

## BLEPHAROCERIDAE (NET-WINGED MIDGES)

The adults are elongated, mosquito-like insects of moderate size, with long legs and broad wings. In addition to veins, the wings have a network of fine lines. These midges are world-wide in distribution, but there are relatively few species. They frequent the borders of streams where they feed on smaller insects. It is thought that the eggs are deposited on wet rocks at the margins of streams and that the larvae migrate into the water. Both the larvae and pupae are usually found in clusters tightly attached to the rocky bottoms of rushing brooks and streams of ravines and hilly and mountainous areas.

The unique larvae are flattened and composed of seven divisions; the first consists of the fused head, thorax, and first abdominal segment; the next five are abdominal segments two to six; the last and smallest division includes three abdominal segments. Each of the first six divisions has a median ventral sucker by which the larva attaches itself tightly to the substrate.

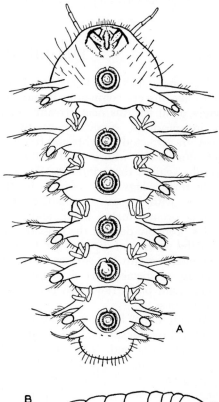

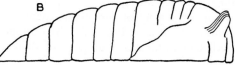

Fig. 388.—Blepharoceridae. A, ventral view of larva of *Bibiocephala*, ×11; B, lateral view of pupa of *Bibiocephala*, ×9. (A redrawn from Johannsen, 1934; B redrawn from Malloch, 1917.)

Each division except the last also has a pair of prolegs. There are paired tufts of tracheal gill filaments on abdominal segments two to six. The antennae are slender and usually short. Total length ranges from 4 to 12 mm.

The pupae are flat, heavily sclerotized, and a shiny brown or black color on the dorsal side. The integument of the ventral surface is very delicate and transparent. There are six pads, three of which are on each side near the lower surface of the abdomen. Unlike the larvae, the pupae remain attached in one spot. There are two sets of flat, leaflike, thoracic respiratory organs.

## KEY TO GENERA OF BLEPHAROCERIDAE LARVAE

1. With paired lateral body processes situated immediately anterior and slightly dorsal to prolegs (Fig. 388A); western; widely distributed.......................2
   Paired lateral body processes absent or rudimentary................Blepharocera
2. With six stout tubercles on dorsal side of each body segment...........Philorus
   Dorsal tubercles lacking.........................................................3
3. Each gill tuft composed of four or six filaments, some of which are directed forward, some backward.........................................................Agathon
   Each gill tuft composed of three or four filaments, all directed forward. Bibiocephala

## TIPULIDAE (CRANE FLIES)

The crane flies are long-legged, mosquito-like insects commonly found flying singly or in swarms near streams, ponds, or in meadows, especially at twilight. They are attracted to lights and frequently get into houses where they flutter awkwardly against the windows. They lose their fragile legs very easily. In those species with aquatic immature stages, mating occurs during flight, and the females probably deposit the eggs by flying over the water and dipping the tip of the abdomen beneath the surface. The great majority of species have a single generation a year, but a few have two or three generations.

Aquatic crane fly larvae may be easily identified by the spiracular disc at the extreme posterior end. This disc, except in *Antocha*, bears a pair of functional spiracles and may be thrust up to the surface of the water for air, particularly when the supply of dissolved oxygen becomes low. It is customarily lobed, fringed with hairs, and has a number of delicate anal gills associated with it. Color ranges from brown to whitish, and the integument is often quite transparent. The common species range from 10 to 50 mm. in length.

As shown below, the larvae exhibit a wide range of habitat preferences; many are semiaquatic and occur in damp sand, organic mud, and wet mosses. Some genera, such as *Tipula*, occur in a variety of habitats; others, such as *Antocha* and *Pilaria*, are restricted to a single type of habitat. The family has both carnivorous and herbivorous representatives. Depending on the species and the environment, the larval period may last from about a month to nearly a year. Probably all crane flies in the United States pass the winter as larvae. Most genera have a wide geographic range.

Habitats of aquatic and semiaquatic crane fly larvae of the United States are here summarized (adapted from Alexander, 1931); uncommon to very rare genera are indicated by asterisks.

Stream bottoms, but not more or less buried in the substrate: *Antocha* and *Eriocera.*

Cold springs: *Aeschnasoma** and *Pedicia.*

On cliffs or rock faces, in or beneath algal scum with percolating or flowing water: *Dactylolabis,** *Elliptera,** *Limonia,* and *Tipula.*

In sphagnum and other aquatic mosses: *Eriocera* and *Pedicia.*

In sandy, gravelly, or loamy soil, poor in humus, on bottoms of streams and ponds or along margins: *Eriocera, Erioptera, Gonomyia,** *Helobia,** *Hexatoma, Limnophila, Longurio,* and *Tipula.*

In rich organic mud at edges of bodies of water; swamps and marshes: *Adelphomyia,** *Dicranota,** *Erioptera, Gonomyia,** *Helius, Limnophila, Limonia, Pilaria, Prionocera, Pseudolimnophila, Tipula,* and *Tricyphona.**

The elongated pupae are formed in the last larval skin which is usually shed. In some species the pupa is enclosed in a silken case, especially in *Antocha.* There are two breathing horns at the anterior end. The pupal stage usually lasts from five to eight days.

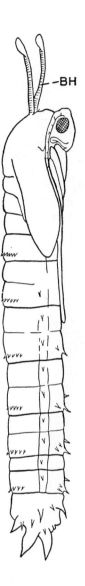

Fig. 389.—Pupa of *Tipula*, ×6. *BH*, breathing horn.

## KEY TO GENERA OF COMMON TIPULIDAE LARVAE

1. Spiracular disc surrounded by six or eight lobes..........................2
   Spiracular disc surrounded by less than six lobes..........................5
2. Spiracular disc surrounded by eight lobes (Fig. 390L); very common ....**Tipula**
   Spiracular disc surrounded by six lobes................................3
3. Anal gills pinnately branched....................................**Longurio**
   Anal gills not pinnately branched....................................4
4. Length of the two ventral lobes of the spiracular disc more than four times the width. ...................................................**Prionocera**
   Length of the two ventral lobes less than four times the width (Fig. 390K); very common. ......................................................**Tipula**

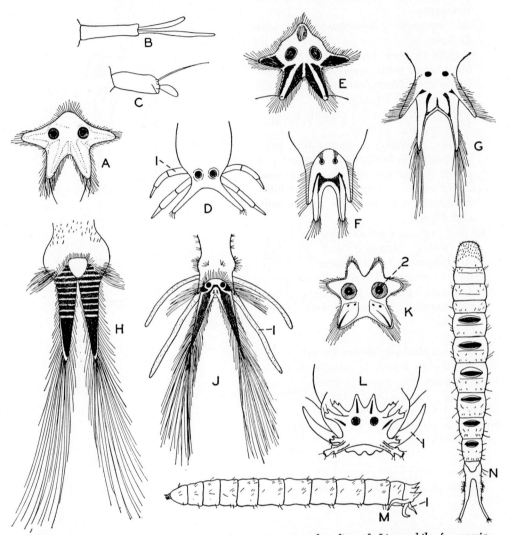

Fig. 390.—Structure of larvae of Tipulidae. A, spiracular disc of *Limnophila fuscovaria* O. S.; B, antenna of *Pseudolimnophila*; C, antenna of *Limnophila fuscovaria*; D, spiracular disc of *Pedicia*; E, spiracular disc of *Helius mainensis* Alexander; F, spiracular disc of *Hexatoma megacera* (O. S.); G, spiracular disc of *H. spinosa* (O. S.); H, spiracular disc of *Pilaria tenuipes* (Say); J, spiracular disc of *Pseudolimnophila luteipennis* (O. S.); K, spiracular disc of *Tipula ignobilis* Loew; L, spiracular disc of *T. abdominalis* (Say); M, lateral view of *Tipula*, ×3; N, dorsal view of *Antocha saxicola* O. S., ×7. 1, anal gill; 2, spiracle. (A to C, E to L, and N redrawn from Alexander, 1920.)

## PTYCHOPTERIDAE (PHANTOM CRANE FLIES)

Although adult phantom crane flies are somewhat similar to true crane flies, the larval stages are different. They may be easily recognized by the presence of a greatly elongated posterior respiratory tube. There is a similar structure in some of the Syrphidae larvae, but these two larval types may be distinguished by the fact that in the Ptychopteridae there is a well-developed head, while the head of a syrphid larva is small, poorly developed, and usually retracted into the thorax.

The immature stages of the Ptychopteridae are typically found in decaying vegetation at the edges of shallow ponds and in marshy areas. Decaying vegetation is the chief food of the larvae. Both the larvae and pupae lie among the debris with the tips of their long breathing tubes thrust up through the surface film. The two most common aquatic forms are *Ptychoptera rufocincta* O. S. and *Bittacomorpha clavipes* (Fabr.). The larvae of the former are 30 to 35 mm. long, whitish or light yellowish in color, and almost smooth; the larvae of the latter are 50 to 60 mm. long, brown or reddish brown, and covered with rows of small tubercles. Members of a third genus, *Bittacomorphella*, are uncommon but may be identified by their blackish coloration, by the many long horny projections covering the body, and by their small size (less than 20 mm. long).

The pupae are similar to those of the Tipulidae, except that one of the pronotal breathing horns is longer than the body and the other is very short.

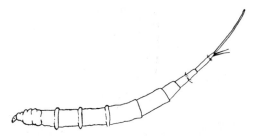

FIG. 391.—Larva of *Ptychoptera rufocincta* O. S., ×2.5.

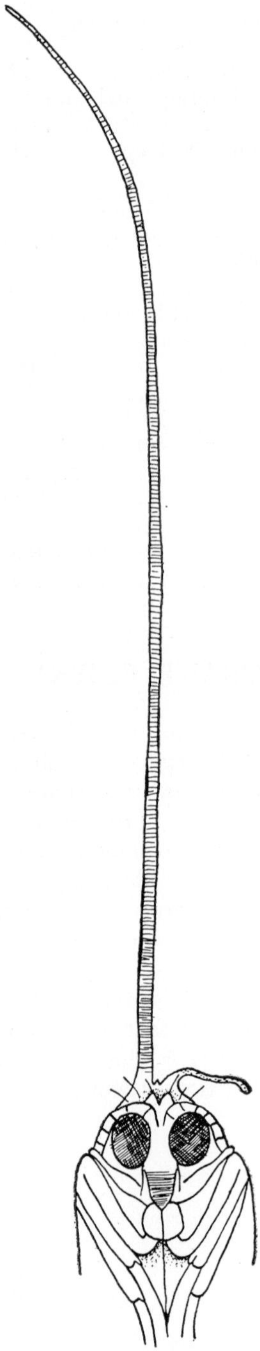

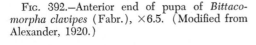

# PSYCHODIDAE (MOTH FLIES)

Adult moth flies are very small, usually less than 4 mm. long; the body is thickly covered with hairs, and the wings are hairy or scaly. They have a world-wide distribution and occur in shady places near water but are often abundant around lights at night.

Although many species have aquatic stages, those commonly encountered in the United States belong to only three genera: *Pericoma, Psychoda*, and *Maruina*. The elongated amphipneustic larvae are characterized by the lack of prolegs and the subdivision of segments into annuli, some of which bear transverse, hardened, dorsal plates. Food consists of algae and decaying vegetation. Body length is 3 to 10 mm.

The parts of the pupal head, legs, and wings are distinct and closely applied to the body. The prothoracic respiratory organs are slender cylindrical or conical processes into which the tracheae extend.

Larvae and pupae of the more common species usually occur in foul water, sewage, filter beds, and decaying organic matter, but some species of *Pericoma* and all species of *Maruina* inhabit rapid, clear streams. *Psychoda* larvae are cylindrical, grayish-white, and have hardened transverse dorsal plates only on the posterior segments. *Pericoma* larvae are also cylindrical, but the coloration is usually brown or blackish and there are dorsal plates on all thoracic and abdominal segments. *Maruina*, however, is strongly depressed, and there are sucker-like discs on the mid-ventral line; coloration is brown or blackish and there are dorsal plates on all segments. *Maruina* appears to be restricted to the western states.

FIG. 392.—Anterior end of pupa of *Bittaco-morpha clavipes* (Fabr.), ×6.5. (Modified from Alexander, 1920.)

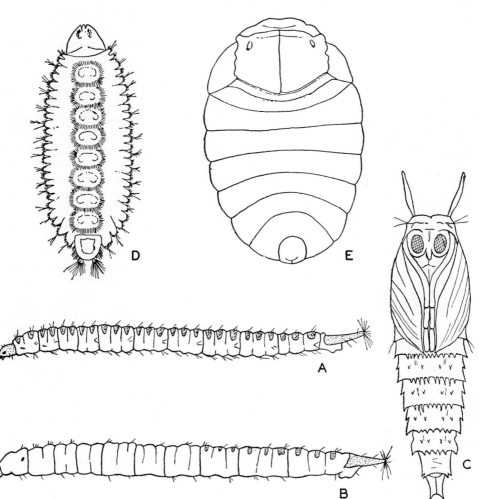

Fig. 393.—Psychodidae. A, larva of *Pericoma*, ×17; B, larva of *Psychoda*, ×16; C, pupa of *Psychoda*, ×25; D, ventral view of larva of *Maruina*, ×30; E, dorsal view of pupa of *Maruina*, ×30. (A and B redrawn from Johannsen, 1934.)

## DIXIDAE (DIXA MIDGES)

Adult dixa midges are small, slender insects which are usually found in small mating swarms near ponds or streams in meadows or wood areas at dusk. During most of the daylight hours they rest on vegetation or shaded rocks near water. Females deposit their eggs in the shallows by swishing the tip of the abdomen in the water as they flutter just above the surface.

All of the larvae are aquatic, and although they resemble mosquito larvae, they have distinct thoracic segments, paired prolegs on the first and usually also the second abdominal segments, and a definite U-shape when at rest. At the caudal end there are two lateral lobes, a long tail process, and two spiracles. Coloration is black or tan. They are found

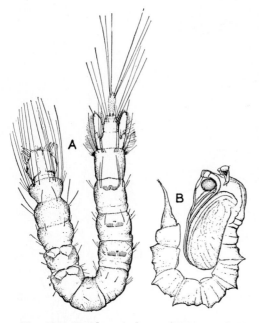

FIG. 394.—Dixidae. A, larva of *Dixa*, ×15; B, pupa of *Dixa*, ×12. (From Johannsen, 1934.)

in puddles, ponds, lakes, slow streams, and in the backwaters of rapid streams. Food consists of microorganisms and detritus filtered from the water by means of the mouth brushes. Total length is 4 to 8 mm. Larvae are most abundant on the shaded, downstream, or protected sides of rocks, vegetation, or debris, always at or near the surface film. Although they may leave the surface when disturbed and swim downward, they return in a few seconds.

Three genera are represented in the United States, each in a different subfamily. *Dixa* is generally distributed and very common; the larva has two pairs of abdominal prolegs (Figure 394), and the dorsal surface of each abdominal segment has a dense corona of setae. *Paradixa* is known only from the District of Columbia area; the larva has two pairs of prolegs, but the dorsal surfaces of the abdominal segments are more sparsely setose. *Meringodixa* has been collected only in the Pacific coast states; it bears only one pair of prolegs, and abdominal coronas of setae are present.

In order to pupate, the larvae crawl a few centimeters above the water's edge and affix themselves lightly to the substrate with a gluelike secretion. The pupa is similar to the pupal stage of mosquitoes. It differs from most mosquito pupae, however, in that it is U-shaped, and the posterior end is on a level with the anterior part of the head. Often the pupae are tightly coiled. They are not truly aquatic and are found floating free in the water only fortuitously. Usually, however, they are fastened in a shaded spot where the humidity is high and where they are occasionally splashed with water so that they do not dry out.

## CULICIDAE (MOSQUITOES, PHANTOM MIDGES)

The Culicidae comprise a large family of world-wide distribution, and because some species are transmitters of malaria and yellow fever, this group has been intensively studied. It is commonly divided into two subfamilies, the Culicinae and the Chaoborinae, the former including the true mosquitoes, the latter the phantom midges. There is much superficial resemblance between these two subfamilies, but the mosquitoes have scaly wings, and the phantom midges have hairy wings, and while many of the female mosquitoes bite, phantom midges do not feed. *Culex* and *Anopheles* are the most common mosquitoes, and *Chaoborus* (formerly called *Corethra*) is the common phantom midge. Aside from the importance of members of this group as disease transmitters and their nuisance as biters, some of the nonbiting Culicidae may occur in such tremendous numbers around lakes as to discourage the use of these bodies of water for summer recreation.

The oviposition habits are diverse but specific for each species. Eggs may be deposited singly, in irregular masses, or in floating rafts, and in such places as tree holes, temporary puddles, rain barrels, marshes, ponds, springs, slow streams and rivers, and lakes.

Culicidae larvae are easily distinguished from other Diptera because of the fact that the fused thoracic segments are thicker than the rest of the body. There are always four instars, the fourth persisting for the longest time. Mature larvae usually range from 3 to 15 mm. in length.

Most Culicinae larvae feed on algae, Protozoa, and bits of organic debris by means of the filtering action of the small mouth brushes. A few species have been observed gnawing on submerged surfaces or scraping the periphyton from such objects. Some species of *Psorophora* feed on other mosquito larvae as well as on entomostraca and rotifers.

The larvae usually lie quietly at the sur-

face of the water, but when they are disturbed they swim downward in a characteristic rapid manner which is responsible for their being called "wrigglers." *Anopheles* normally lies horizontally just beneath the surface film, but *Culex* and *Aedes* are inclined at an angle with only the tip of the respiratory tube at the surface. *Mansonia* (both larvae and pupae) is unique in that it breathes by thrusting the specialized tip of its respiratory tube into air-containing tissues of aquatic plants. *Aedes, Psorophora, Orthopodomyia,* and *Megarhinus septentrionalis* D. and K. larvae are usually found in very small temporary ponds, puddles, tree holes, or water held in plants, while *Uranotaenia* and *Culiseta* are most common in more permanent ponds and marshes. *Anopheles* is usually found in all types of nonstagnant water, from very small puddles to streams. *Culex* is most

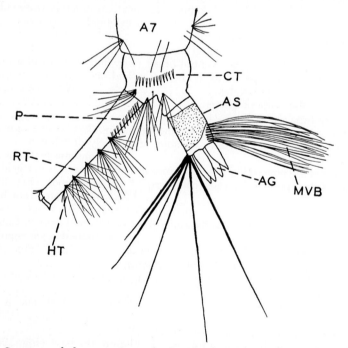

Fig. 395.—Structure of the posterior end of *Culex* larva (somewhat diagrammatic). *A7*, seventh abdominal segment; *AG*, anal gill; *AS*, anal segment; *CT*, comb teeth; *HT*, hair tuft of respiratory tube; *MVB*, median ventral brush of anal segment; *P*, pecten of respiratory tube; *RT*, respiratory tube.

frequently encountered in larger, permanent bodies of water. *Wyeomyia smithi* Coq. is an inhabitant of small bog pools and the water which accumulates in pitcher plants.

Ecological distribution of the various species shows no correlation with the hydrogen ion concentration of their habitats. Many forms are able to tolerate a range as great as pH 5.0 to 9.0.

Chaoborinae larvae are called phantom larvae because of their transparency. They are capable of moving through the water quite rapidly by means of jerky, lashing movements of the body. They are all predatory and catch small Crustacea and insect larvae with their prehensile antennae. There are no specialized respiratory organs, the exchange of oxygen and carbon dioxide occurring through the general body surface. *Corethrella* and *Eucorethra* are inhabitants of cold springs and spring pools; *Mochlonyx* occurs most commonly in pools, ponds, and bogs. *Chaoborus* is abundant everywhere in large ponds and lakes; it is easily distinguished from other Chaoborinae by the presence of a pair of particularly conspicuous pigmented air sacs, or hydrostatic organs, in the thorax and another pair in the posterior end of the abdomen. *Chaoborus* exhibits pronounced daily migratory movements, being confined to the bottom waters during the day and migrating to the surface waters at night.

## KEY TO GENERA OF CULICIDAE LARVAE

1. Antennae prehensile; without mouth brushes..................Chaoborinae, 12
   Antennae not prehensile; mouth brushes present.................Culicinae, 2
2. Spiracles sessile on eighth abdominal segment; respiratory tube absent (Fig. 396G); about a dozen species; widely distributed and common...Anopheles
   Spiracles at tip of a respiratory tube which is at least as long as wide.........3
3. Anal segment with median ventral brush.....................................4
   Anal segment without median ventral brush (Fig. 396E); larva in water of pitcher plants; two rare species in southern Fla. and one common one generally distributed in eastern states....................Wyeomyia smithi (Coq.)
4. Respiratory tube without pecten............................................5
   Respiratory tube with pecten (Fig. 396D)...................................7
5. Respiratory tube greatly modified for piercing (Fig. 396F); two rare species confined to Gulf states; a third common and widely distributed.
   Mansonia perturbans (Walker)
   Respiratory tube not modified for piercing; in tree holes and water held in plants.6
6. Mouth brushes prehensile, each composed of ten stout rods (Fig. 396K); from N. J. to Kan. and Texas..............Megarhinus septentrionalis D. and K.
   Mouth brushes normal; one rare species reported from N. Y. and Mass.; another more common and distributed from Mass. to Fla. and west to Calif.
   Orthopodomyia signifera (Coq.)
7. Respiratory tube with several pairs of ventral tufts of hairs (Fig. 395); widely distributed and common; about 15 species........................Culex
   Respiratory tube with a single pair of ventral tufts of hairs which are occasionally vestigial or absent......................................................8
8. Head elongated, elliptical; in pools; three species, of which one is common in eastern states.............................................Uranotaenia
   Head nearly circular or transversely oval...................................9
9. Respiratory tube with a ventral tuft of hairs close to the base (Fig. 396D); widely distributed; about six species.....................................Culiseta
   Respiratory tube with a ventral tuft of hairs near the middle or beyond, or the tuft may be vestigial or absent.......................................10

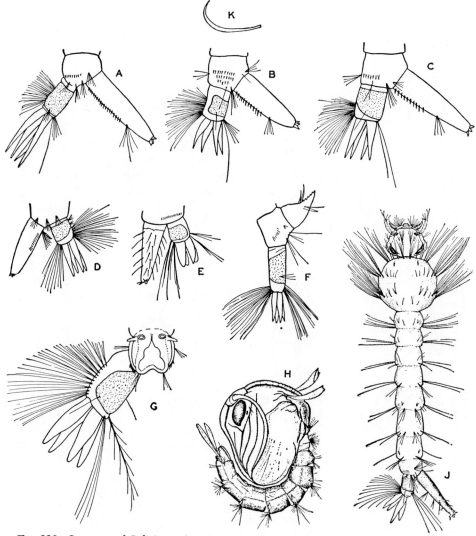

Fig. 396.—Structure of Culicinae. A to G, posterior end of larvae; A, *Psorophora*; B, *Aedes*; C, *Aedes*; D, *Culiseta*; E, *Wyeomyia smithi* Coq:; F, *Mansonia*; G, *Anopheles*; H, pupa of *Culex pipiens* L., ×9; J, larva of *C. pipiens*, ×9; K, rod of larval mouth brush of *Megarhinus septentrionalis* D. and K. (A to G modified from various sources; H and J from Johannsen, 1934.)

10. Head with a prominent triangular pouch on each side; in burrows of marine crabs; several rare species in Gulf states..........................**Deinocerites**
    Head without a prominent triangular pouch on each side; not in burrows of marine crabs. .........................................................................11
11. Anal segment with a complete sclerotized ring and with the median ventral brush piercing the ring (Fig. 396A); widely distributed; about nine species.

**Psorophora**

    Anal segment with a dorsal, saddle-shaped, sclerotized plate; or if completely ringed, the median ventral brush is posterior to the ring (Figs. 396B, C); widely distributed and common; about 50 species...................**Aedes**

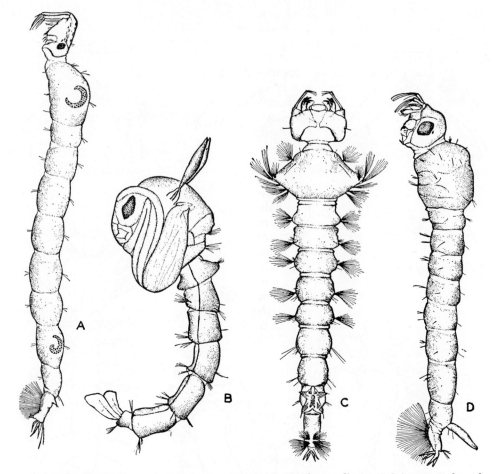

FIG. 397.—Chaoborinae. A, lateral view of larva of *Chaoborus albipes* (Joh.), ×9; B, lateral view of pupa of *C. albipes*, ×10; C, dorsal view of larva of *Eucorethra underwoodi* Underwood, ×5.5; D, lateral view of larva of *Mochlonyx cinctipes* (Coq.), ×15. (From Johannsen, 1934.)

12. Eighth abdominal segment with a single, elongated, dorsal respiratory tube (Fig. 397D). ......................................................13
    No such tube on eighth abdominal segment...............................14
13. Antennae inserted close together, when at rest folded outward against the head; anal brush (fin) not developed; in cold springs; rare; N. J.
                                                      **Corethrella brakeleyi** Coq.
    Antennae inserted far apart, pendent when at rest; anal brush well developed (Fig. 397D); widely distributed; three species.....................**Mochlonyx**
14. Hydrostatic organs (air sacs) present in thorax and in seventh abdominal segment (Fig. 397A); widely distributed; six species.................**Chaoborus**
    Hydrostatic organs absent (Fig. 397C); northern states.
                                                      **Eucorethra underwoodi** Underwood

Like the larvae, all culicid pupae are aquatic. The head and thorax are fused into a somewhat rounded triangular mass from which the elongated curved abdomen projects. The pupae breathe atmospheric air by means of a pair of trumpet-shaped structures on the thorax. They are quite active but do not move about much unless they are disturbed.

There are two paddle-like devices at the posterior end which are fused basally and are not movable in the Chaoborinae but are free and movable in the Culicinae. Though the larvae are relatively long-lived and may even winter over, the pupae live only a few days. The adult is liberated at the surface of the water by a dorsal splitting of the pupal integument.

## SIMULIIDAE (BLACK FLIES)

This small family of world-wide distribution includes the black flies, or buffalo gnats, of which about 50 species are known from North America. They are robust, small insects, seldom being more than 5 mm. long. The color is usually gray, brown, or black. Black flies are found near streams and rivers, and in some areas they may be present in such great numbers at certain times of the year as to be almost unbearable. The females are notorious pests and produce irritating bites on warm-blooded animals. Campers, hunters, fishermen, and farmers are particularly well acquainted with them, the last because of the fact that black flies may cause great damage to livestock.

Depending on the species and habitat, there may be from one to several generations per year. The eggs are deposited on vegetation, rocks, and logs just under the surface of swift streams, especially where the current is broken. Overwintering sometimes occurs in the egg stage.

The larvae are unique and easily identified. They are cylindrical, soft-skinned, a dirty yellow, gray, brown, or black in color, and the caudal third is distinctly swollen. A single stout proleg armed with small hooks projects forward from the prothorax. At the extreme posterior end there is a flat, sessile disc which has 50 to more than 140 radial rows of hooks. Delicate retractile blood gills project from the anus on the dorsal side of the last segment. In addition to the usual mouth parts, there are two prominent fanlike structures located laterally at the extreme anterior end. Each fan consists of a strong peduncle and 30 to 60 long, thin, curved rays.

Black fly larvae are found in the shallows of streams where the current is especially swift. Sometimes they are so abundant that the substrate is almost obscured. With the head downstream, they are tightly attached by the posterior disc to rocks and vegetation. It has been demonstrated that this adhesion may be attributed to the hooks of the disc and to a sticky salivary secretion deposited on the substrate by the mouth. Apparently the posterior disc exerts little if any suctorial action. By means of both the posterior disc and the proleg, the larvae move about in a series of looping movements, trailing a silken thread as they do so. Sometimes, attached to a strand of silk, they swing free of the substrate and may crawl along the strand with the aid of the mouth parts, proleg, and posterior disc. The anterior fans strain plankton and organic debris from the water for food. The larval stage may last from two to six weeks. Total length ranges from 3 to 15 mm.

The generic classification of the Simuliidae is in a state of uncertainty. Some authorities maintain that there are only two American genera, *Parasimulium* and *Simulium*, the latter being divided into three subgenera. For our purposes, however, the suggestions of Smart are followed in which four genera are recognized: *Simulium*, *Prosimulium*, *Cnephia*, and *Parasimulium*, the last of these being known from only a single adult specimen

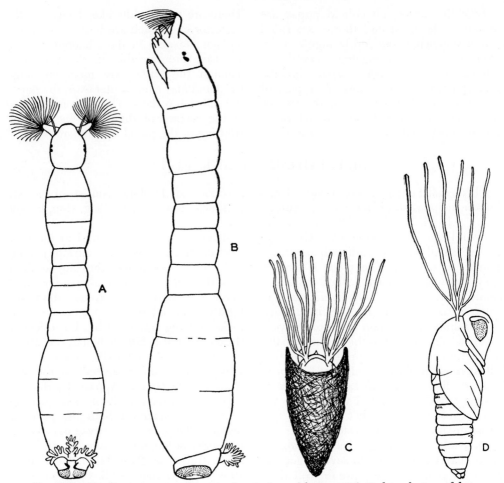

Fig. 398.—*Simulium venustum* Say. A, dorsal view of larva, ×17; B, lateral view of larva, ×21; C, dorsal view of pupa in cocoon, ×15; D, lateral view of pupa, ×21. (Modified from Jobbins-Pomeroy.)

of one Californian species. Unfortunately, there are no known larval characters which can be used to differentiate between them. Identification of species is based largely on minute structural characteristics of the mouth parts. Of the numerous species recorded from the United States, *Cnephia pecuarum* (Riley), *Simulium occidentale* Townsend, *S. venustum* Say, and *S. vittatum* Zett. are among the most common.

During the last instar the larvae construct silken cocoons in which pupation occurs. The cocoons are firmly cemented to the substrate and may be in the form of a wall pocket, slipper, vase, or simply a matted mass of threads. The pupae are oval, enlarged at the anterior end, and yellowish, reddish, or brown. They have small abdominal hooks by which they remain attached to the cocoon. At the anterior end of the thorax are two groups of long, branched, respiratory filaments. *Cnephia pecuarum* has 40 to 48 filaments in each tuft, *Simulium occidentale* has 22 to 25, *S. vittatum* has 16, and *S. venustum* has six. The pupal stage usually lasts from two to eight days.

Generic determinations can often be made with the pupae. *Prosimulium* pupae have a pair of exceptionally large spines, pointing anteriorly, on the last abdominal segment. These spines are absent in *Cnephia* and *Simulium*. The cocoons of some species of *Cnephia* are roughly spun and lacking in definite shape, as in *Prosimulium*; in other species of *Cnephia* the cocoons are slipper-shaped, loosely woven, and without a definite rim to the aperture. Although the shape of *Simulium* cocoons varies greatly from one species to another, they always have a definite, compact, closely woven shape.

## TENDIPEDIDAE (MIDGES)

The true midges are an exceedingly complex family of about 3,000 described species and world-wide distribution. The adults are delicate, nonbiting, and usually less than 10 mm. long. They commonly occur in swarms, especially near bodies of water and near lights at night. In some lake localities they swarm in such enormous numbers that they effectively discourage the use of such areas for recreation and summer homes. The duration of the life cycle is variable; some forms have only one generation in two years, while others have several generations in a single year. The majority of species have aquatic larvae. Eggs may be deposited singly, in irregular or regular masses, or in strings on the surface, the bottom, or aquatic plants.

The larvae are elongated, cylindrical, slender, and range from about 2 to 30 mm. in length. They have a pair of prolegs on both the first thoracic and last abdominal segments. Spiracles are absent, but there are sometimes anal gills on the lateroventral surface of the penultimate abdominal segment. Coloration is white, yellowish, greenish, bluish, pinkish, or a very deep red. This last type of coloration, which is caused by dissolved erythrocruorin in the blood, is characteristic of most of the more abundant species and is responsible for the name "bloodworm." Like hemoglobin, this substance acts as a respiratory pigment and appears to be of particular significance when the larvae are living in water where the concentration of dissolved oxygen is very low.

Tendipedid larvae occur everywhere in aquatic vegetation and on the bottoms of all types of bodies of fresh water. Some species are solitary, while others occur in great concentrations, over 50,000 per square meter of bottom having been found in certain lakes. Many species construct fragile tubes composed of algae, fine silt, or sand grains cemented together with a salivary secretion. These tubes are open at both ends and a current of water is kept passing through by vigorous undulations of the body. Tendipedid larvae are chiefly herbivorous and feed on algae, higher aquatic plants, and organic detritus. Locomotion consists of a series of creeping or looping movements, although some species are active swimmers.

From an economic standpoint, fish biologists know that tendipedid larvae form an important item in the food of young and adult fishes, and that without this group, many good fishing lakes might be relatively barren.

Although dipterists are agreed on the higher taxonomic categories, the classification of tendipedid larvae into species is confused and difficult. This situation is due chiefly to the fact that differences between species are sometimes relatively small and that there may be considerable variations within a single species or genus. *Spaniotoma, Calopsectra* (= *Tanytarsus*), and *Tendipes* (= *Chironomus*), for example, are subdivided into a host of subgenera and groups, and, unfortunately, authorities do not agree as to the limits or method of subdivision. The situation is further complicated by the fact that in certain groups of adult tendipedids there may appear to be close taxonomic affinities, while their larval stages may be quite diverse. The opposite situation is equally true. Also, the immature and adult stages of many species have not yet been associated. Details concerning the subdivision of the more complex genera may be found in papers by Edwards, Goetghebuer, Harnisch, Johannsen, Lenz, Lundbeck, Thienemann, and Townes.

Although it is frequently necessary to make permanent mounts of the head and caudal parts of larvae for detailed work (see Johannsen, 1937, for methods), identification to genus may be accomplished with a binocular dissecting microscope.

The Family Tendipedidae is divided into five subfamilies, of which one, the Podonominae, is very rare. The other four, with their common American genera, are given in the key below.

The larvae of the Subfamily Pelopiinae (= Tanypodinae) are found in ponds, lakes, streams, and rivers. They do not build cases, but are sometimes found in the cases of other tendipedids. They are predaceous, and other insect larvae form a large portion of their diet. *Pentaneura,* *Tanypus,* and *Procladius* are the genera most frequently encountered.

Of the four genera in the Subfamily Diamesinae, *Prodiamesa* occurs in quiet, well-aerated water, while the others are stream forms.

Most Hydrobaeninae (= Orthocladiinae) larvae are found in ponds, lakes, and streams. *Symbiocladius* and some species of *Spaniotoma,* however, are commensals on mayfly and stonefly nymphs, and some species of *Metriocnemus* are found in the water which accumulates in pitcher plants. Some species build cases; others do not. *Spaniotoma, Corynoneura,* and *Cricotopus* are collected most frequently. *Corynoneura* is roughly differentiated from other Hydrobaeninae by the fact that it is usually only 2 or 3 mm. long.

*Calopsectra* and *Tendipes* are by far the most abundant of all Tendipedidae. These two genera, along with about a dozen other uncommon and rare genera, constitute the Subfamily Tendipedinae (= *Chi-*

*ronominae*). A few species of *Calopsectra* are found in swift water, but the great majority of the Tendipedinae occur in sluggish streams, ponds, and lakes, sometimes at great depths. Some species of *Tendipes* that inhabit lakes where there is a deficiency of oxygen have one or two pairs of finger-like gills on the penultimate abdominal segment. Many species are blood red, and those that have a different coloration are usually found in vegetation. The herbivorous and microphagous habit is characteristic, as is the building of flimsy tubes of organic detritus, algae, or small sand grains and silt. Such tubes are lined with a silky substance of the salivary secretion. Usually they are attached, but in a very few species they are movable.

Some mud-inhabiting species have a filter feeding mechanism. The larva spins a concave net of salivary secretion across the lumen of the tube, and by anterior-posterior body undulations a current of water passes through the tube, with the result that plankton and detritus are caught by the net. The larva then eats the whole net and its load of food, after which it spins another net. The whole process is completed in several minutes. Other mud-inhabiting species extend their bodies out of the tube and scrape up detritus, either from the surface or from a depth of 5 to 10 mm.

Certain stream species of *Calopsectra* have a case with several radial and upright projections at the upstream end. Salivary sheets strung between these arms catch food particles from the current. Sections of the net and its entrapped material are removed and eaten periodically, and new net material is spun promptly in places from which it is removed.

Tendipedid larvae inhabiting the tissues of rooted aquatic plants eat only enough plant material to have sufficient room to build and maintain their silk-lined tubes. Most of their food comes from plankton derived from the outside water and caught on temporary nets extending across the diameter of the tube.

# KEY TO GENERA OF TENDIPEDIDAE LARVAE [*]

1. Antennae retractile, usually elongated; prolegs long, stilt-like, anterior pair with a
common base (Fig. 399A) . . . . . . . . . . . . . . PELOPIINAE (=TANYPODINAE), 4
Antennae not retractile, usually short . . . . . . . . . . . . . . . . . . . . . . . . . . . . . . . . . . . . .2

2. Third antennal segment annulated (Fig. 399G); paralabial plates usually absent,
when present they are not striated but are sometimes bearded. DIAMESINAE, 9
Third antennal segment not annulated; paralabial plates, when present, radially
striated (Figs. 400D–F) . . . . . . . . . . . . . . . . . . . . . . . . . . . . . . . . . . . . . . . .3

3. Paralabial plates absent . . . . . . . . . . . . . . HYDROBAENINAE (=ORTHOCLADIINAE), 11
Paralabial plates present (Fig. 400E) . . . . . TENDIPEDINAE (=CHIRONOMINAE), 18

4. Segments of body with a few scattered bristles; body slender; both pairs of anal
gills close to anal opening; most species whitish or yellowish and mottled with
brown. . . . . . . . . . . . . . . . . . . . . . . . . . . . . . . . . . . . . . . . . . . . . . . . . . . . . .Pentaneura
Segments of body with a longitudinal hair fringe on each side; head rather broad;
ventral pair of anal gills attached to base of prolegs, remote from anus . . . . . .5

5. Head never more than one-third longer than broad; antennae one-fourth or one-
third as long as head . . . . . . . . . . . . . . . . . . . . . . . . . . . . . . . . . . . . . . . . . . . . . . . . . . .6
Head about one and one-half times as long as broad; antennae one-half to three-
fourths as long as head . . . . . . . . . . . . . . . . . . . . . . . . . . . . . . . . . . . . . . . . . . . . . .8

6. With four anal gills . . . . . . . . . . . . . . . . . . . . . . . . . . . . . . . . . . . . . . . . . . . . . . . . . . .7
With six anal gills . . . . . . . . . . . . . . . . . . . . . . . . . . . . . . . . . . . . . . . . . . . . . . .Tanypus

7. Lingua of hypopharynx with five teeth (Fig. 399B); larva whitish, yellowish, or
reddish, and somewhat mottled with brownish spots . . . . . . . . . . . .Procladius
Lingua of hypopharynx with four teeth (Fig. 399C); reddish to greenish, with
yellow head . . . . . . . . . . . . . . . . . . . . . . . . . . . . . . . . . . . . . . . . . . . . . . .Anatopynia

8. Antennae about ¾ as long as head; mandibles hooklike (Fig. 399E) . .Clinotanypus
Antennae about ½ as long as head; mandibles curved (Fig. 399D) . . .Coelotanypus

9. Larvae in quiet, well-aerated water . . . . . . . . . . . . . . . . . . . . . . . . . . . . .Prodiamesa
Larvae in swiftly flowing water . . . . . . . . . . . . . . . . . . . . . . . . . . . . . . . . . . . . . . . .10

10. Abdominal segments with numerous small, closely set, stellate hairs on short stalks
(Fig. 399F); head capsule with warts or tubercles . . . . . . . . . . . . . .Heptagyia
Abdomen and head without such processes . . . . . . . . . . . .Syndiamesa, Prodiamesa

11. Antennae at least one-half as long as head, second segment slightly bent (Fig.
399K); mature larva less than 5 mm. long . . . . . . . . . . . . . . . . . .Corynoneura
Antennae shorter, second segment not bent . . . . . . . . . . . . . . . . . . . . . . . . . . . . .12

12. Living on bodies or under wing covers of mayfly or stonefly nymphs . . . . . . . . . .13
Not living on mayfly or stonefly nymphs . . . . . . . . . . . . . . . . . . . . . . . . . . . . . . . .14

13. Head unusually small; larvae under wing covers of mayfly nymphs (Figs. 399L,
M) . . . . . . . . . . . . . . . . . . . . . . . . . . . . . . . . . . . . . . . . . . . . . . . . . . . . .Symbiocladius
Head not unusually small; larvae either under wing covers or clinging to body of
mayfly or stonefly nymphs . . . . . . . . . . . . . . . . . . . . . . . . . . . . . . . . . .Epoicocladius

14. Bristle-bearing preanal papillae of ninth abdominal segment at least twice as long
as broad (Fig. 399J) . . . . . . . . . . . . . . . . . . . . . . . . . . . . . . . . . . . . . . . . . . . . . .15
Preanal papillae shorter or lacking . . . . . . . . . . . . . . . . . . . . . . . . . . . . . . . . . . . . . .16

15. Basal antennal segment slightly but distinctly bent (Fig. 399H) . . . . . . . . .Brillia
Basal antennal segment straight . . . . . . . . . . . . . . . . . . . . . . . . . . . . . .Metriocnemus

16. Labial plates with 11 teeth (Fig. 399N); anterior prolegs single, terminating in
two crowns of claws; mature larva 8 to 10 mm. long, yellowish or dusky
green; in running water . . . . . . . . . . . . . . . . . . . . . . . . . . . . . . . . . . . .Cardiocladius
With another combination of characters . . . . . . . . . . . . . . . . . . . . . . . . . . . . . . . . .17

17. Convex side of mandibles with several transverse wrinkles (Fig. 399O) .Cricotopus
Convex side of mandibles with one or two furrows at most . . . . . . . . . . .Spaniotoma

[*] Greatly modified from Johannsen (1937, 1937a).

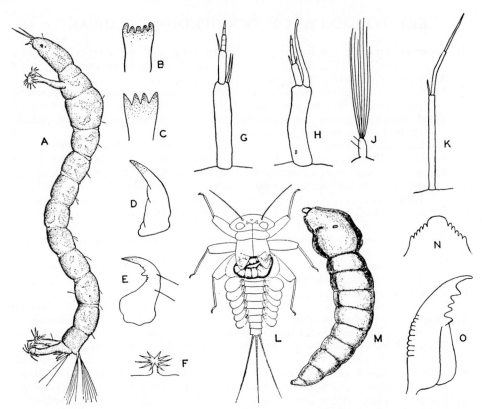

Fig. 399.—Structure of larvae of Pelopiinae, Diamesinae, and Hydrobaeninae. A, *Pentaneura monilis* (L.), ×12; B, lingua of *Procladius*; C, lingua of *Anatopynia*; D, mandible of *Coelotanypus*; E, mandible of *Clinotanypus*; F, stellate hair of *Heptagyia*; G, antenna of *Syndiamesa*; H, antenna of *Brillia*; J, preanal papilla of *Brillia*; K, antenna of *Corynoneura*; L, *Symbiocladius equitans* (Claassen) under wing covers of mayfly nymph, ×2.5; M, lateral view of S. *equitans*, ×7.5; N, labial plate of *Cardiocladius*; O, mandible of *Cricotopus*. (A from Johannsen, 1937; B to G modified from Johannsen, 1937; L and M from Johannsen, 1937a, after Claassen; H to K, N, and O redrawn from Johannsen, 1937a.)

18. Labial plate with a broad toothless middle section flanked on each side by one obliquely placed row of darker lateral teeth (Fig. 400D); antennal blade attached to second segment (Fig. 400B)..............**Cryptochironomus**
    Labial plate toothed in center (Fig. 400E); antennal blade at distal end of basal segment (Fig. 400A).........................................**19**
19. Antennae mounted on prominent tubercles or long prominences and more or less elongated and somewhat curved, five-segmented (Fig. 400A); most abdominal segments with postero-lateral bifid plumose bristles.**Calopsectra** ( =**Tanytarsus**)
    Antennae not mounted on tubercles or prominences, shorter, usually straight, and five- or six-segmented......................................**20**
20. Antennae five-segmented.............................................**25**
    Antennae six-segmented.............................................**21**
21. Two to four middle teeth of labial plate pale, the others dark................**22**
    All labial teeth dark...............................................**23**
22. Two middle teeth of labial plate pale (Fig. 400K)..............**Microtendipes**
    Four middle teeth of labial plate pale..........................**Paratendipes**
23. With a tuft of setae at the base of each paralabial plate; rare..........**Zavreliella**
    With a single seta at the base of each paralabial plate......................**24**

24. Striations of paralabial plates scarcely visible................**Stenochironomus**
    Striations of paralabial plates distinct......................**Lauterborniella**
25. Paralabial plates nearly touching on median line (Fig. 400F); preanal papillae
        nearly three times as long as broad (Fig. 400G)........**Pseudochironomus**
    Paralabial plates broadly separated (Fig. 400E); preanal papillae shorter.....**26**
26. Labial plate with an even number of teeth (Fig. 400J).
                **Phaenopsectra** (=**Tanytarsus** and **Pentapedilum**) and **Polypedilum**
    Labial plate with an odd number of teeth..............................**27**
27. With ventral gills on eleventh segment (Fig. 400H)...**Tendipes** (=**Chironomus**)
    Without ventral gills on eleventh body segment.......................**28**

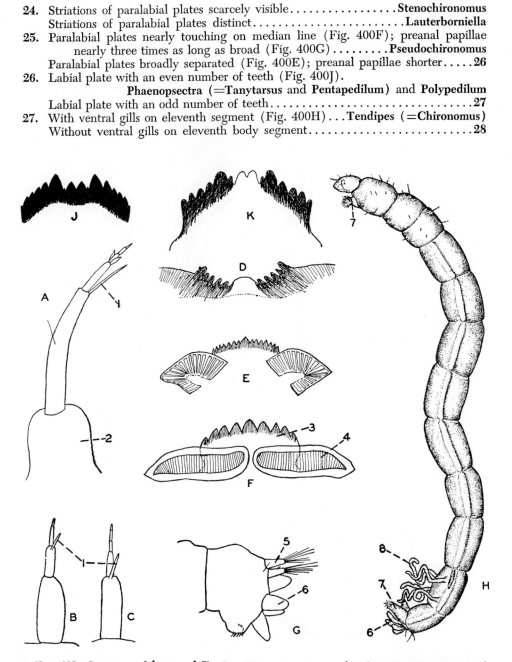

Fig. 400.—Structure of larvae of Tendipedidae. A, antenna of *Calopsectra*; B, antenna of *Cryptochironomus stylifera* (Joh.); C, antenna of *Tendipes*; D, labial plate of *Cryptochironomus stylifera*; E, labial and paralabial plates of *Harnischia abortiva* (Malloch); F, labial and paralabial plates of *Pseudochironomus richardsoni* Malloch; G, posterior end of *P. richardsoni*; H, *Tendipes tentans* (Fabr.), ×8; J, labial plate of *Polypedilum*; K, labial plate of *Microtendipes*. *1*, antennal blade; *2*, tubercle; *3*, labial plate; *4*, paralabial plate; *5*, preanal papilla; *6*, anal gill; *7*, proleg; *8*, abdominal gill. (A to H modified from Johannsen, 1937a.)

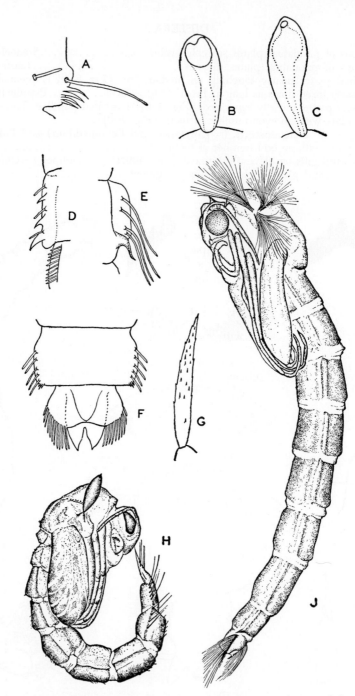

Fig. 401.—Structure of pupae of Tendipedidae. A, comb on penultimate abdominal segment of *Harnischia abortiva*; B and C, typical abdominal respiratory organs of Pelopiinae; D, comb on penultimate abdominal segment of *Calopsectra*; E, comb and spine on penultimate abdominal segment of *Tendipes*; F, posterior end of *Pseudochironomus*; G, respiratory process of *Brillia par* (Coq.); H, *Pentaneura monilis*, ×12; J, *Tendipes tentans*, ×12. (A, D to F redrawn from Johannsen, 1937a; G redrawn from Johannsen, 1937; H from Johannsen, 1937; J from Johannsen, 1937a.)

28. Labial plate with a trilobed middle tooth.........................Harnischia
    Labial plate with a simple middle tooth...................................29
29. Paralabial plates curved laterally (Fig. 400E)....................Harnischia
    Paralabial plates not curved laterally....................................30
30. First and second lateral teeth of labial plate more or less fused at base.
                                            Tendipes (=Chironomus)
    First and second lateral teeth of labial plate not fused at base..............31
31. Nine middle teeth of labial plate alternating large and small.....Xenochironomus
    Middle teeth with other characters........................Glyptotendipes

Superficially, the pupae resemble those of the Culicidae. The head and thorax form a large mass at the anterior end, and the abdomen is elongated, cylindrical, and strongly curved or straight. Some pupae breathe by means of ovate, trumpet-shaped, or cylindrical thoracic respiratory organs, while other forms have tufts of fine filaments in a similar location. The pupae may remain on the bottom in the old larval tube where they keep the water in circulation by movements of the abdomen, or they may swim actively near the surface or among aquatic plants.

## KEY TO SUBFAMILIES OF TENDIPEDIDAE PUPAE

1. Thoracic respiratory organs with open stigmata (Figs. 401B, C).
                                    PELOPIINAE (=TANYPODINAE)
   Thoracic respiratory organs without open stigmata, often composed of numerous filaments, or wholly lacking..........................................2
2. Preanal segment without comb or spines on posterolateral angles...............3
   Preanal segment with comb or spines on posterolateral angles (Figs. 401A, D–F).
                                    TENDIPEDINAE (=CHIRONOMINAE)
3. Thoracic respiratory organ a slender tubular process, or lacking (Fig. 401G).
                    DIAMESINAE, HYDROBAENINAE (=ORTHOCLADIINAE)
   Thoracic respiratory organ a tuft of numerous filaments (Fig. 401J).
                                    TENDIPEDINAE (=CHIRONOMINAE)

## CERATOPOGONIDAE (= HELEIDAE) (BITING MIDGES)

These midges are usually less than 4 mm. long and are commonly called "no-see-ums" or "punkies." The bite of some species is very irritating, and in certain areas around lakes and along the seashore they are present in such enormous numbers as to be serious pests. The immature stages are chiefly aquatic and semiaquatic. Culicoides and Leptoconops are the most common genera, the latter being restricted to the southwest.

Although the elongated larvae may be found in such diverse habitats as springs, streams, ponds, lakes, and wet mud and debris along shores, they are most abundant in floating masses of algae. Some are herbivorous, others are carnivorous, and a few are even cannibalistic. The last seg-ment has retractile gill filaments. Total length ranges from 3 to 12 mm.

Less than half of the American genera are known in the larval stages. The key below nevertheless includes those that are most likely to be encountered.

The pupae are free except in Atrichopogon where the last larval skin remains attached to the posterior end of the pupa. They are rather inactive except when disturbed. There are two respiratory trumpets at the anterior end. The pupal stage lasts only three to five days.

Larvae and pupae are most easily collected by washing out masses of algae with a small stream of water, or by examining the filaments in a shallow white pan.

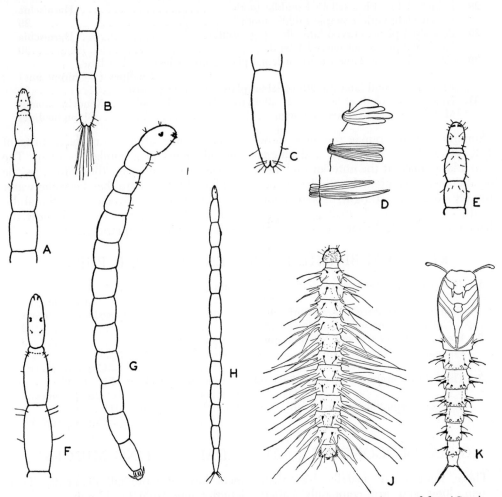

Fig. 402.—Ceratopogonidae. A to J larval structures; K, pupa of *Probezzia glabra* (Coq.), ×13; A, anterior end of *Palpomyia tibialis* (Meigen); B, posterior end of *Alluaudomyia needhami* Thomsen; C, posterior end of *Stilobezzia antennalis* (Coq.); D, flaplike structures attached on inside of last larval exoskeleton of *Palpomyia*; E, anterior end of *Culicoides sanguisuigus*; F, anterior end of *Probezzia opaca* (Loew); G, *Dasyhelea*, ×19; H, *Palpomyia*, ×8; J, *Atrichopogon peregrinus* (Joh.), ×11. (A to C and E to G modified from Thomsen; D, J, and K from Thomsen.)

## KEY TO GENERA OF CERATOPOGONIDAE LARVAE *

1. Prolegs present on prothorax.....................................**Atrichopogon**
   Prolegs lacking on prothorax............................................2
2. Head well developed; head capsule well sclerotized.........................3
   Head not sclerotized but provided with a system of heavily sclerotized rods; western
       and southwestern states....................................**Leptoconops**
3. Head short and thick, the length not exceeding one and one-half times the width;
       body segments each slightly longer than head (Figs. 402A, E, G).........4

* Modified from Thomsen (1937).

Head long, the length more than twice the width; body segments long and slender
(Fig. 402F)................................................................7

4.  Body curved; larva clambering.........................................5
    Body straight; larva swimming.........................................6

5.  Last segment with hooks; mouth directed ventrally (Fig. 402G)........**Dasyhelea**
    Last segment without terminal hooks but with short setae (Fig. 402C); mouth parts
    directed anteriorly......................................**Stilobezzia**

6.  Head pear-shaped; body considerably wider than head (Fig. 402A); larva 9 to 10
    mm. long.................................**Palpomyia tibialis** (Meigen)
    Head oval; body about as wide as head (Fig. 402E); 4 to 5 mm. long...**Culicoides**

7.  Anal hairs as long or longer than last segment (Fig. 402B); larva 5 to 6 mm. long.
                                                              **Alluaudomyia**
    Anal hairs shorter than last segment; 7 to 12 mm. long....................8

8.  With flaplike structures inside of cast skin (Fig. 402D)............**Palpomyia**
    Without such structures.............................**Bezzia, Probezzia**

# STRATIOMYIIDAE (SOLDIER FLIES)

Adult soldier flies are small to moderately large insects with bright green or yellow markings. They are chiefly associated with flowers. In those few species that have aquatic immature stages, the eggs are deposited most frequently on aquatic plants and debris in shallow ponds, slow brooks, and streams.

The larvae are easily identified: (1) they have a heavy opaque deposit of calcium carbonate in the integument; (2) they are stiff and apparently lifeless, spindle-shaped, and somewhat flattened dorsoventrally; and (3) they have a circlet of hairs or bristles around a pair of spiracular openings at the extreme posterior end. These bristles are spread out in a stellate manner on the surface film and act as a float. The larvae may remain submerged for long periods of time, however, utilizing the oxygen contained in the extensive tracheal system. Food includes algae, organic debris, and small Metazoa. Although soldier fly larvae are not common in collections, species of *Stratiomyia* and *Odontomyia* are encountered most frequently. Length ranges from 10 to 50 mm.

The pupae remain within the last larval skin which thus becomes the puparium.

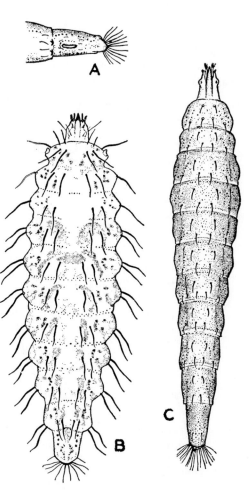

FIG. 403.—Stratiomyiidae larvae. A, posterior end of *Odontomyia cincta*; B, *Oxycera*, ×8; C, *Odontomyia cincta*, ×9. (From Johannsen, 1935.)

## KEY TO COMMON GENERA OF STRATIOMYIIDAE LARVAE [*]

1. Antennae placed laterally on head..................................................2
   Antennae placed dorsally on head, remote from margin........................3

2. Caudal margin of penultimate segment with a pair of ventral, stout, curved, hook-like spines (Fig. 403A); antennae more than three times as long as broad.
   **Odontomyia**

   Caudal margin of penultimate segment without ventral hooks; antennae less than three times as long as broad.................................**Stratiomyia**

3. With a pair of stout, curved, ventral spines on the posterior margin of the penultimate segment; with a transverse ventral row of short, stout spines anterior to the middle of each segment except the last.......................**Euparyphus**

   Stout, curved, ventral spines lacking on the posterior margin of the penultimate segment. .......................................................................4

4. With four or six long setae on the posterior margin of last segment; hair fringe of spiracular chamber short....................................**Nemotelus**

   No long setae on posterior margin of last segment; fringe of spiracular chamber long (Fig. 403B).................................................**Oxycera**

## TABANIDAE (HORSEFLIES)

The horseflies are a large family of world-wide distribution, there being nearly 300 species in the United States alone. They are large (10 to 25 mm. long) and robust. The females of some species bite severely, and many species are seri-

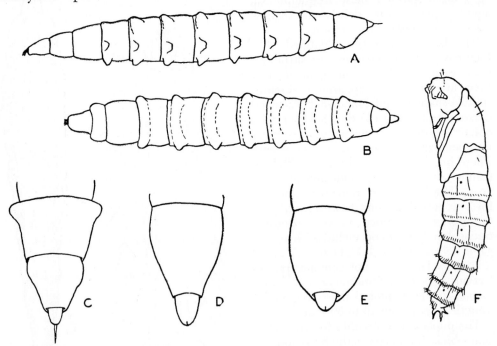

Fig. 404.—Structure of Tabanidae. A to E, larvae; F, pupa of *Chrysops*, ×5; A, *Chrysops*, ×7; B, *Tabanus atratus* Fabr., ×3; C, posterior end of *Chrysops*; D, posterior end of *Tabanus*; E, posterior end of *Haematopota americana* O. S. (B redrawn from Johannsen, 1935.)

[*] Modified from Johannsen (1935).

ous pests to cattle and other domestic animals as well as to man. Although most species are semiaquatic and pupate in damp earth, the immature stages of some are truly aquatic. The eggs of these are laid in masses on foliage, rocks, or sticks just above the surface of ponds, swamps, pools, and streams.

When the larvae hatch they fall into the water. They are elongated, cylindrical, tapered at both ends, and white, yellowish, greenish, or brownish in color. The body is divided into a minute head, three thoracic segments, eight abdominal segments, and a short posterior siphon. The first seven abdominal segments bear a pair of dorsal prolegs (often fused and small) as well as a pair of lateral and a pair of ventral prolegs. The eighth abdominal segment has a broad base but tapers distally. At the tip of the siphon the two tracheal trunks either open as a single vertical slit or end in a sharp com-

pressed spine. The usual length is 15 to 40 mm.

Three genera with aquatic larvae are found in the United States, *Haematopota*, *Chrysops*, and *Tabanus*. The first of these is represented by only one species, *H. americana* O. S., which is confined to the northwest. *Chrysops* and *Tabanus*, however, are widely distributed and common and are represented by many species. A few species of *Tabanus* occur in swift water, but most are found in the muddy shallows of ponds and swamps. *Chrysops* feeds on organic debris, while *Tabanus* and *Haematopota* are predaceous and devour snails, oligochaetes, and insect larvae.

The duration of the larval stage is variable, but in some instances it is known to last as long as three years. Just before pupation the larvae crawl out of the water to the adjacent soil well above water level where they burrow into the ground and pupate at a depth of 2 to 8 cm.

## KEY TO GENERA OF TABANIDAE LARVAE

1. Mature larva small, usually less than 20 mm. long; tracheal trunks not swollen; body almost entirely striated; terminal (third) segment of antennae as long or longer than second; usually with a protrusile stigmatal spine (Fig. 404A, C).**Chrysops**
   Mature larva usually more than 20 mm. long; tracheal trunks usually swollen; ventral and dorsal areas smooth, especially on the thorax; terminal segment of antenna shortest; almost never a protrusile spine at tip of abdomen..................2
2. Anal segment rounded; siphon short (Fig. 404E); dark ornamentation only on anal and thoracic segments......................................**Haematopota**
   Anal segment tapering; siphon elongated when extended (Figs. 404B, D); dark markings, when present, usually on other abdominal segments also, or confined to prothoracic collar only......................................**Tabanus**

## RHAGIONIDAE (SNIPE FLIES)

Snipe flies are Diptera of moderate size which are usually found flying around low bushes, foliage, and tall grasses. Their cone-shaped abdomen is rather characteristic. A few species are bloodsuckers. Only one American genus, *Atherix*, is known to have aquatic larvae. The female fastens her eggs in masses to twigs and

branches which overhang ponds and streams. She dies after oviposition and remains attached to the egg mass. Other females may deposit their eggs on the original mass in the same manner, and in this way eggs and dead females may form a considerable bulk.

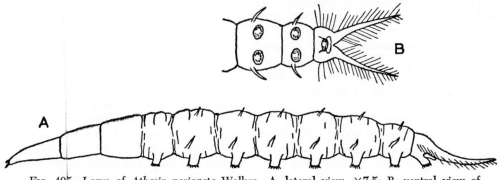

Fig. 405.—Larva of *Atherix variegata* Walker. A, lateral view, ×7.5; B, ventral view of posterior end. (Redrawn from Greene.)

Upon hatching, the larvae fall into the water. They are elongated, cylindrical, slightly flattened, and have the head largely retracted into the thorax. The anterior end is tapered, and there are well-developed, paired, spiny prolegs as well as lateral and dorsal pseudopods on the abdominal segments. They may be most easily identified, however, by the presence of two long, fringed, terminal filaments at the end of the abdomen. Respiration is facilitated by means of two protrusile blood gills situated below the terminal filaments. They are predaceous in their food habits. *Atherix variegata* Walker is the common species found in the eastern states. The total length is 10 to 18 mm. The pupal stage is unknown.

## SYRPHIDAE (FLOWER FLIES)

The members of this family are very common brightly colored insects. The majority feed on pollen and nectar, and their habit of remaining poised in the air is responsible for their being called "hover flies."

The larvae of the majority are found in terrestrial habitats. Many others are semiaquatic and are found in such places as water-filled tree holes and wet, decaying logs. Members of a few genera are truly aquatic and occur in sewage, polluted streams, rivulets, and in decaying vegetation at the edges of ponds.

Species of the genus *Tubifera* (= *Eristalis*) are the only common aquatic larvae in the United States. *T. transversus* Wied., *T. flavipes* Walk., and *T. tenax* (L.) are among the species encountered most frequently. The body is covered with fine spinules, and the thoracic and abdominal segments are wrinkled and indistinct. There are seven pairs of ventral prolegs, a pair of short, dorsal, anterior respiratory horns which terminate in a series of minute openings, and an elongated caudal respiratory tube. This latter structure is three-segmented, telescoping, from two to four times the length of the body proper when extended, and has two spiracular openings at its tip. Respiration is probably further facilitated by a series of delicate retractile anal gills, although some workers believe that these structures are unimportant. The head is small and retracted into the body; it bears reduced mouth parts. *Tubifera* is rather inactive and feeds on decaying organic material in water which is usually sufficiently shallow to permit the tip of the extended caudal respiratory tube to be projected just above the surface. Because of their peculiar appearance, they have long been called "rat-tailed maggots."

In their habits and general structure, most other aquatic and semiaquatic syrphid larvae resemble *Tubifera*. In some of

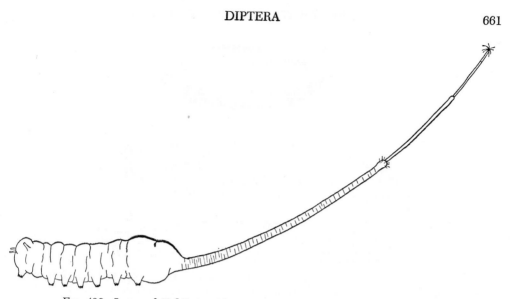

FIG. 406.—Larva of *Tubifera* with respiratory tube partly contracted, ×2.3.

them, however, the caudal respiratory organ may be strongly sclerotized and relatively short. Sometimes it is less than one-tenth as long as the rest of the body. The total length, exclusive of the respiratory tube, ranges from about 5 to 25 mm.

## SCATOPHAGIDAE (DUNG FLIES)

The great majority of dung flies breed in excrement and decaying vegetation, although a few are leaf miners and stem borers. Only one species, *Hydromyza confluens* Loew, is of interest here. The small, dull, whitish larvae are imbedded in the submerged petioles of the yellow water lily where they feed upon the tissues and produce small swellings. The pupae remain with the petiole, and the adults escape from the puparium and leave the petiole through a small trapdoor-like opening in the epidermis and float to the surface and fly off. In the strict sense, the immature stages are not aquatic since they do not actually come in contact with the water.

FIG. 407.—Larva of *Hydromyza confluens* Loew, ×7. (Redrawn from Hickman.)

## TETANOCERIDAE (MARSH FLIES)

Marsh flies are sluggish yellow or brown flies which are found at the edges of ponds, streams, and swamps. Although the imagoes of many species are known, the immature stages of relatively few have been studied.

The larvae are all aquatic. They are cylindrical, yellowish to dark brown, tapered at both ends, and have a series of rounded tubercles over most of the body. At the caudal end there is a lobed spiracular disc which is somewhat similar to the spiracular disc of crane fly larvae. The head is retracted except for a pair of mouth hooks. The larvae are usually found at the surface of the water among floating vegetation. *Sepedon fuscipennis* Loew and *Dictya pictipes* Loew are the only widely

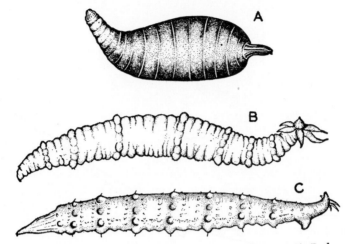

Fig. 408.—Tetanoceridae. A, puparium of *Dictya pictipes* Loew, ×5; B, larva of *Sepedon fuscipennis* Loew, ×5; C, larva of *Dictya pictipes*, ×6. (From Johannsen, 1935.)

distributed American species. *Tetanocera* is less common, and *Hedronema* and *Poecilographa* are rare and poorly known. Total length ranges from 5 to 17 mm.

*Sepedon* larvae have a spiracular disc composed of three pairs of small dorsal lobes and two pairs of larger ventral lobes. *Tetanocera* and *Dictya* larvae have a caudal spiracular disc composed of eight similar lobes. In *Tetanocera* these lobes are triangular, but in *Dictya* they are broadly rounded.

The puparia are swollen, seedlike, and curved upwards at one or both ends, but still have vestiges of certain larval structures on the integument.

## EPHYDRIDAE (SHORE FLIES)

Shore flies are small, brown, gray, or blackish flies which inhabit moist places on the shores of streams, ponds, lakes, and the ocean. A few are leaf and stem miners. The immature stages of relatively few species are known.

The cylindrical larvae are characterized by mouth hooks which have a serrate or digitate margin. The caudal respiratory organs are simple paired tubercles or greatly elongated retractile processes. Numerous larval forms have been described in the literature, but the genera and species noted below are the most common.

*Lemnaphila scotlandae* Cresson is a miner in fronds of *Lemna*. The larvae average only 2.25 mm. in length and may be identified by the fact that each tracheal trunk ends in a tubercle which terminates in a sharp hollow spur. The species of *Hydrellia* are somewhat similar to *L. scotlandae* but are larger and mine in the leaves of *Potamogeton*, *Panicum*, etc. Both *Lemnaphila* and *Hydrellia* obtain oxygen from intercellular air spaces in their food plants.

*Ephydra* and *Setacera* are quite similar. They may be recognized by a long cylindrical postanal process that has two retractile respiratory tubes at its apex. Unlike *Tubifera*, however, they do not obtain their oxygen at the surface film, but swim aimlessly about, sometimes as deep as a meter. There are eight pairs of short, conical, clawed, abdominal prolegs, each pair being fused at the base. The last pair of prolegs are considerably larger than the

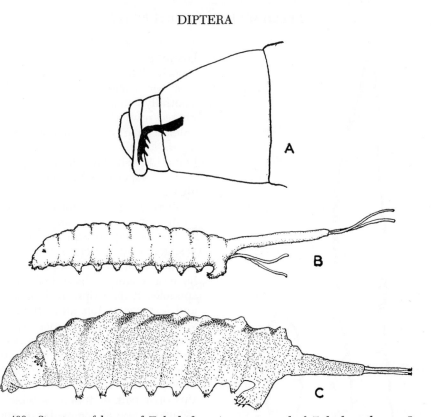

Fig. 409.—Structure of larvae of Ephydridae. A, anterior end of *Ephydra subopaca* Loew, showing mouth hooks; B, *Ephydra gracilis* Packard, ×6; C, *Ephydra subopaca*, ×9. (B and C from Johannsen, 1935.)

others. Immature aquatic stages of *Setacera* have been found only a few times in brine and salt pools, but certain species of *Ephydra* are relatively common. *E. gracilis* Packard is extremely abundant in Great Salt Lake and other similar habitats. *E. millbrae* Jones has been found in California salt marshes and the Salton Sea. *E. subopaca* Loew is widely distributed in salt or alkali ponds and lakes. *E. hians* Say is common in similar locations in the western half of the United States.

The larva of *Scatella stagnalis* Fall is widely distributed in both cold and hot springs. It may be distinguished from both *Ephydra* and *Setacera* by the fact that prolegs are lacking. The segments are provided with creeping welts, however, the spinules of which are a little longer than those on the adjacent body parts.

*Ephydra*, *Setacera*, and *Scatella* range from about 8 to 17 mm. in length.

The pupae of the shore flies are formed in the last larval integument which retains many of the larval characteristics but is considerably swollen.

## ANTHOMYIIDAE (ANTHOMYIIDS)

The anthomyiids are closely related to houseflies and are included in that family (Muscidae) by some authorities. There are more than 500 species in the United States. They are usually found on leaves and flowers.

Of the few genera that have immature aquatic stages *Limnophora* is by far the

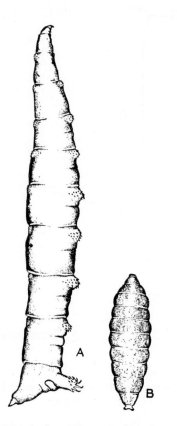

FIG. 410.—Anthomyiidae. A, lateral view of larva of *Limnophora aequifrons* Stein, ×6; B, puparium of *Limnophora torreyae* Joh., ×5. (From Johannsen, 1935.)

most common. The whitish or yellowish larvae are cylindrical and tapered anteriorly. The head is wholly retracted except for a pair of black mouth hooks. Ventrally, there are several closely arranged rows of very short setae along the anterior margin of each abdominal segment. Anthomyiid larvae are usually found in shallow brooks, rivulets, or trickles, especially in moss or masses of algae.

There are three common species in the United States. In *L. aequifrons* Stein all of the prolegs except the last pair are vestigial, and the last segment ends in a pair of retractile conical projections which have a common base and which bear spiracles at their tips. In *L. discreta* Stein and *L. torreyae* Joh. all of the prolegs are vestigial. In the former species the spiracles are borne on two small papillae which are widely separated on the truncate terminal segment. In *L. torreyae*, however, the spiracles are borne at the tips of a pair of tubercles which have a common base at the posterior end of the cone-shaped last segment. Length of the larvae is 7 to 15 mm.

The puparia are ovoid, reddish-brown, and have 11 visible segments. They have much the same general size and proportions as the larvae, and some larval structures still remain more or less visible.

# DIPTERA REFERENCES

ALDRICH, J. M. 1912. The biology of some western species of the dipterous genus Ephydra. *Jour. N. Y. Ent. Soc.* **20**:77–99.

ALEXANDER, C. P. 1920. The crane-flies of New York. Part II. Biology and phylogeny. *Mem. Cornell Univ. Agric. Exp. Sta.* **38**:691–1133.

———. 1931. The crane-flies (Tipulidae, Diptera). Deutsche Limnologische Sunda-Expedition. *Arch. Hydrobiol. Suppl.* **9**:135–191.

BATES, M. 1949. *The natural history of mosquitoes.* 379 pp. New York, N. Y.

BERG, C. O. 1950. Biology of certain Chironomidae reared from Potamogeton. *Ecol. Monogr.* **20**:83–101.

———. 1950a. Hydrellia (Ephydridae) and some other acalyptrate Diptera reared from Potamogeton. *Ann. Ent. Soc. Amer.* **43**:374–398.

BERG, K. 1937. Contributions to the biology of Corethra Meigen (Chaoborus Lichtenstein). *Det. Kgl. Videnskab. Selskab. Biol. Medd.* **13**:1–101.

BRUNDIN, L. 1949. Chironomiden und andere Bodentiere der südschwedischen Urgebirgsseen. *Rept. Inst. Freshwater Res. Drottningholm* **30**:1–915.

CARPENTER, S. J., W. W. MIDDLEKAUFF, and R. W. CHAMBERLAIN. 1946. The mosquitoes of the southern United States east of Oklahoma and Texas. *Amer. Midl. Nat. Monogr.* **3**:1–292.

CAVANAUGH, W. J., and J. E. TILDEN. 1930. Algal food, feeding, and case-building habits of the larvae of the midge fly, Tanytarsus dissimilis. *Ecology* **11**:281–287.

CRESSON, JR., E. T. 1942. Descriptions of two new Nearctic species of the genus Hydrellia reared from pond-weed (Diptera: Ephydridae). *Ent. News* 53:78–79.

CURRAN, C. H. 1934. *The families and genera of North American Diptera*. 512 pp. New York, N. Y.

DUNAVAN, D. 1929. A study of the respiration and respiratory organs of the rat-tailed maggot, Eristalis arbustorum L. (Diptera: Syrphidae). *Ann. Ent. Soc. Amer.* 22:731–753.

DYAR, H. G. 1928. The mosquitoes of the Americas. *Publ. Carnegie Inst.* 387:1–616.

DYAR, H. G., and R. C. SHANNON. 1927. North American two-winged flies of the family Simuliidae. *Proc. U. S. Nat. Mus.* 69:1–54.

EWER, R. F. 1942. On the functions of haemoglobin in Chironomus. *Jour. Exp. Biol.* 18:197–205.

GÄBLER, H. 1930. Die postembryonale Entwicklung des Tracheensystems von Eristalis tenax L. *Zeitschr. Morph. u. Ökol. der Tiere* 19:427–492.

GREENE, C. T. 1926. Descriptions of larvae and pupae of two-winged flies belonging to the family Leptidae. *Proc. U. S. Nat. Mus.* 70:1–20.

HAYES, W. P. 1938, 1939. A bibliography of keys for the identification of immature insects. Part I. Diptera. *Ent. News* 49:246–251; 50:5–10, 76–82.

HICKMAN, C. P. 1935. External features of the larva of Hydromyza confluens. *Proc. Ind. Acad. Sci.* 44:212–216.

HOWARD, L. O., H. G. DYAR, and F. KNAB. 1912–1917. The mosquitoes of North and Central America and the West Indies, Parts I-IV. *Publ. Carnegie Inst.* 159:1–520, 1–150, 1–523, 524–1064.

JOBBINS–POMEROY, A. W. 1916. Notes on five North American buffalo gnats of the genus Simulium. *Bull. U. S. Dept. Agric.* 329:1–48.

JOHANNSEN, O. A. 1934. Aquatic Diptera. Part I. Nemocera, exclusive of Chironomidae and Ceratopogonidae. *Mem. Cornell Univ. Agric. Exp. Sta.* 164:1–70.

———. 1935. Aquatic Diptera. Part II. Orthorrhapha-Brachycera and Cyclorrhapha. *Ibid.* 177:1–62.

———. 1937. Aquatic Diptera. Part III. Chironomidae: subfamilies Tanypodinae, Diamesinae, and Orthocladiinae. *Ibid.* 205:1–84.

———. 1937a. Aquatic Diptera. Part IV. Chironomidae: subfamily Chironominae. *Ibid.* 210:1–56.

KELLOGG, V. L. 1903. The net-winged midges (Blepharoceridae) of North America. *Proc. Calif. Acad. Sci., Zool.*, ser. 3, 3:187–232.

KITAKAMI, S. 1931. The Blepharoceridae of Japan. *Mem. Coll. Sci. Kyoto Imp. Univ.*, Ser B, 6:53–108.

KUSTER, K. C. 1934. A study of the general biology, morphology of the respiratory system, and respiration of certain aquatic Stratiomyia and Odontomyia larvae (Diptera). *Pap. Mich. Acad. Sci., Arts and Lett.* 19:605–657.

LEATHERS, A. L. 1922. Ecological study of aquatic midges and some related insects with special reference to feeding habits. *Bull. U. S. Bur. Fish.* 38:1–61.

LENZ, F. 1941. Die Jugendstadien der Sectio Chironomariae (Tendipedini) connectentes (Subf. Chironominae = Tendipedinae). Zusammenfassung und Revision. *Arch. Hydrobiol.* 38:1–69.

MALLOCH, J. R. 1914. American black flies or buffalo gnats. *U. S. Dept. Agric., Bur. Ent., Tech. Ser.* 26:1–82.

———. 1915. The Chironomidae, or midges, of Illinois, with particular reference to the species occurring in the Illinois River. *Bull. Ill. State Lab. Nat. Hist.* 10:275–543.

———. 1915a. Some additional records of Chironomidae for Illinois and notes of other Illinois Diptera. *Ibid.* 11:301–363.

———. 1917. A preliminary classification of Diptera, exclusive of Pupipara, based upon larval and pupal characters, with keys to imagines in certain families. Part I. *Ibid.* 12:161–409.

MARCHAND, W. 1920. The early stages of the Tabanidae (horse-flies). *Monogr. Rockefeller Inst. Med. Res.* 13:1–203.

MATHESON, R. 1944. *Handbook of the mosquitoes of North America*. 2d ed. 314 pp. Ithaca, N. Y.

METCALF, C. L. 1932. Black flies and other biting flies of the Adirondacks. *Bull. N. Y. State Mus.* 289:1–40.

MILLER, R. B. 1941. A contribution to the ecology of the Chironomidae of Costello Lake, Algonquin Park, Ontario. *Univ. Toronto Studies, Biol. Ser.* 49:1–63.

NICHOLSON, H. P., and C. E. MICKEL. 1950. The black flies of Minnesota (Simuliidae). *Tech. Bull. Univ. Minn. Agric. Exp. Sta.* 192:1–64.

NOWELL, W. R. 1951. The dipterous family Dixidae in western North America (Insecta: Diptera). *Microentomology* 16:187–270.

OWEN, W. B. 1937. The mosquitoes of Minnesota, with special reference to their biologies. *Tech. Bull. Univ. Minn. Exp. Sta.* 126:1–75.

PENNAK, R. W. 1945. Notes on mountain midges (Deuterophlebiidae) with a description of the immature stages of a new species from Colorado. *Amer. Mus. Novit.* 1276:1–10.

PURI, I. M. 1925. On the life-history and structure of the early stages of Simuliidae (Diptera, Nematocera). Parts I and II. *Parasitology* 17:295–369.

REMPEL, J. G. 1936. The life-history and morphology of Chironomus hyperboreus. *Jour Biol. Bd. Can.* 2:209–221.

ROGERS, J. S. 1933. The ecological distribution of the crane-flies of northern Florida. *Ecol. Monogr.* 3:1–74.

———. 1942. The crane flies (Tipulidae) of the George Reserve, Michigan. *Univ. Mich. Mus. Zool. Misc. Publ.* 53:1–128.

ROSS, H. H. 1947. The mosquitoes of Illinois (Diptera, Culicidae). *Bull. Ill. Nat. Hist. Surv.* 24:1–96.

ROZEBOOM, L. E. 1942. The mosquitoes of Oklahoma. *Okla. Agric. Exp. Sta. Tech. Bull.* 16:1–56.

SADLER, W. O. 1934. Biology of the midge Chironomus tentans Fabricius, and methods for its propagation. *Mem. Cornell Univ. Agric. Exp. Sta.* 173:1–25.

SMART, J. 1945. The classification of the Simuliidae (Diptera). *Trans. Royal Ent. Soc. London* 95:463–532.

SMITH, F. K. 1928. Larval characters of the genus Dixa. *Jour. N. Y. Ent. Soc.* 36:263–284.

THIENEMANN, A. 1944. Bestimmungstabellen für die bis jetzt bekannten Larven und Puppen der Orthocladiinen (Diptera Chironomidae). *Arch. Hydrobiol.* 39:551–664.

THOMSEN, L. C. 1937. Aquatic Diptera. Part V. Ceratopogonidae. *Mem. Cornell Univ. Agric. Exp. Sta.* 210:57–80.

TOWNES, H. K. 1945. The Nearctic species of Tendipedini [Diptera, Tendipedidae (= Chironomidae)]. *Amer. Midl. Nat.* 34:1–206.

TWINN, C. R. 1936. The blackflies of eastern Canada (Simuliidae, Diptera). *Canad. Jour. Res. Sect. D,* 14:97–150.

WALSHE, B. M. 1951. The feeding habits of certain chironomid larvae (subfamily Tendipedinae). *Proc. Zool. Soc. London* 121:63–79.

ZAHAR, A. R. 1951. The ecology and distribution of blackflies (Simuliidae) in south-east Scotland. *Jour. Animal Ecol.* 20:33–62.

# Chapter 36

# GASTROPODA (SNAILS, LIMPETS)

ALMOST every conceivable type of fresh-water environment, from the smallest ponds and streams to the largest lakes and rivers, has its characteristic population of snails, or univalve mollusks. Some localities may yield only one or two species, while others may contain dozens. Sometimes the collector needs to hunt assiduously in order to find a few specimens; under other circumstances they may be present in enormous numbers. Snails are animals of the substrate and are found creeping about on all types of submerged surfaces, chiefly in water from ten centimeters to two meters deep.

**General characteristics.** The vast majority of fresh-water gastropods have a spiral or discoidal coiled shell. However, in five American genera (the limpets), the shell is in the form of a very low cone. The range in the maximum dimensions of the shell (length or width) of the mature animal is about 2 to 70 mm.

The muscular portion of the animal which projects from the shell is called the foot. For the most part it is inconspicuously colored, usually being grayish, brownish, or blackish, and often flecked or mottled with yellowish or whitish. The ventral surface of the foot is flat and there is a more or less prominent head at the anterior end. The head bears two tentacles which range in shape from short, blunt, or conical to long and filiform. The eyes are on or near the base of the tentacles. The mouth is on the ventral surface

of the head at the extreme anterior end and in contact with the substrate in most species, but in the Viviparidae, Pleuroceridae, Amnicolidae, and Valvatidae it is at the end of a muscular proboscis, or rostrum. In the Ampullariidae and Neritidae this rostrum is divided into two long tentacle-like lobes. In the Lymnaeidae the head itself is widened into two flat lateral lobes, constituting the velum, a structure which persists from the larval stage.

The foot consists mainly of muscle tissue, but it contains the anterior portions of the digestive tract and reproductive system, as well as most of the nervous system. The rest of the internal organs form the visceral hump which lies within the shell where its shape is a counterpart of the coils. Forming a lining for the shell and enclosing the viscera is a thin layer of specialized tissue, the mantle. The shell grows by the addition of the shell material secreted by the edge of the mantle (collar) at the orifice of the shell.

Although a few snails, such as *Valvata*, have a delicate external gill, most fresh-water gastropods have either internal gills which are specialized folds of the mantle for aquatic respiration, or an internal air-filled "lung" consisting of a special portion of the mantle cavity surrounded by highly vascularized mantle. The respiratory opening (pneumostome) to either the internal gills or lung is usually situated on the right side at the edge of the shell. In those aquatic snails with a lung the edge

667

of the mantle is often elongated into a respiratory siphon through which air is obtained at the surface film.

The exposed portion of the body of a snail is securely fastened to the shell internally by a large columellar muscle, and by the contraction of this muscle the foot may be doubled up and withdrawn from view. Those snails with gills have a discoidal chitinous (rarely calcareous) operculum attached dorsally on the posterior part of the foot, and when the animal is withdrawn into the shell the operculum fits into the opening and effectively closes it.

In some families external reproductive structures may be seen. In the Amnicolidae and Valvatidae, for example, more or less laterally in the region of the neck, is the verge, a projecting male copulatory organ of variable structure and size. In the Viviparidae the right tentacle of the male is much larger than the left and serves as a penis sheath.

**Shell.** Compared with marine and tropical land snails, the fresh-water forms are a rather drab-colored lot. A few species are rich green or yellow with red tinges or bright color bands, but the great majority are nondescript gray, tan, brown, blackish, or "horn-colored," sometimes with indistinct bands or a mottled appearance. The shell proper is covered with a thin organic epidermis in which the pigments are deposited. The epidermis has the important function of protecting the underlying chalky white calcium carbonate from erosion.

In most of the common and widespread species the surface of the shell is superficially smooth, but if it is examined closely, fine longitudinal growth lines and spiral sculpture may be seen. Sometimes these lines can be detected only with the aid of a lens. At the other extreme are a few species whose shells are pronouncedly costate, ridged, carinate, or tuberculate.

When a shell is held with the opening toward the observer and with the tip upward, the shell is said to be dextral if the opening is on the observer's right and sinistral if on the left. The great majority of species are dextral. Some genera contain both dextral and sinistral species, but only in a very few species are both dextral and sinistral specimens known.

The important features of a typical gastropod shell are shown in Fig. 411. The opening of the shell is called the aperture, and the main portion of the shell above the aperture is the spire. The first large coil, or whorl, of the shell is the body whorl, and the nucleus, or protoconch, is the small round knob of from 1¼ to 1½ whorls without distinct sculpturing at the apex of the shell. The whorls are coiled around a central axis, or columella. An inner lip at the columellar margin of the aperture is usually present and reflected over the columellar region. The inner surface of the shell immediately adjacent to the inner lip is termed the parietal wall. The outer lip, or peristome, lies on the opposite side of the aperture; it is often reflected back upon itself. The umbilicus may be a small chink or narrow slit between the reflected inner lip and the body whorl; it may be a definite hole one whorl deep; or it may be complete and well developed so that all of the larger whorls revolve around a thin-walled hollow tube occupying the position of the typical solid columella. In many instances the umbilical opening is sealed, and the shell is said to be imperforate.

Considerable variations in size, shape, shell thickness, and surface markings occur within many genera, and sometimes even within a single species. These variations are particularly striking in the Pleuroceridae. In some cases variations within a species are clearly correlated with certain ecological features of the environment. Thickness of the shell, for example, may be directly related to the amount of calcium in the water. In highly alkaline waters, especially in the western states, many species show increased tendencies toward being ridged, plicate, or rugose.

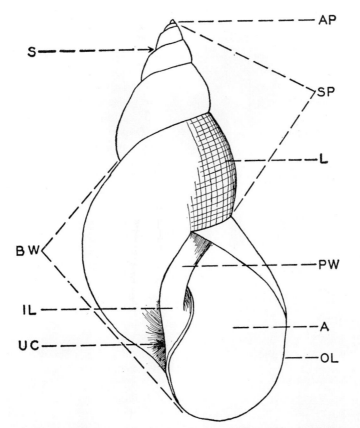

FIG. 411.—Anatomical features of a typical *Lymnaea* shell, ×2.5. *A*, aperture; *AP*, apex; *BW*, body whorl; *IL*, inner lip reflected over columella; *L*, spiral and growth lines; *OL*, outer lip; *PW*, parietal wall; *S*, suture; *SP*, spire; *UC*, umbilical chink. (Modified from Baker, 1928.)

Specimens in such waters are also generally smaller than those in other habitats. On wave-beaten shores and in rapid streams there is usually an increase in the relative size of the aperture and a decrease in the length of the spire.

**Locomotion.** In spite of many close observations, the mechanism of the usual gliding movements is not well understood. As a snail moves along on the underside of the surface film or on the substrate, it leaves a familiar "slime track," a thin, flat ribbon of mucus secreted by the ventral surface of the foot, especially near the anterior end. The secretion of mucus is apparently necessary for locomotion, perhaps only as a lubricant, but it is not definitely known whether the actual movement of the snail is entirely due to indistinct waves of muscular contraction on the ventral surface of the foot, to ciliary action in the same area, or to both.

Another method of locomotion has been called "hunching." It involves obvious muscular contractions of the foot and a jerky pulling forward of the shell. Such movements are not normal, however, and usually occur when the snail is entangled in vegetation or is out of water.

A third method of locomotion, called "spinning," is utilized chiefly by some species of *Physa*, *Lymnaea*, and *Helisoma*; it occurs when the snail is moving through the water rather than over the substrate. For moving upward in this manner the

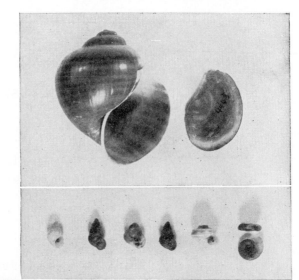

Fig. 412.—Representative American fresh-water gastropod shells. *Top, Pomacea calignosa* (Reeve) and its operculum, ×1; *second row,* left to right, ×1.5: *Hydrobia, Fluminicola, Amnicola limosa* (Say), *Pomatiopsis lapidaria* (Say), *Valvata tricarinata* (Say), and *Gyraulus similaris* Baker (2); *third row,* left to right, ×1: *Helisoma trivolvis* Say (2), *Lymnaea palustris* (Müll.), *Campeloma integrum* (Say), *Viviparus contectoides* Binn., and *Lioplax subcarinata* (Say); *bottom row,* left to right, ×1: *Lanx patelloides* (Lea) (2), *Carinifex newberryi* (Lea), *Physa gyrina* Say, *Goniobasis, Pleurocera,* and *Neritina reclivata* Say.

snail has the ability to decrease its specific gravity. A thread of mucus is fastened to the substrate at the point of leaving, and the snail moves upward with the lateral margins of the foot brought together and leaving a vertical mucus thread behind. Similarly, a snail at the surface film or on some object above the bottom may fasten a thread and move downward, trailing a mucous track. The same thread may be used a number of times by the same or other individuals, but it soon becomes brittle and breaks. For the most part, those snails which spin have slender, tapered, or pointed feet.

**Feeding, digestive system.** The great majority of fresh-water gastropods are normally vegetarians. The coating of living algae which covers most submerged surfaces forms the chief food, but dead plant material is frequently ingested, and occasionally dead animal material is eaten by some species. *Physa* and *Lymnaea*, for example, are good scavengers and essentially omnivorous. There are even a few records of *Lymnaea* feeding on living animals. When first deposited, mucus trails

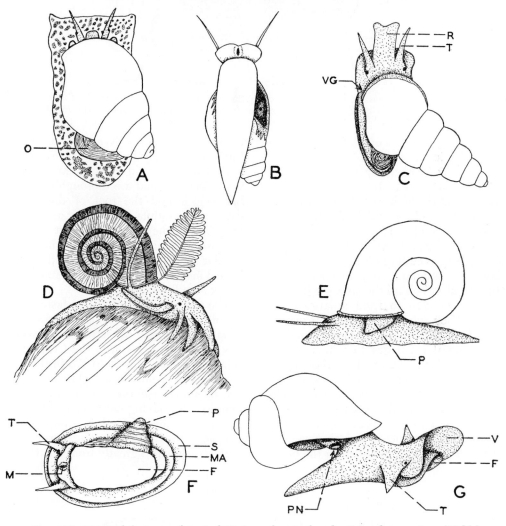

FIG. 413.—External features of typical Gastropoda. A, female *Campeloma rufum* (Hald.), ×1.2; B, ventral view of *Physa gyrina*, ×1.7; C, *Pomatiopsis lapidaria*, ×.8; D, *Valvata tricarinata*, ×5, showing plumose left external gill, rudimentary right gill, verge, tentacles, rostrum, and divided foot; E, *Helisoma trivolvis*, ×1.7; F, ventral view of *Ferrissia tarda* (Say), ×8; G, *Lymnaea*, ×1.5. F, foot; M, mouth; MA, mantle; O, operculum; P, pseudobranch; PN, pneumostome; R, rostrum; S, shell; T, tentacle; V, velum; VG, vertical groove of foot. (A to F modified from Baker, 1928; G modified from Baker, 1911.)

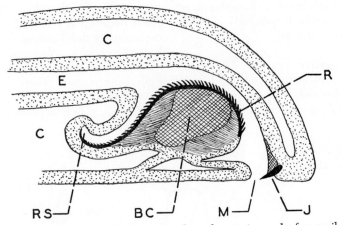

FIG. 414.—Diagrammatic longitudinal section through anterior end of a snail. *BC*, buccal cartilages; *C*, body cavity; *E*, esophagus; *J*, sclerotized jaw; *M*, mouth; *R*, radula; *RS*, radula sac.

are sticky and accumulate debris and microscopic organisms, and as snails move about they incidentally utilize it and its contents as food. It has been clearly shown that the higher the temperature, the greater the activity and food intake.

Just inside of the mouth is a set of one, two, or three small sclerotized jaws (Fig. 415), used in cutting off bits of food. One jaw is dorsal and (or) two are lateral. Immediately behind the jaws the digestive tract is swollen to form a large buccal mass. The ventral portion of this organ is greatly thickened and contains stout, movable buccal cartilages to which muscles are attached. Dorsally, the buccal cartilages and their muscles are covered by the radula, one of the most characteristic features of the Gastropoda. It is essentially a longitudinal, toothed, straplike, chitinoid structure which occupies a position analogous with that of the human

tongue. The radula is moved back and forth very rapidly by means of the underlying cartilages and muscles, and in this way pieces of food are thoroughly ground between it and the roof of the buccal cavity. The radula wears away as a result, especially at the anterior end, but it is continuously replaced since it is formed in a radular sac at the posterior end of the buccal mass and grows outward much like the human fingernail.

The teeth of the radula are fastened to the flat radular membrane in transverse rows. The number of teeth in a transverse row ranges from seven in the Ctenobranchiata to from about 19 to 175 in the Pulmonata and Aspidobranchiata. The number of transverse rows is usually large, some species having more than 150. Thus the total number of teeth in a radula may range into the thousands. The morphology of the teeth varies greatly from one family

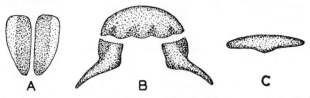

FIG. 415.—Sclerotized jaws of typical Gastropoda. A, *Pleurocera acuta* Raf.; B, *Lymnaea*; C, single dorsal jaw of *Aplexa hypnorum* (L.).

and genus to another (Fig. 416), but all teeth are fundamentally similar; each has a base of attachment and a reflected portion bearing the cutting points, or cusps.

In each transverse row three general types of teeth are usually recognized: (1) a single, distinctive, median central tooth, (2) a series of lateral teeth on each side of it, and (3) a series of marginal teeth located outside of the laterals. Thus, in the families of the Ctenobranchiata the seven teeth in a transverse series are named in order: second marginal, first marginal, lateral, central, lateral, first mar-

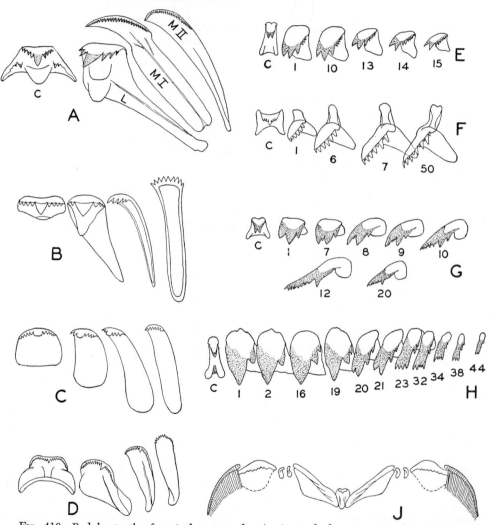

FIG. 416.—Radular teeth of typical gastropods. A, *Amnicola limosa porata* (Say) (Amnicolidae); B, *Goniobasis livescens* (Menke) (Pleuroceridae); C, *Viviparus contectoides* (Binn.) (Viviparidae); D, *Valvata tricarinata* (Valvatidae); E, *Ferrissia parallela* (Hald.) (Ancylidae); F, *Physa sayi Tappan* (Physidae); G, *Helisoma antrosa* (Conrad) (Planorbidae); H, *Lymnaea stagnalis* Say (Lymnaeidae); J, *Neritina reclivata* (Neritidae). *C*, central tooth; *L*, lateral tooth; *MI* and *MII*, first and second marginal teeth; teeth designated by number are a few laterals and marginals selected from the complete series. (A modified from Baker, 1928; B to G redrawn from Baker, 1928; H modified from Baker, 1911.)

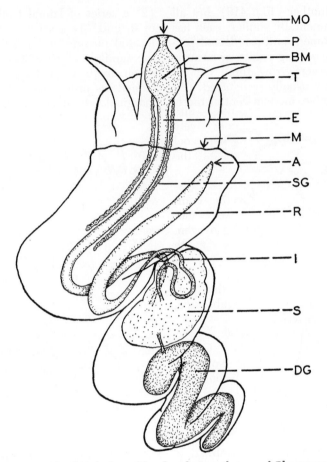

FIG. 417.—Diagrammatic dorsal view of head and visceral mass of *Pleurocera*, showing location of digestive organs. *A*, anus; *BM*, buccal mass; *DG*, digestive gland; *E*, esophagus; *I*, intestine; *M*, edge of mantle; *MO*, mouth; *P*, proboscis; *R*, rectum; *S*, stomach; *SG*, salivary gland; *T*, tentacle. (Modified from Magruder.)

ginal, and second marginal. In the other families there are correspondingly more lateral and marginal teeth, and the morphological gradations between adjacent teeth are very gradual. In the Lymnaeidae it is customary to designate a series of transitional teeth which lie between typical laterals and marginals.

The esophagus, which leaves the buccal mass, is quite long; it passes from the foot into the visceral mass contained within the shell where it may or may not be dilated to form a crop. A pair of salivary glands may be found along the esophagus or on the crop. Shortly behind the crop is the dilated stomach which may have a gizzard associated with it. In some genera the gizzard contains sand, presumably to further macerate the food. The stomach is followed by the long intestine whose posterior end is dilated to form the rectum. The anus opens into the mantle cavity near the edge of the mantle and shell. A very large digestive gland, the so-called liver, empties into the stomach.

**Circulatory system.** The heart is situated in the lower part of the visceral hump, usually on the left side. In mature individuals with thin shells and in immature individuals the beating may be seen through the shell. The heart consists of one auricle (rarely two) and a ventricle. The ventricle pumps the blood through a short aortic trunk to all parts of the body via a series of arteries and capillaries. From the capillaries the blood passes into spaces, or sinuses, in the tissues collectively called the hemocoel. From the hemocoel it passes into veins and thence back to the auricle.

The blood of gastropods contains a dissolved, complex, copper-containing compound, hemocyanin, which, like hemoglobin, is capable of transporting oxygen. Oxidized hemocyanin imparts a definite bluish color to the blood; in the reduced state it is colorless. In some of the Planorbidae it has been found that erythrocruorin, a hemoglobin-like substance, is the respiratory pigment.

**Respiration.** In the orders Ctenobranchiata and Aspidobranchia respiration is strictly aquatic and occurs through an internal gill, or ctenidium, to which the surrounding water has easy access. This structure consists of a series of narrow, flat leaflets well supplied with blood and arranged like the teeth of a comb. It is located on the surface of the mantle within the mantle cavity of the body whorl. In some species there are over 100 leaflets in the ctenidium. In *Valvata* the ctenidium is external and plumose (Fig. 413D). It is possible that the gilled snails may obtain a small amount of oxygen through the general body surface.

The families constituting the order Pulmonata do not have gills, but obtain oxygen through a "lung," or pulmonary cavity. This is an air-filled, saclike, highly vascularized portion of the mantle cavity which occupies as much as one-half of the body whorl. The pneumostome, a small opening to the pulmonary cavity, is situated where the edge of the mantle and shell meet the foot. In the Lymnaeidae and Physidae the edge of the mantle is frequently drawn out into a long, muscular respiratory siphon around the pneumostome.

At variable intervals most pulmonates come to the surface of the water where the pneumostome is brought into contact with the atmosphere and a fresh supply of air is taken into the pulmonary cavity. Under appropriate conditions in the laboratory the opening of the pneumostome at the surface may be heard as a faint clicking sound. The migrations to the surface by spinning or on emergent vegetation appear to be largely governed by temperature and the amount of dissolved oxygen in the water, and under average conditions may occur every few minutes to several hours. Under both natural and experimental conditions, however, it has been found that many pulmonates rarely or never come to the surface for air. This is particularly true of certain species of *Lymnaea*, *Physa*, and *Helisoma* which may pass their entire life cycle without access to the surface. Some pulmonates have been collected in water more than 15 meters deep, and Forel collected *Lymnaea* at a depth of 250 meters in Lake Geneva, Switzerland. Certainly under such circumstances there are no migrations to the surface for air. Although there seems to be little specific information available (Cheatum, 1934), it appears that pulmonates that occur at great depths and some that remain submerged for protracted periods in the shallows fill the pulmonary cavity with water and use it as a gill. In many species, however, it is well established that all oxygen absorption may occur through the general body surface in both immature and mature individuals. Indeed, in the limpets (Ancylidae) the respiratory cavity is vestigial. Individuals in this family, as well as in the Planorbidae, have a pseudobranch. This is a short, blunt to long, conical projection from the dorsal or lateral portion of the foot near the edge of the shell. It is highly vascularized and undoubtedly functions as an accessory gill (Fig. 413F). Under experimental conditions it has been found that few snails can tolerate anaerobic conditions more than 48 hours.

**Excretion.** The renal organ is spongy and of varying size and shape. It is situated near the heart and respiratory cavity or gill, and its small duct opens near the anus.

**Muscles.** Aside from the foot, which is composed mostly of muscle tissue, there are several important free muscles. The columellar muscle is attached to the shell

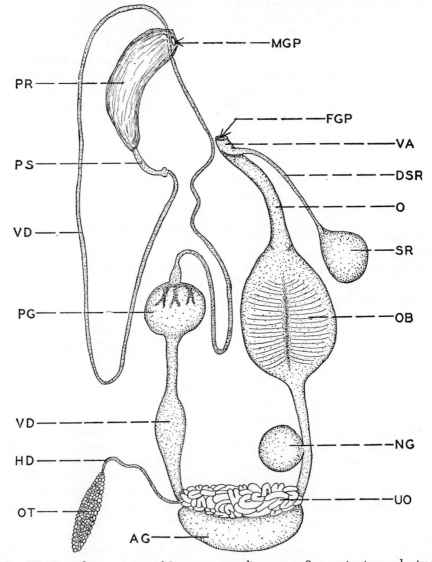

FIG. 418.—Reproductive system of *Lymnaea stagnalis appressa* Say; protractors and retractors of praeputium and penis sheath not shown. *AG*, albumen gland; *DSR*, duct of seminal receptacle; *FGP*, female genital pore; *HD*, hermaphroditic duct; *MGP*, male genital pore; *NG*, nidamental gland; *O*, oviduct; *OB*, oviducal bulb; *OT*, ovotestis; *PG*, prostate gland; *PR*, praeputium; *PS*, penis sheath; *SR*, seminal receptacle; *UO*, uterine portion of oviduct; *VA*, vagina; *VD*, vas deferens. (Modified from Baker, 1911.)

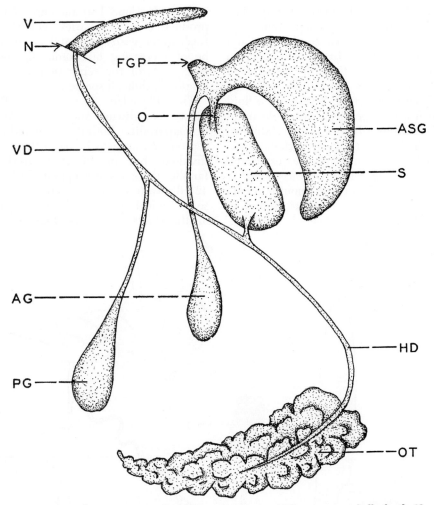

FIG. 419.—Reproductive system of *Valvata tricarinata*. *ASG*, accessory shell gland; *N*, wall of neck; *S*, spermatheca; *V*, verge; see legend of foregoing figure for other structures. (Modified from Bernard.)

internally and serves to withdraw the animal. Sets of muscles protract, retract, or depress the buccal mass. Those parts of the reproductive system directly concerned with copulation are usually supplied with protractors and retractors.

**Nervous system.** The greater portion of the gastropod nervous system (the "brain") usually consists of nine large ganglia, eight of which are paired. They are connected with each other by commissures and are arranged around the esophagus just behind the buccal mass. Large branching nerves originating in these ganglia innervate all parts of the body. Several small accessory ganglia are associated with some of the sense organs.

**Sensory areas and organs.** The eyes, situated at the base of the tentacles, are well developed, although little is known concerning the powers of vision. The sense of smell, or the ability to detect certain substances in solution, is probably centered in the osphradium, a small specialized area of the mantle cavity. The sense of hearing, or perhaps more appropriately the sense of equilibrium and the ability to detect vibrations, is centered in two statocysts. Each of these is a minute sac closely associated with the central nervous system; it contains a fluid in which are suspended a variable number of calcareous bodies called statoliths. Although the general body surface reacts to touch, the tentacles are especially sensitive. It seems logical to assume that taste is centered in the mouth region where this sense has been attributed to Semper's organ.

**Reproduction.** The anatomy of the reproductive system varies widely in the fresh-water gastropods and is coming to be of increasing taxonomic significance, especially for the separation and identification of difficult species.

The Physidae, Lymnaeidae, Planorbidae, Ancylidae, and Valvatidae are hermaphroditic, both the male and female reproductive organs being in the same individual, but in all other fresh-water families the sexes are separate. Figs. 418–421 illustrate the reproductive systems of some typical species. The basal portions of the ducts lie in the foot and body

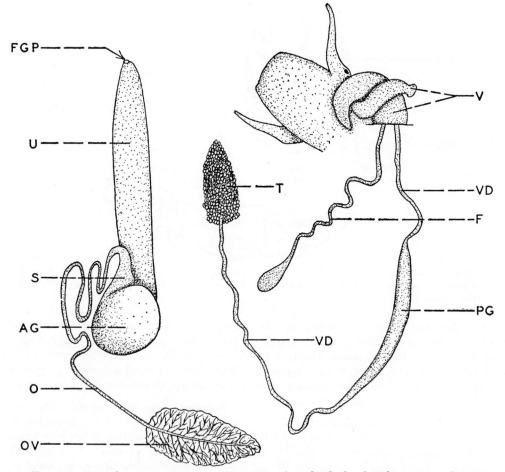

FIG. 420.—Reproductive systems of male and female individuals of *Bithinia tentaculata* L. *F*, flagellum; *OV*, ovary; *T*, testis; *U*, uterus; see legends of foregoing figures for other structures. (Modified from Baker, 1928.)

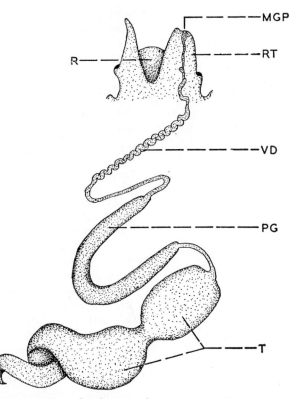

FIG. 421.—Reproductive system of male *Campeloma integrum*. *R*, rostrum; *RT*, right tentacle; see legends of foregoing figures for other structures. (Modified from Baker, 1928.)

whorl; the distal organs, however, occur in the smaller whorls, with the ovotestis, ovary, or testis being more or less imbedded in the digestive gland at the tip of the spire.

The male genital pore is usually located near the base of the right tentacle. It is commonly situated at the end of a muscular, protrusible, intromittent copulatory organ, or penis, which is withdrawn into the body except during copulation. In the Viviparidae the right tentacle is modified as a penis sheath. In the Amnicolidae and Valvatidae the copulatory organ, usually called a verge, remains protruded and cannot be retracted. Sometimes the verge is long and thin; in other genera it is blunt, lobed, or divided. There is no male copulatory organ in the Pleuroceridae and the male genital pore lies at the edge of the mantle cavity.

The female genital pore is unspecialized and usually lies at the base of the neck near the pulmonary aperture or at the edge of the mantle cavity.

Although surprisingly little accurate work has been done, the available information seems to indicate that a variety of conditions exist regarding fertilization in the hermaphroditic fresh-water Gastropoda. In some species isolated individuals have been observed to produce young; under such circumstances both mature sperm and mature eggs are produced simultaneously, and self-fertilization, rather than self-copulation, occurs in the reproductive tract. In other cases two such individuals may copulate and exchange sperm, each animal acting as male and female during the process; this is thought to be the common condition. In still other instances the ovotestis may pro-

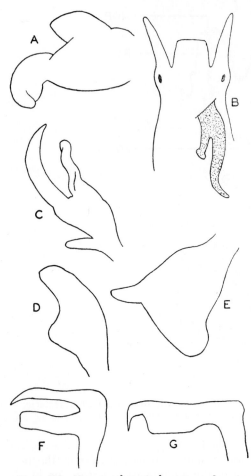

Fig. 422.—Verges of typical gastropods. A, *Somatogyrus subglobosus* (Say); B, *Amnicola limosa porata*; C, *Hydrobia nickliniana* (Lea); D, *Amnicola binneyana* Hann.; E, *A. lacustrica* Pils.; F, *A. walkeri* Pils.; G, *Pomatiopsis cincinnatiensis* (Lea). (A and C to G modified from Berry, 1943; B modified from Baker, 1928.)

duce eggs at one time and sperm at another, and therefore an individual may act as either male or female during copulation, but not both.

Oviposition usually occurs in the spring, although it may continue into the summer and early fall. Some species produce few eggs; others hundreds at a time. They are almost invariably deposited in a gelatinous mass on some substrate.

The early developmental stages occur within the egg mass, and by the time the young snail leaves, it has taken on the basic morphological features of the adult, and the shell has one to two whorls. The Viviparidae are ovoviviparous, the individuals being rather well developed at birth.

It is thought that in the great majority of species the usual length of life is nine to 15 months. Some of the Lymnaeidae, however, are known to live as long as three or four years.

**Predators.** Perhaps the greatest natural enemies of snails are the fishes. It has been estimated that about 20 per cent of our fresh-water species feed to a greater or lesser extent on mollusks. For only a few forms, however, do snails form a significant portion of the diet; some of these are the suckers, perch, sheepshead, pumpkinseed, and whitefish. Some ducks, shore birds, and occasional amphibians may eat snails. Among the invertebrates their most important predators are leeches, beetle larvae, and Hemiptera and Odonata nymphs.

Many species of snails are known to serve as the intermediate hosts of trematodes, but it is thought that such infections are seldom fatal, although the reproductive capacity may be greatly decreased and the digestive gland severely damaged.

**Ecology.** In the words of Boycott (1936), it is difficult to "disentangle the importance of quality of water from geographical distribution, the physical character of the habitat, and available food materials." Nevertheless, it is possible to point out certain ecological factors of the environment that have a pronounced influence in the determination of the habitat and activities.

One of the most important of these factors is the amount of dissolved salts in the water, especially calcium carbonate, which is the essential material for shell construction. It is generally true that soft waters contain few species and individuals, while hard waters contain many species and individuals. The majority of Lymnaeidae, for example, occur in water high in carbonates (more than 15 parts per million of bound carbon dioxide). A few species, however, are striking in their ability to thrive in soft waters which are low in carbonates. The Valvatidae are most common in waters containing less than 8 parts per million. *Campeloma* has been found in abundance in water containing only 1 part per million. It is difficult to understand how calcium carbonate can be utilized at such low concentrations. Many species are of course adapted to a wide range of carbonate content; *Amnicola limosa porata* (Say) has been collected from lakes having a bound carbon dioxide content ranging from 1 to 30 parts per million; and other species undoubtedly have still wider limits.

The pH, or hydrogen ion concentration, is closely associated with, and partly determined by, the carbon dioxide content, and lakes low in carbonates are usually toward the acid side of the scale (below pH 7.0), while those high in carbonates are almost always alkaline. It follows, then, that the great majority of species and the largest numbers of individuals occur under alkaline conditions. All of the Valvatidae and nearly all of the Lymnaeidae, for example, are confined to waters having pH readings of 7.0 or above. Nevertheless, there are some striking exceptions in other families. *Ferrissia parallela* (Haldeman) has been found in waters ranging from pH 6.0 to 8.4, and *Amnicola limosa porata* (Say) from pH 5.7 to 8.3. In general, however, snails are uncommon in lakes and streams whose surface waters are more acid than pH 6.2.

Dissolved oxygen is another important limiting factor, most pulmonate and gilled species requiring rather high concentrations. For this reason polluted rivers and the deeper parts of lakes which become oxygen-deficient during the summer and winter are usually devoid of gastropods. Limpets seem to be found only where the water remains almost saturated.

The great majority of species and individuals occur in the shallows, especially in water less than three meters deep. At greater depths river and lake faunas tend to become more and more depauperate. The fact that the shallows are a favorite habitat is probably correlated with the abundance of food in this zone. Although a few genera, such as *Lymnaea*, occur in a wide variety of habitats, many forms are restricted to particular types of substrates. *Pleurocera* is usually found on rocky or sandy shoals, the Viviparidae are most common on sandy bottoms, and the Ampullariidae are mud lovers. *Physa* occurs in greatest abundance where there is a moderate amount of aquatic vegetation and organic debris, and it is rare among dense mats of vegetation. The Amnicolidae are usually found among aquatic plants, sometimes in enormous numbers. *Hydrobia nickliniana* (Lea), the "water cress snail," is restricted to the dense mats of water cress and other vegetation of cool springs. Swift streams with sand or gravel bottoms and wave-swept beaches are generally poor places for collecting.

Large bodies of water usually have many species and small bodies have few, the reason presumably being the fact that the former have a greater variety of specific subhabitats suitable for the individual species.

Although some gastropods may be active down to the freezing point of water, such conditions are not favorable, and perennially cold lakes and streams and bodies of water in high mountainous areas contain few species and individuals. At the other extreme, a continuous temperature of 30°C. is more than most species can tolerate. Some lake pulmonates exhibit seasonal migrations correlated with temperature; in the fall they move into deeper waters and in spring into the shallows.

**Hibernation, aestivation.** Populations in ponds that freeze solid are able to overwinter by burrowing into the mud and debris on the bottom and hibernating. In intermittent streams and ponds that are dry for a short period in the summer many pulmonates burrow into the mud up to a depth of several inches and aestivate during the unfavorable period. The most effective seal and protection is afforded by a mud bottom that has a high percentage of clay. In *Lymnaea* the formation of an epiphragm has been studied closely. This structure is usually produced when the snail is imbedded in the mud. It is a thin sheet of mucus which is formed just within the aperture by the foot. Upon drying, it hardens and forms an effective seal which aids in protecting the animal during the drought period. This device may account for the presence of *Lymnaea* in some waters to the exclusion of other genera. Viable aestivating *Planorbis* and *Lymnaea* have been kept in the laboratory for more than three years.

**Geographic distribution, dispersal.** The fresh-water gastropod fauna of the United States is rich in species, rich in individuals, and rich in diversity. Not counting additional varieties, Baker (1928) lists 95 species from Wisconsin, Goodrich and van der Schalie (1944) list 99 from Indiana, and Winslow (1926) lists 142 from Michigan. Even Texas, which is by no means a favorable area for the development of an extensive fauna, has 53 species (Strecker, 1935). It is estimated that more than 90 per cent of the species and half of the genera found in North American waters are endemic.

Some genera, such as *Lymnaea*, *Helisoma*, *Gyraulus*, and *Ferrissia*, occur almost everywhere from coast to coast. The Pleuroceridae are confined largely to the states east of the Mississippi except for a few species in the Pacific coast states. The Neritidae occur only in Alabama, Florida, and along the Gulf coast, and the fresh-water species of the Ampullariidae are found only in Florida and Georgia. Some genera are similarly restricted. *Lanx* occurs only in the west coast states, *Aplexa* in the northern states, *Lyogyrus* in the Atlantic coast states, and *Tulotoma* only in the Alabama River and its tributaries. Perhaps the most interesting case of all, *Gyrotoma*, *Amphigyra*, and *Neoplanorbis* are confined to the Coosa River, Alabama.

The general problem of an explanation of the present geographic distribution of American fresh-water snails is extremely complicated, poorly understood, and beyond the scope of this volume. It involves, among other things, a careful consideration of past geological, geographic, and climatic changes.

Presumably it is relatively easy for a species to migrate slowly and extensively throughout an entire, connected drainage system provided that unfavorable environmental conditions are not encountered during such migrations. Movements between normally isolated bodies of water, or between inaccessible parts of the same drainage system, however, are necessarily passive and dependent upon outside agencies. Occasional flood waters may leave their normal channels and carry eggs or adults to distant places. There are numerous instances recorded in the literature where small individuals have been found on the feathers or in mud on the feet and legs of ducks and shore birds, and most authorities are agreed that this is a most important means of increasing the geographical range. Goodrich and van der Schalie (1944) have aptly summarized the essentials of distribution: "Whatever the mode of distribution, it has to be remembered that continued existence of a mollusk in any spot to which it may penetrate depends upon whether that spot is environmentally favorable, particularly for reproduction. It is to be suspected that in times without number migration has proved a failure."

Several species native to Europe, Japan, and the general Pacific area have been introduced into the United States by aquarium fanciers and have "escaped" to natural habitats. *Bithinia tentaculata* (L.), the "faucet snail," was imported to the Great Lakes region from northern Europe in the late 1870's. *Thiara granifera* Lamarck is a species native to the Far East and western Pacific islands, but was introduced into Lithia Spring, Fla., where it is now abundant. *Viviparus malleatus* Reeve is a Japanese species that may now be collected in springs, lakes, and streams near San Francisco, Boston, Philadelphia, Niagara Falls, and St. Petersburg, Fla. Several other introduced fresh-water species have been collected in various parts of the country, and the list will undoubtedly grow with time.

**Collection, preparation.** The nature of collecting apparatus depends on the type of environment being visited. In the shallows of lakes and streams simple hand-picking may be used. In deeper waters a long-handled net or tin strainer is effective. In water more than a meter or two deep it is usually necessary to work from a boat with a dredge. Bottom debris and vegetation should be sifted and examined on shore. Limpets should be carefully removed from the substrate with a knife blade. Wide-mouth bottles may be used to transport specimens to the laboratory.

For anatomical work the animal should preferably be killed and fixed in boiling water, although 75 to 95 per cent alcohol is also useful. In the Amnicolidae and Valvatidae where species identification may be based on the morphology of the undistorted verge, it is best to first narcotize the animal by sprinkling menthol crystals on the surface of the water and waiting until it becomes very sluggish, and then kill and fix in Bouin's solution. Sixty to 75 per cent alcohol is a suitable preservative. Formaldehyde should not be used as it makes the specimens brittle and damages the shell.

Either freshly killed or alcoholic specimens may be used for dissection. The foot and the attached visceral hump should be kept intact by carefully pulling the latter from the shell with a pin or hairpin. If the specimen is small the shell may be broken away from the underlying parts bit by bit, or the shell may be dissolved in dilute hydrochloric or sulphuric acid. The only instruments necessary for the dissection itself are a fine scalpel, forceps, scissors, and needles. First, the foot should be pinned down in a small dish containing a thick layer of paraffin on the bottom. Beginning at the head, a median, dorsal, longitudinal cut should be made through the body wall; it should be carried well into the mantle area, using great care not to injure the underlying parts. The dorsal flaps of the body wall and mantle may then be pinned back, thus exposing most of the viscera.

The radula may be isolated and cleaned by simply placing the whole buccal mass in cold 10 per cent potassium hydroxide for several hours to a day or by heating the solution for a few minutes. After a thorough rinsing in water, the radula should be placed between two slides with a strip of paper on each side of the radula to prevent crushing. The two slides should be bound together with string. While in this flattened position, the radula should be dehydrated in alcohol and cleared. One slide is then removed and the radula is covered with mounting fluid and a cover slip. It is sometimes advantageous to stain it in strong chromic acid or carmine. It is wise to mount the radula with the teeth up and to make several transverse cuts so the surface of the teeth can be more closely examined at the ends of the cuts. It should be borne in mind that the teeth at the anterior end of the radula are too worn to be diagnostic.

If the dry shell is to be preserved, the animal should first be pulled out and then the shell cleaned. It should be rubbed internally with a bit of sponge on a wire and then rinsed with a syringe. The external surface is often encrusted with algae, debris, and calcium carbonate or iron oxide deposits, and the appearance may be much improved by scrubbing with a stiff toothbrush and water, or by placing the shell in a weak solution of oxalic acid for a half hour or longer. Finally the shell should be well rinsed and dried before storage. It is not necessary to remove the animal from the shell in the minute species, but the whole specimen should be kept in 70 per cent alcohol for a day or two and then simply allowed to dry without any resulting offensive odor.

Opercula can be cleaned in oxalic acid, dried, and then placed in the shell whose aperture is plugged with cotton.

Suggestions for storing, arranging, and cataloging a shell collection are given in Ward and Whipple (1918).

**Taxonomy.** Three orders of Gastropoda are represented in American fresh waters. The Ctenobranchiata ( = Pectinibranchiata) includes the families Ampullariidae, Amnicolidae, Viviparidae, Valvatidae, and Pleuroceridae. All of these gastropods except the Valvatidae are dioecious and have an internal gill; all have an operculum, a heart with a single auricle, and a radula with few teeth in a transverse series; the two visceral nerves are crossed, forming an 8-shaped loop. The Order Aspidobranchia, including the single Family Neritidae, is similar to the Ctenobranchiata in the above respects except that the heart has two auricles and the radula has many teeth in a transverse series. The Pulmonata, on the other hand, consisting of the Physidae, Lymnaeidae, Planorbidae, and Ancylidae, are hermaphroditic and have an internal pulmonary cavity, a heart with a single auricle, and a radula consisting of many teeth in a transverse row; the operculum is absent, and the visceral nerves do not cross but form a simple loop.

Much of the generic and specific nomenclature of the past is confused because of descriptions based on one or a few shells taken from one or a few localities, but even with our present knowledge there are many species that are still troublesome to the specialists. This situation is due mainly to individual variations, age differences, and ecological variations within single species. The shells of some species of Pleuroceridae, for example, are said to be "infinitely variable."

During the past twenty years it has become increasingly apparent that more accurate, critical identifications can be made by using the anatomical details of the radula and the internal and external reproductive organs as criteria. Since none of these structures show any considerable variations within a species, they are proving to be particularly valuable in such families as the Amnicolidae where the shells are minute and not particularly distinctive.

F. C. Baker has divided the Lymnaeidae of the United States into seven genera, including *Lymnaea, Stagnicola, Fossaria, Radix, Pseudosuccinea, Bulimnaea,* and *Acella,* but this division has not been generally accepted, and most workers consider them subgenera of the single genus *Lymnaea.* This practice has been followed in the present manual.

Most of the species in the genus *Amnicola* are known only by their shell characteristics. In a few forms, however, the radula and reproductive organs have been studied, and they indicate a wide range of conditions. On the basis of these morphological differences some investigators have placed a few of the species of *Amnicola* in new genera, particularly *Vancleaveia* and *Cincinnatia.* Nevertheless, pending a careful investigation of many species of *Amnicola* in order to establish relationships more completely, it seems judicious to retain the original broad limits of the genus. These same general remarks also apply to the genus *Somatogyrus.*

The key which follows includes all of the known genera occurring in the United States. Only fresh-water forms are indicated, those restricted to brackish waters being omitted.

# KEY TO FAMILIES AND GENERA OF GASTROPODA

1. Without an operculum; mantle cavity a lung. . . . . . . . . . .Order **PULMONATA, 3**
   Operculum present; with gills. . . . . . . . . . . . . . . . . . . . . . . . . . . . . . . . . . . . . . . . . .2
2. Radula small, with few teeth (usually seven) in a transverse series (Figs. 416A–D); widely distributed. . . . . . . . . . . . . .Order **CTENOBRANCHIATA, 6**
   Radula large, with many teeth in a transverse series (Fig. 416J); Ala., Fla., and Gulf coast. . . . . . . . . . . . . . . . .Order **ASPIDOBRANCHIA**, NERITIDAE, **11**
3. Shell spiral and sinistral (Figs. 412; 413B). . . . .PHYSIDAE (pouch snails), **12**
   Shell not both spiral and sinistral. . . . . . . . . . . . . . . . . . . . . . . . . . . . . . . . . . . . .4
4. Shell spiral, elongated, and dextral; spire more or less elongated (Figs. 411, 412, 423); 11 species; usually in quiet waters; common and widely distributed.
                              LYMNAEIDAE (pond snails), **Lymnaea**
   Shell discoidal, patelliform, or rarely with a low spiral (Figs. 426, 427). . . . . . . .5
5. Shell discoidal and orblike, or with a low spiral. .PLANORBIDAE (orb snails), **13**
   Shell patelliform except for several minute species from the Coosa R., Ala., which are coiled, have a flat spire, and a broadly dilated columellar margin.
                              ANCYLIDAE (limpets), **22**
6. Operculum concentric (Fig. 428A). . . . . . . . . . . . . . . . . . . . . . . . . . . . . . . . . . . .7
   Operculum spiral (Fig. 425C). . . . . . . . . . . . . . . . . . . . . . . . . . . . . . . . . . . . . . . . .9
7. Shell very large, the largest American fresh-water snails (Fig. 412); both gill and lung present; proboscis divided into two tentacle-like structures; usually on muddy substrates; several species in Fla. and Ga.
                              AMPULLARIIDAE (apple snails), **Pomacea**
   Shell smaller; animal with gill only. . . . . . . . . . . . . . . . . . . . . . . . . . . . . . . . . . . .8
8. Shell less than 13 mm. long (Fig. 430C); introduced from Europe; in rivers and lakes of the Great Lakes region. .AMNICOLIDAE, **Bithinia tentaculata** (L.)
   Shell more than 15 mm. long; usually on sandy bottoms of lakes and rivers.
                              VIVIPARIDAE, **28**

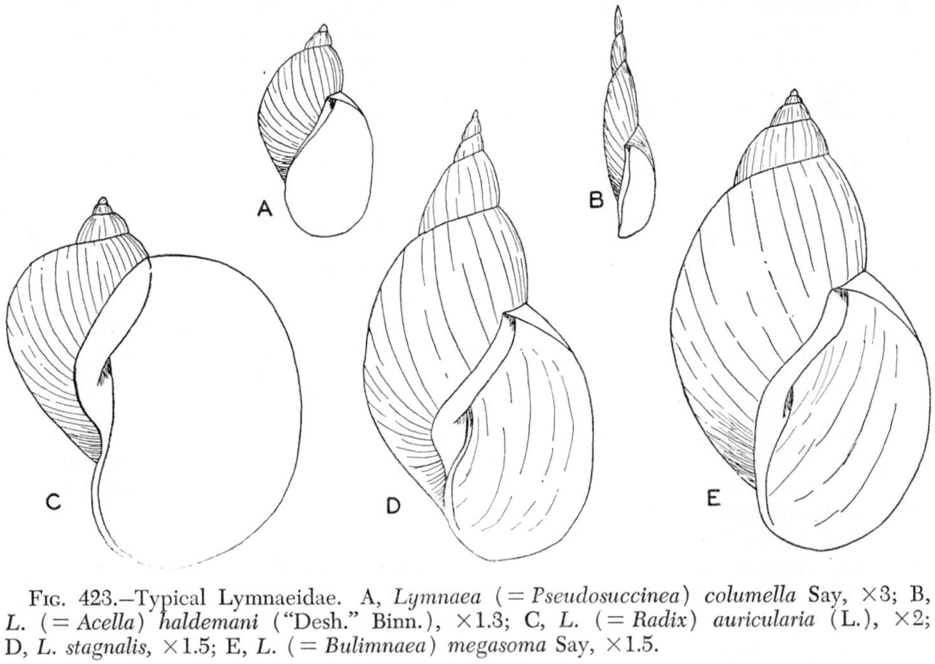

Fig. 423.—Typical Lymnaeidae. A, *Lymnaea* (= *Pseudosuccinea*) *columella* Say, ×3; B, *L.* (= *Acella*) *haldemani* ("Desh." Binn.), ×1.3; C, *L.* (= *Radix*) *auricularia* (L.), ×2; D, *L. stagnalis*, ×1.5; E, *L.* (= *Bulimnaea*) *megasoma* Say, ×1.5.

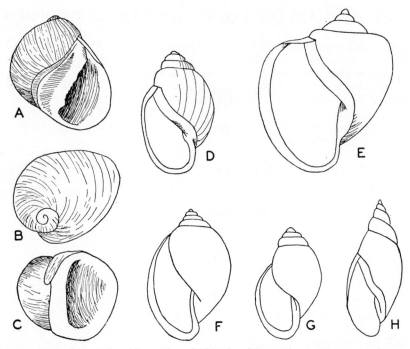

FIG. 424.–Typical Neritidae (A to C) and Physidae (D to H). A, *Neritina reclivata*, ×1.5; B and C, *Lepyrium showalteri* Lea, ×6.5; D, *Physa gyrina*, ×1.7; E, *P. parkeri* "Currier" De Camp, ×2; F, *P. sayi*, ×2; G, *P. integra* Hald., ×2.5; H, *Aplexa hypnorum* (L.), ×2.5.

9.  Operculum circular and multispiral (Fig. 425C); gill external (Fig. 413D); shell
    generally less than 7 mm. in diameter; several species; generally distributed in
    a variety of habitats.......VALVATIDAE (round-mouthed snails), **Valvata**
    Operculum not circular; paucispiral (Fig. 430F) or multispiral; gill internal...**10**
10. Shell more than 15 mm. long, thick, and heavy; male without external verge.
                          PLEUROCERIDAE (river snails), **31**
    Shell less than 10 mm. long; male with external verge......AMNICOLIDAE, **38**
11. Shell globose, thick, and solid; columellar region expanded and flattened (Fig.
    424A); operculum calcareous; few species in fresh and brackish waters of
    Fla. and Gulf coast.........................................**Neritina**
    Shell small and thin; columellar region concavely flattened (Figs. 424B, C); oper-
    culum corneous; one rare species in the Coosa and Cahaba rivers of Ala.
                          **Lepyrium showalteri** (Lea)
12. Shell with body whorl somewhat inflated; inner edge of mantle digitate or lobed
    and extending over shell (Figs. 424D–G); many variable species inhabiting
    all types of waters, especially in northern states...................**Physa**
    Shell more elongated (Fig. 424H); inner edge of mantle simple, not extending over
    shell; in swales, intermittent streams, and stagnant pools; generally distributed
    in northern states..............................**Aplexa hypnorum** (L.)
13. Shell discoidal..............................................**14**
    Shell with a low spiral; western.................................**21**
14. Interior of aperture armed with several lamellae or teeth (Fig. 426J)..........**15**
    Interior of aperture without lamellae or teeth..........................**16**
15. In eastern half of U. S.; several species (Fig. 426J)...............**Planorbula**
    Several uncommon species in southern Texas and La...............**Tropicorbis**

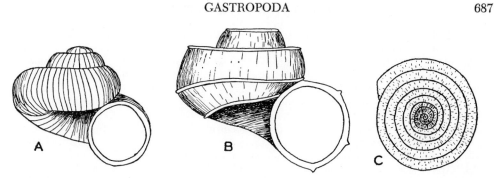

Fig. 425.—Valvatidae. A, *Valvata sincera* Say, ×8; B, *V. tricarinata*, ×11; C, operculum of *V. tricarinata*. (C modified from Baker, 1928.)

16. Shell large, greatest diameter more than 12 mm.; lip usually thickened (Figs. 426F, G); shell ultradextral or ultrasinistral; many species in all types of habitats, but most common in quiet waters; widely distributed........**Helisoma**
    Shell small, greatest diameter less than 9 mm.; lip sharp; dextral.............17
17. Base of body whorl somewhat flattened; one rare species in southern Texas.
                                      **Drepanotrema cultratum** (Orb.)
    Base of body whorl convex (Figs. 426B–D); common and widely distributed...18
18. Shell costate, less than 3 mm. in diameter (Fig. 426E); one or two species in northern states.........................................**Armiger**
    Shell not costate...............................................19
19. Shell rounded, or with carinate or subcarinate periphery (Figs. 426A–D); many species in a great variety of habitats........................**Gyraulus**
    Shell with acutely carinate periphery (Fig. 426H); usually in quiet waters; widely distributed but common only east of the Rockies.....................**20**
20. Penial gland sausage-shaped; several species.......................**Menetus**
    Penial gland flattened; several species..........................**Promenetus**°
21. Shell imperforate (Fig. 426L); several western species.............**Parapholyx**
    Shell deeply umbilicate (Fig. 426K); several western species.........**Carinifex**

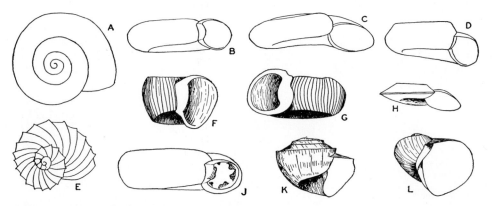

Fig. 426.—Typical Planorbidae. A and B, *Gyraulus circumstriatus* (Tryon), ×6; C, *G. deflectus* (Say), ×6; D, *G. altissimus* (Baker), ×5; E, *Armiger crista* (L.), ×6; F, *Helisoma antrosa*, ×1.7; G, *H. trivolvis*, ×1.2; H, *Promenetus exacuous* (Say), ×4; J, *Planorbula*, ×4; K, *Carinifex newberryi*, ×.9; L, *Parapholyx effusa* (Lea), ×4. (A and B redrawn from Baker, 1928.)

* *Promenetus* is sometimes included in *Menetus*.

22. Shell patelliform . . . . . . . . . . . . . . . . . . . . . . . . . . . . . . . . . . . . . . . . . . . . . . . . . **24**
Shell planorbiform or neritiform, minute; Coosa R., Ala. . . . . . . . . . . . . . . . . . . . . **23**
23. Shell planorbiform, minute (Fig. 427G); several species . . . . . . . . . . **Neoplanorbis**
Shell neritiform (Figs. 427J, K) . . . . . . . . . . . . . . . . . **Amphigyra alabamensis** Pils.
24. Shell and apex unicolored . . . . . . . . . . . . . . . . . . . . . . . . . . . . . . . . . . . . . . . . . . . . . . **25**
Shell with pink apex; several species, mostly in Ala., but some extending into Ky.,
Ind., and Ill. . . . . . . . . . . . . . . . . . . . . . . . . . . . . . . . . . . . . . . . . . . . . . . **Rhodacmea**
25. Shell large, 8 to 18 mm. long; apex subcentral (Figs. 427E, F); few species; con-
fined to west coast states . . . . . . . . . . . . . . . . . . . . . . . . . . . . . . . . . . **Lanx** [*]
Shell small; apex more or less posterior and excentric; widely distributed . . . . . . **26**
26. Apex near posterior margin of shell (Fig. 427H); with a horizontal septum in
maturity; few species; generally but locally distributed . . . . . . . . . **Gundlachia**
Apex only slightly posterior; without horizontal septum . . . . . . . . . . . . . . . . . . . . **27**
27. Apex to the right of the mid-line (Fig. 427A); numerous species in many types of
habitats; widely distributed but usually localized . . . . . . . . . . . . . . . . . **Ferrissia**
Apex to the left of the mid-line; a single species known from Lake Eldora, Colo.
**Ancylus coloradensis** Henderson
28. Operculum wholly concentric (Fig. 428A) . . . . . . . . . . . . . . . . . . . . . . . . . . . . . . . **29**
Center of operculum subspiral (Fig. 428B); several species east of Mississippi R.
**Lioplax**
29. Whorls of shell somewhat flattened and nodulous; inner margin of operculum
reflected, forming an elevated marginal fold (Fig. 428G); several species;
restricted to the Alabama R. and its tributaries . . . . . . . . . . . . . . . . **Tulotoma**
Whorls of shell not flattened, smooth; inner margin of operculum simple . . . . . . . **30**

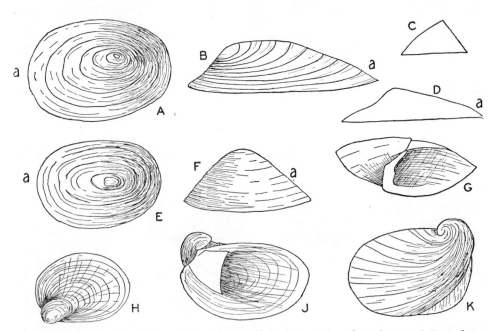

Fig. 427.—Typical Ancylidae. A, dorsal view of *Ferrissia*, ×9; B, lateral view of *F. rivularis* (Say), ×11; C, cross section of *F. rivularis*, ×6; D, longitudinal section of *Ferrissia*, ×8; E, dorsal view of *Lanx newberryi* (Lea), ×2; F, lateral view of *L. newberryi*, ×2; G, *Neoplanorbis tantillus* Pils., ×22; H, *Gundlachia hinkleyi* Walker, ×7; J and K, *Amphigyra alabamensis* Pils., ×17. *a*, anterior.

* Some authorities place this genus in a separate family, the Lancidae.

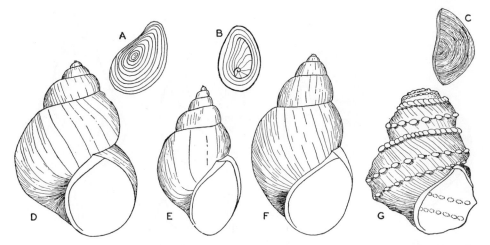

Fig. 428.—Typical Viviparidae. A, operculum of *Viviparus*; B, operculum of *Lioplax subcarinata* (Say); C, operculum of *Tulotoma*; D, *Viviparus subpurpureus* (Say), ×1.5; E, *Lioplax subcarinata*, ×2.5; F, *Campeloma decisum* (Say), ×1.7; G, *Tulotoma magnifica* (Conrad), ×1.

**30.** Shell subconic, thin (Fig. 428D); several species, chiefly eastern; most common in lakes and streams of the Mississippi Valley..................**Viviparus**

Shell turreted, thick (Fig. 428F); numerous species; generally distributed from the Mississippi Valley to the Atlantic coast...................**Campeloma**

**31.** Aperture canaliculate below (Figs. 429D–G)...........................32

Aperture not canaliculate below......................................35

**32.** Shell fusiform, large; canal long (Fig. 429D); in rapid streams of eastern Tenn. and western Va..........................................**Io**

Shell conical; canal short.........................................33

**33.** Spire elongated (Figs. 429F, G); numerous and extremely variable species; from Great Lakes and Mississippi Valley south to Ky., Tenn., and Ala., in which states it is most common...................................**Pleurocera**

Spire short.......................................................34

**34.** Parietal wall callously thickened above and below (Fig. 429E); several species; chiefly in Ky., Tenn., Ala., and Ind............................**Lithasia**

Parietal wall callously thickened above (Fig. 429B); several species in rivers of Tenn. and Ala......................................**Eurycaelon**

**35.** Shell ovate-conic to elongated (Fig. 429H); numerous species; most common in rivers of Tenn. and Ala., but extending north to Great Lakes, St. Lawrence R. basin, and western tributaries of the Mississippi R.; a few species in the Pacific coast states, and two species reported from northwestern Nev.; absent in the Rocky Mountain region...................................**Goniobasis**

Shell more globose.................................................36

**36.** Aperture entire; shell heavy........................................37

Aperture with a sutural fissure above (Fig. 429A); about a dozen highly variable species in the Coosa R., Ala...................................**Gyrotoma**

**37.** Inner marginal teeth of radula with four or five cusps; numerous highly variable species (Fig. 429C); from the Ohio R. south to Ga., Ala., Ark., and Mo., especially abundant in the Coosa R., Ala......................**Anculosa**

Inner marginal teeth of radula with seven cusps; one species in the Atlantic coast streams from N. Y. to S. C., and about five other species in Ohio, Ky., Kanawha R., W. Va., Hiwassee R., N. C., and the Tennessee R.........**Nitocris**

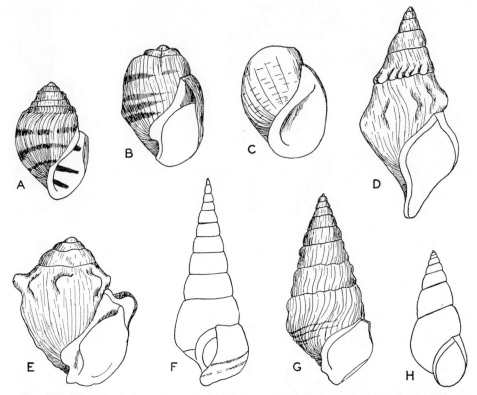

Fig. 429.—Typical Pleuroceridae. A, *Gyrotoma amplum* Anthony, ×2; B, *Eurycaelon anthonyi* (Budd), ×1.5; C, *Anculosa picta* Conrad, ×2; D, *Io spinosa* Lea, ×1.2; E, *Lithasia*, ×2.2; F, *Pleurocera acuta* Raf., ×2; G, *Pleurocera*, ×1.5; H, *Goniobasis livescens* (Menke), ×2. (A redrawn from Goodrich, 1924; C modified from Goodrich, 1922; F modified from Goodrich and van der Schalie.)

38. Operculum multispiral...................................................39
      Operculum paucispiral (Fig. 430F)........................................40
39. Shell amnicoliform (Fig. 430O); five minute species; Atlantic coast states.
                                                                            **Lyogyrus**
      Shell valvataeform (Fig. 430M); southern Texas......**Horatia micra** (P. and F.)
40. Foot divided by a vertical groove (Fig. 413C); usually amphibious but often found
         on submerged substrates; several species; generally distributed in and east of
         the Mississippi Valley, rare farther west....................**Pomatiopsis** *
      Foot not divided..........................................................41
41. Shell thin, subglobose to elongated......................................42
      Shell thick, short; body whorl very large.................................47
42. Shell smooth.............................................................43
      Shell ribbed, carinate, or bluntly spinose................................45
43. Shell slender; body whorl not swollen; spire long (Fig. 430A); usually in cool
         springs; numerous species ranging from Atlantic to Pacific coasts...**Hydrobia**
      Body whorl swollen; spire usually short...................................44

---

* Some authorities place this genus in a separate family, the Pomatiopsidae, because of the unique structure of the verge and radula.

**44.** Shell umbilicate (Fig. 430E); numerous species; widely distributed and common in a variety of habitats, but rare west of the Continental Divide....**Amnicola**

    Shell cleft or imperforate; 3.0 to 3.5 mm. long; known only from deep water of Lake Michigan..................................**Hoyia sheldoni** (Pils.)

**45.** Shell longitudinally ribbed (Fig. 430P); Nev..........**Tryonia clathrata** Stimp.

    Shell not longitudinally ribbed.........................................**46**

**46.** Shell usually strongly carinate (Fig. 430G), but sometimes with the carina hidden in the spire (Fig. 430H); several species in the upper Mississippi Valley, Great Lakes region, Ala., and Nev.........................**Pyrgulopsis**

    Whorls shouldered and usually coronated with spines (Fig. 430N); one species in Fla. and two in Texas..............................**Potamopyrgus**

**47.** Shell widely umbilicate........................................**48**

    Shell imperforate or with a narrow umbilical chink......................**49**

**48.** Shell depressed (Fig. 430L); two species in southern Texas..........**Cochliopa**

    Shell not depressed (Fig. 430Q); Coosa R., Ala.....**Clappia umbilicata** (Walker)

**49.** Edge of aperture sinuous, not in the same plane (Fig. 430J); in rapid streams; several species west of Continental Divide.................**Fluminicola**

    Edge of aperture not sinuous...........................................**50**

**50.** Edge of aperture in a horizontal plane; from N. J. to S. C.......**Gillia altilis** Lea

    Edge of aperture very oblique.........................................**51**

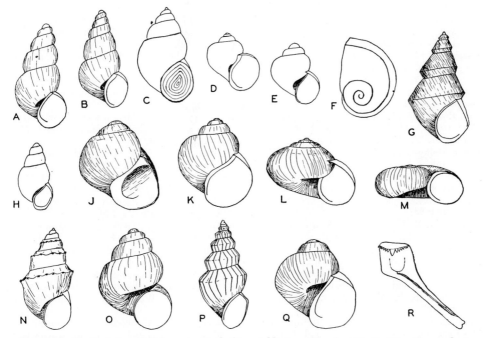

Fig. 430.—Typical Amnicolidae. A, *Hydrobia nickliniana* (Lea), ×7; B, *Pomatiopsis lapidaria* (Say), ×4; C, *Bithinia tentaculata* (L.) with operculum, ×2.5; D, *Somatogyrus subglobosus* (Say), ×2; E, *Amnicola limosa*, ×4; F, operculum of *A. limosa*, with fine striations and growth lines omitted; G, *Pyrgulopsis nevadensis* (Stearns), ×5; H, *P. letsoni* (Walker), ×5; J, *Fluminicola columbiana* Hemp., ×2.5; K, *Gillia altilis* (Lea), ×2.5; L, *Cochliopa riograndensis* P. and F., ×3; M, *Horatia micra* (P. and F.), ×8; N, *Potamopyrgus coronatus* Pfr., ×5; O, *Lyogyrus browni* (Carp.), ×10; P, *Tryonia clathrata* Stimp., ×5; Q, *Clappia umbilicata* Walker, ×8; R, lateral tooth of *C. tryoni* (P. and B.). (R redrawn from Baker, 1928.)

**51.** Each lateral tooth of radula with a prominent central cusp flanked by an equal number of smaller cusps on each side (Fig. 430R); one rare species in Wis. and another in the Potomac drainage....................................**Clappia**

With an unequal number of cusps on each side of the prominent central cusp of the lateral tooth of radula; about ten species east of the Mississippi R. and mostly south of the Ohio R..............................**Somatogyrus**

## GASTROPODA REFERENCES

ADAMSTONE, F. B. 1923. The distribution and economic importance of Mollusca in Lake Nipigon. *Univ. Toronto Studies, Biol. Ser.* 22:67–119.

BAKER, F. C. 1911. The Lymnaeidae of North and Middle America. *Spec. Publ. Chicago Acad. Sci.* 3:1–539.

——. 1916. The relation of mollusks to fish in Oneida Lake. *N. Y. State Coll. Forestry, Tech. Publ.* 4:1–366.

——. 1918. The productivity of invertebrate fish food on the bottom of Oneida Lake, with special reference to mollusks. *Ibid.* 9:1–233.

——. 1918a. The relation of shellfish to fish in Oneida Lake, New York. *N. Y. State Coll. Forestry, Circ.* 21:1–34.

——. 1928. *The fresh water Mollusca of Wisconsin. Part I. Gastropoda.* 507 pp. Wis. Acad. Sci., Arts and Lett. Madison, Wisconsin.

——. 1945. *The molluscan family Planorbidae.* 530 pp. Urbana, Ill.

BERRY, E. G. 1943. The Amnicolidae of Michigan: distribution, ecology, and taxonomy. *Mus. Zool. Univ. Mich. Misc. Publ.* 57:1–68.

BOYCOTT, A. E. 1936. The habitats of fresh-water Mollusca in Britain. *Jour. Animal Ecol.* 5:116–186.

CARRIKER, M. R. 1946. Morphology of the alimentary system of the snail Lymnaea stagnalis appressa Say. *Trans. Wis. Acad. Sci. Arts and Lett.* 38:1–88.

CHAMBERLIN, R. V., and D. T. JONES. 1929. A descriptive catalog of the Mollusca of Utah. *Bull. Univ. Utah* 19:1–203.

CHEATUM. E. P. 1934. Limnological investigations on respiration, annual migratory cycle, and other related phenomena in fresh-water pulmonate snails. *Trans. Amer. Micros. Soc.* 53:348–407.

CRABB, E. D. 1927. Anatomy and function of the reproductive system in the snail, Lymnaea appressa Say. *Biol. Bull.* 53:55–66.

DAWSON, J. 1911. The biology of Physa. *Behavior Monogr.* 1:1–120.

GOODRICH, C. 1922. The Anculosae of the Alabama River drainage. *Mus. Zool. Univ. Mich. Misc. Publ.* 7:1–57.

——. 1924. The genus Gyrotoma. *Ibid.* 12:1–32.

——. 1936. Goniobasis of the Coosa River, Alabama. *Ibid.* 31:1–60.

——. 1941. Distribution of the gastropods of the Cahaba River, Alabama. *Mus. Zool. Univ. Mich. Occ. Pap.* 428:1–30.

——. 1944. Certain operculates of the Coosa River. *Nautilus* 58:1–10.

GOODRICH, C., and H. VAN DER SCHALIE. 1939. Aquatic mollusks of the Upper Peninsula of Michigan. *Mus. Zool. Univ. Mich. Misc. Publ.* 43:1–45.

GUNTER, G. 1936. Radular movements in gastropods. *Jour. Wash. Acad. Sci.* 26:361–365.

HENDERSON, J. 1924. Mollusca of Colorado, Utah, Montana, Idaho, and Wyoming. *Univ. Colo. Studies* 13:65–223.

——. 1929. Non-marine Mollusca of Oregon and Washington. *Ibid.* 17:47–190.

——. 1936. Mollusca of Colorado, Utah, Montana, Idaho, and Wyoming—supplement. *Ibid.* 23:81–145.

——. 1936a. The non-marine Mollusca of Oregon and Washington. Supplement. *Ibid.* 251–280.

HOFF, C. C. 1940. Anatomy of the ancylid snail, Ferrissia tarda (Say). *Trans. Amer. Micros. Soc.* 59:224–242.

HUBENDICK, B. 1947. Die Verbreitungsverhältnisse der limnischen Gastropoden in Südschweden. *Zool. Bidrag Uppsala* 24:419–559.

MACAN, T. T. 1950. Ecology of fresh-water Mollusca in the English Lake District. *Jour. Animal Ecol.* 19:124–146.

MAGRUDER, S. R. 1935. The anatomy of the freshwater prosobranchiate gastropod, Pleurocera canaliculatum undulatum (Say). *Amer. Midl. Nat.* 16:883–912.

MORRISON, J. P. E. 1932. A report on the Mollusca of the northeastern Wisconsin lake district. *Trans. Wis. Acad. Sci., Arts and Lett.* 27:359–396.

NEKRASSOW, A. D. 1928. Vergleichende Morphologie der Laiche von Süsswasser-Gastropoden. *Zeitschr. Morph. u. Ökol. Tiere* 13:1–35.

NOLAND, L. E., and E. REICHEL. 1943. Life cycle of Lymnaea stagnalis completed at room temperature without access to air. *Nautilus* 57:8–13.

PILSBRY, H. E. 1934. Review of the Planorbidae of Florida, with notes on other members of the family. *Proc. Acad. Nat. Sci.* 86:29–66.

SHOUP, C. S. 1943. Distribution of fresh-water gastropods in relation to total alkalinity of streams. *Nautilus* **56**:130–134.

STRECKER, J. K., JR. 1935. Land and fresh-water snails of Texas. *Trans. Tex. Acad. Sci.* **17**:4–44.

THIELE, J. 1931. *Handbuch der systematischen Weichtierkunde. Erster Band.* 778 pp. Jena.

WALKER, B. 1918. A synopsis of the classification of the freshwater Mollusca of North America, north of Mexico, and a catalogue of the more recently described species, with notes. *Mus. Zool. Univ. Mich. Misc. Publ.* **6**:1–213.

WINSLOW, M. L. 1926. A revised check list of Michigan Mollusca. *Mus. Zool. Univ. Mich. Occ. Pap.* **181**:1–28.

# Chapter 37

## PELECYPODA (CLAMS, MUSSELS)

UNLIKE THE Gastropoda, the bivalve mollusks are all aquatic, and although they occur in nearly all types of fresh-water environments, they are most abundant and varied in the larger rivers.

**General characteristics.** The mussels, or clams, of our inland waters range from about 2 to 250 mm. in length. The two valves of the shell are securely attached to each other dorsally by an elastic hinge ligament, and under natural conditions the valves gape slightly to permit the protrusion of the muscular hatchet- or axe-shaped foot at the anteroventral margin and the inhalent and exhalent siphons at the posterior margin. There are no tentacles, head, or eyes. The animal lies obliquely with the ventral half (or more) hidden in the substrate; in some species the shell may be entirely hidden from view with only the siphons appearing at the surface.

**Locomotion.** Mussels move over and through the substrate by means of a series of contractions of the intrinsic muscle fibers of the foot. The foot is first elongated and thrust forward in the substrate; then the distal portion of the foot becomes more or less swollen transversely so that it obtains a purchase, and at the same time the entire foot is shortened; as a result the main portion of the body and its enclosing shell are pulled forward slightly. These repeated muscular contractions therefore result in locomotion which is essentially a series of short "hunching"

movements. Some species are known to move several feet per hour and the resulting long troughlike tracks of larger mussels may often be seen on sandy lake bottoms where there is little wave action. The stimuli responsible for movements of clams are not generally known, but it is thought that stagnation and fall in water level are of primary importance. Thin-shelled species are generally more active than heavy-shelled.

**Shell, muscles.** Mussel shells exhibit a variety of shapes. Some are decidedly elongated or oval; others are subcircular, rhomboidal, quadrate, trapezoidal, or sub-triangular. At the dorsal margin of each valve, just anterior to the hinge ligament, is a raised area, the umbo or beak, which denotes the point at which growth began in the juvenile mussel. Surrounding each umbo and extending out to the edges of the valves is a series of concentric lines which are formed at the edge of the shell as the animal grows. At intervals these rings are more closely grouped, forming a more or less distinct ridge. In many species it can be shown that these markings clearly denote limits of annual growth and winter rest periods, especially if an adequate sample from a particular locality is studied. The annual growth-ring picture is often confused, however, by the presence of accessory rings formed in response to a variety of temporary unfavorable environmental conditions, such as lack of food, low oxygen supply, and

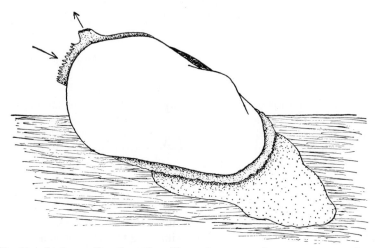

FIG. 431.—Female *Lampsilis siliquoidea* (Barnes) in natural position in river bottom, ×.5. Arrows indicate currents of water. (Modified from Baker, 1928.)

fall in water level. In addition to these concentric markings, many genera bear pustules, rays, knobs, or wrinkles.

External coloration is whitish to brown in the Sphaeriidae, and light yellow, light green, dark green, brown, or blackish in other families. In older shells, especially near the umbones, the outer protective colored layer (periostracum) is often eroded away, exposing the chalky white calcium carbonate layer underneath. The internal surface of the shell is thickly coated with nacre, or mother-of-pearl, which ranges in color from silvery white through pink to dark purple; it is composed of extremely thin alternating laminae of calcium carbonate and an organic substance. Between the nacre and the periostracum is the prismatic layer; it consists of minute, closely packed, prism-like blocks of calcium carbonate (Fig. 432).

The important features of the inner surface of a typical shell are shown in Fig. 433. Near the dorsal margin there is usually a series of projecting and interlocking hinge teeth which aid in keeping the two valves in juxtaposition. In the Unionidae the pseudocardinal teeth are in the anterior part of the shell below the umbones, and the long, narrow, ridgelike

lateral teeth are more posterior and below the region of the ligament. In the Sphaeriidae there are lateral teeth both anterior and posterior to the true cardinals.

The hinge teeth serve as a fulcrum, and the springlike hinge ligament normally keeps the shell slightly open. When the foot and siphons are withdrawn, however, the shell may be tightly closed by the contraction of the two large but short transverse muscles fastened to the inner surface of the valves, the anterior and posterior adductors.

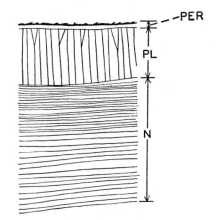

FIG. 432.—Small section of mussel shell. *PER*, periostracum; *PL*, prismatic layer; *N*, nacre.

In addition to the scars produced by the attachment of the adductor muscles, each valve typically contains the scars of three other muscles. Above, and more or less closely associated with the posterior adductor scar, is a small scar produced by the attachment of the posterior retractor of the foot. The anterior adductor has a comparable associated scar for the anterior retractor of the foot, as well as an additional scar for the protractor muscle of the foot. There are also some small and indistinct scars in the cavity of the umbo from muscles which aid in holding the visceral mass in place.

Except where muscles are attached, the inner surface of the shell is completely lined with a sheet of glandular tissue, the mantle. This structure is securely fastened near the edges of the valves along the muscular pallial line. Such an attach-

ment prevents foreign particles from getting between mantle and shell. An indentation in the pallial line may be present near the posterior end of the shell; it is called the pallial sinus and is produced by intrinsic muscles which retract the siphons. The entire lateral surface of the mantle secretes the nacre, but the periostracum and prismatic layer are formed only by the border of the mantle at the periphery of the shell.

**Gross visceral anatomy.** When one valve of a mussel is removed, the underlying mantle can be seen covering the viscera. At the posterior end of a typical animal the edges of the two lobes of the mantle are modified to form three slitlike openings. Uppermost is the smooth supraanal opening; below this is the anal (exhalent) opening, which may be smooth or

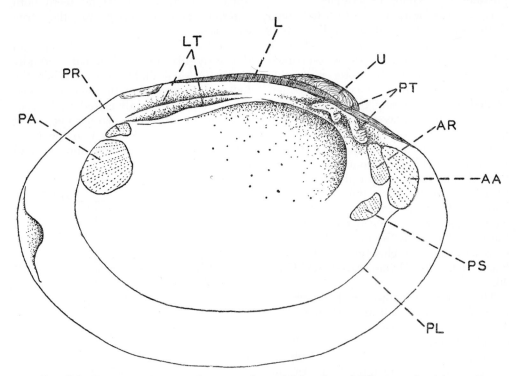

Fig. 433.—Diagrammatic view of inner surface of left valve of *Elliptio*, ×1. *AA,* anterior adductor muscle scar; *AR,* anterior retractor muscle scar; *L,* ligament; *LT,* lateral teeth; *PA,* posterior adductor muscle scar; *PL,* pallial line; *PR,* posterior retractor muscle scar; *PS,* scar of protractor muscle of foot; *PT,* pseudocardinal teeth; *U,* umbo.

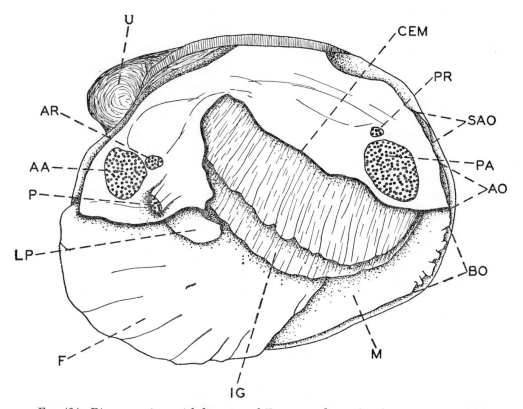

FIG. 434.—Diagrammatic partial dissection of *Fusconaia ebenus* (Lea), ×1.4. *AA*, anterior adductor muscle; *AO*, anal opening; *AR*, anterior retractor muscle; *BO*, branchial opening; *CEM*, cut edge of mantle; *F*, foot; *IG*, inner gill; *LP*, labial palps; *M*, mantle; *P*, protractor muscle of foot; *PA*, posterior adductor muscle; *PR*, posterior retractor muscle; *SAO*, supra-anal opening; *U*, umbo. (Modified from Lefevre and Curtis, 1910.)

crenulated; lowermost is the distinctly papillose branchial (inhalent) opening. In the Unionidae and Margaritanidae the edges of the mantle around the branchial opening project to form a more or less distinct siphon. Some Sphaeriidae have long, cylindrical, protrusible anal and branchial siphons (Fig. 435); in other species only the anal siphon is prominent. Neither the Margaritanidae nor the Sphaeriidae have a supra-anal opening.

When the mantle is removed from one side, the two long flat gills of that side are exposed to view. Each gill is composed of two lamellae which are united at the lower but not the upper margin, the two gills together being roughly W-shaped in cross section. The outer gill is connected

at the outside and top to the mantle, and the inner gill is attached at the inside to the outer surface of the main median visceral mass; the base of the inner lamella of the outer gill and the base of the outer lamella of the inner gill are attached to each other. The cavity between the two lamellae of each gill is subdivided by ver-

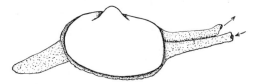

FIG. 435.—*Musculium transversum* (Say), showing branchial and anal siphons, ×2. Arrows indicate currents of water. (Modified from Baker, 1928.)

tical partitions into many narrow chambers or water tubes, closed below but opening above into a longitudinal space along the dorsal portion of the gill called the suprabranchial chamber. At the posterior end of the animal the suprabranchial chambers are fused to form a single cavity, the cloacal chamber. Near the anterior end of the gills and surrounding the small slitlike mouth are two flat labial palps on each side. The upper lip is continuous with the left and right outer palps, and the lower lip is continuous with the left and right inner palps. The greater portion of the foot lies between the gills in the anterior part of the mantle cavity. It tapers posteriorly, and the median visceral mass of the posterior part of the animal is confined to the dorsal part of the mantle cavity.

**Feeding, digestive system.** The food of a mussel consists of zooplankton, phytoplankton, and organic detritus, the feeding processes being specialized for the removal of these suspended microscopic particles from the water. The inner surface of the mantle, the gills, and the visceral mass are covered with cilia which beat in such a coordinated way as to draw a stream of water in through the branchial siphon. This water passes into the mantle cavity and enters the many minute openings, or ostia, of the gill lamellae into the gill chambers, then upward to the suprabranchial chambers, and finally posteriorly through the cloacal chamber and out the exhalent opening. As this continuous stream of water passes over the outer surface of the gills, however, the food particles become entangled in their mucous

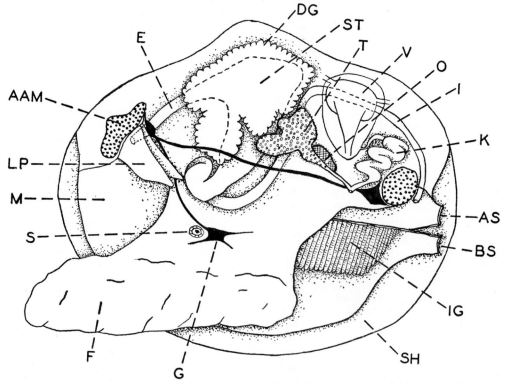

Fig. 436.—Diagrammatic longitudinal section of *Musculium*, ×12. *AAM*, anterior adductor muscle; *AS*, anal siphon; *BS*, branchial siphon; *DG*, digestive gland; *E*, esophagus; *F*, foot; *G*, pedal ganglion; *I*, intestine; *IG*, inner gill; *K*, kidney; *LP*, labial palp; *M*, mantle; *O*, ovary; *S*, statocyst; *SH*, shell; *ST*, stomach; *T*, testis; *V*, ventricle of heart.

covering. The mucus with its contained food is driven by ciliary action along the edge of the gills toward the mouth where it is picked up by cilia on the labial palps and directed into the mouth in a constant ribbon-like stream.

Although some inorganic silt may be mixed with the organic food taken into the mouth, a large portion of the inedible material is separated out beforehand. The mechanisms involved in this selection and separation have been the subject of a long controversy, and it now appears probable that the labial palps are most important, and that by some means much of the indigestible material is separated out on their surface and carried to the ventral edges where it drops off and is carried backward by ciliary action and expelled between the valves just below the inhalent siphon. It is likely that some additional selection and separation of food and inorganic debris is effected by the edge of the inhalent siphon and the mouth. The entire digestive tract is imbedded in the main visceral mass. The mouth opens into a short esophagus which leads to the more or less bulbous stomach situated in the anterior dorsal portion of the foot. The stomach is surrounded by a large green gland, or "liver." The long narrow intestine has several coils behind and below the stomach before it proceeds to the dorsal region and runs posteriorly above the posterior adductor muscle and opens into the mantle cavity through the anus just above the exhalent opening of the mantle cavity.

The anterior part of the intestine of the Unionidae has a lateral diverticulum, or groove, containing the curious crystalline style. This is a cylindrical structure of a hyaline, milky, or brownish color and of a dense gelatinous consistency. During normal feeding activities it is revolved on its long axis by the ciliary epithelium of the style sac. The anterior end of the style usually projects into the stomach where it rubs against a cartilage-like shield and is constantly being eroded away. This ero-sion liberates a polysaccharide-digesting enzyme and is thought to function also in separating food from foreign particles. The style disappears during periods of starvation but is regenerated as a response to ingestion. It is formed only slowly at low temperatures.

**Circulation.** The circulatory system consists of a single ventricle, two auricles, blood vessels, and spaces or sinuses in the tissues. Dorsally and posterior to the stomach is the thin-walled pericardial cavity, containing the heart and through which the posterior part of the intestine passes longitudinally. The ventricle is an oval organ surrounding the intestine, and the two flat auricles lie at the sides of the ventricle and open into it just below the middle of each side.

Arising from the ventricle are an anterior and a posterior artery whose branches supply all of the soft parts of the animal, the mantle and gills being supplied with a particularly large quantity of blood. From the smaller arteries the blood passes into numerous sinuses in the tissues, and thence into veins and back to the auricles.

The blood is colorless or slightly bluish owing to dissolved hemocyanin, a respiratory pigment. The heart rate is usually less than 20 beats per minute, but a rate as high as 100 beats has been recorded.

**Respiration.** Although the entire body surface is in contact with water and probably functions in respiration, the greater portion of the oxygen-carbon dioxide exchance undoubtedly occurs in the mantle and gills.

**Excretion.** The two kidneys, **or** organs of Bojanus, lie in the visceral mass immediately below or behind the pericardial cavity. Each kidney is a dark-colored more or less convoluted tubule with the opening at one end in the pericardial cavity and the opening at the other (external) in a suprabranchial chamber.

**Nervous system.** Unlike snails, mussels have a simple nervous system, with only three pairs of ganglia. The cerebropleural ganglia lie immediately posterior to the anterior adductor muscle, one on each side of the esophagus, and are connected by a short commissure passing over the esophagus; the pedal ganglia are deeply imbedded in the foot and are more or less fused; the visceral ganglia lie just anterior to the posterior adductor and are also partially fused. Connecting the cerebropleural ganglia with the pedal and visceral ganglia are two pairs of long commissures. Each ganglion gives off nerve fibers to the adjacent organs.

**Sense organs.** Maintenance of equilibrium is effected by a pair of minute statocysts situated near the pedal ganglia. Each statocyst is an ovoid or round fluid-filled cavity lined with sensory cells and containing a spherical concretion, the statolith.

The osphradia are two small areas of specialized epithelium on the roof of the cloacal chamber. Their function has never been successfully established, but most writers assume that they are useful in detecting dissolved foreign materials in the water.

In addition to being sensitive to touch, the projecting edges of the mantle are capable of detecting pronounced changes in light intensity, and the valves can be caused to shut by casting a shadow or bright light on the mantle.

**Reproduction.** The Sphaeriidae are uniformly hermaphroditic, but in the Unionidae the sexes are separate except for a few species which are occasionally or consistently hermaphroditic. The ovaries and testes are imbedded in the upper part of the foot and are connected with the suprabranchial chambers by short ducts.

The details of reproduction differ markedly in these two families. In the Sphaeriidae it is thought that self-fertilization occurs in the reproductive ducts.

The zygotes pass into the suprabranchial chambers and then downward into the water tubes of the inner pair of gills. Here they develop and grow, and the gills, becoming greatly distended, are then called marsupia. An adult may contain from one to 20 young in various stages of development. When released from the marsupia, the immature individuals are fully formed, having the shell and all morphological features of adults; sometimes they are surprisingly large, often one-quarter to one-third as long as the parent. Reproduction is thought to continue throughout the year, although very few young are released during the winter months.

In the Unionidae the unfertilized eggs pass into the suprabranchial chambers and then downward into the water tubes of the gills. Depending on the species, all four gills, the two outer gills, or only special parts of the outer gills (Fig. 437) are utilized. Sperm of the male are swept out of the animal through the exhalent opening into the surrounding water. Some of the sperm are then drawn fortuitously into the incurrent siphon of a mature female in the vicinity; they pass through the ostia of the gill lamellae and fertilize the eggs in the water tubes. The embryos are retained only for the early stages of development, but growth is pronounced, and the gills (marsupia) soon become distended. The number of embryos present at one time ranges from several thousand in the smaller species to more than 3,000,-000 in some of the largest mussels.

Depending on the species, breeding may begin in the first to eighth year of life. The Unioninae are short-term breeders and are gravid between April and August; the Anodontinae and Lampsilinae are long-term breeders, the eggs being fertilized in midsummer and carried until the following spring or summer.

Marine bivalves have characteristic ciliated free-swimming larvae, but the American fresh-water mussels have an entirely different type of larva, the glochidium, which becomes a temporary and obligatory parasite on a fish. The mature glochidium which is released from the marsupium of the female mussel ranges from 0.05 to 0.50 mm. in diameter. Superficially, it appears to be a small edition of an adult in its general morphology. There are two chitinoid valves joined at their bases along a hinge, lined by a layer of cells comprising the larval mantle, and held together by a single adductor muscle. The mantle bears several tufts of sensory hairs. In species of *Unio, Anodonta,* and *Quadrula* the glochidium has a peculiar long thread which is thought to be useful in becoming attached to the host fish (Fig. 438A). The general shape of the valves may be simple and oval or rounded, roughly triangular, or ax-head shaped (in *Proptera* only). Sometimes the periphery of the shell opposite the hinge bears teeth.

In the Unionidae and Anodontinae the glochidia leave the female via the supra-

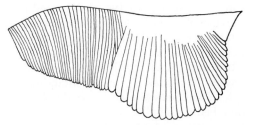
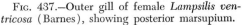

FIG. 437.—Outer gill of female *Lampsilis ventricosa* (Barnes), showing posterior marsupium.

branchial chambers and exhalent siphon; they may be free or more or less imbedded in mucus. In the Lampsilinae irregular masses break through temporary openings in the water tubes. In either case the glochidia become scattered and sink to the bottom where they remain with the valves gaping upward. If they do not come in contact with the body of a fish they usually die within several days. Fish become infected by brushing against the bot-

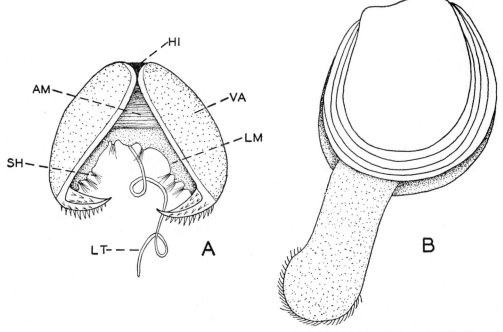

FIG. 438.—Immature Pelecypoda. A, end view of glochidium of *Anodonta imbecillis* Say, ×130. B, lateral view of juvenile stage of *Actinonaias carinata* (Barnes), ×150. AM, adductor muscle; HI, hinge; LM, larval mantle; LT, larval thread; SH, tuft of sensory hairs; VA, valve. (A modified from Tucker; B modified from Lefevre and Curtis, 1912.)

tom, by stirring up the bottom with fin movements, and by taking in water which contains the glochidia in temporary suspension. The larvae are exceedingly sensitive and clamp tightly to the superficial tissues immediately upon contacting the fish. The hookless species usually become attached to the gills, hooked species to the fins or general body surface. Some forms are host-specific and infect only one species of fish; others are capable of infecting several to many species of fish. Sometimes the glochidia become attached to an unsuitable host but soon leave voluntarily.

Within a short time the tissues of the fish begin to grow over the glochidium, and in a day or two the latter is completely encased and forms a small projecting nodule. This parasitic stage usually lasts from ten to 30 days, although some records indicate as long as 190 days; undoubtedly water temperatures influence the duration of the parasitic period.

During encystment the glochidial structures change markedly, and most of the adult organ systems become more or less definitely formed. The single adductor muscle is replaced by two; the mouth and intestine are present; the gills, kidneys, heart, and foot are represented by functional rudiments; and the mantle has taken on a more definitive structure. Usually, however, there is little increase in size.

At the close of the parasitic period the young mussel breaks out of its cyst, falls to the bottom, and enters a period appropriately called the juvenile stage (Fig. 438B). The organ systems begin to develop rapidly, and the beginning of the adult shell appears beneath the glochidial shell. The foot is long and ciliated and provides a means of locomotion. A long, sticky, hyaline thread, or byssus, is secreted by the posterior part of the foot in many species; it apparently facilitates attachment to the substrate and is usually shed in a few weeks. The smaller juvenile mussels burrow into the bottom and for this reason are seldom collected. As growth

proceeds, however, the adult habits are assumed, and the organs take on their adult characteristics. Strictly speaking, the juvenile stage lasts from one to as much as eight years, that is, until the animal is sexually mature.

Several species are known to be able either to complete development to the juvenile stage in the brood chamber or to leave the parent as a glochidium and parasitize a fish in the usual manner. One species, *Simpsoniconcha ambigua* (Say), parasitizes *Necturus*, the mud puppy.

Even though more than 3,000 glochidia have been found parasitizing a single adult fish, there is little evidence that they do any direct harm in natural habitats. Nevertheless, heavy infections (100 or more) have been shown to kill 30-millimeter fingerling trout by causing secondary bacterial infections.

**Growth, longevity.** The period of growth extends from about April to September, and the actual rate of growth is dependent upon numerous factors, including temperature, food supply, current, and the specific chemical nature of the water. Mussels usually grow to a length of 30 to 80 mm. in two growing seasons. Some of the Anodontidae live for ten to 15 years, but the Sphaeriidae are thought to live no longer than 12 to 18 months.

**Enemies.** The Sphaeriidae are eaten regularly by numerous fishes, including the gizzard shad, whitefish, buffalo, sucker, redhorse, and perch, and soft-shelled species of the Anodontidae are eaten to a limited extent by catfish and sheepshead. Muskrats are undoubtedly the most important mammalian enemy of mussels. They usually select thin-shelled forms and either let them die on shore when the shell gapes, or force the shell open with their teeth. Piles of discarded shells near muskrat colonies are said to be an excellent source for some of the uncommon species. Mussels are also occasionally eaten by mink, otter, raccoon, turtles, and hellbenders (*Cryptobranchus*).

The branchial and mantle cavities are often infested with parasitic or commensal Hydracarina. Larval flukes are sometimes found in the branchial and pericardial cavities. Both of these groups may be responsible for the production of small irregular pearls and blisters on the inner surface of the host shell, and sometimes the nacre may be discolored.

**Economic importance.** As a result of the utilization of marine shells, satisfactory synthetic substitutes, and the gradual depletion of mussel beds, the fresh-water pearl button industry has been declining in importance for many years, although the value of the products has held up well. The industry was founded in 1891, and by 1912 there were 196 factories in 20 states along the larger rivers of the Mississippi system and a few rivers entering the Gulf east of the Mississippi. In that year these plants produced $6,173,486 worth of merchandise. In 1941, with far fewer factories, the corresponding figure was about $2,500,000, but in 1944 it was $4,306,353, and in 1949 it was $3,696,452. About 20,300 tons of shell were harvested in 1944 with a value, before processing, of $892,915; Tennessee, Kentucky, and Arkansas rivers yielded 78 per cent of the total.

There are about 40 useful species and 17 species of first importance in the manufacture of buttons; these are included in the following genera: *Fusconaia, Megalonaias, Amblema, Quadrula, Actinonaias, Plagiola, Ligumia,* and *Lampsilis.* The mussels are collected in several ways. One widely used device is the crowfoot dredge. It consists of a long iron bar to which are attached 100 to 200 four-pronged hooks on short lengths of cord. When the dredge is lowered from a flat-bottomed boat and dragged along the bottom, the hooks become lodged between the open valves of mussels, and the animals clamp tightly upon them. At intervals the dredge is raised and the mussels are removed. Other devices include rake-like tongs, stout rakes with large attached bags or nets, and forks for shallow water collecting. Some states outlaw forking in the interests of conservation.

The mussels are killed by steaming in a cooker, and the meat is removed. The shells are then sold by the ton to the buyers. In the factories or along the river's edge they are sorted and soaked in water before the blanks are cut with a tubular saw. The blanks are ground to uniform thickness, drilled, finished, sorted, and carded or packed for sale.

Mussels are seldom collected primarily for their pearls, the fresh-water pearl industry being carried on in conjunction with, and in addition to, the preparation of shells for the button factories. The pearls are more or less imbedded in the soft tissues, and after removal from the shell these parts are examined visually and slipped between the fingers to detect hidden pearls. Small pearls are sometimes recovered by allowing the meats to rot. When reduced to a pulp, the mass is rubbed through a fine sieve which retains the pearls.

Pearls are formed by the secretion of nacre around a foreign body which becomes lodged against the mantle or other tissues. This secretion takes place in a sac lined with epithelium physiologically and histologically similar to the shell-secreting epidermis of the mantle. The foreign body may be a bit of debris, sand grains, or even some kind of a parasite. Though the layman usually thinks of pearls as being "balls," "pears," or "buttons," there are many other irregular shapes habitually produced by certain species. Some of these are called "petal," "lily," "leaf," and "arrowhead," according to their shape. Such curious but natural shapes are determined by pressures and movements of surrounding organs during their formation. Spherical pearls, on the other hand, occur only in a part of the body which is free from unequal pressures and extensive movements; button pearls are formed near the outer surface of the mantle where they are pressed against the shell while nacre deposition is occurring.

The formation of real freak pearls, or "baroques," is usually instigated by the presence of a parasite or by a button or ball pearl becoming lodged in a new location. Baroques may be either attached to the shell or free. They are of irregular shape, but rare specimens may simulate a bird, insect, other object, or even a face. Single unusual and large baroques and perfectly formed regular pearls command high prices, hundreds and even thousands of dollars having been paid for many specimens. One Arkansas pearl, weighing 3.4 grams, is reputed to have been sold for $6,750. Unfortunately, the finding of really fine pearls is an event of increasing rarity because of the great depletion of our mussel resources.

The reported total value of mussel pearls collected in the entire Mississippi River drainage system in 1931 was only $11,436.

In view of our rapidly declining mussel populations, United States government research workers have intermittently been trying to develop effective and economical methods of artificially propagating mussels ever since 1894. Only recently, however, have promising techniques been devised (Jones, 1949). Mature glochidia are taken from gravid females and placed in tanks containing the suitable host species of fish. After infection, these fish are released in appropriate rivers.

**Ecology.** Fresh-water bivalves occur in all types of unpolluted habitats but they are most abundant and varied in the larger rivers. Small creeks and spring brooks are devoid of mussels, although they contain Sphaeriidae. Similarly, small lakes, especially seepage lakes, contain few species, and large drainage lakes contain many. Lake Pepin, for example, which is really a wide place on the Mississippi, contains 32 species of mussels.

Like snails, bivalves are most abundant in the shallows, especially in water less than two meters deep. In the largest rivers and some lakes, however, mussels occur as deep as seven meters, while the Sphaeriidae are found in great abundance on some lake bottoms more than 30 meters below the surface.

The occurrence of the largest species and largest numbers of mussels in rivers where there is a good current has not yet been satisfactorily explained from an ecological standpoint. It is possible that abundant food supply, the specific type of substrate, an abundance of oxygen, water chemistry, or a combination of factors may be significant. River genera have thicker shells than lake genera, and individuals of a single species inhabiting both types of environments usually have heavier shells in running waters. Also, in a single species, flatter and less inflated varieties may occur in upper tributaries, more swollen varieties in the lower parts of a river system. Mussels inhabiting exposed lake shoals may be somewhat stunted and more heavy shelled than specimens from protected waters.

Bare rock bottoms and shifting sands and muds, with their accompanying high turbidities, are completely unsuitable for bivalves, while stable gravel, sand, and substrates composed of sand or gravel mixed with other materials support the largest populations, some such beds having more than 50 mussels per square meter. Though soft mud bottoms are generally uninhabited, there are some common "mud-loving" species of *Anodonta*. Customarily, mussels inhabit substrates free of rooted vegetation, but there are numerous exceptions. The Sphaeriidae are less specific in their occurrence and are found on all types of bottoms except clay and rock; in favorable situations populations of more than 5,000 individuals per square meter may be counted.

To a large extent the geographical distribution of the fresh-water bivalves appears to be determined by the chemical features of waters. The Anodontidae are rarely found in acid waters (pH below 7.0) or in waters having a bound carbon dioxide content of less than 15.0 mg. per liter. Decidedly alkaline waters and an abundance of calcium carbonate for shell construction favor large numbers of individuals and species. The Sphaeriidae, on the other hand, have become adapted to a wider range of conditions, and some species are common in lakes having a pH as low as 6.0 and a bound carbon dioxide content of only 2.0 mg. per liter. It is difficult to understand how a calcium carbonate shell can be secreted and maintained under such unfavorable conditions.

Because of the apparent disappearance of mussels from the shallows during the winter months, it was formerly inferred that they migrated to deeper waters in the fall. It is now believed, however, that migrations are unimportant and that most individuals simply burrow more deeply into the bottom of their summer habitat so that only the inconspicuous edges of the siphons project. The siphons are opened infrequently, and the animals remain in a dormant state throughout the winter. Ten degrees Centigrade is thought to be an average critical hibernation temperature.

Many Sphaeriidae are known to burrow into the substrate in times of drought, and among the Unionidae, species of *Uniomerus, Carunculina, Ligumia,* and *Amblema* have all been found buried in substrates which were moist or dry for several months.

Fresh-water mussels are thought to have first developed in the New World, and, more specifically, in the general area of the Mississippi drainage basin, for it is here that the greatest diversity of species occurs. *Anodonta* is the only genus of the predominantly American subfamily Anodontinae occurring in the United States which is not confined to North America; it is found also in Europe and Asia. The Unioninae occur in North America, Europe, Asia, and Africa, but all genera found in the United States are endemic to North America; about 41 genera occur outside of North America. The Lampsilinae are all confined to North America. The

Margaritanidae are widely distributed throughout the Northern Hemisphere, and the Sphaeriidae are world-wide. The other families mentioned in this chapter are predominantly marine, only a few species having invaded brackish waters and the coastal areas of rivers.

H. and A. van der Schalie (1950) distinguish six mussel faunal regions in the United States. The Atlantic region is characterized by a preponderance of *Elliptio* species and comprises drainages entering the Atlantic Ocean from the St. Lawrence southward into eastern Florida and extending as far west as western Lake Huron, central Pennsylvania, and western Georgia. The Pacific region includes those drainages entering the Pacific Ocean and is characterized mainly by the presence of *Anodonta, Gonidea,* and *Margaritifera.* The Mississippi region includes more than half of the area of the United States, from the Continental Divide on the west to the Atlantic region on the east, and from Canada to the Gulf. It has an extremely rich naiad fauna. The Ozark region is a small area including the eastern half of Oklahoma, southeastern Nebraska, southwestern Missouri, and northwestern Arkansas. It has characteristic species of *Ptychobranchus* and *Arkansia.* The small Cumberlandian region includes southeastern Kentucky, eastern Tennessee, the southernmost tip of West Virginia, and westernmost Virginia. *Conradilla* and *Lexingtonia* are characteristic genera. The sixth region is the Appalachicolan, including northwestern Florida, southeastern Alabama, and southwestern Georgia. It is characterized by certain species of *Quincuncina, Margaritana,* and *Medionidus.*

It should be pointed out that the mussel fauna of the Mississippi region has penetrated into most of the other faunal regions, and especially into the Ozark and Cumberlandian regions. The upper portion of the Mississippi faunal region, however, has a strikingly uniform and characteristic assemblage of species. It contains no species originating in any of the other faunal regions.

Not counting many additional varieties, there are between 500 and 600 species of Unionidae and an unknown number, but probably several hundred, species of Sphaeriidae known from the United States. The Cumberland River has more than 80 species of Unionidae; Michigan has 66 Unionidae and 108 species of Sphaeriidae; Dane County, Wisconsin, has 34 Unionidae and 30 Sphaeriidae; Texas has 44 Unionidae. The known naiad fauna of the Great Lakes comprises six species from Lake Superior, ten from Michigan, 17 from Huron, 40 from Erie, and six from Ontario. The Atlantic coast states, Great Plains, Rocky Mountain region, and the Pacific coast states have very few species of Anodontinae.

By migrating naturally and extensively into suitable habitats, a species may, over a long period of time, come to occupy much of a large drainage area. More rapid migration is undoubtedly effected by fishes carrying the glochidial stage of mussels, and possibly by birds transporting Sphaeriidae and immature Unionidae overland in mud or debris on their legs and feet. There is, however, little actual evidence for the latter mode of transport.

Greater numbers of species are usually found in the lower waters of river systems rather than in the small tributaries. The greater abundance of species in large lakes is probably due to the fact that such environments have a greater variety of subhabitats or niches than small lakes.

Pollution, silting of rivers, and the construction of dams are decidedly inimical to our American mussel fauna. Many of the less common species are fast disappearing, and reduced populations appear to be unsuccessful in increasing their present restricted geographical distribution.

**Collection, preparation.** Little special apparatus is necessary for field collecting. The larger species may easily be hand-picked in the shallows; small forms may be washed from vegetation or sifted from bottom debris. A long-handled rake may be used for collecting mussels in water of moderate depths, and dredges are necessary for sampling in deep lakes.

If mussels are placed in warm water and heated to boiling, the valves will separate, the viscera can be easily removed, and the epidermis will not crack so easily. The judicious use of dilute oxalic or hydrochloric acid and a toothbrush are valuable for removing surface incrustations and restoring the natural brilliance of the nacre. After treatment with acid, shells should be rinsed thoroughly in clear water. The epidermis of study specimens should be varnished or greased lightly with vaseline before the two valves are tied together. The Sphaeriidae should be placed in 40 per cent alcohol for a day or two, the viscera should then be removed, and the shell wrapped in tissue paper to prevent gaping while they are allowed to dry thoroughly. Brief directions for arranging specimens in trays and drawers are contained in Ward and Whipple (1918).

Preservation for the study of soft parts should be in 70 or 80 per cent alcohol, not formaldehyde.

**Taxonomy.** Except for *Margaritifera* and a few representatives of marine families which have invaded brackish waters and coastal regions of rivers, the fresh-water bivalves of the United States are all included in the Unionidae and Sphaeriidae. In the former family, the subfamilies and the great majority of genera and species are well established, although some forms have a lengthy synonymy dating back a century. Many species have several subspecific designations, some of which are useful ecologically. According to Baker (1928), for example, *Strophitus rugosus* (Swainson) occurs in large and medium rivers, *S. rugosus pavonius* (Lea) is a creek form, *S. rugosus pepinensis* Baker a river-lake form, *S. rugosus winnebagoensis* Baker a small river-lake form, and *S. rugosus lacustris* Baker a small lake form. *Quadrula quadrula* (Raf.) is even more variable.

To the pearl fisherman and button industry, mussels are known by highly descriptive vernacular names. Some of these are niggerhead, pimple back, pig toe, washboard, pocketbook, elephant's ear, slop bucket, spectacle case, and paper shells.

The nomenclature of the Sphaeriidae is in a greatly confused state. The late V. Sterki was the outstanding recent authority on the group and he described scores of species and identified specimens sent to him by conchologists all over the country. He appreciated and emphasized the fact that many species are highly variable, as many as 46 forms having been described

for one species. Other workers, however, have felt that the distinctions which he drew between species and varieties were too insignificant and inconstant, and that there are actually far fewer American species than Sterki listed. The situation is now even more complicated and unfortunate because in many instances present investigators find that his published descriptions are too sketchy and generalized to be of any real use. In a recent critical paper, Brooks and Herrington (1944) contend that the whole family should be carefully restudied with a more liberal point of view. They are in agreement with some older American and European workers in their belief that *Musculium* and *Sphaerium* cannot be clearly separated on the basis of conchological characters, and that the former is in reality a division of the latter.

## KEY TO FAMILIES AND GENERA OF PELECYPODA

1. Ligament external..............................................2
   Ligament internal; in brackish waters.............................7
2. Shell with true cardinal teeth (Figs. 439B, 456)......................4
   Shell with well-developed pseudocardinal teeth, occasionally vestigial or absent (Figs. 439A, 440B, 441).........................................3
3. Shell elongated, laterally compressed (Fig. 439A); gills either without distinct interlamellar septa, or, if present, then oblique to the gill filaments; epidermis blackish; 80 to 175 mm. long; lotic.....MARGARITANIDAE, **Margaritifera** *M. margaritifera* L. in the north Atlantic and western states; *M. hembeli* Conrad in Ala. and La.; *M. monodonta* (Say) * in rivers of Mississippi Valley from Ohio to Nebr. and south to Tenn.
   Shell subcircular, oval, subtriangular, or elongated; gills with distinct interlamellar septa, parallel to gill filaments; lotic and lentic; pearly mussels or naiads.
   UNIONIDAE, 8
4. Hinge with anterior and posterior lateral teeth (Fig. 456)...................5
   Hinge without lateral teeth; shell round and thin; 10 to 15 mm. long; a single species in brackish waters of Fla..CYRENELLIDAE, **Cyrenella floridana** Dall
5. Shell thin and fragile, length ranging from about 2 to 20 mm. but rarely more than 10 mm.; concentric growth rings not prominent; pallial line simple; widely distributed and common; fingernail clams, seed shells......SPHAERIIDAE, **48**
   Shell heavy and more than 10 mm. long, with prominent concentric growth rings (Fig. 439B); pallial line sinuate........................CYRENIDAE, **6**
6. More than 25 mm. long (Fig. 439B); a single species in streams and brackish waters near the coast from S. C. to Texas....**Polymesoda caroliniana** (Bosc)
   More than 10 mm. long; introduced from Asia and now occasionally found in sloughs and rivers of Wash., Ore., and Calif....**Corbicula fluminea** (O. F. M.)

---

* This species is sometimes placed in a separate genus, *Cumberlandia*.

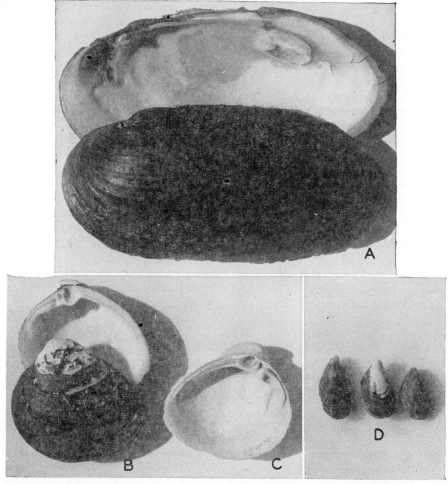

FIG. 439.—Representative Pelecypoda. A, *Margaritifera margaritifera* L., ×0.7; B, *Polymesoda caroliniana* (Bosc), ×0.8; C, *Rangia cuneata* Gray, ×0.8; D, *Mytilopsis leucophaeta* Conrad, ×1.4.

7. Hinge with cardinal and lateral teeth; 25 to 70 mm. long (Fig. 439C); shell thick; Ala. to Texas; a single species........MACTRIDAE, **Rangia cuneata** Gray
   Hinge without distinct teeth; shell mytiliform; with a byssus; 10 to 15 mm. long (Fig. 439D); Md. to Fla.; a single species.
   DREISSENIIDAE, **Mytilopsis leucopheata** Conrad

8. Water tubes simple in gravid female; hinge complete.....................9
   Water tubes in gravid female divided into three longitudinal tubes, of which only the center one is used as an ovisac; hinge rarely complete; length ranging from 25 to 200 mm....................................ANODONTINAE, **10**

9. Marsupium formed of all four gills or of entire outer gills; edge of gravid marsupium always sharp; male and female shells usually similar; 40 to 250 mm. long...............................................UNIONINAE, **17**
   Marsupium nearly always confined to the posterior part of the outer gills (Fig. 437); edge of gravid marsupium distended and bulging; male and female shells usually different; 30 to 150 mm. long..............LAMPSILINAE, **31**

**10.** Beak sculpture concentric (Fig. 440C)....................................11
  Beak sculpture double-looped..........................................13
**11.** Beak sculpture fine; shell thin and smooth (Fig. 440A); streams and wave-swept
  shores; several species in Great Lakes, St. Lawrence, and Mississippi drainages.
  **Anodontoides**
  Beak sculpture coarse (Fig. 440C)....................................12

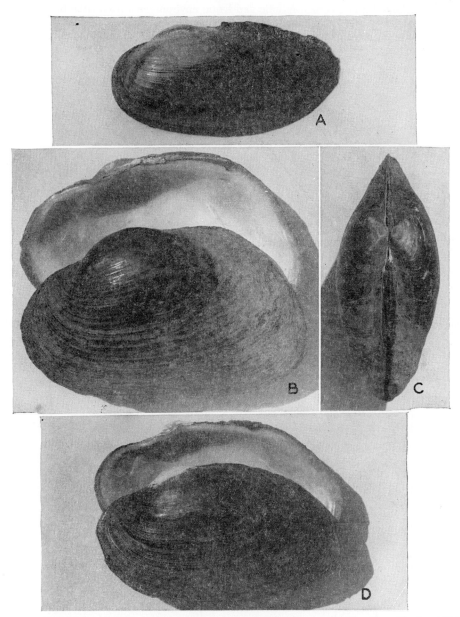

Fig. 440.—Representative Anodontinae.  A, *Anodontoides*,  ×0.9;  B, *Alasmidonta*,  ×0.9;
C, *Alasmidonta*, dorsal, ×0.7;  D, *Strophitus*, ×0.9.

12. Shell rhomboid, with a prominent posterior ridge (Fig. 440B); sand and mud
      bottoms of rivers; generally distributed from the Mississippi Valley eastward;
      about ten species.....................................**Alasmidonta**
    Shell elliptical to rhomboid, with a low posterior ridge (Fig. 440D); common from
      the Mississippi R. to the Atlantic coast but extending as far west as Colo. and
      Texas; about eight species.................................**Strophitus**
13. Hinge wholly edentulous (Fig. 441A); shell thin and highly variable; widely dis-
      tributed and common in lotic and lentic environments from Atlantic to Pacific
      coasts; paper shells; about ten species.......................**Anodonta**
    Hinge teeth more or less developed; shell thick or thin....................**14**

Fig. 441.—Representative Anodontinae. A, *Anodonta*, ×0.7; B, *Arcidens confragosus* (Say),
×0.7.

Fig. 442.—Representative Anodontinae. A, *Lasmigona*, ×0.7; B, *Simpsoniconcha ambigua* (Say), ×1.7.

14. Beak sculpture tubercular (Fig. 441B); surface of shell tubercular or folded; shell thick.................................................................15
    Beak sculpture not tubercular (Fig. 442); surface of shell smooth except on posterior slope; shell thick or thin...................................16
15. Beak sculpture strong and continuous with tubercular surface sculpture (Fig. 441B); common in streams and rivers of the Ohio and Mississippi drainage systems, and southwest to Texas; a single species.**Arcidens confragosus** (Say)
    Beak sculpture poorly developed and not continuous with surface sculpture; a single species in rivers of Ark...............**Arkansia wheeleri** O. and W.
16. Pseudocardinals fully developed; shell elliptic-rhomboid, thin to thick, and corrugated or smooth on posterior slope (Fig. 442A); more than 60 mm. long; generally distributed in rivers and streams east of the Mississippi R., and extending as far west as Nebr.; about eight species.............**Lasmigona**
    With a single pseudocardinal on each valve; shell thin, elongate-elliptical, rounded in front and behind, and usually less than 60 mm. long (Fig. 442B); characteristically under stones in running water; occurring from Mich. to Iowa in the north and from Tenn. to Ark. in the south; a single species.
                                                      **Simpsoniconcha ambigua** (Say)
17. All four gills serving as marsupia.......................................18
    Outer gills only serving as marsupia...................................25

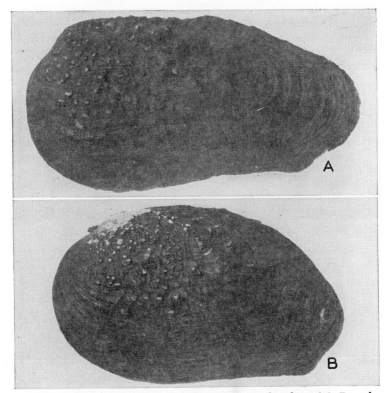

FIG. 443.—*Tritogonia verrucosa* (Barnes) (Unioninae). A, female, ×0.6; B, male, ×0.6.

18. Male and female shells alike............................................**19**
    Male and female shells different (Fig. 443); shell solid and rhomboid; a single
        species in streams and rivers of Mississippi and Alabama drainages.
                                                    **Tritogonia verrucosa** (Barnes)
19. Hinge with perfect pseudocardinals and laterals...........................**20**
    Hinge teeth rudimentary or lacking; shell smooth, elongated, and usually with a
        high, sharp, posterior ridge (Fig. 444A); a single species in west coast states.
                                                    **Gonidea angulata** (Lea)
20. Surface of shell smooth; shell heavy and round, rhomboid, triangular, or short ellip-
        tical (Fig. 444B); N. Y. to Minn. and southward; about 20 species. .**Fusconaia**
    Surface of shell not smooth...........................................**21**
21. Surface of shell pustulose; shell heavy and triangular, quadrate, rounded, or
        rhomboid..........................................................**22**
    Surface of shell plicate (Figs. 445B, 446)..............................**23**
22. With prominent projecting beaks; distributed throughout the Mississippi drainage
        system and as far west as Minn. and Texas; about 25 species (Fig. 445A).
                                                                      **Quadrula**
    Beaks projecting only slightly; Gulf drainages from the Suwanee to the Escambia
        rivers; several species.......................................**Quincuncina**
23. Beaks sculptured with coarse concentric or somewhat double-looped ridges; shell
        moderately large and heavy.........................................**24**
    Beaks sculptured with strong zigzag lines; shell elongate-quadrate, very heavy, and
        large; 80 to 250 mm. long (Fig. 445B); in large, deep rivers; Mississippi sys-
        tem generally and in large rivers from Ala. to Texas; a single species.
                                                    **Megalonaias gigantea** (Barnes)

24. With beak sculpture extending upon the shell; streams flowing into Gulf of Mexico from Ala. to eastern Texas, and northward in the Mississippi system to Tenn; a single species...........................**Plectomerus trapezoides** Lea
    With beak sculpture not extending upon the shell (Fig. 446A); small to large rivers of the Mississippi system generally; five species............**Amblema**
25. Surface of shell tuberculous...........................................26
    Surface of shell smooth or spiny.......................................27
26. Shell rounded (Fig. 446B); nacre deep purple; a single species in rivers of Mississippi drainage system.......................**Cyclonaias tuberculata** Raf.
    Shell irregularly oval (Fig. 447A); nacre white or tinged with pink; Ohio, Cumberland, and Tennessee river systems, and extending as far west as Minn. and Mo.; three species......................................**Plethobasus**

Fig. 444.—Representative Unioninae. A, *Gonidea angulata* Lea, ×0.9; B, *Fusconaia*, ×0.8.

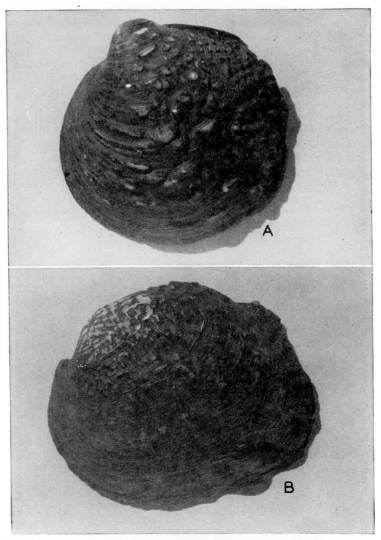

Fig. 445.—Representative Unioninae. A, *Quadrula*, ×0.9; B, *Megalonaias gigantea* Barnes, ×0.9.

**27.** Hinge with perfect pseudocardinals and laterals..........................28
Hinge teeth imperfect and vestigial; shell elongated, rather thin, and smooth; one rare species in Ohio, Cumberland, and Tennessee river systems.

**Lastena lata** (Raf.)

**28.** Shell short, rounded, quadrate, or oblique...............................29
Shell usually elongated and straight....................................30

**29.** Shell subquadrate or subtrapezoidal; beak slightly elevated (Fig. 447B); southeastern states; several species............................**Lexingtonia**
Shell solid, triangular to rhomboid, usually with a prominent beak (Fig. 448A); many species, most of which are in the southeastern states, but a few in the Ohio and Mississippi drainages..............................**Pleurobema**

**30.** Shell elongated, rhomboid, or oval, and more or less angled posteriorly (Fig. 448B); beak sculpture running parallel with the growth lines; many species in a wide variety of lotic and lentic habitats throughout the eastern half of the U. S.

Elliptio

Shell trapezoidal (Fig. 449A); beak sculpture concentric; Ohio and Ind. south to Gulf coast; several species..............................**Uniomerus**

**31.** Male and female shells alike...........................................32

Male and female shells different (Fig. 452)...............................35

**32.** Shell elongate-triangular (Fig. 449B); lateral teeth thickened; Mich. south to Ala., La., and Ark.; about seven species......................**Ptychobranchus**

Shell rounded-triangular or oval; lateral teeth not thickened................33

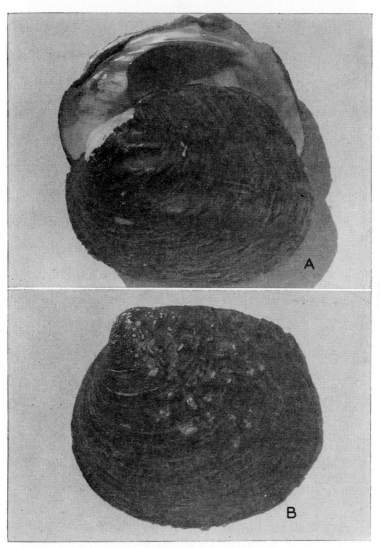

Fig. 446.—Representative Unioninae. A, *Amblema*, ×0.8; B, *Cyclonaias tuberculata* Raf., ×1.

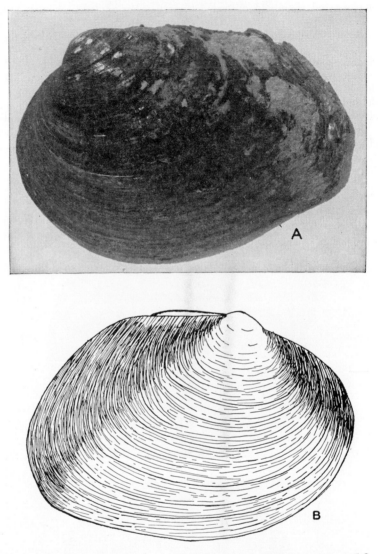

Fig. 447.—Representative Unioninae. A, *Plethobasus*, ×1; B, *Lexingtonia*, ×1.8.

33. Shell oval, with a single row of large tubercles (Fig. 449C); a single species in large rivers of eastern half of U. S.................**Obliquaria reflexa** Raf.
    Shell rounded-triangular, with nodulously wrinkled or lachrymose sculpture....**34**
34. Sculpture of shell nodular, radiately wrinkled, or lachrymose; beak cavities shallow (Fig. 449D); one species in the Ohio, Cumberland, and Tennessee river systems; another from Mo. to Okla.........................**Cyprogenia**
    With a series of humps running from the beaks to the central part of the base of the shell, which is otherwise sculptured by irregular ridges; beak cavities deep and compressed; a single species in the Tennessee and Cumberland river systems.......................................**Dromus dromas** Lea

35. Female shell more or less expanded in the post-basal region (Fig. 452B); shell
    large...................................................................36
    Female shell only slightly swollen just behind the middle of the base; rather small
    and elongated (Fig. 449E); several species in Ala., Tenn., Ga., and Fla.
                                                                **Medionidus**
36. Dorsal margin winged (Fig. 450); shell rather thin; in rivers and lakes........37
    Dorsal margin not winged.................................................38
37. Pseudocardinals heavy, thick, and broadly triangular; St. Lawrence and Mississippi
    drainage systems south to Ala. and Texas; about seven species (Fig. 450A).
                                                                **Proptera**
    Pseudocardinals thin and lamellar; generally distributed in the eastern half of the
    U. S.; several species (Fig. 450B).........................**Leptodea**
38. Pseudocardinals complete and well developed..............................39
    Pseudocardinals divided into irregular radiating laminae; a single species in slow
    streams from Fla. to Texas and north to Ark....**Glebula rotundata** (Lamarck)

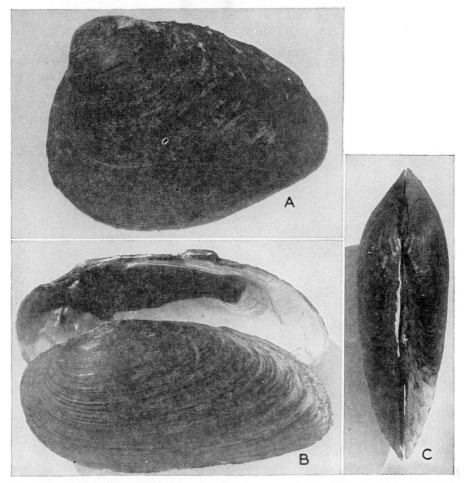

Fig. 448.–Representative Unioninae. A, *Pleurobema*, ×0.7; B, *Elliptio*, ×0.9; C, *Elliptio*,
dorsal view, ×0.8.

39.  Shell with a distinct posterior ridge (Figs. 451A, B); dorsal slope smooth......**40**
     Shell without a distinct posterior ridge, or, if distinct, then the dorsal slope radi-
     ately sculptured..................................................**41**
40.  Hinge heavy and strong; epidermis painted with scattered, broken rays (Fig.
     451A); 45 to 100 mm. long; a single species in large rivers; from Pa. west to
     Iowa and south to Ala., Kan., and Okla...........**Plagiola lineolata** (Raf.)
     Hinge not particularly heavy and strong; epidermis sometimes painted with a
     pattern of broken or arrow-marked rays (Fig. 451B); 25 to 60 mm. long;
     Mississippi drainage generally; several species..................**Truncilla**

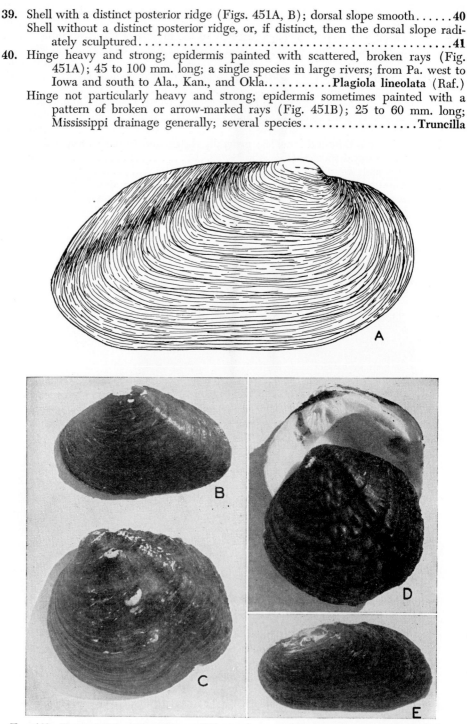

Fig. 449.—Representative Unioninae and Lampsilinae. A, *Uniomerus*, ×1.7; B, *Ptychobran-chus*, ×0.8; C, *Obliquaria reflexa* Raf., ×0.8; D, *Cyprogenia*, ×1; E, female *Medionidus*, ×1.3.

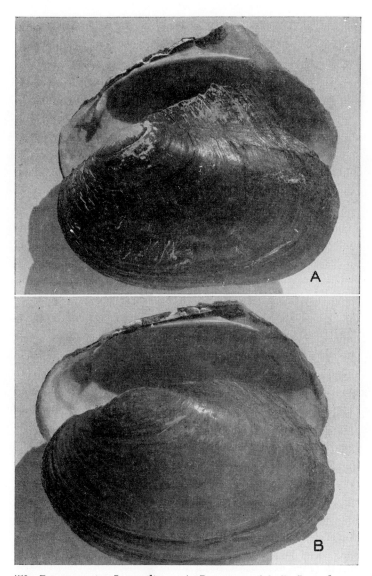

Fig. 450.—Representative Lampsilinae. A, *Proptera*, ×0.9; B, *Leptodea*, ×0.7.

41. Marsupial expansion of female shell of the same texture as the rest of the shell. .42
   Marsupial expansion of the female shell of different texture than the rest of the
      shell, usually radiately sculptured (Fig. 451C); about 25 species in the rivers
      of the eastern half of the U. S..............................................**Dysnomia**
42. Inner edge of mantle in front of branchial opening differentiated into papillae or
      flaps in female....................................................................43
   Inner edge of mantle in front of branchial opening without papillae or flaps in
      female; eastern half of U. S..................................................47

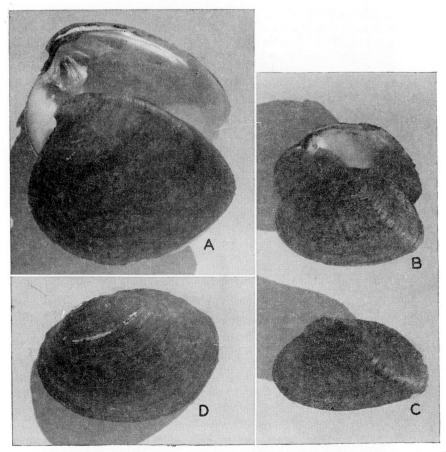

Fig. 451.—Representative Lampsilinae. A, *Plagiola lineolata* (Raf.), ×0.9; B, *Truncilla*, ×1; C, *Dysnomia*, ×1; D, *Carunculina*, ×1.2.

43. Shell smooth (Figs. 452; 453A, B); lentic and lotic; eastern half of U. S........44
    Shell strongly sculptured posteriorly; Tennessee, Elk, and Flint rivers; a single
        species.................................**Conradilla caelata** (Conrad)
44. Shell usually less than 50 mm. long (Fig. 451D); female with a well-developed
        caruncle on the inner edge of the mantle in front of the branchial opening;
        most abundant in the south; about five variable species.........**Carunculina**
    Usually more than 50 mm. long; caruncle absent.........................45
45. Inner edge of mantle in front of branchial opening in female distinctly papillate
        Figs. (455B, C) and sometimes with a ribbon-like flap; shell oval to oblong..46
    Inner edge of mantle in front of branchial opening in female not distinctly papil-
        late but always with a ribbon-like flap (Fig. 455A); shell oval to elliptical
        (Fig. 452); many common species.........................**Lampsilis**

46. Inner edge of mantle in front of branchial opening in female with a row of irregular large and small papillae (Fig. 455B); several small to medium-sized species (Fig. 453A)..........................................**Micromya**

Inner edge of mantle in front of branchial opening in female with a row of small, regular papillae (Fig. 455C); many large species (Fig. 453B)......**Ligumia**

47. Shell inflated, about as high as long (Fig. 453C); about six species......**Obovaria**

Shell subcompressed, clearly longer than high (Fig. 454); several species.
                                                                    **Actinonaias**

48. Shell nearly equipartite, beaks subcentral (Figs. 456B–E); with both anal and branchial siphons (Fig. 435)..........................................**49**

Shell inequipartite, anterior end longer; beaks subterminal (Fig. 456A); with anal siphon only; usually 2 to 6 mm. long, but a few species as long as 11 mm.; generally distributed in many types of habitats; very many species...**Pisidium**

Fig. 452.—*Lampsilis* (Lampsilinae). A, male, ×1; B, female, ×1.2.

FIG. 453.—Representative Lampsilinae. A, *Micromya*, ×0.9; B, *Ligumia*, ×0.8; C, *Obovaria*, ×0.9.

FIG. 454.—*Actinonaias* (Lampsilinae), ×0.8.

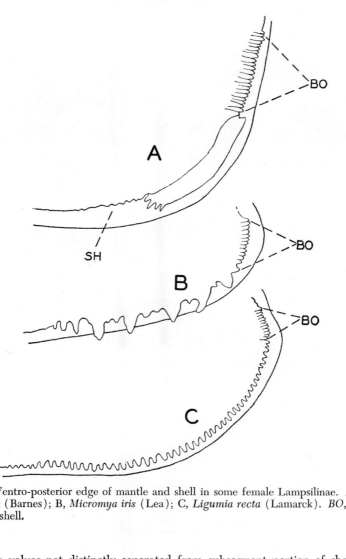

Fig. 455.—Ventro-posterior edge of mantle and shell in some female Lampsilinae. A, *Lampsilis ventricosa* (Barnes); B, *Micromya iris* (Lea); C, *Ligumia recta* (Lamarck). *BO*, branchial opening; *SH*, shell.

**49.** Nepionic valves not distinctly separated from subsequent portion of shell; * usually 7 to 15 mm. long, but a few species attaining 25 mm. . . . . . . . . . . . . . . . . **50**
Nepionic valves inflated, usually separated from subsequent portion of shell by a distinct sulcus * (Figs. 456B, C); cardinal teeth minute or obsolete; shell very thin and polished; usually 5 to 12 mm. long; generally distributed in many types of habitats; many species. . . . . . . . . . . . . . . . . . . . . . **Musculium**
**50.** Shell oval and relatively thick (Fig. 456E); with two small cardinal teeth in the left valve, one in the right (Figs. 456F, G); generally distributed in many types of habitats; many species. . . . . . . . . . . . . . . . . . . . . . . . . . . . . . . **Sphaerium**
Shell subrhomboidal, thin, and mottled (Fig. 456D); one feeble cardinal tooth in each valve; Fla., Ala., La., and Texas; several species. . . . . . . . . . . . . **Eupera**

\* Brooks and Herrington (1944), as well as some earlier American and European workers, believe that this is not a valid separation character and that *Musculium* is in reality a division of *Sphaerium*.

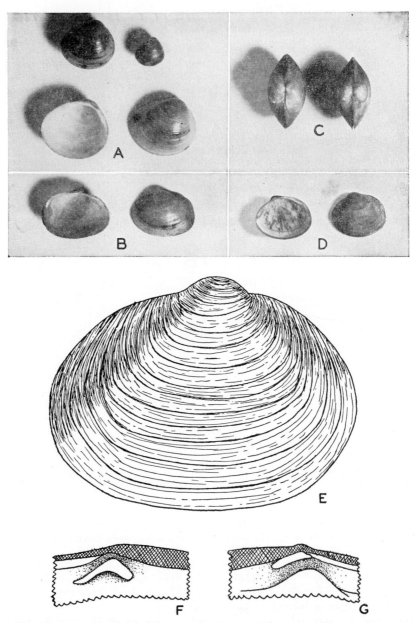

Fig. 456.—Representative Sphaeriidae. A, *Pisidium*, ×1.5; B, *Musculium*, ×1.5; C, *Musculium*, dorsal, ×1.5; D, *Eupera*, ×1.7; E, *Sphaerium simile* (Say), ×5; F, cardinal tooth of right valve of *S. simile*; G, cardinal teeth of left valve of *S. simile*. (F and G modified from Baker, 1928.)

# PELECYPODA REFERENCES

ALLEN, W. R. 1921. Studies of the biology of freshwater mussels. Experimental studies of the food relations of certain Unionidae. *Biol. Bull.* **40**:210–242.

AREY, L. B. 1932. The formation and structure of the glochidial cyst. *Ibid.* **62**:212–221.

BAKER, F. C. 1898. The Mollusca of the Chicago area. The Pelecypoda. *Bull. Nat. Hist. Surv. Chicago Acad. Sci.* **3**:1–130.

——. 1916. The relation of mollusks to fish in Oneida Lake. *N. Y. State Coll. Forestry, Tech. Publ.* **4**:1–366.

——. 1918. The productivity of invertebrate fish food on the bottom of Oneida Lake, with special reference to mollusks. *Ibid.* **9**:1–233.

——. 1918a. The relation of shellfish to fish in Oneida Lake, New York. *N. Y. State Coll. Forestry, Circ.* **21**:1–34.

——. 1928. *The fresh water Mollusca of Wisconsin. Part II. Pelecypoda.* 495 pp. Wis. Acad. Sci., Arts and Lett. Madison, Wisconsin.

BALL, G. H. 1922. Variation in fresh-water mussels. *Ecology* **3**:93–121.

BOYCOTT, A. E. 1936. The habitats of fresh-water Mollusca in Britain. *Jour. Animal Ecol.* **5**:116–186.

BROOKS, S. T., and H. B. HERRINGTON. 1944. The Sphaeriidae, a preliminary survey. *Nautilus* **57**:93–97.

BROWN, C. J. D., C. CLARK, and B. GLEISSNER. 1938. The size of certain naiades from western Lake Erie in relation to shoal exposure. *Amer. Midl. Nat.* **19**:682–701.

CHAMBERLIN, R. V., and D. T. JONES. 1929. A descriptive catalog of the Mollusca of Utah. *Bull. Univ. Utah* **19**:1–203.

CHURCHILL, E. P., JR., and S. I. LEWIS. 1924. Food and feeding in fresh-water mussels. *Bull. U. S. Bur. Fish.* **39**:437–471.

COKER, R. E. 1919. Freshwater mussels and mussel industries of the United States. *Ibid.* **36**:13–89.

COKER, R. E., A. F. SHIRA, H. W. CLARK, and A. D. HOWARD. 1921. Natural history and propagation of fresh-water mussels. Ibid. **37**:76–181.

FOSTER, T. D. 1932. Observations on the life history of a fingernail shell of the genus Sphaerium. *Jour. Morph.* **53**:473–497.

FRIERSON, L. S. 1927. *A classified and annotated check list of the North American Naiades.* 111 pp. Baylor Univ. Press. Waco, Texas.

GILMORE, R. J. 1917. Notes on reproduction and growth in certain viviparous mussels of the family Sphaeriidae. *Nautilus* **31**:16–30.

GOODRICH, C., and H. VAN DER SCHALIE. 1939. Aquatic mollusks of the Upper Peninsula of

Michigan. *Mus. Zool. Univ. Mich. Misc. Publ.* **43**:1–45.

——. 1944. A revision of the Mollusca of Indiana. *Amer. Midl. Nat.* **32**:257–326.

HENDERSON, J. 1924. Mollusca of Colorado, Utah, Montana, Idaho, and Wyoming. *Univ. Colo. Studies* **13**:65–223.

——. 1929. Non-marine Mollusca of Oregon and Washington. *Ibid.* **17**:47–190.

——. 1936. Mollusca of Colorado, Utah, Montana, Idaho, and Wyoming—supplement. *Ibid.* **23**:81–145.

HOWARD, A. D. 1922. Experiments in the culture of fresh-water mussels. *Bull. U. S. Bur. Fish.* **38**:63–89.

INGRAM, W. M. 1948. The larger freshwater clams of California, Oregon, and Washington. *Jour. Ent. and Zool.* **40**:72–92.

JONES, R. O. 1949. Propagation of fresh-water mussels. *Prog. Fish-Cult.* **12**:13–25.

KUNZ, G. F. 1898. The freshwater pearls and pearl fisheries of the United States. *Bull. U. S. Fish Comm.* **17**:373–426.

LEFEVRE, G., and W. C. CURTIS. 1912. Studies of the reproduction and artificial propagation of fresh-water mussels. *Bull. U. S. Bur. Fish.* **30**:105–201.

MONK, C. R. 1925. The anatomy and life-history of a fresh-water mollusk of the genus Sphaerium. *Jour. Morph. and Physiol.* **45**:473–501.

MORRISON, J. P. E. 1932. A report on the Mollusca of the northeastern Wisconsin lake district. *Trans. Wis. Acad. Sci., Arts and Lett.* **27**:359–396.

MURPHY, G. 1942. Relationship of the fresh-water mussel to trout in the Truckee River. *Calif. Fish and Game* **28**:89–102.

NELSON, T. C. 1918. On the origin, nature, and function of the crystalline style of lamellibranchs. *Jour. Morph.* **31**:53–111.

ORTMANN, A. E. 1912. Notes upon the families and genera of the Najades. *Ann. Carnegie Mus.* **8**:222–365.

——. 1919. A monograph of the Naiades of Pennsylvania. Part III. Systematic account of the genera and species. *Mem. Carnegie Mus.* **8**:1–384.

ORTMANN, A. E., and B. WALKER. 1922. On the nomenclature of certain North American naiades. *Mus. Zool. Univ. Mich. Occ. Pap.* **112**:1–75.

SCAMMON, R. E. 1906. The Unionidae of Kansas, Part I. *Kan. Univ. Sci. Bull.* **3**:277–373.

SIMPSON, C. T. 1914. *A descriptive catalogue of the naiades, or pearly freshwater mussels.* 1540 pp. Bryant Walker. Detroit, Mich.

STERKI, V. 1916. A preliminary catalog of the

North American Sphaeriidae. *Ann.. Carnegie Mus.* **10**:429–474.

——. 1916a. Some directions and suggestions for collecting the Sphaeriidae and aquatic gastropods. *Ibid.* 478–486.

STRECKER, J. K. 1931. The distribution of the naiades or pearly fresh-water mussels of Texas. *Baylor Univ. Spec. Bull.* **2**:3–71.

SURBER, T. 1912. Identification of the glochidia of freshwater mussels. *U. S. Bur. Fish. Document No.* **771**:1–10.

THIELE, J. 1935. *Handbuch der systematischen Weichtierkunde.* Zweiter Band. pp. 779–1154. Gustav Fischer, Jena.

TUCKER, M. E. 1927. Morphology of the glochidium and juvenile of the mussel Anodonta imbecillis. *Trans. Amer. Micros. Soc.* **46**:286–293.

UTTERBACK, W. I. 1915–1916. The naiades of Missouri. *Amer. Midl. Nat.* **4**:41–53, 97–152, 181–204, 244–273, 311–327, 339–354, 387–400, 432–464.

VAN CLEAVE, H. J. 1940. Ten years of observation on a fresh-water mussel population. *Ecology* **21**:363–370.

VAN DER SCHALIE, H. 1938. The naiad fauna of the Huron River, in southeastern Michigan. *Mus. Zool. Univ. Mich. Misc. Publ.* **40**:1–83.

——. 1940. Aestivation of fresh-water mussels. *Nautilus* **53**:137–138.

——. 1941. On collecting fresh water mussels. *Amer. Malacological Union Rept.,* pp. 9–14.

——. 1945. The value of mussel distribution in tracing stream confluence. *Pap. Mich. Acad. Sci., Arts and Lett.* **30**:355–373.

VAN DER SCHALIE, H., and A. 1950. The mussels of the Mississippi River. *Amer. Midl. Nat.* **44**:448–466.

WALKER, B. 1918. A synopsis of the classification of the freshwater Mollusca of North America, north of Mexico, and a catalogue of the more recently described species, with notes. *Mus. Zool. Univ. Mich. Misc. Publ.* **6**:1–213.

WILSON, C. B., and H. W. CLARK. 1914. The mussels of the Cumberland River and its tributaries. *Bur. Fish. Doc.* **781**:1–63.

# Appendix A

# FIELD AND LABORATORY APPARATUS

CERTAIN pieces of efficient and time-saving field and laboratory apparatus are frequently unfamiliar to the beginning investigator who is interested in collecting and working with fresh-water invertebrates. In addition, the advanced researcher is sometimes unaware of the advantages inherent in some kinds of equipment that could easily be adapted to his special needs. For these reasons it seems not inappropriate to include this brief pictorial and explanatory appendix. The following photographs are by no means a catalogue of field and laboratory apparatus used in working with fresh-water invertebrates. They represent merely a selection of items that the writer and his students have found especially useful. Most of them are mentioned in one or more places in the appropriate chapters of this volume. Some items are standard in many laboratories; others are seldom seen. Some are expensive; others are trivial in cost. Additional pieces of apparatus and information concerning their use may be found in Welch (1948), *Limnological Methods* and in Galtsoff *et al.* (1937), *Culture Methods for Invertebrate Animals.*

The size and design of containers used for bringing specimens back to the laboratory are of infinite variety and depend to a large extent on the size, nature, and numbers of organisms collected and transported. Regardless of the size of the container, however, it is best to fill it almost to the top with water or preserving fluid. If the container is only one-half or two-thirds full, the fluid and specimens will be sloshed about as they are carried by hand or on the floor of an automobile, and the softer and larger organisms are thereby often damaged or ruined.

If live specimens are being transported over long distances, the lid of the container should be removed at intervals or a portion of the water should be changed in order to renew the supply of oxygen.

Field collecting is a long, hard, and often tedious task. Especially for taxonomic work, the beginner should bear in mind that he must collect large, representative samples consisting of an abundance of individuals. *Specimens without complete accompanying data are worthless.* They should have attached notations of the precise location and habitats (understandable to any colleague), date, name of collector, and any special notes on associated organisms, weather, and water conditions.

With few exceptions, specimens once collected should be attended to promptly in the laboratory. Fluids should be changed, and specimens should be properly killed and fixed where necessary. Much hard-earned material is worthless if the tired collector postpones caring for it until the following day.

727

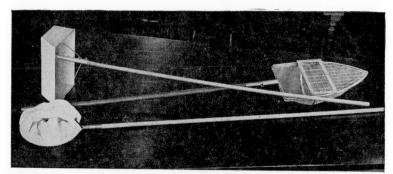

Fig. 457.—Field collecting apparatus. An ordinary long-handled dipnet is shown at the bottom of the photograph. A scraper net is shown in the upper left. It is used for scraping along the bottom of ponds and streams for aquatic insects and other macroscopic forms. The four sides are made of galvanized sheet metal, and the bottom is fine-meshed brass screening. The apron net (right) is perhaps the best single tool for collecting larger aquatic invertebrates. It is pointed at the front so that it may be pushed through vegetation and bottom debris. The wide-meshed cover allows animals to enter while keeping out coarser materials. The curved bottom is made out of heavy brass screening which permits fine debris to pass through. A final vigorous push of the apron net lands the catch toward the rear of the net where it may be removed through a hinged door. Materials should be sorted in a white enameled pan.

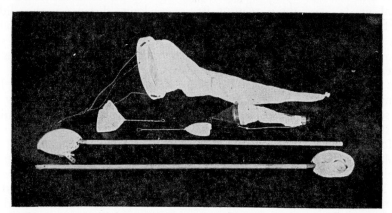

Fig. 458.—Various types of collecting nets. Two "pond-life dipnets" with three-foot handles are shown at the bottom of the photograph. One has a very fine weave suitable for Protozoa (173 meshes to the inch) and a detachable glass vial at its tip; the other has a coarse weave (38 meshes to the inch). A standard plankton townet is shown at the top. The mouth has a diameter of ten inches and the bag is made of fine (number 20) bolting silk (173 meshes to the inch). In the left center are two small aquarium nets. These are useful for collecting in the shallows and in puddles; they are also handy for sorting and washing specimens. A Birge cone net is shown at right center. The conical front end is made from coarse brass screening, and the rear end consists of a shallow cup with a screw cap at the bottom. The two are connected with a tapered bolting silk net. If properly weighted, the cone net may be towed behind a boat. It may also be thrown from shore at the end of a long line. The coarse screen keeps out vegetation and debris but allows small organisms to enter. When the net is retrieved it should be held upright so that the organisms are concentrated in the cup. The screw cap is then carefully removed and the contents emptied into a collecting vial or jar.

Fig. 459.—Juday plankton trap. This quantitative device has an over-all width of about 19 inches and takes a ten-liter water sample. As shown above, the trap is set to be released. On the right side is a brass boxlike portion without top or bottom. When the sampler is lowered to the desired depth a brass weight is allowed to slide down the line. It trips the catch, and a spring draws the top and bottom of the sampler from the left to the right side, thereby enclosing the water sample. The sampler is then hauled up to the surface where the ten liters of water drain out through the fine bolting silk net, and all of the organisms are concentrated in a few ml. of water in a brass and silk "bucket" at the bottom of the net. The bucket is removable, and the contained organisms can be quickly transferred to a vial of preservative. Although the Juday plankton trap is a standard instrument for quantitative zooplankton sampling, the meshes of the net do not retain certain algae.

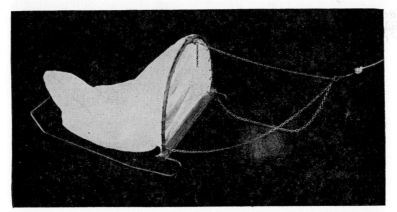

Fig. 460.—Dredge net. This is a strong, light-weight net for bottom collecting from a boat. It consists of a D-shaped frame mounted on runners about 20 inches long. The net has a relatively coarse mesh. Appropriate weights attached to the line several feet in front of the net will permit effective use as it is towed along in deep water. When properly used, the dredge net will take organisms living on the surface of the substrate and just above the surface.

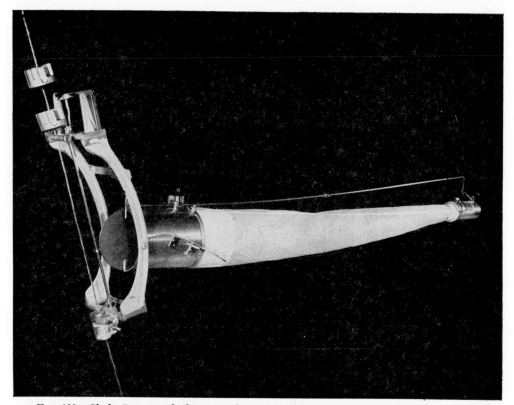

Fɪɢ. 461.—Clarke-Bumpus plankton sampler. This instrument is unexcelled for gross quantitative zooplankton sampling. It is essentially a closing plankton net with a flow meter to indicate the total amount of water passing through the mouth of the net. It is towed at the desired depth from a cable held as nearly vertical as possible by means of a weight attached to the lower end. A net of any desired length and mesh may be attached to the brass collar. (Photo courtesy of G. L. Clarke.)

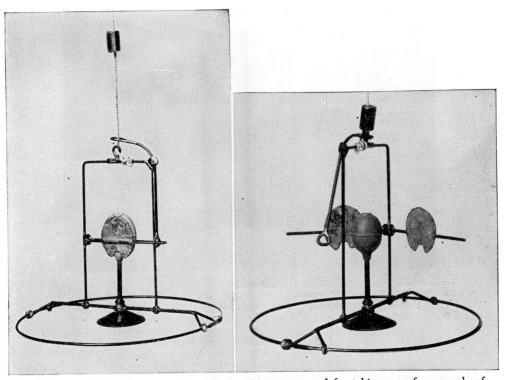

FIG. 462.—Mud-sucker. A semiquantitative instrument used for taking a surface sample of mud and its contained microorganisms in deep water. The photograph on the left shows the mud-sucker as it is lowered to take a sample. When it touches the bottom a brass weight is allowed to slide down the line and trip the catch. The photograph on the right shows the sampler after being tripped. Mud is sucked up into the rubber bulb. (Photo courtesy of George M. Moore.)

FIG. 463.—Bottom sampling materials. The Peterson dredge is a heavy instrument which is especially useful for taking quantitative bottom samples from sand and gravel substrates. Accessory cast iron weights can be attached to make the dredge as heavy as 60 pounds. The dredge covers about one thirteenth of a square meter of bottom. Samples should be mixed and rinsed several times with portions of water in a large metal pan, the supernatant being quickly poured through a sieve to catch the organisms. The piece of brass screening with two wooden handles shown on the left is useful for collecting stream bottom organisms. It should be held obliquely and just downstream from the point where silt, debris, pebbles, and rubble are dislodged and worked over with the fingers or a short stick.

Fig. 464.—Ekman dredge and sieve. This dredge is used for taking quantitative samples from soft, muddy bottoms; it is useless for sand, gravel, rock, and debris substrates. The photograph shows the jaws set for release; they are closed by sending a brass messenger down the taut line to trip the spring catch. This model takes a sample 9 inches square, but a smaller model takes a sample 6 inches square. The depth to which the sampler sinks into the substrate depends partially on the speed with which it is allowed to strike bottom. The brass screen across the top prevents bottom animals from being lost when the sampler sinks into the substrate. If the mud sample is diluted with quantities of water as it is washed through the sieve, the organisms can be separated out relatively quickly.

Fig. 465.—Water "telescope," or viewing box. This device is made of galvanized sheet metal and has the shape of a truncated pyramid. The upper end is open, but the lower end is covered with a piece of heavy glass which is carefully cemented in place so that the box is watertight. The underwater view through this box is surprisingly clear and revealing. It is useful for observing the activities of clams, snails, and crayfish, as well as for locating lost instruments In the photograph it is being used at the edge of a dam, but it is equally advantageous in deeper water from the side or stern of a boat.

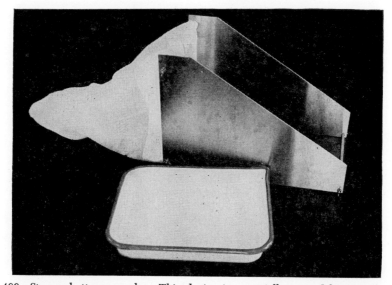

Fig. 466.—Stream bottom sampler. This device is essentially a modification of the well-known square-foot sampler, and the area within the brass or stainless steel frame covers 25 by 40 cm. (one-tenth of a square meter). The mouth of this quantitative sampler is faced upstream so that the conical net bellies downstream. In swift currents the sampler must be held down firmly to prevent shifting. When the gravel, debris, rubble, sand, or silt within the frame are worked over thoroughly with the fingers, the organisms are dislodged and float back with the current into the net. They may then be emptied into a collecting jar or enameled pan for sorting. The model shown in the photograph is fastened together with six wingnuts so that it may be easily disassembled and carried in a more compact manner. The net has a light canvas collar and is made from number OOOXX bolting silk

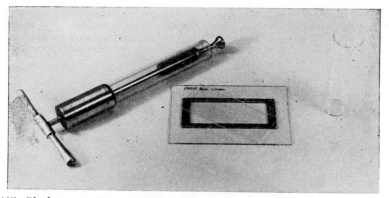

Fig. 467.—Plankton counting materials. An ordinary pipette or Hensen-Stempel pipette (left) is used for placing exactly 1 ml. of a plankton sample in the shallow Sedgwick-Rafter counting cell (center), and the cell is then carefully covered with a large cover slip. The cell consists simply of a thin brass or plastic frame cemented to an extra large glass slide. Since the depth of the chamber plus the cover slip thickness is only about 1.5 mm., an 8 mm. microscope objective can be used for identifying and counting the organisms in the cell.

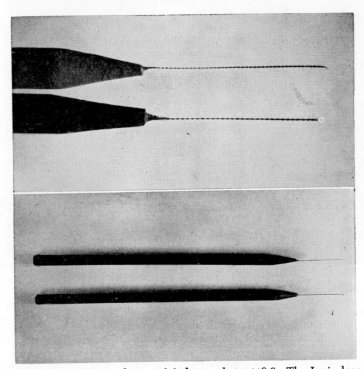

Fig. 468.—Irwin loops. Upper photo, ×2.6; lower photo, ×0.6. The Irwin loop is a highly successful but simple device for picking up and transferring micrometazoans from one fluid to another while working with dissecting binoculars. It consists of a loop at the end of a double strand of fine, twisted, stainless steel wire, the whole being mounted in a slender wooden handle. The loop owes its special usefulness to the fact that it is small, flattened, and bent at an angle of 30 degrees. By sliding the loop under a specimen, the latter may be easily lifted up and through the surface film, usually on the first trial. It is much more efficient than a bristle or fine pipette. Several sizes are available in which the transverse inside diameter of the loop ranges from about 0.3 to 0.8 mm.

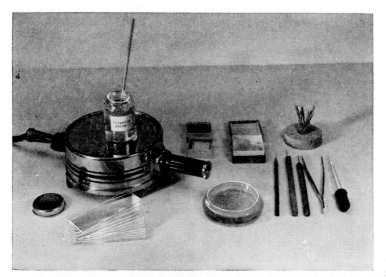

FIG. 469.—Materials used in making glycerin jelly mounts of small invertebrates. Included are: electric hot plate, small jar of glycerin jelly, slide labels, cover slips, mounted bristles and "minuten nadeln" (upper right), slides, Syracuse watch glass containing specimens, Irwin loop, needles, forceps, and pipette. (See p. 738 for method of making mounts.)

FIG. 470.—Materials for sealing slide mounts. Shown are: turntable, Murrayite cement, and camel's hair brush. In general, only round cover slips should be used with glycerin, glycerin jelly, CMC-10, and similar mounting media. The slide should first be centered on the turntable so that the center of the cover slip is over the center of the turntable. Then the wheel is given a moderate spin, and while it is in motion a partial brushful of Murrayite should be held at the edge of the cover slip. In this way the edge of the cover slip is neatly and effectively sealed to the slide with an airtight seal. If too much Murrayite is applied or if the wheel is turned too rapidly, centrifugal force will cause the cement to flow out over the edge of the slide. A needle thrust through the handle of the camel's hair brush will fit across the top of the Murrayite jar so that the brush will not be immersed too deeply.

# Appendix B

## REAGENTS AND SOLUTIONS

For the most part, this brief appendix lists only those reagents and solutions that are mentioned more than once in the text portion of this volume. Information concerning additional reagents and procedures, including fixation, imbedding, sectioning, staining, etc., can be obtained by consulting any of the several standard microtechnique handbooks.

In the writer's laboratory all transfers of small specimens from one solution to another are performed in the same vial. When solutions are added they are squirted into the vial with a pipette so that there is thorough mixing; when solutions are removed they are sucked up with a pipette after the specimens have all settled to the bottom of the vial. Although two or three such portions are usually necessary to effect a complete change of solutions in a vial, the small additional time is well compensated for by the convenience and compactness of the method. Furthermore, there is little danger of drying, spilling, or loss of specimens.

The following list includes a variety of anesthetics. In general, such solutions should be slowly and gradually added to the water containing the specimens. Experience will determine proper amounts.

**Acetic acid.** Usually supplied as glacial acetic acid which is 99.5 per cent $CH_3COOH$. Two to 10 parts of glacial acetic acid are often added to 100 parts saturated mercuric chloride as a fixative.

**Alcohol.** Wherever "alcohol" is indicated in this manual, ethyl alcohol, or $C_2H_5OH$, is meant. It is used in varying concentrations as a fixative and preservative. Alcohol is usually supplied commercially in about 95 per cent concentration (190 proof). All alcohol dilutions are made by measuring out the number of ml. of 95 per cent alcohol equivalent to the percentage of alcohol desired and diluting to 95 ml. with water. For example, to make a 60 per cent solution, add 35 ml. water to 60 ml. of 95 per cent alcohol. Absolute (essentially 100 per cent) alcohol is expensive to buy but may be easily made in the laboratory by dehydrating 95 per cent alcohol with anhydrous copper sulphate. Crystals of copper (cupric) sulphate should first be heated in an evaporating dish until the water of crystallization is driven off and a white powder remains. Place some of this powder in a bottle and add 95 per cent alcohol. The water in the alcohol immediately unites with the copper sulphate, turning it blue. Add more anhydrous copper sulphate until it no longer turns blue. Then quickly filter the alcohol into a dry bottle and stopper with a tight cork or ground glass stopper.

**Alum cochineal.** An excellent wholemount stain for many small invertebrates. Add 6 g. potassium alum and 6 g. powdered cochineal to 90 ml. distilled water and boil for 30 minutes. Allow the fluid to settle, decant the supernatant, add a little water, and boil until about 90 ml. of solution remains. Filter when cool and add 0.5 g. thymol to inhibit molds. Depending on size and density of specimens, stain for 4 to 30 hours. After staining, wash specimens in several changes of water for 15 to 30 minutes to extract the alum. The material is then dehydrated and mounted in balsam, permount, or some similar nonaqueous material.

**Balsam** (Canada balsam). A general permanent mounting medium for dehydrated whole specimens or microtome sections. It is easiest to buy a thick solution and dilute with xylol (xylene) to the proper consistency. Add a marble chip to keep the solution neutral.

**Benzamine hydrochloride, benzamine lactate.** Anesthetics for certain small metazoans; usually used in 2 per cent solutions.

**Bismarck brown.** An intra-vitam stain useful for protozoans. Boil 1 g. of the stain in 100 ml. water and filter.

**Borax carmine.** This is a most useful stain for whole mounts of small metazoans. Boil 2 g. carmine in 100 ml. of 4 per cent borax until dissolved. Then add 100 ml. of 70 per cent alcohol; filter after 24 hours. Stain objects for 10 hours to several days, depending on size and density. Transfer to 70 per cent acid alcohol and keep there until the stain no longer forms clouds. Wash the specimens in neutral alcohol.

**Bouin's fluid.** A general fixative consisting of 75 ml. saturated aqueous picric acid, 25 ml. formalin, and 5 ml. glacial acetic acid. The normal fixing time is 2 to 16 hours, but tissues are not harmed if left in the fluid up to several weeks.

**Butyn, butyn sulphate.** Anesthetics for certain small metazoans; usually used in a 0.1 to 2 per cent solution.

**Chloral hydrate.** A general anesthetic for small metazoans. Make up as a 10 per cent solution.

**Chloretone.** A common anesthetic usually used in 0.1 to 0.6 per cent solution.

**Chloroform.** Occasionally used as a saturated aqueous solution (1.0 per cent) for anesthetizing small metazoans. Chloroform vapors are sometimes useful if the organisms are concentrated in a small amount of water under a bell jar beside a small beaker of chloroform.

**Chloroplatinic acid.** This compound, $H_2PtCl_6 \cdot 6H_2O$, is especially valuable to preserve and keep osmic acid solutions stable. A gram should be added to every 100 ml. of osmic acid solution.

**Clorox.** A commercial caustic useful for isolating small sclerotized structures from musculature and connective tissues, and especially for isolating trophi of rotifers. Usually diluted 1 to 10 with water.

**CMC–10 (Nonresinous mounting medium).** This is a new, permanent mounting material useful for whole mounts of aquatic insects, crustaceans, and possibly certain other small metazoans. It is available in a thick syrupy solution in which specimens may be mounted directly and satisfactorily from water, formalin preservative solutions, alcohols, and glycerin. It dries hard (but slowly) and has the additional advantage of being a clearing agent. For real permanency, however, cover slips should be ringed with Murrayite or some similar cement after the mounts have dried for several days. CMC–10 may be thinned with water. Preliminary tests indicate that it is just as permanent as balsam, and if further tests are corroborated, CMC–10 will indeed be an important contribution to biological technique and slide making. The product is marketed by the General Biological Supply House, Chicago, Ill.

**Cocaine, Novocain.** Excellent anesthetics for small metazoans but extremely difficult to obtain because of narcotics regulations. Best used as a 5 per cent solution in 95 per cent alcohol or water.

**Eosin.** General purpose cytoplasmic stain for small metazoans. Usually used as a 0.5 per cent solution in 95 per cent alcohol or water.

**Euparal.** A permanent slide mounting medium. Specimens may be transferred directly from 95 per cent alcohol into euparal.

**FAA (formalin–aceto–alcohol).** A general purpose fixative in which material may be kept for several days without harm. Numerous modifications of this fixative are used; a typical one consists of 40 ml. distilled water, 2 ml. glacial acetic acid, 50 ml. of 95 per cent alcohol, and 10 ml. formalin.

**Formalin.** A common and cheap preservative consisting of a 37 to 40 per cent aqueous solution of formaldehyde, $H_2CO$. Depending on the nature of the preserved material, 2 to 6 per cent solutions of formalin (*not* 2 to 6 per cent formaldehyde) are usually used. Commercial formalin is slightly acid and may be neutralized by maintaining a slight deposit of magnesium carbonate in the bottom of the reagent bottle. When formalin dries it forms a whitish irreversible polymer.

**Fuchsin (basic).** A nuclear stain sometimes useful in temporary whole mounts of micrometazoans. Make up a 0.5 per cent aqueous solution.

**Gilson's fluid.** (See p. 129.)

**Glycerin.** An excellent medium for temporary and permanent mounts for many kinds of micrometazoans. Directions for making the latter are given on pages 185–186. Glycerin is miscible with water and alcohol at all concentrations and has the advantage of being a slight clearing agent. Because glycerin is nondrying, the writer regularly adds about 5 per cent of it to stored vials of alcoholic and formalin specimens. If such vials should break, or the water and alcohol should dry, the specimens are still available in good condition. Specimens to be used in concentrated glycerin should first be placed in a 5 to 20 per cent solution of glycerin in 50 to 95 per cent alcohol. If the container is uncovered (but protected from dust), the alcohol and water evaporate in a few days, leaving the specimens in pure glycerin.

**Glycerin jelly.** A valuable permanent mounting medium which is solid at ordinary temperatures. Soak 1.5 g. clean gelatin overnight in 100 ml. water, then dissolve with gentle heat. Add half its volume of clean glycerin and 0.5 g. carbolic acid. Warm *gently* and stir for 10 minutes until homogeneous. Store in a small wide-mouth bottle with a screw cap. Specimens to be mounted in glycerin jelly should first be in at least 50 per cent glycerin. Melt the glycerin jelly gently in warm water or on a hot plate. (If it is heated too much it polymerizes and is useless.) Place the specimen on a slide in a droplet of glycerin, drop on one to several drops of liquid glycerin jelly with a thin glass rod, and quickly orient the specimen with a warm needle. Then breathe on the undersurface of a clean circular cover slip and put it in place on top of the fluid. Set the mount aside to congeal. Later the excess glycerin jelly may be removed from the edge of the cover slip with a razor blade and clean cloth. For real permanence the cover slip should be ringed on a turntable with several coats of Murrayite.

**Helly's fluid.** (See p. 129.)

**Hematoxylin.** Delafield's hematoxylin is a general purpose nuclear stain. Dissolve 1 g. of hematoxylin crystals in 10 ml. absolute alcohol and add it drop by drop to 100 ml. of a saturated aqueous solution of aluminum ammonium sulphate. Expose this mixture to air and light for several weeks to "ripen." Then filter, add 25 ml. glycerin, and 25 ml. methyl alcohol.

**Hertwig-Schneider's fluid.** (See p. 109.)

**Hydroxylamine hydrochloride.** Anesthetic for certain small metazoans; usually used in a 2 per cent aqueous solution.

**Isopropyl alcohol.** Occasionally useful as an anesthetic, especially for certain protozoans. Sometimes used in histological work as a substitute for ethyl alcohol.

**Lactophenol.** A special mounting medium with index of refraction especially favorable for cuticular details. Made up of 20 g. phenol crystals, 40 g. glycerin, 20 g. lactic acid, and 20 ml. distilled water.

**Magnesium sulphate.** Occasionally used as an anesthetic for fresh-water invertebrates, but more useful for marine forms.

**Menthol.** An anesthetic occasionally used for fresh-water invertebrates. Sprinkle fine crystals on the surface of the water containing the specimens.

**Methylene blue.** An excellent intravitam stain for translucent forms. Make up a stock of 0.01 g. of methylene blue in 100 ml. absolute alcohol. Add enough of this solution to the water containing the organisms to tinge it a light blue.

**Monk's fluid.** This is an aqueous mounting medium which is useful for making permanent slides of copepods and other small arthropods. It consists of 5 ml. white corn syrup, 5 ml. Certo (fruit pectin), and 3 ml. water. Add a crystal of thymol as a preservative. The mixture sets in a few minutes. Dry to hardness over gentle heat, preferably a hot plate.

**Murrayite.** A synthetic cement which is dissolved in benzol to a thin syrupy consistency. Since it is permanently waterproof, alcohol proof, and glycerin proof, it is an excellent sealing cement for museum jars and cover slips. If circular cover slips are ringed on a turntable, several coats should be applied with a camel's hair brush, allowing at least 10 hours between coats.

**Neosynephrin hydrochloride.** Anesthetic for small metazoans; usually used in a 1 per cent solution.

**Neutral red.** An intra-vitam stain useful for protozoans. Dissolve 1 g. of the powder in 100 ml. water.

**Nicotine sulphate.** This salt is occasionally used as an anesthetic for small fresh-water invertebrates in about 2 per cent solution.

**Nitric acid.** Concentrated nitric acid is used in cleaning and isolating sponge spicules and gemmules. Two per cent nitric acid is useful for fixing turbellarians, and a 1 per cent solution is used for dissociating tissues of hydras.

**Osmic acid.** Really osmium tetroxide, $OsO_4$, this compound is poisonous and extremely volatile. Used in a 1 per cent solution in distilled water, it is an excellent and rapid fixative for a variety of small metazoans. Prepare the solution by crushing the cleaned hermetically sealed glass container in an appropriate amount of water and allowing the released osmic acid crystals to dissolve. This compound is easily oxidized by light and dust and should therefore be kept in a blackened dropping bottle. Solutions have much greater permanence if they contain 1 per cent chloroplatinic acid. If specimens are in a drop of water on a slide, fixation is accomplished in a few seconds if the slide is inverted over the mouth of the osmic acid bottle. A few drops of osmic acid are sufficient for fixing specimens in 5 ml. to 10 ml. of water. All fixed material should be washed in several changes of water. If the material is colored dark brown or black by the action of the osmic acid, place in commercial hydrogen peroxide until sufficiently bleached. Osmic acid is unfortunately very expensive.

**Permount.** A synthetic mounting medium, superior to balsam in some ways.

Dissolve sufficient Permount in toluol or xylol (xylene) to make a syrupy fluid.

**Potassium hydroxide.** A 2 to 10 per cent solution of potassium hydroxide is often used for clearing opaque chitinous insects and other arthropods. Specimens may be heated gently in the solution for a few minutes or left in it cold for 8 to 48 hours. Specimens should then be neutralized with 10 per cent acetic acid and washed with several changes of water.

**Schaudinn's fixative.** A general fixative consisting of 2 parts saturated mercuric chloride and 1 part 95 per cent alcohol.

Fix for 5 minutes to 3 hours, depending on size and density of the objects. Remove all of the salt by washing in several changes of 70 per cent alcohol for a total of 3 to 8 days. Salt removal may be greatly speeded by adding a small amount of tincture of iodine to the alcohol. The action of this fixative is enhanced by the addition of sufficient glacial acetic acid to make a 1 per cent solution immediately before using.

**Terpineol (synthetic oil of lilac).** A good clearing agent, readily miscible with 90 per cent alcohol. Does not make specimens brittle.

# INDEX

This index includes all names of genera, subgenera, species, and subspecies, as well as the other systematic groups that are used in this volume. Peculiar and less generally used anatomical and ecological terms are also listed.

All generic and specific names are italicized. Species names begin with a small letter and each is followed by the name of its genus in parentheses.

All numbers refer to pages of this book. Roman type page numbers indicate key or text locations where items are most extensively discussed or characterized. Boldface page numbers indicate the location of pertinent figures. An italicized page number means that both a figure and a text or key reference appear on that page.

## DATE DUE

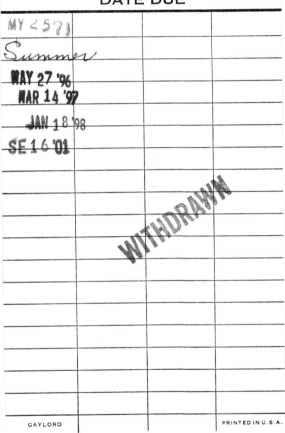